McDougal Littell

CLASSZONE

Visit **classzone.com** and get connected.

ClassZone resources provide instruction, practice and learning support for students and parents.

Help with the Math

- @Home Tutor enables students to focus on the math and be more prepared for class, using animated examples and instruction.
- Extra examples similar to those in the book provide additional support.
- Hints and Homework Help offers assistance solving select homework exercises.

Practice, Practice, Practice

- eWorkbook includes interactive worksheets with additional practice problems.
- Problem of the Week features a new problem to solve every week.

Games and Activities

- Crossword puzzles, memory games, and other activities help students connect to essential math concepts.
- Math Vocabulary Flipcards are a fun way to learn math terminology.

 Math

- Engaging activities with animated problem-solving graphics support each lesson.

Access the online version of your textbook at classzone.com

Your complete text is available for immediate use!

 **McDougal Littell**

Where Great Lessons Begin

McDougal Littell

MATH

Algebra 1

Ron Larson

Laurie Boswell

Timothy D. Kanold

Lee Stiff

 **McDougal Littell**

A DIVISION OF HOUGHTON MIFFLIN COMPANY

Evanston, Illinois • **Boston** • **Dallas**

About *California Math Algebra 1*

The content of *California Math Algebra 1* is organized around and offers complete coverage of California's Algebra 1 Mathematics Content Standards. Mathematics standards from previous grades are reviewed to help with your understanding of the Algebra 1 standards. Activities are provided to develop Algebra 1 concepts. Each lesson has ample skill practice so that you can master the important mathematical processes taught in Algebra 1. *California Math Algebra 1* also teaches you valuable techniques for solving purely mathematical as well as real-world problems. Throughout each chapter you will engage in error analysis and mathematical reasoning to build critical thinking skills and to construct logical arguments. *California Math Algebra 1* thus provides a balance between basic skills, conceptual understanding, and problem solving—all supported by mathematical reasoning.

In *California Math Algebra 1* you will have many opportunities to practice your understanding of the Algebra 1 standards. At the end of each lesson are multiple choice exercises that review standards that you learned in previous lessons. Additionally, multiple choice exercises on chapter content appear in each lesson, on Mixed Review pages twice per chapter, and at the end of each chapter on the Multiple Choice Strategies and Multiple Choice Practice pages. Technology support for learning algebra is available at classzone.com.

ISBN-13: 978-0-618-72652-3
ISBN-10: 0-618-72652-7   7 8 9-1421-13 12 11 10

4500261182

Internet Web Site: http://www.mcdougallittell.com

About the Authors

Ron Larson is a professor of mathematics at Penn State University at Erie, where he has taught since receiving his Ph.D. in mathematics from the University of Colorado. Dr. Larson is well known as the author of a comprehensive program for mathematics that spans middle school, high school, and college courses. Dr. Larson's numerous professional activities keep him in constant touch with the needs of teachers and supervisors. He closely follows developments in mathematics standards and assessment.

Laurie Boswell is a mathematics teacher at The Riverside School in Lyndonville, Vermont, and has taught mathematics at all levels, elementary through college. A recipient of the Presidential Award for Excellence in Mathematics Teaching, she was also a Tandy Technology Scholar. She served on the NCTM Board of Directors (2002–2005), and she speaks frequently at regional and national conferences on topics related to instructional strategies and course content.

Timothy D. Kanold is the superintendent of Adlai E. Stevenson High School District 125 in Lincolnshire, Illinois. Dr. Kanold served as a teacher and director of mathematics for 17 years prior to becoming superintendent. He is the recipient of the Presidential Award for Excellence in Mathematics and Science Teaching, and a past president of the Council for Presidential Awardees in Mathematics. Dr. Kanold is a frequent speaker at national and international mathematics meetings.

Lee Stiff is a professor of mathematics education in the College of Education and Psychology of North Carolina State University at Raleigh and has taught mathematics at the high school and middle school levels. He served on the NCTM Board of Directors and was elected President of NCTM for the years 2000–2002. He is a recipient of the W. W. Rankin Award for Excellence in Mathematics Education presented by the North Carolina Council of Teachers of Mathematics.

Advisers and Reviewers
McDougal Littell's *California Math* series

Program Advisory Panel

Rick Austin
Mathematics Teacher
Daniel Lewis Middle School
Paso Robles, CA

Gregory T. Miyata
EETT/IMaST II Lead
  Coach/Advisor
Robert Louis Stevenson
  Middle School
Los Angeles, CA

Karen Cliffe
Mathematics Curriculum
  Specialist
Sweetwater Union
  High School District
Chula Vista, CA

Yoshiko Okamoto
Mathematics Teacher,
  Department Chair
Hoover Middle School
Lakewood, CA

Stephanie Davis
Mathematics and Science
  Teacher
Jefferson Middle School
San Gabriel, CA

Jane Marie Smith
Mathematics Teacher
Hillview Middle School
Palmdale, CA

Barry Fox
Mathematics Teacher/
  Assistant Principal
Florence Nightingale Middle
  School
Los Angeles, CA

Gwendolyn Walker-Jennels
Mathematics Teacher
Ralph Waldo Emerson
  Middle School
Pomona, CA

Brent T. Kuykendall
Mathematics Teacher
Ridgecrest Intermediate School
Rancho Palos Verdes, CA

Joan Hairston
Mathematics Teacher
Francisco Bravo Medical Magnet
  School
Los Angeles, CA

Textbook Reviewers

José Aguilar
Mathematics Coach
Eagle Rock High School
Los Angeles, CA

Rick Austin
Mathematics Teacher
Daniel Lewis Middle School
Paso Robles, CA

Tamesha Carter
Mathematics Teacher
DeMille Middle School
Long Beach, CA

Gregory T. Miyata
EETT/IMaST II Lead
    Coach/Advisor
Robert Louis Stevenson
    Middle School
Los Angeles, CA

Mark Chavez
Mathematics Teacher
DeMille Middle School
Long Beach, CA

Yoshiko Okamoto
Mathematics Teacher,
    Department Chair
Hoover Middle School
Lakewood, CA

Karen Cliffe
Mathematics Curriculum
    Specialist
Sweetwater Union
    High School District
Chula Vista, CA

Mike Pacheco
Mathematics Teacher
David Wark Griffith Middle School
Los Angeles, CA

Ed Kohn
Professional Development
    Facilitator
Los Angeles Unified School
    District
Los Angeles, CA

Rudy Sass
Mathematics Teacher
Orangeview Junior High School
Anaheim, CA

Chris Martinez
Mathematics Teacher
Arden Middle School
Sacramento, CA

Teacher's Editions Advisory Panel

Edie Birbeck
Mathematics Teacher
William Hopkins Junior
   High School
Fremont, CA

Janet L. Bryson
Mathematics Coach,
TASEL-M
Orange, CA

Ellen Duffy
Mathematics Coach
TASEL-M
Fullerton, CA

Donna Krueger Phair
Mathematics Teacher,
   Department Chair
William Hopkins Junior
   High School
Fremont, CA

Frank Dong
Mathematics Teacher
Marina Middle School
San Francisco, CA

Diane Jacobs
Mathematics Teacher
Fitz Intermediate School
Santa Ana, CA

Ellen Fujii
7–12 Mathematics Program
   Facilitator
Garden Grove Unified
   School District
Garden Grove, CA

Shauna Poong
Mathematics Teacher
Marina Middle School
San Francisco, CA

Douglas Harik
Mathematics Teacher
Westborough Middle School
South San Francisco, CA

Jenita Whiting-Dandridge
Mathematics Teacher
Los Angeles Academy
   Middle School
Los Angeles, CA

Sheila Hernandez
Mathematics Teacher
Horner Junior High School
Fremont, CA

CALIFORNIA

CA

Overview
California Student Edition

California Table of Contents   *Pages TOC2–TOC14*

California Student Guide   *Page SG1*

    Standards Practice   *Pages SG2–SG15*

    Pre-Course Test   *Pages SG16–SG17*

    Scavenger Hunt   *Pages SG18–SG19*

California Chapter Support   *Throughout*

    Multiple choice worked-out examples   *Throughout each chapter*

    California @Home Tutor   *Throughout each chapter*

    Standards references and
About the Standards notes   *Throughout each chapter*

    California Standards Spiral Review   *In every lesson*

    Mixed Review of Skills and Problem Solving   *Twice per chapter*

    Multiple Choice Strategies   *At the end of each chapter*

    Multiple Choice Practice   *At the end of each chapter*

Standards Review Handbook   *Pages 783–809*

Yosemite National Park

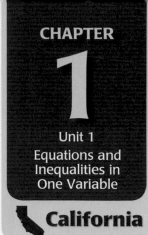

CHAPTER

1

Unit 1
Equations and
Inequalities in
One Variable

California

Evaluating Expressions, p. 16
$3f + 2s + t$

Expressions, Equations, and Problem Solving

Review Prerequisite Skills 2

Gr. 6 AF 1.2   **1.1**   **Evaluate Expressions and Use Exponents** 5

Gr. 7 AF 1.2   **1.2**   **Apply Order of Operations** 11

     Graphing Calculator Activity   Use Order of Operations 17

Gr. 7 AF 1.1   **1.3**   **Write Expressions** 19

     Investigating Algebra Activity: Patterns and Expressions 18

     Mixed Review of Skills and Problem Solving 25

Gr. 7 AF 1.1   **1.4**   **Write Equations and Inequalities** 26

Gr. 7 MR 2.5   **1.5**   **Use a Problem Solving Plan** 32

     Problem Solving Workshop 38

     Mixed Review of Skills and Problem Solving 39

Assessment

     Quizzes 24, 37
     Chapter Summary and Chapter Problem 40
     Chapter Review and Chapter Test 42
     ◆ **Multiple Choice Strategies and Practice** 46

Animated Algebra
classzone.com   **Activities** 10, 12, 18, 26, 33, 38

Chapter 1 Highlights

⚡ TECHNOLOGY

*At **classzone.com**:*
- Animated Algebra, 10, 12, 18, 26, 33, 38
- California @Home Tutor, 4, 9, 15, 23, 30, 36, 42
- Online Quiz, 10, 16, 24, 31, 37

STUDENT HELP

- Vocabulary and Reading, 4, 5, 8, 11, 14, 16, 19, 21, 22, 26, 27, 29, 32, 35, 42, 45
- Notetaking, 4, 35, 42
- Another Way, 32, 38
- Avoid Errors, 5, 12, 19, 20, 34
- Hints and Homework Help, 8, 14, 22, 29, 35

◆ ASSESSMENT

- Multiple choice examples and exercises, 8, 9, 10, 13, 14, 16, 22, 23, 30, 34, 36
- California Standards Spiral Review, 10, 16, 24, 31, 37
- Writing, Open-Ended, and Short Response, 3, 8, 14, 22, 29, 31, 36

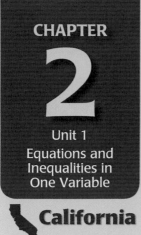

Adding Integers, p. 65
Change in elevation = 150 − (−8)

Properties of Real Numbers

Review Prerequisite Skills **50**

Alg. 2.0, 24.2, 24.3 **2.1 Use Integers and Rational Numbers** **53**

Alg. 1.0, 1.1 **2.2 Add Real Numbers** **60**

Alg. 1.0, 1.1 **2.3 Subtract Real Numbers** **67**
  Spreadsheet Activity Subtract Real Numbers **72**

Alg. 1.0, 1.1 **2.4 Multiply Real Numbers** **74**
  Investigating Algebra Activity: Multiplication by −1 . . . . **73**
  Mixed Review of Skills and Problem Solving **80**

Alg. 1.0, 1.1, 25.2 **2.5 Apply the Distributive Property** **81**
  Problem Solving Workshop **87**

Alg. 1.0, 1.1, 2.0 **2.6 Divide Real Numbers** **88**

Alg. 1.0, 2.0 **2.7 Find Square Roots and Compare Real Numbers** **95**
  Investigating Algebra Activity: Writing Statements in If-Then Form **94**

Alg. 24.0, 25.0, 25.3 **2.8 Use Properties of Real Numbers and Logical Reasoning** **102**
  Mixed Review of Skills and Problem Solving **109**

Assessment

Quizzes **71, 86, 108**
Chapter Summary and Chapter Problem **110**
Chapter Review and Chapter Test **112**
◆ Multiple Choice Strategies and Practice **118**

 Activities **67, 76, 79, 83**

Chapter 2 Highlights

⬀ TECHNOLOGY

At *classzone.com*:
- Animated Algebra, 67, 76, 79, 83
- California @Home Tutor, 52, 58, 65, 70, 78, 85, 92, 100, 112
- Online Quiz, 59, 66, 71, 79, 86, 93, 101, 108

STUDENT HELP
- Vocabulary and Reading, 52, 53, 55, 56, 60, 63, 67, 69, 74, 76, 77, 79, 81, 82, 84, 88, 90, 95, 96, 98, 102, 105, 112, 113, 117
- Notetaking, 52, 63, 112
- Another Way, 63, 83, 87, 90
- Avoid Errors, 55, 68, 88
- Hints and Homework Help, 56, 63, 69, 77, 84, 90, 98, 105

◆ ASSESSMENT
- Multiple choice examples and exercises, 54, 57, 58, 62, 64, 65, 69, 70, 75, 77, 78, 84, 86, 91, 93, 99, 100, 106, 107
- California Standards Spiral Review, 59, w66, 71, 79, 86, 93, 101, 108
- Writing, Open-Ended, and Short Response, 51, 56, 69, 77, 84, 90, 98, 99, 100, 105, 107, 112

CHAPTER

3

Unit 1
Equations and
Inequalities in
One Variable

California

Solving Equations, p. 185
$$\frac{x}{144} = \frac{1}{20}$$

Solving Equations

Review Prerequisite Skills 122

Gr. 6 AF 1.1   **3.1**   **Solve One-Step Equations** 125

Gr. 7 AF 4.1   **3.2**   **Solve Two-Step Equations** 132
                Problem Solving Workshop 138

Alg. 4.0   **3.3**   **Solve Multi-Step Equations** 139

Alg. 5.0   **3.4**   **Solve Equations with Variables on Both Sides** 146
       🔍 **Investigating Algebra Activity:**
       Modeling Equations with Variables on Both Sides 145
       Spreadsheet Activity   Solve Equations Using Tables 153
       Mixed Review of Skills and Problem Solving 154

Gr. 6 NS 1.2   **3.5**   **Write Ratios and Proportions** 155

Gr. 6 NS 1.3   **3.6**   **Solve Proportions Using Cross Products** 161

Gr. 6 AF 3.1   **3.7**   **Rewrite Equations and Formulas** 167
       Mixed Review of Skills and Problem Solving 174

Assessment

Quizzes 152, 173
Chapter Summary and Chapter Problem 175
Chapter Review and Chapter Test 177
◆ Multiple Choice Strategies and Practice 182

Animated Algebra
classzone.com   Activities 131, 146, 168, 170

Chapter 3 Highlights

🔗 TECHNOLOGY

At classzone.com:
- Animated Algebra, 131, 146, 168, 170
- California @Home Tutor, 124, 130, 136, 143, 151, 159, 165, 172, 177
- Online Quiz, 131, 137, 144, 152, 160, 166, 173

STUDENT HELP

- Vocabulary and Reading, 124, 128, 125, 132, 133, 135, 139, 141, 144, 146, 149, 155, 156, 158, 161, 164, 167, 170, 177, 181
- Notetaking, 124, 128, 177
- Another Way, 134, 138, 141, 157, 162
- Avoid Errors, 140, 156
- Hints and Homework Help, 128, 135, 141, 149, 158, 164, 170

◆ ASSESSMENT

- Multiple choice examples and exercises, 127, 129, 130, 132, 135, 137, 140, 142, 143, 146, 149, 151, 158, 159, 164, 165, 170, 171, 172
- California Standards Spiral Review, 131, 137, 144, 152, 160, 166, 173
- Writing, Open-Ended, and Short Response, 123, 130, 131, 135, 137, 141, 143, 149, 150, 158, 164, 166, 170

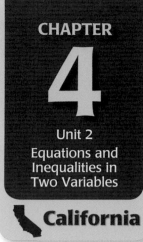

CHAPTER

4

Unit 2
Equations and
Inequalities in
Two Variables

California

Solving Inequalities, p. 201
$$h < \frac{\text{Area}}{400}$$

Solving Inequalities

Review Prerequisite Skills 186

Gr. 7 AF 4.1   **4.1**   **Solve Inequalities Using Addition and Subtraction** 189

Gr. 7 AF 4.1   **4.2**   **Solve Inequalities Using Multiplication and Division** 196
     ○ Investigating Algebra Activity:
     Inequalities with Negative Coefficients 195

Alg. 4.0, 5.0   **4.3**   **Solve Multi-Step Inequalities** 202
     Problem Solving Workshop 208

Alg. 4.0, 5.0   **4.4**   **Solve Compound Inequalities** 210
     ○ Investigating Algebra Activity: Statements with *And* and *Or* 209
     ▮ Graphing Calculator Activity   Solve Compound Inequalities 218
     Mixed Review of Skills and Problem Solving 219

Alg. 3.0   **4.5**   **Solve Absolute Value Equations** 220

Alg. 3.0   **4.6**   **Solve Absolute Value Inequalities** 226
     Mixed Review of Skills and Problem Solving 232

Assessment

     Quizzes 201, 217, 231
     Chapter Summary and Chapter Problem 233
     Chapter Review and Chapter Test 235
     ◆ Multiple Choice Strategies and Practice 240
     Cumulative Review, Chapters 1–4 244

 *Animated* Algebra
classzone.com   Activities 191, 197, 212, 217, 220, 221, 227

Chapter 4 Highlights

⚡ TECHNOLOGY

At _classzone.com_:
- Animated Algebra, 191, 197, 212, 217, 220, 221, 227
- California @Home Tutor, 188, 193, 200, 206, 216, 224, 230, 235
- Online Quiz, 194, 201, 207, 217, 225, 231

STUDENT HELP

- Vocabulary and Reading, 188, 189, 191, 192, 196, 198, 201, 202, 205, 210, 214, 220, 222, 223, 226, 227, 229, 235, 239
- Notetaking, 188, 205. 235
- Another Way, 204, 208, 213
- Avoid Errors, 197, 221
- Hints and Homework Help, 192, 198, 205, 214, 223, 229

◆ ASSESSMENT

- Multiple choice examples and exercises, 192, 194, 199, 200, 202, 205, 207, 214, 215, 216, 221, 223, 225, 227, 229, 230
- California Standards Spiral Review, 194, 201, 207, 217, 225, 231
- Writing, Open-Ended, and Short Response, 187, 192, 193, 198, 199, 209, 214, 223, 229

CHAPTER

5

Unit 2
Equations and
Inequalities in
Two Variables

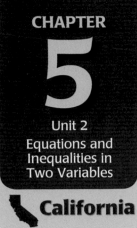

California

Writing Function Rules, p. 253
$y = 2x$

Graphing Linear Equations and Functions

Review Prerequisite Skills 246

Alg. 16.0, 17.0, 18.0 | **5.1** | **Represent Functions as Ordered Pairs and Rules** 249

▦ Graphing Calculator Activity | Make a Table 255

Alg. 17.0, 18.0 | **5.2** | **Represent Functions as Graphs** 257

🔍 Investigating Algebra Activity: Scatter Plots and Functions 256

Alg. 6.0, 7.0 | **5.3** | **Graph Linear Equations and Functions** 264

▦ Graphing Calculator Activity | Graphing Linear Equations 272

Alg. 6.0 | **5.4** | **Graph Using Intercepts** 273

Mixed Review of Skills and Problem Solving 280

Gr. 7 AF 3.3 | **5.5** | **Find Slope and Rate of Change** 282

🔍 Investigating Algebra Activity: Slope 281

Alg. 6.0 | **5.6** | **Graph Using Slope-Intercept Form** 291

🔍 Investigating Algebra Activity: Slope and y-Intercept 290

Alg. 6.0 | **5.7** | **Recognize Direct Variation** 297

Problem Solving Workshop 304

Mixed Review of Skills and Problem Solving 306

Assessment

Quizzes 263, 279, 303
Chapter Summary and Chapter Problem 307
Chapter Review and Chapter Test 309
◆ Multiple Choice Strategies and Practice 314

Animated Algebra
classzone.com | Activities 251, 258, 265, 274, 285, 292, 298

Chapter 5 Highlights

⚙ TECHNOLOGY

At *classzone.com*:
• Animated Algebra, 251, 258, 265, 274, 285, 292, 298
• California @Home Tutor, 248, 253, 262, 270, 277, 278, 288, 295, 302, 309
• Online Quiz, 254, 263, 271, 279, 289, 296, 303

STUDENT HELP

• Vocabulary and Reading, 248, 249, 250, 252, 257, 260, 264, 265, 268, 270, 273, 276, 282, 286, 291, 294, 297, 300, 309, 313
• Notetaking, 248, 276, 309
• Another Way, 299, 304
• Avoid Errors, 282
• Hints and Homework Help, 252, 260, 268, 276, 286, 294, 300

◆ ASSESSMENT

• Multiple choice examples and exercises, 250, 252, 253, 254, 261, 262, 268, 269, 270, 273, 277, 278, 286, 289, 294, 296, 300, 301, 302
• California Standards Spiral Review, 254, 263, 271, 279, 289, 296, 303
• Writing, Open-Ended, and Short Response, 247, 252, 254, 260, 268, 286, 294, 295, 300

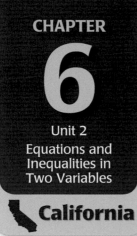

CHAPTER

6

Unit 2
Equations and
Inequalities in
Two Variables

California

Writing Linear Equations, p. 351
$100\ell + 40s =$ Amount available

Writing Linear Equations

Review Prerequisite Skills 318

Alg. 7.0 6.1 Write Linear Equations in Slope-Intercept Form 322
       Investigating Algebra Activity: Modeling Linear Relationships 321

Alg. 7.0 6.2 Use Linear Equations in Slope-Intercept Form 329
       Problem Solving Workshop 337
       Mixed Review of Skills and Problem Solving 339

Alg. 7.0 6.3 Write Linear Equations in Point-Slope Form 340

Alg. 7.0 6.4 Write Linear Equations in Standard Form 347

Alg. 8.0 6.5 Write Equations of Parallel and Perpendicular Lines 354
       Investigating Algebra Activity:
       If-Then Statements and Their Converses 353
       Mixed Review of Skills and Problem Solving 361

Assessment

Quizzes 336, 360
Chapter Summary and Chapter Problem 362
Chapter Review and Chapter Test 364
◆ Multiple Choice Strategies and Practice 368

 **Animated Algebra**
classzone.com   Activities 322, 341, 345, 347, 358

Chapter 6 Highlights

⊘ TECHNOLOGY

At *classzone.com*:
• Animated Algebra, 322, 341, 345, 347, 358
• California @Home Tutor, 327, 334, 335, 345, 351, 359
• Online Quiz, 328, 336, 346, 352, 360

STUDENT HELP

• Vocabulary and Reading, 320, 322, 324, 325, 329, 333, 335, 340, 343, 347, 350, 354, 357, 364, 367
• Notetaking, 320, 343, 364
• Another Way, 330, 332, 337, 348, 357
• Avoid Errors, 341, 342
• Hints and Homework Help, 325, 333, 343, 350, 357

◆ ASSESSMENT

• Multiple choice examples and exercises, 325, 327, 329, 333 334, 335, 343, 344, 345, 350, 351, 354, 358, 359
• California Standards Spiral Review, 328, 336, 346, 352, 360
• Writing, Open-Ended, and Short Response, 319, 325, 326, 333, 350, 357, 358

CHAPTER

7

Unit 2
Equations and
Inequalities in
Two Variables

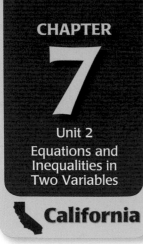

California

Solving Linear Systems, p. 388
$$d = 73t + 350,\ d = 88t$$

Systems of Equations and Inequalities

Review Prerequisite Skills 372

Alg. 9.0   **7.1**   **Solve Linear Systems by Graphing** 376
    Investigating Algebra Activity: Solving Linear Systems 375
    Graphing Calculator Activity   Solving Linear Systems by Graphing 382

Alg. 9.0   **7.2**   **Solve Linear Systems by Substitution** 383
    Problem Solving Workshop 389

Alg. 9.0   **7.3**   **Solve Linear Systems by Adding or Subtracting** 391
    Investigating Algebra Activity: Linear Systems and Elimination 390

Alg. 9.0   **7.4**   **Solve Linear Systems by Multiplying First** 398

Alg. 9.0   **7.5**   **Solve Special Types of Linear Systems** 405
    Mixed Review of Skills and Problem Solving 412

Alg. 15.0   **7.6**   **Solve Rate Problems** 413

Alg. 15.0   **7.7**   **Solve Mixture Problems** 418

Alg. 6.0   **7.8**   **Graph Linear Inequalities in Two Variables** 425
    Investigating Algebra Activity: Linear Inequalities in Two Variables 424

Alg. 9.0   **7.9**   **Solve Systems of Linear Inequalities** 433
    Mixed Review of Skills and Problem Solving 441

Assessment

Quizzes 388, 404, 423, 440
Chapter Summary and Chapter Problem 442
Chapter Review and Chapter Test 444
◆ Multiple Choice Strategies and Practice 450
Cumulative Review, Chapters 1–7 454

Animated Algebra
classzone.com
Activities 377, 383, 388, 399, 405, 414, 427, 433

Chapter 7 Highlights

⊘ TECHNOLOGY

At *classzone.com*:
- Animated Algebra, 377, 383, 388, 399, 405, 414, 427, 433
- California @Home Tutor, 374, 380, 387, 396, 403, 410, 416, 421, 431, 439, 444
- Online Quiz, 381, 388, 397, 404, 411, 417, 423, 432, 440

STUDENT HELP

- Vocabulary and Reading, 374, 376, 378, 383, 386, 391, 394, 398, 401, 405, 408, 413, 415, 418, 425, 429, 431, 433, 437, 444, 449
- Notetaking, 374, 408, 444
- Another Way, 385, 389, 398, 399, 420
- Avoid Errors, 392, 419, 426, 428
- Hints and Homework Help, 378, 386, 394, 401, 408, 415, 421, 429, 437

◆ ASSESSMENT

- Multiple choice examples and exercises, 379, 380, 386, 387, 394, 395, 396, 401, 402, 403, 407, 409, 411, 415, 416, 417, 421, 422, 427, 429, 430, 431, 434, 437, 438, 439
- California Standards Spiral Review, 381, 388, 397, 404, 411, 417, 423, 432, 440
- Writing, Open-Ended, and Short Response, 373, 378, 379, 386, 387, 388, 394, 395, 397, 401, 402, 403, 408, 410, 415, 421, 429, 432, 437, 439

Simplifying Radical Expressions, p. 489
$$d = \sqrt{\frac{3 \cdot 98}{2}}$$

Exponents and Radicals

		Review Prerequisite Skills	456
Alg. 2.0	8.1	**Apply Exponent Properties Involving Products**	460
		Investigating Algebra Activity: Products and Powers	459
Alg. 2.0	8.2	**Apply Exponent Properties Involving Quotients**	467
Alg. 2.0	8.3	**Define and Use Zero and Negative Exponents**	475
		Investigating Algebra Activity: Zero and Negative Exponents	474
		Mixed Review of Skills and Problem Solving	481
Alg. 1.0, 25.1	8.4	**Simplify Radical Expressions**	483
		Investigating Algebra Activity: Properties of Radicals	482
Gr. 7 MG 3.3	8.5	**Apply the Pythagorean Theorem and its Converse**	491
		Problem Solving Workshop	497
Alg. 2.0	8.6	**Use Cube Roots and Fractional Exponents**	498
		Mixed Review of Skills and Problem Solving	504

Assessment

Quizzes	473, 490, 503
Chapter Summary and Chapter Problem	505
Chapter Review and Chapter Test	507
◆ Multiple Choice Strategies and Practice	512

Animated Algebra
classzone.com   Activities 462, 477, 483, 486, 491

Chapter 8 Highlights

⚙ TECHNOLOGY

At *classzone.com*:
- Animated Algebra, 462, 477, 483, 486, 491
- California @Home Tutor, 464, 465, 471, 472, 479, 489, 495, 502, 507
- Online Quiz, 466, 473, 480, 490, 496, 503

STUDENT HELP

- Vocabulary and Reading, 458, 460, 463, 465, 467, 470, 475, 476, 478, 483, 486, 487, 494, 498, 501, 507, 511
- Notetaking, 458, 463, 507
- Another Way, 492, 497
- Avoid Errors, 461, 493
- Hints and Homework Help, 463, 470, 478, 487, 494, 501

◆ ASSESSMENT

- Multiple choice examples and exercises, 461, 464, 465, 470, 471, 478, 479, 487, 488, 489, 492, 494, 496, 498, 501, 502
- California Standards Spiral Review, 466, 473, 480, 490, 496, 503
- Writing, Open-Ended, and Short Response, 457, 464, 470, 471, 478, 487, 488, 494, 495, 501

CHAPTER

9

Unit 3
Exponents
and Polynomials

California

Solving Polynomial Equations, p. 561
$(x - 2)(x - 3) = 56$

Polynomials and Factoring

Review Prerequisite Skills **516**

Alg. 10.0   **9.1 Add and Subtract Polynomials** **520**
    Investigating Algebra Activity: Addition with Algebra Tiles **519**
    Graphing Calculator Activity   Graph Polynomial Functions **526**

Alg. 10.0   **9.2 Multiply Polynomials** **528**
    Investigating Algebra Activity: Multiplication with Algebra Tiles **527**

Alg. 10.0   **9.3 Find Special Products of Polynomials** **534**

Alg. 10.0   **9.4 Divide Polynomials** **541**
    Investigating Algebra Activity: Division with Algebra Tiles **540**
    Mixed Review of Skills and Problem Solving **548**

Alg. 11.0, 14.0, 23.0   **9.5 Solve Polynomial Equations in Factored Form** **549**

Alg. 11.0, 14.0   **9.6 Factor $x^2 + bx + c$** **556**
    Investigating Algebra Activity: Factorization with Algebra Tiles **555**
    Problem Solving Workshop **563**

Alg. 11.0, 14.0   **9.7 Factor $ax^2 + bx + c$** **566**
    Investigating Algebra Activity: More Factorization with Algebra Tiles **565**

Alg. 11.0, 14.0, 25.2   **9.8 Factor Special Products** **573**

Alg. 11.0, 14.0, 25.1   **9.9 Factor Polynomials Completely** **579**
    Mixed Review of Skills and Problem Solving **587**

Assessment

Quizzes **547, 572, 586**
Chapter Summary and Chapter Problem **588**
Chapter Review and Chapter Test **590**
◆ Multiple Choice Strategies and Practice **596**
Cumulative Review, Chapters 1–9 .... **600**

Animated Algebra
classzone.com   Activities **521, 555, 565, 571, 574**

Chapter 9 Highlights

TECHNOLOGY

At classzone.com:
- Animated Algebra, 521, 540, 555, 565, 571, 574
- California @Home Tutor, 518, 524, 532, 533, 538, 546, 553, 561, 571, 577, 585, 590
- Online Quiz, 525, 533, 539, 547, 554, 562, 572, 578, 586

STUDENT HELP

- Vocabulary and Reading, 518, 520, 523, 528, 531, 534, 537, 539, 541, 545, 549, 552, 556, 559, 566, 569, 573, 576, 579, 580, 583, 590, 595
- Notetaking, 518, 531, 590
- Another Way, 522, 558, 563
- Avoid Errors, 522, 529, 536, 542, 567, 582
- Hints and Homework Help, 523, 531, 537, 545, 552, 559, 569, 576, 583

◆ ASSESSMENT

- Multiple choice examples and exercises, 522, 523, 524, 531, 532, 533, 537, 538, 541, 545, 546, 552, 554, 558, 559, 560, 561, 569, 570, 571, 574, 576, 577, 581, 583, 585,
- California Standards Spiral Review, 525, 533, 539, 547, 554, 562, 572, 578, 586
- Writing, Open-Ended, and Short Response, 517, 523, 537, 545, 552, 559, 561, 569, 570, 572, 576, 583, 584, 590

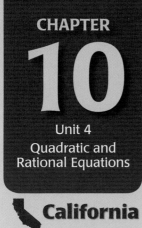

CHAPTER

10

Unit 4
Quadratic and
Rational Equations

California

Graphing Quadratic Equations, p. 661
$y = -0.18x^2 + 1.6x$

Quadratic Equations and Functions

Review Prerequisite Skills 602

Alg. 21.0   **10.1 Graph $y = ax^2 + c$** 605

Alg. 21.0   **10.2 Graph $y = ax^2 + bx + c$** 612

Alg. 21.0   **10.3 Graph $y = a(x - p)(x - q)$** 618

Alg. 21.0   **10.4 Solve Quadratic Equations by Graphing** 624
      Graphing Calculator Activity Find Zeros of a Function 631
      Mixed Review of Skills and Problem Solving 632

Alg. 23.0   **10.5 Use Square Roots to Solve Quadratic Equations** 633
      Problem Solving Workshop 640

Alg. 14.0   **10.6 Solve Quadratic Equations by Completing the Square** 643
      Investigating Algebra Activity: Completing the Square–Algebra Tiles 642

Alg. 19.0, 20.0   **10.7 Solve Quadratic Equations by the Quadratic Formula** 649

Alg. 20.0, 22.0   **10.8 Interpret the Discriminant** 657
      Investigating Algebra Activity: The Discriminant 656
      Mixed Review of Skills and Problem Solving 663

Assessment

Quizzes 623, 639, 662
Chapter Summary and Chapter Problem 664
Chapter Review and Chapter Test 666
◆ Multiple Choice Strategies and Practice 672

Animated Algebra classzone.com   Activities 611, 613, 642, 648

Chapter 10 Highlights

🔎 TECHNOLOGY

At _classzone.com_:
- Animated Algebra, 611, 613, 642, 648
- California @Home Tutor, 610, 616, 617, 622, 629, 637, 638, 647, 654, 661
- Online Quiz, 611, 617, 623, 630, 639, 648, 655, 662

STUDENT HELP

- Vocabulary and Reading, 604, 605, 608, 612, 615, 618, 621, 624, 628, 633, 636, 643, 646, 649, 652, 655, 657, 660, 666, 671
- Notetaking, 604, 621, 666
- Another Way, 633, 635, 640
- Avoid Errors, 613, 619, 625, 644, 658
- Hints and Homework Help, 608, 615, 621, 628, 636, 646, 652, 660

◆ ASSESSMENT

- Multiple choice examples and exercises, 609, 610, 615, 616, 621, 622, 623, 626, 628, 629, 636, 638, 644, 646, 647, 650, 653, 654, 658, 660, 661
- California Standards Spiral Review, 611, 617, 623, 630, 639, 648, 655, 662
- Writing, Open-Ended, and Short Response, 603, 608, 611, 615, 617, 622, 628, 630, 636, 637, 641, 646, 652, 660

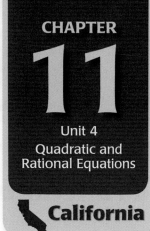

CHAPTER

11

Unit 4
Quadratic and
Rational Equations

California

Solving Rate Problems, p. 737

$$t = \frac{12}{r-4} + \frac{12}{r+4}$$

Rational Expressions and Equations

Review Prerequisite Skills 676

Alg. 15.0 **11.1 Recognize Inverse Variation** 680
    🔍 Investigating Algebra Activity:
    Relationships Between Dimensions of a Rectangle 679

Alg. 12.0 **11.2 Simplify Rational Expressions** 688
    ▦ Graphing Calculator Activity ⟩ Graph Rational Functions 695

Alg. 13.0 **11.3 Multiply and Divide Rational Expressions** 696
    Mixed Review of Skills and Problem Solving 704

Alg. 13.0 **11.4 Add and Subtract Rational Expressions** 705

Alg. 13.0 **11.5 Solve Rational Equations** 713
    Problem Solving Workshop 719

Alg. 15.0 **11.6 Solve Work Problems** 721
    Mixed Review of Skills and Problem Solving 726

Assessment

    Quizzes 703, 725
    Chapter Summary and Chapter Problem 727
    Chapter Review and Chapter Test 729
    ◆ Multiple Choice Strategies and Practice 734
    Cumulative Review, Chapters 1–11 738

Animated Algebra
classzone.com Activities 681, 698, 707

Chapter 11 Highlights

⟲ TECHNOLOGY

At _classzone.com_:
• Animated Algebra, 681, 698, 707
• California @Home Tutor, 678, 685, 686, 693, 701, 702, 710, 711, 717, 724, 729
• Online Quiz, 687, 694, 703, 712, 718, 725

STUDENT HELP

• Vocabulary and Reading, 678, 680, 684, 686, 688, 691, 696, 700, 705, 709, 713, 716, 721, 723, 729, 733
• Notetaking, 678, 700, 729
• Another Way, 715, 719
• Avoid Errors, 681, 689, 707, 714
• Hints and Homework Help, 684, 691, 700, 709, 716, 723

◆ ASSESSMENT

• Multiple choice examples and exercises, 684, 686, 690, 692, 694, 697, 700, 701, 702, 709, 701, 711, 716, 717, 723, 724
• California Standards Spiral Review, 687, 694, 703, 712, 718, 725
• Writing, Open-Ended, and Short Response, 677, 684, 685, 691, 692, 709, 716, 718, 723, 729

Finding Probabilities, p. 748
$$P(A) = \frac{19}{200}$$

Probability:
Review and Preview

Review Prerequisite Skills 740

Gr. 6 SDAP 3.0 **12.1 Find Theoretical and Experimental Probability** 744
    ○ Investigating Algebra Activity: Find a Probability 743

Alg. 2 18.0 **12.2 Find Probabilities Using Permutations** 750

Alg. 2 18.0, 19.0 **12.3 Find Probabilities Using Combinations** 756
    ▤ Graphing Calculator Activity Find Permutations and Combinations 761

Gr. 6 SDAP 3.4, 3.5 **12.4 Find Probabilities of Compound Events** 762
    Problem Solving Workshop 769
    Mixed Review of Skills and Problem Solving 771

Assessment

    Quizzes 755, 768
    Chapter Summary and Chapter Problem 772
    Chapter Review and Chapter Test 774
    ◆ Multiple Choice Strategies and Practice 778

Animated Algebra Activities 746, 749, 756
classzone.com

Chapter 12 Highlights

⊘ TECHNOLOGY

At classzone.com:
- Animated Algebra, 746, 756
- California @Home Tutor, 742, 748, 754, 759, 767, 774
- Online Quiz, 749, 755, 760, 768

STUDENT HELP

- Vocabulary and Reading, 742, 744, 747, 750, 753, 756, 758, 762, 763, 765, 774, 777
- Notetaking, 742, 753, 774
- Another Way, 764, 769
- Hints and Homework Help, 747, 753, 758, 765

◆ ASSESSMENT

- Multiple choice examples and exercises, 746, 747, 748, 752, 753, 754, 757, 758, 759, 765, 766, 767
- California Standards Spiral Review, 749, 755, 760, 768
- Writing, Open-Ended, and Short Response, 741, 747, 753, 758, 760, 765, 767

Standards Review Handbook

pages 783–809

Number Sense

Quotients and Remainders	783
Factors and Multiples	784
Finding Equivalent Fractions and Simplifying Fractions	786
Mixed Numbers and Improper Fractions	787
Adding and Subtracting Fractions	788
Multiplying and Dividing Fractions	789
Comparing and Ordering Decimals	790
Fractions, Decimals, and Percents	791
Finding Percents of Numbers	793

Algebra and Functions

The Coordinate Plane	794
Converting Units of Measurement	795

Measurement and Geometry

Perimeter and Area	796
Circumference and Area of a Circle	798
Surface Area and Volume	799
Translations and Reflections	801

Statistics, Data Analysis, and Probability

Mean, Median, and Mode	803
Line Graphs	804
Counting Methods	805

Mathematical Reasoning

Problem Solving Strategies	807
Venn Diagrams and Logical Reasoning	809

Extra Practice for Chapters 1–12

pages 810–821

Tables

pages 822–829

Symbols	*822*
Formulas	*823*
Properties	*825*
Measures	*828*
Squares and Square Roots	*829*

English-Spanish Glossary

pages 830–858

Index

pages 859–872

Credits

pages 873–874

Selected Answers

page SA1

CALIFORNIA

California Student Guide

Getting Started

The following pages will help you get started by providing a preview of the course and an introduction to your textbook.

California Standards Practice   *Pages SG2 – SG15*

Gives you an overview of the standards for this course. Lists all Algebra 1 standards with two multiple choice exercises for each standard.

California Pre-Course Test   *Pages SG16 – SG17*

Tests prerequisite skills for Algebra 1 with page references to the Standards Review Handbook at the back of the book.

Scavenger Hunt   *Pages SG18 – SG19*

Provides an opportunity to explore student resources at the back of the book.

Yosemite National Park

Standards Practice

As you answer each multiple choice question, you may want to turn to the page given in blue to study the mathematical concepts that the question is addressing.

Algebra 1 | Standards Practice

Standard 1.0 Students identify and use the arithmetic properties of subsets of integers and rational, irrational, and real numbers, including closure properties for the four basic arithmetic operations where applicable:

Standard 1.1 Students use properties of numbers to demonstrate whether assertions are true or false.

1. To show that

$$5(-3 + 7) = 7 \cdot 5 + (-3) \cdot 5$$

Miranda wrote these steps.

Step 1 $5(-3 + 7) = 5(-3) + 5 \cdot 7$
Step 2 $\qquad = 5 \cdot 7 + 5(-3)$
Step 3 $\qquad = 7 \cdot 5 + (-3) \cdot 5$

Which property of numbers did she use to write Step 3? *(p. 74)*

- **A** Distributive property
- **B** Associative property of multiplication
- **C** Commutative property of multiplication
- **D** Commutative property of addition

2. Let a be a positive number. If $a(b - c) < 0$, which statement *must* be true? *(p. 102)*

- **A** $b < 0$
- **B** $b < c$
- **C** $b > c$
- **D** $b = c$

Standard 2.0 Students understand and use such operations as taking the opposite, finding the reciprocal, taking a root, and raising to a fractional power. They understand and use the rules of exponents.

3. $64^{1/2} + (-2)^3 = \underline{\ ?\ }$ *(p. 498)*

- **A** -4
- **B** 0
- **C** 16
- **D** 24

4. Which expression is equivalent to $\left(\dfrac{x^8 y}{x^2 y^3}\right)^2$? *(p. 475)*

- **A** $x^{12}y^4$
- **B** $x^8 y^4$
- **C** $\dfrac{x^{12}}{y^4}$
- **D** $\dfrac{x^8}{y^4}$

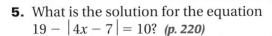

Algebra 1 — Standards Practice

Standard 3.0 Students solve equations and inequalities involving absolute values.

5. What is the solution for the equation $19 - |4x - 7| = 10$? *(p. 220)*

Ⓐ $x = -\frac{1}{2}$ or $x = 4$

Ⓑ $x = -2$ or $x = 4$

Ⓒ $x = -4$ or $x = \frac{1}{2}$

Ⓓ $x = -4$ or $x = 4$

6. What is the solution of the inequality $|2x + 5| \geq 23$? *(p. 226)*

Ⓐ $-9 \leq x \leq 9$

Ⓑ $x \leq -9$ or $x \geq 9$

Ⓒ $-14 \leq x \leq 9$

Ⓓ $x \leq -14$ or $x \geq 9$

Standard 4.0 Students simplify expressions before solving linear equations and inequalities in one variable, such as $3(2x - 5) + 4(x - 2) = 12$.

7. Which equation is equivalent to $5 - 3(7x - 4) + 6x = 4x$? *(p. 146)*

Ⓐ $-15x - 7 = 4x$

Ⓑ $-15x + 17 = 4x$

Ⓒ $-2x = 4x$

Ⓓ $20x - 8 = 4x$

8. Which inequality is equivalent to $8 - 7(x + 4) < 9(1 - 3x)$? *(p. 202)*

Ⓐ $4x > 3$

Ⓑ $20x < -27$

Ⓒ $20x < 29$

Ⓓ $28x < 5$

Standard 5.0 Students solve multistep problems, including word problems, involving linear equations and linear inequalities in one variable and provide justification for each step.

9. The length of a rectangle is 3 centimeters more than two times its width. The perimeter of the rectangle is 84 centimeters. What is the length of the rectangle? *(p. 146)*

Ⓐ 13 centimeters

Ⓑ 17 centimeters

Ⓒ 27 centimeters

Ⓓ 29 centimeters

10. Solve $6x - 2 < -8(5 - x)$.

Step 1 $6x - 2 < -40 + 8x$
Step 2 $-2x - 2 < -40$
Step 3 $-2x < -38$
Step 4 $x < 19$

Which is the first *incorrect* step in the solution shown above? *(p. 202)*

Ⓐ Step 1   Ⓑ Step 2

Ⓒ Step 3   Ⓓ Step 4

Go On

Standard 6.0 Students graph a linear equation and compute the *x*- and *y*-intercepts (e.g., graph 2*x* + 6*y* = 4). They are also able to sketch the region defined by linear inequalities (e.g., they sketch the region defined by 2*x* + 6*y* < 4).

11. What is the *x*-intercept of the graph of −8*x* + *y* = 4? *(p. 273)*

Ⓐ −2

Ⓑ −$\frac{1}{2}$

Ⓒ $\frac{1}{2}$

Ⓓ 4

12. Which graph represents the solution set of the inequality 3*x* + 2*y* > 6? *(p. 425)*

Ⓐ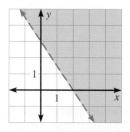

Ⓑ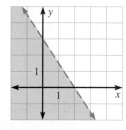

Ⓒ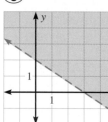

Ⓓ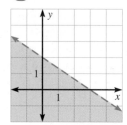

Standard 7.0 Students verify that a point lies on a line, given an equation of the line. Students are able to derive linear equations by using the point-slope formula.

13. Which point lies on the line defined by 7*x* − 2*y* = −2? *(p. 264)*

Ⓐ (−2, 6)

Ⓑ (0, −1)

Ⓒ (2, 6)

Ⓓ (2, 8)

14. What is the equation of the line that passes through the points (−2, −9) and (8, −14)? *(p. 329)*

Ⓐ $y = -\frac{1}{2}x - 10$

Ⓑ $y = -\frac{1}{2}x - 8$

Ⓒ $y = -2x - 13$

Ⓓ $y = -2x + 2$

Algebra 1   Standards Practice

Standard 8.0 Students understand the concepts of parallel lines and perpendicular lines and how their slopes are related. Students are able to find the equation of a line perpendicular to a given line that passes through a given point.

15. The equation of line ℓ is $y = 5x + 20$, and the equation of line q is $10x - 2y = 20$. Which statement about the two lines is true? *(p. 354)*

    Ⓐ Lines ℓ and q have the same x-intercept.

    Ⓑ Lines ℓ and q have the same y-intercept.

    Ⓒ Lines ℓ and q are parallel.

    Ⓓ Lines ℓ and q are perpendicular.

16. Which equation represents a line that is perpendicular to $y = 6x - 5$ and passes through the point $(-6, 3)$? *(p. 354)*

    Ⓐ $y = -6x - 33$

    Ⓑ $y = -\frac{1}{6}x + 2$

    Ⓒ $y = \frac{1}{6}x + 4$

    Ⓓ $y = 6x + 39$

Standard 9.0 Students solve a system of two linear equations in two variables algebraically and are able to interpret the answer graphically. Students are able to solve a system of two linear inequalities in two variables and to sketch the solution sets.

17. What is the solution to this system of equations? *(p. 405)*

$$\begin{cases} x + 3y = -9 \\ -3x + 2y = -17 \end{cases}$$

    Ⓐ $(0, -3)$

    Ⓑ $(3, -4)$

    Ⓒ No solution

    Ⓓ Infinitely many solutions

18. Which system of inequalities is shown on the graph below? *(p. 433)*

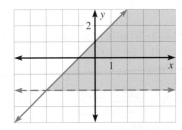

    Ⓐ $y \geq x + 1$ Ⓑ $y > x + 1$
         $y > -2$ $y \leq -2$

    Ⓒ $y < x + 1$ Ⓓ $y \leq x + 1$
         $y \geq -2$ $y > -2$

Go On

Standard 10.0 Students add, subtract, multiply, and divide monomials and polynomials. Students solve multistep problems, including word problems, by using these techniques.

19. $8x^2(-3x^3 + 5x - 1) = \underline{\ ?\ }$ *(p. 528)*

   Ⓐ $-24x^5 + 5x - 1$

   Ⓑ $-24x^5 + 40x^3 - 8x^2$

   Ⓒ $24x^5 + 40x^3 - 8x^2$

   Ⓓ $-24x^6 + 40x^3 - 8x^2$

20. $(9x^2 + 4x - 7) - (-x^2 + 8) = \underline{\ ?\ }$ *(p. 520)*

   Ⓐ $8x^2 + 4x + 1$

   Ⓑ $8x^2 + 4x - 15$

   Ⓒ $10x^2 + 4x + 1$

   Ⓓ $10x^2 + 4x - 15$

Standard 11.0 Students apply basic factoring techniques to second- and simple third-degree polynomials. These techniques include finding a common factor for all terms in a polynomial, recognizing the difference of two squares, and recognizing perfect squares of binomials.

21. Which is a factor of $x^2 - 5x + 6$? *(p. 556)*

   Ⓐ $x - 6$

   Ⓑ $x - 2$

   Ⓒ $x + 2$

   Ⓓ $x + 6$

22. Which of the following shows $20x^2 - 5y^2$ factored completely? *(p. 579)*

   Ⓐ $5(2x - y)^2$

   Ⓑ $5(4x^2 - y^2)$

   Ⓒ $5(2x + y)(2x - y)$

   Ⓓ $5(4x + y)(x - y)$

Standard 12.0 Students simplify fractions with polynomials in the numerator and denominator by factoring both and reducing them to the lowest terms.

23. What is $\dfrac{15a^2 + 5ab}{9a^2 + 6ab + b^2}$ reduced to lowest terms? *(p. 688)*

   Ⓐ $\dfrac{5}{3 + b}$

   Ⓑ $\dfrac{10}{9 + b^2}$

   Ⓒ $\dfrac{2a}{b}$

   Ⓓ $\dfrac{5a}{3a + b}$

24. Simplify $\dfrac{x^2 + x - 12}{2x^2 - 32}$ to lowest terms. *(p. 688)*

   Ⓐ $\dfrac{x - 3}{2(x - 4)}$

   Ⓑ $\dfrac{x - 3}{2(x + 4)}$

   Ⓒ $\dfrac{x + 3}{2(x - 4)}$

   Ⓓ $\dfrac{x + 3}{2(x + 4)}$

Algebra 1 | Standards Practice

Standard 13.0 Students add, subtract, multiply, and divide rational expressions and functions. Students solve both computationally and conceptually challenging problems by using these techniques.

25. $\dfrac{3}{2x^2 - 5x - 3} - \dfrac{1}{x^2 - x - 6} = \underline{\ ?\ }$ *(p. 705)*

  (A) $\dfrac{x - 7}{(2x - 1)(x + 3)(x - 2)}$

  (B) $\dfrac{x - 5}{(2x - 1)(x + 3)(x - 2)}$

  (C) $\dfrac{x + 3}{(2x + 1)(x - 3)(x + 2)}$

  (D) $\dfrac{x + 5}{(2x + 1)(x - 3)(x + 2)}$

26. Which expression equals the product $\left(\dfrac{3a^2 + 11a - 4}{a - 4}\right)\left(\dfrac{1}{3a - 1}\right)$? *(p. 696)*

  (A) -1

  (B) $\dfrac{a - 4}{a + 4}$

  (C) $\dfrac{a + 4}{a - 4}$

  (D) $\dfrac{3a^2 + 11a - 4}{3a^2 + 13a + 4}$

Standard 14.0 Students solve a quadratic equation by factoring or completing the square.

27. What quantity should be added to both sides of the equation

$$x^2 - 10x = 12$$

to complete the square? *(p. 643)*

  (A) -5 (B) 5

  (C) 25 (D) 100

28. What are the solutions for the quadratic equation $2x^2 + 5x = 3$? *(p. 566)*

  (A) $-3, \dfrac{1}{2}$ (B) $-\dfrac{3}{2}, -1$

  (C) $-\dfrac{3}{2}, 1$ (D) $1, \dfrac{3}{2}$

Standard 15.0 Students apply algebraic techniques to solve rate problems, work problems, and percent mixture problems.

29. A boat takes 2 hours to travel 22 miles downstream (with the current) and 4.4 hours to return the 22 miles upstream (against the current). The speed of the current remains constant. What is the speed of the current? *(p. 413)*

  (A) 3 miles per hour

  (B) 5 miles per hour

  (C) 8 miles per hour

  (D) 11 miles per hour

30. John takes 60 minutes to mow the lawn, and his brother Joe takes 90 minutes to mow the lawn. How long do John and Joe working together take to mow the lawn? *(p. 721)*

  (A) 30 minutes

  (B) 36 minutes

  (C) 75 minutes

  (D) 150 minutes

Go On

Standard 16.0 Students understand the concepts of a relation and a function, determine whether a given relation defines a function, and give pertinent information about given relations and functions.

31. Which relation is a function? *(p. 249)*

   Ⓐ {(3, 1), (3, 2), (3, 3), (3, 4)}

   Ⓑ {(4, −2), (4, 2), (9, −3), (9, 3)}

   Ⓒ {(−2, 4), (2, 4), (−3, 9), (3, 9)}

   Ⓓ {(3, 6), (4, 8), (8, 6), (4, 6)}

32. Which relation is *not* a function? *(p. 249)*

   Ⓐ {(−3, 9), (−1, 1), (0, 0), (1, 1), (3, 9)}

   Ⓑ {(−2, 1), (−1, 1), (0, 1), (1, 1), (2, 1)}

   Ⓒ {(−2, −2), (−1, −1), (1, 1), (2, 2)}

   Ⓓ {(−2, −1), (−2, 1), (2, −1), (2, 1)}

Standard 17.0 Students determine the domain of independent variables and the range of dependent variables defined by a graph, a set of ordered pairs, or a symbolic expression.

33. What is the domain of the function shown on the graph below? *(p. 257)*

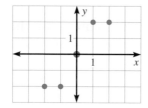

   Ⓐ {−2, 2}

   Ⓑ {−2, 0, 2}

   Ⓒ {−2, −1, 1, 2}

   Ⓓ {−2, −1, 0, 1, 2}

34. The domain of the function $y = x^2 - 2$ is {−2, −1, 0, 1, 2}. What is the range of the function? *(p. 249)*

   Ⓐ {−6, −3, −1, 0, 2}

   Ⓑ {−2, −1, 0, 1, 2}

   Ⓒ {−2, −1, 2}

   Ⓓ {0, 1, 4}

Algebra 1   Standards Practice

Standard 18.0 Students determine whether a relation defined by a graph, a set of ordered pairs, or a symbolic expression is a function and justify the conclusion.

35. Which graph represents a function? *(p. 257)*

Ⓐ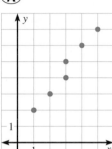

Ⓑ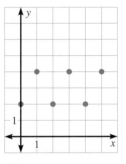

Ⓒ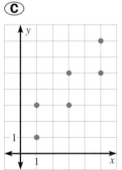

Ⓓ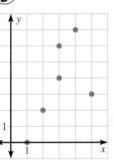

36. Three ordered pairs of a function are $(-4, 5)$, $(0, 1)$, and $(2, 10)$. Which ordered pair *cannot* be a fourth ordered pair of the function? *(p. 249)*

Ⓐ $(-10, 5)$

Ⓑ $(-5, 4)$

Ⓒ $(0, 5)$

Ⓓ $(10, 2)$

Standard 19.0 Students know the quadratic formula and are familiar with its proof by completing the square.

37. Four steps to derive the quadratic formula are shown below.

$$\text{I} \quad x + \frac{b}{2a} = \pm\sqrt{\frac{b^2 - 4ac}{4a^2}}$$

$$\text{II} \quad x = \frac{-b \pm \sqrt{b^2 - 4ac}}{2a}$$

$$\text{III} \quad \left(x + \frac{b}{2a}\right)^2 = \frac{b^2 - 4ac}{4a^2}$$

$$\text{IV} \quad x + \frac{b}{2a} = \frac{\pm\sqrt{b^2 - 4ac}}{2a}$$

What is the correct order for these steps? *(p. 649)*

Ⓐ I, III, IV, II   Ⓑ II, IV, I, III

Ⓒ III, I, IV, II   Ⓓ III, IV, I, II

38. What are the solutions to the equation $rx^2 + sx + t = 0$, where r, s, and t are real numbers and r is not zero? *(p. 649)*

Ⓐ $x = \dfrac{-s \pm \sqrt{s^2 - 4rt}}{2}$

Ⓑ $x = \dfrac{-r \pm \sqrt{r^2 - 4st}}{2s}$

Ⓒ $x = \dfrac{-s \pm \sqrt{s^2 - 4rt}}{2r}$

Ⓓ $x = \dfrac{-t \pm \sqrt{t^2 - 4rt}}{2r}$

Go On

Standard 20.0 Students use the quadratic formula to find the roots of a second-degree polynomial and to solve quadratic equations.

39. Which is one of the roots of the polynomial $x^2 + 2x - 1$? *(p. 649)*

(A) $1 - \sqrt{2}$

(B) 1

(C) $-1 + \sqrt{2}$

(D) $-1 + 2\sqrt{2}$

40. Which statement *best* explains why the equation $-x^2 + 6x - 9 = 0$ has exactly one real solution? *(p. 657)*

(A) The value of $6^2 - 4(-1)(-9)$ is negative.

(B) The value of $6^2 - 4(-1)(-9)$ is 0.

(C) The value of $6^2 - 4(-1)(-9)$ is positive.

(D) The value of $6^2 - 4(-1)(-9)$ is a perfect square.

Standard 21.0 Students graph quadratic functions and know that their roots are the *x*-intercepts.

41. Which graph is the graph of the equation $y = -x^2 - 2x + 4$? *(p. 612)*

(A)

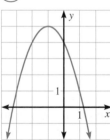

(B)

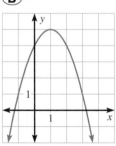

(C)

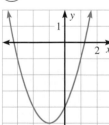

(D)

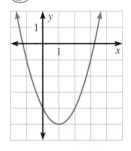

42. The graph of the equation $y = 0.5x^2 - 2.5x + 2$ is shown below.

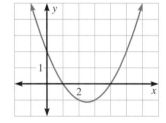

For what value or values of x is $y = 0$? *(p. 624)*

(A) 2 only

(B) 4 only

(C) 1 and 2

(D) 1 and 4

Algebra 1 | Standards Practice

Standard 22.0 Students use the quadratic formula or factoring techniques or both to determine whether the graph of a quadratic function will intersect the *x*-axis in zero, one, or two points.

43. How many times does the graph of $y = 3(x + 4)^2$ intersect the *x*-axis? *(p. 618)*

Ⓐ None

Ⓑ One

Ⓒ Two

Ⓓ Three

44. For which value of *c* will the graph of $y = 2x^2 + 4x + c$ have no *x*-intercepts? *(p. 657)*

Ⓐ −2

Ⓑ 0

Ⓒ 2

Ⓓ 4

Standard 23.0 Students apply quadratic equations to physical problems, such as the motion of an object under the force of gravity.

45. The height *h* (in feet) of an object *t* seconds after it is dropped from an initial height of *s* feet is modeled by the equation $h = -16t^2 + s$. After how many seconds will a penny dropped from a height of 36 feet reach the ground? *(p. 633)*

Ⓐ 1 second

Ⓑ 1.5 seconds

Ⓒ 4 seconds

Ⓓ 6 seconds

46. The area of the rectangle shown below is 12 square feet. What is the length of the shorter side of the rectangle? *(p. 566)*

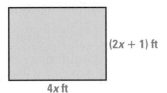

(2x + 1) ft

4x ft

Ⓐ 1 foot

Ⓑ 2 feet

Ⓒ 3 feet

Ⓓ 4 feet

Go On ➡

Standards Practice

Standard 24.0 Students use and know simple aspects of a logical argument:

Standard 24.1 Students explain the difference between inductive and deductive reasoning and identify and provide examples of each.

47. Ben uses the table below to conclude that if n is odd, then $n + 3$ is even.

n	1	3	5	7
$n + 3$	4	6	8	10

Amy uses the following reasoning to make the same conclusion:

If n is odd, then n can be written as $n = 2m + 1$ where m is a whole number. Then $n + 3 = 2m + 4 = 2(m + 2)$. Because $2(m + 2)$ is the product of 2 and a whole number, $2(m + 2)$ is always even.

Which of the following statements is true? *(p. 102)*

(A) Amy used inductive reasoning, and Ben used deductive reasoning.

(B) Amy used deductive reasoning, and Ben used inductive reasoning.

(C) Both Amy and Ben used deductive reasoning.

(D) Both Amy and Ben used inductive reasoning.

48. Look at the following list of calculations:

$$\sqrt{2^{2 \cdot 3}} = \sqrt{2^6} = \sqrt{64} = 8$$
$$\sqrt{2^{2 \cdot 4}} = \sqrt{2^8} = \sqrt{256} = 16$$
$$\sqrt{3^{2 \cdot 2}} = \sqrt{3^4} = \sqrt{81} = 9$$
$$\sqrt{3^{2 \cdot 3}} = \sqrt{3^6} = \sqrt{729} = 27$$

Which statement about two positive real numbers a and b is supported by the calculations? *(p. 483)*

(A) $\sqrt{a^{2b}} = ab$

(B) $\sqrt{a^{2b}} = a^b$

(C) $\sqrt{a^{2b}} = b^a$

(D) $\sqrt{a^{2b}} = a\sqrt{b}$

Algebra 1 — Standards Practice

Standard 24.2 Students identify the hypothesis and conclusion in logical deduction.

49. What is the hypothesis of the following statement? *(p. 53)*

If a number is an even number, then the square of the number is an even number.

- **Ⓐ** A number is an even number
- **Ⓑ** The square of the number is an even number
- **Ⓒ** A number is not an even number
- **Ⓓ** The square of the number is not an even number

50. Consider the statement "No whole number is an irrational number." To write this statement in if-then form, Leah begins by writing, "If a number is a whole number, then…." Which of the following is the correct conclusion for Leah's statement? *(p. 94)*

- **Ⓐ** The number is not a rational number
- **Ⓑ** The number is an irrational number
- **Ⓒ** The number is not an irrational number
- **Ⓓ** The number is not a negative number

Standard 24.3 Students use counterexamples to show that an assertion is false and recognize that a single counterexample is sufficient to refute an assertion.

51. Which number serves as a counterexample to the statement below? *(p. 53)*

The reciprocal of a number is less than the original number.

- **Ⓐ** $-\dfrac{1}{2}$
- **Ⓑ** $\dfrac{1}{2}$
- **Ⓒ** $\dfrac{3}{2}$
- **Ⓓ** 4

52. Emma evaluated the expression $n^2 - n$ for four values of n.

n	3	4	5	6
$n^2 - n$	6	12	20	30

She concluded that for all integers n, $n^2 - n$ represents a positive number. Which number serves as a counterexample to prove Emma's conclusion false? *(p. 102)*

- **Ⓐ** -2
- **Ⓑ** -1
- **Ⓒ** 1
- **Ⓓ** 2

Go On

Standards Practice

Standard 25.0 Students use properties of the number system to judge the validity of results, to justify each step of a procedure, and to prove or disprove statements:

Standard 25.1 Students use properties of numbers to construct simple, valid arguments (direct and indirect) for, or formulate counterexamples to, claimed assertions.

53. Sam claims that $9 \div \frac{1}{4} = 4 \div \frac{1}{9}$. He uses the following steps to prove his claim.

Step 1 $9 \div \frac{1}{4} = 9 \cdot 4$

Step 2 $\quad\quad = 4 \cdot 9$

Step 3 $\quad\quad = 4 \div \frac{1}{9}$

Which property did Sam use for Step 2? *(p. 88)*

  (A) Distributive property

  (B) Division rule

  (C) Commutative property of multiplication

  (D) Associative property of multiplication

54. Which property of equality is used in the statement "If $x = y$ and $y = z$, then $x = z$"? *(p. 102)*

  (A) Reflexive property

  (B) Symmetric property

  (C) Transitive property

  (D) Addition property

Standard 25.2 Students judge the validity of an argument according to whether the properties of the real number system and the order of operations have been applied correctly at each step.

55. Eli wrote these steps to evaluate $5(3 - 2) - 4(1 - 3)$.

$5(3 - 2) - 4(1 - 3)$

$= 15 - 10 - 4 + 12 \quad$ (Step 1)

$= 5 - 16 \quad$ (Step 2)

$= -11 \quad$ (Step 3)

Which of the following is true? *(p. 11)*

  (A) Eli made an error in Step 1.

  (B) Eli made an error in Step 2.

  (C) Eli made an error in Step 3.

  (D) Eli made no errors.

56. Zach wrote these steps to simplify the expression $2 - 12(x + 3) - 7$.

$2 - 12(x + 3) - 7$

$= -10(x + 3) - 7 \quad$ (Step 1)

$= -10x - 30 - 7 \quad$ (Step 2)

$= -10x - 37 \quad$ (Step 3)

Which of the following is true? *(p. 81)*

  (A) Zach made an error in Step 1.

  (B) Zach made an error in Step 2.

  (C) Zach made an error in Step 3.

  (D) Zach made no errors.

Algebra 1 — Standards Practice

Standard 25.3 Given a specific algebraic statement involving linear, quadratic, or absolute value expressions or equations or inequalities, students determine whether the statement is true sometimes, always, or never.

57. When is this statement true? *(p. 103)*

$$|x| < x$$

(A) This statement is never true.

(B) This statement is always true.

(C) This statement is true only for positive values of x.

(D) This statement is true only for negative values of x.

58. When is this statement true? *(p. 102)*

For real numbers x and y,
$x - y > x + y$.

(A) This statement is never true.

(B) This statement is always true.

(C) This statement is true if x is negative.

(D) This statement is true if y is negative.

Pre-Course Test

Number Sense

Factors and Multiples *(Standards Review pp. 784–785)*

Find the greatest common factor and the least common multiple of the numbers.

1. 24, 36   **2.** 4, 16   **3.** 45, 65   **4.** 100, 18

Operations *(Standards Review pp. 783, 786–789)*

Find the quotient and remainder.

5. $113 \div 6$ **6.** $504 \div 8$ **7.** $947 \div 11$ **8.** $1580 \div 25$

Perform the indicated operation. Simplify if possible.

9. $\frac{3}{9} + \frac{7}{9}$ **10.** $\frac{7}{12} - \frac{5}{12}$ **11.** $2\frac{1}{6} - \frac{5}{6}$ **12.** $\frac{3}{8} + 4\frac{1}{12}$

13. $5 - 2\frac{3}{10}$ **14.** $6\frac{11}{16} + 1\frac{3}{4}$ **15.** $\frac{2}{5} \times \frac{3}{4}$ **16.** $8 \times \frac{2}{7}$

17. $\frac{9}{14} \div \frac{5}{7}$ **18.** $\frac{5}{8} \div 2$ **19.** $2\frac{1}{4} \times 4\frac{3}{4}$ **20.** $3\frac{5}{6} \div 2\frac{3}{10}$

Decimals, Fractions, and Percents *(Standards Review pp. 790–793)*

Rewrite the numbers in the list as decimals, if necessary. Then order the numbers from least to greatest.

21. $0.6,\ 1,\ \frac{3}{4},\ 48\%,\ 1\frac{1}{10}$ **22.** $3\frac{1}{3},\ 300\%,\ \frac{25}{8},\ 2\frac{5}{6},\ 250\%$ **23.** $166\frac{2}{3}\%,\ 1.7,\ 1.67,\ \frac{7}{4},\ \frac{8}{5}$

24. $4,\ \frac{25}{6},\ 390\%,\ 4.1,\ 3\frac{5}{6}$ **25.** $1.4,\ 1.43,\ 1.432,\ \frac{10}{7},\ 1\frac{3}{5}$ **26.** $20\%,\ 2,\ 0.22,\ \frac{2}{3},\ \frac{2}{5}$

Find the percent of the number.

27. 30% of 110   **28.** 25% of 66   **29.** 19% of 173   **30.** 205% of 50

Algebra and Functions

Coordinate Plane *(Standards Review p. 794)*

Plot the point in a coordinate plane.

31. $A(2, 6)$ **32.** $B(3, -4)$ **33.** $C(-1, -1)$ **34.** $D(-5, 3)$

35. $E(7, 0)$ **36.** $F(-2, 2)$ **37.** $G(0, -5)$ **38.** $H(-3, -6)$

Converting Units of Measurement *(Standards Review p. 795)*

Copy and complete.

39. $144 \text{ in.} = \underline{\ ?\ } \text{ ft}$ **40.** $187 \text{ m} = \underline{\ ?\ } \text{ cm}$ **41.** $1660 \text{ sec} = \underline{\ ?\ } \text{ min}$

42. $2.5 \text{ h} = \underline{\ ?\ } \text{ min}$ **43.** $59.1 \text{ km} = \underline{\ ?\ } \text{ m}$ **44.** $3 \text{ h} = \underline{\ ?\ } \text{ sec}$

Measurement and Geometry

Two-dimensional and Three-dimensional Figures
(Standards Review pp. 796–800)

45. Find the perimeter and area of a rectangle with a length of 5 feet and a width of 17 feet.

46. Find the circumference and area of a circle with a diameter of 16 centimeters. Give your answer in terms of π.

Find the surface area and volume of the prism, sphere, or cylinder. For the sphere and the cylinder, round your answer to the nearest tenth.

47.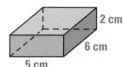

48.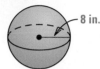

49.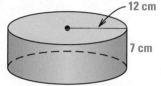

Translations *(Standards Review pp. 801–802)*

50. Draw the polygon with vertices $(-2, -1)$, $(1, -2)$, $(2, 2)$, and $(0, 4)$. Then find the coordinates of the vertices of the image after a translation of 4 units to the right and 3 units down, and draw the image.

51. Draw the line segment with endpoints $(-4, -2)$ and $(2, -3)$. Then draw the reflection of the line segment in the y-axis.

Statistics, Data Analysis, and Probability

Data Analysis *(Standards Review pp. 803–804)*

Use the line graph, which shows the high temperature for each of the first six days of a month.

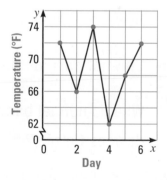

52. On which day was the temperature the coldest?

53. What was the change in temperature from the first day to the second day?

54. Find the mean, median, and mode of the data in the graph.

Mathematical Reasoning

Logical Reasoning and Problem Solving *(Standards Review pp. 805–809)*

55. Four sisters are going to a park together. In how many different ways can the sisters stand in a row for a photo in front of the park?

56. A large pizza with 8 slices costs $10. Carl ate 5 slices of pizza, and Jorge ate 3 slices. How much of the total cost of the pizza should each person pay?

57. Are the following statements *always*, *sometimes*, or *never* true? *Explain.*

    a. A whole number less than 20 that has 3 as a factor also has 6 as a factor.

    b. A factor of 48 that is greater than 1 is even.

Pre-Course Test

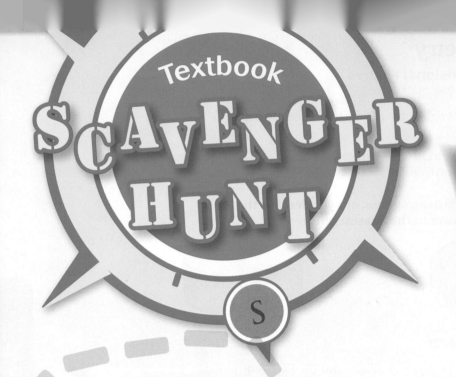

Textbook SCAVENGER HUNT

S

Practice using your textbook!

Use the student resources described on the next page to answer each question. Give page numbers to show where you found the answer to the question.

1 What is a monomial?

2 Tell what each of these symbols means: $\sqrt{a}$, $n!$, $\pm$.

3 How many yards are there in 1 mile?

4 On what page of the book is the distributive property first discussed?

5 What is normal body temperature in degrees Fahrenheit? in degrees Celsius?

6 What is a conjecture?

7 On what page can you review the skill of adding fractions?

8 On what page can you find selected answers for Lesson 1.1?

9 What formula can you use to find the volume of a cylinder?

Student Resources in Your Textbook

Your textbook contains many resources that you can use for reference when you are studying or doing your homework.

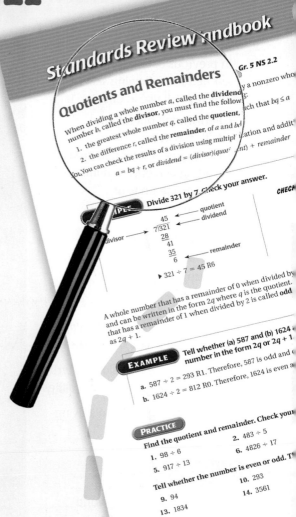

Standards Review Handbook Use the Standards Review Handbook on pages 783–809 to review material learned in previous courses.

Tables Refer to the tables on pages 822–829 if you need information about mathematical symbols, measures, formulas, and properties.

English-Spanish Glossary Use the English-Spanish Glossary on pages 830–858 to look up the meanings of math vocabulary terms in both English and Spanish. Each glossary entry also tells where in your book a term is covered in more detail.

Index Use the Index on pages 859–872 as a quick guide for finding out where a particular math topic is covered in the book.

Selected Answers Use the Selected Answers starting on page SA1 to check your work or to see whether you are on the right track in solving a problem.

Expressions, Equations, and Problem Solving

Before

In previous courses, you learned the following skills, which you'll use in Chapter 1:

- Performing operations with fractions
- Finding perimeter and area
- Finding percents of numbers
- Converting units of measurement

Now

In Chapter 1 you'll study these **Big Ideas:**

1 Writing and evaluating algebraic expressions

2 Using expressions to write equations and inequalities

3 Using a problem solving plan

Why?

So you can solve real-world problems about . . .

- Football, p. 16
- Wildlife education, p. 23
- Digital photos, p. 23
- Triathlons, p. 30
- Part-time jobs, p. 31
- Hiking, p. 36

 **Algebra**
at *classzone.com*

Get-Ready Games

Vacation Views

California Standards

Review adding fractions. **Gr. 6 NS 2.1**
Prepare for evaluating expressions. **Gr. 7 AF 1.2**

KIM	DAVE	ANN	SAM
$\frac{11}{6}$	$2\frac{3}{5}$	$4\frac{7}{12}$	$\frac{4}{5}$
$\frac{5}{12}$	$\frac{1}{3}$	$\frac{5}{6}$	$3\frac{1}{10}$
$5\frac{1}{2}$	$1\frac{11}{15}$	$\frac{8}{3}$	$\frac{7}{2}$
$\frac{1}{8}$	$9\frac{1}{15}$	$6\frac{11}{18}$	$7\frac{1}{4}$
$6\frac{3}{4}$	$\frac{6}{5}$	$\frac{4}{9}$	$\frac{9}{20}$

How to Play

On a family trip, the first stop is a mountain lookout tower. Four ladders lead to the top of the tower. Who reaches the top first?

- Find the sum of the fractions on the rungs of each ladder.
- The ladder with the least sum is the one that is climbed the fastest.

· Next Stop ·

California Standards

Review converting units of measure. *Gr. 6 AF 2.1*
Prepare for problem solving. *Gr. 7 MR 2.5*

| 415 meters | centimeters |
| 41.5 M   4150 E   41,500 U | ? |

| 19 seconds | minutes |
| 0.32 N   41 D   1140 A | ? |

| 8.1 millimeters | centimeters |
| 0.081 A   0.81 H   810 T | ? |

| 588 feet | yards |
| 49 R   196 C   1764 S | ? |

| 60 feet | inches |
| 5 E   120 N   720 L | ? |

5575

How to Play

Find the next stop on the family trip by converting measures. Round to the nearest tenth.

- For each measure, choose the correct equivalent measure using the unit listed on the right.
- In the blank below the new unit, write the letter that corresponds with your choice.
- Rearrange the letters to find the next stop.

Games Wrap-Up

Draw Conclusions

Complete these exercises after playing the games.

1. **WRITING** *Describe* the steps you take to compare mixed numbers.

2. **REASONING** Look back at *Next Stop*. Without performing any calculations, how can you choose the correct conversion of 19 seconds to minutes? *Explain*.

Prerequisite Skills

California @HomeTutor

Prerequisite skills practice
at classzone.com

REVIEW VOCABULARY

- **numerator,** *p. 786*
- **denominator,** *p. 786*
- **equivalent fractions,** *p. 786*
- **percent,** *p. 791*
- **perimeter,** *p. 796*
- **area,** *p. 796*

VOCABULARY CHECK

Copy and complete the statement.

1. In the fraction $\frac{2}{3}$, 2 is the __?__ and 3 is the __?__.

2. Two fractions that represent the same number are called __?__.

3. The __?__ of a figure is the distance around it.

SKILLS CHECK

Perform the indicated operation. *(Review pp. 788–789 for 1.1, 1.2.)*

4. $\frac{2}{3} + \frac{3}{5}$
5. $\frac{5}{6} - \frac{3}{4}$
6. $\frac{3}{5} \times \frac{2}{3}$
7. $\frac{1}{2} \div \frac{5}{8}$

Write the percent as a decimal. *(Review p. 791 for 1.5.)*

8. 4%
9. 23%
10. 1.5%
11. 2.5%

12. Find the perimeter and area of the rectangle. *(Review p. 796 for 1.5.)*

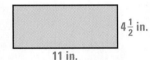

$4\frac{1}{2}$ in.

11 in.

Notetaking Skills

NOW YOU TRY
Make a *formula triangle* for the volume of a rectangular prism, $V = Bh$.

Focus on Graphic Organizers

You can use a *formula triangle* to organize the variables and operations of a formula that involves only multiplication, such as the formula for the area of a rectangle, $A = \ell w$.

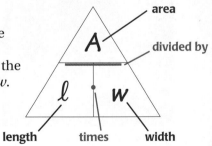

area
divided by
length   times   width

Cover the variable that you want to find.

Use the remaining variables and the operation between them to find the unknown variable.

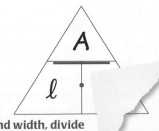

To find width, divide area by length.

1.1 Evaluate Expressions and Use Exponents

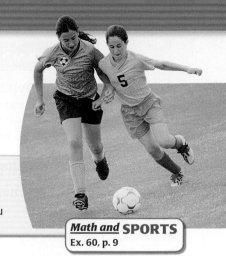

Standards Preparation

Gr. 6 AF 1.2 Write and **evaluate an algebraic expression for a given situation, using up to three variables.**

Connect *Before* you worked with whole numbers, fractions, and decimals. *Now* you will evaluate algebraic expressions to prepare for Algebra 1 Standard 4.0.

Math and SPORTS
Ex. 60, p. 9

Key Vocabulary
• variable
• algebraic expression
• power
• base
• exponent

A **variable** is a letter used to represent one or more numbers. The numbers are the values of the variable. *Expressions* consist of numbers, variables, and operations. An **algebraic expression**, or *variable expression*, is an expression that includes at least one variable.

Algebraic expression	Meaning	Operation
$5(n)$ $5 \cdot n$ $5n$	5 times n	Multiplication
$\dfrac{14}{y}$ $14 \div y$	14 divided by y	Division
$6 + c$	6 plus c	Addition
$8 - x$	8 minus x	Subtraction

To **evaluate an algebraic expression**, substitute a number for each variable, perform the operation(s), and simplify the result, if necessary.

EXAMPLE 1 Evaluate algebraic expressions

Evaluate the expression when $n = 3$.

AVOID ERRORS
Use the multiplication symbol $\cdot$ instead of $\times$ in algebraic expressions to avoid confusing $\times$ with the variable x.

a. $13 \cdot n = 13 \cdot 3$ **Substitute 3 for n.**

      $= 39$ **Multiply.**

b. $\dfrac{9}{n} = \dfrac{9}{3}$ **Substitute 3 for n.**

      $= 3$ **Divide.**

c. $n - 1 = 3 - 1$ **Substitute 3 for n.**

      $= 2$ **Subtract.**

d. $n + 8 = 3 + 8$ **Substitute 3 for n.**

      $= 11$ **Add.**

✓ **GUIDED PRACTICE**   for Example 1

Evaluate the expression when $y = 2$.

1. $6y$ **2.** $\dfrac{8}{y}$ **3.** $y + 4$ **4.** $11 - y$

EXAMPLE 2 **Evaluate an expression in two variables**

MOVIES The total cost of seeing a movie at a theater can be represented by the expression $a + r$ where a is the cost (in dollars) of admission and r is the cost (in dollars) of refreshments. Suppose you pay $7.50 for admission and $7.25 for refreshments. Find the total cost.

Solution

$$\text{Total cost} = a + r \qquad \text{Write expression.}$$
$$= 7.50 + 7.25 \qquad \text{Substitute 7.50 for } a \text{ and 7.25 for } r.$$
$$= 14.75 \qquad \text{Add.}$$

▶ The total cost is $14.75.

EXPRESSIONS USING EXPONENTS A **power** is an expression that represents repeated multiplication of the same factor. For example, 81 is a power of 3 because $81 = 3 \cdot 3 \cdot 3 \cdot 3$. A power can be written in a form using two numbers, a **base** and an **exponent**. The exponent represents the number of times the base is used as a factor, so 81 can be written as 3^4.

base → exponent

$$3^4 = \underbrace{3 \cdot 3 \cdot 3 \cdot 3}_{\text{4 factors of 3}}$$

power

EXAMPLE 3 **Read and write powers**

Write the power in words and as a product.

Power	Words	Product
a. 7^1	seven to the first power	7
b. 5^2	five to the second power, or five *squared*	$5 \cdot 5$
c. $\left(\frac{1}{2}\right)^3$	one half to the third power, or one half *cubed*	$\frac{1}{2} \cdot \frac{1}{2} \cdot \frac{1}{2}$
d. z^5	z to the fifth power	$z \cdot z \cdot z \cdot z \cdot z$

WRITE EXPONENTS For a number raised to the first power, you usually do not write the exponent 1. For instance, you write 7^1 simply as 7.

✓ **GUIDED PRACTICE** for Examples 2 and 3

5. **WHAT IF?** In Example 2, suppose you go back to the theater with a friend to see an afternoon movie. You pay for both admissions. Your total cost (in dollars) can be represented by the expression $2a$. If each admission costs $4.75, what is your total cost?

Write the power in words and as a product.

6. 9^5 　　　　　　　 7. 2^8 　　　　　　　 8. n^4

EXAMPLE 4 **Evaluate powers**

Evaluate the expression.

  a. x^4 when $x = 2$ **b.** n^3 when $n = 1.5$

Solution

  a. $x^4 = 2^4$ **b.** $n^3 = 1.5^3$

        $= 2 \cdot 2 \cdot 2 \cdot 2$ $= (1.5)(1.5)(1.5)$

        $= 16$ $= 3.375$

✔ **GUIDED PRACTICE**   **for Example 4**

Evaluate the expression.

  9. x^3 when $x = 8$ **10.** k^2 when $k = 2.5$ **11.** d^4 when $d = \frac{1}{3}$

REVIEW AREA AND VOLUME
For help with area and volume, see pp. 796 and 799.

AREA AND VOLUME Exponents are used in the formulas for the area of a square and the volume of a cube. In fact, the words *squared* and *cubed* come from the formula for the area of a square and the formula for the volume of a cube.

$A = s^2$ $V = s^3$

EXAMPLE 5 **Evaluate a power**

STORAGE CUBES Each edge of the medium-sized pop-up storage cube shown is 14 inches long. The storage cube is made so that it can be folded flat when not in use. Find the volume of the storage cube.

Solution

  $V = s^3$ **Write formula for volume.**

    $= 14^3$ **Substitute 14 for *s*.**

    $= 2744$ **Evaluate power.**

▶ The volume of the storage cube is 2744 cubic inches.

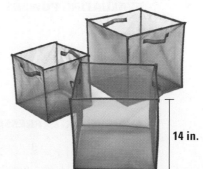

14 in.

✔ **GUIDED PRACTICE**   **for Example 5**

  12. WHAT IF? In Example 5, suppose the storage cube is folded flat to form a square. Find the area of the square.

1.1 EXERCISES

HOMEWORK KEY

◆ = **MULTIPLE CHOICE PRACTICE**
Exs. 18, 52, 53, 61, and 65–67

○ = **HINTS AND HOMEWORK HELP**
for Exs. 21, 39, and 59 at classzone.com

SKILLS · PROBLEM SOLVING · REASONING

1. VOCABULARY Identify the exponent and the base in the expression 6^{12}.

2. WRITING *Describe* the steps you would take to evaluate the expression n^5 when $n = 3$. Then evaluate the expression.

EXAMPLE 1
on p. 5
for Exs. 3–18

EVALUATING EXPRESSIONS Evaluate the expression.

3. $15x$ when $x = 4$
4. $0.4r$ when $r = 6$
5. $w - 8$ when $w = 20$

6. $n + 17$ when $n = 9$
7. $\dfrac{y}{3}$ when $y = 21$
8. $30 - t$ when $t = 8$

9. $1.6 - g$ when $g = 1.2$
10. $5 + m$ when $m = 7$
11. $0.8 + h$ when $h = 3.7$

12. $\dfrac{24}{f}$ when $f = 8$
13. $\dfrac{t}{5}$ when $t = 4.5$
14. $2.5m$ when $m = 4$

15. $\dfrac{1}{2}k$ when $k = \dfrac{2}{3}$
16. $y - \dfrac{1}{2}$ when $y = \dfrac{5}{6}$
17. $h + \dfrac{1}{3}$ when $h = 1\dfrac{1}{3}$

18. ◆ **MULTIPLE CHOICE** What is the value of $2.5z$ when $z = 10$?

(A) 0.25
(B) 2.5
(C) 12.5
(D) 25

EXAMPLE 3
on p. 6
for Exs. 19–26

WRITING POWERS Write the power in words and as a product.

19. 12^5
20. 7^3
21. $(0.3)^4$
22. $(3.2)^2$

23. $\left(\dfrac{1}{2}\right)^8$
24. n^7
25. y^6
26. t^4

EXAMPLE 4
on p. 7
for Exs. 27–40

ERROR ANALYSIS *Describe* and correct the error in evaluating the power.

27. $(0.4)^2 = 2(0.4) = 0.8$ ✗

28. $5^4 = 4 \cdot 4 \cdot 4 \cdot 4 \cdot 4 = 1024$ ✗

EVALUATING POWERS Evaluate the power.

29. 3^2
30. 10^2
31. 1^5
32. 11^3

33. 5^3
34. 4^5
35. 2^6
36. 6^4

37. $\left(\dfrac{1}{4}\right)^2$
38. $\left(\dfrac{2}{3}\right)^4$
39. $\left(\dfrac{3}{5}\right)^3$
40. $\left(\dfrac{1}{6}\right)^3$

EVALUATING EXPRESSIONS Evaluate the expression.

41. x^2 when $x = \dfrac{3}{4}$
42. p^2 when $p = 1.1$

43. b^3 when $b = 4$
44. w^3 when $w = 0.5$

45. $x + y$ when $x = 11$ and $y = 6.4$
46. kn when $k = 9$ and $n = 4.5$

47. $w - z$ when $w = 9.5$ and $z = 2.8$
48. $\dfrac{b}{c}$ when $b = 24$ and $c = 2.5$

49. xyz when $x = 4$, $y = 5.5$, and $z = 2.5$
50. $x + y + z$ when $x = 14$, $y = 8.7$, and $z = 20$

51. ERROR ANALYSIS *Describe* and correct the error in evaluating the expression $\frac{a}{b}$ when $a = 48$ and $b = 12$.

$$\frac{a}{b} = \frac{12}{48} = \frac{1}{4} \quad \times$$

52. ◆ **MULTIPLE CHOICE** Which expression has the greatest value when $x = 10$ and $y = 0.5$?

(A) xy (B) $x - y$ (C) $\frac{x}{y}$ (D) $\frac{y}{x}$

53. ◆ **MULTIPLE CHOICE** Let b be the number of tokens you bought at an arcade, and let u be the number you have used. Which expression represents the number of tokens remaining?

(A) $b + u$ (B) $b - u$ (C) bu (D) $\frac{b}{u}$

CONNECT SKILLS TO PROBLEM SOLVING Exercises 54–56 will help you prepare for problem solving.

54. There are $12x$ eggs in x cartons. How many eggs are in 3 cartons?

55. The value (in cents) of y dimes is $10y$. What is the value (in cents) of 5 dimes?

56. The area of a square with a side length of s is s^2. What is the area of a square with a side length of 3 inches?

EXAMPLES
2 and 5
on pp. 6–7
for Exs. 57–61

57. **GEOMETRY** The perimeter of a square with a side length of s is given by the expression $4s$. What is the perimeter of the square shown?

7.5 m

California @HomeTutor for problem solving help at classzone.com

58. LEOPARD FROG You can estimate the distance (in centimeters) that a leopard frog can jump using the expression 13ℓ where ℓ is the frog's length (in centimeters). What distance can a leopard frog that is 12.5 centimeters long jump?

California @HomeTutor for problem solving help at classzone.com

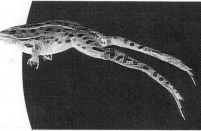

Leopard frog

59. MULTI-STEP PROBLEM You are buying a tank for three fish. You have one fish that is 3.5 inches long, another that is 5.5 inches long, and a third that is 3 inches long. The area (in square inches) of water surface the fish need is given by the expression $12f$ where f is the sum of the lengths (in inches) of all the fish in the tank.

a. What is the total length of the three fish?

b. How many square inches of water surface do the fish need?

60. MULTI-STEP PROBLEM Jen was the leading scorer on her soccer team. She scored 120 goals and had 20 assists in her high school career.

a. The number n of points awarded for goals is given by $2g$ where g is the number of goals scored. How many points did Jen earn for goals?

b. The point total is given by $n + a$ where a is the number of assists. Use your answer from part (a) to find Jen's point total.

61. ◆ **MULTIPLE CHOICE** For a snow sculpture contest, snow is packed into the shape of a cube with an edge length of 8 feet. One cubic foot of the snow weighs about 30 pounds. You can estimate the weight (in pounds) of the cube of snow using the expression $30V$ where V is the volume (in cubic feet) of the snow. About how much does the uncarved cube of snow weigh?

1 ft³ of packed snow weighs about 30 lb.

(A) 240 lb   (B) 1920 lb

(C) 15,360 lb   (D) 216,000 lb

62. COMPARING POWERS Let x and y be whole numbers greater than 0 with $y > x$. Which expression has the greater value, 3^x or 3^y? *Explain.*

63. CHALLENGE For which whole number value(s) of x greater than 0 is the value of x^2 greater than the value of 2^x? *Explain.*

64. CHALLENGE A manufacturer produces three different sizes of cube-shaped stacking bins with edge lengths as shown.

Bin A 6 in.   **Bin B**  12 in.   **Bin C** 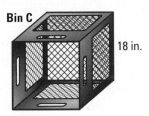 18 in.

a. **Evaluate** Find the volume of each bin.

b. **Compare** How many times greater is the edge length of bin B than the edge length of bin A? How many times greater is the volume of bin B than the volume of bin A?

c. **Compare** Answer the questions in part (b) for bin A and bin C.

d. **Explain** *Explain* how multiplying the edge length of a cube by a number n affects the volume of the cube. *Justify* your explanation.

Animated Algebra at classzone.com

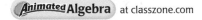

◆ **CALIFORNIA STANDARDS SPIRAL REVIEW**

Gr. 6 NS 2.1 | **65.** What is $\frac{4}{7} \times \frac{7}{9}$? *(p. 789)*

(A) $\frac{4}{9}$ (B) $\frac{11}{16}$ (C) $\frac{36}{49}$ (D) $2\frac{1}{4}$

Gr. 7 NS 1.3 | **66.** Which of the following is equivalent to $\frac{9}{4}$? *(p. 791)*

(A) 1.5   (B) 2.25   (C) 2.5   (D) 9.4

Gr. 6 SDAP 1.1 | **67.** Graciela bought 3 DVDs. She paid $9.99 for one, $14.99 for another, and $16.99 for the third. What was the mean price of the DVDs? *(p. 803)*

(A) $7.00   (B) $13.99   (C) $14.99   (D) $41.97

1.2 Apply Order of Operations

Standards Preparation

Gr. 7 AF 1.2 Use the correct order of operations to evaluate algebraic expressions such as $3(2x + 5)^2$.

Connect

Before you evaluated expressions and used exponents. *Now* you will apply the order of operations to prepare for Algebra 1 Standard 5.0.

Math and MUSIC
Ex. 41, p. 15

Key Vocabulary
• order of operations

Mathematicians have established an **order of operations** to evaluate an expression involving more than one operation.

KEY CONCEPT *For Your Notebook*

Order of Operations

STEP 1 **Evaluate** expressions inside grouping symbols.

STEP 2 **Evaluate** powers.

STEP 3 **Multiply** and **divide** from left to right.

STEP 4 **Add** and **subtract** from left to right.

EXAMPLE 1 Evaluate an expression

Evaluate the expression $27 \div 3^2 \times 2 - 1$.

Solution

There are no grouping symbols in the expression, so begin with Step 2 of the order of operations.

$$27 \div 3^2 \times 2 - 1 = 27 \div 9 \times 2 - 1 \qquad \text{Evaluate power (Step 2).}$$
$$= 3 \times 2 - 1 \qquad \text{Division is to the left of multiplication, so divide first (Step 3).}$$
$$= 6 - 1 \qquad \text{Now multiply (Step 3).}$$
$$= 5 \qquad \text{Subtract (Step 4).}$$

▶ The value of the expression $27 \div 3^2 \times 2 - 1$ is 5.

✓ **GUIDED PRACTICE** for Example 1

Evaluate the expression.

1. $20 - 4^2$ **2.** $2 \cdot 3^2 + 4$ **3.** $32 \div 2^3 + 6$ **4.** $45 - 6^2 + 4$

GROUPING SYMBOLS Grouping symbols such as parentheses ( ) and brackets [ ] indicate that operations inside the grouping symbols should be performed first. For example, to evaluate $2 \cdot 4 + 6$, you multiply first, then add. To evaluate $2(4 + 6)$, you add first, then multiply.

EXAMPLE 2 Evaluate expressions with grouping symbols

Evaluate the expression.

a. $7(\mathbf{13 - 8}) = 7(\mathbf{5})$	Subtract within parentheses.
$= 35$	Multiply.
b. $24 - (\mathbf{3^2} + 1) = 24 - (\mathbf{9} + 1)$	Evaluate power.
$= 24 - 10$	Add within parentheses.
$= 14$	Subtract.
c. $2[30 - (\mathbf{8 + 13})] = 2[30 - \mathbf{21}]$	Add within parentheses.
$= 2[9]$	Subtract within brackets.
$= 18$	Multiply.

AVOID ERRORS
When grouping symbols appear inside other grouping symbols, work from the innermost grouping symbols outward.

FRACTION BARS A fraction bar can act as a grouping symbol. Evaluate the numerator and denominator before you divide:

$$\frac{8 + 4}{5 - 2} = (8 + 4) \div (5 - 2)$$
$$= 12 \div 3$$
$$= 4$$

EXAMPLE 3 Evaluate an algebraic expression

Algebra

For an interactive example of evaluating an algebraic expression, go to **classzone.com**.

Evaluate the expression when $x = 4$.

$\dfrac{9x}{3(x + 2)} = \dfrac{9 \cdot 4}{3(4 + 2)}$	Substitute 4 for x.
$= \dfrac{9 \cdot 4}{3 \cdot 6}$	Add within parentheses.
$= \dfrac{36}{18}$	Multiply.
$= 2$	Divide.

✓ **GUIDED PRACTICE** for Examples 2 and 3

Evaluate the expression.

5. $4(3 + 9)$ **6.** $3(8 - 2^2)$ **7.** $2[(9 + 3) \div 4]$

Evaluate the expression when $y = 8$.

8. $y^2 - 3$ **9.** $12 - y - 1$ **10.** $\dfrac{10y + 1}{y + 1}$

EXAMPLE 4 ◆ **Multiple Choice Practice**

If $w = 5$ and $z = 2$, then $wz + 3w = ?$

Ⓐ 16   Ⓑ 17.5   Ⓒ 25   Ⓓ 65

ELIMINATE CHOICES

A product of whole numbers is a whole number. A sum of whole numbers is a whole number. So, the value of the expression is a whole number. You can eliminate choice B.

Solution

$$wz + 3w = 5 \cdot 2 + 3 \cdot 5 \qquad \text{Substitute 5 for } w \text{ and 2 for } z.$$
$$= 10 + 15 \qquad \text{Multiply.}$$
$$= 25 \qquad \text{Add.}$$

▶ The correct answer is C. Ⓐ Ⓑ Ⓒ Ⓓ

✔ **GUIDED PRACTICE**   for Example 4

11. What is the value of the expression $9c - cd$ when $c = 5$ and $d = 7$?

Ⓐ 10   Ⓑ 28   Ⓒ 98   Ⓓ 210

EXAMPLE 5   **Solve a real-world problem**

A group of 12 students volunteers to collect litter for one day. A sponsor provides:

- 3 juice drinks for each student
- 2 sandwiches for each student
- $30 for trash bags

The sponsor's cost (in dollars) is given by the expression $12(3j + 2s) + 30$ where j is the cost of a juice drink and s is the cost of a sandwich. A juice drink costs $1.25. A sandwich costs $2. What is the sponsor's cost?

Total number of volunteers: 12

Solution

$$12(3j + 2s) + 30 = 12(3 \cdot \mathbf{1.25} + 2 \cdot 2) + 30 \qquad \text{Substitute 1.25 for } j \text{ and 2 for } s.$$
$$= 12(3.75 + 4) + 30 \qquad \text{Multiply within parentheses.}$$
$$= 12(7.75) + 30 \qquad \text{Add within parentheses.}$$
$$= 93 + 30 \qquad \text{Multiply.}$$
$$= 123 \qquad \text{Add.}$$

▶ The sponsor's cost is $123.

✔ **GUIDED PRACTICE**   for Example 5

12. WHAT IF? In Example 5, suppose the number of volunteers doubles. Does the sponsor's cost double as well? *Explain.*

1.2 EXERCISES

HOMEWORK
KEY

◆ = **MULTIPLE CHOICE PRACTICE**
   Exs. 21, 22, 31, 43, and 51–53

◯ = **HINTS** AND **HOMEWORK HELP**
   for Exs. 15, 25, and 41 at classzone.com

SKILLS · PROBLEM SOLVING · REASONING

1. VOCABULARY According to the order of operations, which operation would you perform first in simplifying $50 - 5 \times 4^2 \div 2$?

2. WRITING *Describe* the steps you would use to evaluate the expression $2(3x + 1)^2$ when $x = 3$.

EXAMPLES 1 and 2
on pp. 11–12
for Exs. 3–21

EVALUATING EXPRESSIONS Evaluate the expression.

3. $13 - 8 + 3$

4. $8 - 2^2$

5. $3 \cdot 6 - 4$

6. $5 \cdot 2^3 + 7$

7. $48 \div 4^2 + \dfrac{3}{5}$

8. $1 + 5^2 \div 50$

9. $2^4 \cdot 4 - 2 \div 8$

10. $4^3 \div 8 + 8$

11. $(12 + 72) \div 4$

12. $24 + 4(3 + 1)$

13. $12(6 - 3.5)^2 - 1.5$

14. $24 \div (8 + 4^2)$

15. $\dfrac{1}{2}(21 + 2^2)$

16. $\dfrac{1}{6}(6 + 18) - 2^2$

17. $\dfrac{3}{4}[13 - (2 + 3)]^2$

18. $8[20 - (9 - 5)^2]$

ERROR ANALYSIS *Describe* and correct the error in evaluating the expression.

19.
$$(1 + 13) \div 7 + 7 = 14 \div 7 + 7$$
$$= 14 \div 14$$
$$= 1$$

20.
$$20 - \dfrac{1}{2} \cdot 6^2 = 20 - 3^2$$
$$= 20 - 9$$
$$= 11$$

21. ◆ **MULTIPLE CHOICE** What is the value of $3[20 - (7 - 5)^2]$?

A 48   **B** 56   **C** 192   **D** 972

EXAMPLE 3
on p. 12
for Exs. 22–31

22. ◆ **MULTIPLE CHOICE** What is the value of $\dfrac{x^2}{25} + 3x$ when $x = 10$?

A 26   **B** 34   **C** 43   **D** 105

EVALUATING EXPRESSIONS Evaluate the expression.

23. $4n - 12$ when $n = 7$

24. $6t^2 - 13$ when $t = 2$

25. $11 + r^3 - 2r$ when $r = 5$

26. $5(w - 4)$ when $w = 7$

27. $3(m^2 - 2)$ when $m = 1.5$

28. $y^2 - 2y + 1$ when $y = 7$

29. $\dfrac{k^2 - 1}{k + 3}$ when $k = 5$

30. $\dfrac{b^3 - 21}{5b + 9}$ when $b = 3$

31. ◆ **MULTIPLE CHOICE** Which is the first *incorrect* step in evaluating the expression $p^2 \div 2 + p$ when $p = 6$?

Step 1 $p^2 \div 2 + p = 6^2 \div 2 + 6$

Step 2 $= 36 \div 2 + 6$

Step 3 $= 36 \div 8$

Step 4 $= 4.5$

A Step 1   **B** Step 2   **C** Step 3   **D** Step 4

14   Chapter 1   Expressions, Equations, and Problem Solving

EXAMPLE 4
on p. 13
for Exs. 32–36

EVALUATING EXPRESSIONS Evaluate the expression.

32. $xy - x$ when $x = 6$ and $y = 4$

33. $2(m^2 + n)$ when $m = 5$ and $n = 1$

34. $\dfrac{3a + 4}{2b - 3}$ when $a = 2$ and $b = 9.5$

35. $\dfrac{s^2 - 15}{2t - 7}$ when $s = 7$ and $t = 12$

36. **REASONING** Minh and Carlos each evaluated the expression $2x + y$ when $x = 7$ and $y = 12$. Which student evaluated the expression correctly? *Justify* your reasoning.

> Minh
> $2x + y = 2 \cdot 7 + 12$
> $ = 14 + 12$
> $ = 26$

> Carlos
> $2x + y = 2 \cdot 7 + 12$
> $ = 2 \cdot 19$
> $ = 38$

CONNECT SKILLS TO PROBLEM SOLVING Exercises 37–39 will help you prepare for problem solving.

37. What is the value (in cents) of 3 quarters and 4 dimes?

38. What is the height (in inches) of a person who is 5 feet 9 inches tall?

39. What is the weight (in ounces) of a dog that weighs 8 pounds 4 ounces?

EXAMPLE 5
on p. 13
for Exs. 40–43

40. **SALES** Your school's booster club sells school T-shirts. Half the T-shirts come from one supplier at a cost of $5.95 each, and half from another supplier at a cost of $6.15 each. The average cost (in dollars) of a T-shirt is given by the expression $\dfrac{5.95 + 6.15}{2}$. Find the average cost.

California @HomeTutor for problem solving help at classzone.com

41. **MULTI-STEP PROBLEM** You join an online music service. The total cost (in dollars) of downloading 3 singles and 2 albums is given by the expression $3 \cdot 0.99 + 2 \cdot 9.95$.

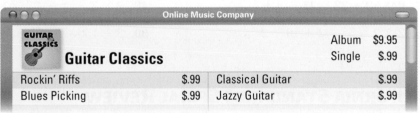

a. Find the total cost of downloading 3 singles and 2 albums.

b. You have $25 to spend. How much will you have left?

California @HomeTutor for problem solving help at classzone.com

42. **PHYSIOLOGY** If you know how tall you were at the age of 2, you can estimate your adult height (in inches). Girls can use the expression $25 + 1.17h$ where h is the height (in inches) at the age of 2. Boys can use the expression $22.7 + 1.37h$. Estimate the adult height of each person to the nearest inch.

a. A girl who was 34 inches tall at age 2

b. A boy who was 33 inches tall at age 2

43. ◆ **MULTIPLE CHOICE** The regular shipping fee (in dollars) for an online computer store is given by the expression $0.5w + 4.49$ where w is the weight (in pounds) of the item. The fee (in dollars) for rush delivery is given by $0.99w + 6.49$. You purchase a 26 pound computer. How much do you save using regular shipping instead of rush delivery?

    A $14.74   **B** $17.49   **C** $32.23   **D** $49.72

READING *IN* MATH   **Read the information below for Exercises 44–46.**

Football Each year Heisman Trophy voters select the outstanding college football player. Each voter selects three players and ranks them first to third. A first place vote is worth 3 points, a second place vote is worth 2 points, and a third place vote is worth 1 point. In 2005, there were 923 voters. Reggie Bush was the winner and Vince Young was the runner-up. The votes for the two players are shown in the table.

Reggie Bush

Player	First place	Second place	Third place
Reggie Bush	784	89	11
Vince Young	79	613	145

44. Explain Let f, s, and t be, respectively, the number of first place, second place, and third place votes a player gets. *Explain* why the expression $3f + 2s + t$ represents a player's point total.

45. Evaluate Use the expression in Exercise 44 to determine how many more points Reggie Bush got than Vince Young got.

46. Explain How many voters did *not* cast a first-place vote for either Reggie Bush or Vince Young? *Explain.*

CHALLENGE **Insert grouping symbols in the expression so that the value of the expression is 14.**

47. $9 + 39 + 22 \div 11 - 9 + 3$ **48.** $2 \times 2 + 3^2 - 4 + 3 \times 5$

49. $2 \times 2 + 5^2 \div 2 + 10 \div 2$ **50.** $3 + 15^2 \div 8 + 4 - 4 + 3^2$

◆ CALIFORNIA STANDARDS SPIRAL REVIEW

Gr. 6 AF 2.1   **51.** How many centimeters are in 3.5 meters? *(p. 795)*

    A 0.035 cm   **B** 35 cm   **C** 350 cm   **D** 355 cm

Gr. 7 AF 2.1   **52.** Which expression could you use to represent y^4? *(p. 5)*

    A $4y$ **B** $y \div 4$ **C** $4y \cdot 4y$ **D** $y \cdot y \cdot y \cdot y$

Gr. 7 MG 2.1   **53.** What is the volume of a cube-shaped block of wood with an edge length of 3 inches? *(p. 5)*

    A 6 in.^3 **B** 9 in.^3 **C** 27 in.^3 **D** 54 in.^3

1.2 Use Order of Operations

Standards Preparation

Gr. 7 AF 1.2 Use the correct order of operations to evaluate algebraic expressions such as $3(2x + 5)^2$.

QUESTION How can you use a graphing calculator to evaluate an expression?

You can use a graphing calculator to evaluate an expression. When you enter the expression, it is important to use grouping symbols so that the calculator performs operations in the correct order.

EXAMPLE Evaluate an expression

Use a graphing calculator to evaluate an expression.

Lean body mass is the mass of the skeleton, muscles, and organs. Physicians use lean body mass to determine dosages of medicine.

Scientists have developed separate formulas for the lean body masses of men and women based on their mass m (in kilograms) and height h (in meters). Lean body mass is measured in units called BMI (Body Mass Index) units.

Men: $1.10m - \dfrac{128m^2}{10{,}000h^2}$ **Women:** $1.07m - \dfrac{148m^2}{10{,}000h^2}$

Find the lean body mass (in BMI units) of a man who is 1.8 meters tall and has a mass of 80 kilograms.

Solution

Enter the expression for men in the calculator. Substitute 80 for m and 1.8 for h. Because the fraction bar is a grouping symbol, enter the numerator and the denominator using parentheses.

Use the following keystrokes.

1.10 ⊠ 80 ⊟ (128 ⊠ 80 x^2) ⊘ (10000 ⊠ 1.8 x^2)

```
1.10*80-(128*80²)/
(10000*1.8²)
        62.71604938
```

▶ The lean body mass of a man who is 1.8 meters tall and has a mass of 80 kilograms is about 62.7 BMI units.

PRACTICE

Use a calculator to evaluate the expression for $n = 4$. Round to the nearest thousandth.

1. $3 + 5 \cdot n \div 10$
2. $2 + \dfrac{3n^2}{4}$
3. $\dfrac{83}{3n^2} - 1.3$

4. $\dfrac{14.2n}{8 + n^3}$
5. $\dfrac{7 - n}{n^2}$
6. $5n^2 + \dfrac{4n^3 + 1}{3}$

7. Find the lean body mass (to the nearest tenth of a BMI unit) of a woman who is 1.6 meters tall and has a mass of 54 kilograms.

1.3 Patterns and Expressions

MATERIALS · graph paper

Standards Preparation

Gr. 7 AF 1.1 Use variables and appropriate operations to write an expression, an equation, an inequality, or a system of equations or inequalities **that represents a verbal description** (e.g., **three less than a number, half as large as area *A*).**

QUESTION How can you use an algebraic expression to describe a pattern?

EXPLORE Create and describe a pattern

STEP 1 *Draw a figure* Draw a unit square on graph paper. Then draw a unit square against each side of the first square to form figure 1.

Copy figure 1 and draw a square on each "arm" to form figure 2. Use the same method to form figure 3.

STEP 2 *Write expressions* For each figure, write a verbal description of the number of squares in the figure. Then write an algebraic expression.

Figure 1	Figure 2	Figure 3

Figure 1	Figure 2	Figure 3
1 + 4	1 + 4 + 4	1 + 4 + 4 + 4

DRAW CONCLUSIONS Use your observations to complete these exercises

In Exercises 1–3, use the pattern in Steps 1 and 2 above.

1. How is the figure number related to the number of times 4 is added in the numerical expression? Predict the number of squares in the fourth figure. Create figure 4 and check your prediction.

2. *Describe* how to calculate the number of squares in the *n*th figure.

3. Write an algebraic expression for the number of squares in the *n*th figure. (*Hint:* Remember that repeated addition can be written as multiplication.)

4. Write a verbal description of the number of squares in the *n*th figure of the pattern. Then write an algebraic expression.

Figure 1   **Figure 2**   **Figure 3**   **Figure 4**

1.3 Write Expressions

Standards Preparation

Gr. 7 AF 1.1 Use variables and appropriate operations to write an expression, an equation, an inequality, or a system of equations or inequalities **that represents a verbal description (e.g., three less than a number, half as large as area A).**

Connect   *Before* you simplified numerical and algebraic expressions. *Now* you will write expressions to prepare for Algebra 1 Standard 5.0.

Math and **PHOTOGRAPHY**
Ex. 36, p. 23

Key Vocabulary
• **verbal model**
• **rate**
• **unit rate**

To translate verbal phrases into expressions, look for words that indicate mathematical operations.

KEY CONCEPT   *For Your Notebook*

Translating Verbal Phrases

Operation	Verbal Phrase	Expression
Addition: sum, plus, total, more than, increased by	The sum of 2 and a number x	$2 + x$
	A number n plus 7	$n + 7$
Subtraction: difference, less than, minus, decreased by	The difference of a number n and 6	$n - 6$
	5 less than a number y	$y - 5$
Multiplication: times, product, multiplied by, of	12 times a number y	$12y$
	$\frac{1}{3}$ of a number x	$\frac{1}{3}x$
Division: quotient, divided by, divided into	The quotient of a number k and 2	$\frac{k}{2}$

Order is important when writing subtraction and division expressions. For instance, "the difference of a number n and 6" is written $n - 6$, *not* $6 - n$, and "the quotient of a number k and 2" is written $\frac{k}{2}$, *not* $\frac{2}{k}$.

EXAMPLE 1   Translate verbal phrases into expressions

AVOID ERRORS
In verbal phrases, the words "the quantity" tell you what to group. In part (a), you write $6n - 4$, *not* $(6 - 4)n$.

Verbal Phrase	Expression
a. 4 less than the quantity 6 times a number n	$6n - 4$
b. 3 times the sum of 7 and a number y	$3(7 + y)$

 GUIDED PRACTICE   for Example 1

1. Translate the phrase "the quotient of 2 and the quantity 10 plus a number x" into an expression.

EXAMPLE 2 Write an expression

CUTTING A RIBBON A piece of ribbon ℓ feet long is cut from a ribbon 8 feet long. Write an expression for the length (in feet) of the remaining piece.

Solution

Draw a diagram and use a specific case to help you write the expression.

Suppose the piece cut is 2 feet long.

|←————8 ft————→|
|←2 ft→|←——(8 − 2) ft——→|

The remaining piece is (8 − 2) feet long.

Suppose the piece cut is ℓ feet long.

|←————8 ft————→|
|←ℓ ft→|←——(8 − ℓ) ft——→|

The remaining piece is (8 − ℓ) feet long.

▶ The expression $8 - \ell$ represents the length (in feet) of the remaining piece.

VERBAL MODEL A **verbal model** describes a real-world situation using words as labels and using math symbols to relate the words. You can replace the words with numbers and variables to create a *mathematical model*, such as an expression, for the real-world situation.

EXAMPLE 3 Use a verbal model to write an expression

TIPS You work with 5 other people at an ice cream stand. All the workers put their tips into a jar and share the amount in the jar equally at the end of the day. Write an expression for each person's share (in dollars) of the tips.

Solution

STEP 1 **Write** a verbal model.

STEP 2 **Translate** the verbal model into an algebraic expression. Let a represent the amount (in dollars) in the jar.

Amount in jar	÷	Number of people
a	÷	6

▶ An expression that represents each person's share (in dollars) is $\dfrac{a}{6}$.

✓ **GUIDED PRACTICE** for Examples 2 and 3

2. **WHAT IF?** In Example 2, suppose that you cut the original ribbon into p pieces of equal length. Write an expression that represents the length (in feet) of each piece.

3. **WHAT IF?** In Example 3, suppose that each of the 6 workers makes the same contribution c (in dollars) for an after-work celebration. Write an expression that represents the total amount (in dollars) contributed.

RATES A **rate** is a fraction that compares two quantities measured in different units. If the denominator of the fraction is 1 unit, the rate is called a **unit rate**.

EXAMPLE 4 **Find a unit rate**

READING
Per means "for each" or "for every" and can also be represented using the symbol /, as in mi/h.

A car travels 110 miles in 2 hours. Find the unit rate.

$$\frac{110 \text{ miles}}{2 \text{ hours}} = \frac{110 \text{ miles} \div 2}{2 \text{ hours} \div 2} = \frac{55 \text{ miles}}{1 \text{ hour}}$$

▶ The unit rate is 55 miles per hour, or 55 mi/h.

EXAMPLE 5 **Solve a multi-step problem**

CELL PHONES Your basic monthly charge for cell phone service is $30, which includes 300 free minutes. You pay a fee for each extra minute you use. One month you paid $3.75 for 15 extra minutes. Find your total bill if you use 22 extra minutes.

Basic charge: $30

Solution

STEP 1 **Calculate** the unit rate.

$$\frac{\$3.75}{15 \text{ min}} = \frac{\$.25}{\text{min}} = \$.25 \text{ per minute}$$

STEP 2 **Write** a verbal model and then an expression. Let m be the number of extra minutes.

Basic charge (dollars)	+	Rate for extra minutes (dollars/minute)	·	Number of extra minutes (minutes)
30	+	0.25	·	m

USE UNIT ANALYSIS
You expect the answer, which is a cost, to be in dollars. You can use unit analysis, also called *dimensional analysis*, to check that the expression produces an answer in dollars.

STEP 3 **Use** *unit analysis* to check that the expression $30 + 0.25m$ is reasonable.

$$\text{dollars} + \frac{\text{dollars}}{\text{minute}} \cdot \text{minutes} = \text{dollars} + \text{dollars} = \text{dollars}$$

Because the final units are dollars, the expression is reasonable.

STEP 4 **Evaluate** the expression when $m = 22$.

$$30 + 0.25(22) = 35.5$$

▶ The total bill is $35.50.

✓ **GUIDED PRACTICE** for Examples 4 and 5

4. **WHAT IF?** Your friend's basic monthly charge for cell phone service is $35, which includes 300 free minutes. One month he paid $8.80 for 40 extra minutes. Find your friend's total bill if he uses 35 extra minutes.

1.3 EXERCISES

HOMEWORK KEY

◆ = **MULTIPLE CHOICE PRACTICE**
Exs. 13, 26, 32, and 39–41

○ = **HINTS** AND **HOMEWORK HELP**
for Exs. 11, 21, and 35 at classzone.com

SKILLS · PROBLEM SOLVING · REASONING

1. VOCABULARY Copy and complete: A(n) _?_ is a fraction that compares two quantities measured in different units.

2. WRITING *Explain* how to write $\frac{20 \text{ miles}}{4 \text{ hours}}$ as a unit rate.

EXAMPLE 1
on p. 19
for Exs. 3–13

TRANSLATING PHRASES **Translate the verbal phrase into an expression.**

3. 8 more than a number x

4. The product of 6 and a number y

5. $\frac{1}{2}$ of a number m

6. 50 divided by a number h

7. The difference of 7 and a number n

8. The sum of 15 and a number x

9. The quotient of twice a number t and 12

10. 3 less than the square of a number p

11. 7 less than twice a number k

12. 3 times the sum of a number w and 5

13. ◆ **MULTIPLE CHOICE** Which expression represents the phrase "the product of 15 and the quantity 12 more than a number x"?

    A $15 + 12 \cdot x$ **B** $(15 + 12)x$ **C** $15(x + 12)$ **D** $15 \cdot 12 + x$

EXAMPLES 2 and 3
on p. 20
for Exs. 14–21

14. ERROR ANALYSIS *Describe* and correct the error in writing an expression for the situation.

Situation: Number of pages of a 5 page article left to read if you've read p pages

Expression: $p - 5$

WRITING EXPRESSIONS **Write an expression for the situation.**

15. Number of tokens needed for v video games if each game takes 4 tokens

16. Each person's share if p people share 16 slices of pizza equally

17. Cost in dollars per pound of grapes if p pounds cost \$2.97

18. Amount you spend if you buy a shirt for \$20 and jeans for j dollars

19. Number of days left in the week if d days have passed so far

20. Number of hours in m minutes

21. Number of months in y years

EXAMPLE 4
on p. 21
for Exs. 22–25

UNIT RATES **Find the unit rate.**

22. $\frac{32 \text{ students}}{4 \text{ groups}}$ **23.** $\frac{4.5 \text{ pints}}{3 \text{ servings}}$ **24.** $\frac{12 \text{ runs}}{5 \text{ innings}}$ **25.** $\frac{\$136}{20 \text{ shares}}$

26. ◆ **MULTIPLE CHOICE** Which expression represents the phrase "twice the quotient of 50 and the sum of a number y and 8"?

    A $\frac{2 \cdot 50}{y} + 8$ **B** $2\left(\frac{50 + y}{8}\right)$ **C** $2\left(\frac{50}{y + 8}\right)$ **D** $\frac{2}{50} + (y + 8)$

ERROR ANALYSIS *Describe* and correct the error in the units.

27.

$$\frac{\$2}{ft} \cdot 24\ ft = \frac{\$48}{ft^2}$$ ✗

28.

$$9\ yd \cdot \frac{3\ ft}{1\ yd} \cdot \frac{\$2}{ft} = \frac{\$54}{ft}$$ ✗

CONNECT SKILLS TO PROBLEM SOLVING Exercises 29–31 will help you prepare for problem solving.

29. Tickets to a game cost $40 each. Renting a bus costs $500. Write a verbal model for the total cost of renting a bus and buying *t* tickets.

30. Sweatshirts cost $35 each. You have a coupon for $25 off your total purchase. Write a verbal model for the total cost when using the coupon and buying *s* sweatshirts.

31. A group of *x* friends split a restaurant bill for $25. One left a $5 tip. Write a verbal model for the amount paid by the friend who left the tip.

EXAMPLE 5
on p. 21
for Exs. 32–35

32. ◆ **MULTIPLE CHOICE** Tickets to a science museum cost $19.95 each. There is a $3 charge for each order no matter how many tickets are bought. Which expression gives the cost (in dollars) of buying *t* tickets?

    (A) $19.95t \div 3$ **(B)** $19.95t + 3$ **(C)** $19.95t + 3t$ **(D)** $19.95t \cdot 3t$

California @HomeTutor for problem solving help at classzone.com

33. FOSSIL FUELS Fossil fuels are produced by the decay of organic material over millions of years. To make one gallon of gas, it takes about 98 tons of organic material. Write an expression for the amount (in tons) of organic material it takes to make *g* gallons of gas. How many tons would it take to make enough gas to fill a car's 20 gallon gas tank?

California @HomeTutor for problem solving help at classzone.com

34. MULTI-STEP PROBLEM A 48 ounce container of juice costs $2.64. A 64 ounce container of the same juice costs $3.84.

   a. Find the cost per ounce of each container.

   b. Which size container costs less per ounce?

   c. You want to buy 192 ounces of juice. How much do you save using the container size from your answer to part (b)?

(35.) WILDLIFE EDUCATION A wildlife center presents a program about birds of prey. The center charges a basic fee of $325 and an additional fee for each bird exhibited. If 5 birds are exhibited, the additional fee is $125. What is the total cost if 7 birds are exhibited?

36. DIGITAL PHOTOS Your printer takes 36 seconds to print a small photo and 60 seconds to print a large one. Write an expression for the time (in seconds) your printer would take to print a batch that includes both small and large photos. Then find the time your printer would take to print 12 small photos and 5 large photos.

Bird of prey: Hawk

37. CHALLENGE Look for a pattern in the expressions below. Generalize the pattern to write an expression for the sum of the whole numbers from 1 to n. Then find the sum of the whole numbers from 1 to 50.

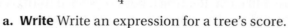

$$1 + 2 = \frac{2 \cdot 3}{2} \qquad\qquad 1 + 2 + 3 = \frac{3 \cdot 4}{2} \qquad\qquad 1 + 2 + 3 + 4 = \frac{4 \cdot 5}{2}$$

38. TREE SURVEY A national survey assigns scores to trees. A tree's score is the sum of the girth in inches, the height in feet, and $\frac{1}{4}$ the crown spread in feet.

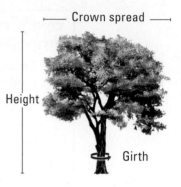

   a. Write Write an expression for a tree's score.

   b. Evaluate Find the score for a tree with a girth of 12 feet, a height of 97 feet, and a crown spread of 24 feet.

   c. CHALLENGE Let n be any number greater than 0. Which change would have the greatest effect on a tree's score, an increase of n feet in the girth, in the height, or in the crown spread? *Explain* your reasoning.

◆ CALIFORNIA STANDARDS SPIRAL REVIEW

Gr. 6 NS 2.1

39. What is $\frac{1}{5} \times \frac{3}{5}$? *(p. 789)*

   (A) $\frac{3}{25}$ **(B)** $\frac{1}{3}$ **(C)** $\frac{2}{5}$ **(D)** $\frac{4}{5}$

Gr. 6 AF 1.3

40. What is the value of the expression $6 + 6 \times 2 + 2$? *(p. 11)*

   (A) 3   **(B)** 8   **(C)** 20   **(D)** 30

Gr. 7 AF 1.2

41. A square with a side of length x units is inside a square with a side of length 3 units, as shown. Which expression represents the area of the shaded region in terms of x? *(p. 11)*

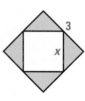

   (A) $9 - x^2$ **(B)** $9 + x^2$

   (C) $9 - 2x$ **(D)** $9 - 4x$

QUIZ *for Lessons 1.1–1.3*

Evaluate the expression.

   1. $y + 10$ when $y = 43$ *(p. 5)*   **2.** $15 - b$ when $b = 9$ *(p. 5)*   **3.** t^2 when $t = 20$ *(p. 5)*

   4. $3n - 5$ when $n = 2.5$ *(p. 11)*   **5.** $2y^2 + 1$ when $y = \frac{1}{2}$ *(p. 11)*   **6.** $\frac{3x - 6}{8}$ when $x = 8$ *(p. 11)*

Translate the verbal phrase into an expression. *(p. 19)*

   7. 7 less than a number y **8.** 5 more than a number t

   9. Twice the sum of a number k and 3   **10.** 8 more than half of a number d

   11. CAMPING The rental cost for a campsite is $25 plus $2 per person. Write an expression for the total cost. Then find the total cost for 5 people. *(p. 19)*

MIXED REVIEW of Skills and Problem Solving

Multiple Choice Practice for Lessons 1.1–1.3

1. You buy 3 quarts of strawberries and receive the receipt below. Later, you realize that you actually need 5 quarts of strawberries. How much will the additional strawberries cost? **Gr. 7 MG 1.3**

    - **A** $2.50
    - **B** $5.00
    - **C** $5.50
    - **D** $12.50

2. What is the value of the expression w^3 when $w = 2.5$? **Gr. 6 AF 1.2**

    - **A** 5.5
    - **B** 7.5
    - **C** 6.25
    - **D** 15.625

3. What is the value of $x^2 - 3x - 1$ when $x = 5$? **Gr. 7 AF 1.2**

    - **A** 9
    - **B** 13
    - **C** 39
    - **D** 41

4. You are comparing the two cube-shaped candles shown below. How many more cubic inches of wax would you need to make the larger candle than to make the smaller one? **Gr. 7 MG 2.1**

    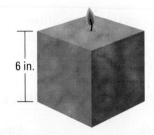

    - **A** 8 in.³
    - **B** 20 in.³
    - **C** 120 in.³
    - **D** 152 in.³

5. What is the value of the expression $\frac{b}{a}$ when $a = 4$ and $b = 16$? **Gr. 6 AF 1.2**

    - **A** $\frac{1}{4}$
    - **B** 4
    - **C** 8
    - **D** 12

6. A retangular garden has a length of 10 feet and a width of 5 feet. A gardener plans to increase the length of the garden by f feet as shown. By how much will the area of the garden increase if the value of f is 3? **Gr. 7 MG 2.1**

    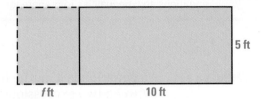

    - **A** 8 ft²
    - **B** 15 ft²
    - **C** 30 ft²
    - **D** 65 ft²

7. Vera and Yen are running a race for charity. Sponsors pledge a given amount for each mile a runner runs. The table shows the total pledges for both runners. Suppose Vera runs v miles and Yen runs y miles. Which expression represents the total amount (in dollars) pledged to the two girls? **Gr. 7 AF 1.1**

Runner	Total pledges (dollars per mile)
Vera	45
Yen	35

    - **A** $80(v + y)$
    - **B** $35v + 45y$
    - **C** $45v + 35y$
    - **D** $(45 + v) + (35 + y)$

8. Which expression represents the phrase "8 less than the quotient of a number x and 20"? **Gr. 7 AF 1.1**

    - **A** $8 - \frac{x}{20}$
    - **B** $8 - \frac{20}{x}$
    - **C** $\frac{x}{20} - 8$
    - **D** $\frac{20}{x} - 8$

1.4 Write Equations and Inequalities

Standards Preparation

Gr. 7 AF 1.1 Use variables and appropriate operations to **write** an expression, **an equation, an inequality**, or a system of equations or inequalities **that represents a verbal description (e.g., three less than a number, half as large as area A).**

Connect   *Before* you simplified numerical and algebraic expressions. *Now* you will write equations and inequalities to prepare for Algebra 1 Standard 5.0.

Math and **SPORTS**
Ex. 43, p. 30

Key Vocabulary
• equation
• inequality
• open sentence
• solution of an equation
• solution of an inequality

An **equation** is a mathematical sentence formed by placing the symbol = between two expressions. An **inequality** is a mathematical sentence formed by placing one of the symbols $<$, $\leq$, $>$, or $\geq$ between two expressions.

An **open sentence** is an equation or an inequality that contains an algebraic expression. For example, $x + 2 = 5$ is an open sentence, but $3 + 2 = 5$ is not.

KEY CONCEPT   *For Your Notebook*

Symbol	Meaning	Associated Words
=	is equal to	the same as
<	is less than	fewer than
≤	is less than or equal to	at most, no more than
>	is greater than	more than
≥	is greater than or equal to	at least, no less than

COMBINING INEQUALITIES Sometimes two inequalities are combined. For example, the inequalities $x > 4$ and $x < 9$ can be combined to form the inequality $4 < x < 9$, which is read "x is greater than 4 and less than 9."

EXAMPLE 1   Write equations and inequalities

Animated Algebra

For an interactive example of writing equations and inequalities, go to **classzone.com**.

Verbal Sentence	Equation or Inequality
a. The difference of twice a number k and 8 is 12.	$2k - 8 = 12$
b. The product of 6 and a number n is at least 24.	$6n \geq 24$
c. A number y is no less than 5 and no more than 13.	$5 \leq y \leq 13$

✓ **GUIDED PRACTICE**   for Example 1

1. Write an equation or an inequality for the sentence "The quotient of a number p and 12 is at least 30."

SOLUTIONS When you substitute a number for the variable in an open sentence like $x + 2 = 5$ or $2y > 6$, the resulting statement is either true or false. If the statement is true, the number is a **solution of the equation** or a **solution of the inequality**.

EXAMPLE 2 Check possible solutions

Check whether 3 is a solution of the equation or inequality.

Equation/Inequality	Substitute	Conclusion
a. $8 - 2x = 2$	$8 - 2(3) \stackrel{?}{=} 2$	$2 = 2$ ✓ 3 is a solution.
b. $4x - 5 = 6$	$4(3) - 5 \stackrel{?}{=} 6$	$7 = 6$ ✗ 3 is *not* a solution.
c. $2z + 5 > 12$	$2(3) + 5 \stackrel{?}{>} 12$	$11 > 12$ ✗ 3 is *not* a solution.
d. $5 + 3n \le 20$	$5 + 3(3) \stackrel{?}{\le} 20$	$14 \le 20$ ✓ 3 is a solution.

READING

A question mark above a symbol indicates a question. For instance, $8 - 2(3) \stackrel{?}{=} 2$ means "Is $8 - 2(3)$ equal to 2?"

USING MENTAL MATH Some equations are simple enough to solve using mental math. Think of the equation as a question. Once you answer the question, check the solution.

EXAMPLE 3 Use mental math to solve an equation

About the Standards

This lesson introduces solving equations. You will learn more about solving equations and inequalities in Chapters 3 and 4 as part of Algebra 1 Standard 5.0.

Equation	Think	Solution	Check
a. $x + 4 = 10$	What number plus 4 equals 10?	6	$6 + 4 = 10$ ✓
b. $20 - y = 8$	20 minus what number equals 8?	12	$20 - 12 = 8$ ✓
c. $6n = 42$	6 times what number equals 42?	7	$6(7) = 42$ ✓
d. $\frac{a}{5} = 9$	What number divided by 5 equals 9?	45	$\frac{45}{5} = 9$ ✓

✓ **GUIDED PRACTICE** for Examples 2 and 3

Check whether the given number is a solution of the equation or inequality.

2. $9 - x = 4$; 5   **3.** $b + 5 < 15$; 7   **4.** $2n + 3 > 21$; 9

Solve the equation using mental math.

5. $m + 6 = 11$ **6.** $5x = 40$ **7.** $\frac{r}{4} = 10$

EXAMPLE 4 **Solve a multi-step problem**

MOUNTAIN BIKING The last time you and 3 friends went to a mountain bike park, you had a coupon for $10 off and paid $17 for 4 tickets. What is the regular price of 4 tickets? If you pay the regular price this time and share it equally, how much does each person pay?

Mountain bike park

Solution

STEP 1 **Write** a verbal model. Let p be the regular price of 4 tickets. Write an equation.

Regular price	−	Amount of coupon	=	Amount paid
↓		↓		↓
p	−	10	=	17

STEP 2 **Use** mental math to solve the equation $p - 10 = 17$. Think: 10 less than what number is 17? Because $27 - 10 = 17$, the solution is 27.

▸ The regular price for 4 tickets is $27.

STEP 3 **Find** the cost per person: $\dfrac{\$27}{4 \text{ people}} = \$6.75$ per person

▸ Each person pays $6.75.

EXAMPLE 5 **Write and check a solution of an inequality**

BASKETBALL A basketball player scored 351 points last year. If the player plays 18 games this year, will an average of 20 points per game be enough to beat last year's total?

Solution

STEP 1 **Write** a verbal model. Let p be the average number of points per game. Write an inequality.

Number of games	·	Points per game	>	Total points last year
↓		↓		↓
18	·	p	>	351

USE UNIT ANALYSIS
Unit analysis shows that $\text{games} \cdot \dfrac{\text{points}}{\text{game}} = \text{points}$, so the inequality is reasonable.

STEP 2 **Check** that 20 is a solution of the inequality $18p > 351$. Because $18(20) = 360$ and $360 > 351$, 20 is a solution. ✓

▸ An average of 20 points per game will be enough.

✓ **GUIDED PRACTICE** **for Examples 4 and 5**

8. **WHAT IF?** In Example 4, suppose that the price of 4 tickets with a half-off coupon for each is $15. What is each person's share if you pay full price?

9. **WHAT IF?** In Example 5, suppose that the player plays 16 games. Would an average of 22 points per game be enough to beat last year's total?

1.4 EXERCISES

HOMEWORK
KEY

◆ = **MULTIPLE CHOICE PRACTICE**
Exs. 16, 37, 45, and 50–53

○ = **HINTS AND HOMEWORK HELP**
for Exs. 7, 23, and 43 at classzone.com

SKILLS · PROBLEM SOLVING · REASONING

1. VOCABULARY Give an example of an open sentence.

2. WRITING *Describe* the difference between an expression and an equation.

EXAMPLE 1
on p. 26
for Exs. 3–16

WRITING OPEN SENTENCES Write an equation or an inequality.

3. The sum of 42 and a number n is equal to 51.

4. The quotient of a number b and 10 is 1.4.

5. The difference of 9 and the quotient of a number t and 6 is 5.

6. The sum of 12 and the quantity 8 times a number k is equal to 48.

7. The product of 9 and the quantity 5 more than a number t is less than 6.

8. The product of 4 and a number w is at most 51.

9. The sum of a number b and 3 is greater than 8 and less than 12.

10. The product of 8 and a number k is greater than 4 and no more than 16.

11. The difference of a number t and 7 is greater than 10 and less than 20.

STORE SALES Write an inequality for the price p (in dollars) described.

12.

Sale! Nothing over $10!

13.

Prices start at $12.⁹⁹

ERROR ANALYSIS *Describe* and correct the error in writing the verbal sentence as an equation or an inequality.

14. The sum of a number n and 4 is no more than 13.

$$n + 4 < 13 \quad ✗$$

15. The difference of a number t and 4.2 is 15.

$$4.2 - t = 15 \quad ✗$$

16. ◆ **MULTIPLE CHOICE** Which equation corresponds to the sentence "The product of 3 and a number b is no less than 12"?

(A) $3b < 12$ **(B)** $3b \leq 12$ **(C)** $3b > 12$ **(D)** $3b \geq 12$

EXAMPLE 2
on p. 27
for Exs. 17–28

CHECK POSSIBLE SOLUTIONS Check whether the given number is a solution of the equation or inequality.

17. $x + 9 = 17$; 8

18. $9 + 4y = 17$; 1

19. $6f - 7 = 29$; 5

20. $\dfrac{k}{5} + 9 = 11$; 10

21. $\dfrac{r}{3} - 4 = 4$; 12

22. $\dfrac{x - 5}{3} \geq 2.8$; 11

23. $15 - 4y > 6$; 2

24. $y - 3.5 < 6$; 9

25. $2 + 3x \leq 8$; 2

26. $\dfrac{2p}{3} - 1 \geq 7$; 3

27. $\dfrac{4z - 5}{3} < 1$; 2

28. $3z + 7 > 20$; 4

EXAMPLE 3
on p. 27
for Exs. 29–34

MENTAL MATH Solve the equation using mental math.

29. $x + 8 = 13$

30. $y + 16 = 25$

31. $z - 11 = 1$

32. $5w = 20$

33. $8b = 72$

34. $\dfrac{f}{6} = 4$

EQUATIONS AND INEQUALITIES In Exercises 35 and 36, write an open sentence. Then check whether 3.5 is a solution of the open sentence.

35. 2 less than the product of 3 and a number x is equal to the sum of x and 5.

36. 4 more than twice a number k is no greater than the sum of k and 11.

37. ◆ **MULTIPLE CHOICE** Which equation has the same solution as $z - 9 = 3$?

(A) $z - 4 = 16$ **(B)** $\dfrac{1}{2}z = 7$ **(C)** $z + 15 = 27$ **(D)** $5z = 45$

CONNECT SKILLS TO PROBLEM SOLVING Exercises 38–40 will help you prepare for problem solving.

Write an equation or inequality for the situation.

38. A kicker who kicked a total of f field goals over a 16 game season averaged 2.25 field goals per game.

39. Your favorite music video program on television runs 60 minutes. Less a minutes for ads, the program has fewer than 45 minutes for videos.

40. A plane has flown 90 miles and has d miles left to fly on a 370 mile trip.

EXAMPLES
4 and 5
on p. 28
for Exs. 41–45

41. **CHARITY WALK** You are taking part in a charity walk, and you have walked 12.5 miles so far. Your goal is to walk 20 miles. How many more miles do you need to walk to meet your goal?

California *@HomeTutor* for problem solving help at classzone.com

42. **COMPACT DISCS** You buy a storage rack that holds 40 CDs. You have 27 CDs. Write an inequality that describes how many more CDs you can buy and still have no more CDs than the rack can hold. You buy 15 CDs. Will they all still fit?

California *@HomeTutor* for problem solving help at classzone.com

43. **TRIATHLON** The first modern triathlon was held in San Diego in 1974. When an international triathlon was held in San Diego in 2005, there were 1350 more participants than in the first triathlon. There were 1396 participants in 2005. How many participants were there in the first triathlon?

44. **BAKING MEASUREMENTS** You are baking batches of cookies for a bake sale. Each batch takes 2.5 cups of flour. You have 18 cups of flour. Can you bake 8 batches? *Explain.*

45. ◆ **MULTIPLE CHOICE** You take a job doing yard work for a neighbor, and ask three friends to help. You share the amount the neighbor pays you equally with your friends. Each of you gets $25. How much did the neighbor pay?

(A) $50 **(B)** $75 **(C)** $100 **(D)** $125

Triathlons involve biking, running, and swimming.

46. OPEN-ENDED Describe a real-world situation you could model using the equation $5x = 50$. Use mental math to solve the equation. *Explain* what the solution means in this situation.

47. PART-TIME JOBS You have two part-time jobs. You earn $6 per hour babysitting and $5 per hour walking dogs. You can work a total of 10 hours this weekend and hope to earn at least $55. Let b be the number of hours you spend babysitting.

Dog walking: $5 per hour

    a. Write an inequality that describes the situation. Your inequality should involve only one variable, b.

    b. If you spend the same amount of time at each job, will you meet your goal? *Explain.*

    c. Can you meet your goal by working all 10 hours at only one job? *Explain.*

48. CHALLENGE Each of the longer sides of a rectangle has a length of x inches. Each of the other sides is 1 inch shorter than the longer sides. The perimeter of the rectangle is 22 inches. Find the length and the width of the rectangle. *Justify* your answer.

49. CHALLENGE You and your friend are reading the same series of science fiction books. You tell your friend, "I've read 3 times as many books as you have." Your friend replies, "You've read only 4 more books than I have." How many books have each of you read?

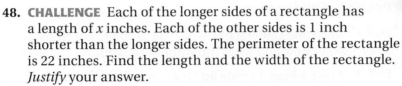

◆ **CALIFORNIA STANDARDS SPIRAL REVIEW**

Gr. 7 AF 1.2

50. What is the value of the expression $9b - 7a$ when $a = 6$ and $b = 7$? *(p. 11)*

    (A) 5   **(B)** 12   **(C)** 14   **(D)** 21

Gr. 7 AF 1.1

51. Which expression represents the difference of y and the product of 5 and x? *(p. 19)*

    (A) $5x - y$ **(B)** $5x - 5y$ **(C)** $y - 5x$ **(D)** $x - 5y$

Gr. 6 AF 2.1

52. Gardeners calculated the average growth rates of four palm trees in their gardens. Which is the greatest of the four average growth rates? *(p. 795)*

    (A) Royal palm: 2.25 inches per month

    (B) Queen palm: 2.5 feet per year

    (C) Majesty palm: 3.5 feet every 2 years

    (D) Fishtail palm: 12 inches every 3 months

Gr. 6 AF 1.2

53. A cell phone company estimates that about 1 minute of airtime is needed to send a picture message and about 2 minutes are needed to send a video message. Which expression could you use to estimate the total airtime needed to send p picture messages and v video messages? *(p. 19)*

    (A) $2(p + v)$ **(B)** $2p + v$ **(C)** $p + 2v$ **(D)** $3(p + v)$

1.5 Use a Problem Solving Plan

Standards Preparation Gr. 7 MR 2.5 **Use a variety of methods, such as words, numbers, symbols,** charts, graphs, **tables, diagrams,** and models **to explain mathematical reasoning.**

Connect *Before* you used problem solving strategies. *Now* you will use a problem solving plan to prepare for Algebra 1 Standard 5.0.

Math and **SPORTS**
Ex. 1, p. 32

Key Vocabulary
• formula

KEY CONCEPT   *For Your Notebook*

A Problem Solving Plan

STEP 1 **Read and Understand** Read the problem carefully. Identify what you know and what you want to find out.

STEP 2 **Make a Plan** Decide on an approach to solving the problem.

STEP 3 **Solve the Problem** Carry out your plan. Try a new approach if the first one isn't successful.

STEP 4 **Look Back** Once you obtain an answer, check that it is reasonable.

EXAMPLE 1   Read a problem and make a plan

RUNNING You run in a city where the short blocks on north-south streets are 0.1 mile long. The long blocks on east-west streets are 0.15 mile long. You will run 2 long blocks east, a number of short blocks south, 2 long blocks west, then back to your starting point. You want to run 2 miles. How many short blocks should you run?

0.1 mi
N
W◇E
0.15 mi
S

Solution

ANOTHER WAY
For an alternative method for solving the problem in Example 1, turn to page 38 for the **Problem Solving Workshop**.

STEP 1 **Read and Understand**

What do you know?

You know the lengths of short blocks and long blocks, the number of long blocks you will run, and the total distance you want to run.

You can conclude that you must run an even number of short blocks because you run the same number of short blocks in each direction.

What do you want to find out?

You want to find out the number of short blocks you should run so that, along with the 4 long blocks, you run 2 miles.

STEP 2 **Make a Plan** Write a verbal model that represents what you want to find out. Then write an equation and solve it, as in Example 2.

EXAMPLE 2   Solve a problem and look back

Solve the problem in Example 1 by carrying out the plan. Then check your answer.

Animated Algebra

For an interactive example of problem solving, go to **classzone.com**.

Solution

STEP 3 **Solve the Problem** Write a verbal model. Then write an equation. Let s be the number of short blocks you run.

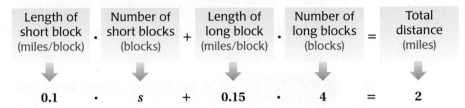

Length of short block (miles/block)	·	Number of short blocks (blocks)	+	Length of long block (miles/block)	·	Number of long blocks (blocks)	=	Total distance (miles)
0.1	·	s	+	0.15	·	4	=	2

REVIEW PROBLEM SOLVING

To review problem solving strategies, see p. 807.

The equation is $0.1s + 0.6 = 2$. One way to solve the equation is to use the strategy *guess, check, and revise.*

Guess an even number that is easily multiplied by 0.1. Try 20.

Check whether 20 is a solution.

$$0.1s + 0.6 = 2 \qquad \text{Write equation.}$$
$$0.1(\mathbf{20}) + 0.6 \stackrel{?}{=} 2 \qquad \text{Substitute 20 for } s.$$
$$2.6 = 2 \; \boldsymbol{X} \qquad \text{Simplify; 20 does not check.}$$

Revise. Because $2.6 > 2$, try an even number less than 20. Try 14.

Check whether 14 is a solution.

$$0.1s + 0.6 = 2 \qquad \text{Write equation.}$$
$$0.1(\mathbf{14}) + 0.6 \stackrel{?}{=} 2 \qquad \text{Substitute 14 for } s.$$
$$2 = 2 \; \checkmark \qquad \text{Simplify; 14 checks.}$$

▶ To run 2 miles, you should run 14 short blocks along with the 4 long blocks you run.

STEP 4 **Look Back** Check your answer by making a table. You run 0.6 mile on the long blocks. Each two short blocks add 0.2 mile.

Short blocks	0	2	4	6	8	10	12	14
Total distance	0.6	0.8	1.0	1.2	1.4	1.6	1.8	2.0

The total distance is 2 miles when you run 4 long blocks and 14 short blocks. The answer in Step 3 is correct.

✓ **GUIDED PRACTICE**   for Examples 1 and 2

1. **WHAT IF?** In Example 1, suppose that you want to run a total distance of 3 miles instead of 2 miles. How many short blocks should you run?

FORMULAS A **formula** is an equation that relates two or more quantities. You may find it helpful to use formulas in problem solving.

REVIEW FORMULAS
For additional formulas, see pp. 796–800 and the Table of Formulas on pp. 823–824.

Temperature	$C = \frac{5}{9}(F - 32)$ where C = degrees Celsius and F = degrees Fahrenheit
Simple interest	$I = Prt$ where I = interest, P = principal, r = interest rate (as a decimal), and t = time
Distance traveled	$d = rt$ where d = distance traveled, r = rate (constant or average speed), and t = time
Profit	$P = I - E$ where P = profit, I = income, and E = expenses

EXAMPLE 3 ◆ **Multiple Choice Practice**

Which equation could be used to find the circumference in inches of a circle with a radius of 8 inches?

(**A**) $C = 4 \times \pi$ (**B**) $C = 8 \times \pi$ (**C**) $C = 16 \times \pi$ (**D**) $C = 64 \times \pi$

AVOID ERRORS
Don't confuse radius with diameter. The problem gives the radius of the circle, so use $C = 2\pi r$. If the diameter were given, you would use $C = \pi d$.

Use the formula for the circumference of a circle with $r = 8$ inches.

$C = 2\pi r$ **Write circumference formula.**

$= 2\pi(8)$ **Substitute 8 for r.**

$= 16\pi$ **Simplify.**

▶ The correct answer is C. (**A**) (**B**) (**C**) (**D**)

EXAMPLE 4 **Use a formula to solve a problem**

CRAFTS You need a rectangular piece of leather to make a book cover as shown. Find the cost of the piece of leather if leather costs $.25 per square inch.

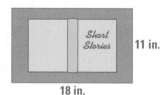

Solution

Use the formula for the area of a rectangle, $A = \ell w$, with $\ell = 18$ inches and $w = 11$ inches.

$A = \ell w$ **Write area formula.**

$= 18(11) = 198$ **Substitute 18 for ℓ and 11 for w, then simplify.**

The area is 198 square inches, so the total cost is $.25(198) = $49.50.

▶ The cost of the piece of leather is $49.50.

 GUIDED PRACTICE for Examples 3 and 4

2. **GARDENING** A gardener determines the cost of planting daffodil bulbs to be $2.40 per square foot. How much will it cost to plant daffodil bulbs in a rectangular garden that is 12 feet long and 5 feet wide?

1.5 EXERCISES

SKILLS · PROBLEM SOLVING · REASONING

1. **VOCABULARY** Give an example of a formula.

2. **NOTETAKING SKILLS** Make a formula triangle like the one on page 4 using the formula for distance traveled, $d = rt$.

EXAMPLES 1 and 2
on pp. 32–33
for Exs. 3–7

READING AND UNDERSTANDING In Exercises 3–5, identify what you know and what you need to find out. You do *not* need to solve the problem.

3. **CRAFT SHOW** You make 35 dog collars and anticipate selling all of them at a craft show. You spent $85 for materials and hope to make a profit of $90. How much should you charge for each collar?

4. **DISTANCE RUNNING** A runner ran at a rate of 0.15 mile per minute for 40 minutes. The next day, the runner ran at a rate of 0.16 mile per minute for 50 minutes. How far did the runner run altogether?

5. **TEMPERATURE** One day, the temperature in Rome, Italy, was 30°C. The temperature in Dallas, Texas, was 83°F. Which temperature was higher?

ERROR ANALYSIS *Describe* and correct the error in solving the problem.

A town is fencing a rectangular field that is 200 feet long and 150 feet wide. At $10 per foot, how much will it cost to fence the field?

6.
$P = 200 + 150 = 350$
$\$10(350) = \$3500$ ✗

7.
$A = (200)(150) = 30,000$
$\$10(30,000) = \$300,000$ ✗

EXAMPLES 3 and 4
on p. 34
for Exs. 8–14

CHOOSING A FORMULA In Exercises 8–12, state the formula that is needed to solve the problem. You do *not* need to solve the problem.

8. The temperature is 68°F. What is the temperature in degrees Celsius?

9. A store buys a baseball cap for $5 and sells it for $20. What is the profit?

10. Find the area of a triangle with a base of 25 feet and a height of 8 feet.

11. A car travels at a constant speed of 50 miles per hour for 4 hours. How far does the car travel?

12. What is the interest on $1000 invested for 3 years in an account that earns simple interest at an annual rate of 2%?

13. ◆ **MULTIPLE CHOICE** What is the interest on $1200 invested for 2 years in an account that earns simple interest at an annual rate of 5%?

Ⓐ $12　　　Ⓑ $60　　　Ⓒ $120　　　Ⓓ $240

14. ◆ **MULTIPLE CHOICE** A car travels at an average speed of 55 miles per hour. How many miles does the car travel in 2.5 hours?

Ⓐ 22 mi　　　Ⓑ 57.5 mi　　　Ⓒ 110 mi　　　Ⓓ 137.5 mi

CONNECT SKILLS TO PROBLEM SOLVING Exercises 15–18 will help you prepare for problem solving.

Use the following question: For how many minutes does a horse run if it travels at a constant speed of 900 feet per minute for 840 yards?

15. Identify what you know and what you need to find out.

16. Make and describe a plan to solve the problem.

17. Carry out the plan and solve the problem.

18. Look back. Check that your answer is reasonable.

EXAMPLES 1, 2, and 4 on pp. 32–34 for Exs. 19–23

19. DVD STORAGE A stackable storage rack holds 22 DVDs and costs $21. How much would it cost to buy enough racks to hold 127 DVDs?

California @HomeTutor for problem solving help at classzone.com

20. FRAMING For an art project, you make a square print with a side length of 8 inches. You make a frame using strips of wood $1\frac{1}{4}$ inches wide. What is the area of the frame?

California @HomeTutor for problem solving help at classzone.com

21. ◆ MULTIPLE CHOICE You have saved $70 to buy a mountain board that costs $250. You plan to save $10 each week. How many weeks will it take to save for the mountain board?

Ⓐ 18   Ⓑ 25   Ⓒ 32   Ⓓ 126

22. HIKING You are hiking. The total weight of your backpack and its contents is $13\frac{3}{8}$ pounds. You want to carry no more than 15 pounds. How many extra water bottles can you add to your backpack if each bottle weighs $\frac{3}{4}$ pound?

Cost of mountain board: $250

23. PIZZA Thick crust pizza requires about 0.15 ounce of dough per square inch of surface area. You have two rectangular pans.

• One pan is 16 inches long and 14 inches wide.

• One pan is 15.5 inches long and 10 inches wide.

How much more dough do you need to make a thick crust pizza in the larger pan than in the smaller one?

24. MULTI-STEP PROBLEM A gardener is reseeding a city park that has the shape of a right triangle with a base of 150 feet and a height of 200 feet. The third side of the park is 250 feet long.

a. One bag of grass seed covers 3750 square feet and costs $27.50. How many bags are needed? What is the total cost?

b. Wire fencing costs $23.19 for each 50 foot roll. How much does it cost to buy fencing to enclose the area?

25. SHORT RESPONSE A farmer plans to build a fence around a rectangular pen that is 16 feet long. The area of the pen is 80 square feet. Is 40 feet of fencing enough to fence in the pen? *Explain.*

26. SONAR A diver uses a sonar device to determine the distance to her diving partner. The device sends a sound wave and records the time it takes for the wave to reach the diving partner and return to the device.

Speed of wave: about 4800 ft/sec

    a. The wave returns 0.2 second after it was sent. How far did it travel?

    b. How far away is the diving partner?

27. CHALLENGE Write a formula for the length ℓ of a rectangle given its perimeter P and its width w. *Justify* your thinking.

28. CHALLENGE You and your friend live 12 miles apart. You leave home at the same time and travel toward each other. You walk at a rate of 4 miles per hour, and your friend bicycles at a rate of 11 miles per hour.

    a. How far from home will each of you be when you meet?

    b. Suppose your friend bicycles at a rate of 12 miles per hour. How far from home will each of you be when you meet?

◆ CALIFORNIA STANDARDS SPIRAL REVIEW

Gr. 5 NS 1.2

29. Jennifer is buying a coat that regularly sells for $75 and is on sale for 20% off. Which expression describes the discount on the jacket? *(p. 793)*

  (A) 0.02×75 **(B)** 0.2×75 **(C)** 0.8×75 **(D)** 1.2×75

Gr. 7 NS 1.3

30. Which fraction is equal to 2.2? *(p. 791)*

  (A) $\dfrac{1}{5}$ **(B)** $\dfrac{11}{5}$ **(C)** $\dfrac{12}{5}$ **(D)** $\dfrac{10}{4}$

Gr. 6 AF 2.1

31. How many inches are in 3.5 feet? *(p. 795)*

  (A) 36 in.   **(B)** 37 in.   **(C)** 41 in.   **(D)** 42 in.

QUIZ *for Lessons 1.4–1.5*

Write an equation or an inequality. *(p. 26)*

  1. 4 more than twice a number n is equal to 25.

  2. The quotient of a number x and 2 is no more than 9.

Check whether the given number is a solution of the equation or inequality. *(p. 26)*

  3. $13 - 2x = 5$; 4   **4.** $5d - 4 \geq 16$; 4   **5.** $4y + 3 \geq 15$; 2

  6. CAR TRAVEL Your family car travels about 28.5 miles on each gallon of gas. Suppose the average price of gas is $3 per gallon. About how much would your family pay for gas for a 912 mile trip? *(p. 32)*

Another Way to Solve Example 1, page 32

Standards
Preparation
Gr. 7 MR 2.5

In Example 1 on page 32, you saw how to solve a problem about running using an equation. You can also solve the problem by using the strategy *draw a diagram*.

PROBLEM

RUNNING You run in a city where the short blocks on north-south streets are 0.1 mile long. The long blocks on east-west streets are 0.15 mile long. You will run 2 long blocks east, a number of short blocks south, 2 long blocks west, then back to your starting point. You want to run a total of 2 miles. How many short blocks should you run?

METHOD **Drawing a Diagram** You can draw a diagram to solve the problem.

STEP 1 **Read** the problem carefully. It tells you the lengths of a short block and a long block. You plan to run 4 long blocks and a distance of 2 miles.

STEP 2 **Draw** a pair of rectangles to represent running 1 short block in each direction. The total distance is 4(0.15) + 2(0.1) = 0.8 mile. Continue adding pairs of rectangles until the total distance run is 2 miles.

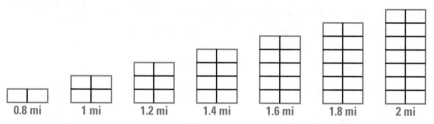

| 0.8 mi | 1 mi | 1.2 mi | 1.4 mi | 1.6 mi | 1.8 mi | 2 mi |

▶ You should run 14 short blocks.

Animated **Algebra** at classzone.com

PRACTICE

1. **BAKING** A cake pan is 9 inches wide and 11 inches long. How many 3 inch by 3 inch square pieces can you cut? Solve this problem using an equation. Then draw a diagram. *Explain* why a diagram is useful.

2. **SWIMMING** A 12 foot rope strung through 4 floats marks off the deep end of a pool. Each end of the rope is 3 feet from a float. The floats are equally spaced. How far apart are they? Solve this problem using two different methods.

3. **ERROR ANALYSIS** *Describe* and correct the error in solving Exercise 2.

$$4x + 6 = 12$$
$$4(1.5) + 6 = 12$$ ✗

The floats are 1.5 feet apart.

4. **⬣ GEOMETRY** The length of a rectangle is twice its width. The perimeter is 72 inches. What is its length? Solve this problem using two different methods.

Multiple Choice Practice for Lessons 1.4–1.5

1. Which equation or inequality represents the verbal sentence "The product of 4 and p is at least 20"? **Gr. 7 AF 1.1**

   Ⓐ $4p = 20$ Ⓑ $4p > 20$

   Ⓒ $4p \leq 20$ Ⓓ $4p \geq 20$

2. You consider 68°F to be a comfortable room temperature. The temperature in the room is 18°C. How many degrees Celsius should you raise the temperature so that it will be 68°F? **Gr. 7 MG 1.1**

   Ⓐ 2°C   Ⓑ 3.6°C

   Ⓒ 20°C   Ⓓ 50°C

3. Which term describes the following most specifically?
   $$8x - 3 = 9$$
   Gr. 7 AF 1.4

   Ⓐ Equation   Ⓑ Expression

   Ⓒ Inequality   Ⓓ Open sentence

4. You plan to attend the dance camp described by taking the bus. Which equation could you use to find the number d of days that you can attend camp if you have a total of $150 to spend? **Gr. 7 AF 1.1**

Dance Camp Just **$100!**

July 1 – July 15
Sign up now!
Bus available for **$5** per day

   Ⓐ $100 = 150 + 5d$

   Ⓑ $100 + 105 = 5d$

   Ⓒ $150 = 100d + 5$

   Ⓓ $150 = 100 + 5d$

5. What number is the solution of $n + 3 = 9$? **Gr. 6 AF 1.1**

   Ⓐ 3   Ⓑ 6

   Ⓒ 9   Ⓓ 27

6. So far this season, baseball player Ted Clark has 17 home runs. The card describes Ted's rookie season, that is, his first season. How many home runs does he have to get by the end of this season to equal his record in his rookie season? **Gr. 6 AF 1.1**

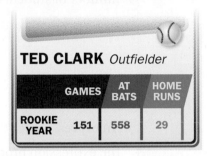

TED CLARK *Outfielder*

	GAMES	AT BATS	HOME RUNS
ROOKIE YEAR	151	558	29

   Ⓐ 12   Ⓑ 17

   Ⓒ 29   Ⓓ 46

7. The Warrens deposited $1000 in an account that earned simple interest. They left their deposit in the account for 2 years and made no other deposits. At the end of the 2 years, the account was worth $1070. What was the annual interest rate? **Gr. 7 NS 1.7**

   Ⓐ 1.75%   Ⓑ 3.5%

   Ⓒ 7%   Ⓓ 14%

8. Your class is planning a car wash. You need $75 worth of materials and plan to charge $5 per car. Which of the following is a verbal model for your class's profit? **Gr. 7 MR 2.5**

   Ⓐ | Cost of materials | + | Charge per car | • | Number of cars washed |

   Ⓑ | Cost of materials | − | Charge per car | • | Number of cars washed |

   Ⓒ | Charge per car | • | Number of cars washed | − | Cost of materials |

   Ⓓ | Charge per car | + | Number of cars washed | − | Cost of materials |

BIG IDEAS
For Your Notebook

Big Idea 1

Writing and Evaluating Algebraic Expressions

The cost of admission for one student at a planetarium is $6. You can use a verbal model to write an expression for the total cost of admission for any number of students.

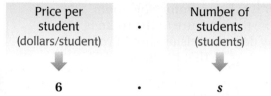

Price per student (dollars/student)	·	Number of students (students)
6	·	*s*

An expression for the total cost is 6*s*. Because $\dfrac{\text{dollars}}{\text{student}} \cdot \cancel{\text{students}} = \text{dollars}$, the expression produces an answer in dollars. The expression is reasonable.

Big Idea 2

Using Expressions to Write Equations and Inequalities

You can use symbols to write an equation or inequality that compares the expression 6*s* with another expression.

Words	Algebra	
The total cost of admission to the planetarium for *s* students at a rate of $6 per student is $150.	$6s = 150$	**Equation**
The total cost of admission to the planetarium for *s* students at a rate of $6 per student is no more than $150.	$6s \leq 150$	**Inequality**
The total cost of admission to the planetarium for *s* students at a rate of $6 per student is at least $150.	$6s \geq 150$	**Inequality**

Big Idea 3

Using a Problem Solving Plan

You can use a problem solving plan to solve a problem.

The cost of admission for one student at a planetarium is $6. How many students are admitted if the total cost is $150?	
Read and Understand	You know the cost of admission for each student and the total cost. You want to know how many students are admitted.
Make a Plan	Solve the equation $6s = 150$ from Big Idea 2.
Solve the Problem	Use mental math. Because $6 \cdot 25 = 150$, $s = 25$.
Look Back	Check reasonableness: $20 < 25 < 30$; $6 \cdot 20 = \mathbf{120}$, $6 \cdot 30 = \mathbf{180}$, and $\mathbf{120} < 150 < \mathbf{180}$.

APPLYING THE
BIG IDEAS

Big Idea 1
You write and evaluate algebraic expressions in **Steps 1 and 2**.

Big Idea 2
You write equations and inequalities in **Step 3**.

Big Idea 3
You use a problem solving plan in **Ex. 1**.

PROBLEM How can you use nutrition information to make good decisions about eating?

STEP 1 Write an algebraic expression.

The number of calories in a serving of food is the sum of the calories from fat, protein, and carbohydrate. The table shows the calories in 1 gram of each of the three food components.

Write an expression for the number of calories in a quantity of food that contains f grams of fat, p grams of protein, and c grams of carbohydrate.

Component	Calories in 1 gram
Fat	9
Protein	4
Carbohydrate	4

STEP 2 Evaluate an algebraic expression.

Plan a lunch. Choose a main dish, a salad, and a drink from the table. Find the total number of grams of fat, protein, and carbohydrate in your lunch. Use your expression from Step 1 to find the total number of calories.

Food (single serving)	Fat (g)	Protein (g)	Carbohydrate (g)
Chicken and bean burrito	15	20	27
Macaroni and cheese	11	14	50
Garden salad	0	2	12
Carrot-raisin salad	30	2	40
1% milk	2	8	12
Fruit smoothie	3	3	41

STEP 3 Write an equation or an inequality.

Suppose you choose a burrito and a fruit smoothie. You want a lunch with 80 grams of carbohydrate. Write an equation you can use to determine how many grams of carbohydrate you can add. Which salad do you choose?

Suppose you choose macaroni and cheese and a garden salad. You want a lunch with at least 20 grams of protein. Write an inequality that describes the situation. Which drink do you choose?

Extending the Problem

1. Plan a meal that provides about one third of your recommended daily intake of fat, protein, carbohydrate, and calories. You can find those recommendations online at www.kidsnutrition.org. You can find the nutrition content of foods online at www.ars.usda.gov/foodsearch.

CHAPTER REVIEW

1

REVIEW KEY VOCABULARY

- variable, *p. 5*
- algebraic expression, *p. 5*
- evaluate an algebraic expression, *p. 5*
- power, *p. 6*
- base, *p. 6*

- exponent, *p. 6*
- order of operations, *p. 11*
- verbal model, *p. 20*
- rate, *p. 21*
- unit rate, *p. 21*
- equation, *p. 26*

- inequality, *p. 26*
- open sentence, *p. 26*
- solution of an equation or inequality, *p. 27*
- formula, *p. 34*

VOCABULARY EXERCISES

In Exercises 1–3, copy and complete the statement.

1. In the power 7^{12}, __?__ is the base and __?__ is the exponent.

2. A(n) __?__ is a statement that contains the symbol =.

3. A(n) __?__ is an expression that includes at least one variable.

4. **NOTETAKING SKILLS** Make a formula triangle like the one on page 4 using the formula for simple interest, $I = Prt$.

REVIEW EXAMPLES AND EXERCISES

Use the review examples and exercises below to check your understanding of the concepts you have learned in each lesson of Chapter 1.

| **1.1** | **Evaluate Expressions and Use Exponents** | *pp. 5–10* |

Gr. 6 AF 1.2

EXAMPLE

Evaluate $6 - n$ when $n = 4$.

$$6 - n = 6 - 4 \qquad \text{Substitute 4 for } n.$$
$$= 2 \qquad \text{Simplify.}$$

EXERCISES

EXAMPLES 1, 4, and 5 on pp. 5–7 for Exs. 5–12

Evaluate the expression.

5. $3 + x$ when $x = 13$

6. $y - 2$ when $y = 18$

7. $\frac{20}{k}$ when $k = 2$

8. $40w$ when $w = 0.5$

9. z^2 when $z = 20$

10. w^3 when $w = 0.1$

11. **DVD STORAGE** A DVD storage sleeve has the shape of a square with an side length of 5 inches. What is the area of the front of the sleeve?

12. **NOTEPAPER** You store square notepaper in a cube-shaped box with an inside edge length of 3 inches. What is the volume of the box?

1.2 Apply Order of Operations

pp. 11–16

Gr. 7 AF 1.2

EXAMPLE

Evaluate $(5 + 3)^2 \div 2 \times 3$.

$$(5 + 3)^2 \div 2 \times 3 = 8^2 \div 2 \times 3 \qquad \text{Add within parentheses.}$$
$$= 64 \div 2 \times 3 \qquad \text{Evaluate power.}$$
$$= 32 \times 3 \qquad \text{Divide.}$$
$$= 96 \qquad \text{Multiply.}$$

EXERCISES

EXAMPLES
1, 2, and 3
on pp. 11–12
for Exs. 13–21

Evaluate the expression.

13. $12 - 6 \div 2$

14. $1 + 2 \cdot 9^2$

15. $3 + 2^3 - 6 \div 2$

16. $15 - (4 + 3^2)$

17. $\dfrac{20 - 12}{5^2 - 1}$

18. $50 - [7 + (3^2 \div 2)]$

Evaluate the expression when $x = 4$.

19. $15x - 8$

20. $3x^2 + 4$

21. $2(x - 1)^2$

1.3 Write Expressions

pp. 19–24

Gr. 7 AF 1.1

EXAMPLE

Write an expression for the entry fee in a jazz band competition if there is a base fee of $50 and a charge of $1 per member.

Write a verbal model. Then translate the verbal model into an algebraic expression. Let n represent the number of band members.

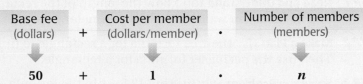

Base fee (dollars)	+	Cost per member (dollars/member)	·	Number of members (members)
50	+	1	·	n

▶ An expression for the entry fee (in dollars) is $50 + n$.

EXERCISES

EXAMPLES
1, 2, and 3
on pp. 19–20
for Exs. 22–27

Translate the verbal phrase into an expression.

22. The sum of a number k and 7

23. 5 less than a number z

24. The quotient of a number k and 12

25. 3 times the square of a number x

26. **TOLL ROADS** A toll road charges trucks a toll of $3 per axle. Write an expression for the total toll for a truck.

27. **SCHOOL SUPPLIES** You purchase some notebooks for $2.95 each and a package of pens for $2.19. Write an expression for the total amount (in dollars) that you spend.

1.4 Write Equations and Inequalities

pp. 26–31

Gr. 7 AF 1.1

EXAMPLE

Write an inequality for the sentence "The sum of 3 and twice a number k is no more than 15." Then check whether 4 is a solution of the inequality.

An inequality is $3 + 2k \leq 15$.

To check whether 4 is a solution of the inequality, substitute 4 for k.

$3 + 2(4) \overset{?}{\leq} 15$ **Substitute 4 for k.**

$11 \leq 15$ ✓   **Inequality is true. So, 4 is a solution.**

EXERCISES

**EXAMPLES
1 and 2**
on pp. 26–27
for Exs. 28–32

Write an equation or an inequality.

28. The product of a number z and 12 is 60.

29. The sum of 13 and a number t is at least 24.

Check whether the given number is a solution of the equation or inequality.

30. $3x - 4 = 10$; 5   **31.** $4y - 2 \geq 2$; 3   **32.** $2d + 4 < 9d - 7$; 3

1.5 Use a Problem Solving Plan

pp. 32–37

Gr. 7 MR 2.5

EXAMPLE

A rectangular banner is 12 feet long and has an area of 60 square feet. What is the perimeter of the banner?

STEP 1 **Read and Understand** You know the length of the rectangular banner and its area. You want to find the perimeter.

STEP 2 **Make a Plan** Use the area formula for a rectangle to find the width. Then use the perimeter formula for a rectangle.

STEP 3 **Solve the Problem** Substituting 12 for ℓ in the formula $A = \ell w$, you get $60 = 12w$. Because $12 \cdot 5 = 60$, $w = 5$. Then substituting 12 for ℓ and 5 for w in the formula $P = 2\ell + 2w$, you get $P = 2(12) + 2(5) = 34$ feet.

STEP 4 **Look Back** Use estimation. Since $\ell \approx 10$ and $A = 60$, $w \approx 6$. Then $P \approx 2(10) + 2(6) = 32$ feet, so your answer is reasonable.

EXERCISES

**EXAMPLES
1, 2, 3, and 4**
on p. 32–34
for Exs. 33–34

33. **U.S. HISTORY** The flag that inspired the national anthem was a rectangle 30 feet wide and 42 feet long. Pieces of the flag have been lost. It is now 30 feet wide and 34 feet long. How many square feet have been lost?

34. **PATTERNS** A grocery clerk stacks three rows of cans of fruit for a display. Each of the top two rows has 2 fewer cans than the row beneath it. There are 30 cans altogether. How many cans are there in each row?

1. **VOCABULARY** Copy and complete: A(n) ? is an equation that relates two or more quantities.

2. **VOCABULARY** Give an example of an inequality.

Evaluate the expression.

3. $7 + 3^2 \cdot 2$

4. $(5^2 + 17) \div 7$

5. $(24 - 11) - (3 + 2) \div 4$

6. $\frac{x}{5}$ when $x = 30$

7. n^3 when $n = 20$

8. $15 - t$ when $t = 3.2$

9. $12 + 4x$ when $x = 1\frac{1}{2}$

10. $3z^2 - 7$ when $z = 6$

11. $2(4n + 5)$ when $n = 2$

Write an expression, an equation, or an inequality.

12. The sum of 19 and the cube of a number x

13. Half the sum of 12 and the quotient of a number t and 4

14. The product of 3 and a number y is no more than 21.

15. Twice the difference of a number z and 12 is equal to 10.

16. The sum of 23 and the square of a number b is greater than 80.

17. The difference of 13 and the product of 3 and a number a is equal to 5.

Check whether the given number is a solution of the equation or inequality.

18. $2 + 3x = 10; 2$

19. $8 + 3b > 15; 2$

20. $11y - 5 \le 30; 3$

21. $15 - 4x = 7; 2$

22. $\frac{n}{3} - 1 \ge 15; 12$

23. $\frac{k}{2} + 3 = 30; 18$

Use mental math to solve the equation.

24. $x + 16 = 24$

25. $w - 9 = 11$

26. $4z = 10$

27. **FOOD PREPARATION** You buy tomatoes at $1.29 per pound and peppers at $3.99 per pound to make salsa. Write an expression for the total cost of the ingredients. Then find the total cost of 5 pounds of tomatoes and 2 pounds of peppers.

28. **FUNDRAISING** A school's service club is sponsoring a dance in the school gym to raise money for a local charity. The expenses will be $625, and tickets to the dance will cost $8.50. The club members hope to raise enough after expenses to donate at least $1000 to the charity. Write an inequality that describes the situation. If the club members sell 195 tickets, will they meet their goal?

29. **CAR EXPENSES** A family determined the average cost of maintaining and operating the family car to be about $.30 per mile. On one trip, the family drove at an average rate of 50 miles per hour for 6.5 hours. On a second trip, the family drove at an average rate of 55 miles per hour for 6 hours. Which trip cost more? How much more?

STRATEGIES YOU'LL USE:
- SOLVE DIRECTLY
- ELIMINATE CHOICES

Standards Preparation

Gr. 6 AF 1.1,
Gr. 7 AF 1.1

If you have difficulty solving a multiple choice problem directly, you may be able to use another approach to eliminate incorrect answer choices and obtain the correct answer.

PROBLEM 1

An airplane flew at 400 miles per hour for 5 hours. Later, the plane flew at 450 miles per hour for 4 hours. How far did the plane fly altogether?

A 1912.5 mi **B** 3800 mi **C** 4050 mi **D** 4500 mi

Strategy 1 SOLVE DIRECTLY

Write and evaluate an expression to find the distance.

STEP 1 **Write** a verbal model. You know the formula for distance traveled, $d = rt$. There are two rates and two times, so the verbal model will represent the sum of two products.

Rate (mi/h)	•	Time (h)	+	Rate (mi/h)	•	Time (h)

STEP 2 **Use** the verbal model to write an expression.

Rate (mi/h)	•	Time (h)	+	Rate (mi/h)	•	Time (h)
400	•	5	+	450	•	4

STEP 3 **Evaluate** the expression.

$$400 \cdot 5 + 450 \cdot 4 = 2000 + 1800$$
$$= 3800$$

The plane flew 3800 miles altogether.

The correct answer is B. **A** **B** **C** **D**

Strategy 2 ELIMINATE CHOICES

Consider the extremes to eliminate incorrect answer choices.

STEP 1 **Consider** flying at the slower rate for the entire time.

$$\frac{400 \text{ mi}}{h} \cdot 9 \text{ h} = 3600 \text{ mi}$$

So, the plane flew farther than 3600 miles because it actually flew at a faster rate for part of the 9 hours. You can eliminate choice A.

STEP 2 **Consider** flying at the faster rate for the entire time.

$$\frac{450 \text{ mi}}{h} \cdot 9 \text{ h} = 4050 \text{ mi}$$

So, the plane flew less than 4050 miles because it actually flew at a slower rate for part of the 9 hours. You can eliminate choices C and D.

The only remaining choice is B.

The correct answer is B. **A** **B** **C** **D**

PROBLEM 2

What is the solution of the equation $x + 15 = 45$?

(A) 3   **(B)** 25   **(C)** 30   **(D)** 60

Strategy 1   SOLVE DIRECTLY

Use mental math to solve the equation.

$$x + 15 = 45$$

Think: What number plus 15 is 45?

Because $30 + 15 = 45$, the solution is 30.

The correct answer is C. **(A) (B) (C) (D)**

Strategy 2   ELIMINATE CHOICES

Substitute each given value for x in the equation.

Choice A: 3   **Choice B:** 25
Substitute 3 for x.   Substitute 25 for x.

$$x + 15 = 45 \qquad\qquad x + 15 = 45$$
$$3 + 15 \overset{?}{=} 45 \qquad\qquad 25 + 15 \overset{?}{=} 45$$
$$18 = 45 \;✗ \qquad\qquad\quad 40 = 45 \;✗$$

Choice C: 30
Substitute 30 for x.

$$x + 15 = 45$$
$$30 + 15 \overset{?}{=} 45$$
$$45 = 45 \;✓$$

The correct answer is C. **(A) (B) (C) (D)**

STRATEGY PRACTICE

Explain why you can eliminate the highlighted answer choice.

1. What is the solution of the equation $x - 25 = 75$?

   (A) 3   **(B)** ✗ **25**   **(C)** 50   **(D)** 100

2. Which number is a solution of the inequality $7x < 28$?

   (A) 3   **(B)** 4   **(C)** 5.5   **(D)** ✗ **7**

3. A high-speed train travels at a rate of 200 miles per hour for 0.5 hour and then at a rate of 160 miles per hour for 1.5 hours. How far does the train travel?

   (A) ✗ **260 mi**   **(B)** 340 mi   **(C)** 380 mi   **(D)** 440 mi

4. One square has a side length of 14 meters. Another square has a side length of 12 meters. How much greater is the area of the larger square?

   (A) 4 m^2 **(B)** 52 m^2 **(C)** 144 m^2 **(D)** ✗ **196 m^2**

1. You receive a $75 gift certificate to a music store. An expression for the total cost (in dollars) of c CDs and d DVDs is $15c + 20d$. Your purchase is shown. How much money is left on the gift certificate? **Gr. 7 AF 1.2**

   (A) $5

   (B) $20

   (C) $25

   (D) $145

   2 CDs
   at $15 each

   2 DVDs
   at $20 each

2. The sum of a number n and 28 is 51. Which equation represents this relationship? **Gr. 7 AF 1.1**

   (A) $28 + n = 51$

   (B) $51n = 28$

   (C) $28 - n = 51$

   (D) $51 + n = 28$

3. The surface area of a cube is given by the expression $6s^2$ where s is the edge length of the cube. What is the surface area of the cube shown? **Gr. 7 AF 1.2**

   5 in.

   5 in.

   5 in.

   (A) 30 in.^{2}

   (B) 125 in.^{2}

   (C) 150 in.^{2}

   (D) 900 in.^{2}

4. What is the interest on $2800 invested for 2 years in an account that earns simple interest at an annual rate of 3%? **Gr. 7 NS 1.7**

   (A) $42

   (B) $84

   (C) $126

   (D) $168

5. Which number is the solution of $\frac{x}{5} - 7 = 5$? **Gr. 7 AF 4.1**

   (A) 10

   (B) 12

   (C) 25

   (D) 60

6. You are shipping books that weigh $\frac{3}{8}$ pound each. The box weighs 1 pound. You want the total weight of the shipment to be less than 8 pounds. Let n be the number of books that you ship. Which statement represents the situation? **Gr. 7 AF 1.1**

   (A) $\frac{3}{8}n + 1 = 8$

   (B) $\frac{3}{8}n + 1 < 8$

   (C) $\frac{3}{8}n + 1 \geq 8$

   (D) $\frac{3}{8}n + 1 \leq 8$

7. What is the value of $5.7 - b$ when $b = 4.2$? **Gr. 6 AF 1.2**

   (A) 1.5

   (B) 2.0

   (C) 4.2

   (D) 9.9

8. A rectangular pool has the same depth throughout. The water in the pool was 4 feet deep before water was added. After, the pool contained 2352 cubic feet of water. How much water was added? **Gr. 7 MG 2.1**

   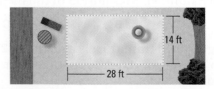

   14 ft

   28 ft

   (A) 392 ft^3

   (B) 588 ft^3

   (C) 784 ft^3

   (D) 1568 ft^3

9. A porch is being completely covered with square and rectangular stone tiles, as shown below. There will be 27 square tiles and 18 rectangular tiles used. What is the area of the porch? **Gr. 7 MG 2.1**

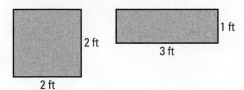

Ⓐ 135 ft²

Ⓑ 162 ft²

Ⓒ 180 ft²

Ⓓ 315 ft²

10. What is the value of the expression $\frac{4(x-2)}{5x}$ when $x = 8$? **Gr. 7 AF 1.2**

Ⓐ $\frac{3}{5}$

Ⓑ $\frac{3}{4}$

Ⓒ $\frac{4}{5}$

Ⓓ $\frac{6}{5}$

11. You travel by train from Sacramento to Emeryville. The train leaves at 12:10 P.M. and travels at an average speed of 50 miles per hour. At about what time do you arrive in Emeryville? **Gr. 7 AF 4.2**

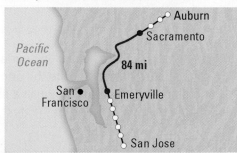

Ⓐ 12:50 P.M.

Ⓑ 1:00 P.M.

Ⓒ 1:35 P.M.

Ⓓ 1:50 P.M.

12. Which expression represents the phrase "5 times the difference of a number x and 4"? **Gr. 7 AF 1.1**

Ⓐ $5 \cdot 4 - x$

Ⓑ $5 \cdot x - 4$

Ⓒ $5(4 - x)$

Ⓓ $5(x - 4)$

13. Workers take 2 hours to load a delivery truck. After the truck is loaded, it is driven at an average speed of 50 miles per hour to a building site 125 miles away. Which of the following is a verbal model for the time required to load the truck and arrive at the building site? **Gr. 7 MR 2.5**

Ⓐ | Time to load truck | + | Average speed | ÷ | Distance to building site |
| --- | --- | --- | --- | --- |

Ⓑ | Time to load truck | + | Distance to building site | ÷ | Average speed |
| --- | --- | --- | --- | --- |

Ⓒ | Time to load truck | + | Average speed | · | Distance to building site |
| --- | --- | --- | --- | --- |

Ⓓ | Time to load truck | · | Average speed | + | Distance to building site |
| --- | --- | --- | --- | --- |

14. Until today, a runner's best time for running 4 laps on her school track was 332 seconds. Today she runs 4 laps and breaks her record. Which inequality represents the possible average speed s (in seconds per lap) that she runs today? **Gr. 7 AF 1.1**

Ⓐ $\frac{s}{4} > 332$

Ⓑ $\frac{4}{s} > 332$

Ⓒ $4s > 332$

Ⓓ $4s < 332$

2 Properties of Real Numbers

Before

In previous courses and in Chapter 1, you learned the following skills, which you'll use in Chapter 2:

- Comparing and ordering numbers
- Evaluating expressions
- Applying the order of operations
- Performing operations with fractions

Now

In Chapter 2 you'll study these **Big Ideas**:

1 Performing operations with real numbers

2 Applying properties of real numbers

3 Classifying and reasoning with real numbers

Why?

So you can solve real-world problems about . . .

- Music, p. 58
- Volcanoes, p. 70
- Movies, p. 85
- Volleyball, p. 93
- Pyramids, p. 101

Animated Algebra
at *classzone.com*

Get-Ready Games

Four Out

California Standards

Review operations with rational numbers. *Gr. 7 NS 1.2*

Prepare for using properties of real numbers. *Alg. 1.0*

Materials

- 2 *Four Out* answer cards
  1 answer card for each player
- 24 *Four Out* expression cards
- 24 markers

How to Play Play in pairs. Fill the blanks on your answer card with 16 of the 24 numbers below. Shuffle the deck of expression cards and place the deck face down in a pile. On each turn, players should follow the steps on the next page.

$\frac{11}{30}$	$\frac{1}{10}$	7	$2\frac{1}{2}$	$1\frac{4}{5}$	$\frac{1}{8}$	$\frac{3}{14}$	$\frac{1}{5}$
$1\frac{1}{8}$	$\frac{13}{20}$	32	$\frac{16}{35}$	$2\frac{1}{4}$	$\frac{1}{18}$	21	$2\frac{1}{3}$
$\frac{3}{35}$	$1\frac{1}{16}$	$\frac{1}{81}$	$3\frac{2}{3}$	$1\frac{2}{21}$	$\frac{1}{12}$	$4\frac{5}{6}$	$\frac{9}{16}$

CALIFORNIA STANDARDS

• **Alg. 1.0** Students identify and use the arithmetic properties of subsets of integers and rational, irrational, and real numbers including closure properties for the four basic arithmetic operations where applicable. *(Lessons 2.2, 2.3, 2.4, 2.5, 2.6, 2.7, 2.8)*

• **Alg. 1.1** Students use properties of numbers to demonstrate whether assertions are true or false. *(Lessons 2.2, 2.3, 2.4, 2.5, 2.6, 2.8)*

$$\frac{3}{7} + \frac{2}{3}$$

1 **Draw** the top card from the deck of expression cards. Both players use this card to complete Steps 2 and 3.

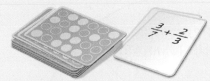

How to Win Be the first player to have four markers in a row on your game board. Markers can be aligned vertically, horizontally, or diagonally.

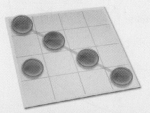

2 **Evaluate** the expression shown on the card.

Games Wrap-Up

3 **Place** a marker on a space of your game board if it contains the value of the expression.

Draw Conclusions

Complete these exercises after playing the game.

1. **WRITING** *Describe* the steps you take to add two mixed numbers with different denominators.

2. **REASONING** What is the greatest number of spaces on your board that can be marked without having four in a row? *Explain.*

51

Prerequisite Skills

California @HomeTutor

Prerequisite skills practice
at classzone.com

REVIEW VOCABULARY

- **variable,** *p. 5*
- **algebraic expression,** *p. 5*
- **order of operations,** *p. 11*
- **least common denominator,** *p. 788*
- **reciprocal,** *p. 789*
- **mean,** *p. 803*

VOCABULARY CHECK

In Exercises 1 and 2, copy and complete the statement.

1. The least common denominator of the fractions $\frac{3}{8}$ and $\frac{5}{12}$ is ___?___.

2. The variable in the expression $5x - 3$ is ___?___.

3. According to the order of operations, what is the first step in simplifying the expression $(3 + 4)^2 - 8$?

SKILLS CHECK

Copy and complete the statement using <, >, or =. *(Review p. 790 for 2.1, 2.7.)*

4. 6.7 ___?___ 9.69   5. 15.09 ___?___ 15.1   6. 0.333 ___?___ 0.34   7. 2.5 ___?___ 2.500

Evaluate the expression when $x = 5$. *(Review p. 5 for 2.2–2.4, 2.6.)*

8. $52 - x$ 9. $1.7x$ 10. $x + 39$ 11. $\frac{125}{x}$

Evaluate the expression. *(Review p. 11 for 2.5.)*

12. $5m - 9$ when $m = 6$ 13. $16 - r - 3$ when $r = 10$

Notetaking Skills

NOW YOU TRY

Make a *concept circle* for the rule for subtracting fractions with unlike denominators.

Focus on Graphic Organizers

You can use a *concept circle* to organize information about a rule or property, such as the rule for adding fractions with unlike denominators.

CONCEPT

ADDING FRACTIONS WITH UNLIKE DENOMINATORS

$$\frac{a}{b} + \frac{c}{d} = \frac{ad + bc}{bd}$$

EXAMPLE

$$\frac{1}{5} + \frac{2}{3} = \frac{1(3) + 5(2)}{5(3)}$$
$$= \frac{13}{15}$$

JUSTIFY

$$\frac{a}{b} + \frac{c}{d} = \frac{ad}{bd} + \frac{bc}{bd}$$
$$= \frac{ad + bc}{bd}$$

Combine $\frac{1}{2}$ and $\frac{2}{3}$ cups of flour. Find the total amount.

$$\frac{1}{2} + \frac{2}{3} = 1\frac{1}{6} \text{ cups}$$

APPLY

2.1 Use Integers and Rational Numbers

Standards

Alg. 2.0 Students understand and use such operations as taking the **opposite**, finding the reciprocal, taking a root, and raising to a fractional power. They understand and use the rules of exponents.

Alg. 24.2 Students identify the hypothesis and conclusion in logical deduction.

Alg. 24.3 Students use counterexamples to show that an assertion is false and recognize that a single counterexample is sufficient to refute an assertion.

Connect *Before* you performed operations with whole numbers. *Now* you will graph and compare positive and negative numbers.

Math and **WEATHER**
Ex. 65, p. 59

Key Vocabulary
• **whole numbers**
• **integers**
• **rational number**
• **opposites**
• **absolute value**
• **conditional statement**

The set of **whole numbers** is {0, 1, 2, 3, . . .}, and the set of **integers** is {. . . , −3, −2, −1, 0, 1, 2, 3, . . .}. The dots indicate that the numbers continue without end in one or both directions. **Positive integers** are integers that are greater than 0. **Negative integers** are integers that are less than 0. The integer 0 is neither negative nor positive.

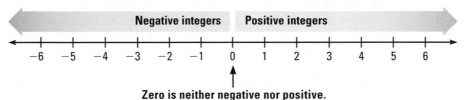

Zero is neither negative nor positive.

EXAMPLE 1 Graph and compare integers

Graph −3 and −4 on a number line. Then tell which number is greater.

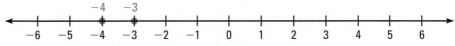

▸ On the number line, −3 is to the right of −4. So, −3 > −4.

RATIONAL NUMBERS The integers belong to the set of *rational numbers*. A **rational number** is a number $\frac{a}{b}$ where a and b are integers and $b \neq 0$. For example, $-\frac{1}{2}$ is a rational number because it can be written as $\frac{-1}{2}$ or $\frac{1}{-2}$. The rational numbers belong to the set of numbers called the *real numbers* (discussed in more detail in Lesson 2.7).

READING
Although you can write a negative fraction in different ways, you usually write it with the negative sign to the left of the fraction.

Real numbers

Rational numbers

Integers

Whole numbers

REVIEW FRACTIONS
For help with writing fractions as decimals, see p. 791.

DECIMALS In decimal form, a rational number either terminates or repeats. For example, $\frac{3}{4} = 0.75$ is a *terminating decimal*, and $\frac{1}{3} = 0.333\ldots = 0.\overline{3}$ is a *repeating decimal*.

EXAMPLE 2 ◆ **Multiple Choice Practice**

Which is *not* a rational number?

Ⓐ $0.\overline{27}$ Ⓑ 0.6 Ⓒ $-\frac{1}{3}$ Ⓓ $0.101101110\ldots$

Solution

Repeating decimals, terminating decimals, and fractions are all rational numbers. While choice D shows a pattern in its digits, the decimal is neither terminating nor repeating. So, choice D is not a rational number.

▶ The correct answer is D. Ⓐ Ⓑ Ⓒ **Ⓓ**

EXAMPLE 3 **Order rational numbers**

ASTRONOMY A star's color index is a measure of the temperature of the star's surface. The greater the color index, the cooler the star. Order the stars in the table from hottest to coolest.

Orion constellation

Star	Rigel	Arneb	Denebola	Bellatrix
Color index	−0.03	0.21	0.09	−0.22

Solution

Begin by graphing the numbers on a number line.

Read the numbers from left to right: −0.22, −0.03, 0.09, 0.21.

▶ From hottest to coolest, the stars are Bellatrix, Rigel, Denebola, and Arneb.

 GUIDED PRACTICE for Examples 1, 2, and 3

Graph the numbers on a number line. Then tell which number is greater.

 1. 4 and 0 **2.** 2 and −5 **3.** −1 and −6

Tell whether each number in the list belongs to each of the following sets: whole numbers, integers, and rational numbers. Then order the numbers from least to greatest.

 4. 4, −1.5, −0.31, −2.8 **5.** $\frac{1}{6}$, 1.75, $-\frac{2}{3}$, 0

OPPOSITES Two numbers that are the same distance from 0 on a number line but are on opposite sides of 0 are called **opposites**. For example, 4 and −4 are opposites because they are both 4 units from 0 but are on opposite sides of 0. The opposite of 0 is 0. You read the expression −*a* as "the opposite of *a*."

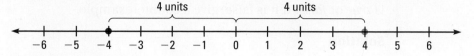

4 units   4 units

$$-6 \quad -5 \quad -4 \quad -3 \quad -2 \quad -1 \quad 0 \quad 1 \quad 2 \quad 3 \quad 4 \quad 5 \quad 6$$

EXAMPLE 4   **Find opposites of numbers**

READING
Do not assume that −*a* is a negative number. Notice that for *a* = −2.5, −*a* = 2.5.

a. If *a* = −2.5, then −*a* = −(−2.5) = 2.5.

b. If $a = \frac{3}{4}$, then $-a = -\frac{3}{4}$.

c. If *a* = 0, then −*a* = 0. (Zero is its own opposite.)

ABSOLUTE VALUE The **absolute value** of a number *a* is the distance between *a* and 0 on a number line. The symbol $|a|$ represents the absolute value of *a*.

KEY CONCEPT   *For Your Notebook*

Absolute Value of a Real Number

Words If *a* is positive, then $|a| = a$.   **Example** $|2| = 2$

Words If *a* is 0, then $|a| = 0$.   **Example** $|0| = 0$

Words If *a* is negative, then $|a| = -a$.   **Example** $|-2| = -(-2) = 2$

EXAMPLE 5   **Find absolute values of numbers**

AVOID ERRORS
The absolute value of a number is never negative. If a number *a* is negative, then its absolute value, −*a*, is positive.

a. If $a = -\frac{2}{3}$, then $|a| = \left|-\frac{2}{3}\right| = -\left(-\frac{2}{3}\right) = \frac{2}{3}$.

b. If *a* = 3.2, then $|a| = |3.2| = 3.2$.

CONDITIONAL STATEMENTS A **conditional statement** has a hypothesis and a conclusion. An **if-then statement** is a form of a conditional statement. The *if* part contains the *hypothesis*. The *then* part contains the *conclusion*.

conditional statement

$$\text{If } \boldsymbol{a} \textbf{ is a positive number}, \text{ then } |a| = a.$$

hypothesis   conclusion

About the Standards

Drawing a conclusion from a hypothesis is part of logical deduction (Algebra 1 Standard 24.2), which is discussed in Lesson 2.8.

In mathematics, if-then statements are either true or false. An if-then statement is true if the conclusion is always true when the hypothesis is satisfied. An if-then statement is false if for just one example, called a **counterexample**, the conclusion is false when the hypothesis is satisfied.

EXAMPLE 6 Analyze a conditional statement

Identify the hypothesis and the conclusion of the statement "If a number is a rational number, then the number is an integer." Tell whether the statement is *true* or *false*. If it is false, give a counterexample.

Solution

Hypothesis: a number is a rational number

Conclusion: the number is an integer

The statement is false. The number 0.5 is a counterexample, because 0.5 is a rational number but not an integer.

 GUIDED PRACTICE for Examples 4, 5, and 6

For the given value of a, find $-a$ and $|a|$.

6. $a = 5.3$ **7.** $a = -7$ **8.** $a = -\dfrac{4}{9}$

Identify the hypothesis and the conclusion of the statement. Tell whether the statement is *true* or *false*. If it is false, give a counterexample.

9. If a number is a rational number, then the number is positive.

10. If the absolute value of a number is positive, then the number is positive.

2.1 EXERCISES

HOMEWORK KEY

◆ = **MULTIPLE CHOICE PRACTICE**
Exs. 23, 45, 54, 63, and 69–71

○ = **HINTS AND HOMEWORK HELP**
for Exs. 15, 31, and 61 at classzone.com

SKILLS • PROBLEM SOLVING • REASONING

1. VOCABULARY Copy and complete: A number is a(n) ? if it can be written in the form $\dfrac{a}{b}$ where a and b are integers and $b \neq 0$.

2. VOCABULARY What is the opposite of -2? *Explain* your answer.

3. WRITING *Describe* the difference between whole numbers and positive integers.

4. WRITING For a negative number x, is the absolute value of x a *positive number* or a *negative number*? *Explain*.

EXAMPLE 1
on p. 53
for Exs. 5–13

GRAPHING AND COMPARING INTEGERS Graph the numbers on a number line. Then tell which number is greater.

5. 0 and 7   **6.** 0 and -4 **7.** -5 and -6

8. -2 and -3 **9.** 5 and -2 **10.** -12 and 8

11. -1 and -5 **12.** 3 and -13 **13.** -20 and -2

EXAMPLES
2 and 3
on p. 54
for Exs. 14–25

CLASSIFYING AND ORDERING NUMBERS Tell whether each number in the list belongs to each of the following sets: whole numbers, integers, and rational numbers. Then order the numbers from least to greatest.

14. $3, -5, -2.4, 1$

15. $1.6, 1, -4, 0$

16. $0.25, -0.5, 0.2, -2$

17. $-\frac{2}{3}, -0.6, -1, \frac{1}{3}$

18. $-0.01, 0.1, 0, -\frac{1}{10}$

19. $16, -1.66, \frac{5}{3}, -1.6$

20. $-2.7, \frac{1}{2}, 0.3, -7$

21. $-4.99, 5, \frac{16}{3}, -5.1$

22. $-\frac{3}{5}, -0.4, -1, -0.5$

23. ◆ **MULTIPLE CHOICE** Which number is a whole number?

(A) $\left| -\frac{18}{9} \right|$
(B) $-\frac{4}{3}$
(C) 1.6
(D) $-(-7.963)$

ERROR ANALYSIS *Describe* and correct the error in the statement.

24.

The numbers $-(-2), -4,$ $-|8|,$ and -0.3 are negative numbers.

25.

The numbers $|-3.4|, -(-8),$ $-|-0.2|,$ and 0.87 are positive numbers.

EXAMPLES
4 and 5
on p. 55
for Exs. 26–37

FINDING OPPOSITES AND ABSOLUTE VALUES For the given value of a, find $-a$ and $|a|$.

26. $a = 6$

27. $a = -3$

28. $a = -18$

29. $a = 0$

30. $a = 13.4$

31. $a = 2.7$

32. $a = -6.1$

33. $a = -7.9$

34. $a = -1\frac{1}{9}$

35. $a = -\frac{5}{6}$

36. $a = \frac{3}{4}$

37. $a = 1\frac{1}{3}$

EXAMPLE 6
on p. 56
for Exs. 38–45

ANALYZING CONDITIONAL STATEMENTS Identify the hypothesis and the conclusion of the conditional statement. Tell whether the statement is *true* or *false*. If it is false, give a counterexample.

38. If a number is a positive integer, then the number is a whole number.

39. If a number is negative, then its absolute value is negative.

40. If a number is positive, then its opposite is positive.

41. If a number is an integer, then the number is a rational number.

42. If a number is a whole number, then its opposite is an integer.

43. If a number is an integer, then its absolute value is a whole number.

44. **ERROR ANALYSIS** *Describe* and correct the error in analyzing the statement "If a number is an integer, then the number is a whole number."

Hypothesis: a number is an integer
Conclusion: the number is a whole number

The statement is false.

The number 0 is a counterexample, because 0 is an integer but not a whole number.

45. ◆ **MULTIPLE CHOICE** Consider the statement "For all positive integers x, the expression $3x - 1$ represents a prime number." Which number serves as a counterexample to the statement?

    (A) 2   (B) 4   (C) 6   (D) 12

EVALUATING EXPRESSIONS Evaluate the expression when $x = -0.75$.

46. $-x$ **47.** $|x| + 0.25$ **48.** $|x| - 0.75$ **49.** $1 + |-x|$

50. $2 \cdot (-x)$ **51.** $(-x) \cdot 3$ **52.** $|x| + |x|$ **53.** $-x + |x|$

54. ◆ **MULTIPLE CHOICE** Which number is a solution of $|x| + 1 = 1.3$?

    (A) -2.3 (B) -0.3 (C) 1.3 (D) 2.3

CONNECT SKILLS TO PROBLEM SOLVING Exercises 55–59 will help you prepare for problem solving.

55. Which temperature is colder, $-2.4°F$ or $0.3°F$?

56. Which elevation is higher, 5 feet or -88 feet?

57. Which weight is heavier, 3.94 ounces or 3.941 ounces?

58. A recipe calls for $1\frac{2}{3}$ cups of bread flour and $1\frac{3}{4}$ cups of whole wheat flour. Which amount is greater?

59. Your savings account balance changed by $-\$250$ in May and $\$240$ in June. In which month was the absolute value of the change the greatest?

EXAMPLE 3
on p. 54
for Exs. 60–61

60. **GEOGRAPHY** The map shows various locations in Imperial County, California, and their elevations above or below sea level. Order the locations from lowest elevation to highest elevation.

    California @*HomeTutor*   for problem solving help at classzone.com

Imperial County, CA

● Frink: -170 ft

● Fondo: -206 ft
● Alamorio: -135 ft

● Date City: 5 ft

Calexico: 2 ft ●

61. **SPORTS** In golf, the goal is to have the least score among all the players. Which golf score, -8 or -12, is the better score?

    California @*HomeTutor*   for problem solving help at classzone.com

EXAMPLE 5
on p. 55
for Exs. 62–63

62. **MUSIC** A guitar tuner is a device that tunes a guitar string to its exact pitch. Some tuners use the measure *cents* to indicate how far the string tone is above or below the exact pitch, marked as 0 cents. Suppose that one string tone measures -3.4 cents, and a second string tone measures -3.8 cents. Which string tone is closer to the exact pitch? *Explain.*

63. ◆ **MULTIPLE CHOICE** The change in the value of a share of stock for several days is shown. On which day was the absolute value of the change the greatest?

    (A) Monday   (B) Tuesday

    (C) Wednesday   (D) Thursday

Day	Change in value
Monday	$-\$.45$
Tuesday	$-\$1.32$
Wednesday	$\$.27$
Thursday	$\$1.03$

64. MULTI-STEP PROBLEM The intensity of a sound is measured in decibels (dB), and the frequency of the sound is measured in hertz (Hz). The table shows the intensity at different frequencies on a stereo system.

Frequency (Hz)	32	64	125	250	500	1000	2000	4000	8000
Intensity (dB)	8.8	7.1	5.8	1.5	−2.8	−1.5	2.7	2.8	2.9

  a. Which frequency has the least sound intensity?

  b. *Describe* the change in sound intensity as the frequency increases from 32 hertz to 8000 hertz.

65. WEATHER A wind chill index describes how much colder it feels outside when wind speed is considered with air temperature. The table shows the wind chill temperatures for given pairs of air temperature and wind speed.

Wind Chill Temperatures (°F)					
Wind speed (mi/h)	Air temperature (°F)				
	20	**10**	**0**	**−10**	**−20**
0	20	10	0	−10	−20
10	9	−4	−16	−28	−41
20	4	−9	−22	−35	−48
30	1	−12	−26	−39	−53

  a. Compare Which conditions feel colder, an air temperature of 0°F with a wind speed of 30 miles per hour, or an air temperature of −10°F with a wind speed of 10 miles per hour?

  b. Analyze How does the wind chill temperature change under constant air temperature and increasing wind speed?

66. CHALLENGE What can you conclude about the opposite of the opposite of a number? *Explain* your reasoning.

67. CHALLENGE For what values of a is the opposite of a greater than a? less than a? equal to a? *Explain* your answer.

68. CHALLENGE In an academic contest, the point values of the questions are given by the expression $50x$ where $x = 1, 2, 3,$ or 4. You earn $50x$ points for a correct answer to a question and $-(50x)$ points for an incorrect answer. Order from least to greatest all the possible points you can earn when answering one question.

◆ CALIFORNIA STANDARDS SPIRAL REVIEW

Gr. 7 AF 1.1

69. The difference of a number x and 5 is more than 7. Which inequality represents this relationship? *(p. 26)*

  (A) $x - 5 > 7$ **(B)** $x - 5 \geq 7$ **(C)** $5 - x > 7$ **(D)** $5 - x < 7$

Gr. 7 AF 1.2

70. What is the value of $3(x + 5)^2$ when $x = 5$? *(p. 11)*

  (A) 100   **(B)** 300   **(C)** 400   **(D)** 900

Gr. 6 NS 2.4

71. Your oregano plant is $\frac{1}{4}$ inch tall. In the next ten days, it grows $\frac{7}{10}$ inch. What is the new height of the plant? *(p. 26)*

  (A) $\frac{7}{40}$ in.   **(B)** $\frac{9}{20}$ in.   **(C)** $\frac{4}{7}$ in.   **(D)** $\frac{19}{20}$ in.

2.2 Add Real Numbers

Standards

Alg. 1.0 Students identify and use the arithmetic properties of subsets of integers and rational, irrational, and real numbers, including closure properties for the four basic arithmetic operations where applicable.

Alg. 1.1 Students use properties of numbers to demonstrate whether assertions are true or false.

Connect *Before* you added positive numbers. *Now* you will add positive and negative numbers.

Math and **SPORTS**
Ex. 61, p. 66

Key Vocabulary
• additive identity
• additive inverse

You can use a number line to add two real numbers. Start at 0, then move the appropriate distance and direction for each number in the sum. Use the sign of the number to decide whether to move left or right.

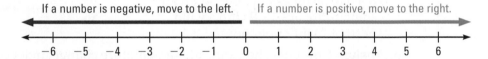

If a number is negative, move to the left.　If a number is positive, move to the right.

EXAMPLE 1 Add two integers using a number line

Find the sum.

a. $2 + (-4)$　　　　　　　　　**b.** $-3 + 6$

Solution

a. Start at 0. Move **2** units to the **right**. Then move **4** units to the **left**.

▶ The final position is -2. So, $2 + (-4) = -2$.

b. Start at 0. Move **3** units to the **left**. Then move **6** units to the **right**.

▶ The final position is 3. So, $-3 + 6 = 3$.

✓ **GUIDED PRACTICE**　for Example 1

Use a number line to find the sum.

1. $7 + (-2)$　　**2.** $8 + (-11)$　　**3.** $-8 + 4$　　**4.** $-1 + (-4)$

RULES OF ADDITION You can use a number line to develop rules for adding numbers. Consider the sum $-3 + (-4)$.

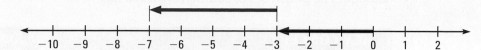

Notice that the arrows point in the same direction and that their combined length is 7 units. Also notice that the numbers being added, -3 and -4, are both negative and that the sum, -7, is negative. So, the absolute value of the sum is found by adding the lengths of the two arrows, and the sign of the sum is the same as the sign of the numbers being added. In other words,

$$-3 + (-4) = -(\left|-3\right| + \left|-4\right|) = -7.$$

In Exercise 62, you will use a number line to develop a rule for adding two integers with different signs.

These results suggest the following rules for adding integers. The rules are also valid for adding real numbers.

KEY CONCEPT *For Your Notebook*

Rules of Addition for Real Numbers

Words To add two numbers with the *same* sign, add their absolute values. The sum has the same sign as the numbers added.

Examples $8 + 7 = 15$ $-6 + (-10) = -16$

Words To add two numbers with *different* signs, subtract the lesser absolute value from the greater absolute value. The sum has the same sign as the number with the greater absolute value.

Examples $-12 + 7 = -5$ $18 + (-4) = 14$

EXAMPLE 2 **Add real numbers**

Find the sum.

a. $-5.3 + (-4.9) = -(\left|-5.3\right| + \left|-4.9\right|)$ **Rule of same signs**

$ = -(5.3 + 4.9)$ **Take absolute values.**

$ = -10.2$ **Add.**

b. $-12.2 + 19.3 = \left|19.3\right| - \left|-12.2\right|$ **Rule of different signs**

$ = 19.3 - 12.2$ **Take absolute values.**

$ = 7.1$ **Subtract.**

✓ **GUIDED PRACTICE** **for Example 2**

Find the sum.

5. $-0.6 + (-6.7)$ **6.** $10.1 + (-16.2)$ **7.** $-13.1 + 8.7$

PROPERTIES OF ADDITION Notice that both $3 + (-2)$ and $-2 + 3$ have the same sum, 1. So, $3 + (-2) = -2 + 3$. This is an example of the *commutative property of addition*. The properties of addition are listed below.

KEY CONCEPT *For Your Notebook*

Properties of Addition for Real Numbers

COMMUTATIVE PROPERTY The order in which you add two numbers does not change the sum.

Algebra $a + b = b + a$ **Example** $3 + (-2) = -2 + 3$

ASSOCIATIVE PROPERTY The way you group three numbers in a sum does not change the sum.

Algebra $(a + b) + c = a + (b + c)$ **Example** $(-3 + 2) + 1 = -3 + (2 + 1)$

IDENTITY PROPERTY The sum of a number and 0 is the number.

Algebra $a + 0 = 0 + a = a$ **Example** $-5 + 0 = -5$

INVERSE PROPERTY The sum of a number and its opposite is 0.

Algebra $a + (-a) = -a + a = 0$ **Example** $-6 + 6 = 0$

CLOSURE PROPERTY A set of numbers is closed under addition if the sum of any two numbers in the set is also a number in the set.

Example The set of whole numbers is closed under addition because the sum of any two whole numbers is a whole number.

About the Standards

You will determine whether subsets of integers and rational, irrational, and real numbers are closed under the four basic arithmetic operations on pages 65, 70, 77, 92, and 99 as part of Algebra 1 Standard 1.0.

The identity property states that the sum of a number a and 0 is a. The number 0 is the **additive identity**. The inverse property states that the sum of a number a and its opposite is 0. The opposite of a is also called the **additive inverse** of a.

EXAMPLE 3 ◆ **Multiple Choice Practice**

> **Which property of addition is used in the equation below?**
>
> $$(x + 9) + 2 = x + (9 + 2)$$
>
> Ⓐ Inverse property Ⓑ Commutative property
> Ⓒ Associative property Ⓓ Identity property

Solution

The equation $(x + 9) + 2 = x + (9 + 2)$ demonstrates the associative property of addition. The way you group the three numbers in the sum does not change the sum.

▶ The correct answer is C. Ⓐ Ⓑ Ⓒ Ⓓ

EXAMPLE 4 **Add three real numbers**

BUSINESS The table shows the annual profits of two piano manufacturers. Which manufacturer had the greater total profit for the three years?

Year	Profit (millions) for manufacturer A	Profit (millions) for manufacturer B
1	−$5.8	−$6.5
2	$8.7	$7.9
3	$6.8	$8.2

Piano maker installing strings

Solution

ANOTHER WAY
You can also find the sums by adding from left to right, as shown for manufacturer A:
−5.8 + 8.7 + 6.8 = 2.9 + 6.8 = 9.7.

Manufacturer A

Total profit = −5.8 + 8.7 + 6.8
$$= -5.8 + (8.7 + 6.8)$$
$$= -5.8 + 15.5$$
$$= 9.7$$

Manufacturer B

Total profit = −6.5 + 7.9 + 8.2
$$= -6.5 + (7.9 + 8.2)$$
$$= -6.5 + 16.1$$
$$= 9.6$$

▶ Because 9.7 > 9.6, manufacturer A had the greater total profit.

✓ **GUIDED PRACTICE** for Examples 3 and 4

Identify the property being illustrated.

8. $7 + (-7) = 0$ **9.** $-12 + 0 = -12$ **10.** $4 + 8 = 8 + 4$

11. WHAT IF? In Example 4, suppose that the profits for year 4 are −$1.7 million for manufacturer A and −$2.1 million for manufacturer B. Which manufacturer has the greater total profit for the four years?

2.2 EXERCISES

HOMEWORK KEY
◆ = **MULTIPLE CHOICE PRACTICE**
Exs. 39, 50, 60, and 66–68

○ = **HINTS AND HOMEWORK HELP**
for Exs. 7, 11, and 57 at classzone.com

SKILLS • PROBLEM SOLVING • REASONING

1. VOCABULARY What number is called the additive identity?

2. NOTETAKING SKILLS Make a concept circle like the one on page 52 for adding two negative numbers.

EXAMPLE 1
on p. 60
for Exs. 3–10

USING A NUMBER LINE Use a number line to find the sum.

3. $-11 + 3$ **4.** $-1 + 6$ **5.** $13 + (-7)$ **6.** $5 + (-10)$

7. $-9 + (-4)$ **8.** $-8 + (-2)$ **9.** $-14 + 8$ **10.** $-11 + (-9)$

EXAMPLE 2
on p. 61
for Exs. 11–24

FINDING SUMS Find the sum.

11. $-2.4 + 3.9$ **12.** $-8.7 + 4.2$ **13.** $4.3 + (-10.2)$

14. $9.1 + (-2.5)$ **15.** $-6.5 + (-7.1)$ **16.** $-11.4 + (-3.8)$

17. $4\frac{1}{5} + \left(-9\frac{1}{2}\right)$ **18.** $8\frac{2}{3} + \left(-1\frac{3}{5}\right)$ **19.** $-12\frac{3}{4} + 6\frac{9}{10}$

20. $-\frac{4}{9} + 1\frac{4}{5}$ **21.** $-3\frac{3}{7} + \left(-14\frac{3}{4}\right)$ **22.** $-7\frac{1}{12} + \left(-13\frac{7}{8}\right)$

ERROR ANALYSIS *Describe* and correct the error in finding the sum.

23.
$$-13 + (-15) = 28 \quad \times$$

24.
$$17 + (-31) = -48 \quad \times$$

EXAMPLE 3
on p. 62
for Exs. 25–32

IDENTIFYING PROPERTIES Identify the property being illustrated.

25. $-3 + 3 = 0$ **26.** $(-6 + 1) + 7 = -6 + (1 + 7)$

27. $9 + (-1) = -1 + 9$ **28.** $-8 + 0 = -8$

29. $(x + 2) + 3 = x + (2 + 3)$ **30.** $y + (-4) = -4 + y$

ERROR ANALYSIS *Describe* and correct the error in identifying the property being illustrated.

31.
$$-1.7 + 1.7 = 0 \quad \times$$
Identity property

32.
$$8 + (-21) = -21 + 8 \quad \times$$
Associative property

EXAMPLE 4
on p. 63
for Exs. 33–39

FINDING SUMS Find the sum.

33. $-13 + 5 + (-7)$ **34.** $-18 + (-12) + (-19)$

35. $0.47 + (-1.8) + (-3.8)$ **36.** $-2.6 + (-3.4) + 7.6$

37. $-3\frac{1}{2} + \left(-7\frac{2}{5}\right) + \left(-9\frac{3}{10}\right)$ **38.** $8\frac{2}{3} + \left(-6\frac{3}{5}\right) + 3\frac{1}{4}$

39. ◆ **MULTIPLE CHOICE** What is the value of the expression $13.7 + (-5) + (-3.7)$?

     (A) 5   **(B)** 12.4   **(C)** 15   **(D)** -2.4

EVALUATING EXPRESSIONS Evaluate the expression for the given value of x.

40. $3 + x + (-7); x = 6$ **41.** $x + (-5) + 5; x = -3$

42. $9.6 + (-x) + 2.3; x = -8.5$ **43.** $-1.7 + (-5.4) + (-x); x = 2.4$

44. $1\frac{1}{4} + |x| + \left(-3\frac{1}{2}\right); x = -8\frac{2}{5}$ **45.** $|x| + \left(-3\frac{1}{4}\right) + \left(7\frac{3}{10}\right); x = -3\frac{1}{3}$

FINDING SOLUTIONS Solve the equation using mental math.

46. $x + (-9) + 9 = 8$ **47.** $(-8) + x + (-2) = -10$

48. $x + (-2.8) + 9.2 = 0$ **49.** $-8.7 + x + 1.3 = 0$

50. ◆ **MULTIPLE CHOICE** If $a + b$ is negative, which statement *must* be true?

     (A) $a < 0, b < 0$ **(B)** $a > 0$ **(C)** $a < 0, b > 0$ **(D)** $a < -b$

51. TRUE OR FALSE Consider the statement $2 + (-3 + 5) = -3 + (2 + 5)$.

    a. Evaluate each side of the equation to determine whether the statement is true or false.

    b. Copy and complete: $2 + (-3 + 5) = (2 + (-3)) + 5$ Associative property

$$= ((-3) + 2) + 5 \qquad \underline{\quad\quad ? \quad\quad}$$

$$= \underline{\quad ? \quad} \qquad \underline{\quad\quad ? \quad\quad}$$

52. REASONING Decide whether the following sets of numbers are closed under addition. *Explain* your reasoning.

    a. $\{-2, 0, 2\}$ **b.** Positive integers   **c.** Negative integers

---

CONNECT SKILLS TO PROBLEM SOLVING Exercises 53–56 will help you prepare for problem solving.

53. The temperature outside a car is $-5°F$. The temperature inside the car is $75°F$ greater. Write an expression for the temperature (in °F) inside the car.

54. A balloon rises 150 meters from an elevation of -8 meters. Write an expression for the new elevation (in meters) of the balloon.

55. A bank account had a balance of $550 before a transaction of $-\$350$. Write an expression for the new balance (in dollars) of the account.

56. A whale rises 60 meters from an elevation of -95 meters. Write an expression for the new elevation (in meters) of the whale.

EXAMPLES 1 and 2
on pp. 60–61
for Ex. 57–59

57. **PARKING GARAGES** The bottom level of a parking garage has an elevation of -45 feet. The top level of the garage is 100 feet higher. What is the elevation of the top level?

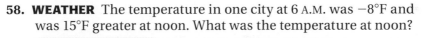

California **@HomeTutor**   for problem solving help at classzone.com

58. **WEATHER** The temperature in one city at 6 A.M. was $-8°F$ and was $15°F$ greater at noon. What was the temperature at noon?

California **@HomeTutor**   for problem solving help at classzone.com

Bottom level: -45 ft

59. **MULTI-STEP PROBLEM** Two eyeglass lenses can be combined to create a new lens, and the sum of their strengths is the strength of the new lens.

    a. A lens of strength -4.75 is combined with a lens of strength 6.25 to form a new lens. What is the strength of the new lens?

    b. A lens of strength -2.5 is combined with a lens of strength -1.25 to form a new lens. What is the strength of the new lens?

    c. The greater the absolute value of the strength of a lens, the stronger the lens. Which new lens is stronger, the one in part (a) or in part (b)?

EXAMPLE 4
on p. 63
for Exs. 60–61

60. ◆ **MULTIPLE CHOICE** The table shows the profits for a company from 2001 to 2006. Which three-year period had the greatest total profit?

Year	2001	2002	2003	2004	2005	2006
Profit (millions of dollars)	−13.76	54.91	38.54	−21.33	123.90	−14.82

  A 2001–2003   **B** 2002–2004   **C** 2003–2005   **D** 2004–2006

61. **GOLF** In golf, your score on a hole is the number of strokes above or below an expected number of strokes needed to hit a ball into the hole. When you compare two scores, the lesser score is the better score.

   a. **Compare** For three holes, you score -2, 2, and -1. Your friend scores 1, -3, and 0. Who has the better total score?

   b. **Explain** Your friend scores -3 and -2 for the next two holes. If you score a -3 for each of your next two holes, will you have a better total score than your friend on all five holes?

62. **REASONING** Consider the sum $5 + (-6)$.

   a. Use a number line to find the sum. Do the arrows point in the same direction or in different directions?

   b. Find a relationship between the sum and the lengths of the two arrows. How is the sign of the sum determined by the arrow lengths?

   c. Use the results of parts (a) and (b) to express the sum $5 + (-6)$ using absolute values.

63. **CHALLENGE** Consider the expression $|x| + (-x)$. Write a simplified expression for the sum if x is positive. Then write a simplified expression for the sum if x is negative. Give examples to support your answers.

64. **CHALLENGE** Evaluate $-50 + (-49) + (-48) + \cdots + 48 + 49 + 50$. *Explain* how you can use the properties of addition to obtain the sum.

65. **CHALLENGE** You sold three items in an Internet auction. The table shows the profit earned for each item. You now plan to sell a floor lamp. What is the least profit that you can earn on the lamp and have a positive total profit for the four items? *Explain* your answer.

Item	Profit (dollars)
Mantel clock	4.13
Framed mirror	−10.65
Metal lunch box	−5.87

◆ CALIFORNIA STANDARDS SPIRAL REVIEW

Gr. 6 NS 1.1

66. Which fraction is closest to 0? *(p. 53)*

   Ⓐ $-\dfrac{1}{7}$　　Ⓑ $-\dfrac{5}{8}$　　Ⓒ $\dfrac{3}{10}$　　Ⓓ $\dfrac{1}{2}$

Gr. 7 NS 2.5

67. What is the value of $|8 - 3| - |5 - 7|$? *(p. 53)*

   Ⓐ 2　　Ⓑ 3　　Ⓒ 5　　Ⓓ 7

Gr. 6 NS 1.1

68. You are making playlists from MP3 files on your computer. The table shows the number of seconds that each playlist is over 80 minutes or under 80 minutes. Which list orders the playlists from shortest to longest? *(p. 53)*

   Ⓐ Hits, Oldies, Top 20, 90s

   Ⓑ Hits, Oldies, 90s, Top 20

   Ⓒ Oldies, Hits, 90s, Top 20

   Ⓓ Oldies, Hits, Top 20, 90s

Playlist	Seconds over or under 80 minutes
Oldies	−26
90s	21
Hits	−142
Top 20	45

EXTRA PRACTICE for Lesson 2.2, p. 811　　🔁 **ONLINE QUIZ** at classzone.com

2.3 Subtract Real Numbers

Math and GEOLOGY
Ex. 49, p. 70

Alg. 1.0 Students identify and use the arithmetic properties of subsets of integers and rational, irrational, and real numbers, including closure properties for the four basic arithmetic operations where applicable.

Alg. 1.1 Students use properties of numbers to demonstrate whether assertions are true or false.

Connect *Before* you added real numbers. *Now* you will subtract real numbers.

Key Vocabulary
• **opposites**, *p. 55*

Because the expressions $12 - 3$ and $12 + (-3)$ are both equal to 9, you can conclude that $12 - 3 = 12 + (-3)$. Subtracting 3 from 12 is equivalent to adding the opposite of 3 to 12. This example illustrates the *subtraction rule*.

KEY CONCEPT   *For Your Notebook*

Subtraction Rule for Real Numbers

Words To subtract b from a, add the opposite of b to a.

Algebra $a - b = a + (-b)$ **Example** $14 - 8 = 14 + (-8)$

EXAMPLE 1   Subtract real numbers

Animated Algebra

For an interactive example of subtracting real numbers, go to **classzone.com**.

Find the difference.

a. $-12 - 19 = -12 + (-19)$

$\qquad\qquad\quad = -31$

b. $18 - (-6.4) = 18 + 6.4$

$\qquad\qquad\quad\;\; = 24.4$

 GUIDED PRACTICE   for Example 1

Find the difference.

1. $-2 - 7$ **2.** $11.7 - (-5)$ **3.** $\frac{1}{3} - \frac{1}{2}$

EXAMPLE 2   Evaluate a variable expression

Evaluate the expression $y - x + 6.8$ when $x = -2$ and $y = 7.2$.

$y - x + 6.8 = 7.2 - (-2) + 6.8$ Substitute -2 for x and 7.2 for y.

$\qquad\qquad\quad = 7.2 + 2 + 6.8$ Add the opposite of -2.

$\qquad\qquad\quad = 16$ Add.

Evaluate the expression when $x = -3$ and $y = 5.2$.

4. $x - y + 8$ **5.** $y - (x - 2)$ **6.** $(y - 4) - x$

EVALUATING CHANGE You can use subtraction to find the change in a quantity, such as elevation or temperature. The change in a quantity is the difference of the new amount and the original amount. If the new amount is greater than the original amount, the change is positive. If the new amount is less than the original amount, the change is negative.

EXAMPLE 3 Evaluate change

TEMPERATURES One of the most extreme temperature changes in United States history occurred in Fairfield, Montana, on December 24, 1924. At noon, the temperature was 63°F. By midnight, the temperature fell to −21°F. What was the change in temperature?

Solution

The change in temperature is the difference of the temperature at midnight and the temperature at noon.

STEP 1 **Write** a verbal model.

$$\boxed{\text{Change in temperature}} = \boxed{\text{Temperature at midnight}} - \boxed{\text{Temperature at noon}}$$

STEP 2 **Find** the change in temperature.

> **AVOID ERRORS**
> When a quantity decreases, the change is negative. So, the change found in Example 3 should be a negative number.

Change $= -21 - 63$	**Substitute values.**
$= -21 + (-63)$	**Add the opposite of 63.**
$= -84$	**Add −21 and −63.**

▶ The change in temperature was −84°F.

CHECKING YOUR WORK You can use a calculator to check your work when subtracting real numbers. To enter a negative number on a calculator, use the $(-)$ key. To enter a subtraction sign, use the $-$ key. To check your answer in Example 3, use the following keystrokes.

$(-)$ 21 $-$ 63 ENTER

7. CAR VALUES A new car is valued at $15,000. One year later, the car is valued at $12,300. What is the change in the value of the car?

2.3 EXERCISES

HOMEWORK KEY
◆ = **MULTIPLE CHOICE PRACTICE**
Exs. 34, 41, 50, and 55–57
○ = **HINTS AND HOMEWORK HELP**
for Exs. 3, 31, and 51 at classzone.com

SKILLS · PROBLEM SOLVING · REASONING

1. **VOCABULARY** Use the subtraction rule to rewrite the expression $-3 - 6$ as an addition expression.

2. **WRITING** Without actually subtracting, how can you tell whether a change in a quantity will be negative?

EXAMPLE 1
on p. 67
for Exs. 3–14

FINDING DIFFERENCES Find the difference.

3. $13 - (-5)$ 　　4. $16 - 32$　　　5. $-11 - (-3)$　　　6. $-15 - 29$

7. $-35.9 - (-50)$　　8. $14.7 - (-2.3)$　　9. $-3.6 - 22.2$　　10. $-18.2 - (-15.4)$

11. $\frac{1}{2} - \frac{5}{6}$　　12. $-\frac{5}{3} - \frac{8}{3}$　　13. $\frac{1}{2} - \left(-\frac{1}{4}\right)$　　14. $-\frac{7}{10} - \left(-\frac{2}{5}\right)$

EXAMPLE 2
on p. 67
for Exs. 15–25

ERROR ANALYSIS *Describe* and correct the error in evaluating the expression when $x = 3$ and $y = -8$.

15.
$$x - y + 2 = 3 - 8 + 2$$
$$= 3 + (-8) + 2$$
$$= -5 + 2$$
$$= -3$$

16.
$$x - (-4 + y) = 3 - [-4 + (-8)]$$
$$= 3 - (-12)$$
$$= 3 - 12$$
$$= -9$$

EVALUATING EXPRESSIONS Evaluate the expression when $x = 7.1$ and $y = -2.5$.

17. $x - (-y)$　　　18. $y - x - 12$　　　19. $x - (-6) + y$

20. $x - (y - 13)$　　21. $-y - (1.9 - x)$　　22. $-y - x$

23. $x - y - 2$　　　24. $5.3 - (y - x)$　　25. $x + y - 2.8$

EXAMPLE 3
on p. 68
for Exs. 26–34

EVALUATING CHANGE Find the change in temperature or elevation.

26. From $-5°C$ to $-13°C$　　　　27. From $-45°F$ to $62°F$

28. From -300 feet to -100 feet　　29. From 1200 meters to -80 meters

30. From $4.8°F$ to $-12.6°F$　　　31. From -90.7 feet to 36.4 feet

32. From -4.37 miles to 2.92 miles　　33. From $-273°C$ to $-115°C$

34. ◆ **MULTIPLE CHOICE** What is the change in elevation from -87.2 feet to 33.6 feet?

　Ⓐ -53.6 ft　　　Ⓑ 53.6 ft　　　Ⓒ 87.2 ft　　　Ⓓ 120.8 ft

EVALUATING EXPRESSIONS Evaluate the expression when $x = 3.6$, $y = 6.6$, and $z = -11$.

35. $(x - y) - |z|$　　　36. $\left(x - |-y|\right) - z$　　　37. $x - |y - z|$

38. $(-x - y) - z - 5$　　39. $x + y - z + 12.9$　　40. $-z + y - x - (-2.4)$

41. ◆ **MULTIPLE CHOICE** If $a - b$ is negative, which statement *must* be true?

(A) $a > b$ **(B)** $a = 0$ **(C)** $a < b$ **(D)** $b = 0$

42. **REASONING** Use the closure property of addition to write a similar property for subtraction. Then decide whether the following sets of numbers are closed under subtraction. *Explain* your reasoning.

a. Integers **b.** Positive integers **c.** Negative integers

43. **REASONING** Tell whether the associative property and the commutative property hold for subtraction. Give examples to support your answers.

44. **TRUE OR FALSE** Consider the statement $11 - (-16) = 16 + 11$.

a. Evaluate each side of the equation to determine whether the statement is true or false.

b. Copy and complete: $11 - (-16) = 11 + 16$ _____?_____

$= $ __?__ Commutative property

CONNECT SKILLS TO PROBLEM SOLVING Exercises 45–47 will help you prepare for problem solving.

45. Yesterday's temperature at noon was 12°F, and at midnight was −3°F. Write an expression for the change in temperature (in °F).

46. A bird flew from an elevation of 48 feet to an elevation of 27 feet. Write an expression for the change in elevation (in feet).

47. At a miniature golf course, your score yesterday was −3 and today it was 14. Write an expression for the change in the scores.

EXAMPLE 3
on p. 68
for Exs. 48–49

48. **VOLCANOES** Mahukona is a Hawaiian volcano whose summit has an elevation of −3600 feet. The summit once had an elevation of 800 feet. What was the change in elevation of the volcano's summit?

California*@HomeTutor* for problem solving help at classzone.com

49. **CAVES** The temperature inside Mammoth Cave in Kentucky is about 12.2°C year round. If the temperature outside the cave is −2.4°C, what is the change in temperature from outside to inside the cave?

California*@HomeTutor* for problem solving help at classzone.com

50. ◆ **MULTIPLE CHOICE** In four plays a football team gains 3 yards, loses 7 yards, loses 2 yards, and gains 15 yards. What is the team's net yards gained after four plays?

(A) 3 yd **(B)** 9 yd **(C)** 15 yd **(D)** 27 yd

51. **TRACK AND FIELD** In order to qualify for a girls' regional 1500 meter race, an athlete's personal best time for the season must be under the qualifying time of 5 minutes 42 seconds. Sue's personal best time is 341.7 seconds. Find the difference of her personal best time and the qualifying time. Does Sue qualify for the race? How can you tell from the difference you calculated?

Second play: −7 yards

52. SNOWBOARDS Snowboarders can rotate the shoe bindings on their snowboards. The binding setup shown below is written +24°/−18°. This means that the front angle is 24° counterclockwise from vertical, and the rear angle is 18° clockwise from vertical. Your setup is initially +30°/+15°. Find the changes in angle measures needed to match the diagram.

53. CHALLENGE Let a and b be negative numbers. Tell whether the value of the expression is positive or negative. *Explain* your reasoning.

a. $|a + b|$ **b.** $-a - b$ **c.** $-|a| - |b|$ **d.** $a + b$

54. CHALLENGE Greenwich Mean Time (GMT) is the time at the Royal Observatory in Greenwich, England. A location that is $+n$ hours from GMT is n hours ahead of GMT, and a location that is $-n$ hours from GMT is n hours behind GMT. Costa Rica is -6 hours from GMT, and India is $+5.5$ hours from GMT. If it is 7:45 A.M. in India, what time is it in Costa Rica?

◆ CALIFORNIA STANDARDS SPIRAL REVIEW

Alg. 1.0

55. Which property of addition is used in the equation $x + 9 = 9 + x$? *(p. 60)*

A Inverse property   **B** Commutative property

C Associative property   **D** Identity property

Gr. 7 NS 2.5

56. Which expression has the least value? *(p. 53)*

A $|-13|$ **B** $|-20|$ **C** $|-8|$ **D** $|5|$

Alg. 2.0

57. For a video game, when you wager x points and are incorrect, the opposite of x is added to your score. You wager 2500 points and are wrong. How many points are added to your score? *(p. 53)*

A -2500 **B** -50 **C** 0 **D** 2500

QUIZ *for Lessons 2.1–2.3*

1. Tell whether the numbers $-\dfrac{5}{6}$, -8.2, 0, and -9 belong to each of the following sets: whole numbers, integers, and rational numbers. Then order the numbers from least to greatest. *(p. 53)*

Find the sum or difference.

2. $5 + (-36)$ *(p. 60)*   **3.** $-8.2 + (-2.3)$ *(p. 60)*   **4.** $3.46 + (-2.9)$ *(p. 60)*

5. $-18 - (-9)$ *(p. 67)*   **6.** $-11.2 - 21.7$ *(p. 67)*   **7.** $6.1 - (-14.4)$ *(p. 67)*

Evaluate the expression when $x = 2.5$ and $y = -3.4$. *(p. 67)*

8. $x + y - 9$ **9.** $x - (y - 5.1)$ **10.** $12.1 - (y - x)$

2.3 Subtract Real Numbers

Standards Preparation

Gr. 7 NS 1.2 Add, **subtract**, multiply, and divide **rational numbers** (integers, fractions, and terminating decimals) and take positive rational numbers to whole-number powers.

QUESTION How can you use a spreadsheet to subtract the same number from various numbers?

In a spreadsheet, the columns are identified by letters, and the rows are identified by numbers. Each cell has a name that is made up of a letter and a number. For example, B2 is the cell in column B and row 2. A cell can contain a label, a number, or a formula.

	A	B	C
1			
2			

EXAMPLE Find the difference of two numbers

Hand grips

A manufacturing company is making foam hand grips for bicycles and jump ropes. The ideal length of a hand grip is 5 inches. In a batch of ten hand grips, the actual lengths (in inches) are 4.878, 4.902, 5.115, 5.13, 4.877, 4.874, 4.799, 4.819, 4.879, and 5.124. Create a spreadsheet to find the difference of the actual length and the ideal length for each hand grip.

Solution

STEP 1 *Enter data*
Enter the labels in the first row of the spreadsheet. Then enter the grip numbers and grip lengths in the next ten rows.

	A	B	C
1	Grip	Length (inches)	Difference
2	1	4.878	
3	2	4.902	

STEP 2 *Calculate differences*
For each of the ten hand grips, enter the formula for the difference of the actual and ideal lengths in the appropriate cell in column C.

	A	B	C
1	Grip	Length (inches)	Difference
2	1	4.878	=B2−5
3	2	4.902	=B3−5

After you enter a formula, the cell should display the difference of the length of the grip and the ideal length. For example, C2 should display −0.122.

DRAW CONCLUSIONS

1. The manufacturer will consider a hand grip acceptable if the absolute value of the difference of the actual length and the ideal length is at most 0.125 inch. How many hand grips from the batch are acceptable?

2. What are the least and greatest possible lengths that a hand grip can have and still be acceptable? *Explain* your reasoning.

3. For which of the ten hand grips is the length closest to the ideal length? How can you tell from the differences in column C?

2.4 Multiplication by −1

MATERIALS · paper and pencil

Standards Preparation

Gr. 7 MR 1.2 Formulate and justify **mathematical conjectures based on a general description of the mathematical question or problem posed.**

QUESTION What is the product of any integer a and −1?

You can rewrite a multiplication expression as repeated addition. For example, 3 · 8 can be rewritten as 8 + 8 + 8. Because the sum is 24, you can conclude that 3 · 8 = 24.

EXPLORE Find the product of an integer and −1

STEP 1 Copy and complete the table.

Multiplication expression	Addition expression	Sum
5 · (−1)	−1 + (−1) + (−1) + (−1) + (−1)	−5
4 · (−1)	?	?
3 · (−1)	?	?
2 · (−1)	?	?

STEP 2 Copy and complete the multiplication equations below.

$5 \cdot (-1) = \underline{?}$
$4 \cdot (-1) = \underline{?}$
$3 \cdot (-1) = \underline{?}$
$2 \cdot (-1) = \underline{?}$

Complete using the table from Step 1.

$1 \cdot (-1) = \underline{?}$
$0 \cdot (-1) = \underline{?}$
$-1 \cdot (-1) = \underline{?}$
$-2 \cdot (-1) = \underline{?}$
$-3 \cdot (-1) = \underline{?}$

Complete by extending the pattern in the first four products.

DRAW CONCLUSIONS Use your observations to complete these exercises

1. Copy and complete: For any integer a, $a \cdot (-1) = \underline{?}$.

Find the product.

2. $12 \cdot (-1)$ 3. $10 \cdot (-1)$ 4. $-23 \cdot (-1)$

5. $-47 \cdot (-1)$ 6. $-18 \cdot (-1)$ 7. $15 \cdot (-1)$

2.4 Multiply Real Numbers

Standards Alg. 1.0 Students identify and use the arithmetic properties of subsets of integers and rational, irrational, **and real numbers, including closure properties for the four basic arithmetic operations where applicable.**

Alg. 1.1 Students use properties of numbers to demonstrate whether assertions are true or false.

Connect *Before* you added and subtracted real numbers. *Now* you will multiply real numbers.

Math and GEOGRAPHY
Example 4, p. 76

Key Vocabulary
• multiplicative identity

The activity on page 73 suggests that $a \cdot (-1) = -a$ for any integer a. This rule not only lets you write the product of a and -1 as $-a$, but it also lets you write $-a$ as $(-1)a$ and as $a(-1)$. Using this rule, you can multiply any two real numbers. Here are two examples:

$$-2(3) = -1(2)(3) \qquad\qquad (-2)(-3) = -2(3)(-1)$$
$$= -1(6) \qquad\qquad\qquad\qquad = -6(-1)$$
$$= -6 \qquad\qquad\qquad\qquad\qquad = 6$$

KEY CONCEPT *For Your Notebook*

The Sign of a Product

Words The product of two real numbers with the *same* sign is positive.

Examples $3(4) = 12$ $\qquad\qquad -6(-3) = 18$

Words The product of two real numbers with *different* signs is negative.

Examples $2(-5) = -10$ $\qquad\qquad -7(2) = -14$

EXAMPLE 1 Multiply real numbers

MULTIPLY NEGATIVES
• A product is negative if it has an *odd* number of negative factors.
• A product is positive if it has an *even* number of negative factors.

Find the product.

a. $2(-5)(-4) = (-10)(-4)$ **Multiply 2 and -5.**

$\qquad\qquad\quad = 40$ **Same signs; product is positive.**

b. $-\dfrac{1}{2}(-4)(-3) = 2(-3)$ **Multiply $-\dfrac{1}{2}$ and -4.**

$\qquad\qquad\qquad = -6$ **Different signs; product is negative.**

✓ **GUIDED PRACTICE** for Example 1

1. Find the product. **a.** $-2(-7)$ **b.** $-0.5(-4)(-9)$

PROPERTIES OF MULTIPLICATION Notice that both $4(-5)$ and $-5(4)$ have a product of -20, so $4(-5) = -5(4)$. This is an example of the *commutative property of multiplication*. Properties of multiplication are listed below.

KEY CONCEPT   *For Your Notebook*

Properties of Multiplication for Real Numbers

COMMUTATIVE PROPERTY The order in which you multiply two numbers does not change the product.

Algebra $a \cdot b = b \cdot a$ **Example** $4 \cdot (-5) = -5 \cdot 4$

ASSOCIATIVE PROPERTY The way you group three numbers in a product does not change the product.

Algebra $(a \cdot b) \cdot c = a \cdot (b \cdot c)$ **Example** $(-2 \cdot 7) \cdot 4 = -2 \cdot (7 \cdot 4)$

IDENTITY PROPERTY The product of a number and 1 is that number.

Algebra $a \cdot 1 = 1 \cdot a = a$ **Example** $(-5) \cdot 1 = -5$

PROPERTY OF ZERO The product of a number and 0 is 0.

Algebra $a \cdot 0 = 0 \cdot a = 0$ **Example** $-3 \cdot 0 = 0$

PROPERTY OF -1 The product of a number and -1 is the opposite of the number.

Algebra $a \cdot (-1) = -1 \cdot a = -a$ **Example** $-2 \cdot (-1) = 2$

CLOSURE PROPERTY A set of numbers is closed under multiplication if the product of any two numbers in the set is also a number in the set.

Example The set of integers is closed under multiplication because the product of any two integers is an integer.

USE CLOSURE PROPERTY

Although the set of integers is closed under multiplication, a *subset* of the set may not be closed under multiplication. For example, $\{-1, 0, 1, 2\}$ is not closed under multiplication because $-1 \cdot 2 = -2$.

The identity property states that the product of a number a and 1 is a. The number 1 is called the **multiplicative identity**.

 EXAMPLE 2 ◆ **Multiple Choice Practice**

> **Which property of multiplication is used in the equation $9 \cdot (-1) = -9$?**
>
> **Ⓐ** Commutative property   **Ⓑ** Property of zero
>
> **Ⓒ** Identity property   **Ⓓ** Property of -1

Solution

The equation $9 \cdot (-1) = -9$ demonstrates the property of -1 because it shows that the product of 9 and -1 is the opposite of 9.

▶ The correct answer is D. Ⓐ Ⓑ Ⓒ **Ⓓ**

✔ **GUIDED PRACTICE** for Example 2

2. Which property is used in the equation $5 \cdot (-6) = -6 \cdot 5$?

EXAMPLE 3   Use properties of multiplication

Animated Algebra

For an interactive example of using properties of multiplication, go to **classzone.com**.

Find the product $(-4x) \cdot 0.25.$ **Justify your steps.**

$$
\begin{aligned}
(-4x) \cdot 0.25 &= 0.25 \cdot (-4x) && \text{Commutative property of multiplication} \\
&= [0.25 \cdot (-4)]x && \text{Associative property of multiplication} \\
&= -1 \cdot x && \text{Product of 0.25 and } -4 \text{ is } -1. \\
&= -x && \text{Multiplicative property of } -1
\end{aligned}
$$

EXAMPLE 4   Solve a multi-step problem

Mono Lake, California

LAKES In 1900 the elevation of Mono Lake in California was about 6416 feet. Approximate the elevation in 2000 given the following information.

- From 1900 to 1950, the average rate of change in elevation was about -0.12 foot per year.
- From 1950 to 2000, the average rate of change in elevation was about -0.526 foot per year.

READING
The average rate of change in elevation is the total change in elevation divided by the number of years that have passed.

Solution

STEP 1   **Write** a verbal model.

New elevation (feet)	=	Original elevation (feet)	+	Average rate of change (feet/year)	·	Time span (years)

STEP 2   **Calculate** the elevation in 1950. Use the elevation in 1900 as the original elevation. The time span is $1950 - 1900 = 50$ years.

$$
\begin{aligned}
\text{New elevation} &= 6416 + (-0.12)(50) && \text{Substitute values.} \\
&= 6416 + (-6) && \text{Multiply } -0.12 \text{ and } 50. \\
&= 6410 && \text{Add 6416 and } -6.
\end{aligned}
$$

STEP 3   **Calculate** the elevation in 2000. Use the elevation in 1950 as the original elevation. The time span is $2000 - 1950 = 50$ years.

$$
\begin{aligned}
\text{New elevation} &= 6410 + (-0.526)(50) && \text{Substitute values.} \\
&= 6410 + (-26.3) && \text{Multiply } -0.526 \text{ and } 50. \\
&= 6383.7 && \text{Add 6410 and } -26.3.
\end{aligned}
$$

▶ The elevation in 2000 was about 6383.7 feet above sea level.

✓   **GUIDED PRACTICE**   for Examples 3 and 4

Find the product. *Justify* **your steps.**

3. $\dfrac{3}{10}(5y)$ **4.** $0.8(-x)(-1)$ **5.** $(-y)(-0.5)(-6)$

6. Using the data in Example 4, approximate the elevation of Mono Lake in 1925 and in 1965.

2.4 EXERCISES

HOMEWORK KEY

◆ = **MULTIPLE CHOICE PRACTICE**
Exs. 28, 50, 57, and 64–66

◯ = **HINTS AND HOMEWORK HELP**
for Exs. 11, 33, and 55 at classzone.com

SKILLS · PROBLEM SOLVING · REASONING

1. **VOCABULARY** What number is called the multiplicative identity?

2. **WRITING** *Describe* the difference between the identity property of multiplication and the multiplicative property of −1.

EXAMPLE 1
on p. 74
for Exs. 3–18

FINDING PRODUCTS Find the product.

3. $-4(7)$

4. $11(-2)$

5. $-9(-10)$

6. $-8(-11)$

7. $5(-7.2)$

8. $(-2.5)(-1.3)$

9. $-42\left(-\dfrac{1}{6}\right)$

10. $-\dfrac{1}{2}(-32)$

11. $-1.9(3.3)(7)$

12. $0.5(-20)(-3)$

13. $-\dfrac{5}{6}(-12)(-4)$

14. $-\dfrac{3}{4}(2)(-6)$

15. $-8(-4)(-2.5)$

16. $-1.6(-2)(-10)$

17. $18\left(-\dfrac{2}{3}\right)\left(-\dfrac{1}{5}\right)$

18. $-\dfrac{3}{4}\left(-\dfrac{1}{3}\right)\left(-\dfrac{8}{9}\right)$

EXAMPLE 2
on p. 75
for Exs. 19–28

IDENTIFYING PROPERTIES Identify the property illustrated.

19. $-\dfrac{2}{5} \cdot 0 = 0$

20. $0.3 \cdot (-3) = -3 \cdot 0.3$

21. $-143 \cdot 1 = -143$

22. $-1 \cdot (-6) = 6$

23. $(-2 \cdot 5) \cdot 4 = -2 \cdot (5 \cdot 4)$

24. $0 \cdot (-76.3) = 0$

25. $1 \cdot (ab) = ab$

26. $(3x)y = 3(xy)$

27. $s \cdot (-1) = -s$

28. ◆ **MULTIPLE CHOICE** Which statement illustrates the associative property of multiplication?

Ⓐ $(-5 \cdot 3) \cdot 3 = -5 \cdot (3 \cdot 3)$

Ⓑ $-5 \cdot 3 = 3 \cdot (-5)$

Ⓒ $-3 \cdot 1 = -3$

Ⓓ $-5 \cdot 0 = 0$

EXAMPLE 3
on p. 76
for Exs. 29–38

USING PROPERTIES Find the product. *Justify* your steps.

29. $y(-2)(-8)$

30. $-18(-x)$

31. $\dfrac{3}{5}(-5q)$

32. $-2(-6)(-7z)$

33. $-5(-4)(-2.1)(-z)$

34. $-\dfrac{1}{5}(-10)(4)(-5c)$

35. $-5t(-t)$

36. $-6r(-2.8r)$

37. $\dfrac{1}{3}\left(-\dfrac{9}{10}\right)(-m)(-m)$

38. **REASONING** Decide whether the following sets of numbers are closed under multiplication. *Explain* your reasoning.

a. $\{-1, 0, 1\}$

b. Whole numbers

c. Negative integers

EVALUATING EXPRESSIONS Evaluate the expression when $x = -2$ and $y = 3.6$.

39. $2x + y$

40. $-x - 3y$

41. $xy - 5.4$

42. $|y| - 4x$

43. $1.5x - |-y|$

44. $x^2 - y^2$

45. $|1.25xy|$

46. $|x^2 - y|$

47. $\left|\dfrac{1}{8}xy\right|$

ERROR ANALYSIS *Describe* and correct the error in finding the product.

48.
$$-1(7)(-3)(-2x) = 7(-3)(-2x)$$
$$= -21(-2x)$$
$$= [-21 \cdot (-2)]x$$
$$= 42x$$

49.
$$(-5z)(-8)(z) = (-8)(-5z)(z)$$
$$= (-8)(-5)(z)(z)$$
$$= -40(z \cdot z)$$
$$= -40z^2$$

50. ◆ **MULTIPLE CHOICE** If $a < 0$ and $abc > 0$, which statement *must* be true?

    (A) $bc > 0$ **(B)** $bc < 0$ **(C)** $ac > 0$ **(D)** $ab < 0$

51. **TRUE OR FALSE** Consider the statement $4 \cdot (-9 \cdot 3) = -9 \cdot (4 \cdot 3)$.

   a. Evaluate each side of the equation to determine whether the statement is true or false.

   b. Copy and complete: $4 \cdot (-9 \cdot 3) = (-9 \cdot 3) \cdot 4$ Commutative property

$$= \underline{?} \quad \text{Associative property}$$
$$= -9 \cdot (4 \cdot 3) \quad \underline{?}$$

CONNECT SKILLS TO PROBLEM SOLVING Exercises 52–54 will help you prepare for problem solving.

52. A pond's water level is changing at an average rate of −1.5 feet per year. Write an expression for the change in water level (in feet) after 4 years.

53. The change in value of a car is −$1200 per year. Write an expression for the change in value (in dollars) after 3.5 years.

54. A tire changes pressure at a rate of −4 pounds per square inch (psi) per hour. Write an expression for the change in pressure (in psi) after 3 hours.

EXAMPLE 4
on p. 76
for Exs. 55–57

55. **DEAD SEA** In 1940 the surface area of the Dead Sea was about 980 square kilometers. From 1940 to 2001, the average rate of change in surface area was about −5.7 square kilometers per year. Find the surface area of the Dead Sea in 2001.

California @HomeTutor   for problem solving help at classzone.com

56. **STOCKS** An investor purchases 50 shares of a stock at $3.50 per share. The next day, the change in value of a share of the stock is −$.25. What is the total value of the shares the next day?

California @HomeTutor   for problem solving help at classzone.com

57. ◆ **MULTIPLE CHOICE** The Rialto Bridge in Venice, Italy, is a footbridge built in the late 16th century. The maximum clearance between the water and the bridge is about 7.32 meters. Because of a rising sea level and a gradual sinking of the city, the clearance changes at an average rate of about −2 millimeters per year. Approximate the clearance after 15 years.

   (A) 5.32 m   **(B)** 7.02 m

   (C) 7.29 m   **(D)** 7.318 m

Rialto Bridge

Glaciers When viewed from above, an area of about 90 square kilometers of Mount Rainier in Washington is covered by glaciers. In 1913 the volume of glaciers on Mount Rainier was 5.62 cubic kilometers. The table shows the average rate of change in volume for two time periods.

Time period	Rate of change (km³/yr)
1913–1971	−0.02241
1971–1994	−0.00565

58. **Calculate** Find the total volume of the glaciers in 1971.

59. **Calculate** Find the total volume of the glaciers in 1994.

60. **Explain** About one third of the change in volume during the period 1913–1994 took place in the northeastern glaciers on Mount Rainier. Find the change in the volume of the northeastern glaciers. *Explain* your steps.

61. **MULTI-STEP PROBLEM** A skydiver in free fall will eventually reach a constant velocity, called terminal velocity. The skydiver shown reaches a terminal velocity of −160 feet per second at an altitude of 3200 feet.

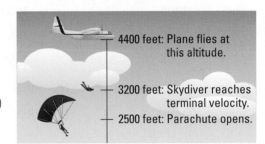

4400 feet: Plane flies at this altitude.

3200 feet: Skydiver reaches terminal velocity.

2500 feet: Parachute opens.

   a. Write an equation for the altitude a (in feet) of the skydiver in terms of the time t (in seconds) after reaching terminal velocity.

   b. Make a table that shows the value of a for $t = 1, 2, 3, 4,$ and 5 seconds. The skydiver wants to open the parachute at an altitude of 2500 feet. After how many seconds should the skydiver open the parachute?

Animated Algebra at classzone.com

62. **CHALLENGE** The product of n factors is negative. What is the greatest possible number of negative factors if n is even? odd? Give examples.

63. **CHALLENGE** Due to soil erosion, Dongting Lake in China is decreasing in surface area. Its surface area was about 2626.5 square kilometers in 1995. From 1950–1995, the average rate of change in surface area was about −38.3 square kilometers per year. From 1825–1950, the change was about −13.2 square kilometers per year. Approximate the surface area in 1825.

◆ CALIFORNIA STANDARDS SPIRAL REVIEW

Gr. 7 AF 1.1

64. The sum of −3 and a number n is 5. Which equation shows this relationship? *(p. 26)*

   (A) $-3 + n = 5$ (B) $-3 - n = 5$ (C) $-3n = 5$ (D) $-3 + 5 = n$

Gr. 7 AF 1.2

65. What is the value of $2y - x$ when $x = 8$ and $y = -4$? *(p. 11)*

   (A) −16   (B) 0   (C) 12   (D) 20

Gr. 7 NS 2.3

66. The change in an elephant's weight was −2.5 pounds yesterday and −1.7 pounds today. How much did its weight change over the two days? *(p. 60)*

   (A) −4.2 lb   (B) −0.8 lb   (C) 0.8 lb   (D) 4.2 lb

Multiple Choice Practice for Lessons 2.1–2.4

1. The table shows the number of people who migrated into and out of a city during the period 2002–2005. When was the absolute value of the change in the population (based on migration) the greatest? **Gr. 7 NS 2.3**

Year	Number migrating into city	Number migrating out of city
2002	3179	3623
2003	3053	3632
2004	3180	3695
2005	3174	3396

Ⓐ 2002   Ⓑ 2003

Ⓒ 2004   Ⓓ 2005

2. Which number serves as a counterexample to the statement "If x is a positive integer, then $3x - 4$ is a whole number"? **Alg. 24.3**

Ⓐ 0   Ⓑ $\frac{1}{3}$

Ⓒ 1   Ⓓ 3

3. An SUV's tire is inflated at the pressure and temperature shown below. Suppose the pressure changes 0.085 psi for every 1°F change in temperature. What is the pressure at 42°F? **Gr. 7 NS 2.3**

Pressure: 35 psi at 72°F

Ⓐ 28.88 psi   Ⓑ 31.43 psi

Ⓒ 32.45 psi   Ⓓ 37.55 psi

4. Which set is closed under multiplication? **Alg. 1.0**

Ⓐ $\{-8, 0, 1\}$ Ⓑ $\{-5, -1, 0, 1\}$

Ⓒ $\{-1, 0, 1\}$ Ⓓ $\{0, 1, 2\}$

5. What is the hypothesis of the statement "If x is negative, then $-x$ is positive"? **Alg. 24.2**

Ⓐ $-x$ is negative   Ⓑ $-x$ is positive

Ⓒ x is negative   Ⓓ x is positive

6. The photo below shows dry ice changing directly from a solid to a gas. Dry ice may exist as a gas, liquid, and solid at the same time when it is at a certain pressure and its temperature is 22.4°C warmer than shown below. What is the temperature at which this occurs? **Gr. 7 NS 2.3**

Temperature: −79°C

Ⓐ −101.4°C   Ⓑ −57.6°C

Ⓒ −57.4°C   Ⓓ −56.6°C

7. Which list is correctly ordered from least to greatest? **Gr. 7 NS 1.1**

Ⓐ $|-1|, |0|, |1|, |2|$

Ⓑ $\frac{1}{2}, \frac{1}{3}, \frac{1}{4}, \frac{1}{5}$

Ⓒ $-7.8, -8.7, 7.8, 8.7$

Ⓓ $0.6, 0.66, 0.666, \frac{2}{3}$

8. Which if-then statement is *always* true? **Alg. 24.0**

Ⓐ If x is a whole number, then $2x$ is odd.

Ⓑ If x is a whole number, then $2x$ is positive.

Ⓒ If x is a whole number, then $2x$ is greater than x.

Ⓓ If x is a whole number, then $2x$ is a whole number.

2.5 Apply the Distributive Property

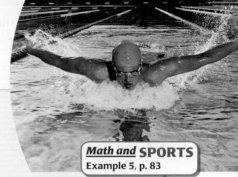

Math and SPORTS
Example 5, p. 83

Standards

Alg. 1.0 Students identify and use the arithmetic properties of subsets of integers and rational, irrational, and real numbers, including closure properties for the four basic arithmetic operations where applicable.

Alg. 1.1 Students use properties of numbers to demonstrate whether assertions are true or false.

Alg. 25.2 Students judge the validity of an argument according to whether the properties of the real number system and the order of operations have been applied correctly at each step.

Connect

Before you used properties to add, subtract, and multiply real numbers. *Now* you will apply the distributive property.

Key Vocabulary
- **equivalent expressions**
- **distributive property**
- **term**
- **coefficient**
- **like terms**
- **constant term**

The models below show two methods for finding the area of a rectangle that has a length of $(x + 2)$ units and a width of 3 units.

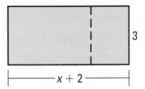

Area = $3(x + 2)$

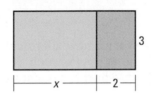

Area = $3(x) + 3(2)$

$3(x + 2)$ and $3(x) + 3(2)$ represent the same area, so the expressions are equal. These expressions are equal no matter what the value of x is. Two expressions that are equal for all values of the variable are called **equivalent expressions**.

The equation $3(x + 2) = 3(x) + 3(2)$ illustrates the **distributive property**, which can be used to find the product of a number and a sum or difference.

KEY CONCEPT   *For Your Notebook*

About the Standards

The distributive property, along with the properties of addition and multiplication on pages 62 and 75, are the arithmetic properties in Algebra 1 Standard 1.0.

The Distributive Property

Let a, b, and c be real numbers.

Words	Algebra	Examples
The product of a and $(b + c)$:	$a(b + c) = ab + ac$	$3(4 + 2) = 3(4) + 3(2)$
	$(b + c)a = ba + ca$	$(3 + 5)2 = 3(2) + 5(2)$
The product of a and $(b - c)$:	$a(b - c) = ab - ac$	$5(6 - 4) = 5(6) - 5(4)$
	$(b - c)a = ba - ca$	$(8 - 6)4 = 8(4) - 6(4)$

EXAMPLE 1 Apply the distributive property

a. $4(y + 3) = 4y + 12$ **b.** $(y + 7)y = y^2 + 7y$ **c.** $n(n - 9) = n^2 - 9n$

EXAMPLE 2   Distribute a negative number

Use the distributive property to write an equivalent expression.

a. $-2(x + 7) = -2(x) + (-2)(7)$ Distribute −2.

$\qquad\qquad\quad = -2x - 14$ Simplify.

b. $(5 - y)(-3y) = 5(-3y) - y(-3y)$ Distribute −3y.

$\qquad\qquad\qquad = -15y + 3y^2$ Simplify.

c. $-(2x - 11) = (-1)(2x - 11)$ Multiplicative property of −1

$\qquad\qquad\quad = (-1)(2x) - (-1)(11)$ Distribute −1.

$\qquad\qquad\quad = -2x + 11$ Simplify.

TERMS AND COEFFICIENTS The parts of an expression that are added together are called **terms**. The number part of a term with a variable part is called the **coefficient** of the term.

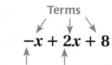

Terms

$$-x + 2x + 8$$

Coefficients are −1 and 2.

READING

Note that $-x$ has a coefficient of −1 even though the 1 isn't written. Similarly, x has a coefficient of 1.

Like terms have identical variable parts with corresponding variables raised to the same power, such as $-x$ and $2x$ in the expression above. A term that has no variable part is a **constant term**. Constant terms are also like terms.

EXAMPLE 3   Identify parts of an expression

Identify the terms, like terms, coefficients, and constant terms of the expression $3x - 4 - 6x + 2$.

Solution

Write the expression as a sum: $3x + (-4) + (-6x) + 2$

Terms: $3x, -4, -6x, 2$ **Like terms:** $3x$ and $-6x$; -4 and 2

Coefficients: $3, -6$ **Constant terms:** $-4, 2$

 GUIDED PRACTICE   for Examples 1, 2, and 3

Use the distributive property to write an equivalent expression.

1. $2(x + 3)$ **2.** $-(4 - y)$ **3.** $(m - 5)(-3m)$ **4.** $(2n + 6)\left(\frac{1}{2}\right)$

5. Identify the terms, like terms, coefficients, and constant terms of the expression $-7y + 8 - 6y - 13$.

COMBINING LIKE TERMS The distributive property allows you to combine like terms that have variable parts. For example, $5x + 6x = (5 + 6)x = 11x$. A quick way to combine like terms with variable parts is to mentally add the coefficients and use the common variable part. An expression is *simplified* if it has no grouping symbols and if all of the like terms have been combined.

EXAMPLE 4 Simplify an expression

ANOTHER WAY

In Example 4, you can rewrite the expression $4(n + 9) - 3(2 + n)$ as $4(n + 9) + (-3)(2 + n)$ and then distribute -3 to the terms in $2 + n$.

Simplify the expression $4(n + 9) - 3(2 + n)$.

Solution

$$4(n + 9) - 3(2 + n) = 4n + 36 - 6 - 3n \qquad \text{Distributive property}$$
$$= n + 30 \qquad \text{Combine like terms.}$$

EXAMPLE 5 Solve a multi-step problem

EXERCISING Your daily workout plan involves a total of 50 minutes of running and swimming. You burn 15 calories per minute when running and 9 calories per minute when swimming. Let r be your running time (in minutes). Find the number of calories you burn in your 50 minute workout if you run for 20 minutes.

Solution

ANOTHER WAY

For an alternative method for solving the problem in Example 5, turn to page 87 for the **Problem Solving Workshop**.

The workout lasts 50 minutes, and your running time is r minutes. So, your swimming time is $(50 - r)$ minutes.

Running: 15 Cal/min

STEP 1 **Write** a verbal model. Then write an equation.

Amount burned (calories)	=	Burning rate when running (calories/minute)	·	Running time (minutes)	+	Burning rate when swimming (calories/minute)	·	Swimming time (minutes)
C	=	15	·	r	+	9	·	$(50 - r)$

$$C = 15r + 9(50 - r) \qquad \text{Write equation.}$$
$$= 15r + 450 - 9r \qquad \text{Distributive property}$$
$$= 6r + 450 \qquad \text{Combine like terms.}$$

STEP 2 **Find** the value of C when $r = 20$.

$$C = 6r + 450 \qquad \text{Write equation.}$$
$$= 6(20) + 450 = 570 \qquad \text{Substitute 20 for } r. \text{ Then simplify.}$$

▶ You burn 570 calories in your 50 minute workout if you run for 20 minutes.

Animated **Algebra**

For an interactive example of using the distributive property, go to **classzone.com**.

✓ **GUIDED PRACTICE** for Examples 4 and 5

Simplify the expression.

6. $5(6 + n) - 2(n - 2)$ **7.** $4(x - 5) + 3(3 + x)$

8. WHAT IF? In Example 5, suppose your workout lasts 45 minutes. How many calories do you burn if you run for 20 minutes? 30 minutes?

2.5 EXERCISES

HOMEWORK KEY

◆ = MULTIPLE CHOICE PRACTICE
Exs. 21, 28, 54, and 58–60

◯ = HINTS AND HOMEWORK HELP
for Exs. 9, 37, and 53 at classzone.com

SKILLS · PROBLEM SOLVING · REASONING

1. VOCABULARY What are the coefficients of the expression $4x + 8 - 9x + 2$?

2. WRITING Are the expressions $2(x + 1)$ and $2x + 1$ equivalent? *Explain.*

EXAMPLES 1 and 2
on pp. 81–82
for Exs. 3–21

ERROR ANALYSIS *Describe* and correct the error in simplifying the expression.

3.
$$5y - (2y - 8) = 5y - 2y - 8$$
$$= 3y - 8 \qquad ✗$$

4.
$$8 + 2(4 + 3x) = 8 + 8 + 6x$$
$$= 22x \qquad ✗$$

USING THE DISTRIBUTIVE PROPERTY Use the distributive property to write an equivalent expression.

5. $4(x + 3)$ **6.** $8(y + 2)$ **7.** $(m + 5)5$ **8.** $(n + 6)3$

9. $(p - 3)(-8)$ **10.** $-4(q - 4)$ **11.** $2(2r - 3)$ **12.** $(s - 9)9$

13. $6v(v + 1)$ **14.** $-w(2w + 7)$ **15.** $-2x(3 - x)$ **16.** $3y(y - 6)$

17. $\frac{1}{2}\left(\frac{1}{2}m - 4\right)$ **18.** $-\frac{3}{4}(p - 1)$ **19.** $\frac{2}{3}(6n - 9)$ **20.** $\frac{5}{6}r(r - 1)$

21. ◆ **MULTIPLE CHOICE** Which expression is equivalent to $4x - 6$?

   (A) $4(x - 2)$ **(B)** $-4(x + 2)$ **(C)** $2(2x - 3)$ **(D)** $-2x$

EXAMPLE 3
on p. 82
for Exs. 22–28

IDENTIFYING PARTS OF AN EXPRESSION Identify the terms, like terms, coefficients, and constant terms of the expression.

22. $-7 + 13x + 2x + 8$ **23.** $9 + 7y - 2 - 5y$ **24.** $7x^2 - 10 - 2x^2 + 5$

25. $-3y^2 + 3y^2 - 7 + 9$ **26.** $2 + 3xy - 4xy + 6$ **27.** $6xy - 11xy + 2xy - 4xy$

28. ◆ **MULTIPLE CHOICE** Which two terms are like terms?

   (A) $-2, -5x$ **(B)** $4x, -x$ **(C)** $-2, -2y$ **(D)** $5x, -3y$

EXAMPLE 4
on p. 83
for Exs. 29–40

SIMPLIFYING EXPRESSIONS Simplify the expression.

29. $7x + (-11x)$ **30.** $6y - y$ **31.** $5 + 2n + 2$ **32.** $(4a - 1)2 + a$

33. $3(2 - c) - c$ **34.** $6r + 2(r + 4)$ **35.** $15t - (t - 4)$ **36.** $3(m + 5) - 10$

37. $-6(v + 1) + v$ **38.** $7(w - 5) + 3w$ **39.** $6(5 - z) + 2z$ **40.** $(s - 3)(-2) + 17s$

⊘ **GEOMETRY** Find the perimeter and area of the rectangle.

41.

5

$v + 3$

42.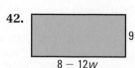

9

$8 - 12w$

43.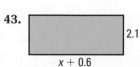

2.1

$x + 0.6$

44. TRUE OR FALSE Consider the statement $3(6 + 1 + 8) = 3(6) + 3(1) + 3(8)$.

    a. Evaluate each side of the equation to determine whether the statement is true or false.

    b. Copy and complete: $3(6 + 1 + 8) = 3((6 + 1) + 8)$ Order of operations

$$= 3(6 + 1) + 3(8) \quad \underline{\quad ? \quad}$$

$$= \underline{\quad ? \quad} \quad \text{Distributive property}$$

ERROR ANALYSIS Tell whether the order of operations or property has been applied correctly at each step in the evaluation or simplification.

45.

$$2(7 + (-1)^2) = 14 + 2(-1)^2 \quad \text{Distributive property}$$
$$= 14 + (-2)^2 \quad \text{Multiply.}$$
$$= 18 \quad \text{Evaluate power and add.}$$

46.

$$2 - 3(-4 + 9) = -1(-4 + 9) \quad \text{Subtract.}$$
$$= 4 + 9 \quad \text{Distributive property}$$
$$= 13 \quad \text{Add.}$$

47.

$$6n + 2(1 - 8n) = 6n + 2(8n - 1) \quad \text{Commutative property}$$
$$= 6n + 16n - 1 \quad \text{Distributive property}$$
$$= 22n - 1 \quad \text{Combine like terms.}$$

48.

$$x - (y + z) = x + (-1)(y + z) \quad \text{Subtraction rule, property of } -1$$
$$= x + (-1)y + z \quad \text{Distributive property}$$
$$= x - y + z \quad \text{Property of } -1, \text{ subtraction rule}$$

CONNECT SKILLS TO PROBLEM SOLVING Exercises 49–51 will help you prepare for problem solving. Write an expression for the situation.

49. Perimeter of a sign with a width of x inches and length of $(x + 11)$ inches

50. Area of an envelope with a width of $(x - 2)$ inches and length of x inches

51. Area of a triangular garden with a base of x feet and a height of $(x + 1)$ feet

EXAMPLE 5
on p. 83
for Exs. 52–54

52. SPORTS An archer shoots 6 arrows at a target. Some arrows hit the 9 point ring and the rest hit the 10 point bull's-eye. Write an equation that gives the score s in terms of the number a of arrows that hit the 9 point ring. Then find the score if 2 arrows hit the 9 point ring.

    California @HomeTutor for problem solving help at classzone.com

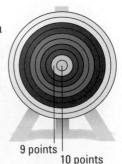

9 points
10 points

53. MOVIES You rent 3 movies for the same price and have a coupon for $2 off the regular cost per rental. Write an equation that gives the total cost C (in dollars) in terms of the regular cost r (in dollars) of a rental. Then find the total cost if a rental regularly costs $3.99.

    California @HomeTutor for problem solving help at classzone.com

54. ◆ **MULTIPLE CHOICE** In a diving competition, a diver's score is the product of the difficulty level d of a dive and the sum of the scores x, y, and z of 3 judges. Which expression represents the diver's score?

(**A**) $x + y + z$ (**B**) $d(xyz)$ (**C**) $d(x + y + z)$ (**D**) $d \cdot x + y + z$

55. MUSIC During the summer you give one hour saxophone lessons to 20 students each week. Use the information in the advertisement.

a. **Model** Write an equation that gives your weekly earnings y (in dollars) in terms of the number x of beginning students that you teach.

b. **Calculate** Find your weekly earnings if 15 of your 20 students are beginners.

56. CHALLENGE How can you use $a(b + c) = ab + ac$ to show that $(b + c)a = ba + ca$ is also true? *Justify* your steps.

57. CHALLENGE A drama club plans to sell 100 tickets to a school musical. An adult ticket costs $6, and a student ticket costs $4. Students who attend the school get a $1 discount. The club expects two thirds of the student tickets to be discounted. Write an equation that gives the total revenue r (in dollars) in terms of the number a of adult tickets sold.

◆ CALIFORNIA STANDARDS SPIRAL REVIEW

Alg. 1.0   **58.** Which property is used in the statement $2x \cdot 1 = 2x$? *(p. 74)*

(**A**) Commutative property   (**B**) Identity property

(**C**) Property of zero   (**D**) Property of -1

Gr. 7 NS 1.2   **59.** When $a = -2$ and $b = 2$, which expression does *not* have a value of -4? *(p. 5)*

(**A**) ab (**B**) $a - b$ (**C**) $b - a$ (**D**) $3a + b$

Gr. 6 AF 1.2   **60.** A hardware store charges $.30 for a certain bolt. The store obtains the bolts from the manufacturer for a price of $.19 per bolt. Which expression gives the profit earned by the store for selling x bolts? *(p. 19)*

(**A**) $0.3 - 0.19x$ (**B**) $0.3x - 0.19x$ (**C**) $0.19x - 0.30x$ (**D**) $0.3x + 0.19x$

QUIZ *for Lessons 2.4–2.5*

Find the product. *(p. 74)*

1. $-5 \cdot (-5)$ **2.** $18 \cdot \left(-\dfrac{7}{6}\right)$ **3.** $8 \cdot \dfrac{4}{5} \cdot (-10)$ **4.** $9 \cdot (-7) \cdot (-1.2)$

5. $(-3x) \cdot (-4)$ **6.** $-\dfrac{2}{3}x \cdot 15$ **7.** $x \cdot 1.5 \cdot (-6.4)$ **8.** $(-2)(13x)$

Use the distributive property to write an equivalent expression. *(p. 81)*

9. $7(x + 14)$ **10.** $-4(5x + 9)$ **11.** $-5(2x - 6)$ **12.** $(3 - x)6$

Using ALTERNATIVE METHODS

Another Way to Solve Example 5, page 83

In Example 5 on page 83, you saw how to solve a problem about exercising using a verbal model and an equation. You can also solve the problem by breaking it into parts.

PROBLEM

EXERCISING Your daily workout plan involves a total of 50 minutes of running and swimming. You burn 15 calories per minute when running and 9 calories per minute when swimming. Find the number of calories you burn in your 50 minute workout if you run for 20 minutes.

METHOD **Breaking into Parts** You can solve the problem by breaking it into parts.

STEP 1 **Find** the number of calories you burn when running.

$$\frac{15 \text{ calories}}{\text{per minute}} \cdot 20 \text{ minutes} = 300 \text{ calories}$$

Your running time is 20 minutes, so your swimming time is 50 − 20 = 30 minutes.

STEP 2 **Find** the calories you burn when swimming.

$$\frac{9 \text{ calories}}{\text{per minute}} \cdot 30 \text{ minutes} = 270 \text{ calories}$$

STEP 3 **Add** the calories you burn when doing each activity. You burn a total of 570 calories.

$$300 \text{ calories} + 270 \text{ calories} = 570 \text{ calories}$$

PRACTICE

1. **VACATIONING** Your family is taking a vacation for 10 nights. You will spend some nights at a campground and the rest of the nights at a motel. A campground stay costs $15 per night, and a motel stay costs $60 per night. Find the total cost of lodging if you stay at a campground for 6 nights. Solve this problem using two different methods.

2. **WHAT IF?** In Exercise 1, suppose the vacation lasts 12 days. Find the total cost of lodging if you stay at the campground for 6 nights. Solve this problem using two different methods.

3. **FLORIST** During the summer, you work 35 hours per week at a florist shop. You get paid $8 per hour for working at the register and $9.50 per hour for making deliveries. Find the total amount you earn this week if you spend 5 hours making deliveries. Solve this problem using two different methods.

4. **ERROR ANALYSIS** *Describe* and correct the error in solving Exercise 3.

$8 per hour • 5 hours = $40

$9.50 per hour • 30 hours = $285

$40 + $285 = $325

2.6 Divide Real Numbers

Standards

Alg. 1.0 Students identify and use the arithmetic properties of subsets of integers and rational, irrational, **and real numbers, including closure properties for the four basic arithmetic operations where applicable.**

Alg. 1.1 Students use properties of numbers to demonstrate whether assertions are true or false.

Alg. 2.0 Students understand and use such operations as taking the opposite, **finding the reciprocal,** taking a root, and raising to a fractional power. They understand and use the rules of exponents.

Math and SPORTS
Ex. 61, p. 93

Connect *Before* you multiplied real numbers. *Now* you will divide real numbers..

Key Vocabulary
- **multiplicative inverse**
- **reciprocal,** *p. 789*
- **mean,** *p. 803*

Reciprocals like $\frac{2}{3}$ and $\frac{3}{2}$ have the property that their product is 1. The reciprocal of a nonzero number a, written $\frac{1}{a}$, is called the **multiplicative inverse** of a. Zero does not have a multiplicative inverse because there is no number a such that $0 \cdot a = 1$.

KEY CONCEPT   *For Your Notebook*

Inverse Property of Multiplication for Real Numbers

Words The product of a nonzero number and its multiplicative inverse is 1.

Algebra $a \cdot \frac{1}{a} = \frac{1}{a} \cdot a = 1, a \neq 0$ **Example** $8 \cdot \frac{1}{8} = 1$

EXAMPLE 1   Find multiplicative inverses of numbers

a. The multiplicative inverse of $-\frac{1}{5}$ is -5 because $-\frac{1}{5} \cdot (-5) = 1$.

b. The multiplicative inverse of $-\frac{6}{7}$ is $-\frac{7}{6}$ because $-\frac{6}{7} \cdot \left(-\frac{7}{6}\right) = 1$.

WRITE INVERSES
You can find the inverse of $-\frac{6}{7}$ as follows:

$$\frac{1}{-\frac{6}{7}} \cdot 1 = \frac{1}{-\frac{6}{7}} \cdot \frac{7}{7}$$

$$= \frac{7}{-6}, \text{ or } -\frac{7}{6}$$

DIVISION Because the expressions $6 \div 3$ and $6 \cdot \frac{1}{3}$ have the same value, 2, you can conclude that $6 \div 3 = 6 \cdot \frac{1}{3}$. This example illustrates the *division rule*.

KEY CONCEPT   *For Your Notebook*

Division Rule for Real Numbers

Words To divide a number a by a nonzero number b, multiply a by the multiplicative inverse of b.

Algebra $a \div b = a \cdot \frac{1}{b}, b \neq 0$ **Example** $5 \div 2 = 5 \cdot \frac{1}{2}$

SIGN OF A QUOTIENT Because division can be expressed as multiplication, the sign rules for division are the same as the sign rules for multiplication.

AVOID ERRORS
You cannot divide a real number by 0, because 0 does not have a multiplicative inverse.

> **KEY CONCEPT**   *For Your Notebook*
>
> **The Sign of a Quotient**
>
> • The quotient of two real numbers with the *same* sign is positive.
> • The quotient of two real numbers with *different* signs is negative.
> • The quotient of 0 and any nonzero real number is 0.

EXAMPLE 2   Divide real numbers

Find the quotient.

a. $-16 \div 4 = -16 \cdot \dfrac{1}{4}$
$= -4$

b. $-20 \div \left(-\dfrac{5}{3}\right) = -20 \cdot \left(-\dfrac{3}{5}\right)$
$= 12$

EXAMPLE 3   Find the mean

TEMPERATURES Barrow, Alaska, is the northernmost settlement in the United States. The daily minimum temperatures in Barrow for February 1–5, 2004 are shown. Find the mean daily minimum temperature.

Day in February	1	2	3	4	5
Minimum temperature (°F)	−21	−29	−39	−39	−22

Point Barrow Observatory

Solution

To find the mean daily minimum temperature, find the sum of the minimum temperatures for the 5 days and then divide the sum by 5.

REVIEW MEAN
For help with finding a mean, see p. 803.

$\text{Mean} = \dfrac{-21 + (-29) + (-39) + (-39) + (-22)}{5}$

$= \dfrac{-150}{5} = -30$

▸ The mean daily minimum temperature was −30°F.

✔ **GUIDED PRACTICE**   for Examples 1, 2, and 3

1. Find the multiplicative inverse of -8, $-\dfrac{4}{7}$, and $\dfrac{1}{3}$.

2. Find the quotient $18 \div \left(-\dfrac{2}{9}\right)$.

3. **TEMPERATURES** In Example 3, the minimum temperatures for the next two days of February were −27°F and −28°F. Find the mean daily minimum temperature for the first 7 days of February.

EXAMPLE 4 Simplify an expression

Simplify the expression $\dfrac{36x - 24}{6}$.

ANOTHER WAY
You can simplify the expression by first rewriting it as a difference of two fractions: $\dfrac{36x - 24}{6} = \dfrac{36x}{6} - \dfrac{24}{6} = 6x - 4$.

$$\frac{36x - 24}{6} = (36x - 24) \div 6 \qquad \text{Rewrite fraction as division.}$$

$$= (36x - 24) \cdot \frac{1}{6} \qquad \text{Division rule}$$

$$= 36x \cdot \frac{1}{6} - 24 \cdot \frac{1}{6} \qquad \text{Distributive property}$$

$$= 6x - 4 \qquad \text{Simplify.}$$

✔ **GUIDED PRACTICE** for Example 4

4. Simplify the expression $\dfrac{-10z - 20}{-5}$.

CONCEPT SUMMARY   *For Your Notebook*

Rules for Addition, Subtraction, Multiplication, and Division

Let a and b be real numbers.

Expression	$a + b$	$a - b$	$a \cdot b$	$a \div b$
Positive if...	the number with the greater absolute value is positive.	$a > b$.	a and b have the same sign ($a \neq 0$, $b \neq 0$).	a and b have the same sign ($a \neq 0$, $b \neq 0$).
Negative if...	the number with the greater absolute value is negative.	$a < b$.	a and b have different signs ($a \neq 0$, $b \neq 0$).	a and b have different signs ($a \neq 0$, $b \neq 0$).
Zero if...	a and b are additive inverses.	$a = b$.	$a = 0$ or $b = 0$.	$a = 0$ and $b \neq 0$.

2.6 EXERCISES

HOMEWORK KEY

◆ = **MULTIPLE CHOICE PRACTICE**
Exs. 11, 50, 60, and 65–67

◯ = **HINTS AND HOMEWORK HELP**
for Exs. 31, 35, and 57 at classzone.com

SKILLS • PROBLEM SOLVING • REASONING

1. VOCABULARY What is a multiplicative inverse?

2. WRITING How can division be expressed as multiplication?

EXAMPLE 1
on p. 88
for Exs. 3–11

FINDING INVERSES Find the multiplicative inverse of the number.

3. -18 **4.** 9 **5.** -1 **6.** $-\dfrac{1}{2}$

7. $-\dfrac{3}{4}$ **8.** $-\dfrac{5}{9}$ **9.** $4\dfrac{1}{3}$ **10.** $-2\dfrac{2}{5}$

11. ◆ **MULTIPLE CHOICE** If $-\dfrac{5}{7}x = 1$, what is the value of x?

    Ⓐ $-1\dfrac{2}{5}$ Ⓑ $\dfrac{5}{7}$ Ⓒ 1 Ⓓ $\dfrac{12}{5}$

EXAMPLE 2
on p. 89
for Exs. 12–23

FINDING QUOTIENTS Find the quotient.

12. $-21 \div 3$ **13.** $-18 \div (-6)$ **14.** $-1 \div \left(-\dfrac{7}{2}\right)$ **15.** $15 \div \left(-\dfrac{3}{4}\right)$

16. $13 \div \left(-4\dfrac{1}{3}\right)$ **17.** $-\dfrac{2}{3} \div 2$ **18.** $-\dfrac{1}{2} \div \dfrac{1}{5}$ **19.** $-\dfrac{1}{5} \div (-6)$

20. $-\dfrac{4}{7} \div (-2)$ **21.** $-1 \div \left(-\dfrac{6}{5}\right)$ **22.** $8 \div \left(-\dfrac{4}{11}\right)$ **23.** $-\dfrac{1}{3} \div \dfrac{5}{3}$

EXAMPLE 3
on p. 89
for Ex. 24–32

FINDING MEANS Find the mean of the numbers.

24. $-10, -8, 3$ **25.** $12, -8, -9$ **26.** $18, -9, 0, -5$

27. $-2, 9, -3, 5$ **28.** $-1, -4, -5, 10$ **29.** $7, -4, 1, -9, -6$

30. $-5.3, -2, 1.3$ **31.** $0.25, -4, -0.75, -1, 6$ **32.** $-0.6, 0.18, -2, 5, -0.5$

EXAMPLE 4
on p. 90
for Exs. 33–43

SIMPLIFYING EXPRESSIONS Simplify the expression.

33. $\dfrac{6x - 14}{2}$ **34.** $\dfrac{12y - 8}{-4}$ **35.** $\dfrac{9z - 6}{-3}$

36. $\dfrac{-6p + 15}{6}$ **37.** $\dfrac{5 - 25q}{10}$ **38.** $\dfrac{-18 - 21r}{-12}$

39. $\dfrac{-24a - 10}{-8}$ **40.** $\dfrac{-20b + 12}{-5}$ **41.** $\dfrac{36 - 27c}{9}$

ERROR ANALYSIS *Describe* and correct the error in simplifying the expression.

42.

$$\dfrac{12 - 18x}{6} = (12 - 18x) \cdot \left(-\dfrac{1}{6}\right)$$
$$= 12\left(-\dfrac{1}{6}\right) - 18x\left(-\dfrac{1}{6}\right)$$
$$= -2 + 3x$$

43.

$$\dfrac{-15x - 10}{-5} = (-15x - 10) \cdot \left(-\dfrac{1}{5}\right)$$
$$= -15x\left(-\dfrac{1}{5}\right) - 10\left(-\dfrac{1}{5}\right)$$
$$= 3x - 2$$

44. REASONING Use the multiplicative property of -1 and the division rule to establish a property of -1 for division. *Explain* your reasoning.

EVALUATING EXPRESSIONS Evaluate the expression.

45. $\dfrac{2y - x}{x}$ when $x = 1$ and $y = -4$ **46.** $\dfrac{4x}{3y + x}$ when $x = 6$ and $y = -8$

47. $\dfrac{-9x}{y^2 - 1}$ when $x = -3$ and $y = -2$ **48.** $\dfrac{y - x}{xy}$ when $x = -6$ and $y = -2$

49. REASONING Tell whether the associative property and the commutative property hold for division. Give examples to support your answers.

50. ◆ **MULTIPLE CHOICE** Let a and b be positive numbers, and let c and d be negative numbers. Which quotient has a value that is always negative?

    Ⓐ $\dfrac{a}{b} \div \dfrac{c}{d}$ Ⓑ $\dfrac{a}{c} \div \dfrac{b}{d}$ Ⓒ $\dfrac{c^2}{a} \div \dfrac{b}{d}$ Ⓓ $\dfrac{a}{cd} \div b$

51. REASONING Use the closure property of multiplication to write a similar property for division. Then decide whether the following sets of numbers are closed under division. *Explain* your reasoning.

a. Positive integers   **b.** Nonzero rational numbers   **c.** $\left\{\frac{1}{4}, \frac{1}{2}, 1, 2, 4\right\}$

52. TRUE OR FALSE Consider the statement $8 \div 5 = \frac{1}{5} \div \frac{1}{8}$.

a. Evaluate each side of the equation to determine whether the statement is true or false.

b. Copy and complete: $8 \div 5 = 8 \cdot \frac{1}{5}$ _____?_____

$= \frac{1}{5} \cdot 8$ _____?_____

$= \underline{\ ?\ }$ Division rule

CONNECT SKILLS TO PROBLEM SOLVING Exercises 53–55 will help you prepare for problem solving.

53. A drill bit used for drilling ice descends from ground level to an elevation of −54 feet after 4.5 minutes. Write an expression for the average rate of change in the drill bit's elevation (in feet per minute).

54. At dawn, the air temperature is −3.5°C. Two hours later, the air temperature is 1.7°C. Write an expression for the average rate of change of the temperature (in degrees Celsius per hour) for the period.

55. Your team scores −20, 125, and −150 on the last three questions in a competition. Write an expression for the average of the scores.

Elevation: −42 m

EXAMPLES
2 and 3
on p. 89
for Exs. 56–57

56. SPORTS Free diving means diving without the aid of breathing equipment. Suppose that an athlete free dives to an elevation of −42 meters in 60 seconds. Find the average rate of change in the diver's elevation.

California *@HomeTutor* for problem solving help at classzone.com

57. WEATHER The daily mean temperature is the mean of the high and low temperatures for a given day. The high temperature for Boston, Massachusetts, on January 10, 2004, was −10.6°C. The low temperature was −18.9°C. Find the daily mean temperature.

California *@HomeTutor* for problem solving help at classzone.com

58. INVESTING The table shows the changes in the values of one share of stock A and one share of stock B over 5 days.

Day of week	Monday	Tuesday	Wednesday	Thursday	Friday
Change in share value for stock A (dollars)	−0.45	−0.32	0.66	−1.12	1.53
Change in share value for stock B (dollars)	−0.37	0.14	0.59	−0.53	1.02

a. Find the average daily change in share value for each stock.

b. Which stock performed better over the 5 days? How much more money did the better performing stock earn, on average, per day?

◆ = **MULTIPLE CHOICE PRACTICE**   ◯ = **HINTS** AND **HOMEWORK HELP** at classzone.com

59. MULTI-STEP PROBLEM The South Aral Sea in Russia was about 57 meters above sea level in 1965. Scientists once predicted that the elevation would be about 34 meters above sea level in 2002.

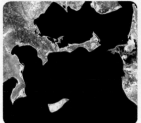 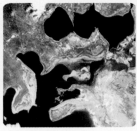

South Aral Sea, 1973   **South Aral Sea, 2000**

   a. Estimate the average rate of change in elevation for the period 1965–2002 using the scientists' prediction.

   b. More recent research suggests that the elevation decreased to about 30.5 meters above sea level in 2002. Use this information to predict the elevation in 2010. *Explain* your steps.

60. ◆ **MULTIPLE CHOICE** In a trivia competition, your team earned 60, −100, 300, 120, and −80 points on 5 questions. The sixth question has a value of 300 points. By how many points will your team's mean score per question change if you answer the sixth question correctly?

   (A) 40 points   **(B)** 50 points   **(C)** 60 points   **(D)** 100 points

61. VOLLEYBALL Ace efficiency is a measure of a volleyball player's serving ability. The ace efficiency f is given by the formula $f = \dfrac{a - e}{s}$ where a is the number of aces (a serve that the opponent is unable to hit), e is the number of service errors, and s is the total number of serves.

   a. Find f for a player who has 108 aces and 125 errors in 500 serves.

   b. If the player makes 30 more aces and 20 more service errors in the next 100 serves, will the ace efficiency increase? *Explain.*

62. CHALLENGE Find the mean of the integers from −410 to 400. *Explain* how you got your answer.

63. CHALLENGE What is the mean of a number and three times its opposite? *Explain* your reasoning.

64. CHALLENGE The average daily balance of a checking account is the sum of the daily balances in a given period divided by the number of days in the period. Suppose that a period has 30 days. Find the average daily balance of an account that has a balance of $110 for 18 days, a balance of −$300 for 10 days, and a balance of $100 for the rest of the period.

◆ CALIFORNIA STANDARDS SPIRAL REVIEW

Gr. 7 NS 1.3

65. Which fraction is equal to 4.16? *(p. 791)*

   (A) $\dfrac{4}{25}$ **(B)** $\dfrac{84}{25}$ **(C)** $\dfrac{104}{25}$ **(D)** $\dfrac{129}{25}$

Alg. 2.0

66. Which of the following is equal to 4? *(p. 53)*

   (A) $-|-4|$ **(B)** $-|4|$ **(C)** $|-4|$ **(D)** $|-16|$

Gr. 6 AF 2.1

67. A yardstick is about 0.914 meter long. About how long is the yardstick in centimeters? *(p. 795)*

   (A) 9.14 cm   **(B)** 91.4 cm   **(C)** 914 cm   **(D)** 9140 cm

2.7 Writing Statements in If-Then Form

MATERIALS · paper and pencil

QUESTION How can you write an *all* or *none* statement in if-then form?

EXPLORE Tell whether certain statements are true about a group

STEP 1 *Answer questions* Copy the questions shown at the right and write your answers beside them.

1. Do you play an instrument?
2. Do you participate in a school sport?
3. Are you taking an art class?
4. Do you walk to school?

Standards
Alg. 24.2 Students identify the hypothesis and conclusion in logical deduction.

STEP 2 *Write if-then statements* Each of the *all* or *none* statements below can be written in if-then form. Copy each statement and complete its equivalent if-then form. The first one is done for you as an example.

1. All of the students in our group play an instrument.
   If a student is in our group, then the student plays an instrument.

2. None of the students in our group participates in a school sport.
   If ___?___, then ___?___.

3. None of the students in our group is taking an art class.
   If ___?___, then ___?___.

4. All of the students in our group walk to school.
   If ___?___, then ___?___.

STEP 3 *Analyze statements* Form a group with 2 or 3 classmates. Tell whether each if-then statement in Step 2 is *true* or *false* for your group. If the statement is false, give a counterexample.

DRAW CONCLUSIONS Use your observations to complete these exercises

1. *Describe* the similarity and difference in the if-then forms of the following statements:

   All of the students in our group listen to rock music.

   None of the students in our group listens to rock music.

Rewrite the given conditional statement in if-then form. Then tell whether the statement is *true* or *false*. If it is false, give a counterexample.

2. All positive numbers are integers.

3. All rational numbers can be written as quotients of integers.

4. None of the negative numbers is a whole number.

5. None of the rational numbers has an opposite equal to itself.

2.7 Find Square Roots and Compare Real Numbers

Math and ARCHITECTURE
Ex. 51, p. 101

Standards
Alg. 1.0 Students identify and use the arithmetic properties of subsets of integers and rational, irrational, and real numbers, including closure properties for the four basic arithmetic properties where applicable.

Alg. 2.0 Students understand and use such operations as taking the opposite, finding the reciprocal, **taking a root**, and raising to a fractional power. They understand and use the rules of exponents.

Connect
Before you found squares of numbers and compared rational numbers.
Now you will find square roots and compare real numbers.

Key Vocabulary
• square root
• radicand
• perfect square
• irrational number
• real numbers

Recall that the square of 4 is $4^2 = 16$ and the square of -4 is $(-4)^2 = 16$. The numbers 4 and -4 are called the *square roots* of 16. In this lesson, you will find the square roots of nonnegative numbers.

KEY CONCEPT   *For Your Notebook*

Square Root of a Real Number

Words A **square root** of a real number a is a real number b such that $b^2 = a$.

Example $3^2 = 9$ and $(-3)^2 = 9$, so 3 and -3 are square roots of 9.

All positive real numbers have two square roots, a positive (or *principal*) square root and a negative square root, each written with the radical symbol $\sqrt{}$. The number or expression inside a radical symbol is the **radicand**.

$$\text{radical symbol} \longrightarrow \sqrt{a} \longleftarrow \text{radicand}$$

Zero has only one square root, 0. Negative real numbers do not have real square roots because the square of every real number is either positive or 0.

EXAMPLE 1   **Find square roots**

READING
The symbol ± is read as "plus or minus" and refers to both the positive square root and the negative square root.

Evaluate the expression.

  a. $\sqrt{49} = 7$ The positive square root of 49 is 7.

  b. $-\sqrt{4} = -2$ The negative square root of 4 is -2.

  c. $\pm\sqrt{36} = \pm 6$ The square roots of 36 are 6 and -6.

✓ **GUIDED PRACTICE**   for Example 1

Evaluate the expression.

  1. $-\sqrt{9}$ **2.** $\sqrt{25}$ **3.** $\pm\sqrt{64}$ **4.** $-\sqrt{81}$

PROOFS A logical argument consisting of a sequence of deductions, as in Example 3, is called a *proof*. You can use the properties below, along with those given earlier in Chapter 2, to provide justification for each step in a proof.

REVIEW PROPERTIES

The properties of addition are listed on p. 62, the properties of multiplication on p. 75 and p. 88, and the distributive property on p. 81.

KEY CONCEPT   *For Your Notebook*

Properties of Equality

REFLEXIVE PROPERTY
A quantity is equal to itself.

Algebra $a = a$

Example $3 = 3$

SYMMETRIC PROPERTY
If one quantity equals a second, then the second quantity equals the first.

Algebra If $a = b$, then $b = a$.

Example If $1 + 3 = 4$,
then $4 = 1 + 3$.

TRANSITIVE PROPERTY
If one quantity equals a second and the second quantity equals a third, then the first quantity equals the third.

Algebra If $a = b$ and $b = c$,
then $a = c$.

Example If $6 + 3 = 5 + 4$ and
$5 + 4 = 9$, then $6 + 3 = 9$.

ADDITION PROPERTY OF EQUALITY
If the same quantity is added to two equal quantities, then the resulting quantities are equal.

Algebra If $a = b$, then $a + c = b + c$.

Example If $2(4) = 8(1)$, then
$2(4) + 7 = 8(1) + 7$.

EXAMPLE 4   **Write a proof**

Prove that $a \cdot (-1)$ is the additive inverse of a.

Solution

To prove that $a \cdot (-1)$ is the additive inverse of a, show that $a + a \cdot (-1) = 0$.

WRITE PROOFS

Proofs can be written in a two-column format, with statements listed on the left and the justification for each statement on the right.

$a = a \cdot 1$	**Multiplicative identity property**
$a + a \cdot (-1) = a \cdot 1 + a \cdot (-1)$	**Addition property of equality**
$a + a \cdot (-1) = a[1 + (-1)]$	**Distributive property**
$a + a \cdot (-1) = a \cdot 0$	**Additive inverse property**
$a + a \cdot (-1) = 0$	**Multiplicative property of zero**

✓ **GUIDED PRACTICE**   for Example 4

5. Copy and complete the proof of this statement: $a + c = b + c$, then $a = b$.

$a + c = b + c$	Write original equation.
$[a + c] + (-c) = [b + c] + (-c)$	?
$a + [c + (-c)] = b + [c + (-c)]$	?
$a + 0 = b + 0$	?
$a = b$	?

2.8 EXERCISES

◆ = **MULTIPLE CHOICE PRACTICE**
Exs. 18, 31, 34, and 42–44

○ = **HINTS AND HOMEWORK HELP**
for Exs. 7, 11, and 33 at classzone.com

SKILLS · PROBLEM SOLVING · REASONING

1. **VOCABULARY** What is a conjecture?

2. **WRITING** *Explain* why inductive reasoning may lead to false conclusions.

EXAMPLE 1
on p. 102
for Exs. 3–12

DETERMINE TYPES OF REASONING **Determine whether inductive or deductive reasoning is used.**

3. John noticed that on a certain TV channel there were 2 game shows followed by 2 daytime dramas starting at 11 a.m. on Monday and Tuesday. He decided that this arrangement is true for any weekday.

4. Ken uses the examples shown in the table below to determine that the product of two even integers is always even.

Expression	−2 (−4)	−12(20)	36(−16)	100(200)
Result	8	−240	−576	20,000

5. Sheila agrees with Ken in Exercise 4 that the product of two even integers is always even. She writes the argument below for justification.

Let the two even integers be 2m and 2n where m and n are integers. Then their product is 4mn, which equals 2(2mn). Because 4mn is the product of 2 and an integer, it is always even.

6. Kira claims that the sum of two odd integers is even. She writes the paragraph below for justification.

Let m and n be integers. The products 2m and 2n are even, so 2m + 1 and 2n + 1 are odd. The sum of the odd numbers is:

(2m + 1) + (2n + 1) = 2m + 2n + 2

= 2(m + n + 1)

The result is divisible by 2, so the sum of two odd integers is even.

MAKING CONJECTURES **Use inductive reasoning to make a conjecture.**

7. This year's rainfall in March, April, and May is shown at the right. Make a conjecture about the number of inches of rain in June.

8. The first 5 numbers in a pattern are 1, 4, 16, 64, and 256. Make a conjecture about the pattern and use it to find the next number.

9. During each of the last 5 games, your school's basketball team scored more than 50 points. Make a conjecture about your school's score in the next game.

Rainfall by Month

2.1 (March), 1.8 (April), 1.5 (May)

DRAW CONCLUSIONS Use deductive reasoning to draw a conclusion.

10. There are 4 angles of equal measure in a square. The sum of the measures of the angles is 360°. Draw a conclusion about the measure of each angle.

11. The rectangular room shown at the right has a width of 15 feet. Draw a conclusion about the perimeter and area of the room.

 x ft

 $(x + 10)$ ft

12. A particular whole number is a prime number between 20 and 25. Draw a conclusion about the number.

PROPERTIES OF EQUALITY Tell which property of equality is illustrated by the statement.

13. If $x + y = 7$ and $7 = z$, then $x + y = z$.

14. If $x + 1 = y - 3$, then $x + 1 + (-1) = y - 3 + (-1)$.

15. If $5x - 2 = y$, then $y = 5x - 2$.

ERROR ANALYSIS *Describe* and correct the error in the argument.

16.
> The equation $5x + 3 = 3 + 5x$ is always true because of the symmetric property of equality.

17.
> The equation $(2y + 8) \cdot 4z = 2y + (8 \cdot 4z)$ is always true because of the associative properties of addition and multiplication.

EXAMPLE 4
on p. 104
for Ex. 18

18. ◆ **MULTIPLE CHOICE** The deductive reasoning steps shown below prove that $(-a) + (-b) = -(a + b)$ for any real numbers a and b. Which property of real numbers justifies Step 1?

Step 1 $(-a) + (-b) = (-1)a + (-1)b$

Step 2 $\qquad\qquad = -1(a + b)$

Step 3 $\qquad\qquad = -(a + b)$

Ⓐ Distributive property Ⓑ Commutative property of addition

Ⓒ Multiplicative property of -1 Ⓓ Multiplicative identity property

REASONING Determine whether the statement is *sometimes, always,* or *never* true. *Explain* your reasoning.

19. $n > -n$ for a whole number n. 20. $2(x + 1) = 2x + 2$ for a real number x.

21. $(x + 1)^2 = x^2 + 1$ for a real number x. 22. If $x > y$, then $x^2 > y^2$ for real numbers x, y.

23. $|2x| > |x|$ for a real number $x \neq 0$. 24. $|-3x| = -3|x|$ for a real number $x \neq 0$.

25. $x^2 < 0$ for a real number x. 26. $|x + 1| = |x| + 1$ for a real number x.

27. For any positive integer n, the value of $2n - 1$ is odd.

28. For any positive integer n, the value of $n^2 + n + 11$ is prime.

29. For any nonzero real number x, the value of $\dfrac{|x|}{x}$ is 1.

30. If two nonzero real numbers are reciprocals, then their product is 1.

◆ = **MULTIPLE CHOICE PRACTICE** ◯ = **HINTS** AND **HOMEWORK HELP** at classzone.com

31. ◆ **MULTIPLE CHOICE** Consider the statement "The opposite of a number is less than the original number." When is the statement true?

    (A) Never true   (B) True only for negative numbers

    (C) Always true   (D) True only for positive numbers

32. **WRITING** Suppose Alec found the opposites of several positive numbers and several negative numbers to help find the answer to Exercise 31. Did he use inductive or deductive reasoning? *Explain.*

(33.) **SHORT RESPONSE** For a simple pendulum like the one shown, the tables below give the period (the time that the pendulum takes to make a complete swing) for various pendulum masses and lengths. How is the period of a pendulum affected by its mass? by its length? *Explain* your reasoning.

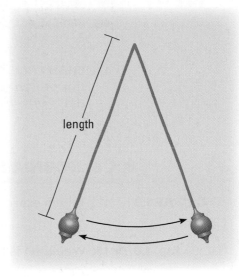

length

Mass = 3 kg		Length = 3 m	
Length (meters)	Period (seconds)	Mass (kilograms)	Period (seconds)
1	2.01	1	3.47
2	2.84	2	3.47
3	3.47	3	3.47
4	4.01	4	3.47

34. ◆ **MULTIPLE CHOICE** Hal claims that for any real number x, $x^2 \geq x$. He supports his claim by stating $(-3)^2 = 9$ and $9 > -3$, as well as $(2)^2 = 4$ and $4 > 2$. Which number x serves as a counterexample to Hal's claim?

    (A) 0   (B) 0.5   (C) 1   (D) 5

EXAMPLES
2 and 3
on p. 103
for Exs. 35–37

MAKING AND PROVING CONJECTURES **Perform the number trick for three different numbers and make a conjecture based on the results. Then prove the conjecture.**

35. Choose any number. Then double it. Then add 12. Then multiply by 4. Then divide by 8. Then subtract the number you chose.

36. Choose any number. Then triple it. Then subtract 12. Then multiply by −2. Then divide by 3. Then subtract 8.

37. Choose any number. Then multiply it by one half. Then add 5. Then multiply by 6. Then subtract 15. Then divide by 3.

EXAMPLE 4
on p. 104
for Exs. 38–39

38. **REASONING** Copy and complete the proof of this statement: $a = -(-a)$.

$$a + (-a) = 0 \qquad \underline{\qquad ? \qquad}$$
$$[a + (-a)] + (-(-a)) = 0 + (-(-a)) \qquad \underline{\qquad ? \qquad}$$
$$[a + (-a)] + (-(-a)) = -(-a) \qquad \underline{\qquad ? \qquad}$$
$$a + [-a + (-(-a))] = -(-a) \qquad \underline{\qquad ? \qquad}$$
$$a + 0 = -(-a) \qquad \underline{\qquad ? \qquad}$$
$$a = -(-a) \qquad \underline{\qquad ? \qquad}$$

39. REASONING Copy and complete the proof of this statement: $a(-b) = -(ab)$.

$a(-b) = a \cdot [(-1)b]$		_____?_____
$= $ _____?_____		Associative property
$= [(-1)a]b$		_____?_____
$= (-1)(ab)$		_____?_____
$= $ _____?_____		Multiplicative property of -1

40. CHALLENGE Make a conjecture about the relationship between $a - b$ and $b - a$ where a and b are real numbers. Prove the conjecture.

41. CHALLENGE Prove that $(-a)b = -(ab)$. (*Hint:* See Exercise 39.) Then use this proven statement along with those from Exercises 38 and 39 to prove that $(-a)(-b) = ab$.

◆ CALIFORNIA STANDARDS SPIRAL REVIEW

Gr. 7 AF 1.3

42. Which expression is equivalent to $-3x - 9y$? *(p. 81)*

   A $-3(x - y)$ **B** $-3(x + 3y)$ **C** $3(x - y)$ **D** $3(x + y)$

Alg. 1.0

43. Which set is closed under subtraction? *(p. 67)*

   A Whole numbers   **B** $\{-2, 0, 2\}$

   C Rational numbers   **D** $\{-2, -1, 0, 1, 2\}$

Alg. 2.0

44. The expression $\sqrt{A}$ gives the side length of a square with area A. What is the side length of a square garage floor whose area is 121 square feet? *(p. 95)*

   A 10 ft   **B** 11 ft   **C** 12.1 ft   **D** 60.5 ft

QUIZ *for Lessons 2.6–2.8*

Find the quotient. *(p. 88)*

1. $-20 \div (-5)$ **2.** $-12 \div \dfrac{2}{3}$ **3.** $\dfrac{4}{5} \div \left(-\dfrac{3}{10}\right)$ **4.** $-18.2 \div (-4)$

5. Tell whether the numbers -3, $-\sqrt{5}$, -3.7, and $\sqrt{3}$ belong to each of the following sets: real numbers, rational numbers, irrational numbers, integers, and whole numbers. Then order the numbers from least to greatest. *(p. 95)*

6. Rewrite the following conditional statement in if-then form: "No irrational numbers are negative numbers." Tell whether the statement is *true* or *false*. If it is false, give a counterexample. *(p. 95)*

7. Josh claims that the result of doubling a number is always greater than the number. He supports his claim with the examples at the right. Did Josh use *inductive reasoning* or *deductive reasoning* to make his conjecture? Is his claim correct? If not, give a counterexample. *(p. 102)*

> 10 doubled is 20, and 20 > 10.
>
> 100 doubled is 200, and 200 > 100.
>
> 1.6 doubled is 3.2, and 3.2 > 1.6.

Multiple Choice Practice for Lessons 2.5–2.8

1. The table shows the areas of two square rugs. How many inches longer is the side length of the sorrel rug than the side length of the shaw rug? **Alg. 2.0**

Type of rug	Area (in.²)
Sorrel rug	8281
Shaw rug	7744

Ⓐ 3 in.   Ⓑ 9 in.

Ⓒ 23 in.   Ⓓ 537 in.

2. Which number is between 15 and 18? **Alg. 2.0**

Ⓐ $\sqrt{100}$ Ⓑ $\sqrt{230}$

Ⓒ $\sqrt{400}$ Ⓓ $\sqrt{475}$

3. The signs below show the average cost of three items at a stadium's concession stand in 2004 and 2006. What is the change in the total amount spent from 2004 to 2006 if two of each item are bought? **Gr. 7 NS 2.3**

Souvenirs	
T-SHIRT	$15.00
HAT	$14.00
PENNANT	$4.75

2004

Souvenirs	
T-SHIRT	$11.50
HAT	$14.75
PENNANT	$5.25

2006

Ⓐ −$4.50   Ⓑ −$6.50

Ⓒ −$7.00   Ⓓ −$9.50

4. Which numbers are ordered from least to greatest? **Gr. 7 NS 1.1**

Ⓐ $-2, \frac{3}{4}, 1.7, \sqrt{9}$

Ⓑ $\sqrt{1}, 4.1, -0.6, \sqrt{4}$

Ⓒ $-0.01, \sqrt{4}, 1, \frac{7}{5}$

Ⓓ $\frac{1}{2}, 0.05, \sqrt{1}, 2$

5. The ocean floor adjacent to a certain beach has an elevation of −60 feet at a distance of 0.3 mile from the shore. What is the average rate of change in the elevation of the ocean floor (in feet per mile)? **Gr. 7 NS 2.3**

Ⓐ −18   Ⓑ −20

Ⓒ −180   Ⓓ −200

6. Your friend is comparing cubic gift boxes. What logical conclusion can you draw? **Alg. 24.0**

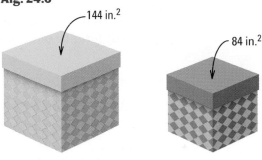

144 in.²   84 in.²

Ⓐ The edge length of the yellow box is 14 inches.

Ⓑ The edge length of the blue box is 5 inches.

Ⓒ The edge length of the yellow box is less than 10 inches.

Ⓓ The edge length of the blue box is greater than 9 inches.

7. Which of the following is an example of deductive reasoning? **Alg. 24.1**

Ⓐ Because 3, 5, 7, and 11 are prime numbers, all prime numbers are odd.

Ⓑ Because $2n + 2 = 2(n + 1)$ and $n + 1$ is an integer when n is an integer, $2n + 2$ is even.

Ⓒ Because $\frac{1}{2}, \frac{1}{3}$, and $\frac{1}{4}$ are not integers, all numbers of the form $\frac{1}{n}$ are not integers when n is a positive integer.

Ⓓ Because the numbers 21, 51, and 81 are all divisible by 3, any whole number that ends in 1 is divisible by 3.

BIG IDEAS
For Your Notebook

Performing Operations with Real Numbers

To add or multiply two real numbers a and b, you can use the following rules:

Expression	Rule when a and b have the same sign	Rule when a and b have different signs
$a + b$	Add $|a|$ and $|b|$. The sum has the same sign as a and b.	Subtract the lesser absolute value from the greater absolute value. The sum has the same sign as the number with the greater absolute value.
ab	The product is positive.	The product is negative.

You can use these rules to subtract or divide numbers, but first you rewrite the difference or quotient using the subtraction rule or the division rule.

Applying Properties of Real Numbers

You can use properties of real numbers to evaluate and simplify expressions.

Property	Addition	Multiplication
Commutative property	$a + b = b + a$	$ab = ba$
Associative property	$(a + b) + c = a + (b + c)$	$(ab)c = a(bc)$
Identity property	$a + 0 = 0 + a = a$	$a \cdot 1 = 1 \cdot a = a$
Inverse property	$a + (-a) = -a + a = 0$	$a \cdot \frac{1}{a} = \frac{1}{a} \cdot a = 1, a \neq 0$
Distributive property	$a(b + c) = ab + ac$ (For variations, see p. 81.)	
Closure property	For all a and b in a set, if $a + b$ is in the set, the set is closed under addition.	For all a and b in a set, if $a \cdot b$ is in the set, the set is closed under multiplication.

Classifying and Reasoning with Real Numbers

Being able to classify numbers can help you tell whether a conditional statement about real numbers is true or false. For example, the following statement is false: "All real numbers are integers." A counterexample is 3.5.

Numbers	Description
Whole numbers	The numbers 0, 1, 2, 3, 4, . . .
Integers	The numbers . . . , $-3, -2, -1, 0, 1, 2, 3, . . .$
Rational numbers	Numbers of the form $\frac{a}{b}$ where a and b are integers and $b \neq 0$
Irrational numbers	Numbers that cannot be written as a quotient of two integers
Real numbers	All rational and irrational numbers

PROBLEM What can you prove about the sum of the deviations from the mean of a set of data?

STEP 1 Collect data.

Talk to at least 10 students who are involved in after-school activities. Record the number of hours each student spends participating in after-school activities in a normal week.

STEP 2 Calculate the mean.

Find the mean of the data collected in Step 1.

STEP 3 Find the deviations from the mean.

Each data value that is not the same as the mean is said to *deviate* from the mean. Make a table like the one below. Write the data values you collected in Step 1 in the first row. Then subtract the mean from each data value and place it in the second row. The values in the second row are called *deviations* from the mean.

EXAMPLE For the sample set of data below, the mean time spent in after-school activities is 4.9 hours per week. The deviations from 4.9 have been calculated.

Time spent at activities (hours per week)	2	6	5	4	8	3.5	5	6	3	6.5
Deviation from the mean	−2.9	1.1	0.1	−0.9	3.1	−1.4	0.1	1.1	−1.9	1.6

STEP 4 Compare positive and negative deviations.

Find the sum of the positive deviations for the data. Then find the sum of the negative deviations for the data. What do you notice about these two sums?

STEP 5 Find a sum of deviations from the mean for unknown data.

Let a and b be two data values. Find the mean of the data. Then find the deviation from the mean of each data value. Finally, find the sum of the deviations. What have you proved?

Extending the Problem

1. Let a set of n data values be represented by $x_1, x_2, x_3, \ldots, x_n$. Let $\overline{x}$ represent the mean of the data. Prove that the sum of the deviations from the mean is 0. *Explain* in general terms what you have proved.

2. How could you use the result of Exercise 1 to check whether you have correctly calculated the mean of a set of data?

REVIEW KEY VOCABULARY

- whole numbers, integers, positive integer, negative integer, *p. 53*
- rational number, *p. 53*
- opposites, absolute value, *p. 55*
- conditional statement, *p. 55*
- if-then statement, *p. 55*
- counterexample, *p. 55*
- additive identity, *p. 62*

- additive inverse, *p. 62*
- multiplicative identity, *p. 75*
- equivalent expressions, *p. 81*
- distributive property, *p. 81*
- term, coefficient, like terms, constant term, *p. 82*
- multiplicative inverse, *p. 88*

- square root, radicand, *p. 95*
- perfect square, *p. 96*
- irrational number, *p. 96*
- real numbers, *p. 97*
- inductive reasoning, *p. 102*
- deductive reasoning, *p. 102*
- conjecture, *p. 102*

VOCABULARY EXERCISES

Identify the terms, coefficients, constant terms, and like terms of the expression.

1. $-3x - 5 - 7x - 9$

2. $-10c - 6 + c$

Tell whether the number belongs to each of the following sets: real numbers, rational numbers, irrational numbers, integers, and whole numbers.

3. 0.3

4. $-\sqrt{8}$

5. -15

6. NOTETAKING SKILLS Make a concept circle like the one on page 52 for multiplying a negative number and a positive number.

REVIEW EXAMPLES AND EXERCISES

Use the review examples and exercises below to check your understanding of the concepts you have learned in each lesson of Chapter 2.

2.1 Use Integers and Rational Numbers

pp. 53–59

EXAMPLE

Order the following numbers from least to greatest: $\frac{1}{5}$, -0.10, 0.25, and $-\frac{1}{6}$.

From least to greatest, the numbers are $-\frac{1}{6}$, -0.10, $\frac{1}{5}$, and 0.25.

Alg. 2.0

EXAMPLE

Find $-a$ and $|a|$ when $a = -3$.

$-a = -(-3) = 3$

$|a| = |-3| = 3$

EXAMPLES
3, 4, and 5
....
on pp. 54–55
for Exs. 7–15

Order the numbers in the list from least to greatest.

7. $-5.2, -\frac{3}{8}, -6, 0.3, -\frac{1}{4}$

8. $2.1, 0, -\frac{13}{10}, -1.38, \frac{3}{5}$

9. $0.66, -0.6, \frac{2}{3}, -\frac{2}{3}, -0.666$

10. $1\frac{5}{7}, -1\frac{5}{7}, -1.57, 1.75, \frac{15}{7}$

For the given value of a, find $-a$ and $|a|$.

11. $a = -0.2$

12. $a = 3$

13. $a = \frac{7}{8}$

14. $a = -\frac{6}{11}$

15. WEATHER The difference between the actual temperature and the normal daily high temperature in a city was 11°F on Monday, −2°F on Tuesday, −13°F on Wednesday, and −8°F on Thursday. On which day was the absolute value of the temperature difference the greatest?

2.2 Add Real Numbers

pp. 60–66

Alg. 1.0

EXAMPLE

Find the sum.

a. $-3.6 + (-5.5) = -(|-3.6| + |-5.5|)$ **Rule of same signs**

$= -(3.6 + 5.5)$ **Take absolute values.**

$= -9.1$ **Add.**

b. $16.1 + (-9.3) = |16.1| - |-9.3|$ **Rule of different signs**

$= 16.1 - 9.3$ **Take absolute values.**

$= 6.8$ **Subtract.**

c. $\frac{1}{3} + \left(-\frac{4}{5}\right) = -\left(\left|-\frac{4}{5}\right| - \left|\frac{1}{3}\right|\right)$ **Rule of different signs**

$= -\left(\frac{4}{5} - \frac{1}{3}\right)$ **Take absolute value.**

$= -\left(\frac{12}{15} - \frac{5}{15}\right)$ **Rewrite with common denominator.**

$= -\frac{7}{15}$ **Subtract.**

EXERCISES

EXAMPLES
1, 2, and 4
....
on pp. 60–63
for Exs. 16–22

Find the sum.

16. $-2 + 5$

17. $-6 + (-4)$

18. $6.2 + (-9.7)$

19. $-4.61 + (-0.79)$

20. $-\frac{4}{7} + \left(-\frac{9}{14}\right)$

21. $-\frac{4}{5} + \frac{11}{12}$

22. BUSINESS A company has a profit of \$2.07 million in its first year, −\$1.54 million in its second year, and −\$.76 million in its third year. Find the company's total profit for the three years.

2.3 Subtract Real Numbers

pp. 67–71

Alg. 1.0   **EXAMPLE**

Find the difference.

a. $12 - 19 = 12 + (-19)$ **Add the opposite of 19.**

$ = -7$ **Simplify.**

b. $8.2 - (-1.6) = 8.2 + 1.6$ **Add the opposite of –1.6.**

$ = 9.8$ **Simplify.**

EXERCISES

EXAMPLES
1 and 2
on p. 67
for Exs. 23–31

Find the difference.

23. $-8 - 3$

24. $1 - 11$

25. $7.7 - 16.3$

26. $-20.3 - (-14.2)$

27. $\dfrac{7}{3} - \dfrac{11}{3}$

28. $-\dfrac{4}{9} - \dfrac{5}{12}$

Evaluate the expression when $x = 2$ and $y = -3$.

29. $(x - 7) + y$

30. $\dfrac{3}{2} - x - y$

31. $y - (2.4 - x)$

2.4 Multiply Real Numbers

pp. 74–79

Alg. 1.0   **EXAMPLE**

Find the product.

a. $-4(12) = -48$ **Different signs; product is negative.**

b. $\dfrac{1}{2}(-3)(-6) = \dfrac{1}{2}[(-3)(-6)]$ **Associative property**

$\phantom{\dfrac{1}{2}(-3)(-6)} = \dfrac{1}{2}(18)$ **Same signs; product is positive.**

$\phantom{\dfrac{1}{2}(-3)(-6)} = 9$ **Multiply $\dfrac{1}{2}$ and 18.**

EXERCISES

EXAMPLES
1, 3, and 4
on pp. 74–76
for Exs. 32–38

Find the product.

32. $15(-4)$

33. $-7.5(-8)$

34. $-\dfrac{2}{5}(-5)(-9)$

Find the product. *Justify* **your steps.**

35. $-4(-y)(-7)$

36. $-\dfrac{1}{3}x \cdot (-18)$

37. $2.5(-4z)(-2)$

38. SWIMMING POOLS The water level of a swimming pool is 3.3 feet and changes at an average rate of −0.14 feet per day due to water evaporation. What will the water level of the pool be after 4 days?

2.5 Apply the Distributive Property

pp. 81–86

Alg. 1.0

EXAMPLE

Use the distributive property to write an equivalent expression.

a. $5(x + 3) = 5(x) + 5(3)$ **Distribute 5.**

            $= 5x + 15$ **Simplify.**

b. $(7 - y)(-2y) = 7(-2y) - y(-2y)$ **Distribute −2y.**

            $= -14y + 2y^2$ **Simplify.**

EXERCISES

EXAMPLES
1, 2, 4, and 5
on pp. 81–83
for Exs. 39–45

Use the distributive property to write an equivalent expression.

39. $8(5 - x)$ **40.** $-3(y + 9)$ **41.** $(z - 4)(-z)$

Simplify the expression.

42. $3(x - 2) + 14$ **43.** $9.1 - 4(m + 3.2)$ **44.** $5n + \frac{1}{2}(8n - 7)$

45. PARTY COSTS You are buying 10 pizzas for a party. Cheese pizzas cost $11 each, and single topping pizzas cost $13 each. Write an equation that gives the total cost C (in dollars) in terms of the number p of cheese pizzas that you buy. Then find the total cost if you buy 4 cheese pizzas.

2.6 Divide Real Numbers

pp. 88–93

Alg. 1.0

EXAMPLE

Find the quotient.

a. $196 \div (-7) = 196 \cdot \left(-\frac{1}{7}\right)$ **b.** $-\frac{14}{15} \div \left(-\frac{7}{3}\right) = -\frac{14}{15} \cdot \left(-\frac{3}{7}\right)$

                $= -28$ $= \frac{2}{5}$

EXERCISES

EXAMPLES
2, 3, and 4
on pp. 89–90
for Exs. 46–52

Find the quotient.

46. $56 \div (-4)$ **47.** $-6 \div \frac{3}{13}$ **48.** $-\frac{4}{9} \div \left(-\frac{2}{3}\right)$

49. SCIENCE A scientist studies the diving abilities of 3 seals and records the elevations they reach before swimming back up to the surface. Find the mean of the following elevations (in meters) recorded: −380, −307, −354.

Simplify the expression.

50. $\frac{24x - 40}{8}$ **51.** $\frac{-36m + 18}{6}$ **52.** $\frac{-18n - 9}{-9}$

2.7 Find Square Roots and Compare Real Numbers

pp. 95–101

Alg. 2.0

EXAMPLE

Order the following numbers from least to greatest: $\sqrt{25}$, $-\sqrt{18}$, -4, 3.2.

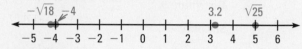

From least to greatest, the numbers are $-\sqrt{18}$, -4, 3.2, and $\sqrt{25}$.

EXERCISES

EXAMPLES
1, 2, 4, and 5
on pp. 95–98
for Exs. 53–63

Evaluate the expression.

53. $\sqrt{121}$ **54.** $-\sqrt{36}$ **55.** $\pm\sqrt{81}$ **56.** $\pm\sqrt{225}$

Approximate the square root to the nearest integer.

57. $\sqrt{97}$ **58.** $-\sqrt{48}$ **59.** $-\sqrt{142}$ **60.** $\sqrt{300}$

Order the numbers in the list from least to greatest.

61. $-\sqrt{49}$, -6.8, 2, $\sqrt{3}$, 1.58 **62.** 1.25, $\sqrt{11}$, -0.3, 0, $-\sqrt{4}$

63. Rewrite the following conditional statement in if-then form: "All real numbers are irrational numbers." Tell whether the statement is *true* or *false*. If it is false, give a counterexample.

2.8 Properties of Real Numbers and Logical Reasoning

pp. 102–108

Alg. 24.1

EXAMPLE

Determine whether inductive reasoning or deductive reasoning is used.

a. During the week, you notice that the mail is delivered on your street between 12:30 P.M. and 1:30 P.M. You conclude through *inductive* reasoning that if today is a weekday, your mail will be delivered between 12:30 P.M. and 1:30 P.M.

b. Your fish tank is a rectangular prism with a square base. The height of the tank is 12 inches, and the length of a side of the base is 8 inches. You conclude through *deductive* reasoning that the volume of the tank is equal to the square of the base length times the height, or 768 cubic inches.

EXERCISES

EXAMPLE 1
on p. 102
for Exs. 64–65

Determine whether inductive or deductive reasoning is used.

64. Last week, you saw your neighbor walk his dog at 6:30 A.M. each day. You conclude that your neighbor will walk his dog at 6:30 A.M. today.

65. One side of a square garden is 12 feet. You conclude that the perimeter of the garden is 48 feet.

VOCABULARY Match the statement with the property that it illustrates.

1. $-1 \cdot 8 = -8$
2. $3(-2) = (-2)3$
3. If $5 \cdot x = 15$, then $15 = 5 \cdot x$.
4. $0 \cdot 6 = 0$

    A. Symmetric property of equality
    B. Commutative property of multiplication
    C. Multiplicative property of zero
    D. Multiplicative property of -1

Tell whether the number belongs to each of the following sets: real numbers, rational numbers, irrational numbers, integers, and whole numbers.

5. $-\dfrac{1}{4}$
6. $\sqrt{90}$
7. $-\sqrt{144}$
8. 8.95

Order the numbers in the list from least to greatest.

9. $-\dfrac{5}{3}, -2, 3, \dfrac{1}{2}, -1.07$

10. $\sqrt{15}, -4.3, 4.2, 0, -\sqrt{25}$

Find the sum, difference, product, or quotient.

11. $1.3 + (-10.4)$

12. $-\dfrac{1}{3} + \dfrac{1}{6}$

13. $-\dfrac{2}{7} - \dfrac{5}{14}$

14. $7.2 - (-11.6)$

15. $-11(-7)$

16. $-\dfrac{1}{5}(-20)(-5)$

17. $-\dfrac{3}{5} \div 12$

18. $5 \div \left(-\dfrac{10}{11}\right)$

Simplify the expression.

19. $-9(y - 7)$

20. $8(x - 4) - 10x$

21. $\dfrac{-7w - 21}{7}$

22. $\dfrac{-16v + 8}{-4}$

Rewrite the conditional statement in if-then form. Then tell whether the statement is *true* or *false*. If it is false, give a counterexample.

23. No rational numbers are integers.

24. All irrational numbers are real numbers.

Determine whether the statement is *sometimes*, *always*, or *never* true.

25. If the last digit of an integer is even, then the integer is divisible by 2.

26. The opposite of an integer is negative.

27. **MUSIC** The revenue from sales of digital pianos in the United States was $152.4 million in 2001 and $149.0 million in 2002. Find the change in revenue from 2001 to 2002.

28. **ELEVATORS** An elevator moves at a rate of -5.8 feet per second from a height of 300 feet above the ground. The elevator takes 3 seconds to make its first stop. How many feet above the ground is the elevator now?

29. **TEMPERATURES** The low temperatures for Montreal, Quebec, in Canada on February 12 for each year during the period 2000–2004 are $-6.7°F$, $-4.2°F$, $4.1°F$, $-3.6°F$, and $0.3°F$. Find the mean of the temperatures.

MULTIPLE CHOICE STRATEGIES

STRATEGIES YOU'LL USE:
- SOLVE DIRECTLY
- ELIMINATE CHOICES

Standards
Alg. 1.0

If you have trouble solving a multiple choice problem directly, you may be able to use another approach to eliminate incorrect answer choices and obtain the correct answer.

PROBLEM 1

The *Alvin* is an HOV (human-operated vehicle) used to explore the ocean. The table shows the capabilities of the vehicle.

Vehicle	Lowest elevation (m)	Velocity (m/sec)
Alvin	−4500	−30

The vehicle begins a dive from the surface of the ocean. What is its elevation after 90 seconds?

(A) −27,000 m   **(B)** −2700 m   **(C)** 150 m   **(D)** 2700 m

Strategy 1   SOLVE DIRECTLY

STEP 1 **Write** a verbal model.

$$\text{Elevation (m)} = \text{Velocity (m/sec)} \cdot \text{Time (sec)}$$

STEP 2 **Calculate** the elevation after 90 seconds.

Elevation $= -30 \cdot 90$ **Substitute.**

$ = -2700$ **Multiply.**

The elevation of the vehicle after 90 seconds is −2700 meters.

The correct answer is B. **(A) (B) (C) (D)**

Strategy 2   ELIMINATE CHOICES

In some cases, you can identify answers that are unreasonable given the information in the problem.

STEP 1 **Compare** choices with limitations stated in the problem.

The table shows that the lowest possible elevation for the vehicle is −4500 meters. Because −27,000 meters is a lower elevation, the choice is unreasonable. You can eliminate choice A.

STEP 2 **Determine** whether the answer is a positive number or a negative number.

The vehicle starts from the surface of the ocean where the elevation is 0 feet. The elevation changes by −30 feet each second because the vehicle is descending. So, the elevation after 90 seconds is a negative number. You can eliminate choices C and D.

The correct answer is B. **(A) (B) (C) (D)**

PROBLEM 2

Which statement illustrates the associative property of multiplication?

(A) $(5 - 3) + 7 = 7 + (5 - 3)$ **(B)** $(8 + 9) + 10 = 8 + (9 + 10)$

(C) $4 \cdot (-4) = -4 \cdot 4$ **(D)** $(11 \cdot 4) \cdot 7 = 11 \cdot (4 \cdot 7)$

Strategy 1   SOLVE DIRECTLY

The associative property of multiplication states that the way you group three numbers in a product does not change the product.

The algebraic representation of this property is shown below.

$$(a \cdot b) \cdot c = a \cdot (b \cdot c)$$

You can see that choice D has this form.

The correct answer is D. **(A)** **(B)** **(C)** **(D)**

Strategy 2   ELIMINATE CHOICES

In some cases, you can identify answers that are not related to vocabulary in the problem.

STEP 1 **Look** for products.

You can eliminate choices A and B because they do not involve multiplication.

STEP 2 **Consider** the meaning of *associative*.

The root of *associative* is *associate*, which suggests a grouping of numbers. You can eliminate choice C because it does not involve grouping numbers.

The correct answer is D. **(A)** **(B)** **(C)** **(D)**

STRATEGY PRACTICE

Explain why you can eliminate the highlighted answer choice.

1. The table shows the change in the balance of your bank account after withdrawals from automated teller machines (ATMs). Banks other than your own charge a $1.50 service fee for each withdrawal. You have $230 in your bank account. You make 8 withdrawals of $20 each, and 3 of the withdrawals are made from your bank's ATM. How much money is left in your account?

Change in Balance after x Withdrawals of $20	
Your bank's ATM	**Another bank's ATM**
$-20x$	$-21.50x$

(A) ✗ $-\$167.50$ **(B)** $-\$161.50$ **(C)** $\$62.50$ **(D)** $\$68.50$

2. Which *best* describes the terms $3x$ and $2x$ in the expression $2x + 1 + 3x$?

(A) Coefficients   **(B)** ✗ Variables   **(C)** Like terms   **(D)** Constant terms

3. Which number is irrational?

(A) $2\sqrt{9}$ **(B)** $\frac{1}{7}$ **(C)** $\sqrt{21}$ **(D)** ✗ 7.236

1. What is the hypothesis of the statement "If x is a real number, then x is also a rational number"? **Alg. 24.2**

   Ⓐ x is a real number

   Ⓑ x is a rational number

   Ⓒ x is a whole number

   Ⓓ x is not an irrational number

2. A farmer is planting corn and soybeans in the rectangular field shown. The farmer spends $.09 per square yard to plant corn and $.07 per square yard to plant soybeans. Which expression represents the total cost (in dollars) of planting corn and soybeans if the corn section has a length of x yards? **Alg. 1.0**

   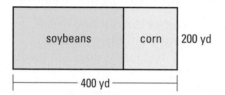

   soybeans   corn   200 yd

   ├── 400 yd ──┤

   Ⓐ $0.07[200(400 - x)] + 0.09(200x)$

   Ⓑ $0.09[400(200 + x)] + 0.07(600x)$

   Ⓒ $0.07[300(400 - x)] + 0.09(400x)$

   Ⓓ $0.09[600(300 + x)] + 0.07(200x)$

3. The modern pentathlon consists of 5 events, including a distance run. For the men's run, each athlete starts with 1000 points. The final score is determined by the amount of time an athlete finishes above or below 10 minutes. An athlete finishes the run in 10 minutes 34 seconds. Based on the table, what is his final score? **Gr. 7 NS 2.3**

Each 0.5 second over 10 minutes	Each 0.5 second under 10 minutes
−2 points	2 points

   Ⓐ 864 points

   Ⓑ 932 points

   Ⓒ 1068 points

   Ⓓ 1136 points

4. A cooler in the shape of a rectangular prism has a volume of 8100 cubic inches. The sides of the cooler with handles are squares. Which of the following is the side length of the square end? **Alg. 2.0**

   Ⓐ 18 in.

   Ⓑ 19 in.

   Ⓒ 20 in.

   Ⓓ 25 in.

   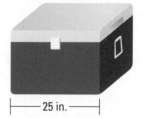

   ├── 25 in. ──┤

5. Which properties justify the steps in the proof shown below of the statement $2 + (-3 + 4) = -3 + (4 + 2)$? **Alg. 25.0**

   Step 1: $2 + (-3 + 4) = (-3 + 4) + 2$
   Step 2: $\qquad\qquad = -3 + (4 + 2)$

   Ⓐ Step 1: Associative property
   Step 2: Commutative property

   Ⓑ Step 1: Commutative property
   Step 2: Associative property

   Ⓒ Step 1: Associative property
   Step 2: Distributive property

   Ⓓ Step 1: Distributive property
   Step 2: Commutative property

6. A store's revenue and expenses for the months of May and June are shown in the table. What is the change in profit (profit = revenue − expenses) from May to June? **Gr. 7 NS 2.3**

Month	Revenue	Expenses
May	$22,556	$17,491
June	$24,950	$19,418

   Ⓐ −$532

   Ⓑ −$467

   Ⓒ $467

   Ⓓ $532

7. The table shows the lowest temperatures on record for several states in the United States. Which states in the table serve as counterexamples to the statement "No state in the United States has a record low as cold as or colder than −37°F"? **Alg. 25.1**

State	Temperature
Alaska	−80°F
Arkansas	−29°F
California	−45°F
Hawaii	12°F
Kentucky	−37°F

(A) Alaska and Arkansas

(B) Arkansas and Hawaii

(C) Alaska, California, and Kentucky

(D) Arkansas, California, and Kentucky

8. Which set is closed under division? **Alg. 1.0**

(A) $\{-1, 1\}$

(B) $\left\{\frac{1}{2}, 1, 2\right\}$

(C) The set of whole numbers

(D) The set of positive integers

9. The table lists the most recent transactions (in dollars) for a checking account that had a balance of $10.49 on January 1. Which statement is true? **Alg. 1.1**

Date	Details	Amount
Jan 4	Deposit	+61.25
Jan 15	ATM Withdrawal/Fee	−41.25
Jan 18	New checks	−15.00

(A) The current balance is negative.

(B) The beginning balance is greater than the current balance.

(C) The sum of the absolute values of the three transactions is over $100.

(D) The change in the balance due to the last three transactions is $35.

10. The table shows the change in the surface height (in centimeters) for a certain lake for each of five weeks. What is the mean weekly change in the lake's height? **Gr. 7 NS 2.3**

Week	Height change
1	−3 cm
2	−1 cm
3	−2 cm
4	0 cm
5	1 cm

(A) −5 cm

(B) −1 cm

(C) 0 cm

(D) 1 cm

11. Consider the statement "The absolute value of a number is greater than the original number." Which of the following is a counterexample to the statement? **Alg. 24.3**

(A) −3

(B) −2

(C) −1

(D) 4

12. Which of the following correctly completes the statement "If x^2 is a perfect square, then   ? "? **Alg. 25.3**

(A) x is sometimes an irrational number

(B) x is never a rational number

(C) x is always a whole number

(D) x is sometimes a negative integer

13. Which property of equality is illustrated by the statement "If $2x + 1 = 7$ and $7 = 5x - 8$, then $2x + 1 = 5x - 8$"? **Alg. 25.2**

(A) Addition property

(B) Reflexive property

(C) Symmetric property

(D) Transitive property

3 Solving Equations

Get-Ready Games

Name that Planet

California Standards

Review solving equations with mental math. **Gr. 6 AF 1.1**
Prepare for solving equations algebraically. **Alg. 4.0**

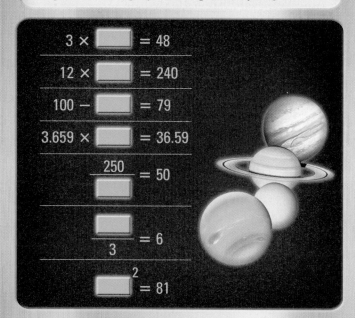

$$3 \times \boxed{} = 48$$

$$12 \times \boxed{} = 240$$

$$100 - \boxed{} = 79$$

$$3.659 \times \boxed{} = 36.59$$

$$\frac{250}{\boxed{}} = 50$$

$$\frac{\boxed{}}{3} = 6$$

$$\boxed{}^{2} = 81$$

How to Play

Find the name of a planet.

- Use mental math to find the missing number in each equation.
- For each answer, find the corresponding letter in the alphabet (1 = A, 2 = B, 3 = C, and so on).
- Rearrange the letters to find the name of a planet.

122

CALIFORNIA STANDARDS

- **Alg. 4.0** Students simplify expressions before solving linear equations and inequalities **in one variable, such as** $3(2x - 5) + 4(x - 2) = 12.$ *(Lesson 3.3)*

- **Alg. 5.0** Students solve multistep problems, including word problems, involving linear equations and linear inequalities **in one variable and provide justification for each step.** *(Lesson 3.4)*

Planet Pinball

California Standards

Review operations with rational numbers. *Gr. 7 NS 1.2*

Prepare for solving equations. *Alg. 4.0*

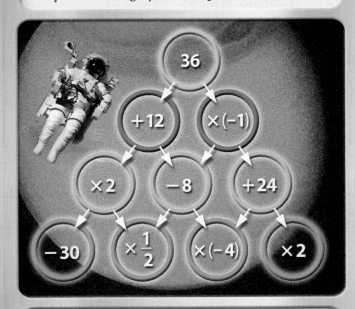

How to Play

Two players each begin at the top planet with a score of 36 points.

- On each turn, toss a coin. If you get heads, move down and to the left. If you get tails, move down and to the right.
- Perform the operation to find your new score.
- When both players reach the bottom row, the player with the greater score wins.

Games Wrap-Up

Draw Conclusions

Complete these exercises after playing the games.

1. **WRITING** Without tossing a coin, find the route through the planets in *Planet Pinball* that gives the greatest possible score. *Explain* your reasoning.

2. **REASONING** Choose a planet name other than the one used in *Name that Planet*. Write a puzzle like *Name that Planet* with your planet name as the solution.

Prerequisite Skills

California @HomeTutor

Prerequisite skills practice at classzone.com

REVIEW VOCABULARY

- **formula,** *p. 34*
- **distributive property,** *p. 81*
- **like terms,** *p. 82*
- **simplest form,** *p. 786*
- **reciprocal,** *p. 789*

VOCABULARY CHECK

Copy and complete the statement.

1. In the expression $3x + 7 + 7x$, ___?___ and ___?___ are like terms.

2. The reciprocal of $\frac{5}{8}$ is ___?___.

SKILLS CHECK

Perform the indicated operation. *(Review pp. 788–789 for 3.1–3.4.)*

3. $\frac{3}{4} + \frac{1}{6}$

4. $\frac{7}{8} - \frac{3}{5}$

5. $\frac{2}{9} \times \frac{7}{10}$

6. $15 \div \frac{1}{3}$

Simplify the expression. *(Review p. 81 for 3.2–3.6.)*

7. $5x - (6 - x)$

8. $3(x - 9) - 16$

9. $23 + 4(x + 2)$

10. $x(7 + x) + 9x^2$

Find the perimeter of the rectangle. *(Review p. 796 for 3.7.)*

11. 7 ft, 16 ft

12. 14 cm, 20 cm

13. 4 in., 11 in.

Notetaking Skills

NOW YOU TRY

Make an *information frame* for the identity property of addition. You may want to use colored pencils.

Focus on Graphic Organizers

You can use an *information frame* to organize information about a mathematical property, such as the commutative property of addition.

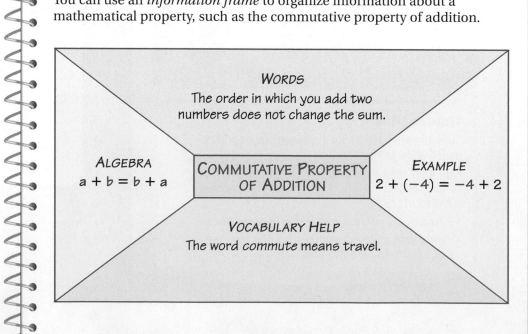

WORDS
The order in which you add two numbers does not change the sum.

ALGEBRA
$a + b = b + a$

COMMUTATIVE PROPERTY OF ADDITION

EXAMPLE
$2 + (-4) = -4 + 2$

VOCABULARY HELP
The word *commute* means travel.

3.1 Solve One-Step Equations

Math and TRANSPORTATION
Ex. 72, p. 130

Standards Preparation

Gr. 6 AF 1.1 Write and solve one-step linear equations in one variable.

Connect

Before you solved equations using mental math.
Now you will solve one-step equations using algebra to prepare for Algebra 1 Standard 5.0.

Key Vocabulary
• inverse operations
• equivalent equations
• reciprocal, *p. 789*

Inverse operations are two operations that undo each other, such as addition and subtraction. When you perform the same inverse operation on each side of an equation, you produce an *equivalent equation*. **Equivalent equations** have the same solution.

> **READING**
> The addition property of equality stated here is another form of the property stated in Lesson 2.8.

KEY CONCEPT   *For Your Notebook*

Addition Property of Equality

Words Adding the same number to each side of an equation produces an equivalent equation.

Algebra If $x - a = b$, then $x - a + a = b + a$, or $x = b + a$.

Subtraction Property of Equality

Words Subtracting the same number from each side of an equation produces an equivalent equation.

Algebra If $x + a = b$, then $x + a - a = b - a$, or $x = b - a$.

EXAMPLE 1   Solve an equation using subtraction

> **USE HORIZONTAL FORMAT**
> Both horizontal and vertical formats are correct. In the rest of the book, however, equations will be solved using the horizontal format.

Solve $x + 7 = 4$.

Horizontal format   **Vertical format**

	Horizontal		Vertical
Write original equation.	$x + 7 = 4$		$x + 7 = 4$
Use subtraction property: Subtract 7 from each side.	$x + 7 - 7 = 4 - 7$		$-7 \quad -7$
Simplify.	$x = -3$		$x = -3$

✔ **GUIDED PRACTICE**   for Example 1

   1. Solve $x + 5 = 3$. Check your solution.

EXAMPLE 2 **Solve an equation using addition**

Solve $x - 12 = 3$.

$$x - 12 = 3$$ Write original equation.

$$x - 12 + 12 = 3 + 12$$ Use addition property: Add 12 to each side.

$$x = 15$$ Simplify.

CHECK You can check the solution by substituting 15 for x in the original equation.

MULTIPLICATION AND DIVISION EQUATIONS Multiplication and division are inverse operations. So, the multiplication property of equality can be used to solve equations involving division, and the division property of equality can be used to solve equations involving multiplication.

KEY CONCEPT   *For Your Notebook*

Multiplication Property of Equality

Words Multiplying each side of an equation by the same nonzero number produces an equivalent equation.

Algebra If $\frac{x}{a} = b$ and $a \neq 0$, then $a \cdot \frac{x}{a} = a \cdot b$, or $x = ab$.

Division Property of Equality

Words Dividing each side of an equation by the same nonzero number produces an equivalent equation.

Algebra If $ax = b$ and $a \neq 0$, then $\frac{ax}{a} = \frac{b}{a}$, or $x = \frac{b}{a}$.

EXAMPLE 3 **Solve an equation using division**

Solve $-6x = 48$.

$$-6x = 48$$ Write original equation.

$$\frac{-6x}{-6} = \frac{48}{-6}$$ Use division property: Divide each side by -6.

$$x = -8$$ Simplify.

✓ **GUIDED PRACTICE**   for Examples 2 and 3

Solve the equation. Check your solution.

2. $x - 8 = 5$

3. $a - 4 = -17$

4. $6 = t - 2$

5. $4x = 48$

6. $-65 = -5y$

7. $6w = -54$

EXAMPLE 4 ◆ Multiple Choice Practice

What value of x makes the equation $x \div 4 = 5$ true?

  (A) 1   (B) 1.25   (C) 9   (D) 20

Solution

$x \div 4 = 5$ Write original equation.

$\dfrac{x}{4} = 5$ Rewrite equation.

$4 \cdot \dfrac{x}{4} = 4 \cdot 5$ Use multiplication property: Multiply each side by 4.

$x = 20$ Simplify.

▶ The correct answer is D. (A) (B) (C) (D)

✓ **GUIDED PRACTICE**   for Example 4

Solve the equation. Check your solution.

8. $\dfrac{t}{-3} = 9$ **9.** $6 = \dfrac{c}{7}$ **10.** $13 = \dfrac{z}{-2}$ **11.** $\dfrac{a}{5} = -10$

USING RECIPROCALS Recall that the product of a number and its reciprocal is 1. You can isolate a variable with a fractional coefficient by multiplying each side of the equation by the reciprocal of the fraction.

EXAMPLE 5   **Solve an equation by multiplying by a reciprocal**

Solve $-\dfrac{2}{7}x = 4$.

REVIEW RECIPROCALS
For help with finding reciprocals, see p. 789.

Solution

The coefficient of x is $-\dfrac{2}{7}$. The reciprocal of $-\dfrac{2}{7}$ is $-\dfrac{7}{2}$.

$-\dfrac{2}{7}x = 4$ Write original equation.

$-\dfrac{7}{2}\left(-\dfrac{2}{7}x\right) = -\dfrac{7}{2}(4)$ Multiply each side by $-\dfrac{7}{2}$, the reciprocal of $-\dfrac{2}{7}$.

$x = -14$ Simplify.

✓ **GUIDED PRACTICE**   for Example 5

Solve the equation. Check your solution.

12. $\dfrac{5}{6}w = 10$ **13.** $\dfrac{2}{3}p = 14$ **14.** $12 = -\dfrac{3}{4}m$ **15.** $-8 = -\dfrac{4}{5}v$

EXAMPLE 6 **Write and solve an equation**

OLYMPICS In the 2004 Olympics, Shawn Crawford won the 200 meter dash. His winning time was 19.79 seconds. Find his average speed to the nearest tenth of a meter per second.

Solution

Let r represent Crawford's average speed in meters per second. Write a verbal model. Then write and solve an equation.

Shawn Crawford

Distance (meters)	=	Rate (meters/second)	·	Time (seconds)
200	=	r	·	19.79

$$\frac{200}{19.79} = \frac{19.79r}{19.79}$$ **Divide each side by 19.79.**

$$10.1 \approx r$$ **Use a calculator.**

▸ Crawford's average speed was about 10.1 meters per second.

✓ **GUIDED PRACTICE** for Example 6

16. WHAT IF? In Example 6, suppose Shawn Crawford ran 100 meters at the same average speed he ran the 200 meters. How long would it take him to run 100 meters? Round your answer to the nearest tenth of a second.

3.1 EXERCISES

HOMEWORK KEY

◆ = **MULTIPLE CHOICE PRACTICE**
Exs. 19, 20, 62, 71, and 81–83

○ = **HINTS AND HOMEWORK HELP**
for Exs. 15, 57, and 71 at classzone.com

SKILLS · PROBLEM SOLVING · REASONING

1. VOCABULARY Copy and complete: Two operations that undo each other are called __?__.

2. NOTETAKING SKILLS Make an information frame like the one on page 124 for the addition property of equality.

EXAMPLES 1 and 2
on pp. 125–126
for Exs. 3–20

SOLVING ADDITION AND SUBTRACTION EQUATIONS Solve the equation. **Check your solution.**

3. $x + 5 = 8$ **4.** $m + 9 = 2$ **5.** $11 = f + 6$ **6.** $13 = 7 + z$

7. $6 = 9 + h$ **8.** $-3 = 5 + a$ **9.** $-7 = 13 + c$ **10.** $-4 = 8 + d$

11. $y - 4 = 3$ **12.** $t - 5 = 7$ **13.** $1 = h - 10$ **14.** $14 = k - 3$

15. $6 = w - 7$ **16.** $-2 = n - 6$ **17.** $-11 = b - 9$ **18.** $-21 = j - 8$

19. ◆ **MULTIPLE CHOICE** What is the solution of $-8 = d - 13$?

    Ⓐ -21 Ⓑ -5 Ⓒ 5 Ⓓ 21

20. ◆ **MULTIPLE CHOICE** What is the solution of $22 + v = -65$?

    Ⓐ -87 Ⓑ -43 Ⓒ 43 Ⓓ 87

EXAMPLES
3 and 4
on pp. 126–127
for Exs. 21–40

SOLVING MULTIPLICATION AND DIVISION EQUATIONS Solve the equation. Check your solution.

21. $5g = 20$ **22.** $9k = 72$ **23.** $48 = 8c$

24. $-18 = 3a$ **25.** $-4q = 52$ **26.** $33 = -11b$

27. $15 = -h$ **28.** $-96 = 8j$ **29.** $187 = -17r$

30. $\dfrac{y}{3} = 5$ **31.** $\dfrac{m}{2} = 14$ **32.** $8 = \dfrac{x}{6}$

33. $\dfrac{n}{13} = 7$ **34.** $76 = \dfrac{p}{4}$ **35.** $-81 = \dfrac{f}{6}$

36. $7 = \dfrac{t}{-7}$ **37.** $-11 = \dfrac{z}{-2}$ **38.** $-3 = \dfrac{d}{14}$

ERROR ANALYSIS *Describe* and correct the error in solving the equation.

39.

$$x + 3.8 = 2.3$$
$$x + 3.8 - 3.8 = 2.3 + 3.8$$
$$x = 6.1$$

40.

$$\frac{x}{3} = 27$$
$$3 \cdot \frac{x}{3} = \frac{27}{3}$$
$$x = 9$$

SOLVING EQUATIONS Solve the equation. Check your solution.

41. $b - 0.4 = 3.1$ **42.** $-3.2 + z = -7.4$ **43.** $-5.7 = w - 4.6$

44. $-6.1 = p + 2.2$ **45.** $8.2 = -4g$ **46.** $-3.3a = 19.8$

47. $\dfrac{3}{4} = \dfrac{1}{8} + v$ **48.** $\dfrac{n}{4.6} = -2.5$ **49.** $-0.12 = \dfrac{y}{-0.5}$

EXAMPLE 5
on p. 127
for Exs. 50–62

50. $\dfrac{1}{2}m = 21$ **51.** $\dfrac{1}{3}c = 32$ **52.** $-7 = \dfrac{1}{5}x$

53. $\dfrac{3}{2}k = 18$ **54.** $-21 = -\dfrac{3}{5}t$ **55.** $-\dfrac{2}{7}v = 14$

56. $\dfrac{5}{4}d = -15$ **㊗57.** $-\dfrac{7}{13}f = 35$ **58.** $-\dfrac{11}{8}h = -132$

59. $\dfrac{8}{5}x = \dfrac{4}{15}$ **60.** $\dfrac{1}{3}y = \dfrac{1}{5}$ **61.** $-\dfrac{4}{3} = \dfrac{2}{3}z$

62. ◆ **MULTIPLE CHOICE** What is the solution of $\dfrac{4}{5}x = -\dfrac{2}{3}$?

    Ⓐ $-\dfrac{6}{5}$ Ⓑ $-\dfrac{5}{6}$ Ⓒ $-\dfrac{8}{15}$ Ⓓ $\dfrac{5}{6}$

63. **REASONING** *Explain* how you can solve the equation $x + 9 = 14$ using the addition property of equality rather than the subtraction property of equality.

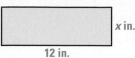 **GEOMETRY** Find the value of *x* for the rectangle or triangle.

64. Area = 54 in.²

x in.

12 in.

65. Area = 72 cm²

x cm

16 cm

CONNECT SKILLS TO PROBLEM SOLVING Exercises 66–68 will help you prepare for problem solving.

Write an equation that represents the situation.

66. The total distance you biked one day, 5 miles, is the product of the rate *r* you biked and the number of minutes, 25, you biked at this rate.

67. As part of a group of 5 people who are sharing the cost *C* of a meal equally, you pay $6.

68. Your total savings this week, $200, is the sum of your savings this week, $20, and the amount *a* you had saved prior to this week.

EXAMPLE 6
on p. 128
for Exs. 69–72

69. **THE DEAD SEA** For the period 1999–2004, the maximum depth of the Dead Sea decreased by 9.9 feet. The maximum depth in 2004 was 1036.7 feet. What was the maximum depth in 1999?

California @*Home*Tutor for problem solving help at classzone.com

70. **CRAFTS** You purchase a stick of clay to make disks for earrings. The stick is 50 millimeters long. How thick should you make each disk so that you will have 20 disks of uniform thickness?

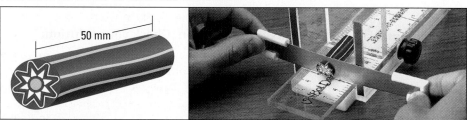

50 mm

California @*Home*Tutor for problem solving help at classzone.com

71. ◆ **MULTIPLE CHOICE** A rectangular trampoline has an area of 187 square feet. The length of the trampoline is 17 feet. Which equation can be used to find the width *w*?

(A) $\frac{w}{17} = 187$ **(B)** $17w = 187$ **(C)** $187w = 17$ **(D)** $w + 17 = 187$

72. **WHEELCHAIRS** The van used to transport patients to and from a treatment center is equipped with a wheelchair lift. The maximum lifting capacity for the lift is 300 pounds. The wheelchairs used by the facility weigh 55 pounds each. What is the maximum weight of a wheelchair occupant who can use the lift?

73. **OPEN-ENDED** *Describe* a real-world situation that can be modeled by the equation $15x = 135$. Solve the equation and explain what the solution means in this situation.

74. JELLYFISH A box jellyfish can travel at a rate of 6.5 feet per second.

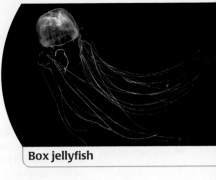

Box jellyfish

   a. Making a Table Make a table that shows the distance d the jellyfish can travel after 1, 2, 3, 4, and 5 seconds.

   b. Using a Table Use the table to determine how long it takes the jellyfish to travel 26 feet.

   c. Writing an Equation Write and solve an equation to find the time it takes the jellyfish to travel 26 feet.

   Animated Algebra at classzone.com

75. SHORT RESPONSE In Everglades National Park in Florida, there are 200 species of birds that migrate. This accounts for $\frac{4}{7}$ of all the species of birds sighted in the park. Write and solve an equation to find the number of species of birds that have been sighted in the park.

76. MULTI-STEP PROBLEM Tatami mats are a floor covering used in Japan. Tatami mats are equal in size, unless they are cut in half. The floor shown has an area of 81 square feet and is covered with 4.5 tatami mats.

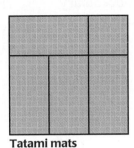

Tatami mats

   a. What is the area of one tatami mat?

   b. What is the length of one tatami mat if it has a width of 3 feet?

77. AMERICAN FLAGS An American flag has a length that is 1.9 times its width. What is the area of a flag that has a length of 9.5 feet?

CHALLENGE Find the value of b using the given information.

78. $4a = 6$ and $b = a - 2$ **79.** $a - 6.7 = 3.1$ and $b = 5a$

80. CHALLENGE At a farm where you can pick your own strawberries, the cost of picked strawberries is calculated using only the weight of the strawberries. The total weight of a container full of strawberries is 2.1 pounds. The cost of the strawberries is $4.68. The weight of the container is 0.3 pound. What is the cost per pound for strawberries?

◆ CALIFORNIA STANDARDS SPIRAL REVIEW

Gr. 7 NS 1.4

81. Which number is irrational? *(p. 95)*

   (A) $-\frac{2}{3}$ (B) 1   (C) $\sqrt{10}$ (D) $\sqrt{16}$

Alg. 2.0

82. What is the value of $\sqrt{196}$? *(p. 95)*

   (A) 12   (B) 14   (C) 16   (D) 19.6

Gr. 6 NS 2.3

83. At midday, the temperature was −2°F. The temperature dropped 9°F by midnight. What was the temperature at midnight? *(p. 67)*

   (A) −11°F   (B) −9°F   (C) 7°F   (D) 11°F

3.2 Solve Two-Step Equations

Standards Preparation

Gr. 7 AF 4.1 Solve two-step linear equations and inequalities in one variable over the rational numbers, interpret the solution or solutions in the context from which they arose, and verify the reasonableness of the results.

Connect *Before* you solved one-step equations. *Now* you will solve two-step equations to prepare for Algebra 1 Standard 5.0.

Math and RECREATION
Example 4, p. 134

Key Vocabulary
• like terms, *p. 82*

The equation $\frac{x}{2} + 5 = 11$ involves two operations performed on x: division by 2 and addition by 5. You typically solve such an equation by applying the inverse operations in the reverse order of the order of operations. This is shown in the table below.

Operations performed on x	Operations to isolate x
1. Divide by 2. 2. Add 5.	1. Subtract 5. 2. Multiply by 2.

EXAMPLE 1 ◆ Multiple Choice Practice

What is the value of x if $\frac{x}{2} + 5 = 11$?

(A) $x = 3$ **(B)** $x = 6$ **(C)** $x = 12$ **(D)** $x = 32$

Solution

$$\frac{x}{2} + 5 = 11$$ **Write original equation.**

$$\frac{x}{2} + 5 - 5 = 11 - 5$$ **Subtract 5 from each side.**

$$\frac{x}{2} = 6$$ **Simplify.**

$$2 \cdot \frac{x}{2} = 2 \cdot 6$$ **Multiply each side by 2.**

$$x = 12$$ **Simplify.**

▶ The correct answer is C. (A) (B) **(C)** (D)

CHECK $\frac{x}{2} + 5 = 11$ **Write original equation.**

$$\frac{12}{2} + 5 \stackrel{?}{=} 11$$ **Substitute 12 for x.**

$$11 = 11 \checkmark$$ **Simplify. Solution checks.**

EXAMPLE 2 **Solve a two-step equation by combining like terms**

**REVIEW
LIKE TERMS**
For help with combining like terms, see p. 82.

Solve $7x - 4x = 21$.

$$7x - 4x = 21 \qquad \text{Write original equation.}$$

$$3x = 21 \qquad \text{Combine like terms.}$$

$$\frac{3x}{3} = \frac{21}{3} \qquad \text{Divide each side by 3.}$$

$$x = 7 \qquad \text{Simplify.}$$

 GUIDED PRACTICE | **for Examples 1 and 2**

Solve the equation. Check your solution.

1. $-1 = \frac{z}{3} - 7$ **2.** $4w + 2w = 24$ **3.** $-16 = 5d - 9d$

EXAMPLE 3 **Write an equation and solve**

READING
Note that "3 less than" means "3 is subtracted from."

The value of y is 3 less than 5 times the value of x. Find x when $y = 17$.

Solution

STEP 1 **Write** an equation.

$$y = 5x - 3 \qquad \text{\textit{y} is 3 less than 5 times \textit{x}.}$$

STEP 2 **Solve** the equation for x when $y = 17$.

$$y = 5x - 3 \qquad \text{Write original equation.}$$

$$17 = 5x - 3 \qquad \text{Substitute 17 for \textit{y}.}$$

$$17 + 3 = 5x - 3 + 3 \qquad \text{Add 3 to each side.}$$

$$20 = 5x \qquad \text{Simplify.}$$

$$\frac{20}{5} = \frac{5x}{5} \qquad \text{Divide each side by 5.}$$

$$4 = x \qquad \text{Simplify.}$$

▸ The value of x is 4 when $y = 17$.

CHECK $y = 5x - 3$ Write original equation.

$$17 \stackrel{?}{=} 5(4) - 3 \qquad \text{Substitute 17 for \textit{y} and 4 for \textit{x}.}$$

$$17 \stackrel{?}{=} 20 - 3 \qquad \text{Multiply 5 and 4.}$$

$$17 = 17 \checkmark \qquad \text{Simplify. Solution checks.}$$

 GUIDED PRACTICE | **for Example 3**

4. The value of y is 4 less than -3 times the value of x. Find x when $y = 14$.

5. The value of y is 5 more than -2 times the value of x. Find x when $y = 11$.

EXAMPLE 4 **Solve a multi-step problem**

SCUBA DIVING As a scuba diver descends into deeper water, the pressure of the water on the diver's body steadily increases. The total pressure on the diver is the sum of the pressure from the atmosphere and the pressure from the water. Use the information below to find the depth at which a diver experiences a pressure of 8517 pounds per square foot (lb/ft^2).

Pressure from atmosphere at surface of water: 2117 lb/ft²

Increase in pressure from water as diver descends: 64 lb/ft² for each foot of depth

ANOTHER WAY
For an alternative method for solving Example 4, turn to page 138 for the **Problem Solving Workshop**.

Solution

STEP 1 **Write** a verbal model. Then write an equation.

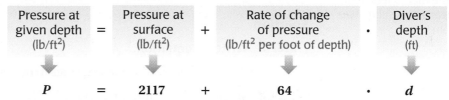

Pressure at given depth (lb/ft^2)	=	Pressure at surface (lb/ft^2)	+	Rate of change of pressure (lb/ft^2 per foot of depth)	·	Diver's depth (ft)
P	=	2117	+	64	·	d

STEP 2 **Find** the depth at which the pressure is 8517 pounds per square foot.

$P = 2117 + 64d$	**Write equation.**
$8517 = 2117 + 64d$	**Substitute 8517 for P.**
$8517 - \mathbf{2117} = 2117 - \mathbf{2117} + 64d$	**Subtract 2117 from each side.**
$6400 = 64d$	**Simplify.**
$\dfrac{6400}{64} = \dfrac{64d}{64}$	**Divide each side by 64.**
$100 = d$	**Simplify.**

▶ A diver experiences a pressure of 8517 pounds per square foot at a depth of 100 feet.

CHECK You can check the solution by substituting 8517 for P and 100 for d in the original equation.

✔ **GUIDED PRACTICE** for Example 4

6. **WHAT IF?** In Example 4, suppose the diver experiences a pressure of 5317 pounds per square foot. Find the diver's depth.

7. **JOBS** Kim has a job where she makes $8 per hour plus tips. Yesterday, Kim made $53, including $13 from tips. How many hours did she work?

3.2 EXERCISES

HOMEWORK KEY

◆ = **MULTIPLE CHOICE PRACTICE**
Exs. 21, 22, 45, and 51–53

○ = **HINTS AND HOMEWORK HELP**
for Exs. 13, 19, and 43 at classzone.com

SKILLS · PROBLEM SOLVING · REASONING

1. VOCABULARY Copy and complete: To solve the equation $2x + 3x = 20$, you would begin by combining $2x$ and $3x$ because they are __?__.

2. WRITING *Describe* the steps you would use to solve the equation $4x + 7 = 15$.

EXAMPLE 1
on p. 132
for Exs. 3–14,
21, 23

SOLVING TWO-STEP EQUATIONS Solve the equation. Check your solution.

3. $3x + 7 = 19$ **4.** $5h + 4 = 19$ **5.** $7d - 1 = 13$

6. $2g - 13 = 3$ **7.** $10 = 7 - m$ **8.** $11 = 12 - q$

9. $\frac{a}{3} + 4 = 6$ **10.** $17 = \frac{w}{5} + 13$ **11.** $\frac{b}{2} - 9 = 11$

12. $-6 = \frac{z}{4} - 3$ **13.** $7 = \frac{5}{6}c - 8$ **14.** $10 = \frac{2}{7}n + 4$

EXAMPLE 2
on p. 133
for Exs. 15–20,
22, 24

COMBINING LIKE TERMS Solve the equation. Check your solution.

15. $8y + 3y = 44$ **16.** $2p + 7p = 54$ **17.** $11x - 9x = 18$

18. $36 = 9x - 3x$ **19.** $-32 = -5k + 13k$ **20.** $6 = -7f + 4f$

21. ◆ **MULTIPLE CHOICE** What is the first step you can take to solve the equation $6 + \frac{x}{3} = -2$?

  A Subtract 2 from each side.   **B** Add 6 to each side.

  C Divide each side by 3.   **D** Subtract 6 from each side.

22. ◆ **MULTIPLE CHOICE** What is the value of x if $3x + x = 24$?

  A $x = -7$ **B** $x = -6$ **C** $x = 6$ **D** $x = 7$

ERROR ANALYSIS *Describe* and correct the error in solving the equation.

23.
$$7 - 3x = 12$$
$$\frac{4x}{4} = \frac{12}{4}$$
$$x = 3$$

24.
$$-2x + x = 10$$
$$\frac{-2x + x}{-2} = \frac{10}{-2}$$
$$x = -5$$

EXAMPLE 3
on p. 133
for Exs. 25–28

WRITING AND SOLVING TWO-STEP EQUATIONS Write an equation for the verbal sentence. Then find the value of x.

25. The value of y is 7 more than 3 times the value of x. Find x when $y = -8$.

26. The value of y is 4 more than 2 times the value of x. Find x when $y = -10$.

27. The value of y is 9 less than 10 times the value of x. Find x when $y = 11$.

28. The value of y is 5 less than 12 times the value of x. Find x when $y = -53$.

SOLVING EQUATIONS Solve the equation. Check your solution.

29. $5.6 = 1.1p + 1.2$

30. $7.2y + 4.7 = 62.3$

31. $1.2j - 4.3 = 1.7$

32. $16 - 2.4d = -8$

33. $14.4m - 5.1 = 2.1$

34. $-5.3 = 2.2v - 8.6$

35. $\dfrac{c}{5.3} + 8.3 = 11.3$

36. $3.2 + \dfrac{x}{2.5} = 4.6$

37. $-1.2 = \dfrac{z}{4.6} - 2.7$

38. REASONING Use the equation $ax + b = c$.

　　a. Solve the equation for x when $a = 3$, $b = 7$, and $c = -2$.

　　b. Solve the equation for x when $a = 2$, $b = 6$, and $c = 11$.

　　c. If a, b, and c are integers, will x always be an integer? *Explain.*

CONNECT SKILLS TO PROBLEM SOLVING Exercises 39–41 will help you prepare for problem solving.

Match the real-world situation with the equation that represents it.

39. After a discount of $5, the total cost of 4 T-shirts that cost x dollars each is $35.

A. $4x - 5 = 35$

40. You order 5 pizzas that cost x dollars each. Including the $4 tip for the driver, you pay a total of $35.

B. $4x + 5 = 35$

41. You pay $5 for parking and buy 4 movie tickets that cost x dollars each. Your total cost is $35.

C. $5x + 4 = 35$

EXAMPLE 4
on p. 134
for Exs. 42–45

42. DANCE CLASSES A dance academy charges $24 per class and a one-time registration fee of $15. A student paid a total of $687 to the academy. Find the number of classes the student took.

California @HomeTutor for problem solving help at classzone.com

Cost: $24 per class

43. CAR REPAIR Tyler paid $124 to get his car repaired. The total cost for the repairs was the sum of the amount paid for parts and the amount paid for labor. Tyler was charged $76 for parts and $32 per hour for labor. Find the amount of time it took to repair his car.

California @HomeTutor for problem solving help at classzone.com

44. ADVERTISING A science museum wants to promote an upcoming exhibit by advertising on city buses for one month. The costs of the two types of advertisements being considered are shown. The museum has budgeted $6000 for the advertisements. The museum decides to have 1 full bus wrap advertisement. How many half-side advertisements can the museum have?

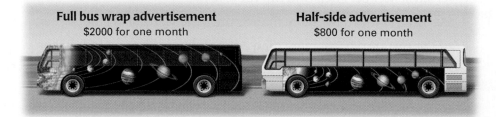

Full bus wrap advertisement
$2000 for one month

Half-side advertisement
$800 for one month

◆ = **MULTIPLE CHOICE PRACTICE**　　　　◯ = **HINTS AND HOMEWORK HELP** at classzone.com

45. ◆ **MULTIPLE CHOICE** A skateboarding park charges $7 per session to skate and $4 per session to rent safety equipment. Jared rents safety equipment every time he skates. The total cost C for Jared to attend n sessions is given by the equation $C = 4n + 7n$. Last year Jared spent a total of $99 at the park. How many sessions did Jared attend last year?

Ⓐ 5 Ⓑ 7 Ⓒ 9 Ⓓ 11

46. **SHORT RESPONSE** A guitar store offers a finance plan where you give a $50 down payment on a guitar and pay the remaining balance in 6 equal monthly payments. You have $50, and you can afford to pay up to $90 per month for a guitar. Can you afford a guitar that costs $542? *Explain.*

47. **MULTI-STEP PROBLEM** The capacity of a landfill is 4,756,505 tons. The landfill currently holds 2,896,112 tons. A cell is added to the landfill every day, and each cell averages 1600 tons.

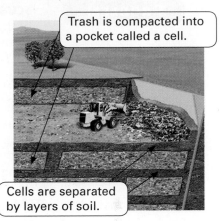

Trash is compacted into a pocket called a cell.

Cells are separated by layers of soil.

   a. Write an equation that gives the amount y (in tons) in the landfill x days from now.

   b. After how many days will the landfill reach capacity? Round your answer to the nearest day.

   c. Use estimation to check your answer to part (b).

48. **SHORT RESPONSE** At a restaurant, customers can dine inside the restaurant or pick up food at the take-out window. On an average day, 400 customers are served inside the restaurant, and 120 customers pick up food at the take-out window. After how many days will the restaurant have served 2600 customers? *Explain.*

49. **CHALLENGE** Solve the equations $3x + 2 = 5$, $3x + 2 = 8$, and $3x + 2 = 11$. Predict the solution of the equation $3x + 2 = 14$. *Explain* your reasoning.

50. **CHALLENGE** During a 1 mile race, one runner is running at a rate of 14.6 feet per second, and another runner is running at a rate of 11.3 feet per second. One lap around the track is 660 feet. After how many seconds will the faster runner be exactly one lap ahead of the other runner?

◆ CALIFORNIA STANDARDS SPIRAL REVIEW

Gr. 6 NS 2.3

51. What is the value of $28 \div (-7)$? *(p. 88)*

Ⓐ −4 Ⓑ −0.25 Ⓒ 4 Ⓓ 21

Alg. 2.0

52. What is the opposite of −4? *(p. 53)*

Ⓐ −4 Ⓑ $-\frac{1}{4}$ Ⓒ $\frac{1}{4}$ Ⓓ 4

Gr. 6 AF 1.1

53. You have some change in your pocket. After you gave your friend $.40, you had $1.10 left. Which equation can you use to find the amount a of money you originally had in your pocket? *(p. 26)*

Ⓐ $a + 1.1 = 0.4$ Ⓑ $a + 0.4 = 1.1$ Ⓒ $a - 1.1 = -0.4$ Ⓓ $a - 0.4 = 1.1$

Using ALTERNATIVE METHODS

Another Way to Solve Example 4, page 134

Standards
Preparation
Gr. 7 MR 2.5

In Example 4 on page 134, you saw how to solve a problem about scuba diving by using an equation. You can also solve the problem using a table.

PROBLEM

SCUBA DIVING As a scuba diver descends into deeper water, the pressure of the water on the diver's body steadily increases. Use the information below to find the depth at which a diver experiences a pressure of 8517 pounds per square foot (lb/ft^2).

- Pressure from atmosphere at surface of water: 2117 lb/ft^2
- Increase in pressure from water as diver descends: 64 lb/ft^2 for each foot of depth

METHOD

Making a Table An alternative approach is to make a table.

STEP 1 **Make** a table that shows the pressure as the depth increases. Because you are looking for a fairly high pressure, use larger increments in depth, such as 20 feet.

Every 1 ft of depth increases the pressure by 64 lb/ft^2.

Every 20 ft of depth increases the pressure by 64(20) = 1280 lb/ft^2.

Depth (ft)	Pressure (lb/ft²)
0	2117
1	2181
2	2245
20	3397
40	4677
60	5957
80	7237
100	8517

STEP 2 **Look** for the depth at which the pressure reaches 8517 pounds per square foot. This happens at a depth of 100 feet.

PRACTICE

1. **BASKETBALL** A sports club offers an organized basketball league. A team pays $600 to join the league. In addition to paying their share of the $600, team members who are not members of the sports club must pay a $25 fee to play. A team pays a total of $775. How many team members who are not club members are on the team? Solve this problem using two different methods.

2. **WHAT IF?** In Exercise 1, suppose you are on a team, but not a club member. The $600 cost is divided equally among the team members. How many players must there be on your team for you to pay $100 to play? Make a table to find the answer.

3. **FURNITURE** You have $370 to spend on a dining table and chairs. A table costs $220, and each chair costs $35. How many chairs can you buy in addition to the table? Solve this problem using two different methods.

3.3 Solve Multi-Step Equations

Math and SAFETY
Ex. 56, p. 143

Standards Alg. 4.0 Students simplify expressions before solving linear equations and inequalities **in one variable**, such as $3(2x − 5) + 4(x − 2) = 12$.

Connect *Before* you solved one-step and two-step equations.
Now you will solve multi-step equations.

Key Vocabulary
• **like terms,** *p. 82*
• **distributive property,** *p. 81*
• **reciprocal,** *p. 789*

Solving a linear equation may take more than two steps. Start by simplifying one or both sides of the equation, if possible. Then use inverse operations to isolate the variable.

EXAMPLE 1 Solve an equation by combining like terms

Solve $8x − 3x − 10 = 20$.

About the Standards

In this chapter, the equations that you're solving involve variables raised only to the first power. Such equations are called *linear*.

$8x − 3x − 10 = 20$	**Write original equation.**
$5x − 10 = 20$	**Combine like terms.**
$5x − 10 + 10 = 20 + 10$	**Add 10 to each side.**
$5x = 30$	**Simplify.**
$\dfrac{5x}{5} = \dfrac{30}{5}$	**Divide each side by 5.**
$x = 6$	**Simplify.**

EXAMPLE 2 Solve an equation using the distributive property

Solve $7x + 2(x + 6) = 39$.

Solution

When solving an equation, you may feel comfortable doing some steps mentally. Method 2 shows a solution where some steps are done mentally.

REVIEW PROPERTIES
For help with using the distributive property, see p. 81.

METHOD 1 Show all steps

$7x + 2(x + 6) = 39$

$7x + 2x + 12 = 39$

$9x + 12 = 39$

$9x + 12 − 12 = 39 − 12$

$9x = 27$

$\dfrac{9x}{9} = \dfrac{27}{9}$

$x = 3$

METHOD 2 Do some steps mentally

$7x + 2(x + 6) = 39$

$7x + 2x + 12 = 39$

$9x + 12 = 39$

$9x = 27$

$x = 3$

EXAMPLE 3 ◆ **Multiple Choice Practice**

Which equation is equivalent to $5(4x + 1) - 3(5x - 6) = 38$?

(A) $5x = 15$ (B) $5x = 61$ (C) $35x = 41$ (D) $35x = 15$

AVOID ERRORS
When you use the distributive property here, remember that you are distributing -3, not 3.

$5(4x + 1) - 3(5x - 6) = 38$ **Write original equation.**

$20x + 5 - 15x + 18 = 38$ **Distributive property**

$5x + 23 = 38$ **Combine like terms.**

$5x = 15$ **Subtract 23 from each side.**

$x = 3$ **Divide each side by 5.**

The answer choice $5x = 15$ appears in the solution.

▶ The correct answer is A.   (A) (B) (C) (D)

USING RECIPROCALS Although you can use the distributive property to solve an equation such as $\frac{3}{2}(3x + 5) = -24$, it is easier to multiply each side of the equation by the reciprocal of the fraction.

EXAMPLE 4   **Multiply by a reciprocal to solve an equation**

Solve $\frac{3}{2}(3x + 5) = -24$.

$\frac{3}{2}(3x + 5) = -24$ **Write original equation.**

$\frac{2}{3} \cdot \frac{3}{2}(3x + 5) = \frac{2}{3}(-24)$ **Multiply each side by $\frac{2}{3}$, the reciprocal of $\frac{3}{2}$.**

$3x + 5 = -16$ **Simplify.**

$3x = -21$ **Subtract 5 from each side.**

$x = -7$ **Divide each side by 3.**

CHECK $\frac{3}{2}(3x + 5) = -24$ **Write original equation.**

$\frac{3}{2}[3(-7) + 5] \stackrel{?}{=} -24$ **Substitute -7 for x.**

$\frac{3}{2}[-16] \stackrel{?}{=} -24$ **Simplify expression within brackets.**

$-24 = -24$ ✓   **Multiply. Solution checks.**

✓ **GUIDED PRACTICE**   for Examples 1, 2, 3, and 4

Solve the equation. Check your solution.

  1. $9d - 2d + 4 = 32$ **2.** $2y + 3(y + 4) = 27$

  3. $4(3x - 1) - (x + 5) = 24$ **4.** $-\frac{4}{5}(4a - 1) = 28$

EXAMPLE 5 **Write and solve an equation**

BIRD MIGRATION A flock of cranes migrates from Canada to Texas. The cranes take 14 days (336 hours) to travel 2500 miles. The cranes fly at an average speed of 25 miles per hour. For how many hours of the migration are the cranes *not* flying?

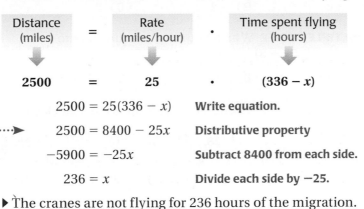

Crane

Solution

Let x be the amount of time the cranes are not flying. Then $336 - x$ is the amount of time the cranes are flying.

Distance (miles)	=	Rate (miles/hour)	·	Time spent flying (hours)
2500	=	25	·	$(336 - x)$

$$2500 = 25(336 - x)$$ Write equation.

$$2500 = 8400 - 25x$$ Distributive property

$$-5900 = -25x$$ Subtract 8400 from each side.

$$236 = x$$ Divide each side by -25.

ANOTHER WAY
You can also begin solving the equation by dividing each side of the equation by 25.

▶ The cranes are not flying for 236 hours of the migration.

 GUIDED PRACTICE for Example 5

  5. WHAT IF? In Example 5, suppose the cranes take 12 days (288 hours) to travel 2500 miles. For how many hours of this migration are the cranes *not* flying?

3.3 **EXERCISES**

HOMEWORK KEY

◆ = **MULTIPLE CHOICE PRACTICE**
Exs. 25, 26, 54, and 63–65

○ = **HINTS AND HOMEWORK HELP**
for Exs. 21, 43, and 55 at classzone.com

SKILLS · PROBLEM SOLVING · REASONING

  1. VOCABULARY What is the reciprocal of the fraction in the equation $\frac{3}{5}(2x + 8) = 18$?

  2. WRITING *Describe* the steps you would use to solve $3(4y - 7) = 11$.

EXAMPLE 1
on p. 139
for Exs. 3–14

COMBINING LIKE TERMS Solve the equation. Check your solution.

  3. $p + 2p - 3 = 6$

  4. $12v + 14 + 10v = 80$

  5. $11w - 9 - 7w = 15$

  6. $5a + 3 - 3a = -7$

  7. $6c - 8 - 2c = -16$

  8. $9 = 7z - 13z - 21$

  9. $-2 = 3y - 18 - 5y$

  10. $23 = -4m + 2 + m$

  11. $35 = -5 + 2x - 7x$

  12. $4d - 13 + 7d = -24$

  13. $-9 = 2b - 11b - 27$

  14. $-23 = 26h - 7 + 6h$

USING THE DISTRIBUTIVE PROPERTY Solve the equation. Check your
solution.

15. $3 + 4(z + 5) = 31$

16. $14 + 2(4g − 3) = 40$

17. $5m + 2(m + 1) = 23$

18. $5h + 2(11 − h) = −5$

19. $27 = 3c − 3(6 − 2c)$

20. $−3 = 12y − 5(2y − 7)$

21. $5(2x − 4) − 3(3x − 7) = 6$

22. $−2(4x − 5) + 6(2x + 1) = 6$

23. $2(3y − 1) + 3(y − 4) = 13$

24. $6(z + 2) − 2(2z + 5) = 18$

25. ◆ **MULTIPLE CHOICE** What is the solution of $7v − (6 − 2v) = 12$?

　　(**A**) $−3.6$　　　(**B**) $−2$　　　(**C**) 2　　　(**D**) 3.6

26. ◆ **MULTIPLE CHOICE** Which equation is equivalent to
$3(4x + 2) − 2(5x − 3) = 12$?

　　(**A**) $2x = 0$　　(**B**) $2x = 24$　　(**C**) $22x = 0$　　(**D**) $22x = 12$

EXAMPLE 4
·····················
on p. 140
for Exs. 27–35,
37

MULTIPLYING BY A RECIPROCAL Solve the equation. Check your solution.

27. $\frac{1}{3}(d + 3) = 5$

28. $\frac{3}{2}(x − 5) = −6$

29. $\frac{4}{3}(7 − n) = 12$

30. $\frac{6}{5}(a + 4) = −18$

31. $\frac{5}{8}(g − 6) = −35$

32. $\frac{2}{11}(3 + 2n) = 10$

33. $4 = \frac{2}{9}(4y − 2)$

34. $−32 = \frac{8}{7}(3w − 1)$

35. $−14 = \frac{2}{5}(9 − 2b)$

ERROR ANALYSIS *Describe* and correct the error in solving the equation.

36.
$$5x − 3(x − 6) = 2$$
$$5x − 3x − 18 = 2$$
$$2x − 18 = 2$$
$$2x = 20 ✗$$
$$x = 10$$

37.
$$\frac{1}{2}(2x − 10) = 4$$
$$2x − 10 = 2$$
$$2x = 12 ✗$$
$$x = 6$$

SOLVING EQUATIONS Solve the equation. Check your solution.

38. $8.9 + 1.2(3a − 1) = 14.9$

39. $−11.2 + 4(2.1 + q) = −0.8$

40. $1.3t + 3(t + 8.2) = 37.5$

41. $1.6 = 7.6 − 5(k + 1.1)$

42. $0.5 = 4.1x − 2(1.3x − 4)$

43. $8.7 = 3.5m − 2.5(5.4 − 6m)$

44. $3(2x − 1.4) − \frac{1}{2}(7x + 5.6) = 0$

45. $3.5(2x + 1.8) − 2(3.2x + 5) = 8.9$

GEOMETRY Find the value of x for the triangle or rectangle.

46. Perimeter = 24 ft

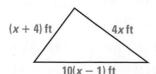

$(x + 4)$ ft　　$4x$ ft

$10(x − 1)$ ft

47. Perimeter = 26 m

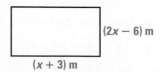

$(2x − 6)$ m

$(x + 3)$ m

　　◆ = **MULTIPLE CHOICE PRACTICE**　　　◯ = **HINTS** AND **HOMEWORK HELP** at classzone.com

48. GEOMETRY The length of a rectangle is 3.5 inches more than its width. The perimeter of the rectangle is 31 inches. Find the length and the width of the rectangle.

49. SHORT RESPONSE Consider the equations $9(x - 4) = 72$ and $8(x + 5) = 59$.

    a. Solve each equation by first dividing each side of the equation by the number outside the parentheses.

    b. When would you recommend the method in part (a) to solve an equation? *Explain*.

CONNECT SKILLS TO PROBLEM SOLVING Exercises 50–53 will help you prepare for problem solving.

Write an equation that represents the situation.

50. During a 105 mile trip, you travel x hours at a speed of 55 miles per hour and $(x - 2)$ hours at a speed of 45 miles per hour.

51. You spend $55 while shopping. You buy x books for $8 each and x bookmarks for $2 each. Then you spend your last $5 on food.

52. You have $73 in a bank account. You deposit x dollars into the account each week for 3 weeks. Then you take $20 out, leaving $80 in the account.

53. A farmer needs to build a rectangular pen that has a perimeter of 102 feet. The length of the pen is x feet, and the width is $(x - 5)$ feet.

EXAMPLE 5
on p. 141
for Exs. 54–56

54. ◆ MULTIPLE CHOICE A ticket agency sells tickets to a professional basketball game. The agency charges $32.50 for each ticket, a convenience charge of $3.30 for each ticket, and a processing fee of $5.90 for the entire order. The total charge for an order is $220.70. How many tickets were purchased?

   A 5 tickets   **B** 6 tickets   **C** 7 tickets   **D** 8 tickets

California@HomeTutor for problem solving help at classzone.com

55. HANGING POSTERS You want to hang 3 equally-sized travel posters on the wall in your room so that the posters on the ends are each 3 feet from the end of the wall. You want the spacing between posters to be equal. How much space should you leave between the posters?

California@HomeTutor for problem solving help at classzone.com

13.5 ft

56. LIFEGUARD TRAINING To qualify for a lifeguard training course, you have to swim continuously for 500 yards using either the front crawl or the breaststroke. You swim the front crawl at a rate of 45 yards per minute and the breaststroke at a rate of 35 yards per minute. You take 12 minutes to swim 500 yards. How much time did you spend swimming the front crawl? Use the verbal model below.

| Distance | = | Rate for front crawl | · | Time for front crawl | + | Rate for breaststroke | (| Total time | − | Time for front crawl |) |

Railways The Busk-Ivanhoe Tunnel on the Colorado Midland Railway was built in the 1890s with separate work crews starting on opposite ends at different times. The crew working from Ivanhoe started 0.75 month later than the crew working from Busk.

Ivanhoe crews completed 115 feet per month.
Busk crews completed 137 feet per month.

Cutaway of Busk-Ivanhoe Tunnel

57. **Calculate** Starting at the time construction began on the Busk end, find the time it took to complete a total of 8473 feet of the tunnel. Round your answer to the nearest month.

58. **Calculate** After 8473 feet were completed, the work crews merged under the same supervision. The combined crew took 3 months to complete the remaining 921 feet of the tunnel. Find the rate at which the remainder of the tunnel was completed.

59. **Reasoning** Was the tunnel being completed more rapidly before or after the work crews merged? *Explain* your reasoning.

60. **CHALLENGE** Solve $5[4(3x - 2) + 9x] - 7(x + 5) = 170$.

61. **CHALLENGE** An even integer can be represented by the expression $2n$, and the next even integer by $2n + 2$, where n is an integer. Find three consecutive even integers that have a sum of 54.

62. **CHALLENGE** A person has quarters and dimes that total $2.80. The number of dimes is 7 more than the number of quarters. How many of each coin does the person have?

◆ CALIFORNIA STANDARDS SPIRAL REVIEW

Gr. 7 NS 2.5

63. What is the value of $|-4.2| + |-3.3|$? *(p. 53)*

   (A) -7.5 **(B)** -0.9 **(C)** 0.9 **(D)** 7.5

Alg. 2.0

64. What is the reciprocal of $\frac{2}{3}$? *(p. 88)*

   (A) $\frac{3}{2}$ **(B)** 2 **(C)** $-\frac{2}{3}$ **(D)** 3

Gr. 7 AF 4.1

65. Ted needs $424 to buy a surfboard. He has $214 and earns $7 per hour bagging groceries. How many hours must Ted work to have the money he needs? *(p. 132)*

   (A) 21 h   **(B)** 30 h   **(C)** 61 h   **(D)** 92 h

3.4 Modeling Equations with Variables on Both Sides

Standards

Alg. 5.0 Students solve multistep problems, including word problems, involving linear equations and linear inequalities in one variable and provide justification for each step.

MATERIALS · algebra tiles

QUESTION How can you solve equations with variables on both sides?

You can model equations with variables on both sides using algebra tiles.

1-tile

A 1-tile represents the number 1.

x-tile

An x-tile represents the variable x.

EXPLORE Solve an equation with variables on both sides

Solve $3x + 2 = 6 + x$.

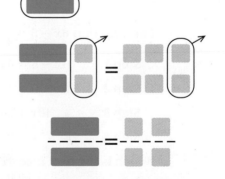

STEP 1 Model $3x + 2 = 6 + x$ using algebra tiles.

STEP 2 Remove one x-tile from each side.

STEP 3 Remove two 1-tiles from each side.

STEP 4 Divide the remaining tiles into two equal groups. Each x-tile is equal to two 1-tiles, so the solution is 2.

DRAW CONCLUSIONS Use your observations to complete these exercises

Use algebra tiles to model and solve the equation.

1. $2x + 1 = x + 4$
2. $x + 7 = 2x + 2$
3. $3x + 4 = 2x + 6$
4. $2x + 6 = 4x + 2$
5. $4x + 2 = x + 8$
6. $2x + 10 = 5x + 1$

7. **REASONING** Look back at the Explore. If you performed Step 3 before Step 2, would you get the same answer? *Explain.*

3.4 Solve Equations with Variables on Both Sides

Standards Alg. 5.0 **Students solve multistep problems, including word problems, involving linear equations** and linear inequalities **in one variable and provide justification for each step.**

Connect *Before* you solved equations with variables on one side. *Now* you will solve equations with variables on both sides.

Math and **RECREATION**
Ex. 57, p. 151

Key Vocabulary
• identity

Some equations have variables on both sides. To solve such equations, you can collect the variable terms on one side of the equation and the constant terms on the other side of the equation.

EXAMPLE 1 Solve an equation with variables on both sides

Solve $7 - 8x = 4x - 17$.

$7 - 8x = 4x - 17$	Write original equation.
$7 - 8x + 8x = 4x - 17 + 8x$	Add $8x$ to each side.
$7 = 12x - 17$	Simplify each side.
$24 = 12x$	Add 17 to each side.
$2 = x$	Divide each side by 12.

Animated Algebra

For an interactive example of solving an equation with variables on both sides, go to **classzone.com**.

EXAMPLE 2 ◆ Multiple Choice Practice

The equation $6x - 5 = \frac{1}{4}(16x + 60)$ is solved below.

Step 1	$6x - 5 = 4x + 15$
Step 2	$10x - 5 = 15$
Step 3	$10x = 20$
Step 4	$x = 2$

Which is the first *incorrect* step in the solution?

  A Step 1   **B** Step 2   **C** Step 3   **D** Step 4

Solution

In Step 1, the distributive property was used correctly to simplify the right side of the equation. However, in Step 2, $4x$ should have been subtracted from the left side of the equation instead of being added.

▸ The correct answer is B. **A** **B** **C** **D**

Solve the equation. Check your solution.

1. $9 - 3k = 17 - 2k$ 2. $3 - 4a = 5(a - 3)$ 3. $8y - 6 = \frac{2}{3}(6y + 15)$

EXAMPLE 3 Solve a real-world problem

CAR SALES The annual sales report for a car dealership is shown. If these trends continue, in how many years will the number of new cars sold be twice the number of used cars sold?

ANNUAL SALES REPORT

 78 new cars sold this year

 67 used cars sold this year

 Number of new cars sold has been increasing by 6 cars per year.

 Number of used cars sold has been decreasing by 4 cars per year.

Solution

Let x represent the number of years from now. Then $6x$ represents the increase in the number of new cars sold over x years, and $-4x$ represents the decrease in the number of used cars sold over x years. Write a verbal model.

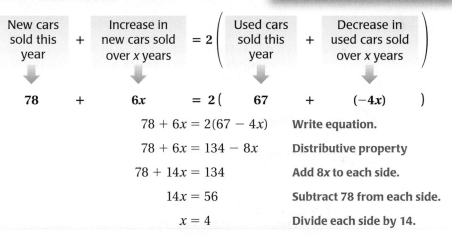

$$78 + 6x = 2(67 - 4x) \quad \text{Write equation.}$$
$$78 + 6x = 134 - 8x \quad \text{Distributive property}$$
$$78 + 14x = 134 \quad \text{Add } 8x \text{ to each side.}$$
$$14x = 56 \quad \text{Subtract 78 from each side.}$$
$$x = 4 \quad \text{Divide each side by 14.}$$

▸ The number of new cars sold will be twice the number of used cars sold in 4 years.

CHECK You can use a table to check the solution.

Year	0	1	2	3	4
Used cars sold	67	63	59	55	51
New cars sold	78	84	90	96	102

The number of new cars sold is twice the number of used cars sold in 4 years.

About the Standards

Think of this solution as a proof of the statement "If $78 + 6x = 2(67 - 4x)$, then $x = 4$." The blue text next to each step is a justification for that step. For example, "Add $8x$ to each side" indicates the addition property of equality.

---

4. **WHAT IF?** In Example 3, suppose the car dealership sold 50 new cars this year instead of 78. In how many years will the number of new cars sold be twice the number of used cars sold?

NUMBER OF SOLUTIONS Equations do not always have one solution. An equation that is true for all values of the variable is an **identity**. So, an identity has all real numbers as solutions. Some equations have no solution.

EXAMPLE 4 | **Identify the number of solutions of an equation**

Solve the equation, if possible.

   a. $3x = 3(x + 4)$ **b.** $2x + 10 = 2(x + 5)$

Solution

  a. $3x = 3(x + 4)$ **Original equation**

      $3x = 3x + 12$ **Distributive property**

The equation $3x = 3x + 12$ is not true because the number $3x$ cannot be equal to 12 more than itself. So, the equation has no solution. This can be demonstrated by continuing to solve the equation.

    $3x - 3x = 3x + 12 - 3x$ **Subtract $3x$ from each side.**

          $0 = 12$ ✗   **Simplify.**

> The statement $0 = 12$ is not true, so the equation has no solution.

  b. $2x + 10 = 2(x + 5)$ **Original equation**

      $2x + 10 = 2x + 10$ **Distributive property**

> Notice that the statement $2x + 10 = 2x + 10$ is true for all values of x. So, the equation is an identity, and all real numbers are solutions.

USE SET NOTATION
In part (a) of Example 4, the solution set of the equation is empty. You can write the solution set as { } or ∅, both symbols for the empty set.

✔ **GUIDED PRACTICE** | for Example 4

Solve the equation, if possible.

  5. $9z + 12 = 9(z + 3)$ **6.** $7w + 1 = 8w + 1$ **7.** $3(2a + 2) = 2(3a + 3)$

SOLVING LINEAR EQUATIONS You have learned several ways to transform an equation into an equivalent equation. These methods are combined in the steps listed below.

CONCEPT SUMMARY   *For Your Notebook*

Steps for Solving Linear Equations

  STEP 1 **Use** the distributive property to remove any grouping symbols.

  STEP 2 **Simplify** the expression on each side of the equation.

  STEP 3 **Use** properties of equality to collect the variable terms on one side of the equation and the constant terms on the other side of the equation.

  STEP 4 **Use** properties of equality to solve for the variable.

  STEP 5 **Check** your solution in the original equation.

3.4 EXERCISES

SKILLS · PROBLEM SOLVING · REASONING

1. **VOCABULARY** Copy and complete: An equation that is true for all values of the variable is called a(n) __?__.

2. **WRITING** *Explain* why the equation $4x + 3 = 4x + 1$ has no solution.

EXAMPLES 1 and 2
on p. 146
for Exs. 3–17

SOLVING EQUATIONS Solve the equation. Check your solution.

3. $8t + 5 = 6t + 1$

4. $k + 1 = 3k - 1$

5. $8c + 5 = 4c - 11$

6. $8 + 4m = 9m - 7$

7. $10b + 18 = 8b + 4$

8. $19 - 13p = -17p - 5$

9. $9a = 6(a + 4)$

10. $5h - 7 = 2(h + 1)$

11. $3(d + 12) = 8 - 4d$

12. $7(r + 7) = 5r + 59$

13. $40 + 14j = 2(-4j - 13)$

14. $5(n + 2) = \frac{3}{5}(5 + 10n)$

15. ◆ **MULTIPLE CHOICE** What is the solution of the equation $8x + 2x = 15x - 10$?

(A) -2 (B) 0.4 (C) 2 (D) 5

16. ◆ **MULTIPLE CHOICE** What is the solution of the equation $4y + y + 1 = 7(y - 1)$?

(A) -4 (B) -3 (C) 3 (D) 4

17. **REASONING** The steps and reasons in solving $4(x + 3) = 6x - 4$ are shown below in no particular order. Correctly order the steps and corresponding reasons.

Steps	Reasons
$12 = 2x - 4$	Divide each side by 2.
$16 = 2x$	Subtract $4x$ from each side.
$8 = x$	Add 4 to each side.
$4x + 12 = 6x - 4$	Distributive property

EXAMPLE 4
on p. 148
for Exs. 18–26, 28–29

SOLVING EQUATIONS Solve the equation, if possible.

18. $w + 3 = w + 6$

19. $16d = 22 + 5d$

20. $8z = 4(2z + 1)$

21. $12 + 5v = 2v - 9$

22. $22x + 70 = 17x - 95$

23. $2 - 15n = 5(-3n + 2)$

24. $12y + 6 = 6(2y + 1)$

25. $5(1 + 4m) = 2(3 + 10m)$

26. $2(3g + 2) = \frac{1}{2}(12g + 8)$

27. ◆ **MULTIPLE CHOICE** Which equation is equivalent to $\frac{2}{3}(9x - 3) = 5(2x + 7)$?

(A) $-3 = 4x + 35$

(B) $-2 = 4x + 35$

(C) $-2 = 7x + 35$

(D) $2 = 16x + 35$

ERROR ANALYSIS *Describe* and correct the error in solving the equation.

28.
$$3(x + 5) = 3x + 15$$
$$3x + 5 = 3x + 15$$
$$5 = 15$$
The equation has no solution. ✕

29.
$$6(2y + 6) = 4(9 + 3y)$$
$$12y + 36 = 36 + 12y$$
$$12y = 12y$$
$$0 = 0$$
The solution is 0. ✕

30. OPEN-ENDED Give an example of an equation that has no solution. *Explain* why your equation does not have a solution.

SOLVING EQUATIONS Solve the equation, if possible.

31. $8w - 8 - 6w = 4w - 7$

32. $3x - 4 = 2x + 8 - 5x$

33. $-15c + 7c + 1 = 3 - 8c$

34. $d + 3 = -d - 10 - \frac{7}{3}d$

35. $\frac{3}{2} + \frac{3}{4}a = \frac{1}{4}a - \frac{1}{2}$

36. $n - 10 = \frac{5}{6}n - 7 - \frac{1}{3}n$

37. $\frac{5}{8}m - \frac{3}{8} = \frac{1}{2}m + \frac{7}{8}$

38. $2.7p - 4 = 1.5p + 2$

39. $3.7b + 7 = 8.1b - 19.4$

40. $6.2h + 5 - 1.4h = 4.8h + 5$

41. $0.7z + 1.9 + 0.1z = 5.5 - 0.4z$

42. $5.4t + 14.6 - 10.1t = 12.8 - 3.5t - 0.6$

43. $\frac{1}{8}(5y + 64) = \frac{1}{4}(20 + 2y)$

44. $14 - \frac{1}{5}(j - 10) = \frac{2}{5}(25 + j)$

45. $5(1.2k + 6) = 7.1k + 34.4$

46. $-0.25(4v - 8) = 0.5(4 - 2v)$

GEOMETRY Find the perimeter of the square.

47.
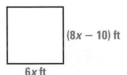
$(8x - 10)$ ft
$6x$ ft

48.

$5x$ ft
$(3x + 6)$ ft

49.
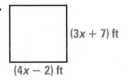
$(3x + 7)$ ft
$(4x - 2)$ ft

CONNECT SKILLS TO PROBLEM SOLVING Exercises 50–53 will help you prepare for problem solving.

Write an equation that represents the situation.

50. Linda had $6 and spent x dollars. Malcolm had $2x$ dollars and spent $3. They have the same amount of money left.

51. During a road trip, you cover the same distance traveling $(x - 3)$ hours at 60 miles per hour as you do traveling x hours at 40 miles per hour.

52. Buying x CDs for $11 each and receiving a $10 discount costs the same as buying x CDs for $9.75 each.

53. You earn x dollars per hour for babysitting and $(x - 2)$ dollars per hour for yard work. One week, you spend 3 hours babysitting. The next week you earn the same amount by doing yard work for 4 hours.

EXAMPLE 3
on p. 147
for Exs. 54–56

54. ◆ **MULTIPLE CHOICE** The membership fee for joining a camping association is $45. A local campground charges members of the camping association $35 per night for a campsite and nonmembers $40 per night for a campsite. After how many nights of camping is the total cost for members, including the membership fee, the same as the total cost for nonmembers?

(A) 4 nights   **(B)** 7 nights   **(C)** 8 nights   **(D)** 9 nights

California @HomeTutor   for problem solving help at classzone.com

55. **HIGH-SPEED INTERNET** Dan and Sydney are getting high-speed Internet access at the same time. Dan's provider charges $60 for installation and $42.95 per month. Sydney's provider has free installation and charges $57.95 per month. After how many months will Dan and Sydney have paid the same amount for high-speed Internet service?

California @HomeTutor   for problem solving help at classzone.com

56. **LANGUAGES** Information about students who take Spanish and students who take French at a high school is shown in the table. If the trends continue, in how many years will there be 3 times as many students taking Spanish as French?

Language	Students enrolled this year	Average rate of change
Spanish	555	30 more students each year
French	233	2 fewer students each year

57. **ROCK CLIMBING** For $360, a rock-climbing gym offers a yearly membership where members can climb as many days as they want and pay $4 per day for equipment rental. Nonmembers pay $10 per day to use the gym and $6 per day for equipment rental. After how many visits is the total cost for a member and a nonmember the same?

58. **MULTI-STEP PROBLEM** Flyball is a relay race for dogs. In each of the four legs of the relay, a dog jumps over hurdles, retrieves a ball from a flybox, and runs back over the hurdles. The last leg of a relay is shown below. The collie starts the course 0.3 second before the sheepdog.

flybox

51 ft

The collie is running 23.4 feet per second.

The sheepdog is running 24 feet per second.

  a. Let t represent the time (in seconds) it takes the collie to run the last leg. Write and solve an equation to find the number of seconds after which the sheepdog would catch up with the collie.

  b. How long does it take the collie to run the last leg?

  c. Use your answers from parts (a) and (b) to determine whether the sheepdog catches up and passes the collie during the last leg of the relay. *Explain* your reasoning.

CHALLENGE Find the value(s) of a for which the equation is an identity.

59. $a(2x + 3) = 9x + 12 - x$

60. $10x - 35 + 3ax = 5ax - 7a$

CHALLENGE Find the length and the width of the rectangle described.

61. The length is 12 units more than the width. The perimeter is 7 times the width.

62. The length is 4 units less than 3 times the width. The perimeter is 22 units more than twice the width.

◆ CALIFORNIA STANDARDS SPIRAL REVIEW

Gr. 6 AF 1.1

63. What is the solution of $\frac{z}{4} = 8$? *(p. 125)*

  (**A**) 2   (**B**) 12   (**C**) 24   (**D**) 32

Alg. 4.0

64. Which equation is equivalent to $7x - \frac{1}{2}(8x + 14) = 17$? *(p. 139)*

  (**A**) $3x + 7 = 17$ (**B**) $3x - 7 = 17$

  (**C**) $11x + 7 = 17$ (**D**) $11x - 7 = 17$

Gr. 6 NS 2.3

65. The low temperature on Wednesday was 12°F. The low temperature on Thursday was 16°F colder than the low temperature on Wednesday. What was the low temperature on Thursday? *(p. 67)*

  (**A**) $-28°F$ (**B**) $-4°F$ (**C**) $4°F$ (**D**) $28°F$

QUIZ *for Lessons 3.1–3.4*

Solve the equation. Check your solution.

1. $x + 9 = 7$ *(p. 125)*   **2.** $-7b = -56$ *(p. 125)*

3. $\frac{z}{4} = 6$ *(p. 125)*   **4.** $-\frac{4}{3}t = -12$ *(p. 125)*

5. $9w - 4 = 14$ *(p. 132)*   **6.** $23 = 1 - d$ *(p. 132)*

7. $66 = 4m + 7m$ *(p. 132)*   **8.** $-104 = -5p - 3p$ *(p. 132)*

9. $2v + 5v - 8 = 13$ *(p. 139)*   **10.** $2a - 6(a - 4) = -4$ *(p. 139)*

11. $\frac{6}{5}(5 - 4g) = -18$ *(p. 139)*   **12.** $3c - \frac{1}{2}(c - 14) = 2$ *(p. 139)*

13. $8x - 7 = 5x - 1$ *(p. 146)*   **14.** $33 + 13k = -(5k + 21)$ *(p. 146)*

15. $4(-y - 5) = \frac{1}{2}(8 - 4y)$ *(p. 146)* **16.** $2(h + 3) = \frac{1}{6}(12h + 36)$ *(p. 146)*

17. **INTERNET SHOPPING** Lana purchases DVDs from a website. Each DVD costs $11, and the shipping and handling fees are $6.95 regardless of the number of DVDs purchased. Lana pays a total of $50.95. How many DVDs does she purchase? *(p. 132)*

3.4 Solve Equations Using Tables

Standards Preparation

Gr. 7 MR 2.5 Use a variety of methods, such as words, numbers, symbols, charts, graphs, **tables**, diagrams, and models, **to explain mathematical reasoning.**

QUESTION How can you use a spreadsheet to solve an equation with variables on both sides?

You can use a spreadsheet to evaluate the left and right sides of an equation.

EXAMPLE Solve an equation using a spreadsheet

Solve $19(x - 1) - 72 = 6x$.

STEP 1 *Enter data and formulas*

Label columns for possible solutions, left side, and right side in row 1. Enter the integers from 0 through 10 as possible solutions in column A. Then enter the formulas for the left side and the right side of the equation in columns B and C.

	A	B	C
1	Possible solutions	Left side	Right side
2	0	=19*(A2−1)−72	=6*A2
3	1	=19*(A3−1)−72	=6*A3
⋮	⋮	⋮	⋮
12	10	=19*(A12−1)−72	=6*A12

STEP 2 *Compare columns*

Compare the values of the left side and the values of the right side. The solution of the equation is 7.

	A	B	C
1	Possible solutions	Left side	Right side
⋮	⋮	⋮	⋮
8	6	23	36
9	7	42	42
10	8	61	48

DRAW CONCLUSIONS Use your observations to complete these exercises

1. **REASONING** In Step 2 above, explain why you can conclude that 7 is the solution of the equation $19(x - 1) - 72 = 6x$.

In Exercises 2–4, use a spreadsheet to solve the equation.

2. $15x + 6 = 6x + 24$ 3. $8x - 17 = 5x + 70$ 4. $18 - 2(x + 3) = x$

5. Not all equations have integer solutions. Consider the equation $4.9 + 4.8(7 - x) = 6.2x$.

   a. Follow Step 1 above using $4.9 + 4.8(7 - x) = 6.2x$.

   b. Add a fourth column that shows the difference of the value of the left side and the value of the right side. Find consecutive possible solutions between which the numbers in the fourth column change sign.

   c. Repeat Step 1. This time use the lesser of the two possible solutions from part (b) as the first possible solution, and increase each possible solution by 0.1. Can you identify a solution now? If so, what is it?

Multiple Choice Practice for Lessons 3.1–3.4

1. The eruption of Mount St. Helens in 1980 decreased its elevation by 1313 feet. The current elevation is shown in the digram below. Which equation can be used to find the original elevation *e* (in feet) of the volcano before the eruption? **Gr. 6 AF 1.1**

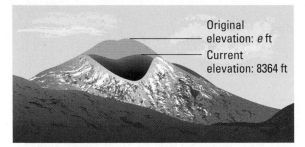

Original elevation: *e* ft
Current elevation: 8364 ft

   (A) $e - 1313 = 8364$

   (B) $e + 1313 = 8364$

   (C) $1313 -wswe = 8364$

   (D) $1313e = 8364$

2. Jorge solved the equation $3(x + 7) = 5x - 21$ as shown.

   Step 1 $3x + 21 = 5x - 21$

   Step 2 $3x - 42 = 5x$

   Step 3 $-42 = 2x$

   Step 4 $-21 = x$

   Which is the first *incorrect* step in Jorge's solution? **Alg. 5.0**

   (A) Step 1   (B) Step 2

   (C) Step 3   (D) Step 4

3. The triangle has a perimeter of 82 inches. What is the value of *x*? **Alg. 5.0**

   $10(x - 1)$ in. $(4x + 14)$ in.

   22 in.

   (A) 3   (B) 4

   (C) 7   (D) 8

4. What is the solution of $\frac{y}{3} = 8$? **Gr. 6 AF 1.1**

   (A) 2   (B) 12

   (C) 24   (D) 32

5. You borrow $432 from your friend. You plan to make one payment of $60, then pay the rest in 12 equal payments. The equation $12x + 60 = 432$ represents this situation. How much is each of the 12 payments? **Gr. 7 AF 4.1**

   (A) $31   (B) $36

   (C) $124   (D) $144

6. What is the solution of $\frac{x}{5} - 7 = 3$? **Gr. 7 AF 4.1**

   (A) 10   (B) 20

   (C) 35   (D) 50

7. A ski resort offers a super-saver pass. The lift ticket rates with and without the super-saver pass are shown. After how many visits to the ski resort will the cost of the super-saver pass and the lift tickets be equal to the cost of the lift tickets without the pass? **Alg. 5.0**

SUPER-SAVER PASS $90
LIFT TICKETS
$22⁵⁰ $45⁰⁰
with pass   without pass

   (A) 3 visits   (B) 4 visits

   (C) 6 visits   (D) 7 visits

8. Which equation is equivalent to $9(2x - 5) = 5(3x + 1) - 32$? **Alg. 4.0**

   (A) $3x = -72$

   (B) $3x = 18$

   (C) $33x = -72$

   (D) $33x = 18$

3.5 Write Ratios and Proportions

Math and COMPETITIONS
Ex. 52, p. 159

Standards Preparation

Gr. 6 NS 1.2 Interpret and use ratios in different contexts (e.g., batting averages, miles per hour) to show the relative sizes of two quantities, using appropriate notations $\left(\frac{a}{b}, a \text{ to } b, a : b\right)$.

Connect

Before you solved equations using division. *Now* you will find ratios and write and solve proportions to prepare for Algebra 1 Standard 7.0.

Key Vocabulary
• ratio
• proportion
• simplest form, p. 786

Throughout this book you have been using rates, such as 50 miles per hour. A rate is a special type of *ratio*.

KEY CONCEPT   *For Your Notebook*

Ratios

A **ratio** uses division to compare two quantities. You can write the ratio of two quantities a and b, where b is not equal to 0, in three ways.

$$a \text{ to } b \qquad\qquad a : b \qquad\qquad \frac{a}{b}$$

Each ratio is read "the ratio of a to b." Ratios should be written in simplest form.

EXAMPLE 1   **Write a ratio**

VOLLEYBALL A volleyball team plays 14 home matches and 10 away matches.

  a. Find the ratio of home matches to away matches.

  b. Find the ratio of home matches to all matches.

Solution

  a. $\dfrac{\text{home matches}}{\text{away matches}} = \dfrac{14}{10} = \dfrac{7}{5}$

  b. $\dfrac{\text{home matches}}{\text{all matches}} = \dfrac{14}{14 + 10} = \dfrac{14}{24} = \dfrac{7}{12}$

✓ **GUIDED PRACTICE**   **for Example 1**

Derek and his brother decide to combine their CD collections. Derek has 44 CDs, and his brother has 52 CDs. Find the specified ratio.

  1. The number of Derek's CDs to the number of his brother's CDs

  2. The number of Derek's CDs to the number of CDs in the entire collection

PROPORTIONS A **proportion** is an equation that states that two ratios are equivalent. The general form of a proportion is given below.

READING
This proportion is read
"*a* is to *b* as *c* is to *d*."

$$\frac{a}{b} = \frac{c}{d} \text{ where } b \neq 0, d \neq 0$$

If one of the numbers in a proportion is unknown, you can solve the proportion to find the unknown number. To solve a proportion with a variable in the numerator, you can use the same methods you used to solve equations.

EXAMPLE 2 Solve a proportion

Solve the proportion $\frac{11}{6} = \frac{x}{30}$.

$\dfrac{11}{6} = \dfrac{x}{30}$	Write original proportion.
$30 \cdot \dfrac{11}{6} = 30 \cdot \dfrac{x}{30}$	Multiply each side by 30.
$\dfrac{330}{6} = x$	Simplify.
$55 = x$	Divide.

✓ **GUIDED PRACTICE** for Example 2

Solve the proportion. Check your solution.

3. $\dfrac{w}{35} = \dfrac{4}{7}$ 4. $\dfrac{9}{2} = \dfrac{m}{12}$ 5. $\dfrac{z}{54} = \dfrac{5}{9}$

SETTING UP A PROPORTION There are different ways to set up a proportion. Consider the following problem.

A recipe for tomato salsa calls for 30 tomatoes to make 12 pints of salsa. How many tomatoes are needed to make 4 pints of salsa?

The tables below show two ways of arranging the information from the problem. In each table, *x* represents the number of tomatoes needed to make 4 pints of salsa. The proportions follow from the tables.

AVOID ERRORS
You cannot write a proportion that compares pints to tomatoes and tomatoes to pints.

$\dfrac{\text{pints}}{\text{tomatoes}} \neq \dfrac{\text{tomatoes}}{\text{pints}}$

	Tomatoes	Pints of salsa
Smaller recipe	*x*	4
Normal recipe	30	12

Proportion: $\dfrac{x}{30} = \dfrac{4}{12}$

	Smaller recipe	Normal recipe
Tomatoes	*x*	30
Pints of salsa	4	12

Proportion: $\dfrac{x}{4} = \dfrac{30}{12}$

EXAMPLE 3 Solve a multi-step problem

ELEVATORS The elevator that takes passengers from the lobby of the John Hancock Center in Chicago to the observation level travels 150 feet in 5 seconds. Find the time the elevator takes to travel from the lobby to the observation level.

1029 ft

ANOTHER WAY

You can find the time by dividing the distance the elevator travels by the elevator's speed, which

is $\frac{150 \text{ ft}}{5 \text{ sec}} = 30$ ft/sec.

$\frac{\text{distance}}{\text{speed}} = \frac{1029 \text{ ft}}{30 \text{ ft/sec}}$

$= 34.3$ sec

Solution

STEP 1 **Write** a proportion involving two ratios that compare the amount of time the elevator moves with the distance it travels.

$$\frac{5}{150} = \frac{x}{1029} \quad \xleftarrow{\text{—— seconds}} \\ \xleftarrow{\text{—— feet}}$$

STEP 2 **Solve** the proportion.

$$\frac{5}{150} = \frac{x}{1029} \qquad \text{Write proportion.}$$

$$1029 \cdot \frac{5}{150} = 1029 \cdot \frac{x}{1029} \qquad \text{Multiply each side by 1029.}$$

$$\frac{5145}{150} = x \qquad \text{Simplify.}$$

$$34.3 = x \qquad \text{Use a calculator.}$$

▶ The elevator travels from the lobby to the observation level in 34.3 seconds.

CHECK You can use a table to check the reasonableness of the solution.

GENERATE TABLE

As the amount of time increases by 5 seconds, the distance traveled increases by 150 feet.

Time (sec)	5	10	15	20	25	30	35
Distance traveled (ft)	150	300	450	600	750	900	1050

The solution, 34.3 seconds, is slightly less than 35 seconds, and 1029 feet is slightly less than 1050 feet. So, the solution is reasonable.

✓ **GUIDED PRACTICE** for Example 3

6. **WHAT IF?** In Example 3, suppose the elevator travels 125 feet in 5 seconds. Find the time the elevator takes to travel from the lobby to the observation level.

7. **ASTRONOMY** When two full moons appear in the same month, the second full moon is called a blue moon. On average, 2 blue moons occur every 5 years. Find the number of blue moons that are likely to occur in the next 25 years.

3.5 EXERCISES

SKILLS · PROBLEM SOLVING · REASONING

1. **VOCABULARY** Copy and complete: A proportion is an equation that states that two __?__ are equal.

2. **WRITING** Write a ratio of two quantities in three different ways.

SIMPLIFYING RATIOS Tell whether the ratio is in simplest form. If not, write it in simplest form.

3. 14 to 18

4. $5 : 13$

5. $\dfrac{24}{25}$

6. 28 to 32

EXAMPLE 2
on p. 156
for Exs. 7–26

SOLVING PROPORTIONS Solve the proportion. Check your solution.

7. $\dfrac{2}{5} = \dfrac{x}{3}$

8. $\dfrac{4}{1} = \dfrac{z}{16}$

9. $\dfrac{c}{8} = \dfrac{11}{4}$

10. $\dfrac{36}{12} = \dfrac{x}{2}$

11. $\dfrac{16}{7} = \dfrac{m}{21}$

12. $\dfrac{k}{9} = \dfrac{10}{18}$

13. $\dfrac{5}{8} = \dfrac{t}{24}$

14. $\dfrac{d}{5} = \dfrac{80}{100}$

15. $\dfrac{v}{20} = \dfrac{8}{4}$

16. $\dfrac{r}{60} = \dfrac{40}{50}$

17. $\dfrac{16}{48} = \dfrac{n}{36}$

18. $\dfrac{49}{98} = \dfrac{s}{112}$

19. $\dfrac{6}{26} = \dfrac{a}{39}$

20. $\dfrac{b}{100} = \dfrac{13}{25}$

21. $\dfrac{h}{66} = \dfrac{38}{44}$

22. $\dfrac{y}{7} = \dfrac{45}{21}$

23. ◆ **MULTIPLE CHOICE** What is the value of x in the proportion $\dfrac{8}{5} = \dfrac{x}{20}$?

　(**A**) 2　　　　(**B**) 23　　　　(**C**) 32　　　　(**D**) 40

24. ◆ **MULTIPLE CHOICE** What is the value of z in the proportion $\dfrac{z}{15} = \dfrac{28}{35}$?

　(**A**) 8　　　　(**B**) 12　　　　(**C**) 18.75　　　　(**D**) 425

ERROR ANALYSIS *Describe* and correct the error in solving the proportion.

25.

$$\frac{3}{4} = \frac{x}{6}$$
$$\frac{1}{6} \cdot \frac{3}{4} = \frac{1}{6} \cdot \frac{x}{6}$$
$$\frac{1}{8} = x$$　✗

26.

$$\frac{m}{10} = \frac{50}{20}$$
$$10 \cdot \frac{m}{10} = 20 \cdot \frac{50}{20}$$
$$m = 50$$　✗

WRITING PROPORTIONS Write the sentence as a proportion.

27. 3 is to 8 as x is to 32.

28. 5 is to 7 as a is to 49.

29. x is to 4 as 8 is to 16.

30. y is to 20 as 9 is to 5.

31. b is to 10 as 7 is to 2.

32. 4 is to 12 as n is to 3.

33. 12 is to 18 as d is to 27.

34. t is to 21 as 40 is to 28.

SOLVING PROPORTIONS Solve the proportion. Check your solution.

35. $\dfrac{b}{0.5} = \dfrac{9}{2.5}$

36. $\dfrac{1.1}{1.2} = \dfrac{n}{3.6}$

37. $\dfrac{2.1}{7.7} = \dfrac{v}{8.8}$

38. $\dfrac{36}{54} = \dfrac{2x}{6}$

39. $\dfrac{3a}{4} = \dfrac{36}{12}$

40. $\dfrac{10h}{108} = \dfrac{5}{9}$

41. $\dfrac{6r}{10} = \dfrac{36}{15}$

42. $\dfrac{12}{42} = \dfrac{4w}{56}$

43. $\dfrac{m+3}{8} = \dfrac{40}{64}$

44. $\dfrac{5}{13} = \dfrac{k-4}{39}$

45. $\dfrac{7}{112} = \dfrac{c-3}{8}$

46. $\dfrac{6+n}{60} = \dfrac{15}{90}$

47. REASONING Write a proportion that does not have any variables and uses 4 different numbers. How many ways can you rearrange the numbers so that the ratios are still equal?

CONNECT SKILLS TO PROBLEM SOLVING Exercises 48–50 will help you prepare for problem solving.

Write a proportion that represents the situation.

48. A job requires an employee to be able to type 120 words in 2 minutes. The employee should be able to type x words in 7 minutes.

49. A traffic light is yellow for 3 seconds out of every 30 seconds. The light will be yellow for a total of x seconds in 8 minutes.

50. You can buy 6 bottles of water for $5. You can buy x bottles of water for $12.50.

EXAMPLE 1
on p. 155
for Exs. 51–55

51. GOVERNMENT There are 435 representatives in the U.S. House of Representatives. Of the 435 representatives, 6 are from Kentucky. Find the ratio of the number of representatives from Kentucky to the total number of representatives.

California @HomeTutor for problem solving help at classzone.com

52. CONTEST Of the 30 champions of the National Spelling Bee from 1974 to 2003, 16 are boys. Find the ratio of the number of champions who are girls to the number who are boys.

California @HomeTutor for problem solving help at classzone.com

Representatives in U.S. House: 435

PIZZA SALES The table shows the number of pizzas sold at a pizzeria during a week. Use the information to find the specified ratio.

53. Small pizzas to large pizzas

54. Medium pizzas to large pizzas

55. Large pizzas to all pizzas

Size	Small	Medium	Large
Pizzas	96	144	240

EXAMPLE 3
on p. 157
for Exs. 56–58

56. ◆ MULTIPLE CHOICE A student can read 7 pages of a book in 10 minutes. Which proportion can be used to find x, the number of pages of the book the student read in 30 minutes?

(A) $\dfrac{7}{10} = \dfrac{x}{30}$

(B) $\dfrac{7}{10} = \dfrac{30}{x}$

(C) $\dfrac{7}{30} = \dfrac{x}{10}$

(D) $\dfrac{7}{10} = \dfrac{x+7}{30}$

57. SOCCER In the first 4 games of the season, a soccer team scored a total of 10 goals. If this trend continues, how many goals will the team score in the 18 remaining games of the season?

58. MOVIES A movie is filmed so that the ratio of the length to the width of the image on the screen is 1.85 : 1.

    a. Writing a Proportion Write and solve a proportion to find the length of the image on the screen when the width of the image is 38 feet.

    b. Making a Table Rewrite the ratio of the length of the image to the width using whole numbers. Then write the ratio in simplified form. Make a table that shows the length of an image when the width of the image is 20 and 40 feet. Use your table to check the reasonableness of your answer to part (a).

59. MULTI-STEP PROBLEM One day, the ratio of skiers to snowboarders on the mountain at a ski resort was 13 : 10. The resort sold a total of 253 lift tickets during the day.

    a. Find the ratio of snowboarders on the mountain to all of the skiers and snowboarders on the mountain.

    b. Use the ratio from part (a) to find the number of lift tickets sold to snowboarders during the day.

    c. During the same day, the ratio of snowboarders who rented snowboards to snowboarders who used their own snowboards is 4 : 7. Find the number of snowboarders who rented a snowboard.

60. SPEED OF LIGHT Light travels about 18.6 million miles in 100 seconds. Light takes about 193.5 seconds to travel from the Sun to Mercury.

    a. Use a proportion to find the distance between the Sun and Mercury.

    b. Find the speed of light (in miles per second). Use this value to find the distance between the Sun and Mercury. *Explain* your method.

61. CHALLENGE If $\dfrac{a}{b} = \dfrac{c}{d}$ for nonzero numbers a, b, c, and d, is it also true that $\dfrac{a}{c} = \dfrac{b}{d}$? *Explain.*

62. CHALLENGE A car traveling 50 miles per hour goes 15 miles farther in the same amount of time as a car traveling 30 miles per hour. Find the distance that each car travels.

◆ CALIFORNIA STANDARDS SPIRAL REVIEW

Gr. 7 AF 1.4

63. Which of the following words best describes the 3 in the equation $3x - 2 = 5$? *(p. 81)*

    (A) Expression   **(B)** Coefficient   **(C)** Variable   **(D)** Term

Gr. 7 NS 1.2

64. What is the value of $-\dfrac{4}{3} \times \dfrac{6}{13}$? *(p. 74)*

    (A) $-\dfrac{5}{8}$ **(B)** $-\dfrac{8}{13}$ **(C)** $\dfrac{1}{8}$ **(D)** 1

Alg. 24.2

65. Which of the following is the hypothesis of the statement "If a number is divisible by 2, then the number is even"? *(p. 53)*

    (A) A number is divisible by 2   **(B)** A number is not divisible by 2

    (C) A number is even   **(D)** A number is even and divisible by 2

3.6 Solve Proportions Using Cross Products

Math and MODELS
Ex. 49, p. 166

Standards Preparation

Gr. 6 NS 1.3 Use proportions to solve problems (e.g., determine the value of *N* if $\frac{4}{7} = \frac{N}{21}$, find the length of a side of a polygon similar to a known polygon). **Use cross-multiplication as a method for solving such problems, understanding it as the multiplication of both sides of an equation by a multiplicative inverse.**

Connect

Before you solved proportions using the multiplication property of equality. *Now* you will solve proportions using cross products to prepare for Algebra 1 Standard 7.0.

Key Vocabulary
• cross product
• scale drawing
• scale model
• scale

In a proportion, a **cross product** is the product of the numerator of one ratio and the denominator of the other ratio. The following property involving cross products can be used to solve proportions. You will prove the cross products property in Exercise 39.

KEY CONCEPT   *For Your Notebook*

Cross Products Property

Words The cross products of a proportion are equal.

Example $\frac{3}{4} = \frac{6}{8}$ $4 \cdot 6 = 24$
$3 \cdot 8 = 24$

Algebra If $\frac{a}{b} = \frac{c}{d}$ where $b \neq 0$ and $d \neq 0$, then $ad = bc$.

EXAMPLE 1   Use the cross products property

Solve the proportion $\frac{8}{x} = \frac{6}{15}$.

$\frac{8}{x} = \frac{6}{15}$ **Write original proportion.**

$8 \cdot 15 = x \cdot 6$ **Cross products property**

$120 = 6x$ **Simplify.**

$20 = x$ **Divide each side by 6.**

▶ The solution is 20. You can check the solution by substituting 20 for *x* in the original proportion.

✓ **GUIDED PRACTICE**   for Example 1

1. Solve the proportion $\frac{4}{a} = \frac{24}{30}$. Check your solution.

EXAMPLE 2 **Use the cross products property**

Solve the proportion $\dfrac{4}{x} = \dfrac{8}{x-3}$.

ANOTHER WAY
Because 8 is twice 4, you can reason that $x - 3$ must be twice x:
$$x - 3 = 2x$$
$$-3 = x$$

$\dfrac{4}{x} = \dfrac{8}{x-3}$ **Write original proportion.**

$4(x - 3) = x \cdot 8$ **Cross products property**

$4x - 12 = 8x$ **Simplify.**

$-12 = 4x$ **Subtract 4x from each side.**

$-3 = x$ **Divide each side by 4.**

▶ The solution is −3. Check by substituting −3 for x in the original proportion.

CHECK $\dfrac{4}{-3} \overset{?}{=} \dfrac{8}{-3-3}$ **Substitute −3 for x.**

$\dfrac{4}{-3} \overset{?}{=} \dfrac{8}{-6}$ **Simplify denominator.**

$\dfrac{4}{-3} \overset{?}{=} \dfrac{4}{-3}$ ✓   **Simplify ratio. Solution checks.**

EXAMPLE 3 **Write and solve a proportion**

SEALS Each day, the seals at an aquarium are each fed 8 pounds of food for every 100 pounds of their body weight. A seal at the aquarium weighs 280 pounds. How much food should the seal be fed per day?

Solution

STEP 1 **Write** a proportion involving two ratios that compare the amount of food with the weight of the seal.

$\dfrac{8}{100} = \dfrac{x}{280}$ ◀— **amount of food**
                 ◀— **weight of seal**

STEP 2 **Solve** the proportion.

ANOTHER WAY
You can also solve the proportion by multiplying each side of the equation by 280.

$\dfrac{8}{100} = \dfrac{x}{280}$ **Write proportion.**

$8 \cdot 280 = 100 \cdot x$ **Cross products property**

$2240 = 100x$ **Simplify.**

$22.4 = x$ **Divide each side by 100.**

▶ A 280 pound seal should be fed 22.4 pounds of food per day.

✓   **GUIDED PRACTICE**   for Examples 2 and 3

Solve the proportion. Check your solution.

2. $\dfrac{2}{a} = \dfrac{7}{a+5}$ **3.** $\dfrac{3}{x} = \dfrac{2}{x-6}$ **4.** $\dfrac{m}{5} = \dfrac{m-6}{4}$

5. **WHAT IF?** In Example 3, suppose the seal weighs 260 pounds. How much food should the seal be fed per day?

3.7 Rewrite Equations and Formulas

Standards Preparation

Gr. 6 AF 3.1 Use variables in expressions describing geometric quantities (e.g., $P = 2w + 2\ell$, $A = \frac{1}{2}bh$, $C = \pi d$—the formulas for the perimeter of a rectangle, the area of a triangle, and the circumference of a circle, respectively).

Connect *Before* you solved equations and used formulas. *Now* you will rewrite equations and formulas to prepare for Algebra 1 Standard 7.0.

Math and **RECREATION**
Ex. 44, p. 172

Key Vocabulary
• literal equation
• formula, *p. 34*

The equations $2x + 5 = 11$ and $6x + 3 = 15$ have the general form $ax + b = c$. The equation $ax + b = c$ is called a **literal equation** because the coefficients and constants have been replaced by letters. When you solve a literal equation, you can use the result to solve any equation that has the same form as the literal equation.

EXAMPLE 1 Solve a literal equation

READING
When you solve an equation or formula in two or more variables for one of the variables, you are expressing that variable in terms of the other variables.

Solve $ax + b = c$ for x. Then use the solution to solve $2x + 5 = 11$.

Solution

STEP 1 Solve $ax + b = c$ for x.

$ax + b = c$	**Write original equation.**
$ax = c - b$	**Subtraction property of equality**
$x = \dfrac{c - b}{a}$	**Assume $a \neq 0$. Division property of equality**

STEP 2 Use the solution to solve $2x + 5 = 11$.

$x = \dfrac{c - b}{a}$	**Solution of literal equation**
$= \dfrac{11 - 5}{2}$	**Substitute 2 for a, 5 for b, and 11 for c.**
$= 3$	**Simplify.**

▶ The solution of $2x + 5 = 11$ is 3.

VARIABLES IN DENOMINATORS In Example 1, you must assume that $a \neq 0$ in order to divide by a. In general, if you have to divide by a variable when solving a literal equation, you should assume that the variable does not equal 0.

 GUIDED PRACTICE for Example 1

Solve the literal equation for x. Then use the solution to solve the specific equation.

1. $a - bx = c$; $12 - 5x = -3$
2. $ax = bx + c$; $11x = 6x + 20$

TWO OR MORE VARIABLES An equation in two variables, such as $3x + 2y = 8$, or a formula in two or more variables, such as $A = \frac{1}{2}bh$, can be solved for a specific variable.

EXAMPLE 2 Rewrite an equation

Solve the equation $3x + 2y = 8$ for y.

$3x + 2y = 8$	**Write original equation.**
$2y = 8 - 3x$	**Subtraction property of equality**
$y = 4 - \frac{3}{2}x$	**Division property of equality**

EXAMPLE 3 Rewrite and use a geometric formula

Animated Algebra

For an interactive example of solving a geometry formula, go to **classzone.com**.

The area A of a triangle is given by the formula $A = \frac{1}{2}bh$ where b is the base and h is the height.

a. Solve the formula for the height h.

b. Use the rewritten formula to find the height of the triangle shown, which has an area of 64.4 square meters.

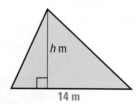

h m

14 m

Solution

a.

$A = \frac{1}{2}bh$	**Write original formula.**
$2A = bh$	**Multiplication property of equality**
$\frac{2A}{b} = h$	**Division property of equality**

USE UNIT ANALYSIS

When area is measured in square meters and the base is measured in meters, dividing twice the area by the base gives a result measured in meters.

b. Substitute 64.4 for A and 14 for b in the rewritten formula.

$h = \frac{2A}{b}$	**Write rewritten formula.**
$= \frac{2(64.4)}{14}$	**Substitute 64.4 for A and 14 for b.**
$= 9.2$	**Simplify.**

▶ The height of the triangle is 9.2 meters.

✓ **GUIDED PRACTICE** for Examples 2 and 3

3. Solve the equation $5x + 4y = 20$ for y.

4. The perimeter P of a rectangle is given by the formula $P = 2\ell + 2w$ where ℓ is the length and w is the width.

a. Solve the formula for the width w.

b. Use the rewritten formula to find the width of the rectangle shown.

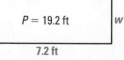

$P = 19.2$ ft

w

7.2 ft

EXAMPLE 4 Solve a multi-step problem

PHOTOGRAPHY As part of a photography class project, you need to print, trim, and frame a photo. You want the length of the photo to be twice its width. You can choose one of two different framing kits.

- One kit has framing that is 1 inch wide and includes 26 inches of framing.

- The other kit has framing that is 1 inch wide and includes 29 inches of framing.

Suppose you plan to use all of the framing in either kit. What should the dimensions of your trimmed photo be?

Solution

STEP 1 **Draw** a diagram and use it to write a formula for the perimeter P (in inches) of the frame in terms of x, the width (in inches) of the photo.

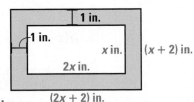

$$P = 2\ell + 2w \qquad \text{Write formula.}$$

$$= 2(2x + 2) + 2(x + 2) \qquad \text{Substitute } 2x + 2 \text{ for } \ell \text{ and } x + 2 \text{ for } w.$$

$$= 4x + 4 + 2x + 4 \qquad \text{Distributive property}$$

$$= 6x + 8 \qquad \text{Combine like terms.}$$

REWRITE FORMULAS
When using a formula for multiple calculations, you may find it easier to rewrite the formula first.

STEP 2 **Solve** the formula for x.

$$P = 6x + 8 \qquad \text{Write original formula.}$$

$$P - 8 = 6x \qquad \text{Subtraction property of equality}$$

$$\frac{P - 8}{6} = x \qquad \text{Division property of equality}$$

STEP 3 **Find** the dimensions of the photo for each frame.

Using 26 inches of framing	**Using 29 inches of framing**
$x = \dfrac{P - 8}{6}$	$x = \dfrac{P - 8}{6}$
$= \dfrac{26 - 8}{6}$	$= \dfrac{29 - 8}{6}$
$= 3$	$= 3.5$

▶ If $x = 3$, then $2x = 6$. If $x = 3.5$, then $2x = 7$. So, if you use 26 inches of framing, your trimmed photo should be 3 inches wide and 6 inches long. If you use 29 inches of framing, your trimmed photo should be 3.5 inches wide and 7 inches long.

✓ **GUIDED PRACTICE** for Example 4

5. **WHAT IF?** In Example 4, suppose you choose a kit with framing that is 2 inches wide and includes 52 inches of framing. What should the dimensions of your trimmed photo be if you plan to use all of the framing?

3.7 EXERCISES

HOMEWORK KEY

◆ = **MULTIPLE CHOICE PRACTICE**
Exs. 25, 29, 30, 46, and 52–54

○ = **HINTS AND HOMEWORK HELP**
for Exs. 9, 21, and 47 at classzone.com

SKILLS · PROBLEM SOLVING · REASONING

1. **VOCABULARY** Copy and complete: When you write the equation $3x + 2 = 8$ as $ax + b = c$, the equation $ax + b = c$ is called a(n) __?__ because the coefficients and constants have been replaced by letters.

2. **WRITING** *Describe* the steps you would take to solve $I = Prt$ for t.

EXAMPLE 1
on p. 167
for Exs. 3–12

LITERAL EQUATIONS Solve the literal equation for x. Then use the solution to solve the specific equation.

3. $ax = bx - c$; $8x = 3x - 10$

4. $a(x + b) = c$; $2(x + 1) = 9$

5. $a(x - b) = c$; $11(x - 4) = 121$

6. $c = \dfrac{x + a}{b}$; $2 = \dfrac{x + 5}{7}$

7. $\dfrac{x}{a} = \dfrac{b}{c}$; $\dfrac{x}{8} = \dfrac{4.5}{12}$

8. $\dfrac{a}{x} = \dfrac{b}{c}$; $\dfrac{5.4}{x} = \dfrac{9.6}{8}$

9. $\dfrac{x}{a} + b = c$; $\dfrac{x}{4} + 6 = 13$

10. $ax + b = cx - d$; $2x + 9 = 7x - 1$

ERROR ANALYSIS *Describe* and correct the error in solving the equation for x.

11.
$$ax + b = 0$$
$$ax = b$$
$$x = \frac{b}{a}$$

12.
$$c = ax - bx$$
$$c = (a - b)x$$
$$c(a - b) = x$$

EXAMPLE 2
on p. 168
for Exs. 13–25

REWRITING EQUATIONS Solve the equation for y.

13. $2x + y = 7$

14. $5x + 4y = 10$

15. $12 = 9x + 3y$

16. $18x - 2y = 26$

17. $14 = 7y - 6x$

18. $8x - 8y = 5$

19. $124 = 4x - 10y$

20. $16y + 12x = 28$

21. $30 = 9x - 5y$

22. $3 + 6x = 11 - 4y$

23. $1 - 7x = 2 - y$

24. $2 + 6y = 3x + 4$

25. ◆ **MULTIPLE CHOICE** Which equation is equivalent to $9x - 3y = 15$?

(A) $y = -3x - 5$

(B) $y = -3x + 5$

(C) $y = 3x - 5$

(D) $y = 3x + 5$

EXAMPLE 3
on p. 168
for Exs. 26–30

REWRITING FORMULAS Solve the formula for the indicated variable.

26. Volume of a rectangular prism: $V = \ell wh$. Solve for w.

27. Surface area of a prism: $S = 2B + Ph$. Solve for h.

28. Length (in seconds) of a movie projected at 24 frames per second: $\ell = 24f$. Solve for f.

Animated Algebra at classzone.com

29. ◆ MULTIPLE CHOICE The formula for the area of a trapezoid is $A = \frac{1}{2}(b_1 + b_2)h$. Which equation is *not* equivalent to the formula?

(A) $h = \dfrac{2A}{b_1 + b_2}$

(B) $b_1 = \dfrac{2A}{h} - b_2$

(C) $b_2 = \dfrac{2A}{b_1} - h$

(D) $b_2 = \dfrac{2A}{h} - b_1$

30. ◆ MULTIPLE CHOICE Which equation can be used to find the value of x given the perimeter P of the triangle shown?

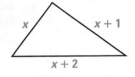

(A) $x = \dfrac{P - 3}{2}$

(B) $x = \dfrac{P - 3}{3}$

(C) $x = \dfrac{P + 3}{3}$

(D) $x = P - 3$

REWRITING EQUATIONS Solve the equation for y.

31. $4.2x - 2y = 16.8$

32. $9 - 0.5y = 2.5x$

33. $-6.5x + 28 = 2 - 1.3y$

34. $8x - 5x + 21 = 36 - 6y$

35. $3.8 - 4.9x + 0.1x = 2.4y + 0.2$

36. $5.4y - 1.2y + 9.8 = 2.1x - 7$

◈ GEOMETRY Solve the formula for the indicated variable. Then evaluate the rewritten formula for the given values. (Use 3.14 for π.)

37. Surface area of a cone:
$S = \pi r \ell + \pi r^2$.
Solve for ℓ. Find ℓ when
$S = 283$ cm^2 and $r = 5$ cm.

38. Area of a circular ring:
$A = 4\pi p w$.
Solve for p. Find p when
$A = 905$ ft^2 and $w = 9$ ft.

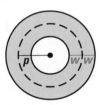

39. REASONING In the steps below, the equation $ax + by = c$ has been solved for y. Copy and complete.

$ax + by = c$ Write original equation.

$by = -ax + c$ **a.** ___?___

$y = \frac{1}{b}(-ax + c)$ **b.** ___?___

$y = -\frac{a}{b}x + \frac{c}{b}$ **c.** ___?___

CONNECT SKILLS TO PROBLEM SOLVING Exercises 40–42 will help you prepare for problem solving.

Use the following information: The perimeter P of a square with a side length of s is given by $P = 4s$.

40. Solve the formula for s.

41. Find the side lengths of squares having perimeters of 4 cm, 8 cm, 16 cm, and 32 cm.

42. What is the effect on the perimeter P of a square when the side length is doubled?

EXAMPLE 4
on p. 169
for Exs. 43–48

43. **CARPENTRY** The penny size s of a nail is given by $s = 4\ell - 2$ where ℓ is the length (in inches) of the nail.

   a. Solve the formula for ℓ.

   b. Use the new formula to find the lengths of nails with the following penny sizes: 5, 12, 16, and 20.

   California **@Home Tutor** for problem solving help at classzone.com

44. **BOWLING** To participate in a bowling league, you pay a $25 sign-up fee and $12 for each league night that you bowl. So, the total cost C (in dollars) is given by the equation

$$C = 12x + 25$$

   where x is the number of league nights you bowled.

   a. Solve the equation for x.

   b. How many league nights have you bowled if you spent a total of $145? $181? $205?

   California **@Home Tutor** for problem solving help at classzone.com

45. **MULTI-STEP PROBLEM** One type of stone formation found in Carlsbad Caverns in New Mexico is called a column. This cylindrical stone formation is connected to the ceiling and the floor of a cave.

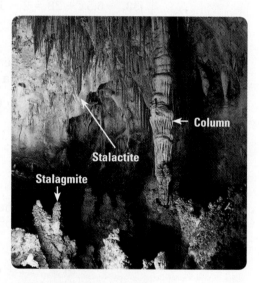

← Column

Stalactite

Stalagmite
↓

   a. Rewrite the formula for the circumference of a circle, $C = 2\pi r$, so that you can easily calculate the radius of a column given its circumference.

   b. What is the radius, to the nearest tenth of a foot, of a column that has a circumference of 7 feet? 8 feet? 9 feet? (Use 3.14 for π.)

   c. *Explain* how you can find the *area* of a cross section of a column if you know its circumference.

46. ◆ **MULTIPLE CHOICE** You are helping to plant a community flower garden. The garden is a rectangle with a width of 25 feet. You are asked to put edging around the garden and are told that the perimeter of the garden is 135 feet. What is the length of the garden?

   (A) 5.4 ft   **(B)** 42.5 ft   **(C)** 85 ft   **(D)** 110 ft

47. **TEMPERATURE** You plan to travel to Vancouver, Canada. You check the weather on a news website. The formula

$$C = \frac{5}{9}(F - 32)$$

   gives the temperature C in degrees Celsius in terms of the temperature F in degrees Fahrenheit. Solve the formula for F to find the predicted temperatures in degrees Fahrenheit. Round your answers to the nearest degree.

   a. Saturday's predicted low temperature: 3°C

   b. Sunday's predicted low temperature: 7°C

48. INDOOR TRACK An athletic facility is building an indoor track like the one shown. The perimeter P of the track is given by $P = 2\pi r + 2x$. The facility is deciding between a track with a perimeter of 660 feet and a track with a perimeter of 1320 feet. Given that $x = 4r$, solve the formula for r. Use the rewritten formula to find the radius and length of each track. (Use 3.14 for π.)

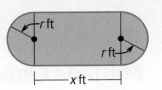

CHALLENGE Solve the literal equation for a.

49. $x = \dfrac{a + b + c}{ab}$

50. $y = x\left(\dfrac{ab}{a - b}\right)$

51. CHALLENGE The distance d (in miles) traveled by a car is given by $d = 55t$ where t is the time (in hours) the car has traveled at 55 mi/h. The distance d (in miles) traveled is also given by $d = 20g$ where g is the number of gallons of gasoline used by the car if it gets 20 mi/gal. Write an equation that expresses g in terms of t.

◆ CALIFORNIA STANDARDS SPIRAL REVIEW

Alg. 2.0

52. What is the value of $\sqrt{16} + \sqrt{4}$? *(p. 95)*

    (A) 4   **(B)** 6   **(C)** 8   **(D)** 10

Alg. 4.0

53. Which equation is equivalent to $-2(4x + 7) = 8 + 3(3x - 5)$? *(p. 146)*

    (A) $-21 = -x$ **(B)** $-7 = 17x$

    (C) $7 = 17x$ **(D)** $-14 = 12x$

Gr. 6 NS 1.3

54. A map uses a scale of 1 inch : 75 miles. How many miles are represented by 4 inches on the map? *(p. 161)*

    (A) 4 mi   **(B)** 75 mi   **(C)** 150 mi   **(D)** 300 mi

QUIZ *for Lessons 3.5–3.7*

Solve the proportion. Check your solution. *(pp. 155, 161)*

1. $\dfrac{7}{1} = \dfrac{x}{4}$ **2.** $\dfrac{4}{5} = \dfrac{d}{25}$ **3.** $\dfrac{s}{90} = \dfrac{24}{60}$

4. $\dfrac{8}{x} = \dfrac{12}{15}$ **5.** $\dfrac{2}{11} = \dfrac{x}{x + 9}$ **6.** $\dfrac{15}{x - 3} = \dfrac{10}{x}$

Solve the equation for y. *(p. 167)*

7. $5x - 3y = 9$ **8.** $3x + 2y + 5x = 12$ **9.** $4(2x - y) = 6$

10. WALKING You take 16.5 minutes to walk 1.5 miles. At this rate, how long will you take to walk 5 miles? *(p. 155)*

11. ◎ GEOMETRY The volume V of a cylinder is given by the formula $V = \pi r^2 h$ where r is the radius of the cylinder and h is the height of the cylinder. Solve the formula for h. *(p. 167)*

Multiple Choice Practice for Lessons 3.5–3.7

1. Which equation is equivalent to $39x - 3y = 18$? **Gr. 6 AF 3.1**

   Ⓐ $y = 13x - 6$

   Ⓑ $y = 13x + 6$

   Ⓒ $y = -13x - 6$

   Ⓓ $y = -13x + 6$

2. The table below shows the results of a survey in which students at a school were asked to name their favorite sport to watch on TV. There are 1209 students in the school. Which proportion could be used to predict the number s of students in the school who would name baseball as their favorite sport to watch on TV? **Gr. 6 NS 1.3**

Sport	Students
Baseball	7
Basketball	6
Football	10
Other	8

   Ⓐ $\frac{7}{24} = \frac{s}{1209}$ Ⓑ $\frac{7}{31} = \frac{s}{1209}$

   Ⓒ $\frac{7}{31} = \frac{1209}{s}$ Ⓓ $\frac{7}{1209} = \frac{s}{31}$

3. Which proportion represents the sentence "x is to 18 as 70 is to 84"? **Gr. 7 AF 1.1**

   Ⓐ $\frac{x}{18} = \frac{70}{84}$ Ⓑ $\frac{x}{18} = \frac{84}{70}$

   Ⓒ $\frac{x}{70} = \frac{84}{18}$ Ⓓ $\frac{18x}{1} = \frac{70}{84}$

4. There are 15 male students and 25 female students in the drama club at a school. What is the ratio of male students in the drama club to female students in the drama club? **Gr. 6 NS 1.2**

   Ⓐ $3:5$ Ⓑ $3:8$

   Ⓒ $5:3$ Ⓓ $5:8$

5. A landscape designer made the scale drawing of a garden shown below. She used a scale of 2 cm : 5 m. What are the dimensions of the actual garden? **Gr. 6 NS 1.3**

   3 cm

   6 cm

   Ⓐ 1.2 m by 2 m Ⓑ 6 m by 12 m

   Ⓒ 7.5 m by 15 m Ⓓ 15 m by 30 m

6. What is the value of x in the proportion $\frac{x+1}{3} = \frac{x}{12}$? **Gr. 6 NS 1.3**

   Ⓐ -4 Ⓑ $-\frac{4}{3}$

   Ⓒ $\frac{4}{3}$ Ⓓ 4

7. The area A of a rhombus is given by the formula $A = \frac{1}{2}d_1 d_2$ where d_1 and d_2 are the lengths of the diagonals. Which equation shows the formula solved for the length d_1? **Gr. 6 AF 3.1**

   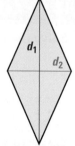

   d_1

   d_2

   Ⓐ $d_1 = \frac{Ad_2}{2}$

   Ⓑ $d_1 = 2Ad_2$

   Ⓒ $d_1 = \frac{A}{2d_2}$

   Ⓓ $d_1 = \frac{2A}{d_2}$

8. Which fraction represents the ratio of 12 to 42 in simplest form? **Gr. 6 NS 1.2**

   Ⓐ $\frac{1}{4}$ Ⓑ $\frac{2}{7}$

   Ⓒ $\frac{3}{7}$ Ⓓ $\frac{6}{21}$

BIG IDEAS
For Your Notebook

Big Idea 1

Solving Equations in One Variable

You can solve equations in one variable by adding, subtracting, multiplying by, or dividing by the same number on each side.

Property	Words	Algebra
Addition property of equality	Add the same number to each side.	If $x - a = b$, then $x - a + a = b + a$, or $x = b + a$.
Subtraction property of equality	Subtract the same number from each side.	If $x + a = b$, then $x + a - a = b - a$, or $x = b - a$.
Multiplication property of equality	Multiply each side by the same nonzero number.	If $\frac{x}{a} = b$ and $a \neq 0$, then $a \cdot \frac{x}{a} = a \cdot b$, or $x = ab$.
Division property of equality	Divide each side by the same nonzero number.	If $ax = b$ and $a \neq 0$, then $\frac{ax}{a} = \frac{b}{a}$, or $x = \frac{b}{a}$.

Big Idea 2

Solving Proportion Problems

You can use the cross products property to solve proportions.

$\dfrac{x - 3}{40} = \dfrac{4}{5}$	**Original proportion**
$5(x - 3) = 40 \cdot 4$	**Cross products property**
$5x - 15 = 160$	**Use distributive property. Multiply 40 and 4.**
$5x = 175$	**Addition property of equality: Add 15 to each side.**
$x = 35$	**Division property of equality: Divide each side by 5.**

Big Idea 3

Rewriting Equations and Formulas

If you have an equation or formula in two or more variables, you can solve for one variable in terms of the others. For example, the formula for the perimeter P of a rectangle can be solved for the length ℓ.

$$P = 2\ell + 2w \qquad w$$
$$\ell$$

$P = 2\ell + 2w$	**Original formula**
$P - 2w = 2\ell$	**Subtraction property of equality: Subtract $2w$ from each side.**
$\dfrac{P - 2w}{2} = \ell$	**Division property of equality: Divide each side by 2.**

Alg. 4.0, 5.0

Big Idea 1
You solve an equation in one variable in **Step 3**.

Big Idea 2
You solve a proportion in **Ex. 1**.

Big Idea 3
You rewrite equations in two variables in **Step 1**.

PROBLEM How can you use equations to design a spirit banner for your school?

STEP 1 Find the length of the banner.

You have limited vertical space in which to hang a rectangular banner. You want the banner to be 4 feet high. A manufacturer offers two banners with a height of 4 feet. One has an area of 68 square feet, and the other has an area of 52 square feet. Write the formula for the area A of the banner in terms of the length ℓ (in feet). Solve the formula for ℓ. Find the value of ℓ for each banner.

STEP 2 Choose the wording for the banner.

Choose a word or phrase to write on the banner. You want a word or phrase that represents your school and fits on one line, such as GO EAGLES. Count the number of letters and the number of spaces, if any, between words. The total number of letters and spaces should be at least 5.

STEP 3 Choose a banner based on letter width.

Allow the same space for each letter and for any space between words. Allow a 1 foot space between each end of the banner and the letter closest to that end. Let x be the width (in feet) of each letter or space. For each banner, write an equation for the length ℓ of the banner in terms of x, and solve for x. Decide which letter width you prefer and choose a banner accordingly.

4 ft

GO EAC

$\vdash 1 \!+\! x \!+\! x \!+\! x \!+\! x \!+\! x \dashv$

STEP 4 Find the letter height.

The manufacturer suggests that the height of each letter be 1.5 times the width x. Find the height of each letter.

Extending the Problem

1. You want to submit a scale drawing of the banner you chose in Step 3 with your order.

   a. Choose a scale for your drawing. Find the dimensions of the scale drawing of the banner.

   b. Find the width and height of each letter on the banner for the scale drawing.

   c. You want the word or phrase on the banner to be centered vertically, so you want the vertical distance y (in feet) above and below the letters to be equal. Write and solve an equation for y.

   d. Make the scale drawing.

REVIEW KEY VOCABULARY

- inverse operations, *p. 125*
- equivalent equations, *p. 125*
- identity, *p. 148*
- ratio, *p. 155*
- proportion, *p. 156*
- cross product, *p. 161*
- scale drawing, *p. 163*
- scale model, *p. 163*
- scale, *p. 163*
- literal equation, *p. 167*

VOCABULARY EXERCISES

1. Copy and complete: A(n) __?__ is a two-dimensional drawing of an object in which the dimensions of the drawing are in proportion to the dimensions of the object.

2. Copy and complete: When you perform the same inverse operation on each side of an equation, you produce a(n) __?__ equation.

3. *Explain* why the equation $2x + 8x = 3x + 7x$ is an identity.

4. Copy and complete: In the proportion $\frac{7}{8} = \frac{28}{32}$, $7 \cdot 32$ and $8 \cdot 28$ are __?__ .

5. **NOTETAKING SKILLS** Make an information frame like the one on page 124 for the multiplication property of equality.

REVIEW EXAMPLES AND EXERCISES

Use the review examples and exercises below to check your understanding of the concepts you have learned in each lesson of Chapter 3.

3.1 Solve One-Step Equations
pp. 125–131

Gr. 6 AF 1.1

EXAMPLE

Solve $\frac{x}{5} = 14$.

$\frac{x}{5} = 14$	Write original equation.
$5 \cdot \frac{x}{5} = 5 \cdot 14$	Multiply each side by 5.
$x = 70$	Simplify.

EXERCISES

**EXAMPLES
1, 2, 3, 4, and 5**
on pp. 125–127
for Exs. 6–12

Solve the equation. Check your solution.

6. $x - 4 = 3$

7. $-8 + a = 5$

8. $4m = -84$

9. $-5z = 75$

10. $11 = \frac{r}{6}$

11. $-27 = \frac{3}{4}w$

12. **PARKS** A rectangular city park has an area of 211,200 square feet. The length of the park is 660 feet. What is the width of the park?

3.2 Solve Two-Step Equations

pp. 132–137

Gr. 7 AF 4.1

EXAMPLE

Solve $4x - 9 = 3$.

$4x - 9 = 3$	Write original equation.
$4x - 9 + 9 = 3 + 9$	Add 9 to each side.
$4x = 12$	Simplify.
$\dfrac{4x}{4} = \dfrac{12}{4}$	Divide each side by 4.
$x = 3$	Simplify.

EXERCISES

**EXAMPLES
1 and 2**
on pp. 132–133
for Exs. 13–18

Solve the equation. Check your solution.

13. $9b + 5 = 23$

14. $11 = 5y - 4$

15. $\dfrac{n}{3} - 4 = 2$

16. $\dfrac{3}{2}v + 2 = 20$

17. $3t + 9t = 60$

18. $-110 = -4c - 6c$

3.3 Solve Multi-Step Equations

pp. 139–144

Alg. 4.0

EXAMPLE

Solve $5x - 2(4x + 3) = 9$.

$5x - 2(4x + 3) = 9$	Write original equation.
$5x - 8x - 6 = 9$	Distributive property
$-3x - 6 = 9$	Combine like terms.
$-3x = 15$	Add 6 to each side.
$x = -5$	Divide each side by -3.

EXERCISES

**EXAMPLES
1, 2, 3, 4, and 5**
on pp. 139–141
for Exs. 19–28

Solve the equation. Check your solution.

19. $3w + 4w - 2 = 12$

20. $z + 5 - 4z = 8$

21. $c + 2c - 5 - 5c = 7$

22. $4y - (y - 4) = -20$

23. $8a - 3(2a + 5) = 13$

24. $16h - 4(5h - 7) = 4$

25. $\dfrac{3}{2}(b + 1) = 3$

26. $\dfrac{4}{3}(2x - 1) = -12$

27. $\dfrac{6}{5}(8k + 2) = -36$

28. FOOTBALL You purchase 5 tickets to a football game from an Internet ticket agency. In addition to the cost per ticket, the agency charges a convenience charge of $2.50 per ticket. You choose to pay for rush delivery, which costs $15. The total cost of your order is $352.50. What is the price per ticket not including the convenience charge?

3.4 Solve Equations with Variables on Both Sides

pp. 146–152

Alg. 5.0

EXAMPLE

Solve $-2(x - 5) = 7 - 2x$, if possible.

$$-2(x - 5) = 7 - 2x \qquad \text{Original equation}$$

$$-2x + 10 = 7 - 2x \qquad \text{Distributive property}$$

$$-2x + 3 = -2x \qquad \text{Subtract 7 from each side.}$$

▶ The equation $-2x + 3 = -2x$ is not true because the number $-2x$ cannot be equal to 3 more than itself. So, the equation has no solution.

EXERCISES

EXAMPLES 1, 2, and 4
on pp. 146–148
for Exs. 29–36

Solve the equation, if possible.

29. $-3z - 1 = 8 - 3z$

30. $16 - 2m = 5m + 9$

31. $2.9w + 5 = 4.7w - 7.6$

32. $2y + 11.4 = 2.6 - 0.2y$

33. $4(x - 3) = -2(6 - 2x)$

34. $6(2a + 10) = 5(a + 5)$

35. $\frac{1}{12}(48 + 24b) = 2(17 - 4b)$

36. $1.5(n + 20) = 0.5(3n + 60)$

3.5 Write Ratios and Proportions

pp. 155–160

Gr. 6 NS 1.2

EXAMPLE

You know that 5 pizzas will feed 20 people. How many pizzas do you need to order to feed 88 people?

$$\frac{5}{20} = \frac{x}{88} \quad \begin{array}{l} \longleftarrow \text{ number of pizzas} \\ \longleftarrow \text{ number of people} \end{array}$$

$$88 \cdot \frac{5}{20} = 88 \cdot \frac{x}{88} \qquad \text{Multiply each side by 88.}$$

$$22 = x \qquad \text{Simplify.}$$

▶ You need to order 22 pizzas.

EXERCISES

EXAMPLES 2 and 3
on pp. 156–157
for Exs. 37–43

Solve the proportion. Check your solution.

37. $\frac{56}{16} = \frac{x}{2}$

38. $\frac{y}{9} = \frac{25}{15}$

39. $\frac{2}{7} = \frac{m}{91}$

40. $\frac{5z}{3} = \frac{105}{6}$

41. $\frac{9}{4} = \frac{3a}{20}$

42. $\frac{c + 2}{45} = \frac{8}{5}$

43. PAINTING The label on a can of paint states that one gallon of the paint will cover 560 square feet. How many gallons of the paint are needed to cover 1400 square feet?

3.6 Solve Proportions Using Cross Products

pp. 161–166

Gr. 6 NS 1.3

EXAMPLE

Solve the proportion $\frac{3}{10} = \frac{12}{x}$.

$\frac{3}{10} = \frac{12}{x}$	Write original proportion.
$3 \cdot x = 10 \cdot 12$	Cross products property
$3x = 120$	Simplify.
$x = 40$	Divide each side by 3.

EXERCISES

EXAMPLES
1, 2, and 3
on pp. 161–162
for Exs. 44–50

Solve the proportion. Check your solution.

44. $\frac{5}{7} = \frac{20}{r}$

45. $\frac{6}{z} = \frac{12}{5}$

46. $\frac{126}{56} = \frac{9}{4b}$

47. $\frac{10}{3m} = \frac{-5}{6}$

48. $\frac{n+8}{5n-2} = \frac{3}{8}$

49. $\frac{5-c}{3} = \frac{2c+2}{-4}$

50. TYPING RATES A student can type 65 words in 2 minutes. How many words can the student type in 20 minutes?

3.7 Rewrite Equations and Formulas

pp. 167–173

Gr. 6 AF 3.1

EXAMPLE

Solve the equation $5x + 4y - 7 = 5$ for y.

$5x + 4y - 7 = 5$	Write original equation.
$5x + 4y = 12$	Adddition property of equality
$4y = 12 - 5x$	Subtraction property of equality
$y = 3 - \frac{5}{4}x$	Division property of equality

EXERCISES

EXAMPLES
2 and 3
on p. 168
for Exs. 51–54

Solve the equation for y.

51. $x + 7y = 0$

52. $3x = 2y - 18$

53. $4y - x = 20 - y$

54. AQUARIUMS A pet store sells aquariums that are rectangular prisms. The volume V of an aquarium is given by the formula $V = \ell w h$ where ℓ is the length, w is the width, and h is the height.

   a. Solve the formula for h.

   b. Use the rewritten formula to find the height of the aquarium shown, which has a volume of 5850 cubic inches.

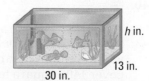

h in.

30 in.   13 in.

1. **VOCABULARY** Copy and complete: A(n) _?_ uses division to compare two quantities.

2. **VOCABULARY** Copy and complete: A(n) _?_ is a three-dimensional model of an object in which the dimensions of the model are in proportion to the dimensions of the object.

Solve the equation. Check your solution.

3. $5 + r = -19$

4. $z - 8 = -12$

5. $-11x = -77$

6. $\dfrac{a}{9} = 6$

7. $15q - 17 = 13$

8. $3y + 2 = 26$

9. $\dfrac{b}{4} + 5 = 14$

10. $\dfrac{m}{10} - 6 = 20$

11. $6j + 5j = 33$

12. $4k - 9k = 10$

13. $14c - 8c + 7 = 37$

14. $4w - 21 + 5w = 51$

15. $-19.4 - 15d + 22d = 4.4$

16. $-12h + 39 = -4h - 17$

17. $-5.7v - 44.2 = -8.3v$

18. $-6.5t + 15 = -9.7t + 43.8$

19. $3(3n + 4) = 54 + 6n$

20. $\dfrac{1}{3}(24p - 66) = 3p + 43$

21. How many solutions does $2(3t - 5) = 6t - 10$ have? How many solutions does $2(3t - 5) = 6t + 10$ have? *Explain* your reasoning.

Solve the proportion. Check your solution.

22. $\dfrac{3}{4} = \dfrac{z}{16}$

23. $\dfrac{72}{45} = \dfrac{8}{w}$

24. $\dfrac{k}{9} = \dfrac{63}{81}$

25. $\dfrac{-5n}{4} = \dfrac{15}{2}$

26. $\dfrac{34}{6} = \dfrac{2x + 1}{3}$

27. $\dfrac{-4a - 1}{-10a} = \dfrac{3}{8}$

Solve the equation for *y*.

28. $8x + y = 14$

29. $-9x + 3y = 18$

30. $4x = -2y + 26$

31. **MOVIES** The ticket prices at a movie theater are shown in the table. A family purchases tickets for 2 adults and 3 children, and the family purchases 3 boxes of popcorn of the same size. The family spends a total of $40.25. How much does each box of popcorn cost?

Ticket	Price
Adults	$8.50
Children	$5.50

32. **ICE SKATING** To become a member of an ice skating rink, you have to pay a $30 membership fee. The cost of admission to the rink is $5 for members and $7 for nonmembers. After how many visits to the rink is the total cost for members, including the membership fee, the same as the total cost for nonmembers?

33. **SCALE DRAWING** You are making a scale drawing of your classroom using the scale 1 inch : 3 feet. The floor of your classroom is a rectangle with a length of 21 feet and a width of 18 feet. What should the length and width of the floor in your drawing be?

3 ◆ MULTIPLE CHOICE STRATEGIES

STRATEGIES YOU'LL USE:
- SOLVE DIRECTLY
- ELIMINATE CHOICES

Standards
Alg. 4.0, 5.0

If you have difficulty solving a multiple choice problem directly, you may be able to use another approach to eliminate incorrect answer choices and obtain the correct answer.

PROBLEM 1

Sid's car gets 34 miles per gallon when driven on the highway and 26 miles per gallon when driven in the city. Sid drove 414 miles on 13 gallons of gas. How many highway miles and how many city miles did he drive?

(A) 91 highway miles, 323 city miles   (B) 182 highway miles, 232 city miles

(C) 232 highway miles, 182 city miles   (D) 323 highway miles, 91 city miles

Strategy 1   SOLVE DIRECTLY

Write and solve an equation to find the distances.

STEP 1 Write an equation. Let x represent the amount of gas (in gallons) used for highway driving. Then $13 - x$ represents the amount of gas (in gallons) used for city driving.

$$414 = 34x + 26(13 - x)$$

STEP 2 Solve the equation.

$$414 = 34x + 338 - 26x$$
$$414 = 8x + 338$$
$$76 = 8x$$
$$9.5 = x$$

STEP 3 Calculate the number of highway miles driven.

$$34(9.5) = 323$$

STEP 4 Calculate the number of city miles driven.

$$26(13 - 9.5) = 91$$

Sid drove 323 highway miles and 91 city miles.

The correct answer is D. (A) (B) (C) **(D)**

Strategy 2   ELIMINATE CHOICES

Consider the extremes to eliminate incorrect answer choices.

STEP 1 Consider driving all highway miles and all city miles.

All highway: $13 \text{ gal} \cdot \dfrac{34 \text{ mi}}{1 \text{ gal}} = 442 \text{ mi}$

All city: $13 \text{ gal} \cdot \dfrac{26 \text{ mi}}{1 \text{ gal}} = 338 \text{ mi}$

Because 414 is closer to 442 than to 338, you know that more highway miles were driven than city miles. So, you can eliminate choices A and B.

STEP 2 Calculate the gallons of gas that would be used for the remaining choices.

Choice C: $232 \text{ mi} \cdot \dfrac{1 \text{ gal}}{34 \text{ mi}} \approx 6.8 \text{ gal}$

$182 \text{ mi} \cdot \dfrac{1 \text{ gal}}{26 \text{ mi}} = 7 \text{ gal}$

Choice D: $323 \text{ mi} \cdot \dfrac{1 \text{ gal}}{34 \text{ mi}} = 9.5 \text{ gal}$

$91 \text{ mi} \cdot \dfrac{1 \text{ gal}}{26 \text{ mi}} = 3.5 \text{ gal}$

In choice D, the total number of gallons of gas is 13.

The correct answer is D. (A) (B) (C) **(D)**

PROBLEM 2

What is the solution of the equation $6(7 - 2x) = 12 + 3(x - 5)$?

(A) 1   (B) 3   (C) 7   (D) 9

Strategy 1   SOLVE DIRECTLY

Solve the equation by first using the distributive property.

$$6(7 - 2x) = 12 + 3(x - 5)$$
$$42 - 12x = 12 + 3x - 15$$
$$42 - 12x = -3 + 3x$$
$$42 = -3 + 15x$$
$$45 = 15x$$
$$3 = x$$

The correct answer is B.   (A) (B) (C) (D)

Strategy 2   ELIMINATE CHOICES

Substitute each answer choice for x in the original equation and simplify.

Choice A: $6(7 - 2 \cdot 1) \stackrel{?}{=} 12 + 3(1 - 5)$
$$6(7 - 2) \stackrel{?}{=} 12 + 3(-4)$$
$$6(5) \stackrel{?}{=} 12 - 12$$
$$30 = 0 ✗$$

Choice B: $6(7 - 2 \cdot 3) \stackrel{?}{=} 12 + 3(3 - 5)$
$$6(7 - 6) \stackrel{?}{=} 12 + 3(-2)$$
$$6(1) \stackrel{?}{=} 12 - 6$$
$$6 = 6 ✓$$

The correct answer is B.   (A) (B) (C) (D)

STRATEGY PRACTICE

Explain why you can eliminate the highlighted answer choice.

1. What is the solution of the equation $5(x + 13) = 8(4 + x)$?

   (A) -11 (B) -4 (C)✗ 0   (D) 11

2. A grocery store sells apples by the pound. A 3 pound bag of apples costs $2.99. About how much does a 5 pound bag of apples cost?

   (A) $3.24   (B) $3.45   (C) $4.98   (D)✗ **$5.98**

3. What is the value of x in the proportion $\dfrac{6}{x + 9} = \dfrac{18}{5x - 3}$?

   (A) -3 (B)✗ 3   (C) 10   (D) 15

4. The surface area S of a cylinder is given by the formula $S = 2\pi rh + 2\pi r^2$ where r is the radius and h is the height of the cylinder. Which formula is *not* equivalent to the original formula?

   (A) $S = 2\pi r(h + r)$ (B) $h = 2\pi rS + 2\pi r^2$

   (C)✗ $h = \dfrac{S - 2\pi r^2}{2\pi r}$ (D) $h = \dfrac{S}{2\pi r} - r$

1. What is the solution of the equation $\frac{3}{5}x = -6$? **Gr. 6 AF 1.1**

   (A) $-\frac{18}{5}$

   (B) -10

   (C) 10

   (D) $\frac{18}{5}$

2. The record for the longest distance and time ever flown by a model airplane was set in 2003 by Maynard Hill of Maryland. The airplane flew from Canada to Ireland in 38 hours and 53 minutes. What was the plane's average speed? **Gr. 6 AF 1.1**

   (A) About 36 mi/h

   (B) About 45 mi/h

   (C) About 49 mi/h

   (D) About 71,744 mi/h

3. The table shows the number of trails at a mountain biking park. What is the ratio of expert trails to total trails? **Gr. 6 NS 1.2**

Type of trail	Number of trails
Beginner	22
Intermediate	13
Expert	13

   (A) 1 : 3

   (B) 13 : 26

   (C) 13 : 22

   (D) 13 : 48

4. The rates for using a swimming facility are given below. A father and his 12-year-old son pay for admission on each visit. After how many visits will the father and son spend the same amount as they would have paid for a family membership? **Gr. 6 AF 1.1**

   (A) 18 visits

   (B) 20 visits

   (C) 35 visits

   (D) 47 visits

5. How many solutions does the equation $3(x - 3) = 3x - 6$ have? **Alg. 4.0**

   (A) None

   (B) 1

   (C) 2

   (D) Infinitely many

6. What is the solution of the proportion $\frac{40}{15} = \frac{8}{x - 5}$? **Gr. 6 NS 1.3**

   (A) 4

   (B) 5

   (C) 8

   (D) 10

7. Which equation is equivalent to $\frac{7}{2}(2x + 4) + 2x - 3 = -5$? **Alg. 4.0**

   (A) $9x = -16$

   (B) $9x = -6$

   (C) $16x = -30$

   (D) $16x = -6$

8. The photo of the Golden Gate Bridge shows the height of each tower above the roadbed of the bridge. A sculptor makes a model of the bridge using a scale of 1 in. : 20 ft. How high is the top of each tower above the roadbed of the model bridge? **Gr. 6 NS 1.3**

144 ft

Ⓐ 0.6 in.

Ⓑ 7.2 in.

Ⓒ 86.4 in.

Ⓓ 240 in.

9. Which equation is equivalent to

$\dfrac{8}{x+1} = \dfrac{11}{8}$? **Alg. 4.0**

Ⓐ $11x = 53$

Ⓑ $11x = 64$

Ⓒ $11x = 65$

Ⓓ $11x = 75$

10. Which equation can be used to find the value of x given the surface area S of the rectangular prism shown? **Gr. 6 AF 3.1**

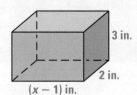

3 in.

2 in.

$(x - 1)$ in.

Ⓐ $x = \dfrac{S-5}{10}$

Ⓑ $x = \dfrac{S-2}{10}$

Ⓒ $x = \dfrac{S-1}{5}$

Ⓓ $x = \dfrac{S+2}{10}$

11. Which of the following is the ratio $\dfrac{36}{30}$ in simplest form? **Gr. 6 NS 1.2**

Ⓐ $5 : 6$

Ⓑ 6 to 5

Ⓒ 16 to 15

Ⓓ $\dfrac{18}{15}$

12. The perimeter of the triangle shown is 16.5 inches. What is the length of the shortest side? **Alg. 5.0**

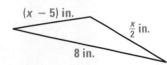

$(x - 5)$ in.

$\frac{x}{2}$ in.

8 in.

Ⓐ 3.5 in.

Ⓑ 4 in.

Ⓒ 4.5 in.

Ⓓ 9 in.

13. Andrew pays $49 for cable TV installation and $43 per month for programming. Doug buys a satellite dish for $145 and pays $35 per month for programming. After how many months will Andrew and Doug have paid the same amount for their TV services? **Alg. 5.0**

Ⓐ 10 months

Ⓑ 12 months

Ⓒ 24 months

Ⓓ 25 months

14. Which equation is equivalent to $4y - 2x = 28$? **Gr. 6 AF 3.1**

Ⓐ $y = \dfrac{1}{2}x + 7$

Ⓑ $y = \dfrac{1}{2}x + 28$

Ⓒ $y = 2x - 28$

Ⓓ $y = 2x + 7$

4 Solving Inequalities

Before

In previous chapters, you learned the following skills, which you'll use in Chapter 4:

- Using a number line to compare and order numbers
- Writing equations and inequalities
- Solving equations
- Finding the absolute value of a number

Now

In Chapter 4 you'll study these

Big Ideas:

1. Applying properties of inequality

2. Using statements with *and* or *or*

3. Graphing inequalities

Why?

So you can solve real-world problems about . . .

- Traveling, p. 200
- Wild horses, p. 201
- Baseball, p. 207
- Weather, p. 216
- Cheerleading, p. 224
- Baking, p. 230

Animated Algebra
at *classzone.com*

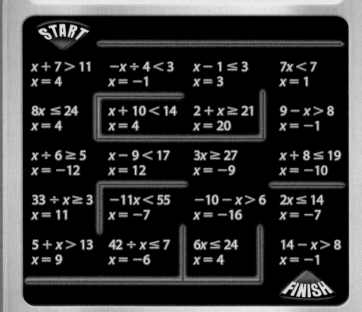

Video Maze

California Standards

Review evaluating expressions. **Gr. 7 AF 1.2**
Prepare for solving inequalities. **Gr. 7 AF 4.1**

START

$x + 7 > 11$ $x = 4$	$-x \div 4 < 3$ $x = -1$	$x - 1 \le 3$ $x = 3$	$7x < 7$ $x = 1$
$8x \le 24$ $x = 4$	$x + 10 < 14$ $x = 4$	$2 + x \ge 21$ $x = 20$	$9 - x > 8$ $x = -1$
$x \div 6 \ge 5$ $x = -12$	$x - 9 < 17$ $x = 12$	$3x \ge 27$ $x = -9$	$x + 8 \le 19$ $x = -10$
$33 \div x \ge 3$ $x = 11$	$-11x < 55$ $x = -7$	$-10 - x > 6$ $x = -16$	$2x \le 14$ $x = -7$
$5 + x > 13$ $x = 9$	$42 \div x \le 7$ $x = -6$	$6x \le 24$ $x = 4$	$14 - x > 8$ $x = -1$

FINISH

How to Play

Find a path through the maze from start to finish. An inequality can be visited only once.

- You start with a score of 0. If the given value of *x* is a solution of the inequality in your path, then add that value of *x* to your score. Otherwise, your score does not change.
- Find the path that results in the greatest score.

CALIFORNIA STANDARDS

• **Alg. 3.0** Students solve equations and inequalities involving **absolute values**. *(Lessons 4.5, 4.6)*

• **Alg. 4.0** Students simplify expressions before solving linear equations and **inequalities in one variable**, such as $3(2x - 5) + 4(x - 2) = 12$. *(Lessons 4.3, 4.4)*

• **Alg. 5.0** Students solve multistep problems, including word problems, involving linear equations and **inequalities in one variable and provide justification for each step**. *(Lessons 4.3, 4.4)*

ASTRO MATH

California Standards

Review solving multi-step equations. **Alg. 5.0**
Prepare for solving multi-step inequalities. **Alg. 5.0**

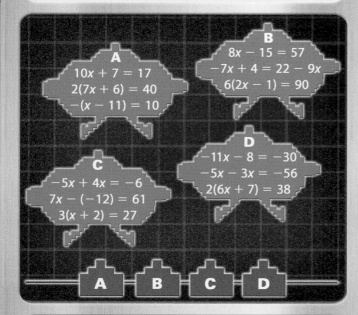

A
$10x + 7 = 17$
$2(7x + 6) = 40$
$-(x - 11) = 10$

B
$8x - 15 = 57$
$-7x + 4 = 22 - 9x$
$6(2x - 1) = 90$

C
$-5x + 4x = -6$
$7x - (-12) = 61$
$3(x + 2) = 27$

D
$-11x - 8 = -30$
$-5x - 3x = -56$
$2(6x + 7) = 38$

A B C D

How to Play

Find the year in which the first handheld electronic game was made. The year is written ABCD.

• Solve each equation.

• In each group of equations, there are two identical solutions. Use that solution in place of the group's letter to find the year.

Games Wrap-Up

Draw Conclusions

Complete these exercises after playing the games.

1. **WRITING** *Explain* why the equation $2x - 3 = 2x - 5$ has no solution.

2. **REASONING** How many different paths are there through the video maze where the inequalities in each path are visited only once?

Prerequisite Skills

California @HomeTutor

Prerequisite skills practice at classzone.com

REVIEW VOCABULARY

- equivalent equations, *p. 125*
- absolute value, *p. 55*
- inequality, *p. 26*
- solution of an inequality, *p. 27*
- mean, *p. 803*

VOCABULARY CHECK

1. Are $7x - 4 = 10$ and $x = 3$ equivalent equations? *Explain*.

2. Copy and complete: The absolute value of a number a is the distance between a and __?__ on a number line.

SKILLS CHECK

Check whether the given number is a solution of the equation or inequality. *(Review p. 26 for 4.1–4.6.)*

3. $x - 2 = 3$; 5   4. $s + 3 = 12$; 9   5. $6y > 20$; 3   6. $\dfrac{p - 3}{5} \le 4$; 23

Solve the equation. Check your solution. *(Review pp. 125, 132, 139 for 4.1–4.6.)*

7. $m + 8 = -20$ 8. $-7x = 35$ 9. $-9r - 4 = 25$ 10. $4t - 7t = 9$

Graph the numbers on a number line. Then tell which number is greater. *(Review p. 53 for 4.1–4.6.)*

11. -3 and 4   12. -8 and -6 13. -5 and 0

For the given value of a, find $-a$ and $|a|$. *(Review p. 53 for 4.5–4.6.)*

14. $a = -3$ 15. $a = -5.6$ 16. $a = 14$ 17. $a = 0$

Notetaking Skills

NOW YOU TRY
Use a *notetaking organizer* to write your notes about solving an equation. You may want to use colored pencils.

Focus on Graphic Organizers

You can use a *notetaking organizer* to write your notes about a topic, such as solving proportions.

Write important vocabulary or formulas in the narrow column.

$\dfrac{a}{b} = \dfrac{c}{d}$

$ad = bc$
(b and d not 0)

Use cross products to solve a proportion.

$4x = 2 \cdot 5$

$4x = 10$

$x = \dfrac{5}{2} = 2\dfrac{1}{2}$

Write your notes about solving a proportion in the wide column.

How can you solve this: $\dfrac{1}{3} = \dfrac{x + 1}{x}$?

Write any questions about solving proportions in the space at the bottom of the page.

4.1 Solve Inequalities Using Addition and Subtraction

Standards Preparation

Gr. 7 AF 4.1 Solve two-step **linear** equations and **inequalities in one variable** over the rational numbers, interpret the solution or solutions in the context from which they arose, and verify the reasonableness of the results.

Connect   *Before* you solved equations using addition and subtraction. *Now* you will solve inequalities using addition and subtraction to prepare for Algebra 1 Standard 4.0.

Math and
EARTH SCIENCE
Example 1, p. 189

Key Vocabulary
- **graph of an inequality**
- **equivalent inequalities**
- inequality, *p. 26*
- **solution of an inequality,** *p. 27*

On a number line, the **graph of an inequality** in one variable is the set of points that represent all solutions of the inequality. To graph an inequality in one variable, use an open circle for < or > and a closed circle for ≤ or ≥. The graphs of $x < 3$ and $x \geq -1$ are shown below.

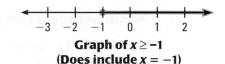

Graph of x < 3
(Does not include x = 3)

Graph of x ≥ −1
(Does include x = −1)

EXAMPLE 1   Write and graph an inequality

DEATH VALLEY The highest temperature recorded in the United States was 134°F at Death Valley, California, in 1913. Use only this fact to write and graph an inequality that describes the temperatures in the United States.

Solution

Let *T* represent a temperature (in degrees Fahrenheit) in the United States. The value of *T* must be less than or equal to 134. So, an inequality is $T \leq 134$.

EXAMPLE 2   Write inequalities from graphs

Write an inequality represented by the graph.

a.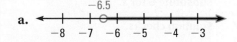

b.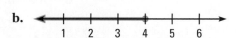

Solution

a. The shading includes all numbers to the right of (greater than) −6.5.

  ▶ An inequality represented by the graph is $x > -6.5$.

b. The shading includes 4 and all numbers to the left of (less than) 4.

  ▶ An inequality represented by the graph is $x \leq 4$.

1. **ANTARCTICA** The lowest temperature recorded in Antarctica was −129°F at the Russian Vostok station in 1983. Use only this fact to write and graph an inequality that describes the temperatures in Antarctica.

Write an inequality represented by the graph.

2.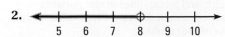

3.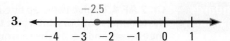

EQUIVALENT INEQUALITIES Just as you used properties of equality to produce equivalent equations, you can use properties of inequality to produce *equivalent inequalities*. **Equivalent inequalities** are inequalities that have the same solutions.

KEY CONCEPT *For Your Notebook*

Addition Property of Inequality

Words Adding the same number to each side of an inequality produces an equivalent inequality.

Algebra If $a > b$, then $a + c > b + c$.   If $a \geq b$, then $a + c \geq b + c$.

If $a < b$, then $a + c < b + c$.   If $a \leq b$, then $a + c \leq b + c$.

EXAMPLE 3 **Solve an inequality using addition**

Solve $x - 5 > -3.5$. Graph your solution.

$x - 5 > -3.5$ **Write original inequality.**

$x - 5 + 5 > -3.5 + 5$ **Add 5 to each side.**

$x > 1.5$ **Simplify.**

SET NOTATION
The solution $x > 1.5$ can also be written as a set, $\{x : x > 1.5\}$. This notation is read as "the set of all x such that x is greater than 1.5."

▶ The solutions are all real numbers greater than 1.5. Check by substituting a number greater than 1.5 for x in the original inequality.

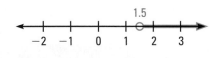

CHECK $x - 5 > -3.5$ **Write original inequality.**

$6 - 5 \overset{?}{>} -3.5$ **Substitute 6 for x.**

$1 > -3.5$ ✓   **Solution checks.**

Solve the inequality. Graph your solution.

4. $x - 9 \leq 3$ 5. $p - 9.2 < -5$ 6. $-1 \geq m - \dfrac{1}{2}$

Subtraction Property of Inequality

Words Subtracting the same number from each side of an inequality produces an equivalent inequality.

Algebra If $a > b$, then $a - c > b - c$.   If $a \geq b$, then $a - c \geq b - c$.

If $a < b$, then $a - c < b - c$.   If $a \leq b$, then $a - c \leq b - c$.

EXAMPLE 4 **Solve an inequality using subtraction**

Animated **Algebra**

For an interactive example of solving an inequality, go to **classzone.com**.

Solve $9 \geq x + 7$. Graph your solution.

$$9 \geq x + 7 \qquad \text{Write original inequality.}$$

$$9 - 7 \geq x + 7 - 7 \qquad \text{Subtract 7 from each side.}$$

$$2 \geq x \qquad \text{Simplify.}$$

▶ You can rewrite $2 \geq x$ as $x \leq 2$. The solutions are all real numbers less than or equal to 2.

EXAMPLE 5 **Solve a real-world problem**

READING
The phrase "no more than" indicates that you use the $\leq$ symbol.

LUGGAGE WEIGHTS You are checking a bag at an airport. Bags can weigh no more than 50 pounds. Your bag weighs 16.8 pounds. Find the possible weights w (in pounds) that you can add to the bag.

Solution

Write a verbal model. Then write and solve an inequality.

Weight of bag	+	Weight you can add	$\leq$	Weight limit
⬇		⬇		⬇
16.8	**+**	**w**	**$\leq$**	**50**

$$16.8 + w \leq 50 \qquad \text{Write inequality.}$$

$$16.8 + w - 16.8 \leq 50 - 16.8 \qquad \text{Subtract 16.8 from each side.}$$

$$w \leq 33.2 \qquad \text{Simplify.}$$

▶ You can add no more than 33.2 pounds.

Bag weight: 16.8 lb

✓ **GUIDED PRACTICE** for Examples 4 and 5

Solve the inequality. Graph your solution.

7. $y + 5 > 6$ **8.** $x + 7 \geq -4$ **9.** $-2 < y + 15$

10. WHAT IF? In Example 5, suppose your bag weighs 29.1 pounds. Find the possible weights (in pounds) that you can add to the bag.

4.1 EXERCISES

HOMEWORK KEY

◆ = MULTIPLE CHOICE PRACTICE
Exs. 10, 23, 38, and 44–46

○ = HINTS AND HOMEWORK HELP
for Exs. 7, 15, and 39 at classzone.com

SKILLS · PROBLEM SOLVING · REASONING

1. **VOCABULARY** Copy and complete: To graph $x < -8$, you draw a(n) __?__ circle at -8, and you draw an arrow to the __?__.

2. **WRITING** Are $x + 7 \geq 18$ and $x \geq 25$ equivalent inequalities? *Explain.*

EXAMPLES
1 and 2
on p. 189
for Exs. 3–10

WRITING AND GRAPHING INEQUALITIES Write and graph an inequality that describes the situation.

3. The speed limit on a highway is 60 miles per hour.

4. You must be at least 16 years old to go on a field trip.

5. A child must be taller than 48 inches to get on an amusement park ride.

WRITING INEQUALITIES Write an inequality represented by the graph.

6.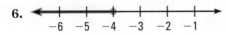

7.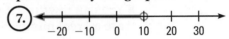

8.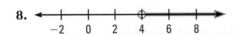

9.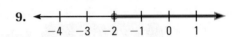

10. ◆ **MULTIPLE CHOICE** Which inequality is represented by the graph?

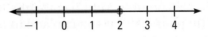

A $x > 2$ **B** $x \geq 2$ **C** $x \leq 2$ **D** $x < 2$

EXAMPLES
3 and 4
on pp. 190–191
for Exs. 11–25

SOLVING INEQUALITIES Solve the inequality. Graph your solution.

11. $x + 4 < 5$

12. $-8 \leq 8 + y$

13. $-1\frac{1}{4} \leq m + 3$

14. $n + 17 \leq 16\frac{4}{5}$

15. $w + 14.9 > -2.7$

16. $8.2 + v > -7.6$

17. $r - 4 < -5$

18. $1 \leq s - 8$

19. $-1\frac{1}{3} \leq p - 8\frac{1}{3}$

20. $q - 1\frac{1}{3} > -2\frac{1}{2}$

21. $2.1 \geq c - 6.7$

22. $d - 1.92 > -8.76$

23. ◆ **MULTIPLE CHOICE** What is the solution of the inequality $m + 7 \geq -10$?

A $m \geq -3$ **B** $m \geq -17$ **C** $m \leq 3$ **D** $m \leq 17$

ERROR ANALYSIS *Describe* and correct the error in solving the inequality or in graphing the solution.

24.
$$x + 8 < -3$$
$$x + 8 - 8 < -3 + 8$$
$$x < 5$$

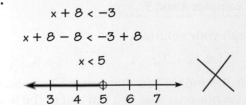

25.
$$-17 \leq x - 14$$
$$-17 + 14 \leq x - 14 + 14$$
$$-3 \leq x$$

TRANSLATING SENTENCES Write the verbal sentence as an inequality.
Then solve the inequality and graph your solution.

26. The sum of 11 and *m* is greater than −23.

27. The difference of *n* and 15 is less than or equal to 37.

28. The difference of *c* and 13 is less than −19.

GEOMETRY Write and solve an inequality to find the possible values of *x*.

29. Perimeter < 51.3 inches

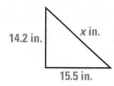

30. Perimeter ≤ 18.7 feet

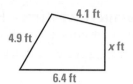

31. REASONING *Explain* how you can use the addition property of
inequality to solve $x + 3 > -5$.

32. WRITING Is it possible to check all the numbers that are solutions of an
inequality? Does checking one solution guarantee that you have solved
an inequality correctly? *Explain* your answers.

CONNECT SKILLS TO PROBLEM SOLVING Exercises 33–35 will help you
prepare for problem solving.

Write an inequality that represents the situation.

33. In a trivia game, team A has 4 points and team B has 12 points. Let *r*
represent the possible numbers of points team A must score to win if
team B scores no more points.

34. The maximum weight that a truck can carry is 1500 pounds. Let *w*
represent the possible weights that can be added to a 780 pound load.

35. A friend has $100. She would like to purchase a $75 tennis racket and
several cans of tennis balls. Let *b* represent the possible dollar amounts
she can spend on tennis balls.

EXAMPLE 5
on p. 191
for Exs. 36–39

36. INTERNET You earn points from buying items at an Internet shopping
site. You would like to redeem 2350 points to get an item for free, but you
want to have at least 6000 points left over. What are the possible
numbers of points you can have before making a redemption?

California @*HomeTutor* for problem solving help at classzone.com

37. SPORTS RECORDS Suppose a quarterback has 24 touchdown
passes so far in a season. What are the possible numbers of
additional touchdown passes that the quarterback can throw
in order to equal or exceed Peyton Manning's record?

California @*HomeTutor* for problem solving help at classzone.com

38. ◆ MULTIPLE CHOICE You can spend at most $30 on a jacket at a
clothing store. You have a coupon for $3 off any item. Which inequality
can you use to find the original prices *p* of jackets that you can buy?

(A) $3 + p \geq 30$ **(B)** $30 + p \leq 3$ **(C)** $p - 3 \leq 30$ **(D)** $p - 30 \geq 3$

39. MULTI-STEP PROBLEM In aerial ski competitions, the scores of two acrobatic ski jumps are added together. The table shows your competitor's first and second scores and your first score.

Ski jump	Competitor's score	Your score
1	127.04	129.49
2	129.98	?

a. Write and solve an inequality to find the scores s that you can earn in your second jump in order to beat your competitor.

b. Will you beat your competitor if you earn 128.13 points? 126.78 points? 127.53 points? *Justify* your answers.

40. VEHICLE WEIGHTS The maximum total weight allowed for a vehicle and its contents depends on the number of axles the vehicle has.

Maximum Total Weights

| 2 axles | 3 axles | 4 axles | 5 axles |
| 34,000 lb | 54,000 lb | 69,000 lb | 80,000 lb |

For each type of vehicle, write and solve an inequality to find the possible weights w (in pounds) of a vehicle when its contents weigh 14,200 pounds. Can a vehicle that has 2 axles and weighs 20,000 pounds hold 14,200 pounds of contents? *Explain.*

41. REASONING The inequality $a < b$ means that $a + n = b$ for some positive number n. Use this definition, the addition property of equality, and the commutative and associative properties of addition to prove the statement "If $a < b$, then $a + c < b + c$."

42. CHALLENGE Write and graph an inequality that represents the numbers that are *not* solutions of $x - 12 \geq 5.7$.

43. CHALLENGE A public television station wants to raise at least $72,000 in a pledge drive. The station raised an average of $5953 per day for the first 3 days and an average of $6153 per day for the next 3 days. What are the possible additional amounts that the station can raise to meet its goal?

◆ **CALIFORNIA STANDARDS SPIRAL REVIEW**

Gr. 7 AF 4.1

44. What is the solution of $5 + 8m = 13$? *(p. 132)*

    (A) −1   (B) 0   (C) 1   (D) 2

Alg. 4.0

45. What is the solution of $6(5y - 3) + 2 = 14$? *(p. 139)*

    (A) −1   (B) $\frac{1}{3}$ (C) $\frac{1}{2}$ (D) 1

Alg. 5.0

46. The bill for the repair on a SUV is $545. The cost of parts is $377. The cost of labor is $42 per hour. Which equation can you use to find the number of hours of labor? *(p. 146)*

    (A) $42(x + 377) = 545$ (B) $42 + 377x = 545$

    (C) $42x + 377 = 545$ (D) $42 + x + 377 = 545$

4.2 Inequalities with Negative Coefficients

MATERIALS · index cards

Standards

Alg. 25.3 Given a specific algebraic statement **involving linear,** quadratic, or absolute value expressions or equations or **inequalities, students determine whether the statement is true sometimes, always, or never.**

QUESTION How do you solve an inequality with a negative coefficient?

EXPLORE Check solutions of inequalities

STEP 1 *Write integers* Write the integers from −5 to 5 on index cards as shown.

| −5 | −4 | −3 | −2 | −1 | 0 | 1 | 2 | 3 | 4 | 5 |

STEP 2 *Check solutions* Determine whether each integer is a solution of $4x \geq 8$. If the integer is *not* a solution, turn over the card.

| | | | | | | | 2 | 3 | 4 | 5 |

STEP 3 *Check solutions* Turn all the cards face up. Repeat Step 2 for $-4x \geq 8$.

| −5 | −4 | −3 | −2 | | | | | | | |

DRAW CONCLUSIONS Use your observations to complete these exercises

1. State an operation that you can perform on both sides of $4x \geq 8$ to obtain the solutions found in Step 2. Then solve the inequality.

2. Copy and complete the steps below for solving $-4x \geq 8$.

   $-4x \geq 8$ Write original inequality.

   __?__   Add $4x$ to each side.

   __?__   Subtract 8 from each side.

   __?__   Divide each side by 4.

   __?__   Rewrite inequality with x on the left side.

3. **REASONING** Does dividing both sides of $-4x \geq 8$ by -4 give the solution found in Exercise 2? If not, what else must you do to the inequality when you divide by -4?

4. **REASONING** How do you solve the inequality $ax \geq b$ when $a > 0$? when $a < 0$?

Solve the inequality.

5. $5x \geq 20$ 6. $-9x \leq 45$ 7. $-8x > 40$ 8. $7x < 21$

4.2 Solve Inequalities Using Multiplication and Division

Standards Preparation

Gr. 7 AF 4.1 Solve two-step linear equations and inequalities in one variable over the rational numbers, interpret the solutions or solutions in the context from which they arose, and verify the reasonableness of the results.

Connect *Before* you solved inequalities using addition and subtraction. *Now* you will solve inequalities using multiplication and division to prepare for Algebra 1 Standard 4.0.

Math and **SPORTS**
Ex. 50, p. 200

Key Vocabulary
• inequality, *p. 26*
• equivalent inequalities, *p. 190*

Solving an inequality using multiplication is similar to solving an equation using multiplication, but it is different in an important way.

KEY CONCEPT — *For Your Notebook*

Multiplication Property of Inequality

Words Multiplying each side of an inequality by a *positive* number produces an equivalent inequality.

Multiplying each side of an inequality by a *negative* number and *reversing the direction of the inequality symbol* produces an equivalent inequality.

Algebra If $a < b$ and $c > 0$, then $ac < bc$.   If $a < b$ and $c < 0$, then $ac > bc$.

If $a > b$ and $c > 0$, then $ac > bc$.   If $a > b$ and $c < 0$, then $ac < bc$.

This property is also true for inequalities $a \geq b$ and $a \leq b$.

EXAMPLE 1   Solve an inequality using multiplication

Solve $\dfrac{x}{4} < 5$. Graph your solution.

$\dfrac{x}{4} < 5$ Write original inequality.

$4 \cdot \dfrac{x}{4} < 4 \cdot 5$ Multiply each side by 4.

$x < 20$ Simplify.

▶ The solutions are all real numbers less than 20. Check by substituting a number less than 20 in the original inequality.

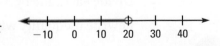

CHECK $\dfrac{x}{4} < 5$ Write original inequality.

$\dfrac{16}{4} \overset{?}{<} 5$ Substitute 16 for *x*.

$4 < 5 ✓$ Solution checks.

EXAMPLE 2 Solve an inequality using multiplication

Solve $\dfrac{x}{-6} < 7$. Graph your solution.

$$\dfrac{x}{-6} < 7 \qquad \text{Write original inequality.}$$

$$-6 \cdot \dfrac{x}{-6} > -6 \cdot 7 \qquad \text{Multiply each side by } -6. \text{ Reverse inequality symbol.}$$

$$x > -42 \qquad \text{Simplify.}$$

▶ The solutions are all real numbers greater than -42. Check by substituting a number greater than -42 in the original inequality.

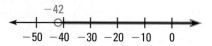

AVOID ERRORS
Because you are multiplying by a negative number, be sure to reverse the inequality symbol.

USING DIVISION The rules for solving an inequality using division are similar to the rules for solving an inequality using multiplication.

KEY CONCEPT   *For Your Notebook*

Division Property of Inequality

Words Dividing each side of an inequality by a *positive* number produces an equivalent inequality.

Dividing each side of an inequality by a *negative* number and *reversing the direction of the inequality symbol* produces an equivalent inequality.

Algebra If $a < b$ and $c > 0$, then $\dfrac{a}{c} < \dfrac{b}{c}$.   If $a < b$ and $c < 0$, then $\dfrac{a}{c} > \dfrac{b}{c}$.

If $a > b$ and $c > 0$, then $\dfrac{a}{c} > \dfrac{b}{c}$.   If $a > b$ and $c < 0$, then $\dfrac{a}{c} < \dfrac{b}{c}$.

This property is also true for inequalities $a \geq b$ and $a \leq b$.

EXAMPLE 3 Solve an inequality using division

Animated Algebra

For an interactive example of solving an inequality, go to **classzone.com**.

Solve $-3x > 24$.

$$-3x > 24 \qquad \text{Write original inequality.}$$

$$\dfrac{-3x}{-3} < \dfrac{24}{-3} \qquad \text{Divide each side by } -3. \text{ Reverse inequality symbol.}$$

$$x < -8 \qquad \text{Simplify.}$$

✓ **GUIDED PRACTICE** for Examples 1, 2, and 3

Solve the inequality. Graph your solution.

1. $\dfrac{x}{3} > 12$ **2.** $\dfrac{m}{-7} < 1.6$ **3.** $-12 \geq \dfrac{r}{2}$ **4.** $6 \leq \dfrac{t}{-5}$

5. $5v \geq 45$ **6.** $-6n < 24$ **7.** $-64 \leq 8b$ **8.** $28 > -4y$

EXAMPLE 4   Solve a real-world problem

PILOTING A student pilot plans to spend 80 hours on flight training to earn a private license. The student has saved $6000 for training. What are the possible hourly rates that the student can afford to pay for training?

Solution

The total cost of training can be at most the amount of money that the student has saved. Write a verbal model for the situation. Then write an inequality and solve.

Student pilot with trainer

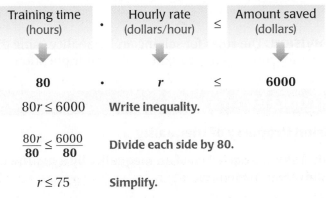

Training time (hours)	·	Hourly rate (dollars/hour)	≤	Amount saved (dollars)
80	·	r	≤	6000

$80r \leq 6000$ **Write inequality.**

$\dfrac{80r}{80} \leq \dfrac{6000}{80}$ **Divide each side by 80.**

$r \leq 75$ **Simplify.**

▶ The student can afford to pay at most $75 per hour for training.

 GUIDED PRACTICE   for Example 4

9. **WHAT IF?** In Example 4, suppose the student plans to spend 90 hours on flight training and has saved $6300. Write and solve an inequality to find the possible hourly rates that the student can afford to pay for training.

4.2 EXERCISES

HOMEWORK KEY

◆ = **MULTIPLE CHOICE PRACTICE**
Exs. 29, 34, 46, and 56–58

○ = **HINTS AND HOMEWORK HELP**
for Exs. 7, 11, and 49 at classzone.com

SKILLS · PROBLEM SOLVING · REASONING

1. **VOCABULARY** Which property are you using when you solve $5x \geq 30$ by dividing each side by 5?

2. **VOCABULARY** Which property are you using when you solve $5x \geq 30$ by multiplying each side by $\frac{1}{5}$?

3. **WRITING** Are $\dfrac{x}{-4} < -9$ and $x < 36$ equivalent inequalities? *Explain* your answer.

4. **WRITING** *Explain* how the multiplication property of inequality is similar to the division property of inequality.

EXAMPLES
1, 2, AND 3
on pp. 196–197
for Exs. 5–34

5. $2p \geq 14$

6. $\dfrac{x}{-3} < -10$

7. $-6y < -36$

8. $40 > \dfrac{w}{5}$

9. $\dfrac{q}{4} < 7$

10. $72 \leq 9r$

11. $\dfrac{g}{6} > -20$

12. $-11m \leq -22$

13. $-90 \geq 4t$

14. $\dfrac{n}{3} < -9$

15. $60 \leq -12s$

16. $\dfrac{v}{-4} \geq -8$

17. $-8.4f > 2.1$

18. $\dfrac{d}{-2} \leq 18.6$

19. $9.6 < -16c$

20. $0.07 \geq \dfrac{k}{7}$

21. $-1.5 \geq 6z$

22. $\dfrac{x}{-5} \leq -7.5$

23. $1.02 < -3j$

24. $\dfrac{y}{-4.5} \geq -10$

25. $\dfrac{r}{-30} < 1.8$

26. $1.9 \leq -5p$

27. $\dfrac{m}{0.6} > -40$

28. $-2t > -1.22$

29. ◆ **MULTIPLE CHOICE** What is the solution of the inequality $\dfrac{n}{3} \geq 6$?

(A) $n \geq 2$ **(B)** $n \geq 18$ **(C)** $n \leq 18$ **(D)** $n \leq 2$

30. WRITING How is solving $ax > b$ where $a > 0$ similar to solving $ax > b$ where $a < 0$? How is it different?

31. REASONING *Explain* how the inequality $ax \geq b$ can be solved for x using *either* the division property or the multiplication property of inequality.

ERROR ANALYSIS *Describe* and correct the error in solving the inequality.

32.

$-15x > 45$

$\dfrac{-15x}{-15} > \dfrac{45}{-15}$

$x > -3$

33.

$\dfrac{x}{9} \leq -7$

$9 \cdot \dfrac{x}{9} \leq 9 \cdot (-7)$

$x \geq -63$

34. ◆ **MULTIPLE CHOICE** What is the solution of the inequality $-8x > 96$?

(A) $x \geq -12$ **(B)** $x > -12$ **(C)** $x \leq -12$ **(D)** $x < -12$

TRANSLATING SENTENCES Write the verbal sentence as an inequality.
Then solve the inequality and graph your solution.

35. The product of -15 and y is less than or equal to 90.

36. The product of $\dfrac{2}{3}$ and x is greater than -12.

37. The quotient of v and -9 is less than -18.

38. The quotient of w and 24 is greater than or equal to $-\dfrac{1}{6}$.

REASONING Complete the statement with *always*, *sometimes*, or *never*.

39. If k is greater than 0 and x is greater than 0, then kx is __?__ greater than 0.

40. If k is less than 0 and x is greater than 0, then kx is __?__ greater than 0.

41. If k is greater than 0, then kx is __?__ greater than 0.

CONNECT SKILLS TO PROBLEM SOLVING Exercises 42–45 will help you prepare for problem solving.

Write an inequality that represents the situation.

42. You have $8 and want to buy some 39-cent stamps. Let s represent the possible numbers of stamps that you can buy.

43. Your average running speed is 6.5 miles per hour. You plan to run at least 10 miles a day as part of a training program. Let t represent the amount of time you spend running.

44. You can read 10 pages per hour. You need to read at least 115 pages of a book for your English class. Let t represent the amount of time you spend reading.

45. Maria plans to save at least $100 each week. She earns $7.50 per hour working at her job. Let h represent the possible numbers of hours Maria should work each week.

EXAMPLE 4
on p. 198
for Exs. 46–49

46. ◆ **MULTIPLE CHOICE** You have $90 to buy CDs for your friend's birthday. The CDs cost $18 each. Which inequality represents the possible numbers of CDs that you can buy?

(A) $x \le 3$ **(B)** $x \le 4$ **(C)** $x \le 5$ **(D)** $x \le 6$

California @HomeTutor for problem solving help at classzone.com

47. **JOB SKILLS** John applies for a job that requires the ability to type 40 words per minute. He practices typing on a keyboard for 5 minutes. The average number of words he types per minute must at least meet the job requirement. What are the possible numbers of words that John can type in 5 minutes in order to meet or exceed the job requirement?

California @HomeTutor for problem solving help at classzone.com

48. **TRAVELING** The driving distance between San Francisco and Los Angeles is about 385 miles. Write and solve an inequality that represents the possible average speeds s (in miles per hour) needed to drive from San Francisco to Los Angeles in less than 7 hours.

49. **MANUFACTURING** A manufacturer of architectural moldings recommends that the length of a piece be no more than 15 times its minimum width w (in inches) in order to prevent cracking. For the piece shown, what could the values of w be?

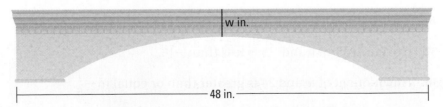

w in.

48 in.

50. **RECREATION** A water-skiing instructor recommends that a boat pulling a beginning skier have a speed less than 18 miles per hour. Write and solve an inequality that you can use to find the possible distances d (in miles) that a beginner can travel in 45 minutes of practice time.

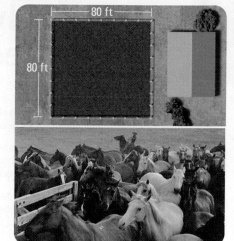

Wild Horses A state agency that offers wild horses for adoption requires that a farmer reserve at least 400 square feet of land per horse in a corral.

51. **Calculate** Write and solve an inequality to find the possible numbers h of horses that the corral shown at the right can hold.

52. **Calculate** By how many feet could the farmer increase just one dimension of the corral to gain enough room for one more horse? *Explain.*

53. **Justify** The farmer decides to increase both dimensions of the corral by 20 feet. *Explain* how the number of additional horses in this case is greater than if the farmer increased just one dimension by 40 feet.

54. **CHALLENGE** For the given values of a and b, tell whether the solution of $ax > b$ consists of *positive numbers*, *negative numbers*, or *both*. *Explain.*

    a. $a < 0, b > 0$ **b.** $a > 0, b > 0$ **c.** $a > 0, b < 0$ **d.** $a < 0, b < 0$

55. **CHALLENGE** An electronics store is selling a laptop computer for $1050. You can spend no more than $900 for the laptop, so you wait for it to go on sale. Also, you plan to use a store coupon for 5% off the sale price. For which decreases in price will you consider buying the laptop?

◆ CALIFORNIA STANDARDS SPIRAL REVIEW

Gr. 7 AF 1.2   56. What is the value of $2[15 - (2 + 10)]^2$? *(p. 11)*

      (A) 9   **(B)** 11   **(C)** 18   **(D)** 27

Alg. 4.0   57. What is the solution of $3x - 12 = 7x + 2x$? *(p. 139)*

      (A) -2 **(B)** -1 **(C)** 1   **(D)** 2

Gr. 6 NS 1.3   58. A recipe that yields 19 chocolate chip cookies calls for 2 cups of flour. How many cups of flour are needed to make 38 cookies? *(p. 161)*

      (A) 2 cups   **(B)** 4 cups   **(C)** 6 cups   **(D)** 8 cups

QUIZ *for Lessons 4.1–4.2*

Solve the inequality. Graph your solution.

1. $x + 8 \geq -5$ *(p. 189)*   2. $-8 \leq v - 5$ *(p. 189)*   3. $w - 11 > 2$ *(p. 189)*

4. $-40 < -5r$ *(p. 196)*   5. $\dfrac{n}{-4} > -7$ *(p. 196)*   6. $\dfrac{c}{6} \leq -8$ *(p. 196)*

7. **MOVIES** You have a $100 gift certificate to spend on DVDs. Each DVD costs $23. What are the possible numbers of DVDs that you can buy? *(p. 196)*

4.3 Solve Multi-Step Inequalities

Standards Alg. 4.0 Students simplify expressions before solving linear equations and **inequalities in one variable**, such as $3(2x − 5) + 4(x − 2) = 12$.

Alg. 5.0 Students solve multi-step problems, including word problems, involving linear equations and **linear inequalities in one variable** and provide justification for each step.

Math and BIOLOGY
Ex. 41, p. 206

Connect *Before* you solved one-step inequalities. *Now* you will solve multi-step inequalities.

Key Vocabulary
• inequality, *p. 26*

The steps for solving two-step and multi-step equations can be applied to linear inequalities. For inequalities, be sure to reverse the inequality symbol when multiplying or dividing by a negative number.

EXAMPLE 1 ◆ Multiple Choice Practice

What is the solution set to the inequality $3x − 7 < 8$?

Ⓐ $\left\{x : x > \frac{1}{3}\right\}$ Ⓑ $\{x : x < 5\}$ Ⓒ $\left\{x : x < \frac{1}{3}\right\}$ Ⓓ $\{x : x > 5\}$

Solution

$3x − 7 < 8$	**Write original inequality.**
$3x < 15$	**Add 7 to each side.**
$x < 5$	**Divide each side by 3.**

The solution set is $\{x : x < 5\}$.

▶ The correct answer is B. Ⓐ ● Ⓒ Ⓓ

EXAMPLE 2 Solve a multi-step inequality

Solve $−0.6(x − 5) \le 15$. Graph your solution.

About the Standards

In this chapter, the inequalities that you are solving involve variables raised only to the first power. Such inequalities are called *linear*.

Solution

$−0.6(x − 5) \le 15$	**Write original inequality.**
$−0.6x + 3 \le 15$	**Distributive property**
$−0.6x \le 12$	**Subtract 3 from each side.**
$x \ge −20$	**Divide each side by −0.6. Reverse inequality symbol.**

▶ The solutions are all real numbers greater than or equal to −20.

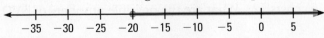

EXAMPLE 3 **Solve a multi-step inequality**

Solve $6x - 7 > 2x + 17$. Graph your solution.

Solution

$6x - 7 > 2x + 17$	Write original inequality.
$6x > 2x + 24$	Add 7 to each side.
$4x > 24$	Subtract $2x$ from each side.
$x > 6$	Divide each side by 4.

▸ The solutions are all real numbers greater than 6.

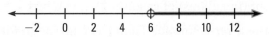

✓ **GUIDED PRACTICE** for Examples 1, 2, and 3

Solve the inequality. Graph your solution.

1. $2x - 5 \leq 23$ **2.** $-6y + 5 \leq -3y - 16$ **3.** $-\frac{1}{4}(p - 12) > -2$

SPECIAL CASES OF SOLUTIONS If an inequality is equivalent to an inequality that is true, such as $-3 < 0$, then the solutions of the inequality are *all real numbers.* If an inequality is equivalent to an inequality that is false, such as $4 < -1$, then the inequality has *no solution.*

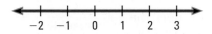

Graph of an inequality whose solutions are all real numbers

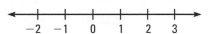

Graph of an inequality that has no solution

EXAMPLE 4 **Identify the number of solutions of an inequality**

Solve the inequality, if possible.

a. $14x + 5 < 7(2x - 3)$ **b.** $12x - 1 > 6(2x - 1)$

Solution

a.

$14x + 5 < 7(2x - 3)$	Write original inequality.
$14x + 5 < 14x - 21$	Distributive property
$5 < -21$	Subtract $14x$ from each side.

▸ There are no solutions because $5 < -21$ is false.

b.

$12x - 1 > 6(2x - 1)$	Write original inequality.
$12x - 1 > 12x - 6$	Distributive property
$-1 > -6$	Subtract $12x$ from each side.

▸ All real numbers are solutions because $-1 > -6$ is true.

EXAMPLE 5 Solve a multi-step problem

CAR WASH A gas station offers gasoline and car washes at the prices shown. The gas station charges $.10 less per gallon of gasoline if a customer also gets a car wash. What are the possible amounts (in gallons) of gasoline that you can buy if you also get a car wash and can spend at most $30?

Gasoline 3.33
Car Wash 10.00

ANOTHER WAY
For an alternative method for solving the problem in Example 5, turn to page 208 for the **Problem Solving Workshop**.

Solution

Because you are getting a car wash, you will pay $3.33 − $.10 = $3.23 per gallon of gasoline. Let g be the amount (in gallons) of gasoline that you buy.

STEP 1 **Write** a verbal model. Then write an inequality.

Price of gasoline (dollars/gallon)	·	Amount of gasoline (gallons)	+	Price of car wash (dollars)	≤	Maximum amount (dollars)
3.23	·	g	+	10	≤	30

STEP 2 **Solve** the inequality.

$3.23g + 10 \leq 30$	**Write inequality.**
$3.23g \leq 20$	**Subtract 10 from each side.**
$g \leq 6.19195\ldots$	**Divide each side by 3.23.**

▶ You can buy up to slightly more than 6 gallons of gasoline.

CHECK You can use a table to check the reasonableness of your answer.

The table shows that you will pay $29.38 for exactly 6 gallons of gasoline. Because $29.38 is less than $30, it is reasonable to conclude that you can buy slightly more than 6 gallons of gasoline.

Gasoline (gal)	Total amount spent (dollars)
0	10.00
1	13.23
2	16.46
3	19.69
4	22.92
5	26.15
6	29.38

 GUIDED PRACTICE for Examples 4 and 5

Solve the inequality, if possible. Graph your solution.

4. $3x - 12 \leq 3x - 4$ **5.** $5(m + 5) < 5m - 17$ **6.** $1 - 8s \leq -4(2s - 1)$

7. CAMP COSTS You are saving money for a summer camp that costs $1800. You have saved $500 so far, and you have 14 more weeks to save the total amount. What are the possible average amounts of money that you can save per week in order to have a total of at least $1800 saved?

4.3 **EXERCISES**

HOMEWORK KEY

◆ = **MULTIPLE CHOICE PRACTICE**
Exs. 15, 33, 42, and 48–50

○ = **HINTS AND HOMEWORK HELP**
for Exs. 5, 19, and 41 at classzone.com

SKILLS · PROBLEM SOLVING · REASONING

1. **VOCABULARY** Copy and complete: The inequalities $3x - 1 < 11$, $3x < 12$, and $x < 4$ are called __?__ .

2. **NOTETAKING SKILLS** Use a notetaking organizer like the one on page 188 to write your notes about solving an inequality.

EXAMPLES 1, 2, and 3
on pp. 202–203
for Exs. 3–17

SOLVING INEQUALITIES Solve the inequality. Graph your solution.

3. $2x - 3 > 7$

4. $5y + 9 \le 4$

5. $8v - 3 \ge -11$

6. $3(w + 12) < 0$

7. $7(r - 3) \ge -13$

8. $2(s + 4) \le 16$

9. $4 - 2m > 7 - 3m$

10. $8n - 2 > 17n + 9$

11. $-10p > 6p - 8$

12. $4 - \frac{1}{2}q \le 33 - q$

13. $-\frac{2}{3}d - 2 < \frac{1}{3}d + 8$

14. $8 - \frac{4}{5}f > -14 - 2f$

15. ◆ **MULTIPLE CHOICE** What is the solution of $2(w + 4) \ge 3w - 7$?

Ⓐ $w \ge 15$ Ⓑ $w \le 15$ Ⓒ $w \le 11$ Ⓓ $w \ge 11$

ERROR ANALYSIS *Describe* and correct the error in solving the inequality.

16.
$$17 - 3x \ge 56$$
$$-3x \ge 39$$
$$x \ge -13$$

17.
$$-4(2x - 3) < 28$$
$$-8x - 12 < 28$$
$$-8x < 40$$
$$x > -5$$

EXAMPLE 4
on p. 203
for Exs. 18–29

SOLVING INEQUALITIES Solve the inequality, if possible.

18. $3p - 5 > 2p + p - 7$

19. $3(s - 4) \ge 2(s - 6)$

20. $5d - 8d - 4 \le -4 + 3d$

21. $2(t - 3) > 2t - 8$

22. $4 + 9y - 3 \ge 3(3y + 2)$

23. $2(4c - 7) \ge 8(c - 3)$

24. $6(x + 3) < 5x + 18 + x$

25. $5(b + 9) \le 5b + 45$

26. $2.2h + 0.4 \le 2(1.1h - 0.1)$

27. $9.5j - 6 + 5.5j \ge 3(5j - 2)$

28. $\frac{1}{5}(4m + 10) < \frac{4}{5}m + 2$

29. $\frac{3}{4}(8n - 4) < -3(1 - 2n)$

TRANSLATING SENTENCES Write the verbal sentence as an inequality. Then solve the inequality and graph your solution.

30. Four more than the product of 3 and x is less than or equal to 40.

31. Twice the sum of x and 8 is greater than the difference of 32 and $6x$.

32. **REASONING** Write a proof of the statement "If $-15 + 3x > 9x + 3$, then $x < -3$."

33. ◆ **MULTIPLE CHOICE** For which values of a and b are all the solutions of $ax + b > 0$ positive?

Ⓐ $a > 0, b > 0$ Ⓑ $a < 0, b < 0$ Ⓒ $a > 0, b < 0$ Ⓓ $a < 0, b = 0$

⊘ **GEOMETRY** Write and solve an inequality to find the possible values of *x*.

34. Area > 81 square feet

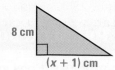

9 ft

(*x* + 2) ft

35. Area ≥ 44 square centimeters

8 cm

(*x* + 1) cm

CONNECT SKILLS TO PROBLEM SOLVING Exercises 36–38 will help you prepare for problem solving.

Write an inequality that represents the situation.

36. You have $15 to spend on a notebook and pens. A notebook costs $2, and each pen costs $.75. Let *p* represent the possible numbers of pens that you can buy.

37. A fish tank holds 60 gallons of water. To do a partial water change, you use a pump that removes water at a rate of 5 gallons per minute. You want to remove no more than 25% of the water. Let *t* represent the possible amounts of time (in minutes) that the pump runs.

38. While taking a trip, a family wants to drive at least 500 miles today. So far today the family has traveled 120 miles at an average speed of 50 miles per hour. Let *t* represent the possible amounts of time (in hours) that the family will continue to drive today.

EXAMPLE 5
on p. 204
for Exs. 39–42

39. CD BURNING A blank CD can hold 70 minutes of music. So far you have burned 25 minutes of music onto the CD. You estimate that each song lasts 4 minutes. What are the possible numbers of additional songs that you can burn onto the CD?

California @HomeTutor for problem solving help at classzone.com

40. BUSINESS You spend $46 on supplies to make wooden ornaments and plan to sell the ornaments for $8.50 each. What are the possible numbers of ornaments that you can sell in order for your profit to be positive?

California @HomeTutor for problem solving help at classzone.com

41. **MULTI-STEP PROBLEM** A zookeeper is designing a rectangular habitat for swans, as shown. The zookeeper needs to reserve 500 square feet for the first 2 swans and 125 square feet for each additional swan.

20 ft

50 ft

a. What are the possible numbers of swans that the habitat can hold?

b. Suppose that the zookeeper increases both the length and width of the habitat by 20 feet. What are the possible numbers of additional swans that the habitat can hold?

42. ◆ **MULTIPLE CHOICE** A gym is offering a trial membership for 3 months by discounting the regular monthly rate by $50. You will consider joining the gym if the total cost of the trial membership is less than $100. Which inequality can you use to find the possible regular monthly rates that you are willing to pay?

  Ⓐ $3x - 50 < 100$ **Ⓑ** $3x - 50 > 100$

  Ⓒ $3(x - 50) < 100$ **Ⓓ** $3(x - 50) > 100$

43. BASEBALL A baseball pitcher makes 53 pitches in the first four innings of a game and plans to pitch in the next 3 innings. The baseball coach assigns a maximum of 105 pitches to the pitcher for the game. Write and solve an inequality to find the possible average numbers of pitches that the pitcher can make in each of the next three innings.

44. SALES TAX A state imposes a sales tax on items of clothing that cost more than $175. The tax applies only to the difference of the price of the item and $175.

  a. Calculate Use the receipt shown to find the tax rate (as a percent). *Explain* how you got your answer.

  b. Apply A shopper has $400 to spend on a winter coat. Write and solve an inequality to find the prices p of coats that the shopper can afford. Assume that $p \geq 175$.

  c. Compare Another state imposes a 4% sales tax on the entire price of an item of clothing. For which prices would paying the 4% tax be cheaper than paying the tax described above?

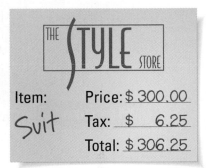

THE STYLE STORE

Item: Suit
Price: $ 300.00
Tax: $ 6.25
Total: $ 306.25

45. REASONING Given $3x + 2 > ax + b$, what values of a and b make the inequality false for all real numbers x? true for all real numbers x?

46. CHALLENGE For which value of a are all the solutions of the inequality $2(x - 5) \geq 3x + a$ less than or equal to 5?

47. CHALLENGE Your scores in four bowling league tournaments are 157, 161, 149, and 172. After the next game, you want your average score to be at least 167. What are the possible scores that you can earn in your next tournament in order to meet your goal?

◆ CALIFORNIA STANDARDS SPIRAL REVIEW

Gr. 7 AF 4.1 **48.** What is the solution set of the inequality $m + 8 \geq 4$? *(p. 189)*

  Ⓐ $\{m : m \geq 12\}$ **Ⓑ** $\{m : m \geq -4\}$ **Ⓒ** $\{m : m \geq 4\}$ **Ⓓ** $\{m : m \geq -12\}$

Alg. 4.0 **49.** What is the solution of $3x + 2 + x = 5(x - 2)$? *(p. 146)*

  Ⓐ -10 **Ⓑ** 0 **Ⓒ** 8 **Ⓓ** 12

Gr. 6 NS 1.2 **50.** An aquarium contains only goldfish and catfish. There are twice as many goldfish as catfish. Which ratio represents the number of catfish to the total number of fish? *(p. 155)*

  Ⓐ $1 : 2$ **Ⓑ** $1 : 3$ **Ⓒ** $1 : 4$ **Ⓓ** $2 : 3$

Using ALTERNATIVE METHODS

Another Way to Solve Example 5, page 204

In Example 5 on page 204, you saw how to solve a problem about buying gasoline using an inequality. You can also solve the problem by working backward.

PROBLEM

CAR WASH A gas station offers gasoline and car washes at the prices shown. The gas station charges $.10 less per gallon of gasoline if a customer also gets a car wash. What are the possible amounts (in gallons) of gasoline that you can buy if you also get a car wash and can spend at most $30?

Gasoline 3.33
Car Wash 10.00

METHOD

Work backward An alternative approach is to work backward.

- Start with the amount you have to spend: $30.
- Subtract the cost of a car wash: $30 − $10 = $20.
- Find the discounted price of gasoline: $3.33 − $.10 = $3.23 per gallon.
- Make a table of values showing the amount of money you have left after buying various amounts of gasoline.

Gasoline (in gallons)	0	1	2	3	4	5	6
Amount of money left	$20.00	$16.77	$13.54	$10.31	$7.08	$3.85	$.62

− $3.23 − $3.23 − $3.23 − $3.23 − $3.23 − $3.23

▶ You can buy up to slightly more than 6 gallons of gasoline.

PRACTICE

1. **BAKING** You need to bake at least 100 cookies for a bake sale. You can bake 12 cookies per batch of dough. What are the possible numbers of batches that will allow you to bake enough cookies? Solve this problem using two different methods.

2. **VIDEO GAMES** A video game console costs $259, and games cost $29 each. You saved $400 to buy a console and games. What are the possible numbers of games that you can buy? Solve this problem using two different methods.

3. **WHAT IF?** In Exercise 2, suppose that you saved $500 and decide to buy a video game console that costs $299. What are the possible numbers of games that you can buy?

4. **MONEY** You need to have at least $100 in your checking account to avoid a fee. You have $247 in your account, and you make withdrawals of $20 per week. What are the possible numbers of weeks that you can withdraw money and avoid the fee? Solve this problem using two different methods.

4.4 Statements with *And* and *Or*

MATERIALS • paper and pencil

Standards Preparation

Gr. 7 MR 2.5 Use a variety of methods, **such as words**, numbers, symbols, charts, graphs, tables, **diagrams**, and models, **to explain mathematical reasoning.**

QUESTION What is the difference between a statement with *and* and a statement with *or*?

EXPLORE Use a Venn diagram to answer questions about a group of students

STEP 1 *Answer questions* Copy the questions shown at the right and write your answers beside them.

> 1. Are you taking an art class?
>
> 2. Are you taking a foreign language class?

STEP 2 *Complete a Venn diagram* Form a group with 3 or 4 classmates. Draw a Venn diagram, like the one shown below, where set *A* consists of students taking an art class and set *B* consists of students taking a foreign language class. Then write the name of each student in the appropriate section of the diagram.

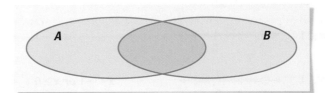

DRAW CONCLUSIONS Use your observations to complete these exercises

In Exercises 1–3, use your Venn diagram to list the students who belong in the given set.

1. Set *A*
2. Set *B*
3. Set *A and* set *B*

4. The students who belong in set *A or* set *B* are all of the students who belong only in set *A*, only in set *B*, or in set *A and* set *B*. List the students in your group who belong in set *A or* set *B*.

5. **OPEN-ENDED** Write a statement with *and* so that the statement is true for all students in your group.

6. **OPEN-ENDED** Write a statement with *or* so that the statement is true for all students in your group.

REASONING Tell whether the statement is *true* or *false*.

7. If a student belongs in set *A and* set *B*, then the student belongs in set *A or* set *B*.

8. If a student belongs in set *A or* set *B*, then the student belongs in set *A and* set *B*.

4.4 Solve Compound Inequalities

Standards

Alg. 4.0 Students **simplify expressions before solving linear** equations and **inequalities in one variable,** such as $3(2x - 5) + 4(x - 2) = 12$.

Alg. 5.0 Students solve multi-step problems, including word problems, involving linear equations and **linear inequalities in one variable and provide justification for each step.**

Connect   *Before* you solved one-step and multi-step inequalities. *Now* you will solve compound inequalities.

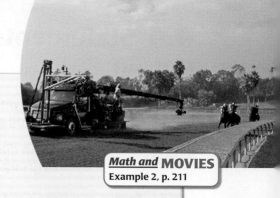

Math and MOVIES
Example 2, p. 211

Key Vocabulary
• compound inequality

A **compound inequality** consists of two inequalities joined by *and* or *or*.

The graph of a compound inequality with *and* is the *intersection* of the graphs. The intersection consists of points that the graphs have in common.

The graph of a compound inequality with *or* is the *union* of the graphs. The union consists of points that are part of either graph.

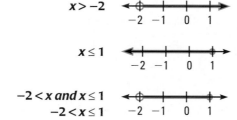

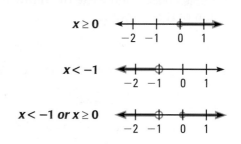

EXAMPLE 1   Write and graph compound inequalities

Translate the verbal phrase into an inequality. Then graph the inequality.

a. All real numbers that are greater than -2 *and* less than 3

Inequality: $-2 < x < 3$ **Graph:**

b. All real numbers that are less than 0 *or* greater than or equal to 2

Inequality: $x < 0$ *or* $x \geq 2$ **Graph:**

✓ **GUIDED PRACTICE**   for Example 1

Translate the verbal phrase into an inequality. Then graph the inequality.

1. All real numbers that are less than -1 *or* greater than or equal to 4

2. All real numbers that are greater than or equal to -3 *and* less than 5

EXAMPLE 2 Write and graph a real-world compound inequality

MOVIES A camera car with a crane is used to film a movie. The crane's maximum height and minimum height above the ground are shown. Write and graph a compound inequality that describes the possible heights of the crane.

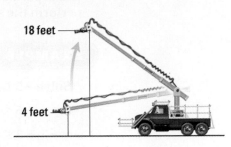

18 feet

4 feet

Solution

Let h represent the height (in feet) of the crane. All possible heights are greater than or equal to 4 feet *and* less than or equal to 18 feet. So, the inequality is $4 \le h \le 18$.

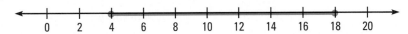

SOLVING COMPOUND INEQUALITIES A number is a solution of a compound inequality with *and* if the number is a solution of *both* inequalities. A number is a solution of a compound inequality with *or* if the number is a solution of *at least one* of the inequalities.

EXAMPLE 3 Solve a compound inequality with *and*

Solve $2 < x + 5 < 9$. Graph your solution.

Solution

Separate the compound inequality into two inequalities. Then solve each inequality separately.

$2 < x + 5$	*and*	$x + 5 < 9$	Write two inequalities.
$2 - 5 < x + 5 - 5$	*and*	$x + 5 - 5 < 9 - 5$	Subtract 5 from each side.
$-3 < x$	*and*	$x < 4$	Simplify.

The compound inequality can be written as $-3 < x < 4$.

▶ The solutions are all real numbers greater than -3 *and* less than 4.

✓ **GUIDED PRACTICE** for Examples 2 and 3

3. **INVESTING** An investor buys shares of a stock and will sell them if the change c in value from the purchase price of a share is less than $-\$3.00$ or greater than $\$4.50$. Write and graph a compound inequality that describes the changes in value for which the shares will be sold.

Solve the inequality. Graph your solution.

4. $-7 < x - 5 < 4$　　　　5. $10 \le 2y + 4 \le 24$　　　　6. $-7 < -z - 1 < 3$

ANOTHER WAY In Example 3, you could solve $2 < x + 5 < 9$ by subtracting 5 from 2, $x + 5$, and 9 without first separating the compound inequality into two separate inequalities. To solve a compound inequality with *and*, you perform the same operation on each expression.

EXAMPLE 4 **Solve a compound inequality with *and***

Solve $-5 \le -x - 3 \le 2$. Graph your solution.

$-5 \le -x - 3 \le 2$	**Write original inequality.**
$-5 + 3 \le -x - 3 + 3 \le 2 + 3$	**Add 3 to each expression.**
$-2 \le -x \le 5$	**Simplify.**
$-1(-2) \ge -1(-x) \ge -1(5)$	**Multiply each expression by -1 and reverse *both* inequality symbols.**
$2 \ge x \ge -5$	**Simplify.**
$-5 \le x \le 2$	**Rewrite in the form $a \le x \le b$.**

▶ The solutions are all real numbers greater than or equal to -5 *and* less than or equal to 2.

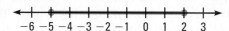

EXAMPLE 5 **Solve a compound inequality with *or***

Solve $2x + 3 < 9$ *or* $3x - 6 > 12$. Graph your solution.

Solution

Solve the two inequalities separately.

$2x + 3 < 9$	*or*	$3x - 6 > 12$	**Write original inequality.**
$2x + 3 - 3 < 9 - 3$	*or*	$3x - 6 + 6 > 12 + 6$	**Addition or subtraction property of inequality**
$2x < 6$	*or*	$3x > 18$	**Simplify.**
$\dfrac{2x}{2} < \dfrac{6}{2}$	*or*	$\dfrac{3x}{3} > \dfrac{18}{3}$	**Division property of inequality**
$x < 3$	*or*	$x > 6$	**Simplify.**

▶ The solutions are all real numbers less than 3 *or* greater than 6.

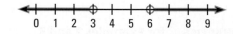

Animated **Algebra**

For an interactive example of solving a compound inequality, go to **classzone.com**.

✔ **GUIDED PRACTICE** for Examples 4 and 5

Solve the inequality. Graph your solution.

7. $-14 < x - 8 < -1$

8. $-1 \le -5t + 2 \le 4$

9. $3h + 1 < -5$ *or* $2h - 5 > 7$

10. $4c + 1 \le -3$ *or* $5c - 3 > 17$

EXAMPLE 6 Solve a multi-step problem

ASTRONOMY The Mars Exploration Rovers *Opportunity* and *Spirit* are robots that were sent to Mars in 2003 in order to gather geological data about the planet. The temperature at the landing sites of the robots can range from −100°C to 0°C.

- Write a compound inequality that describes the possible temperatures (in degrees Fahrenheit) at a landing site.

- Solve the inequality. Then graph your solution.

- Identify three possible temperatures (in degrees Fahrenheit) at a landing site.

Landing site temperatures: −100°C to 0°C

Solution

Let F represent the temperature in degrees Fahrenheit, and let C represent the temperature in degrees Celsius. Use the formula $C = \frac{5}{9}(F - 32)$.

STEP 1 **Write** a compound inequality. Because the temperature at a landing site ranges from −100°C to 0°C, the lowest possible temperature is −100°C, and the highest possible temperature is 0°C.

$-100 \le C \le 0$ **Write inequality using *C*.**

$-100 \le \frac{5}{9}(F - 32) \le 0$ **Substitute $\frac{5}{9}(F - 32)$ for *C*.**

STEP 2 **Solve** the inequality. Then graph your solution.

ANOTHER WAY

You can solve the compound inequality by multiplying through by 9:

$-100 \le \frac{5}{9}(F - 32) \le 0$

$-900 \le 5(F - 32) \le 0$

$-900 \le 5F - 160 \le 0$

$-740 \le 5F \le 160$

$-148 \le F \le 32$

$-100 \le \frac{5}{9}(F - 32) \le 0$ **Write inequality from Step 1.**

$-180 \le F - 32 \le 0$ **Multiply each expression by $\frac{9}{5}$.**

$-148 \le F \le 32$ **Add 32 to each expression.**

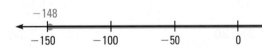

STEP 3 **Identify** three possible temperatures.

The temperature at a landing site is greater than or equal to −148°F *and* less than or equal to 32°F. Three possible temperatures are −115°F, 15°F, and 32°F.

✓ **GUIDED PRACTICE**   **for Example 6**

11. **MARS** Mars has a maximum temperature of 27°C at the equator and a minimum temperature of −133°C at the winter pole.

- Write and solve a compound inequality that describes the possible temperatures (in degrees Fahrenheit) on Mars.

- Graph your solution. Then identify three possible temperatures (in degrees Fahrenheit) on Mars.

4.4 EXERCISES

HOMEWORK KEY

◆ = **MULTIPLE CHOICE PRACTICE**
Exs. 7, 22, 31, 42, and 53–55

◯ = **HINTS AND HOMEWORK HELP**
for Exs. 5, 9, and 43 at classzone.com

SKILLS · PROBLEM SOLVING · REASONING

1. **VOCABULARY** Copy and complete: A(n) ? is an inequality that consists of two inequalities joined by *and* or *or*.

2. **WRITING** *Describe* the difference between the graphs of $-6 \le x \le -4$ and $x \le -6 \ or \ x \ge -4$.

EXAMPLE 1
on p. 210
for Exs. 3–7

TRANSLATING VERBAL PHRASES **Translate the verbal phrase into an inequality. Then graph the inequality.**

3. All real numbers that are less than 6 *and* greater than 2

4. All real numbers that are less than or equal to -8 *or* greater than 12

5. All real numbers that are greater than or equal to -1.5 *and* less than 9.2

6. All real numbers that are greater than or equal to $-7\frac{1}{2}$ *or* less than or equal to -10

7. ◆ **MULTIPLE CHOICE** Which inequality is represented by the graph?

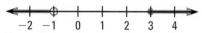

Ⓐ $x \ge -1 \ or \ x \le 3$
Ⓑ $x < -1 \ or \ x > 3$
Ⓒ $x < -1 \ or \ x \ge 3$
Ⓓ $x \le -1 \ or \ x \ge 3$

EXAMPLES 3, 4, and 5
on pp. 211–212
for Exs. 8–22

SOLVING COMPOUND INEQUALITIES **Solve the inequality. Graph your solution.**

8. $6 < x + 5 \le 11$

9. $-1 \le -4m \le 16$

10. $-7 > y - 8 \ge -12$

11. $-6 \le 3n + 9 < 21$

12. $-15 \le 5(3p - 2) < 20$

13. $7 > \frac{2}{3}(6q + 18) \ge -9$

14. $2r + 3 < 7 \ or \ -r + 9 \le 2$

15. $16 < -s - 6 \ or \ 2s + 5 \ge 11$

16. $v + 13 < 8 \ or \ -8v < -40$

17. $-14 > w + 3 \ or \ 5w - 13 > w + 7$

18. $c + 2 \le 2c \ or \ 7 < -\frac{2}{3}c - 5$

19. $-t + 8 \ge t + 4 \ or \ \frac{1}{2}(t - 6) > 11$

20. $9g - 6 > 12g + 1 \ or \ 4 > -\frac{2}{5}g + 8$

21. $-2h - 7 > h + 5 \ or \ \frac{1}{4}(h + 8) \ge 9$

22. ◆ **MULTIPLE CHOICE** What is the solution of $4 \le \frac{1}{2}(4x - 8) < 14$?

Ⓐ $4 \le x < 9$
Ⓑ $0 \le x < 5$
Ⓒ $4 \le x < 5$
Ⓓ $0 \le x < 9$

23. **REASONING** *Describe* the solution set of the compound inequality $x > a \ and \ x < b$ when $a > b$.

24. **REASONING** *Describe* the solution set of the compound inequality $x > a \ or \ x < b$ when $a < b$.

ERROR ANALYSIS *Describe* and correct the error in solving the inequality or in graphing the solution.

25.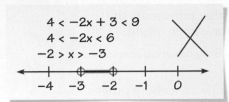

$$4 < -2x + 3 < 9$$
$$4 < -2x < 6$$
$$-2 > x > -3$$

26.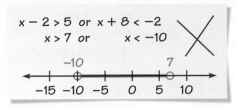

$$x - 2 > 5 \text{ or } x + 8 < -2$$
$$x > 7 \text{ or } \quad x < -10$$

TRANSLATING SENTENCES Write the verbal sentence as an inequality. Then solve the inequality and graph your solution.

27. Five more than x is less than 8 *or* 3 less than x is greater than 5.

28. Three less than x is greater than -4 *and* less than -1.

29. Three times the difference of x and 4 is greater than or equal to -8 *and* less than or equal to 10.

30. The sum of $-2x$ and 8 is less than or equal to -5 *or* 6 is less than $-2x$.

31. ◆ **MULTIPLE CHOICE** Consider the compound inequality $a > 3x + 8$ *and* $a > -4x - 1$. For which value of a does the solution consist of numbers greater than -6 *and* less than 5?

    Ⓐ 16   **Ⓑ** 19   **Ⓒ** 23   **Ⓓ** 26

REASONING In Exercises 32–35, tell whether the statement is *true* or *false*. If it is false, give a counterexample.

32. If a is a solution of $x < 5$, then a is also a solution of $x < 5$ *and* $x \geq -4$.

33. If a is a solution of $x > 5$, then a is also a solution of $x > 5$ *or* $x \leq -4$.

34. Is a is a solution of $x < 5$ and $x \geq -4$, then a is also a solution of $x < 5$.

35. If a is a solution of $x > 5$ or $x \leq -4$, then a is also a solution of $x > 5$.

36. ⊘ **GEOMETRY** The sum of the lengths of any two sides of a triangle is greater than the length of the third side.

    a. Write and solve three inequalities for the triangle shown.

    b. Use the inequalities that you wrote in part (a) to write one inequality that describes all the possible values of x.

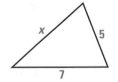

CONNECT SKILLS TO PROBLEM SOLVING Exercises 37–39 will help you prepare for problem solving.

    Write a compound inequality that represents the situation.

37. The preferred water temperatures for blue catfish are between 68°F and 80°F. Let T represent the preferred water temperatures.

38. The minimum speed on a highway is 40 miles per hour, and the maximum speed is 60 miles per hour. Let s represent the possible speeds allowed on the highway.

39. Admission to an amusement park is reduced for children under 6 years of age and adults over 65. Let a represent the ages that qualify for a reduced admission fee.

Blue catfish

EXAMPLE 2
on page 211 for
Exs. 40, 42, 44

40. SLITSNAILS Slitsnails are large mollusks that live in deep waters. Slitsnails have been found at elevations from −2600 feet to −100 feet. Write and graph a compound inequality that represents the elevations at which slitsnails have been found.

California @HomeTutor for problem solving help at classzone.com

EXAMPLE 6
on p. 213 for
Exs. 41, 43, 45

41. ICEBERGS The temperature inside an iceberg ranges from −20°C to −15°C. Write and graph a compound inequality that describes the possible temperatures (in degrees Fahrenheit) of the iceberg's interior.

California @HomeTutor for problem solving help at classzone.com

Slitsnails

42. ◆ MULTIPLE CHOICE The euro is the currency in several countries in Europe. In 2003, the dollar value of one euro ranged from $1.0361 to $1.2597. Which inequality represents the dollar values v that the euro was *not* worth during the year?

(A) $1.0361 < v < 1.2597$

(B) $v < 1.0361$ *or* $v > 1.2597$

(C) $1.0361 \leq v \leq 1.2597$

(D) $v \leq 1.0361$ *or* $v \geq 1.2597$

43. ANIMALS A deer can eat 2% to 4% of its body weight in food per day. The percent p of the deer's body weight eaten in food is given by the equation $p = \dfrac{f}{d}$ where f is the amount (in pounds) of food eaten and d is the weight (in pounds) of the deer. Find the possible amounts of food that a 160 pound deer can eat per day.

44. CURRENCY On October 25, 1865, the steamship *S.S. Republic* sank along with a cargo of gold and silver coins. The list below gives the prices of several recovered gold coins. Use the least price and greatest price to write a compound inequality that describes the prices p of the coins.

Prices of Recovered Gold Coins

$9,098	$20,995	$9,798	$33,592	$12,597
$16,796	$9,798	$10,498	$5,319	$73,486
$11,897	$32,895	$7,349	$6,578	$29,395

45. SKIS A ski shop sells recreational skis with lengths ranging from 150 centimeters to 220 centimeters. The shop recommends that recreational skis be 1.16 times the skier's height (in centimeters). For which heights of skiers does the shop *not* provide recreational skis?

46. WEATHER Wind chill temperature describes how much colder it feels when the speed of the wind is combined with air temperature. At a wind speed of 20 miles per hour, the wind chill temperature w (in degrees Fahrenheit) can be given by the model $w = -22 + 1.3a$ where a is the air temperature (in degrees Fahrenheit). What are the possible air temperatures if the wind chill temperature ranges from −9°F to −2.5°F at a wind speed of 20 miles per hour?

47. **MUSIC** Some musicians use audio amplifiers so that everyone in the audience can hear the performance. The amount y of amplification per person is given by the equation $y = \frac{w}{p}$ where w is the total amount (in watts) of amplification provided by the amplifier and p is the number of people in the audience.

   a. Solve Each person requires 8 watts to 10 watts of amplification. Write and solve an inequality to find the possible total amounts of amplification that an amplifier would need to provide for 300 people.

   b. Decide Will an amplifier that provides 2900 watts of amplification be strong enough for an audience of 350 people? 400 people? *Explain.*

   Animated Algebra at classzone.com

CHALLENGE Solve the inequality, if possible. Graph your solution.

48. $-18 < x - 23$ *and* $x - 16 < -22$

49. $-3y + 7 \leq 11$ *and* $y + 4 > 11$

50. $2m - 1 \geq 5$ *or* $5m > -25$

51. $n + 19 \geq 10$ *or* $-5n + 3 > 33$

52. **CHALLENGE** You and three friends are planning to eat at a restaurant, and all of you agree to divide the total cost of the meals and the 15% tip equally. Each person agrees to pay at least $10 but no more than $20. How much can you spend altogether on meals before the tip is applied?

◆ CALIFORNIA STANDARDS SPIRAL REVIEW

Alg. 1.0

53. Which expression is equivalent to $\dfrac{-44 - 8t}{-4}$? *(p. 88)*

   (A) $11 + 2t$ (B) $22 - 4t$ (C) $-10 - 2t$ (D) $11 - 2t$

Alg. 2.0

54. What is the value of the expression $|x| + 1$ when $x = -1.7$? *(p. 53)*

   (A) 3.7 (B) 2.7 (C) -1.7 (D) -3.7

Gr. 7 AF 4.1

55. Your parents are willing to spend no more than $17,000 for a new car. The car dealership offers $3000 cash back for the purchase of a new car. Which inequality represents the original prices p of the cars that your parents will consider buying? *(p. 189)*

   (A) $p < 14,000$ (B) $p < 20,000$ (C) $p \leq 14,000$ (D) $p \leq 20,000$

QUIZ for Lessons 4.3–4.4

Solve the inequality, if possible. Graph your solution.

1. $-\frac{1}{5}(x - 5) > x - 9$ *(p. 202)*

2. $\frac{1}{2}y - 8 \geq -2y + 3$ *(p. 202)*

3. $-4r + 7 \leq r + 10$ *(p. 202)*

4. $-2(s + 6) \leq -2s + 8$ *(p. 202)*

5. $5(v + 2) > -(v + 12)$ *(p. 202)*

6. $2 < -3t - 7 \leq 14$ *(p. 210)*

7. $a - 4 \geq -1$ *or* $3a < -24$ *(p. 210)*

8. $22 > -3c + 4 > 14$ *(p. 210)*

9. $-27 \leq 9m \leq -18$ *(p. 210)*

10. $5n + 2 > -18$ *or* $-3(n + 4) > 21$ *(p. 210)*

4.4 Solve Compound Inequalities

Standards

Alg. 5.0 Students solve multi-step problems, including word problems, **involving** linear equations and **linear inequalities in one variable** and provide justification for each step.

QUESTION How can you use a graphing calculator to display the solutions of a compound inequality?

EXAMPLE Display the solutions of $12 \le 3x \le 21$ on a graphing calculator

STEP 1 *Rewrite inequality*

Rewrite $12 \le 3x \le 21$ as two separate inequalities joined by *and*.

$12 \le 3x \le 21$ **Write original inequality.**

$12 \le 3x$ *and* $3x \le 21$ **Write as two inequalities joined by** *and*.

STEP 2 *Enter inequalities*

Press Y= and enter the two inequalities, as shown. Inequality signs can be found in the TEST menu, and *and* and *or* can be found in the LOGIC menu.

STEP 3 *Display solutions*

Press GRAPH to display the solutions of $12 \le 3x$ *and* $3x \le 21$. For each value of x that makes the inequality true, the calculator assigns a value of 1 to y and plots the point $(x, 1)$. For each value of x that makes the inequality false, the calculator assigns a value of 0 to y and plots the point $(x, 0)$.

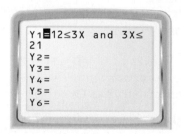

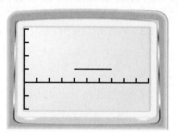

STEP 4 *Interpret the graph*

The screen in Step 3 shows the graph of $y = 1$ over the interval $4 \le x \le 7$. This suggests that the solutions are all real numbers greater than or equal to 4 *and* less than or equal to 7.

DRAW CONCLUSIONS

1. Display the solutions of $12 < 3x < 21$ on a graphing calculator. Then compare the graph of $12 < 3x < 21$ with the graph of $12 \le 3x \le 21$.

2. When displaying the solutions of an inequality on a graphing calculator, how do you know which inequality symbols you should use in your solution?

Display the solutions of the inequality on a graphing calculator.

3. $9 \le 3x \le 21$

4. $4 < 4x < 8$

5. $2 \le \frac{1}{4}x \le 12$

6. $-6x > 18$ *or* $9x > 45$

7. $4x \le 18$ *or* $5x \ge 25$

8. $8x \le 16$ *or* $3x \ge 30$

MIXED REVIEW of Skills and Problem Solving

Multiple Choice Practice for Lessons 4.1–4.4

1. What is the solution of the inequality
   $-100x > 4$? **Gr. 7 AF 4.1**

   (A) $x < -25$ (B) $x < -\frac{1}{25}$

   (C) $x > -\frac{1}{25}$ (D) $x > -25$

2. The table shows the scores you received
   on the five math tests you have taken this
   semester. Which inequality describes the
   possible scores s you can earn on your sixth
   test if you want a mean score of at least 80?
   Alg. 5.0

Test	1	2	3	4	5
Score	75	82	90	84	71

   (A) $s > 76$ (B) $s \geq 78$

   (C) $s > 78$ (D) $s \geq 80$

3. Which inequality is represented by the
   graph? **Gr. 7 AF 4.1**

   (A) $x > 1$ (B) $x \geq 1$

   (C) $x \leq 1$ (D) $x < 1$

4. Which inequality represents the verbal
   statement "Half the sum of b and 3 is
   greater than or equal to 23"? **Alg. 4.0**

   (A) $\frac{1}{2}b + 3 \geq 23$

   (B) $\frac{1}{2}(b + 3) \leq 23$

   (C) $\frac{1}{2}b + 3 \leq 23$

   (D) $\frac{1}{2}(b + 3) \geq 23$

5. What is the solution of the inequality
   $\frac{y}{9} \leq -3$? **Gr. 7 AF 4.1**

   (A) $y \geq -27$ (B) $y \geq -\frac{1}{3}$

   (C) $y \leq -\frac{1}{3}$ (D) $y \leq -27$

6. You have a $140 gift card to use at a sporting
   goods store. The ad below shows this week's
   sale items. You plan to buy 2 pairs of shoes
   and spend the rest of the money on socks.
   What are the possible numbers of pairs of
   socks s you can buy? **Alg. 5.0**

   (A) $0 \leq s \leq 6$ (B) $0 \leq s \leq 5$

   (C) $0 \leq s < 5$ (D) $0 \leq s < 6$

7. Which inequality is represented by the
   graph? **Gr. 7 AF 4.1**

   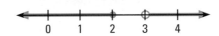

   (A) $x \leq 2$ *or* $x \leq 3$

   (B) $x \leq 2$ *or* $x > 3$

   (C) $x < 2$ *or* $x \geq 3$

   (D) $x \geq 2$ *or* $x < 3$

8. What is the solution of the inequality
   $f + 11 \leq -47$? **Gr. 7 AF 4.1**

   (A) $f \leq -58$ (B) $f \leq -36$

   (C) $f \leq 36$ (D) $f \leq 58$

9. Water can exist as a solid, a liquid, or a
   gas. The table shows the temperatures
   at which water can exist in each form.
   Which compound inequality represents
   the temperatures T at which water is *not*
   a liquid? **Alg. 5.0**

Form of water	Solid	Liquid	Gas
Temperature (°C)	Less than 0	0 to 100	Greater than 100

   (A) $0 < T < 100$ (B) $T > 0$ *or* $T < 100$

   (C) $T > 100$ (D) $T < 0$ *or* $T > 100$

4.5 Solve Absolute Value Equations

Standards Alg. 3.0 **Students solve equations** and inequalities **involving absolute values.**

Connect *Before* you solved linear equations. *Now* you will solve absolute value equations.

Math and **SPORTS**
Ex. 48, p. 224

Key Vocabulary
• **absolute value equation**
• **absolute deviation**
• **absolute value,** *p. 55*

The absolute value of a number a, written $|a|$, is the distance between a and 0 on a number line. An **absolute value equation**, such as $|x| = 4$, is an equation that contains an absolute value expression. The equation $|x| = 4$ means that the distance between x and 0 is 4. The solutions of the equation are 4 and -4, because they are the only numbers whose distance from 0 is 4.

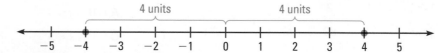

4 units   4 units

$-5 \quad -4 \quad -3 \quad -2 \quad -1 \quad 0 \quad 1 \quad 2 \quad 3 \quad 4 \quad 5$

EXAMPLE 1 Solve an absolute value equation

Solve $|x| = 7$.

Solution

Animated Algebra

For an interactive example of solving an absolute value equation, go to **classzone.com**.

The distance between x and 0 is 7. So, $x = 7$ *or* $x = -7$.

▶ The solutions are 7 and -7.

 GUIDED PRACTICE for Example 1

Solve the equation.

1. $|x| = 3$ **2.** $|x| = 15$ **3.** $|x| = 7.8$ **4.** $|x| = \dfrac{3}{5}$

SOLVING ABSOLUTE VALUE EQUATIONS In Example 1, notice that the expression inside the absolute value symbol equals 7 or the opposite of 7. This suggests the following rule for solving an absolute value equation.

KEY CONCEPT *For Your Notebook*

Solving an Absolute Value Equation

The equation $|ax + b| = c$ where $c \geq 0$ is equivalent to the statement $ax + b = c$ *or* $ax + b = -c$.

Example: $|3x + 2| = 5$ is equivalent to $3x + 2 = 5$ *or* $3x + 2 = -5$.

EXAMPLE 2 ◆ **Multiple Choice Practice**

What is the solution for this equation?
$$|2x - 3| = 9$$

(A) $x = -6 \text{ or } x = 3$ **(B)** $x = -6 \text{ or } x = 4$

(C) $x = -3 \text{ or } x = 6$ **(D)** $x = -3 \text{ or } x = 4$

Solution

Rewrite the absolute value equation as two equations.

$|2x - 3| = 9$	**Write original equation.**
$2x - 3 = 9 \quad or \quad 2x - 3 = -9$	**Rewrite as two equations.**
$2x = 12 \quad or \qquad 2x = -6$	**Add 3 to each side.**
$x = 6 \quad or \qquad x = -3$	**Divide each side by 2.**

▶ The correct answer is C. Ⓐ Ⓑ ● Ⓓ

AVOID ERRORS
Do not start solving for x until you have rewritten the absolute value equation as two equivalent equations without absolute values.

REWRITING EQUATIONS To solve an absolute value equation, you may first need to rewrite the equation in the form $|ax + b| = c$.

EXAMPLE 3 **Rewrite an absolute value equation**

Solve $3|2x + 7| - 5 = 4$.

Solution

First, rewrite the equation in the form $|ax + b| = c$.

$3|2x + 7| - 5 = 4$	**Write original equation.**
$3|2x + 7| = 9$	**Add 5 to each side.**
$|2x + 7| = 3$	**Divide each side by 3.**

Next, solve the absolute value equation.

$|2x + 7| = 3$	**Write absolute value equation.**
$2x + 7 = 3 \quad or \quad 2x + 7 = -3$	**Rewrite as two equations.**
$2x = -4 \quad or \qquad 2x = -10$	**Subtract 7 from each side.**
$x = -2 \quad or \qquad x = -5$	**Divide each side by 2.**

▶ The solutions are -2 and -5. Check your solutions by substituting each answer into the original equation.

Animated Algebra

For an interactive example of solving an absolute value equation, go to **classzone.com**.

✓ **GUIDED PRACTICE** for Examples 2 and 3

Solve the equation.

5. $|r - 7| = 9$ **6.** $2|s| + 4.1 = 18.9$ **7.** $4|t + 9| - 5 = 19$

NO SOLUTIONS The absolute value of a number is never negative. So, when an absolute value expression equals a negative number, there are *no solutions*.

EXAMPLE 4 **Decide if an equation has no solutions**

Solve $|3x + 5| + 6 = -2$, if possible.

$|3x + 5| + 6 = -2$ **Write original equation.**

$|3x + 5| = -8$ **Subtract 6 from each side.**

▶ The absolute value of a number is never negative. So, there are no solutions.

ABSOLUTE DEVIATION The **absolute deviation** of a number x from a given value is the absolute value of the difference of x and the given value:
absolute deviation $= |x - \text{given value}|$.

EXAMPLE 5 **Use absolute deviation**

Ball inflated to 8 psi

BASKETBALLS Before the start of a professional basketball game, a basketball must be inflated to an air pressure of 8 pounds per square inch (psi) with an absolute error of 0.5 psi. Find the minimum and maximum acceptable air pressures for the basketball.

READING
Absolute error is the deviation of a measured value from an accepted value.

Solution

Let p be the air pressure (in psi) of a basketball. Write a verbal model. Then write and solve an absolute value equation.

Absolute error	=	Measured air pressure	−	Accepted air pressure
0.5	= $|$	p	−	8 $|$

$0.5 = |p - 8|$ **Write original equation.**

$0.5 = p - 8$ *or* $-0.5 = p - 8$ **Rewrite as two equations.**

$8.5 = p$ *or* $7.5 = p$ **Add 8 to each side.**

▶ The minimum and maximum acceptable pressures are 7.5 psi and 8.5 psi.

✓ **GUIDED PRACTICE** for Examples 4 and 5

Solve the equation, if possible.

8. $2|m - 5| + 4 = 2$ **9.** $-3|n + 2| - 7 = -10$

10. FOOTBALL An NCAA football must be inflated to an air pressure of 13 psi with an absolute error of 0.5 psi. Find the minimum and maximum acceptable air pressures for an NCAA football.

4.5 EXERCISES

HOMEWORK KEY

◆ = **MULTIPLE CHOICE PRACTICE**
Exs. 21, 36, 50, and 56–58

○ = **HINTS AND HOMEWORK HELP**
for Exs. 11, 25, and 49 at classzone.com

SKILLS · PROBLEM SOLVING · REASONING

1. **VOCABULARY** Copy and complete: The equation $|x - 7| = 0.15$ is an example of a(n) __?__ .

2. **WRITING** Given $|x - 9| = 5$, describe the relationship between x, 9, and 5 using absolute deviation.

EXAMPLES 1, 2, and 3
on pp. 220–221
for Exs. 3–21

SOLVING EQUATIONS Solve the equation.

3. $|x| = 5$

4. $|y| = 36$

5. $|v| = 0.7$

6. $|w| = 9.2$

7. $|r| = \frac{1}{2}$

8. $|s| = \frac{7}{4}$

9. $|m + 3| = 7$

10. $|4n - 5| = 18$

11. $|3p + 7| = 4$

12. $|q + 8| = 2$

13. $|2d + 7| = 11$

14. $|f - 8| = 14$

15. $3|13 - 2t| = 15$

16. $4|b - 1| - 7 = 17$

17. $\frac{1}{3}|2c - 5| + 3 = 7$

18. $\frac{7}{4}|3j + 5| + 1 = 15$

19. $4|2k + 3| - 2 = 6$

20. $-3|5g + 1| - 6 = -9$

21. ◆ **MULTIPLE CHOICE** What is the solution of this equation $|3x + 2| = 1$?

Ⓐ $x = -1$ or $x = -\frac{1}{3}$

Ⓑ $x = -1$ or $x = \frac{1}{3}$

Ⓒ $x = -\frac{1}{3}$ or $x = 1$

Ⓓ $x = \frac{1}{3}$ or $x = 1$

ERROR ANALYSIS *Describe* and correct the error in solving the absolute value equation.

22.
$$|x + 4| = 13$$
$$x + 4 = 13$$
$$x = 9$$

23.
$$|x - 6| = -2$$
$$x - 6 = -2 \text{ or } x - 6 = 2$$
$$x = 4 \quad \text{or} \quad x = 8$$

EXAMPLE 4
on p. 222
for Exs. 24–36

SOLVING EQUATIONS Solve the equation, if possible.

24. $|y - 4| + 8 = 6$

25. $|x - 1| + 5 = 2$

26. $|m + 5| + 1.5 = 2$

27. $|p - 7| + 13 = 5$

28. $-4|8 - 5n| = 13$

29. $2|4 - \frac{1}{2}v| = 8$

30. $-5|10 - \frac{2}{5}x| = 15$

31. $-3|1 - \frac{2}{3}v| = -9$

32. $-5|\frac{4}{5}w + 6| = -10$

33. $-10|14 - r| - 2 = -7$

34. $-2|\frac{1}{3}s - 5| + 3 = 8$

35. $-9|4p + 2| - 8 = -35$

36. ◆ **MULTIPLE CHOICE** Which number is a solution of $|4x - 1| + 2 = 1$?

Ⓐ $-\frac{1}{2}$

Ⓑ 0

Ⓒ 1

Ⓓ There is no solution.

USING ABSOLUTE DEVIATION Find the values of *x* that satisfy the definition of absolute deviation for the given value and the given absolute deviation.

37. Given value: 5;
absolute deviation: 8

38. Given value: 20;
absolute deviation: 5

39. Given value: −9.1;
absolute deviation: 1.6

40. Given value: −3.4;
absolute deviation: 6.7

TRANSLATING SENTENCES In Exercises 41 and 42, write the verbal sentence as an absolute value equation. Then solve the equation.

41. Four more than the absolute deviation of *x* from 3 is 8.

42. Five times the absolute deviation of 2*x* from −9 is 15.

43. REASONING Is $a|x|$ equivalent to $|ax|$ when *a* is positive? when *a* is negative? when *a* is 0? Give examples to support your answers.

CONNECT SKILLS TO PROBLEM SOLVING Exercises 44–46 will help you prepare for problem solving.

Write an absolute value equation that can be used to solve the problem.

44. What are the minimum and maximum weights of a soccer ball that is required to weigh 15 ounces with an absolute deviation of 1 ounce?

45. In February, 2006, the average temperature in Fresno, California, was 52°F with an absolute deviation of 21°F. What were the minimum and maximum temperatures recorded that month?

46. What are the minimum and maximum distances a car can travel if it has a 15 gallon tank and can travel 26 miles per gallon with an absolute deviation of 4 miles per gallon?

EXAMPLE 5
on p. 222
for Exs. 47–51

47. GUARDRAILS A safety regulation requires that the height of a guardrail be 42 inches with an absolute deviation of 3 inches. Find the minimum and maximum heights of a guardrail.

California @HomeTutor for problem solving help at classzone.com

48. CHEERLEADING A cheerleading team is preparing a dance program for a competition. The program must last 4 minutes with an absolute deviation of 5 seconds. Find the least and greatest possible times (in seconds) that the program can last.

California @HomeTutor for problem solving help at classzone.com

49. SPORTS In gymnastics meets last year, the mean of your friend's least and greatest scores on the floor exercise was 7.641 points. The absolute deviation of her least and greatest scores from the mean was 1.013 points.

a. What were the least and greatest scores that she earned?

b. This year the mean of her least and greatest scores is 8.435 points, and the absolute deviation of the least and greatest scores from the mean is 0.45 point. How many points more than last year's greatest score is this year's greatest score?

Floor exercise

◆ = **MULTIPLE CHOICE PRACTICE**   ◯ = **HINTS AND HOMEWORK HELP** at classzone.com

50. ◆ MULTIPLE CHOICE The diameter of a billiard ball must be 2.25 inches with an absolute error of 0.005 inch. What is the maximum possible radius that a billiard ball can have?

    (A) 1.1225 in.   **(B)** 1.1275 in.

    (C) 2.245 in.   **(D)** 2.255 in.

51. JEWELRY A jewelry store advertisement states that a certain diamond bracelet weighs 12 carats, but the actual weight can vary by as much as 5%. Find the minimum and maximum possible weights of the bracelet.

52. CONTESTS You currently have 450 points in an academic contest. You choose the value p of the question you want to answer. The value p represents the absolute deviation of your new score s from 450.

    a. Write an absolute value equation that gives p in terms of s.

    b. If you choose a question worth 150 points, what are the possible new scores that you can have after answering the question?

53. MULTI-STEP PROBLEM The percent p of United States residents who were foreign born, or born outside of the United States, during the period 1910–2000 can be modeled by the equation $p = 0.165|t - 60| + 4.8$ where t is the number of years since 1910.

    a. Approximate During the period 1910–2000, in approximately what year did foreign-born residents account for 13% of all residents?

    b. Predict If the model holds for years after 2000, predict the year in which foreign-born residents will again account for 13% of all residents.

54. CHALLENGE How many solutions does the equation $a|x + b| + c = d$ have if $a > 0$ and $c = d$? if $a < 0$ and $c > d$?

55. CHALLENGE In a recent Olympics, swimmers in a men's 200 meter butterfly event finished with times from 1 minute 54.04 seconds to 1 minute 57.48 seconds. Let t represent the slowest or fastest time (in seconds). Write an absolute value equation that describes the situation.

◆ CALIFORNIA STANDARDS SPIRAL REVIEW

Alg. 2.0   **56.** The reciprocal of a number is $\frac{2}{x}$. What is the number? *(p. 88)*

    (A) $2x$ **(B)** 2 **(C)** x **(D)** $\frac{x}{2}$

Alg. 4.0   **57.** Which inequality is equivalent to $-3 < 2x - 4 < 8$? *(p. 210)*

    (A) $-7 < 2x < 4$ **(B)** $-7 < 2x < 12$

    (C) $1 < 2x < 4$ **(D)** $1 < 2x < 12$

Alg. 5.0   **58.** A deposit of $1250 into an account earning simple annual interest earns more than $50 and less than $75 in interest in 2 years. Which inequality gives the possible interest rates r (in decimal form)? *(p. 202)*

    (A) $0.02 < r < 0.03$ **(B)** $0.04 < r < 0.06$

    (C) $0.2 < r < 0.3$ **(D)** $0.4 < r < 0.6$

4.6 Solve Absolute Value Inequalities

Standards Alg. 3.0 **Students solve** equations and **inequalities involving absolute values.**

Connect *Before* you solved absolute value equations. *Now* you will solve absolute value inequalities.

Math and SPORTS
Ex. 39, p. 230

Key Vocabulary
• **absolute value,** *p. 55*
• **equivalent inequalities,** *p. 190*
• **compound inequality,** *p. 210*
• **mean,** *p. 803*

Recall that $|x| = 3$ means that the distance between x and 0 is 3. The inequality $|x| < 3$ means that the distance between x and 0 is *less than* 3, and $|x| > 3$ means that the distance between x and 0 is *greater than* 3. The graphs of $|x| < 3$ and $|x| > 3$ are shown below.

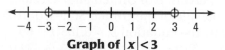 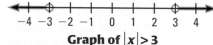

Graph of $|x| < 3$ **Graph of $|x| > 3$**

EXAMPLE 1 **Solve absolute value inequalities**

Solve the inequality. Graph your solution.

a. $|x| \geq 6$ **b.** $|x| \leq 0.5$

Solution

a. The distance between x and 0 is greater than or equal to 6. So, $x \leq -6$ *or* $x \geq 6$.

▶ The solutions are all real numbers less than or equal to -6 *or* greater than or equal to 6.

b. The distance between x and 0 is less than or equal to 0.5. So, $-0.5 \leq x \leq 0.5$.

▶ The solutions are all real numbers greater than or equal to -0.5 *and* less than or equal to 0.5.

✓ **GUIDED PRACTICE** for Example 1

Solve the inequality. Graph your solution.

1. $|x| \leq 8$ **2.** $|u| < 3.5$ **3.** $|v| > \frac{2}{3}$

SOLVING ABSOLUTE VALUE INEQUALITIES In Example 1, the solutions of $|x| \geq 6$ and $|x| \leq 0.5$ suggest that you can rewrite an absolute value inequality as a compound inequality.

KEY CONCEPT   *For Your Notebook*

Solving Absolute Value Inequalities

- The inequality $|ax + b| < c$ where $c > 0$ is equivalent to the compound inequality $-c < ax + b < c$.

- The inequality $|ax + b| > c$ where $c > 0$ is equivalent to the compound inequality $ax + b < -c$ or $ax + b > c$.

These statements are also true for inequalities involving $\geq$ and $\leq$.

EXAMPLE 2   **Solve an absolute value inequality**

Solve $|2x - 10| \geq 14$. Graph your solution.

$$|2x - 10| \geq 14 \qquad \text{Write original inequality.}$$

$$2x - 10 \leq -14 \quad or \quad 2x - 10 \geq 14 \qquad \text{Rewrite as compound inequality.}$$

$$2x \leq -4 \quad or \quad 2x \geq 24 \qquad \text{Add 10 to each side.}$$

$$x \leq -2 \quad or \quad x \geq 12 \qquad \text{Divide each side by 2.}$$

▶ The solutions are all real numbers less than or equal to -2 *or* greater than or equal to 12. Check several solutions in the original inequality.

EXAMPLE 3   ◆ **Multiple Choice Practice**

What is the solution of the inequality $9 - |x - 5| > 3$?

  (A) $x < 11$ (B) $-11 < x < 1$ (C) $-1 < x < 11$ (D) $x < -1$ *or* $x > 11$

Solution

$$9 - |x - 5| > 3 \qquad \text{Write original inequality.}$$

$$-|x - 5| > -6 \qquad \text{Subtract 9 from each side.}$$

$$|x - 5| < 6 \qquad \text{Multiply each side by } -1. \text{ Reverse inequality symbol.}$$

$$-6 < x - 5 < 6 \qquad \text{Rewrite as compound inequality.}$$

$$-1 < x < 11 \qquad \text{Add 5 to each expression.}$$

▶ The correct answer is C. (A) (B) (C) (D)

 GUIDED PRACTICE   for Examples 2 and 3

Solve the inequality. Graph your solution.

  4. $|x + 3| > 8$ **5.** $|2w - 1| < 11$ **6.** $3|5m - 6| - 8 \leq 13$

EXAMPLE 4 Solve a multi-step problem

COMPUTERS You are buying a new computer and find 10 models in a store advertisement. The prices are $890, $750, $650, $370, $660, $670, $450, $650, $725, and $825.

• Find the mean of the computer prices.

• You are willing to pay the mean price with an absolute deviation of at most $100. How many of the computer prices meet your condition?

Solution

STEP 1 Find the mean by dividing the sum of the prices by 10.

$$\text{Mean} = \frac{890 + 750 + 650 + 370 + 660 + 670 + 450 + 650 + 725 + 825}{10}$$

$$= \frac{6640}{10} = 664$$

REVIEW MEAN
For help with finding a mean, see p. 803.

STEP 2 Write and solve an inequality. An absolute deviation of at most $100 from the mean, $664, is given by the inequality $|x - 664| \le 100$.

$$|x - 664| \le 100 \qquad \text{Write absolute value inequality.}$$

$$-100 \le x - 664 \le 100 \qquad \text{Write as compound inequality.}$$

$$564 \le x \le 764 \qquad \text{Add 664 to each expression.}$$

▶ The prices you will consider must be at least $564 and at most $764. Six prices meet your condition: $750, $650, $660, $670, $650, and $725.

✔ **GUIDED PRACTICE** for Example 4

7. **WHAT IF?** In Example 4, suppose that you are willing to pay the mean price with an absolute deviation of at most $75. How many of the computer prices meet this condition?

CONCEPT SUMMARY   *For Your Notebook*

Solving Inequalities

One-Step and Multi-Step Inequalities

• Follow the steps for solving an equation, but reverse the inequality symbol when multiplying or dividing by a negative number.

Compound Inequalities

• If necessary, rewrite the inequality as two separate inequalities. Then solve each inequality separately. Include *and* or *or* in the solution.

Absolute Value Inequalities

• If necessary, isolate the absolute value expression on one side of the inequality. Rewrite the absolute value inequality as a compound inequality. Then solve the compound inequality.

4.6 EXERCISES

SKILLS · PROBLEM SOLVING · REASONING

1. **VOCABULARY** Copy and complete: The inequalities $|x| > 8$ and $x > 8$ or $x < -8$ are __?__ .

2. **WRITING** *Describe* the difference between solving $|x| \le 5$ and solving $|x| \ge 5$.

EXAMPLES
1, 2, and 3
on pp. 226–227
for Exs. 3–23

SOLVING INEQUALITIES Solve the inequality. Graph your solution.

3. $|x| < 4$

4. $|y| \ge 3$

5. $|h| > 4.5$

6. $|p| < 1.3$

7. $|t| \le \dfrac{3}{5}$

8. $|j| \ge 1\dfrac{3}{4}$

9. $|d + 4| \ge 3$

10. $|b - 5| < 10$

11. $|14 - m| > 6$

12. $|2s - 7| < 1$

13. $|4c + 5| \ge 7$

14. $|9 - 4n| \le 5$

15. $5\left|\dfrac{1}{2}r + 3\right| > 5$

16. $\left|\dfrac{4}{3}s - 7\right| - 8 > 3$

17. $-3\left|2 - \dfrac{5}{4}u\right| \le -18$

18. $2|3w + 8| - 13 < -5$

19. $2\left|\dfrac{1}{4}v - 5\right| - 4 > 3$

20. $\dfrac{2}{7}|4f + 6| - 2 \ge 10$

ERROR ANALYSIS *Describe* and correct the error in solving the inequality.

21.
$$|x + 4| > 13$$
$$-13 > x + 4 > +13$$
$$9 > x > -17$$

22.
$$|x - 5| < 20$$
$$x - 5 < 20$$
$$x < 25$$

23. ◆ **MULTIPLE CHOICE** What is the solution of the inequality $|x - 9| + 4 \ge 13$?

   (A) $x \le -8$ or $x \ge -6$

   (B) $x \le 0$ or $x \ge 18$

   (C) $-8 \le x \le -6$

   (D) $0 \le x \le 18$

TRANSLATING SENTENCES Write the verbal sentence as an inequality. Then solve the inequality and graph your solution.

24. The absolute deviation of x from 6 is less than or equal to 4.

25. The absolute deviation of $2x$ from -7 is greater than or equal to 15.

26. Three more than the absolute deviation of $-4x$ from 7 is greater than 10.

27. Four times the absolute deviation of x from 9 is less than 8.

28. ◆ **MULTIPLE CHOICE** Which inequality is equivalent to $x < 1$ or $x > 5$?

   (A) $|x + 8| - 2 > 10$

   (B) $3|6 - 2x| > 12$

   (C) $|5x + 9| < 10$

   (D) $|7 - 4x| - 9 < 8$

REASONING Tell whether the statement is *true* or *false*. If it is false, give a counterexample.

29. If a is a solution of $|x + 3| \le 8$, then a is also a solution of $x + 3 \ge -8$.

30. If a is a solution of $|x + 3| > 8$, then a is also a solution of $x + 3 > 8$.

31. If a is a solution of $|x + 3| \ge 8$, then a is also a solution of $x + 3 \le -8$.

32. If a is a solution of $x + 3 \le -8$, then a is also a solution of $|x + 3| \ge 8$.

CONNECT SKILLS TO PROBLEM SOLVING Exercises 33–35 will help you prepare for problem solving.

Write an absolute value inequality that can be used to solve the problem.

33. The weather forecast for Redding, California, is predicting 3 inches of rain with an absolute deviation of at most 0.5 inch. What are the possible amounts r of rain that Redding could receive according to the forecast?

34. The mean time it takes you to bike to school is 20 minutes with an absolute deviation of at most 2 minutes. What are the possible times t that it takes you to bike to school?

35. Your friend's mean distance in the long jump is 5 meters with an absolute deviation of at least 0.25 meter. What are the possible distances d that your friend can jump?

EXAMPLE 4
on p. 228
for Exs. 36–39

36. ◆ **MULTIPLE CHOICE** An essay contest requires that essay entries consist of 500 words with an absolute deviation of at most 30 words. What are the possible numbers w of words that the essay can have?

(A) $470 < w < 530$

(B) $w < 470$ or $w > 530$

(C) $w \le 470$ or $w \ge 530$

(D) $470 \le w \le 530$

California @HomeTutor for problem solving help at classzone.com

37. SWIMMING POOL The pH scale can be used to determine whether the water in a swimming pool is too acidic or too basic. Balanced pool water has a pH value of 7.4. Pool water is highly acidic or highly basic if the absolute deviation of the pH value from 7.4 is greater than 0.2. Find the pH values for which pool water is highly acidic or highly basic.

California @HomeTutor for problem solving help at classzone.com

38. BAKING You are preheating an oven to 350°F before you bake cookies. Several minutes later, the oven thermometer reads 346°F. The measured temperature has an absolute deviation of at most 2°F. Write and solve an inequality to find the possible temperatures in the oven.

39. **SOFTBALL** A softball compression test measures the hardness of a softball. A softball organization requires that the compression of a softball be 350 pounds with an absolute deviation of at most 50 pounds. Write and solve an inequality to find the softball compressions that the organization will allow.

Baking temperature: 350°F

◆ = **MULTIPLE CHOICE PRACTICE**   ○ = **HINTS AND HOMEWORK HELP** at classzone.com

40. ANIMAL POPULATION *Relative absolute deviation* of a number from a given value is the absolute deviation expressed as a percent of the given value. A wildlife biologist estimates that the number of pronghorn antelope in Nevada is 18,000 with a relative absolute deviation of at most 20%.

   a. Find the absolute deviation from the estimated population of pronghorn antelope by multiplying the estimated population by the relative absolute deviation.

   b. Write and solve an inequality to find the possible numbers of pronghorn antelope in Nevada.

Pronghorn antelope

41. CHALLENGE If $|ax + b| < c$ where $c < 0$, what is the solution of the inequality? If $|ax + b| > c$ where $c < 0$, what is the solution of the inequality? *Explain* your answers.

42. CHALLENGE According to the rules for a women's figure skating event, a skater should finish a routine in an ideal time of 3 minutes 30 seconds. The skater receives a 0.1 point penalty if the absolute deviation of the finishing time from the ideal time is greater than 10 seconds *and* less than or equal to 20 seconds. Write and solve an inequality to find the finishing times for which the skater receives a 0.1 penalty point.

◆ CALIFORNIA STANDARDS SPIRAL REVIEW

Alg. 3.0

43. Which number is a solution of $|6c - 1| = 8$? *(p. 220)*

   (A) $\frac{2}{3}$ **(B)** 1   **(C)** 1.5   **(D)** $2\frac{6}{7}$

Alg. 2.0

44. Which of the following is *not* equivalent to $\sqrt{81}$? *(p. 95)*

   (A) -9 **(B)** 9   **(C)** 3^2 **(D)** $(-3)^2$

Gr. 6 NS 2.3

45. You and a friend are splitting the cost of a meal. The cost of the food is $32, and you have a coupon for $10 off. The expression $\frac{1}{2}[32 + (-10)]$ gives the amount that each person pays. How much do you pay? *(p. 81)*

   (A) $6   **(B)** $11   **(C)** $16   **(D)** $21

QUIZ *for Lessons 4.5–4.6*

Solve the equation, if possible. *(p. 220)*

   1. $|x| = 2.5$ **2.** $|2c + 8| = -6$ **3.** $-2|r - 5| = -6$

Solve the inequality. Graph your solution. *(p. 226)*

   4. $|m| > 4$ **5.** $|2t - 5| < 3$ **6.** $4|3s + 7| - 5 \geq 7$

   7. HEART RATE An athlete's target heart rate while exercising is 145 beats per minute with an absolute deviation of at most 10 beats per minute. What are the possible heart rates that an athlete should aim for? *(p. 226)*

Multiple Choice Practice for Lessons 4.5–4.6

1. You pick peaches at an orchard and plan to use them to make peach pies. The recipe card shows the amount of peaches you use for each pie. What are the possible amounts p (in cups) of peaches you can use for a pie? **Alg. 3.0**

> ### PEACH PIE
> 2 cups peaches (give or take 1/2 cup)
> 2 teaspoons flour
> 1 teaspoon lemon juice

Ⓐ $1\frac{1}{2} \le p \le 2$ Ⓑ $1 \le p \le 2$

Ⓒ $1 \le p \le 2\frac{1}{2}$ Ⓓ $1\frac{1}{2} \le p \le 2\frac{1}{2}$

2. What is the solution of the inequality $2|x + 12| - 7 > 5$? **Alg. 3.0**

Ⓐ $-18 < x < -6$ Ⓑ $-6 < x < 18$

Ⓒ $x < 6 \text{ or } x > 18$ Ⓓ $x < -18 \text{ or } x > -6$

3. You will be making a presentation in your history class. Your teacher gives you a time limit of 16 minutes with an absolute deviation of at most 3 minutes. Which graph represents the possible time lengths your presentation can be? **Alg. 3.0**

Ⓐ   12 13 14 15 16 17 18 19 20

Ⓑ   10 11 12 13 14 15 16 17 18

Ⓒ   12 13 14 15 16 17 18 19 20

Ⓓ   10 11 12 13 14 15 16 17 18

4. What solution(s) does the equation $|2x - 4| + 15 = 12$ have? **Alg. 3.0**

Ⓐ $-\frac{1}{2}$ and $3\frac{1}{2}$ Ⓑ $\frac{1}{2}$ and $-3\frac{1}{2}$

Ⓒ $-\frac{1}{2}$ Ⓓ No solution

5. The table below shows the results of a poll taken before an election. Which inequality can you use to find the possible voting percentages x that candidate A could receive in the election? **Alg. 3.0**

Poll Results for Candidate A	
Percent of vote predicted to receive	**Absolute deviation**
47%	At most 4%

Ⓐ $|x + 4| \le 47$ Ⓑ $|x - 47| \le 4$

Ⓒ $|x - 4| \le 47$ Ⓓ $|x + 47| \le 4$

6. You are buying a new cell phone and see 6 phones listed in an advertisement. The prices of the phones are shown below. You are willing to pay the mean price with an absolute deviation of $50. What are the minimum and maximum prices that you will consider? **Alg. 3.0**

Special Cell Phone Offer!

$139   Model X15 $160   Model S132

Model T14 $179
Model XL6 $228
Model S24 $249
Model Y32 $359

ww   Ⓐ $169 and $269

Ⓑ $169 and $244

Ⓒ $194 and $244

Ⓓ $194 and $269

7. Consider the verbal sentence "Four more than the absolute deviation of x from 16 is 12." What solution(s) does the absolute value equation that represents the verbal sentence have? **Alg. 3.0**

Ⓐ $x = 0$ and $x = -24$

Ⓑ $x = 24$ and $x = -8$

Ⓒ $x = 8$ and $x = 24$

Ⓓ No solution

4 CHAPTER SUMMARY

Standards
Alg. 3.0, 4.0, 5.0

BIG IDEAS
For Your Notebook

Big Idea 1

Applying Properties of Inequality

You can apply the properties of inequality to solve inequalities. The properties listed below are also true for the inequalities $a \geq b$ and $a \leq b$.

Property	If $a < b$, then ...	If $a > b$, then ...
Addition property of inequality	$a + c < b + c$.	$a + c > b + c$.
Subtraction property of inequality	$a - c < b - c$.	$a - c > b - c$.
Multiplication property of inequality	$ac < bc$ if $c > 0$. $ac > bc$ if $c < 0$.	$ac > bc$ if $c > 0$. $ac < bc$ if $c < 0$.
Division property of inequality	$\frac{a}{c} < \frac{b}{c}$ if $c > 0$. $\frac{a}{c} > \frac{b}{c}$ if $c < 0$.	$\frac{a}{c} > \frac{b}{c}$ if $c > 0$. $\frac{a}{c} < \frac{b}{c}$ if $c < 0$.

Big Idea 2

Using Statements with *And* or *Or*

An absolute value equation can be rewritten as two equations joined by *or*. An absolute value inequality can be rewritten as a compound inequality with *and* or *or*. In the statements below, $<$ can be replaced by $\leq$, and $>$ can be replaced by $\geq$.

Absolute value equation or inequality	Equivalent statement with *and* or *or*
$|ax + b| = c, c \geq 0$	$ax + b = c$ or $ax + b = -c$
$|ax + b| < c, c \geq 0$	$-c < ax + b < c$
$|ax + b| > c, c \geq 0$	$ax + b < -c$ or $ax + b > c$

Big Idea 3

Graphing Inequalities

You use a number line to graph an inequality in one variable.

| Graphing simple inequalities | 1. Solve for the variable. 2. Draw an open circle for $<$ or $>$ and a closed circle for $\leq$ or $\geq$. Draw an arrow in the appropriate direction. | $-5x \leq 10$ $x \geq -2$
 number line: $-3, -2, -1, 0$ |
| Graphing compound inequalities | 1. Solve the compound inequality. 2. Use the union of graphs of simple inequalities for *or*. Use the intersection for *and*. | $-5 < x - 3 \leq 1$ $-2 < x \leq 4$
 number line: $-4, -2, 0, 2, 4, 6$ |

Chapter Summary   **233**

APPLYING THE
BIG IDEAS

Big Idea 1
You apply properties of inequality in **Step 3**.

Big Idea 2
You use statements with *and* or *or* in **Steps 1–3**.

Big Idea 3
You graph inequalities in **Steps 1–3**

> **PROBLEM** How can you use inequalities to determine the possible numbers of songs that can be downloaded onto an MP3 player?

STEP 1 Write a compound inequality.

Suppose there are nine songs that you would like to download onto an player. The MP3 player has 22.5 megabytes of storage space available, and you want to use as much of the space as possible. The table below shows the file size (in megabytes) of each song.

Song	1	2	3	4	5	6	7	8	9
File size	5.5	7.5	5.2	4.1	3.7	6.0	6.7	3.8	5.8

Let *s* represent the file size of a song. Use the least and greatest file sizes in the table to write and graph a compound inequality that represents the possible values of *s*.

STEP 2 Make a table of values.

Let *n* represent the number of songs of a given size that can be downloaded onto the MP3 player. Copy and complete the table below using the formula $n = \frac{22.5}{s}$. Round your answers to the nearest tenth.

s	5.5	7.5	5.2	4.1	3.7	6.0	6.7	3.8	5.8
n	4.1	?	?	?	?	?	?	?	?

Use the least and greatest file sizes in the table to write and graph a compound inequality that represents the possible values of *n*.

STEP 3 Solve a compound inequality.

Multiply the compound inequality from Step 1 by *n*. Using the fact that $n \cdot s = 22.5$, write the compound inequality as two separate inequalities joined by *and*, then solve each inequality for *n*. Graph the result on a number line. Compare the compound inequality and its graph from this step with those from Step 2.

Extending the Problem

1. Suppose the MP3 player has 15 megabytes of storage space available, and you want to use as much of the storage space as possible. Write and graph a compound inequality that represents the possible numbers of songs that can be downloaded onto the MP3 player.

2. Choose a number n_1 that is a solution of the compound inequality you wrote in Exercise 1. Then choose n_1 songs from the list of nine songs in Step 1 such that the sum of the file sizes is less than or equal to 15 megabytes. Is there more than one way to do this? *Explain.*

California @HomeTutor
classzone.com
• Multi-Language Visual Glossary
• Vocabulary practice

REVIEW KEY VOCABULARY

• graph of an inequality, *p. 189*   • compound inequality, *p. 210*   • absolute deviation, *p. 222*
• equivalent inequalities, *p. 190*   • absolute value equation, *p. 220*

VOCABULARY EXERCISES

1. Translate the verbal sentence into an absolute value equation: "The absolute deviation of *x* from 19 is 8."

2. Copy and complete: Inequalities that have the same solutions are called __?__.

3. Copy and complete: On a number line, the __?__ of an inequality in one variable is the set of points that represent all solutions of the inequality.

4. **WRITING** *Describe* the steps you would use to solve the inequality $11 - 2n > -5$.

5. **NOTETAKING SKILLS** Use a notetaking organizer like the one on page 188 to write your notes about solving an absolute value equation.

REVIEW EXAMPLES AND EXERCISES

Use the review examples and exercises below to check your understanding of the concepts you have learned in each lesson of Chapter 4.

4.1 Solve Inequalities Using Addition and Subtraction   *pp. 189–194*

Gr. 7 AF 4.1

EXAMPLE

Solve $x - 2.1 \le 1.4$. Graph your solution.

$x - 2.1 \le 1.4$	**Write original inequality.**
$x - 2.1 + 2.1 \le 1.4 + 2.1$	**Add 2.1 to each side.**
$x \le 3.5$	**Simplify.**

▶ The solutions are all real numbers less than or equal to 3.5.

EXERCISES

EXAMPLES 1, 2, 3, and 4 on pp. 189–191 for Exs. 6–9

6. **GEOGRAPHY** The lowest elevation in Mexico is −10 meters at Laguna Salada. Use only this fact to write and graph an inequality that describes the elevations in Mexico.

Solve the inequality. Graph your solution.

7. $x + 5 > -13$ 8. $m - 9 \ge -4$ 9. $s + 3.7 < 1$

4.2 Solve Inequalities Using Multiplication and Division
pp. 196–201

Gr. 7 AF 4.1

EXAMPLE

Solve $\dfrac{x}{-4} < 9$. Graph your solution.

$$\dfrac{x}{-4} < 9 \qquad \text{Write original inequality.}$$

$$-4 \cdot \dfrac{x}{-4} > -4 \cdot 9 \qquad \text{Multiply each side by } -4. \text{ Reverse inequality symbol.}$$

$$x > -36 \qquad \text{Simplify.}$$

▸ The solutions are all real numbers greater than −36.

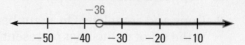

EXERCISES

EXAMPLES
1, 2, 3, and 4
on pp. 196–198
for Exs. 10–14

Solve the inequality. Graph your solution.

10. $\dfrac{p}{2} \le 5$

11. $\dfrac{n}{-4.5} < -8$

12. $-3x > 27$

13. $2y \ge 18$

14. GYMNASTICS In men's gymnastics, an athlete competes in 6 events. Suppose that an athlete's average score per event is at most 9.7 points. Write and solve an inequality to find the possible total scores for the athlete.

4.3 Solve Multi-Step Inequalities
pp. 202–207

Alg. 4.0
Alg. 5.0

EXAMPLE

Solve $-(4x - 7) \ge -13$. Graph your solution.

$$-(4x - 7) \ge -13 \qquad \text{Write original inequality.}$$

$$-4x + 7 \ge -13 \qquad \text{Distributive property}$$

$$-4x \ge -20 \qquad \text{Subtract 7 from each side.}$$

$$x \le 5 \qquad \text{Divide each side by } -4. \text{ Reverse inequality symbol.}$$

▸ The solutions are all real numbers less than or equal to 5.

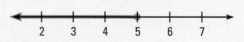

EXERCISES

EXAMPLES
1, 2, 3, 4, and 5
on pp. 202–204
for Exs. 15–21

Solve the inequality, if possible. Graph your solution.

15. $2g + 11 < 25$

16. $\dfrac{2}{3}r - 4 \ge 1$

17. $1 - 3x \le -14 + 2x$

18. $3(q + 1) < 3q + 7$

19. $8(t - 1) > -8 + 8t$

20. $-3(2n - 1) \ge 1 - 8n$

21. TICKET PURCHASES You can order discount movie tickets from a website for $7 each. You must also pay a shipping fee of $4. You want to spend no more than $40. Find the possible numbers of movie tickets that you can order.

Alg. 4.0
Alg. 5.0

EXAMPLE

Solve $-1 < -2x + 7 < 9$. Graph your solution.

$-1 < -2x + 7 < 9$ **Write original inequality.**

$-8 < -2x < 2$ **Subtract 7 from each expression.**

$4 > x > -1$ **Divide each expression by −2. Reverse both inequality symbols.**

$-1 < x < 4$ **Rewrite in the form $a < x < b$.**

▸ The solutions are all real numbers greater than −1 *and* less than 4.

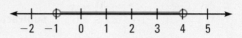

$\begin{array}{ccccccccc} & & & & & & & & \\ -2 & -1 & 0 & 1 & 2 & 3 & 4 & 5 \end{array}$

EXERCISES

EXAMPLES
3, 4, and 5
on pp. 211–212
for Exs. 22–25

Solve the inequality. Graph your solution.

22. $-6 \le 2t - 5 \le -3$

23. $-3 < -3x + 8 < 11$

24. $9s - 6 < 12 \ or \ 3s + 1 > 13$

25. $-4w + 12 \ge 10 \ or \ 5w - 14 > -4$

Alg. 3.0

EXAMPLE

Solve $4\left|5x - 3\right| + 6 = 30$.

First, rewrite the equation in the form $\left|ax + b\right| = c$.

$4\left|5x - 3\right| + 6 = 30$ **Write original equation.**

$4\left|5x - 3\right| = 24$ **Subtract 6 from each side.**

$\left|5x - 3\right| = 6$ **Divide each side by 4.**

Next, solve the absolute value equation.

$5x - 3 = 6 \quad or \quad 5x - 3 = -6$ **Rewrite as two equations.**

$5x = 9 \quad or \quad 5x = -3$ **Add 3 to each side.**

$x = 1.8 \ or \quad\quad x = -0.6$ **Divide each side by 5.**

▸ The solutions are −0.6 and 1.8.

EXERCISES

EXAMPLES
1, 2, 3, 4, and 5
on pp. 220–222
for Exs. 26–32

Solve the equation, if possible.

26. $\left|r\right| = 7$

27. $\left|a + 6\right| = 2$

28. $\left|2c + 5\right| = -1$

29. $2\left|x - 3\right| + 1 = 5$

30. $3\left|2q + 1\right| + 5 = 1$

31. $4\left|3p - 2\right| + 5 = 11$

32. BOWLING In tenpin bowling, the height of each bowling pin must be 15 inches with an absolute deviation of 0.03125 inch. Find the minimum and maximum possible heights of a bowling pin.

Alg. 3.0

EXAMPLE

Solve $3|2x + 11| + 2 \leq 17$. **Graph your solution.**

$3|2x + 11| + 2 \leq 17$	**Write original inequality.**
$3|2x + 11| \leq 15$	**Subtract 2 from each side.**
$|2x + 11| \leq 5$	**Divide each side by 3.**
$-5 \leq 2x + 11 \leq 5$	**Rewrite as compound inequality.**
$-16 \leq 2x \leq -6$	**Subtract 11 from each expression.**
$-8 \leq x \leq -3$	**Divide each expression by 2.**

▸ The solutions are all real numbers greater than or equal to -8 *and* less than or equal to -3.

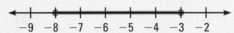

EXAMPLE

Solve $-\frac{1}{3}|4x + 3| < -5$. **Graph your solution.**

$-\frac{1}{3}|4x + 3| < -5$	**Write original inequality.**
$|4x + 3| > 15$	**Multiply each side by -3.** **Reverse inequality symbol.**
$4x + 3 < -15$ *or* $4x + 3 > 15$	**Rewrite as compound inequality.**
$4x < -18$ *or* $4x > 12$	**Subtract 3 from each side.**
$x < -4.5$ *or* $x > 3$	**Divide each side by 4.**

▸ The solutions are all real numbers less than -4.5 *or* greater than 3.

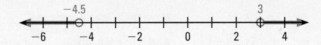

EXERCISES

Solve the inequality. Graph your solution.

EXAMPLES
1, 2, and 3
on pp. 226–227
for Exs. 33–39

33. $|m| \leq 8$ **34.** $-2|g - 2| < -10$ **35.** $|6k + 1| \geq 2$

36. $|2j - 9| - 2 > 10$ **37.** $-6|3x + 5| + 14 \leq 2$ **38.** $\left|\frac{2}{3}n - 9\right| + 2 \leq 7$

39. PARALLEL BARS In gymnastics events, the parallel bars are placed 78.75 inches above the ground with an absolute deviation of 0.4 inch. What are the possible heights h (in inches) that the bars can be placed above the ground?

1. VOCABULARY Copy and complete: The inequality $x < 2$ *or* $x \geq 3$ is an example of a(n) __?__.

2. VOCABULARY Copy and complete: The __?__ of a number x from a given value is the absolute value of the difference of x and the given value.

Translate the verbal phrase into an inequality. Then graph the inequality.

3. All real numbers that are greater than or equal to -1

4. All real numbers that are greater than -2 *and* less than or equal to 7

5. All real numbers that are greater than 8 *or* less than -4

Solve the inequality, if possible. Graph your solution.

6. $x - 9 \geq -5$

7. $-2 > 5 + y$

8. $-0.8 \leq z + 7.7$

9. $5m \geq 35$

10. $\dfrac{n}{6} < -1$

11. $\dfrac{r}{-3} \leq 4$

12. $-4s < 6s + 1$

13. $4t - 7 \leq 13$

14. $-8 > 5 - v$

15. $3(5w + 4) < 12w - 11$

16. $4p - 3 > 2(2p + 1)$

17. $9q - 12 \geq 3(3q - 4)$

18. $2(x + 1) \geq 6$

19. $3x + 5 \leq 2x - 1$

20. $-2(x + 4) > 3x + 17$

21. $-2 \leq 4 - 3a \leq 13$

22. $-7 < 2c - 1 < 10\frac{1}{2}$

23. $-5 \leq 2 - h$ *or* $6h + 5 \geq 71$

Solve the equation, if possible.

24. $-\dfrac{3}{4}\left|x - 3\right| = \dfrac{1}{4}$

25. $\left|3y + 1\right| - 6 = -2$

26. $4\left|2z + 5\right| + 9 = 5$

Solve the inequality, if possible. Graph your solution.

27. $\left|2d + 8\right| > 3$

28. $2\left|3f - 7\right| + 5 < 11$

29. $\left|j - 7\right| - 1 \leq \dfrac{5}{6}$

30. AMUSEMENT PARK An amusement park charges \$7 for admission and \$1.50 for each ride. You have \$30. What are the possible numbers of rides that you can go on?

31. BUSINESS Your cousin is starting a small business baking and decorating cakes and wants to make a profit of at least \$250 for the first month. The expenses for the first month are \$155. What are the possible revenues that your cousin can earn in order to meet the profit goal?

32. CAMPING Michael is planning to ride a horse to a campsite. The sum of Michael's weight and the combined weight of his camping supplies must be at most 20% of the weight of the horse. Michael weighs 177 pounds, and the horse weighs 1000 pounds. What are the possible weights of the camping supplies?

33. BICYCLES A manufacturer of bicycle parts requires that a bicycle chain have a width of 0.3 inch with an absolute error of at most 0.0003 inch. Find the possible widths of bicycle chains that the manufacturer will accept.

4 ◆ MULTIPLE CHOICE STRATEGIES

STRATEGIES YOU'LL USE:
• SOLVE DIRECTLY
• ELIMINATE CHOICES

Standards
Alg. 5.0, 3.0

If you have difficulty solving a multiple choice problem directly, you may be able to use another approach to eliminate incorrect answer choices and obtain the correct answer.

PROBLEM 1

You have $32 and want to buy an MP3 player that costs $200. You earn $8 per hour at your job. What are the possible numbers x of hours that you need to work to afford an MP3 player?

(A) $x \geq 5$ **(B)** $x \geq 10$ **(C)** $x \geq 16$ **(D)** $x \geq 21$

Strategy 1   SOLVE DIRECTLY

Write and solve an inequality for the situation.

STEP 1 **Write** a verbal model. To find your total income, multiply your hourly rate by the number of hours you work and add your savings. This amount must be greater than or equal to the cost of the MP3 player.

Hourly rate	·	Number of hours	+	Money saved	≥	Cost of player

STEP 2 **Use** the verbal model to write an inequality.

Hourly rate	·	Number of hours	+	Money saved	≥	Cost of player
↓		↓		↓		↓
8	·	x	+	32	≥	200

STEP 3 **Solve** the inequality.

$8x + 32 \geq 200$ **Write inequality.**

$8x \geq 168$ **Subtract 32 from each side.**

$x \geq 21$ **Divide each side by 8.**

The correct answer is D. **(A)** **(B)** **(C)** **(D)**

Strategy 2   ELIMINATE CHOICES

Calculate your total income to eliminate incorrect answer choices.

STEP 1 **Choose** a value for x. Start with a value between 10 and 16, say 12.

STEP 2 **Calculate** your total income. Multiply your hourly rate by 12 hours, then add your savings.

$$8 \cdot 12 + 32 = 96 + 32 = 128$$

You can see that working at least 12 hours will not give you enough money to purchase an MP3 player. So, both choices A and B can be eliminated.

STEP 3 **Choose** a value for x that is between 16 and 21, say 20.

STEP 4 **Calculate** your total income.

$$8 \cdot 20 + 32 = 160 + 32 = 192$$

You will not save enough money working 20 hours. So, choice C can be eliminated.

The correct answer is D. **(A)** **(B)** **(C)** **(D)**

PROBLEM 2

Which number is a solution of $|2x - 4| = 6$?

(A) -2 **(B)** -1 **(C)** 0 **(D)** 1

Strategy 1 SOLVE DIRECTLY

Solve the absolute value equation.

STEP 1 **Write** the absolute value equation as two equations joined by *or*.

$$|2x - 4| = 6$$

$$2x - 4 = 6 \quad or \quad 2x - 4 = -6$$

STEP 2 **Solve** each equation.

$$2x - 4 = 6 \quad or \quad 2x - 4 = -6$$
$$2x = 10 \quad or \quad 2x = -2$$
$$x = 5 \quad or \quad x = -1$$

The correct answer is B. **(A)** **(B)** **(C)** **(D)**

Strategy 2 ELIMINATE CHOICES

Substitute the number given in each answer choice for x in the equation.

Choice A:
$$|2(-2) - 4| \overset{?}{=} 6$$
$$|-4 - 4| \overset{?}{=} 6$$
$$|-8| \overset{?}{=} 6$$
$$8 = 6 \; ✗$$

Choice B:
$$|2(-1) - 4| \overset{?}{=} 6$$
$$|-2 - 4| \overset{?}{=} 6$$
$$|-6| \overset{?}{=} 6$$
$$6 = 6 \; ✓$$

The correct answer is B. **(A)** **(B)** **(C)** **(D)**

STRATEGY PRACTICE

Explain why you can eliminate the highlighted answer choice.

1. Which number is a solution of the inequality $-2x > 20$?

   (A) -11 **(B)** -9 **(C)** -8 **(D)** ✗ 10

2. Which number is a solution of $|2x + 6| + 1 \geq 9$?

   (A) -8 **(B)** -6 **(C)** -4 **(D)** ✗ 0

3. The perimeter of a rectangle is less than 35 units. The width of the rectangle is 6 units. What are the possible values for the length ℓ of the rectangle?

   (A) ✗ $\ell < 29$ **(B)** $\ell < 11.5$ **(C)** $\ell > 29$ **(D)** $\ell > 11.5$

4. The battery for your MP3 player will work for at most 20 hours before it must be recharged. You have been listening to your MP3 player for 3 hours after recharging it. What are the possible numbers x of hours the battery will work before it needs to be recharged again?

   (A) $x \leq 3$ **(B)** ✗ $x \leq 7$ **(C)** $x \leq 17$ **(D)** $x \leq 19$

1. The graph of which inequality is shown?
Gr. 7 AF 4.1

Ⓐ $x > -7$

Ⓑ $x \geq -7$

Ⓒ $x \leq -7$

Ⓓ $x < -7$

2. Which absolute value inequality is equivalent to $x > 8$ *or* $x < -15$? **Alg. 3.0**

Ⓐ $|3x + 8| > 45$

Ⓑ $|3x| - 2 < 12$

Ⓒ $|4x - 2| > 33$

Ⓓ $|2x + 7| > 23$

3. You order one lunch item from the menu below. Which inequality describes the possible total costs c (in dollars) of your lunch? **Alg. 5.0**

LUNCH

Chicken Wrap	$5.99
California Wrap	$7.69
Southwestern Wrap	$6.79
Vegetable Wrap	$5.49

Side salad included

Ⓐ $5.49 \leq c \leq 6.79$

Ⓑ $5.99 \leq c \leq 6.79$

Ⓒ $5.99 \leq c \leq 7.69$

Ⓓ $5.49 \leq c \leq 7.69$

4. Which number is a solution of the equation $3|2t - 1| - 7 = 20$? **Alg. 3.0**

Ⓐ -9

Ⓑ -8

Ⓒ -4

Ⓓ -5

5. You decide to eat oatmeal for breakfast. You want to eat at most 200 calories. What are the possible amounts x (in grams) of oatmeal you could eat? **Alg. 5.0**

OATMEAL

Nutrition Facts
Serving Size 1 Packet (28 grams)

Amount Per Serving

Calories 100   Calories from Fat 25

Ⓐ $x \leq 28$

Ⓑ $x \leq 56$

Ⓒ $x \geq 28$

Ⓓ $x \geq 56$

6. In a piano competition, a pianist must perform a piece of music that lasts no less than 8 minutes and no more than 10 minutes. Which inequality represents the amount of time t (in minutes) that a pianist has to perform? **Alg. 4.0**

Ⓐ $8 < t < 10$

Ⓑ $t \leq 8 \ or \ t \geq 10$

Ⓒ $8 \leq t \leq 10$

Ⓓ $t < 8 \ or \ t > 10$

7. While training to work at an ice cream shop, you learn that the weight of a scoop of ice cream should be 4 ounces with an absolute deviation of at most 0.5 ounce. The table shows the weights of your first 10 scoops. What percent of your scoops meet the weight requirement? **Alg. 3.0**

Weights (ounces)				
3.8	4.2	3.9	4.5	3.7
4.6	4.1	3.3	4.3	4.2

Ⓐ 60%

Ⓑ 70%

Ⓒ 80%

Ⓓ 90%

8. The graph of which inequality is shown? **Alg. 4.0**

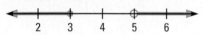

(A) $x \le 3 \; or \; x \ge 5$

(B) $x \le 3 \; or \; x > 5$

(C) $x < 3 \; or \; x \ge 5$

(D) $x < 3 \; or \; x > 5$

9. Which situation can be represented by the inequality $17x \le 240$? **Gr. 7 AF 4.1**

(A) A store sells 17 DVDs for $240. Each DVD costs x dollars.

(B) You spend at least $240 on 17 CDs. Each CD costs x dollars.

(C) A business purchases 17 training manuals for x dollars each. The business spends at most $240.

(D) You save x dollars every week in order to buy a bike that costs $240. After 17 weeks, you still cannot afford the bike.

10. What is the solution of the inequality $4 > -\frac{1}{3}y$? **Gr. 7 AF 4.1**

(A) $y > -12$

(B) $y < -12$

(C) $y > -7$

(D) $y < -7$

11. You are designing an obstacle course for a dog agility event. The course includes a tunnel that must have a height of 24 inches with an absolute deviation of 2 inches. Which equation can you use to find the minimum and maximum heights of the tunnel? **Alg. 3.0**

(A) $|x + 24| = 2$

(B) $|x - 24| = 2$

(C) $|x + 2| = 24$

(D) $|x - 2| = 24$

12. What is the solution of the inequality $2f - 2 \le 8$? **Gr. 7 AF 4.1**

(A) $f \le \frac{1}{20}$

(B) $f \le \frac{1}{5}$

(C) $f \le 5$

(D) $f \le 20$

13. The perimeter of the rectangle shown is greater than 50 inches. What are the possible values of x? **Alg. 4.0**

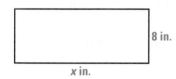

8 in.

x in.

(A) $x > 10$

(B) $x > 17$

(C) $x > 25$

(D) $x > 33$

14. You are performing a music act in a talent show. The talent show entry form lists time limits for each type of act. The director of the show gives each act an absolute deviation of 2 minutes. What is the maximum amount of time (in minutes) that you have to perform? **Alg. 3.0**

Talent Show Entry Form

Name: _____ Grade: _____

Check one category

☐ Comedy (*4 minutes*)

☐ Dance (*3 minutes*)

☐ Music (*5 minutes*)

(A) 3 min

(B) 6 min

(C) 7 min

(D) 8 min

Evaluate the expression. *(p. 11)*

1. $3 \cdot 4^2 - 21$

2. $4 + 4^2 \div 8$

3. $77 \div (11 - 4)$

4. $\frac{1}{2}(8 \cdot 6) - 4^2$

5. $3[50 - (13 - 7)^2]$

6. $\frac{3}{4}[(6 + 4)^2 - 40]$

Check whether the given number is a solution of the equation or inequality. *(p. 26)*

7. $7t - 11 = 52$; 9

8. $3b - 2 = 2b + 3$; 4

9. $8z - 11 > 21$; 4

10. $5a + 3 \le 13$; 2

11. $5 - y \ge 5$; 3

12. $8x - 15 < 8$; 7

Find the sum, difference, product, or quotient.

13. $-2\frac{1}{6} + \left(-4\frac{2}{3}\right)$ *(p. 60)*

14. $2.5 - (-2.05)$ *(p. 67)*

15. $-24.6 - (-5.5)$ *(p. 67)*

16. $\frac{5}{2}(-8)(-5)$ *(p. 74)*

17. $9 \div \left(-\frac{3}{7}\right)$ *(p. 88)*

18. $-\frac{7}{8} \div \frac{1}{2}$ *(p. 88)*

Evaluate the expression for the given value of the variable(s).

19. $\frac{32}{w} - 2$ when $w = 4$ *(p. 11)*

20. $\frac{5y}{32 - y^3}$ when $y = 3$ *(p. 11)*

21. $5.15 + (-h) + 6.6$ when $h = 4.3$ *(p. 60)*

22. $17.4 - \left|-p\right|$ when $p = 3.5$ *(p. 67)*

23. $-x(8.3y)$ when $x = 6$ and $y = 9$ *(p. 74)*

24. $\frac{y}{5x - y}$ when $x = 2$ and $y = 4$ *(p. 88)*

Determine whether the statement is *sometimes*, *always*, or *never* true. *(p. 102)*

25. $n > \frac{1}{n}$ for any real number n

26. $k(-k) < 0$ for any real number k

Solve the equation. Check your solution.

27. $m + 16 = 5$ *(p. 125)*

28. $-4 = \frac{w}{7}$ *(p. 125)*

29. $5 + 3x = 23$ *(p. 132)*

30. $\frac{a}{3} - 4 = 29$ *(p. 132)*

31. $-4 = -2b - 18 + 5b$ *(p. 139)*

32. $\frac{3}{8}(16n + 48) = 72$ *(p. 139)*

33. $-8z + 18 = 2(2z - 9)$ *(p. 146)*

34. $15c + 30 = \frac{1}{3}(102 - 12c)$ *(p. 146)*

35. $\left|5c - 11\right| = 36$ *(p. 220)*

36. $4\left|z + 8\right| + 12 = 46$ *(p. 220)*

Solve the proportion. *(p. 161)*

37. $\frac{6}{d} = \frac{12}{17}$

38. $\frac{1}{9} = \frac{5}{3x}$

39. $\frac{2}{11} = \frac{4}{t - 1}$

40. $\frac{w + 2}{8} = \frac{w}{3}$

Solve the inequality. Then graph your solution.

41. $x - 9 < -13$ *(p. 189)*

42. $\frac{x}{-4} > 7$ *(p. 196)*

43. $1 - 2x \le -13$ *(p. 202)*

44. $8 > -3x - 1$ *(p. 202)*

45. $4x - 10 \le 7x + 8$ *(p. 202)*

46. $-4 < 3x - 1 < 5$ *(p. 210)*

47. $3 < 9 - 2x < 15$ *(p. 210)*

48. $|3x| < 15$ *(p. 226)*

49. $|4x - 2| \ge 18$ *(p. 226)*

50. GARDENS You want to put edging around a rectangular flower garden that is 15 feet long and 12 feet wide. The edging comes in 3 foot pieces, as shown. How many pieces of edging do you need to buy? *(p. 32)*

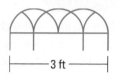
$\vdash$ 3 ft $\dashv$

51. STOCKS The daily change in the price of a share of stock is the difference of the price of a share when trading closes and the price of a share when trading opened earlier that day. The table shows the prices of a share of stock during a 5 day period. Find the change in price for each day. *(p. 67)*

Day	1	2	3	4	5
Opening price (dollars)	39.16	38.82	38.37	38.12	39.14
Closing price (dollars)	38.82	38.37	38.12	39.14	39.22

52. CRAFTS You want to make a square mirror by applying silver leaf to a piece of glass. You have enough silver leaf to cover 854 square inches. Determine the side length of the square piece of glass you need to have cut for this project. Round your answer to the nearest inch. *(p. 95)*

53. BANQUETS The senior class at your high school has its prom at a banquet facility. The banquet facility charges $15.95 per person for a dinner buffet and $400 to rent the banquet hall for an evening. The class paid the banquet facility a total of $2633 for the dinner buffet and use of the banquet hall. How many people attended the prom? *(p. 132)*

54. TELEVISIONS The ratio of the length to the width of two different television screens is shown. The width of each screen is 16.2 inches. Find the length of each screen. *(p. 155)*

Standard

Wide screen

55. BATTERIES A manufacturer of nickel-cadmium batteries recommends storing the batteries at temperatures ranging from $-20°C$ to $45°C$. Use an inequality to describe the temperatures (in degrees Fahrenheit) at which the batteries are recommended to be stored. *(p. 210)*

56. MANUFACTURING A company manufactures bottles of shampoo that each contain 16 fluid ounces with an absolute deviation of 0.05 fluid ounce. Write and graph a compound inequality that gives the possible amounts of shampoo in a bottle. *(p. 226)*

5 Graphing Linear Equations and Functions

Before

In previous courses and chapters, you learned the following skills, which you'll use in Chapter 5:

- Graphing ordered pairs
- Solving equations
- Writing fractions in simplest form

Now

In Chapter 5 you'll study these **Big Ideas:**

1 Representing functions as verbal rules, equations, ordered pairs, and graphs

2 Graphing linear equations and functions

3 Using graphs to solve real-world problems

Why?

So you can solve real-world problems about . . .

- Cell phones, p. 270
- Recycling, p. 278
- Amusement parks, p. 287
- Oceanography, p. 288
- Hockey, p. 295
- Bicycles, p. 302

Animated Algebra

at *classzone.com*

Get-Ready Games

FIND THE FLAGS

California Standards

Review graphing ordered pairs. *Gr. 5 AF 1.4*
Prepare for graphing linear equations. *Alg. 6.0*

Materials

- 2 *Find the Flags* boards, 1 for each player
- Pencils

How to Play Play in pairs. On the grid labeled *My Flags*, each player draws 4 flags, following these steps:

- Draw a horizontal or vertical line segment exactly 2 units in length for the flagpole.

- Draw 3 segments, each 1 unit in length, to form a square flag at one end of the flagpole.

- Use endpoints that have integer coordinates.

Players should not show each other their flags. Players take turns following the steps on the next page.

1 **Name** a point on your *Guesses* grid. Your opponent must tell you whether this point is on one of his or her flags.

(2,3)

How to Win Be the first player to find all of the points on each of the other player's flags.

2 **Use** Xs and Os on your *Guesses* grid to keep track of the points you choose. Mark an X on a point if it is not on one of your opponent's flags. Mark an O if it is a point on one of your opponent's flags.

3 **Name** another point if you found a point on one of your opponent's flags in Step 1.

Games Wrap-Up

Draw Conclusions

Complete these exercises after playing the game.

1. WRITING *Describe* the strategy you used to discover your opponent's flags.

2. REASONING Is it possible that (−1, 2), (−1, 3), and (4, −1) are points on the same flag? *Explain* why or why not.

Prerequisite Skills

California @HomeTutor

Prerequisite skills practice
at classzone.com

**REVIEW
VOCABULARY**

•**solution of an
equation,** *p. 27*

•**ratio,** *p. 155*

•**coordinate plane,**
p. 794

•**ordered pair,** *p. 794*

•**origin,** *p. 794*

•**x-axis, y-axis,** *p. 794*

VOCABULARY CHECK

Copy and complete the statement.

1. When a(n) __?__ of the form (x, y) is graphed, the first number is the x-coordinate and the second number is the y-coordinate.

2. A(n) __?__ uses division to compare two quantities.

SKILLS CHECK

Plot the point in a coordinate plane. *(Review p. 794 for 5.2.)*

3. $A(-2, 0)$ 4. $B(1, 5)$ 5. $C(4, -4)$ 6. $D(0, 3)$

Solve the equation for y. *(Review p. 167 for 5.3, 5.6–5.7.)*

7. $6x + 4y = 16$ 8. $x + 2y = 5$ 9. $-12x + 6y = -12$

Write the fraction in simplest form. *(Review p. 786 for 5.5.)*

10. $\dfrac{9}{12}$ 11. $\dfrac{16}{48}$ 12. $\dfrac{27}{60}$ 13. $\dfrac{40}{55}$

Notetaking Skills

NOW YOU TRY
Make a *sequence
diagram* for solving
an inequality.

Focus on Graphic Organizers

You can use a *sequence* diagram to organize the steps of a process, such as solving an equation.

SOLVING AN EQUATION		
	SEQUENCE:	*EXAMPLE:*
Step 1	Use the distributive property to remove parentheses.	$2 + 2(x + 3) = 14$ $2 + 2x + 6 = 14$
Step 2	Simplify the expression on each side of the equation.	$2x + 8 = 14$
Step 3	Collect variable terms on one side and constant terms on the other.	$2x + 8 - 8 = 14 - 8$ $2x = 6$
Step 4	Solve for the variable.	$x = 3$

5.1 Represent Functions as Ordered Pairs and Rules

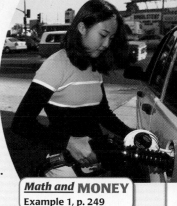

Standards

Alg. 16.0 Students understand the concepts of a relation and a function, determine whether a given relation defines a function, and give pertinent information about given relations and functions.

Alg. 17.0 Students determine the domain of independent variables and the range of dependent variables defined by a graph, **a set of ordered pairs, or a symbolic expression.**

Alg. 18.0 Students determine whether a relation defined by a graph, **a set of ordered pairs, or a symbolic expression is a function and justify the conclusion.**

Math and **MONEY**
Example 1, p. 249

Connect *Before* you wrote algebraic expressions and equations. *Now* you will represent functions as ordered pairs and rules.

Key Vocabulary
- **relation**
- **domain**
- **range**
- **function**
- **independent variable**
- **dependent variable**

A **relation** is a pairing of the elements of one set, called the **domain**, with the elements of another set, called the **range**.

A relation can be represented by a set of ordered pairs of the form (x, y) where x is an element of the domain and y is an element of the range. Ordered pairs can be organized in a table.

EXAMPLE 1 Identify the domain and range of a relation

The table shows the cost of various amounts of regular unleaded gas from the same pump.

a. Write the table as a set of ordered pairs.

b. Identify the domain and range of the relation.

29.99
THIS SALE $

10.000
GALLONS

2.999
PRICE PER GALLON $
ALL TAXES INCLUDED

USE SET NOTATION
Domain and range can also be written as sets. Another way to write the answer to part (b) of Example 1 is:
Domain = {10, 12, 13, 17}
Range = {29.99, 35.99, 38.99, 50.98}

Amount (gallons)	10	12	13	17
Cost (dollars)	29.99	35.99	38.99	50.98

Solution

a. The table can be written as {(10, 29.99), (12, 35.99), (13, 38.99), (17, 50.98)}.

b. The domain is 10, 12, 13, 17. The range is 29.99, 35.99, 38.99, 50.98.

✓ **GUIDED PRACTICE** for Example 1

1. Identify the domain and range of the relation {(−1, 9), (0, 4), (3, 1), (8, −2)}.

RELATIONS AND FUNCTIONS A relation is a **function** if for each domain element there is exactly one range element. Each domain element of a function is called an *input*, and the corresponding range element is called an *output*.

EXAMPLE 2 ◆ **Multiple Choice Practice**

Which relation is a function?

(A) {(0, −2), (0, 3), (5, −4), (10, 5)}   **(B)** {(0, −1), (1, 2), (4, 8), (6, 12)}

(C) {(0, 7), (−1, 7), (−2, 7), (−2, 8)}   **(D)** {(−2, 9), (4, 7), (4, 5), (6, −3)}

Solution

Choices A, C, and D are not functions because each relation contains a domain element that is paired with two different range elements. For instance, 0 is paired with both −2 and 3 in choice A.

The relation {(0, −1), (1, 2), (4, 8), (6, 12)} in choice B is a function because each domain element is paired with exactly one range element.

▶ The correct answer is B. (A) **(B)** (C) (D)

✔ **GUIDED PRACTICE** for Example 2

Determine whether the relation is a function.

2. {(3, 1), (6, 2), (9, 2), (12, 1)}   **3.** {(2, 0), (2, −1), (4, −2), (7, −3)}

FUNCTION RULES A function may be represented using a rule that relates one variable to another. The input variable is called the **independent variable.** The output variable is called the **dependent variable** because its value depends on the value of the input variable.

READING
Function rules typically give the dependent variable in terms of the independent variable. In an equation like $y = x + 3$, y is the dependent variable.

KEY CONCEPT   *For Your Notebook*

Functions

Verbal Rule	Equation	Set of Ordered Pairs
The output is 3 more than the input. The inputs are −2, −1, 0, 1.	$y = x + 3$ with domain −2, −1, 0, 1	{(−2, 1), (−1, 2), (0, 3), (1, 4)}

EXAMPLE 3 **Use a function rule**

The domain of the function $y = 2x$ is −2, 0, 2, 5, 7. Make a table of ordered pairs that represents the function. Then identify the range of the function.

Solution

x	−2	0	2	5	7
$y = 2x$	$2(−2) = −4$	$2(0) = 0$	$2(2) = 4$	$2(5) = 10$	$2(7) = 14$

The range of the function is −4, 0, 4, 10, 14.

EXAMPLE 4 Write a function rule

Write a rule for the function.

x	−1	0	1	4	6
y	1	2	3	6	8

Solution

Notice that each output y is 2 more than the corresponding input x. So, a rule for the function is $y = x + 2$.

EXAMPLE 5 Write a function rule for a real-world situation

Animated Algebra

For an interactive example of identifying domain and range, go to **classzone.com**.

CONCERT TICKETS You are buying concert tickets that cost $15 each. You can buy up to 6 tickets.

- Write the total cost (in dollars) of the tickets as a function of the number of tickets you buy.

- Identify the independent and dependent variables.

- Identify the domain and the range of the function.

Ticket cost: $15

Solution

Write a verbal model. Then write a function rule. Let t represent the number of tickets bought and C represent the total cost (in dollars).

Total cost (dollars)	=	Cost per ticket (dollars/ticket)	·	Tickets bought (tickets)
↓		↓		↓
C	=	15	·	t

CHOOSE A VARIABLE
To write a function rule for a real-world situation, choose letters for the variables that remind you of the quantities represented.

So, the function rule is $C = 15t$. The total cost depends on the tickets bought, so t is the independent variable and C is the dependent variable.

Because you can buy up to 6 tickets, the domain of the function is 0, 1, 2, 3, 4, 5, 6. Make a table to identify the range.

Number of tickets, t	0	1	2	3	4	5	6
Cost (dollars), C	0	15	30	45	60	75	90

The range of the function is 0, 15, 30, 45, 60, 75, 90.

✓ **GUIDED PRACTICE** for Examples 3, 4, and 5

4. The domain of the function $y = x - 5$ is −5, 5, 10, 12, 15. Make a table of ordered pairs that represents the function. Then identify the range of the function.

5. Write a rule for the function. Identify the domain and the range.

Time (hours)	1	2	3	4
Pay (dollars)	8	16	24	32

5.1 EXERCISES

HOMEWORK KEY

◆ = **MULTIPLE CHOICE PRACTICE**
Exs. 9, 18, 19, 33, and 38–40

◯ = **HINTS AND HOMEWORK HELP**
for Exs. 7, 21, and 31 at classzone.com

SKILLS · PROBLEM SOLVING · REASONING

1. **VOCABULARY** Copy and complete: A relation is a function if for each ? element there is exactly one ? element.

2. **WRITING** In the equation $b = a - 2$, which variable is the independent variable and which is the dependent variable? *Explain.*

EXAMPLE 1
on p. 249
for Exs. 3–9

DOMAIN AND RANGE Identify the domain and range of the relation.

3. {(−2, 5), (0, 3), (2, 5)}

4. {(1, 4), (2, 3), (3, 2), (4, 1)}

5. {(8, −1), (18, 9), (28, 20)}

6.

x	y
0	5
1	7
2	15
3	44

7.

x	y
3	7
5	5
7	−3
8	−2

8.

x	y
−6	5
−2	7
−1	10
4	17

9. ◆ **MULTIPLE CHOICE** What is the domain of the relation {(0, 3), (1, 3), (1, 5), (2, 9)}?

Ⓐ 1, 3

Ⓑ 3, 5, 9

Ⓒ 0, 1, 2

Ⓓ 0, 1, 2, 3, 5, 9

EXAMPLE 2
on p. 250
for Exs. 10–17

IDENTIFYING FUNCTIONS Determine whether the relation is a function.

10. {(0, 0), (1, 1), (2, 2), (3, 3)}

11. {(5, −6), (6, −5), (7, −5)}

12. {(9, 10), (9, 11), (10, 11)}

13.

Months	Cost
0	$7.50
1	$9.50
2	$11.50
3	$13.50

14.

Songs	Length
8	20.0 min
10	30.5 min
10	32.2 min
12	35.5 min

15.

Hour	Temperature
0	−4°F
1	−2°F
2	1°F
3	1°F

ERROR ANALYSIS *Describe* and correct the error in describing the relation {(1, 6), (2, 7), (3, 8), (4, 6), (5, 9)}.

16.

The relation is not a function. One range element is paired with two domain elements. ✗

17.

The relation is a function. The range is 1, 2, 3, 4, 5. ✗

EXAMPLES 3 and 4
on pp. 250–251
for Exs. 18–27

18. ◆ **MULTIPLE CHOICE** The domain of the function $y = 5x − 1$ is −1, 3, 5, 6. Which number is in the range of the function?

Ⓐ −6

Ⓑ 4

Ⓒ 6

Ⓓ 15

19. ◆ MULTIPLE CHOICE Each output of a function is 0.5 less than the corresponding input. Which equation is a rule for the function?

(A) $y = x - 0.5$ (B) $y = x + 0.5$ (C) $y = 0.5 - x$ (D) $y = 0.5x$

TABLES Make a table of ordered pairs that represents the function. Then identify the range of the function.

20. $y = x - 3$
Domain: 12, 15, 22, 30

21. $y = x + 3.5$
Domain: −5, −2, 7, 8, 12

22. $y = 3x + 4$
Domain: 0, 5, 7, 10

23. $y = \frac{1}{2}x + 3$
Domain: 4, 6, 9, 11

24. $y = \frac{2}{3}x + \frac{1}{3}$
Domain: −9, −6, −4, −2

25. $y = \frac{0.5x + 1}{2}$
Domain: −4, 0, 2, 4, 6

FUNCTION RULES Write a rule for the function.

26.

x	0	1	2	3
y	2.2	3.2	4.2	5.2

27.

x	6	15	20	21	30
y	−2	7	12	13	22

CONNECT SKILLS TO PROBLEM SOLVING Exercises 28–30 will help you prepare for problem solving.

28. There are 8 oranges in a bowl. Write a rule for the number y of oranges that are left in the bowl as a function of the number x of oranges that are taken from the bowl.

29. Each lap at the California Speedway is 2 miles. Write a rule for the number y of miles driven as a function of the number x of finished laps.

30. DVDs are on sale for $10.50 each. Write a rule for the amount y (in dollars) you spend as a function of the number x of DVDs you buy.

EXAMPLE 5
on p. 251
for Exs. 31–34

31. MULTI-STEP PROBLEM You have 10 quarters that you can use for a parking meter.

   a. Describing in Words Copy and complete: Each time you put 1 quarter in the meter, you have 1 less quarter, so __?__ is a function of __?__.

   b. Writing a Rule Write a rule for the number y of quarters that you have left as a function of the number x of quarters you have used so far. Identify the domain of the function.

   c. Making a Table Make a table that represents the set of ordered pairs for the function. Then identify the range of the function.

   California @HomeTutor for problem solving help at classzone.com

32. YARD SALE At a yard sale, you find 5 paperback books by your favorite author. Each book is priced at $.75.

   a. Copy and complete: For each book you buy, you spend $.75, so __?__ is a function of __?__.

   b. Write a rule for the amount (in dollars) you spend as a function of the number of books you buy. Identify the domain of the function.

   c. Make a table that represents the set of ordered pairs for the function. Then identify the range of the function.

   California @HomeTutor for problem solving help at classzone.com

33. ◆ **MULTIPLE CHOICE** You have $100 saved and plan to save $20 each month. Which rule represents the amount y (in dollars) saved as a function of the number x of months from now?

    Ⓐ $y = 20x$ Ⓑ $x = 20y + 100$

    Ⓒ $y = 20x + 100$ Ⓓ $y = 100x + 20$

34. **SHORT RESPONSE** Consider a relation that pairs the digits 2 through 9 on a telephone keypad with the associated letters.

    a. If the digits are the domain and the associated letters are the range, is the relation a function? *Explain.*

    b. If the letters are the domain and the associated digits are the range, is the relation a function? *Explain.*

35. **REASONING** Consider the relation {(a, b), (c, d)}. What must be true about a, b, c, and d for the relation to be a function? What must be true for the relation *not* to be a function?

36. **CHALLENGE** Consider the relations $y = |x|$ and $x = |y|$, each with the following domain: $x = 0, 1, 2, 3$. What is the range of each function? For which relation is y a function of x? For which relation is y *not* a function of x? *Explain.*

37. **CHALLENGE** Each week you spend a total of 5 hours exercising. You swim part of the time and bike the rest.

        300 calories per hour   **440 calories per hour**

    a. Write a rule for the total number of calories you burn for the entire 5 hours as a function of the time you spend swimming.

    b. One week you spend half the time swimming. How many calories do you burn during the entire 5 hours?

◆ CALIFORNIA STANDARDS SPIRAL REVIEW

Alg. 3.0   **38.** What is the solution of $|x - 3| > 4$? *(p. 226)*

    Ⓐ $x < -1$ or $x > 7$ Ⓑ $-1 < x < 7$

    Ⓒ $x < -7$ or $x > 1$ Ⓓ $-7 < x < 1$

Alg. 5.0   **39.** The total cost C (in dollars) to pre-order t tickets for a baseball game is given by the equation $C = 21.95t + 4.50$. If the total cost was $136.20, how many tickets were bought? *(p. 139)*

    Ⓐ 5   Ⓑ 6   Ⓒ 7   Ⓓ 8

Alg. 24.3   **40.** Which number is a counterexample to the statement "All integers are whole numbers"? *(p. 53)*

    Ⓐ -2 Ⓑ 0   Ⓒ 1   Ⓓ 23

5.1 Make a Table

Standards

Alg. 16.0 Students understand the concepts of a relation and a function, determine whether a given relation defines a function, **and give pertinent information about given relations and functions.**

QUESTION How can you use a graphing calculator to create a table for a function?

You can use a graphing calculator to create a table for a function when you want to display many pairs of input values and output values or when you want to find the input value that corresponds to a given output value.

In the example below, you will make a table to compare temperatures in degrees Celsius and temperatures in degrees Fahrenheit for temperatures at or above the temperature at which water freezes, 32°F.

EXAMPLE Use a graphing calculator to make a table

The formula $C = \frac{5}{9}(F - 32)$ gives the temperature in degrees Celsius as a function of the temperature in degrees Fahrenheit. Make a table for the function.

STEP 1 *Enter equation*
Rewrite the function using x for F and y for C. Press Y= and enter $\frac{5}{9}(x - 32)$.

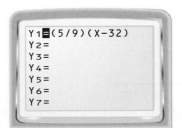

STEP 2 *Set up table*
Go to the TABLE SETUP screen. Use a starting value (TblStart) of 32 and an increment ($\triangle$Tbl) of 1.

```
TABLE SETUP
 TblStart=32
 △Tbl=1
Indpnt:Auto Ask
Depend:Auto Ask
```

STEP 3 *View table*
Display the table. Scroll down to see pairs of inputs and outputs.

PRACTICE

1. You see a sign that indicates that the outdoor temperature is 10°C. Find the temperature in degrees Fahrenheit. *Explain* how you found your answer.

2. Water boils at 100°C. What is the temperature in degrees Fahrenheit?

Make a table for the function. Use the given starting value and increment.

3. $y = \frac{3}{4}x + 5$
   TblStart = 0, $\triangle$Tbl = 1

4. $y = 4x + 2$
   TblStart = 0, $\triangle$Tbl = 0.5

5. $y = 7.5x - 0.5$
   TblStart = 1, $\triangle$Tbl = 1

6. $y = 0.5x + 6$
   TblStart = 3, $\triangle$Tbl = 3

Standards

Alg. 18.0 Students determine whether a relation defined by a graph, a set of ordered pairs, or a symbolic expression **is a function and justify the conclusion.**

5.2 Scatter Plots and Functions

MATERIALS · tape measure · graph paper

QUESTION How can you tell whether a graph represents a function?

A *scatter plot* is a type of display for paired data. Each data pair is plotted as a point. In this activity, you will work in a group to make a scatter plot. You will measure the height of each student in your group and the length of his or her forearm. The length of the forearm is the distance from the elbow to the wrist.

EXPLORE Collect data and make a scatter plot

STEP 1 *Collect data* Measure the height of each student in your group and the length of his or her forearm. Record the results for each student in one row of a table like the one shown.

Height (inches)	Forearm length (inches)
63	10
?	?

STEP 2 *Make a scatter plot* Use graph paper to draw axes labeled as shown. Then plot the data pairs (*height, forearm length*). For example, plot the point (**63, 10**) for a student with a height of 63 inches and a forearm length of 10 inches.

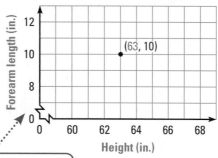

The symbol on an axis represents a break in the axis.

DRAW CONCLUSIONS Use your observations to complete these exercises

1. Examine your scatter plot. What general relationship exists between a person's height and the person's forearm length?

2. Compare your table with those of the other groups in your class. Determine which of the tables represent functions and which do not if you treat height as the independent variable and forearm length as the dependent variable.

3. Is it possible to determine whether a table represents a function by looking at the corresponding scatter plot? *Explain.*

5.2 Represent Functions as Graphs

Math and
HOURS OF DAYLIGHT
Ex. 26, p. 262

Standards Alg. 17.0 Students determine the domain of independent variables and the range of dependent variables defined by **a graph**, a set of ordered pairs, **or a symbolic expression.**

Alg. 18.0 Students determine whether a relation defined by **a graph**, a set of ordered pairs, **or a symbolic expression is a function and justify the conclusion.**

Connect *Before* you represented functions as ordered pairs and rules.
Now you will represent functions as graphs.

Key Vocabulary
• **function,** *p. 249*
• **domain,** *p. 249*
• **range,** *p. 249*

REVIEW THE COORDINATE PLANE
For help with the coordinate plane, see p. 794.

You can use a graph to represent a function. Given a function represented by a set of ordered pairs, each ordered pair can be plotted as a point. The *x*-coordinate is the input. The *y*-coordinate is the output.

Ordered Pairs	Graph
(input, output)	
(−1, 2)	
(1, 4)	
(4, 3)	

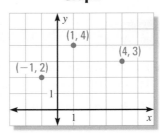

EXAMPLE 1 Graph a function

Graph the function $y = \frac{1}{2}x$ with domain −2, 0, 2, 4.

Solution

STEP 1 **Make** a table of ordered pairs for the function.

x	−2	0	2	4
y	−1	0	1	2

STEP 2 **Plot** a point for each ordered pair (x, y).

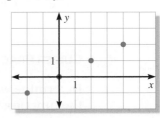

✓ **GUIDED PRACTICE** for Example 1

Graph the function.

1. $y = 2x − 1$; domain: −3, −1, 2, 5

2. $y = −4x + 2$; domain: −1, 0, 1, 2

ANALYZING THE GRAPH OF A RELATION When a relation is *not* a function, its graph contains at least two points with the same *x*-coordinate and different *y*-coordinates. Those points lie on a vertical line. So, you can use a vertical line to determine whether a relation represented by a graph is a function.

EXAMPLE 2 Determine whether a graph represents a function

Animated Algebra

For an interactive example of determining whether a graph represents a function, go to **classzone.com**.

Determine whether the graph represents a function.

a.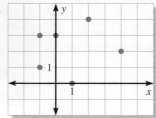

b.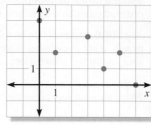

You can draw a vertical line through the points (−1, 1) and (−1, 3). The graph does *not* represent a function.

No vertical line can be drawn through more than one point. The graph represents a function.

EXAMPLE 3 Write a function rule for a graph

Write a rule for the function represented by the graph. Identify the domain and the range of the function.

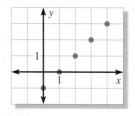

STEP 1 **Make** a table for the graph.

x	0	1	2	3	4
y	−1	0	1	2	3

STEP 2 **Find** a relationship between the inputs and the outputs. Notice from the table that each output *y* is 1 less than the corresponding input *x*.

STEP 3 **Write** a function rule that describes the relationship: $y = x - 1$.

▶ A rule for the function is $y = x - 1$. The domain of the function is 0, 1, 2, 3, 4. The range is −1, 0, 1, 2, 3.

✓ GUIDED PRACTICE for Examples 2 and 3

Determine whether the graph represents a function. If so, write a rule for the function and identify the domain and the range of the function.

3.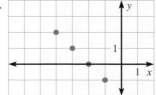

4.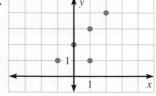

EXAMPLE 4 **Graph and analyze a function**

Presidential campaign button

VOTING In 1920 the ratification of the 19th amendment to the United States Constitution gave women the right to vote. The table shows the number (to the nearest million) of votes cast in presidential elections both before and since women were able to vote.

> **−4 means 4 years before 1920, or 1916.**

> **0 represents the year 1920.**

Years before or since 1920	−12	−8	−4	0	4	8	12
Votes (millions)	15	15	19	27	29	37	40

a. Graph the function represented by the table.

b. Explain how you know the graph represents a function.

c. Describe any trend in the number of votes cast.

Solution

> **LABEL AXES**
> The horizontal axis is labeled with the independent variable, t. The vertical axis is labeled with the dependent variable, v.

a. To graph the function, let t be the number of years before or since 1920. Let v be the number of votes cast (in millions). The graph is shown at the right.

b. The graph represents a function because no vertical line can be drawn to pass through two points.

c. In the three election years before 1920, the number of votes cast was less than 20 million. In 1920, the number of votes cast was greater than 20 million. The number of votes cast continued to increase in the three election years since 1920.

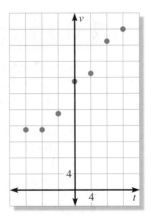

✓ **GUIDED PRACTICE** for Example 4

5. VOTING The presidential election in 1972 was the first election in which 18-year-olds were allowed to vote. The table shows the number (to the nearest million) of votes cast in presidential elections both before and since 1972.

Years before or since 1972	−12	−8	−4	0	4	8	12
Votes (millions)	69	71	73	78	82	87	93

a. Graph the function represented by the table.

b. *Explain* how you know that the graph represents a function.

c. *Describe* any trend in the number of votes cast.

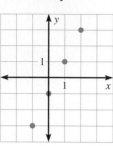
5.2 EXERCISES

SKILLS • PROBLEM SOLVING • REASONING

1. **VOCABULARY** Copy and complete: Each point on the graph of a function corresponds to an ordered pair (x, y) where x is in the __?__ of the function and y is in the __?__ of the function.

2. **WRITING** Given the graph of a function, describe how to write a rule for the function.

EXAMPLE 1
on p. 257
for Exs. 3−12

GRAPHING FUNCTIONS Graph the function.

3. $y = x + 3$; domain: 0, 1, 2, 3, 4, 5

4. $y = \frac{1}{2}x + 1$; domain: 0, 1, 2, 3, 4, 5

5. $y = 2x + 2$; domain: −2, −1, 0, 1, 3, 7

6. $y = 3x − 1$; domain: −3, −1, 2, 3, 5

7. $y = x + 5$; domain: −4, −2, 0, 2, 4, 6

8. $y = −5x + 6$; domain: −1, 0, 1, 2

9. $y = 2.5x$; domain: −1, 0, 1, 2, 3

10. $y = 0.2x − 4$; domain: 0, 5, 10, 15

ERROR ANALYSIS *Describe* and correct the error in graphing the function with domain −2, −1, 0, 1, 2.

11. $y = x − 1$

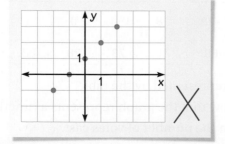

12. $y = 2x$

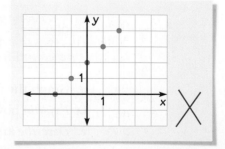

EXAMPLE 2
on p. 258
for Exs. 13–15

IDENTIFYING FUNCTIONS Determine whether the graph represents a function.

13.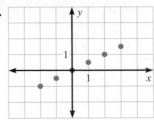

14.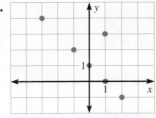

15.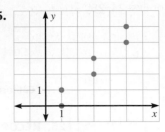

EXAMPLE 3
on p. 258
for Exs. 16–20

WRITING FUNCTION RULES Write a rule for the function represented by the graph. Identify the domain and the range of the function.

16.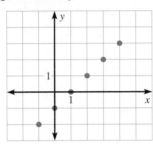

17.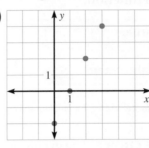

18.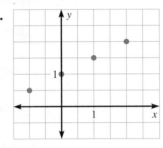

19. ◆ **MULTIPLE CHOICE** What is the domain of the function represented by the graph?

   Ⓐ $-3, -1, 1, 2, 3$ Ⓑ $-2, -1, 0, 1, 2$

   Ⓒ $-2.5, -1, 0.5, 2, 3.5$ Ⓓ $0, 1, 2, 3, 4, 5$

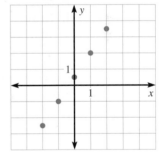

20. ◆ **MULTIPLE CHOICE** The graph of which function is shown in Exercise 19?

   Ⓐ $y = \frac{1}{2}x + \frac{1}{2}$ Ⓑ $y = x + \frac{1}{2}$

   Ⓒ $y = \frac{3}{2}x + \frac{1}{2}$ Ⓓ $y = 2x + \frac{1}{2}$

CONNECT SKILLS TO PROBLEM SOLVING Exercises 21–23 will help you prepare for problem solving.

Describe the input and the output of the function. Then assign variables to the input and output.

21. The table shows the height (in inches) of a plant each year since 2004.

Years since 2004	0	1	2	3
Height (inches)	3	4	6	11

22. The table shows the cost (in dollars) of a hot dog at Dodger Stadium each year since 1995.

Years since 1995	0	3	6	10
Cost (dollars)	2.50	3.00	3.25	4.00

23. The table shows the cost (in dollars) for tickets to a school play.

Tickets	2	4	6	8
Cost (dollars)	8	16	24	32

EXAMPLE 4
on p. 259
for Exs. 24–28

24. ADVERTISING The table shows the cost (in millions of dollars) of a 30 second Super Bowl ad on TV each year since 1997. Graph the data.

Years since 1997	0	1	2	3	4	5	6	7
Cost (millions of dollars)	1.2	1.3	1.6	2.1	2.1	1.9	2.1	2.3

California **@HomeTutor** for problem solving help at classzone.com

25. RECORD TEMPERATURES The table shows the record low temperatures (in degrees Fahrenheit) for a city for each day in the first week of February. Graph the data. *Explain* how you know that the graph represents a function.

Day in February	1	2	3	4	5	6	7
Record low (degrees Fahrenheit)	−8	−11	10	8	10	9	11

California **@HomeTutor** for problem solving help at classzone.com

26. ◆ MULTIPLE CHOICE The graph shows the number of hours of daylight in San Francisco, California, on the fifteenth day of each month in a year. In the graph, 1 represents January, 2 represents February, and so on. Which statement *best* describes the graph?

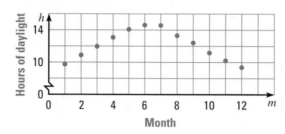

(A) The number of hours of daylight increases throughout the year.

(B) The number of hours of daylight decreases throughout the year.

(C) The number of hours of daylight increases each month from January to June and decreases each month from July to December.

(D) The number of hours of daylight decreases each month from January to June and increases each month from July to December.

27. GUITAR SALES The table shows the guitar sales (in millions of dollars) for a chain of music stores each year since 2001.

Years since 2001	0	1	2	3	4
Sales (millions of dollars)	0.6	0.8	0.9	1.1	1.3

a. Graph the function represented by the table.

b. *Explain* how you know the graph represents a function.

c. *Describe* any trend in the sales.

28. SAT SCORES The math section of the Scholastic Aptitude Test (SAT) is scored using a scale of 0 to 800. The scale was adjusted in 1996. The table shows the average score on the math section of the SAT for the given years.

Years before or since 1996	−3	−2	−1	0	1	2	3
Average score	478	479	482	508	511	512	511

   a. Graph the function represented by the table.

   b. *Explain* how you know the graph represents a function.

   c. *Describe* any trend in the scores.

29. RUNNING Women first officially ran in the Boston Marathon in 1972. The graph shows the winning times (in minutes) for both men and women for 1972 and for every five years thereafter.

   a. CHALLENGE *Explain* how you can estimate the difference in the men's and women's winning time for any year shown.

   b. CHALLENGE *Compare* any trends you see in the graphs.

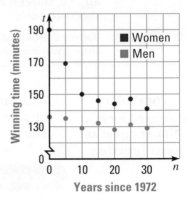

◆ CALIFORNIA STANDARDS SPIRAL REVIEW

Alg. 4.0

30. What is the solution of $-8 \le -2x \le 6$? *(p. 210)*

   Ⓐ $-4 < x < 3$ **Ⓑ** $-4 \le x \le 3$ **Ⓒ** $-4 \ge x \ge 3$ **Ⓓ** $-3 \le x \le 4$

Alg. 16.0

31. Which relation is a function? *(p. 249)*

   Ⓐ {(−3, 2), (−1, 2), (−1, 3), (3, 3)}   **Ⓑ** {(1, 4), (2, 3), (3, 2), (4, 1)}

   Ⓒ {(2, 4), (2, 3), (2, 2), (2, 1)}   **Ⓓ** {(2, 9), (5, 7), (5, 3), (1, −2)}

Gr. 6 AF 3.1

32. The length of a rectangle is 1 more than twice its width x. Which expression represents the perimeter of the rectangle? *(p. 167)*

   Ⓐ $2x + 1$ **Ⓑ** $3x + 1$ **Ⓒ** $6x + 2$ **Ⓓ** $8x$

QUIZ *for Lessons 5.1–5.2*

1. The domain of the function $y = 12 - 2x$ is 0, 2, 3, 4, 5. Make a table of ordered pairs for the function. Then identify the range of the function. *(p. 249)*

Determine whether the relation is a function. *(p. 249)*

   2. {(5, 1), (6, 2), (7, 3), (11, 7)}   **3.** {(4, −3), (6, −1), (6, 6), (9, −3)}

Graph the function. *(p. 257)*

   4. $y = 2x - 5$; domain: 0, 1, 2, 3, 4   **5.** $y = 7 - x$; domain: −1, 1, 3, 7, 10

5.3 Graph Linear Equations and Functions

Standards **Alg. 6.0 Students graph a linear equation** and compute the *x*- and *y*-intercepts (e.g., graph $2x + 6y = 4$). They are also able to sketch the region defined by linear inequalities (e.g., they sketch the region defined by $2x + 6y < 4$).

Alg. 7.0 Students verify that a point lies on a line, given an equation of the line. Students are able to derive linear equations by using the point-slope formula.

Connect *Before* you plotted points in a coordinate plane to represent functions.
Now you will graph linear equations and linear functions in a coordinate plane.

Math and **SCIENCE**
Ex. 60, p. 271

Key Vocabulary
• **standard form of a linear equation**
• **linear function**

An example of an equation in two variables is $3x - y = 7$. A **solution of an equation in two variables**, *x* and *y*, is an ordered pair (x, y) that produces a true statement when the values of *x* and *y* are substituted into the equation.

EXAMPLE 1 Check solutions of an equation

a. The ordered pair $(1, -4)$ is a solution of $3x - y = 7$ because $3(1) - (-4) = 7$.

b. The ordered pair $(-1, -2)$ is *not* a solution of $3x - y = 7$ because $3(-1) - (-2) \neq 7$.

GRAPHS The **graph of an equation in two variables** is the set of points in a coordinate plane that represent all solutions of the equation.

EXAMPLE 2 Graph an equation

Graph the equation $-2x + y = -3$.

Solution

STEP 1 **Solve** the equation for *y*.

$$-2x + y = -3$$
$$y = 2x - 3$$

STEP 2 **Make** a table by choosing a few values for *x* and finding the values of *y*.

x	−2	−1	0	1	2
y	−7	−5	−3	−1	1

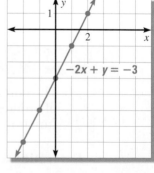

DRAW A GRAPH
If you continued to find solutions of the equation and plotted them, the line would fill in.

STEP 3 **Plot** the points. Notice that the points appear to lie on a line.

STEP 4 **Connect** the points by drawing a line through them. Use arrows to indicate that the graph goes on without end.

POINTS ON LINES A point (x, y) lies on a line if the ordered pair (x, y) is a solution of the equation of the line.

EXAMPLE 3 Determine whether a point lies on a line

READING

In Example 3, the phrase "the line $-2x + y = -3$" is a shorter way of saying "the line with equation $-2x + y = -3$."

Tell whether the point lies on the line $-2x + y = -3$.

a. $(4, 7)$ **b.** $(6, 9)$

Solution

a. The point $(4, 7)$ does *not* lie on the line $-2x + y = -3$ because $-2(4) + 7 \neq -3$.

b. The point $(6, 9)$ lies on the line $-2x + y = -3$ because $-2(6) + 9 = -3$.

✓ **GUIDED PRACTICE**   for Examples 1, 2, and 3

1. Tell whether $\left(4, -\dfrac{1}{2}\right)$ is a solution of $x + 2y = 5$.

2. Graph the equation $y + 3x = -2$.

3. In Example 3, tell whether the point $(-4, 5)$ lies on the line.

LINEAR EQUATIONS A **linear equation** is an equation whose graph is a line or part of a line, such as the equation in Example 2. The **standard form** of a linear equation is

$$Ax + By = C$$

where A, B, and C are real numbers and A and B are not both zero. Special cases of the standard form occur when $A = 0$ or when $B = 0$. Consider these examples:

- The equation $0x + 3y = 6$ simplifies to $3y = 6$, or $y = 2$.
- The equation $4x + 0y = -4$ simplifies to $4x = -4$, or $x = -1$.

In general, the equations $y = b$ and $x = a$ are also linear.

EXAMPLE 4 Graph $y = b$ and $x = a$

Graph (a) $y = 2$ and (b) $x = -1$.

Animated Algebra

For an interactive example of graphing horizontal and vertical lines, go to **classzone.com**.

a. For every value of x, the value of y is 2. The graph of the equation $y = 2$ is a horizontal line 2 units above the x-axis.

b. For every value of y, the value of x is -1. The graph of the equation $x = -1$ is a vertical line 1 unit to the left of the y-axis.

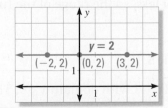

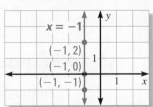

Equations of Horizontal and Vertical Lines

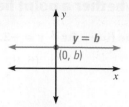

The graph of $y = b$ is a horizontal line. The line passes through the point $(0, b)$.

The graph of $x = a$ is a vertical line. The line passes through the point $(a, 0)$.

✓ **GUIDED PRACTICE**   for Example 4

Graph the equation.

4. $x = 3$ **5.** $y = 2.5$ **6.** $x = -4$

LINEAR FUNCTIONS In Example 4, $y = 2$ is a function, while $x = -1$ is not a function. The equation $Ax + By = C$ represents a **linear function** provided $B \neq 0$ (that is, provided the graph of the equation is not a vertical line). If the domain of a linear function is not specified, it is understood to be all real numbers. The domain can be restricted, as shown in Example 5.

EXAMPLE 5   **Graph a linear function**

Graph the function $y = -\frac{1}{2}x + 4$ with domain $x \geq 0$. Then identify the range of the function.

Solution

USE SET NOTATION
In Example 5, the domain of the function can also can be written as a set, $\{x : x \geq 0\}$. The set is read as "the set of all x such that x is greater than or equal to 0." Similarly, the range can be written as a set, $\{y : y \leq 4\}$.

STEP 1 **Make** a table.

x	0	2	4	6	8
y	4	3	2	1	0

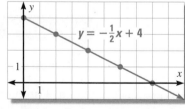

STEP 2 **Plot** the points.

STEP 3 **Connect** the points with a ray because the domain is restricted.

STEP 4 **Identify** the range. From the graph, you can see that all points have a y-coordinate of 4 or less, so the range of the function is $y \leq 4$.

✓ **GUIDED PRACTICE**   for Example 5

7. Graph the function $y = -3x + 1$ with domain $x \leq 0$. Then identify the range of the function.

EXAMPLE 6 **Solve a multi-step problem**

RUNNING The distance d (in miles) that a runner travels is given by the function $d = 6t$ where t is the time (in hours) spent running. The runner plans to run for up to 1.5 hours. Graph the function and identify its domain and range.

Time: Up to 1.5 hours

Solution

STEP 1 **Identify** whether the problem specifies the domain or the range. Time is the independent variable, and you know the runner's time. So, the domain is specified in this problem. The domain of the function is $0 \le t \le 1.5$.

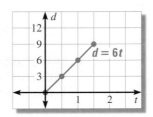

STEP 2 **Graph** the function. Make a table of values. Then plot and connect the points.

t (hours)	0	0.5	1	1.5
d (miles)	0	3	6	9

STEP 3 **Identify** the unspecified domain or range. From the table or graph, you can see that the range of the function is $0 \le d \le 9$.

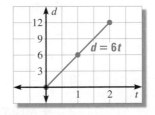

EXAMPLE 7 **Solve a related problem**

WHAT IF? Suppose the runner in Example 6 instead plans to run up to 12 miles. Graph the function and identify its domain and range.

Solution

STEP 1 **Identify** whether the domain or the range is specified. Distance is the dependent variable, and you know the runner's distance. So, the range is specified in this problem. The range is $0 \le d \le 12$.

STEP 2 **Graph** the function. To make a table, you can substitute d-values into the function $d = 6t$ and solve for t.

t (hours)	0	1	2
d (miles)	0	6	12

STEP 3 **Identify** the unspecified domain or range. From the table or graph, you can see that the domain of the function is $0 \le t \le 2$.

✓ **GUIDED PRACTICE** for Examples 6 and 7

8. **GAS COSTS** For gas that costs $3 per gallon, the equation $C = 3g$ gives the cost C (in dollars) of pumping g gallons of gas. You plan to pump up to $15 worth of gas. Graph the function and identify its domain and range.

ANALYZE GRAPHS
In Example 2, the domain is unrestricted, and the graph is a *line*. In Example 5, the domain is restricted to $x \ge 0$, and the graph is a *ray*. Here, the domain is restricted to $0 \le t \le 1.5$, and the graph is a *line segment*.

SOLVE FOR t
To find the time it takes the runner to run 12 miles, solve the equation $6t = 12$ to get $t = 2$.

5.3 EXERCISES

HOMEWORK KEY

◆ = **MULTIPLE CHOICE PRACTICE**
Exs. 13, 35, 42, 43, 55, and 63–65

○ = **HINTS AND HOMEWORK HELP**
for Exs. 3, 17, and 55 at classzone.com

SKILLS · PROBLEM SOLVING · REASONING

1. **VOCABULARY** The equation $Ax + By = C$ represents a(n) _?_ provided $B \neq 0$.

2. **WRITING** Is the equation $y = 6x + 4$ in standard form? *Explain.*

EXAMPLE 1
on p. 264
for Exs. 3–13

CHECKING SOLUTIONS Tell whether the ordered pair is a solution of the equation.

3. $x + 2y = 4$; $(-2, 3)$

4. $3x - 2y = -5$; $(-1, 1)$

5. $9y - x = 35$; $(5, 10)$

6. $-8x + 5y = 12$; $(4, 4)$

7. $-7x - 4y = 1$; $(-3, -5)$

8. $-5y - 6x = 0$; $(-6, 5)$

9. $x = 9$; $(9, 6)$

10. $y = -7$; $(-7, 0)$

11. $x = \frac{3}{4}$; $\left(\frac{1}{2}, \frac{3}{4}\right)$

12. **ERROR ANALYSIS** *Describe* and correct the error in determining whether $(8, 11)$ is a solution of $y - x = -3$.

$$y - x = -3$$
$$8 - 11 \stackrel{?}{=} -3$$
$$-3 = -3 \quad (8, 11) \text{ is a solution.}$$

13. ◆ **MULTIPLE CHOICE** Which ordered pair is a solution of the equation $6x + 3y = 18$?

Ⓐ $(-2, -10)$ Ⓑ $(-2, 10)$ Ⓒ $(2, 10)$ Ⓓ $(10, -2)$

EXAMPLES 2 and 4
on pp. 264–265
for Exs. 14–25

GRAPHING EQUATIONS Graph the equation.

14. $x + y = 2$

15. $-2x + y = 5$

16. $y - 3x = 0$

17. $y + 4x = 1$

18. $2y - 6x = 10$

19. $3y + 4x = 12$

20. $x - 2y = 3$

21. $3x + 2y = 8$

22. $x = 0$

23. $y = 0$

24. $y = -4$

25. $x = 2$

EXAMPLE 3
on p. 265
for Exs. 26–35

CHECKING POINTS Tell whether the point lies on the graph of the equation.

26. $y - x = 11$; $(9, -2)$

27. $x + y = -6$; $(-2, -3)$

28. $2x + y = -1$; $(7, -8)$

29. $4x - 3y = 0$; $(4, 3)$

30. $x - 12y = 7$; $(-5, -1)$

31. $7x - 6y = -21$; $(0, -3)$

32. $x = -8$; $(6, -8)$

33. $y = 3$; $(-7, 3)$

34. $-4y - 15x = 5$; $(10, -3)$

35. ◆ **MULTIPLE CHOICE** Which point does *not* lie on the line $5y - 3x = -20$?

Ⓐ $(-5, -1)$ Ⓑ $(0, -4)$ Ⓒ $(10, 2)$ Ⓓ $(15, 5)$

EXAMPLE 5
on p. 266
for Exs. 36–43

GRAPHING FUNCTIONS Graph the function with the given domain. Then identify the range of the function.

36. $y = 3x - 2$; domain: $x \geq 0$

37. $y = -5x + 3$; domain: $x \leq 0$

38. $y = 4$; domain: $x \leq 5$

39. $y = -6$; domain: $x \geq 5$

40. $y = 2x + 3$; domain: $-4 \leq x \leq 0$

41. $y = -x - 1$; domain: $-1 \leq x \leq 3$

42. ◆ **MULTIPLE CHOICE** What is the range of the function $y = 2x - 6$ given that its domain is $0 \le x \le 4$?

(**A**) $y \le -6$ (**B**) $-6 \le y \le 2$

(**C**) $0 \le y \le 4$ (**D**) $3 \le y \le 5$

43. ◆ **MULTIPLE CHOICE** Which statement is true for the function whose graph is shown?

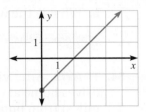

(**A**) The domain is unrestricted.

(**B**) The domain is $x \le -2$.

(**C**) The range is $y \le -2$.

(**D**) The range is $y \ge -2$.

USING FUNCTION NOTATION In Exercises 44–49, use the information and example below to find the value of the function when $x = -3$, 0, and 2.

You have seen functions written in the form $y = ax + b$ where a and b are real numbers. By naming a function f, you can write it using *function notation* as follows: $f(x) = ax + b$. The symbol $f(x)$ is read as "the value of f at x," or simply as "f of x."

EXAMPLE   **Use function notation**

Find the value of the function $f(x) = 3x - 15$ when $x = -3$.

Solution

$f(x) = 3x - 15$	**Write original function.**
$f(-3) = 3(-3) - 15$	**Substitute −3 for x.**
$= -24$	**Simplify.**

▸ When $x = -3$, $f(x) = -24$.

---

44. $f(x) = 2x + 7$ **45.** $f(x) = -9x + 8$ **46.** $f(x) = -2.5x$

47. $f(x) = -x - 11$ **48.** $f(x) = \frac{1}{2}x - 1$ **49.** $f(x) = \frac{5}{6}x - \frac{1}{6}$

CONNECT SKILLS TO PROBLEM SOLVING Exercises 50–52 will help you prepare for problem solving.

Tell whether the problem specifies the domain or range of the function.

50. The cooking time t (in hours) for a roast is given by the function $t = 0.5w$ where w is the weight (in pounds) of the roast. The roast cooks for 3 hours.

51. The amount a (in dollars) of money in an account is given by the function $a = 500 + 10t$ where t is the time (in years) since the account was opened. The account has been open for 4 years.

52. You travel in a canoe at a rate of 4 miles per hour. Your distance d (in miles) traveled is given by $d = 4t$ where t is the time (in hours) spent canoeing. You travel a total of 15 miles.

53. **BAKING** The weight w (in pounds) of a loaf of bread that a recipe yields is given by the function $w = \frac{1}{2}f$ where f is the number of cups of flour used. You have 4 cups of flour.

   a. Graph the function and identify its domain and range.

   b. What is the weight of the largest loaf of bread you can make?

   California @*HomeTutor*   for problem solving help at classzone.com

54. **TRAVEL** After visiting relatives who live 200 miles away, your family drives home at an average speed of 50 miles per hour. Your distance d (in miles) from home is given by $d = 200 - 50t$ where t is the time (in hours) spent driving. Graph the function and identify its domain and range. What is your distance from home after driving for 1.5 hours?

   California @*HomeTutor*   for problem solving help at classzone.com

55. ◆ **MULTIPLE CHOICE** An in-line skater skates 15 miles at an average speed of 10 miles per hour. The distance d traveled after skating for h hours at this speed is given by the function $d = 10h$. What is the domain of the function?

   (A) $0 \le d \le 15$ **(B)** $0 \le h \le 1.5$

   (C) $0 \le d \le 1.5$ **(D)** $0 \le h \le 15$

56. **CELL PHONES** You can recharge a cell phone's battery by turning a small crank on emergency cell phone charger. If you turn the crank 120 times per minute, the total number r of revolutions that you turn the crank is given by $r = 120t$ where t is the time (in minutes) spent turning the crank.

   a. Graph the function and identify its domain and range.

   b. Identify the domain and range if you stop turning the crank after 4 minutes. *Explain* how this affects the appearance of the graph.

READING IN MATH   Read the information below for Exercises 57–59.

Geology Earth is made up of four layers. The outer layer is called the crust, as shown in the diagram. The temperature of Earth's crust increases as the distance from the surface increases. The temperature T (in degrees Celsius) of Earth's crust can be modeled by the function $T = 20 + 25d$ where d is the distance (in kilometers) from the surface.

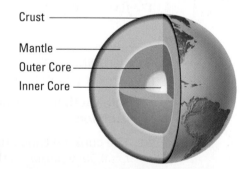

Crust
Mantle
Outer Core
Inner Core

57. **Calculate** What is the temperature of Earth's crust at the surface?

58. **Graph** A scientist studies organisms in a section of crust where the temperature is between 20°C and 95°C. Graph the function and identify its domain and range. How many kilometers deep is the section of crust?

59. **Describe** Use the function to describe the change in temperature from a distance of x kilometers below the surface to a distance of $(x + 1)$ kilometers below the surface.

60. WEATHER BALLOONS The National Weather Service releases weather balloons twice daily at over 90 locations in the United States in order to collect data for meteorologists. The height h (in feet) of a balloon is a function of the time t (in seconds) after the balloon is released, as shown.

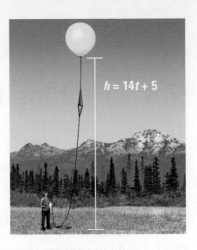

$h = 14t + 5$

a. Make a table showing the height of a balloon after t seconds for $t = 0$ through $t = 10$.

b. A balloon bursts after a flight of about 7200 seconds. Graph the function and identify the domain and range.

61. CHALLENGE If $(3, n)$ is a solution of $Ax + 3y = 6$ and $(n, 5)$ is a solution of $5x + y = 20$, what is the value of A?

62. MULTI-STEP PROBLEM Students can pay for lunch at a school in one of two ways. Students can either make a payment of $30 per month or buy lunch daily for $2.50 per lunch.

a. **Graph** Graph the function $y = 30$ to represent the monthly payment plan. Using the same coordinate plane, graph the function $y = 2.5x$ to represent the daily payment plan.

b. **CHALLENGE** What are the coordinates of the point that is a solution of both functions? What does that point mean in this situation?

c. **CHALLENGE** A student eats an average of 15 school lunches per month. How should the student pay, daily or monthly? *Explain.*

◆ CALIFORNIA STANDARDS SPIRAL REVIEW

Alg. 2.0

63. The opposite of which number is a whole number? *(p. 53)*

(A) -5 (B) -1.5 (C) $\frac{1}{4}$ (D) 8

Alg. 18.0

64. Which relation is *not* a function? *(p. 249)*

(A)

x	−1	1	3	5
y	−2	0	2	4

(B)

x	−3	−2	0	3
y	4	4	4	4

(C)

x	7	7	7	7
y	9	10	11	12

(D)

x	−1	0	1	2
y	−1	0	1	2

Alg. 17.0

65. The graph shows the value (in dollars) of a stock over five days. What is the range of the function? *(p. 257)*

(A) 1, 2, 3, 4, 5   (B) 6, 8, 9, 10

(C) 6, 7, 8, 9, 10   (D) 6, 8, 8.5, 10

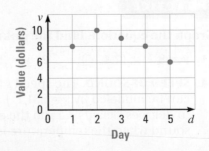

5.3 Graphing Linear Equations

Standards

Alg. 6.0 Students graph **a linear equation** and compute the *x*- and *y*-intercepts (e.g., graph $2x + 6y = 4$). They are also able to sketch the region defined by linear inequalities (e.g., they sketch the region defined by $2x + 6y < 4$).

QUESTION How do you graph an equation on a graphing calculator?

EXAMPLE Use a graph to solve a problem

The formula to convert temperature from degrees Fahrenheit to degrees Celsius is $C = \frac{5}{9}(F - 32)$. Graph the equation. At what temperature are degrees Fahrenheit and degrees Celsius equal?

STEP 1 *Rewrite and enter equation*

Rewrite the equation using *x* for *F* and *y* for *C*.

Press Y= and enter $\frac{5}{9}(x - 32)$. Put parentheses around the fraction $\frac{5}{9}$.

STEP 2 *Set window*

The screen is a "window" that lets you look at part of a coordinate plane. Press WINDOW to set the borders of the graph. For this equation, use $-94 \le x \le 94$ and $-100 \le y \le 100$.

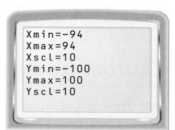

STEP 3 *Graph and trace equation*

Press TRACE and use the left and right arrows to move the cursor along the graph until the *x*-coordinate and *y*-coordinate are equal. From the graph, you can see that degrees Fahrenheit and degrees Celsius are equal at -40.

PRACTICE

Graph the equation. Find the unknown value in the ordered pair.

1. $y = 8 - x$; (2.4, ?)   **2.** $y = 2x + 3$; (? , 0.8)   **3.** $y = -4.5x + 1$; (1.4, ?)

4. SPEED OF SOUND The speed *s* (in meters per second) of sound in air can be modeled by $s = 331.1 + 0.61T$ where *T* is the air temperature in degrees Celsius. Graph the equation. Estimate the speed of sound when the temperature is 20°C.

5.4 Graph Using Intercepts

Math and SCIENCE
Example 4, p. 275

Standards **Alg. 6.0** Students graph a linear equation and compute the *x*- and *y*-intercepts (e.g., graph $2x + 6y = 4$). They are also able to sketch the region defined by linear inequalities (e.g., they sketch the region defined by $2x + 6y < 4$).

Connect *Before* you graphed linear equations by plotting points. *Now* you will graph linear equations using intercepts.

Key Vocabulary
• *x*-intercept
• *y*-intercept

You can use the fact that two points determine a line to graph a linear equation. Two convenient points are the points where the graph crosses the axes.

An ***x*-intercept** of a graph is the *x*-coordinate of a point where the graph crosses the *x*-axis. A ***y*-intercept** of a graph is the *y*-coordinate of a point where the graph crosses the *y*-axis.

To find the *x*-intercept of the graph of a linear equation, find the value of *x* when $y = 0$. To find the *y*-intercept of the graph, find the value of *y* when $x = 0$.

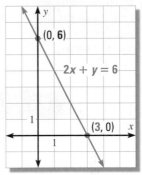

EXAMPLE 1 ◆ Multiple Choice Practice

What are the *x*-intercept and the *y*-intercept of the graph of $2x + 7y = 28$?

A *x*-intercept: 0; *y*-intercept: 4   **B** *x*-intercept: 14; *y*-intercept: 4

C *x*-intercept: 4; *y*-intercept: 14   **D** *x*-intercept: 14; *y*-intercept: −1

ELIMINATE CHOICES
When the *x*-intercept of a linear equation is 0, the *y*-intercept must also be 0 because the graph crosses both axes at (0, 0). So, you can eliminate choice A.

Solution

To find the *x*-intercept, substitute 0 for *y* and solve for *x*.

$$2x + 7y = 28 \qquad \text{Write original equation.}$$

$$2x + 7(\mathbf{0}) = 28 \qquad \text{Substitute 0 for } \textbf{\textit{y}}.$$

$$x = \frac{28}{2} = 14 \qquad \text{Solve for } \textbf{\textit{x}}.$$

To find the *y*-intercept, substitute 0 for *x* and solve for *y*.

$$2x + 7y = 28 \qquad \text{Write original equation.}$$

$$2(\mathbf{0}) + 7y = 28 \qquad \text{Substitute 0 for } \textbf{\textit{x}}.$$

$$y = \frac{28}{7} = 4 \qquad \text{Solve for } \textbf{\textit{y}}.$$

The *x*-intercept is 14, and the *y*-intercept is 4.

▶ The correct answer is B. Ⓐ **Ⓑ** Ⓒ Ⓓ

EXAMPLE 2 Use intercepts to graph an equation

Graph the equation $x + 2y = 4$.

Solution

STEP 1 Find the intercepts.

$$x + 2y = 4 \qquad\qquad x + 2y = 4$$
$$x + 2(\mathbf{0}) = 4 \qquad\qquad 0 + 2y = 4$$
$$x = 4 \leftarrow \textbf{\textit{x}-intercept} \qquad y = 2 \leftarrow \textbf{\textit{y}-intercept}$$

STEP 2 Plot points. The x-intercept is 4, so plot the point (4, 0). The y-intercept is 2, so plot the point (0, 2). Draw a line through the points.

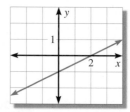

EXAMPLE 3 Use a graph to find intercepts

Identify the x-intercept and the y-intercept of the graph.

Solution

The graph crosses the x-axis at (2, 0). The x-intercept is 2. The graph crosses the y-axis at (0, −1). The y-intercept is −1.

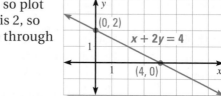

✓ **GUIDED PRACTICE** for Examples 1, 2, and 3

Find the x-intercept and the y-intercept of the graph of the equation.

1. $3x + 2y = 6$ **2.** $4x - 2y = 10$ **3.** $-3x + 5y = -15$

4. Graph $6x + 7y = 42$. Label the points where the line crosses the axes.

5. Identify the x-intercept and the y-intercept of the graph shown at the right.

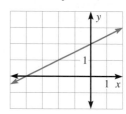

KEY CONCEPT   *For Your Notebook*

Relating Intercepts, Points, and Graphs

Intercepts	Points
The x-intercept of a graph is a.	The graph crosses the x-axis at $(a, 0)$.
The y-intercept of a graph is b.	The graph crosses the y-axis at $(0, b)$.

EXAMPLE 4 Use a linear model

SCIENCE A submersible designed to explore the ocean floor is at an elevation of −13,000 feet (13,000 feet below sea level). The submersible ascends to the surface at an average rate of 650 feet per minute. The elevation *e* (in feet) of the submersible is given by the function

$$e = 650t - 13,000$$

where *t* is the time (in minutes) since the submersible began to ascend.

Submersible

- Find the intercepts of the graph of the function and state what the intercepts represent.

- Graph the function and identify its domain and range.

Solution

STEP 1 Find the intercepts.

$$0 = 650t - 13,000 \qquad\qquad e = 650(0) - 13,000$$

$$13,000 = 650t \qquad\qquad e = -13,000 \leftarrow \textbf{\textit{e}-intercept}$$

$$20 = t \leftarrow \textbf{\textit{t}-intercept}$$

:**NAME INTERCEPTS**
:Because *t* is the
:independent variable,
:the horizontal axis
:is the *t*-axis, and you
:refer to the "*t*-intercept"
:of the graph of the
:function. Similarly, the
:vertical axis is the
:*e*-axis, and you refer to
:the "*e*-intercept."

The *t*-intercept represents the number of minutes the submersible takes to reach an elevation of 0 feet (sea level). The *e*-intercept represents the elevation of the submersible after 0 minutes (the time the ascent begins).

STEP 2 Graph the function using the intercepts.

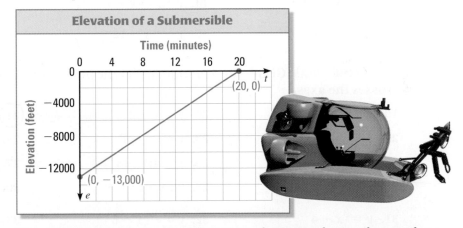

The submersible starts at an elevation of −13,000 feet and ascends to an elevation of 0 feet. So, the range of the function is −13,000 ≤ *e* ≤ 0. From the graph, you can see that the domain of the function is 0 ≤ *t* ≤ 20.

 GUIDED PRACTICE for Example 4

6. **WHAT IF?** In Example 4, suppose the elevation of a second submersible that is ascending to the surface is given by *e* = 500*t* − 10,000. Graph the function and identify its domain and range.

5.4 EXERCISES

HOMEWORK KEY

◆ = MULTIPLE CHOICE PRACTICE
Exs. 43, 44, 45, 53, and 57–59

○ = HINTS AND HOMEWORK HELP
for Exs. 9, 21, and 53 at classzone.com

SKILLS · PROBLEM SOLVING · REASONING

1. **VOCABULARY** Copy and complete: The __?__ of the graph of an equation is the value of x when $y = 0$.

2. **NOTETAKING SKILLS** Make a sequence diagram like the one on page 248 for graphing an equation using intercepts.

3. **ERROR ANALYSIS** *Describe* and correct the error in finding the intercepts of the line shown.

The x-intercept is 1,
and the y-intercept is −2.

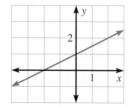

EXAMPLE 1
on p. 273
for Exs. 4–18

FINDING INTERCEPTS Find the x-intercept and the y-intercept of the graph of the equation.

4. $5x - y = 35$

5. $3x - 3y = 9$

6. $-3x + 9y = -18$

7. $4x + y = 4$

8. $2x + y = 10$

9. $2x - 8y = 24$

10. $3x + 0.5y = 6$

11. $0.2x + 3.2y = 12.8$

12. $7.2x - 2.4y = 21.6$

13. $y = 2x + 24$

14. $y = -14x + 7$

15. $y = -4.8x + 1.2$

16. $y = \frac{1}{2}x + 8$

17. $y = \frac{3}{5}x - 12$

18. $y = -\frac{2}{3}x - 30$

EXAMPLE 2
on p. 274
for Exs. 19–33

GRAPHING LINES Graph the equation. Label the points where the line crosses the axes.

19. $y = x + 3$

20. $y = x - 2$

21. $y = 4x - 8$

22. $y = 5 + 10x$

23. $y = -2 + 8x$

24. $y = -4x + 3$

25. $3x + y = 15$

26. $x - 4y = 18$

27. $8x - 5y = 80$

28. $-2x + 5y = 15$

29. $0.5x + 3y = 9$

30. $1.5x - 2y = 6$

31. $y = \frac{3}{4}x + 4$

32. $y = -\frac{1}{3}x - 6$

33. $y = \frac{1}{2}x + \frac{1}{4}$

EXAMPLE 3
on p. 274
for Exs. 34–36

USING GRAPHS TO FIND INTERCEPTS Identify the x-intercept and the y-intercept of the graph.

34.

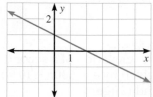

35.

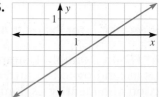

36.

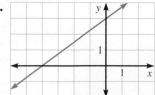

USING INTERCEPTS Draw the line that has the given intercepts.

37. *x*-intercept: 3
y-intercept: 5

38. *x*-intercept: −2
y-intercept: 4

39. *x*-intercept: −5
y-intercept: 6

40. *x*-intercept: 9
y-intercept: −1

41. *x*-intercept: −8
y-intercept: −11

42. *x*-intercept: −2
y-intercept: −6

43. ◆ **MULTIPLE CHOICE** The graph of which equation is shown?

Ⓐ $5x + 2y = -10$

Ⓑ $5x + 2y = 10$

Ⓒ $2x + 5y = -10$

Ⓓ $2x + 5y = 10$

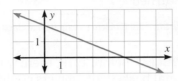

44. ◆ **MULTIPLE CHOICE** The *x*-intercept of the graph of $Ax + 5y = 20$ is 2. What is the value of *A*?

Ⓐ 2   Ⓑ 5   Ⓒ 7.5   Ⓓ 10

45. ◆ **MULTIPLE CHOICE** What is the *y*-intercept of the graph of $Ax + By = 12$ where *A* and *B* are not 0?

Ⓐ 12   Ⓑ *B*   Ⓒ $\dfrac{12}{A}$ Ⓓ $\dfrac{12}{B}$

46. **OPEN-ENDED** Write an equation of a line that has no *x*-intercept and of a line that has no *y*-intercept. *Describe* the graph of each equation.

CONNECT SKILLS TO PROBLEM SOLVING Exercises 47–49 will help you prepare for problem solving.

State what the intercepts of the graph of the equation represent for the situation described.

47. You have $2.30 in dimes and nickels. The situation is given by $0.10d + 0.05n = 2.30$ where *d* is the number of dimes and *n* is the number of nickels.

48. You earn 80 points on a test that has questions worth 4 points and questions worth 5 points. The situation is given by $4x + 5y = 80$ where *x* is the number of 4 point questions answered correctly and *y* is the number of 5 point questions answered correctly.

49. In one month you earn $240 babysitting for $10 per hour and dog walking for $8 per hour. The situation is given by $10b + 8d = 240$ where *b* is the number of hours you spend babysitting and *d* is the number of hours you spend dog walking.

EXAMPLE 4
on p. 275
for Exs. 50–53

50. **GARDENS** The perimeter of a rectangular garden at the Filoli gardens in Woodside, California, is 900 feet. The garden has a width of *x* feet and a length of *y* feet.

   a. Write an equation for the perimeter.

   b. Find the intercepts of the graph of the equation in part (a). Then graph the equation.

California @HomeTutor for problem solving help at classzone.com

Gardens at Filoli

51. RECYCLING In one state, small bottles have a refund value of $.04 each, and large bottles have a refund value of $.08 each. Your friend returns both small and large bottles and receives $.56. This situation is given by $4x + 8y = 56$ where x is the number of small bottles and y is the number of large bottles.

a. Find the intercepts of the graph of the equation. Graph the equation.

b. Give three possibilities for the number of each size bottle your friend could have returned.

California **@HomeTutor** for problem solving help at classzone.com

52. MULTI-STEP PROBLEM Before 1979, there was no 3-point shot in professional basketball; players could score only 2-point field goals and 1-point free throws. In a game before 1979, suppose a team scored a total of 128 points. This situation is given by the equation $2x + y = 128$ where x is the possible number of field goals and y is the possible number of free throws.

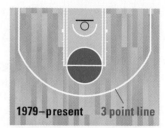

1979–present   3 point line

a. Find the intercepts of the graph of the equation. Graph the equation.

b. What do the intercepts mean in this situation?

c. What are three possible numbers of field goals and free throws the team could have scored?

d. If the team made 24 free throws, how many field goals did it make?

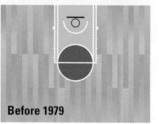

Before 1979

(53.) ◆ **MULTIPLE CHOICE** A family has a plot in a community garden. The family is going to plant vegetables, flowers, or both. The diagram shows the area used by one vegetable plant and the area of the entire plot. The area f (in square feet) of the plot left for flowers is given by the function $f = 180 - 1.5v$ where v is the number of vegetable plants the family plants. Which statement about the function is true?

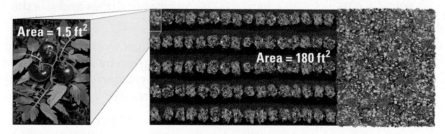

Area = 1.5 ft² Area = 180 ft²

(A) The f-intercept of the graph of the function is 180.

(B) The v-intercept of the graph of the function is 1.5.

(C) The domain of the function is $0 \le v \le 180$.

(D) The domain of the function is $0 \le f \le 180$.

54. REASONING Consider the equation $3x + 5y = k$. What values could k have so that the x-intercept and the y-intercept of the equation's graph would both be integers? *Explain.*

55. CHALLENGE If $a \ne 0$, find the intercepts of the graph of $y = ax + b$ in terms of a and b.

◆ = **MULTIPLE CHOICE PRACTICE**   ○ = **HINTS AND HOMEWORK HELP** at classzone.com

56. MULTI-STEP PROBLEM You borrow $180 from a friend who doesn't charge you interest. You work out a payment schedule in which you will make weekly payments to your friend. The balance B (in dollars) of the loan is given by the function $B = 180 - pn$ where p is the weekly payment and n is the number of weeks you make payments.

   a. Interpret Without finding the intercepts, state what they represent.

   b. Graph Graph the function if you make weekly payments of $20.

   c. Identify Find the domain and range of the function in part (b). How long will it take to pay back your friend?

   d. CHALLENGE Suppose you make payments of $20 for three weeks. Then you make payments of $15 until you have paid your friend back. How does this affect the graph? How many payments do you make?

◆ CALIFORNIA STANDARDS SPIRAL REVIEW

Alg. 24.2

57. What is the conclusion of the statement "If a number is odd, then twice the number is even"? *(p. 53)*

   (A) A number is odd   **(B)** A number is even

   (C) Twice the number is even   **(D)** Twice the number is odd

Alg. 17.0

58. What is the domain of the function represented by the graph? *(p. 257)*

   (A) $-2, 0, 3, 4$ **(B)** $-2, 1, 3, 4$

   (C) $0, 1, 2, 3$ **(D)** $1, 2, 3, 4$

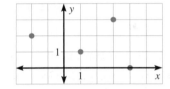

Alg. 3.0

59. A figure skater is preparing a routine for a competition. The routine must last 2 minutes with an absolute deviation of 10 seconds. What is the greatest possible time that the routine can last? *(p. 220)*

   (A) 110 sec   **(B)** 120 sec   **(C)** 130 sec   **(D)** 210 sec

---

QUIZ *for Lessons 5.3–5.4*

Graph the equation. *(p. 264)*

   1. $-4x - 2y = 12$ **2.** $y = -5$ **3.** $x = 6$

Find the x-intercept and the y-intercept of the graph of the equation. *(p. 273)*

   4. $y = x + 7$ **5.** $y = x - 3$ **6.** $y = -5x + 2$

   7. $x + 3y = 15$ **8.** $3x - 6y = 36$ **9.** $-2x - 5y = 22$

10. ⬡ **GEOMETRY** A rectangle with length ℓ and width w has a perimeter of 24 inches. This situation is given by the equation $2\ell + 2w = 24$. *(p. 273)*

   a. Find the intercepts of the graph of the equation. Graph the equation.

   b. Give three possibilities for the length and width of the rectangle.

Multiple Choice Practice for Lessons 5.1–5.4

1. The graph shows the cost *C* (in dollars) of renting in-line skates for *t* hours where *t* = 1, 2, 3, 4, 5. What is the range of the function represented by the graph? **Alg. 17.0**

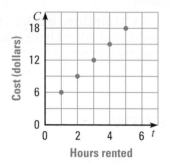

(A) 1, 2, 3, 4, 5
(B) 6, 9, 12, 15, 18
(C) 2, 4
(D) 6, 12, 18

2. What are the *x*-intercept and the *y*-intercept of the graph of $5x + 3y = 30$? **Alg. 6.0**

(A) *x*-intercept: 6; *y*-intercept: 10

(B) *x*-intercept: 10; *y*-intercept: 6

(C) *x*-intercept: 5; *y*-intercept: 10

(D) *x*-intercept: 6; *y*-intercept: 5

3. A violin player replaces the strings on her violin every 6 months. The strings cost $24 per pack. The table shows the total amount *a* (in dollars) spent on replacement strings over time *t* (in months). Which statement about the relation is true? **Alg. 16.0**

t (months)	*a* (dollars)
6	24
12	48
18	72
24	96
30	120

(A) The domain is 24, 48, 72, 96, 120.

(B) The range is 6, 12, 18, 24, 30.

(C) The relation is a function.

(D) The relation is *not* a function.

4. Which statement about the graph of $y = 3$ is *not* true? **Alg. 6.0**

(A) The graph is a horizontal line.

(B) The graph has no *x*-intercept.

(C) The graph is a vertical line.

(D) The *y*-intercept of the graph is 3.

5. Which relation is *not* a function? **Alg. 18.0**

(A)

x	−3	4	4	6
y	1	1	2	5

(B)

x	−3	−2	−1	0
y	7	7	7	7

(C)

x	−4	−1	0	3
y	−2	−2	3	6

(D)

x	−5	0	5	10
y	−5	0	5	10

6. The graph shows the possible combinations of T-shirts and tank tops you can buy with the amount of money you have. You decide to buy only T-shirts. What is the greatest number that you can buy? **Alg. 6.0**

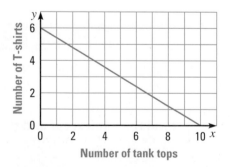

(A) 4 T-shirts

(B) 6 T-shirts

(C) 10 T-shirts

(D) 16 T-shirts

5.5 Slope

MATERIALS · several books · two rulers

Standards Preparation

Gr. 7 AF 3.3 Graph linear functions, noting that the vertical change (change in *y*-value) per unit of horizontal change (change in *x*-value) is always the same and **know that the ratio ("rise over run") is called the slope of a graph.**

QUESTION How can you use a ratio to describe the slope of a ramp?

The ratio of the vertical rise to the horizontal run describes the *slope* of a ramp.

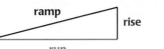

$$\text{slope} = \frac{\text{rise}}{\text{run}}$$

EXPLORE Calculate the slopes of ramps

| STEP 1 | STEP 2 | STEP 3 |

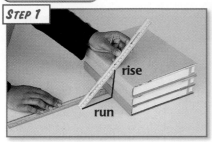 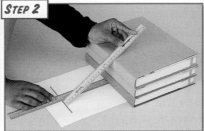 

Make a ramp Make a stack of three books. Use a ruler as a ramp. Measure the rise and run of the ramp, and record them in a table. Calculate and record the slope of the ramp in your table.

Change the run Without changing the rise, make three ramps with different runs by moving the lower end of the ruler. Measure and record the rise and run of each ramp. Calculate and record each slope.

Change the rise Without changing the run, make three ramps with different rises by adding or removing books. Measure and record the rise and run of each ramp. Calculate and record each slope.

DRAW CONCLUSIONS Use your observations to complete these exercises

Describe how the slope of the ramp changes given the following conditions. Give three examples that support your answer.

1. The run of the ramp increases, and the rise stays the same.

2. The rise of the ramp increases, and the run stays the same.

In Exercises 3–5, describe the relationship between the rise and the run of the ramp.

3. A ramp with a slope of 1

4. A ramp with a slope greater than 1

5. A ramp with a slope less than 1

6. Ramp A has a rise of 6 feet and a run of 2 feet. Ramp B has a rise of 10 feet and a run of 4 feet. Which ramp is steeper? How do you know?

5.5 Find Slope and Rate of Change

Standards Preparation Gr. 7 AF 3.3 Graph linear functions, noting that the vertical change (change in *y*-value) per unit of horizontal change (change in *x*-value) is always the same and know that the ratio ("rise over run") is called the slope of a graph.

Connect *Before* you graphed linear equations using intercepts. *Now* you will find the slope of a line to prepare for Algebra 1 Standard 7.0.

Math and **SPORTS**
Ex. 21, p. 287

Key Vocabulary
• slope
• rate of change

The **slope** of a nonvertical line is the ratio of the vertical change (the *rise*) to the horizontal change (the *run*) between any two points on the line. A line's slope, represented by the letter *m*, is constant.

KEY CONCEPT   *For Your Notebook*

Finding the Slope of a Line

Words	**Symbols**	**Graph**

The slope *m* of the nonvertical line passing through the two points (x_1, y_1) and (x_2, y_2) is the ratio of the rise (change in *y*) to the run (change in *x*).

$$m = \frac{y_2 - y_1}{x_2 - x_1}$$

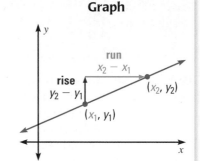

$$\text{slope} = \frac{\text{rise}}{\text{run}} = \frac{\text{change in } y}{\text{change in } x}$$

READING
Read x_1 as "x sub one." Think "x-coordinate of the first point."
Read y_1 as "y sub one." Think "y-coordinate of the first point."

EXAMPLE 1 **Find a positive slope**

Find the slope of the line shown.

Let $(x_1, y_1) = (-4, 2)$ and $(x_2, y_2) = (2, 6)$.

$m = \dfrac{y_2 - y_1}{x_2 - x_1}$ Write formula for slope.

$= \dfrac{6 - 2}{2 - (-4)}$ Substitute.

$= \dfrac{4}{6} = \dfrac{2}{3}$ Simplify.

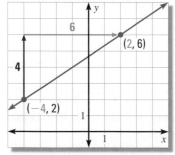

The line rises from left to right. The slope is positive.

AVOID ERRORS
Be sure to keep the *x*- and *y*-coordinates in the same order in both the numerator and denominator when calculating slope.

✓ **GUIDED PRACTICE** for Example 1

1. Find the slope of the line that passes through (5, 2) and (4, −1).

EXAMPLE 2 Find a negative slope

Find the slope of the line shown.

Let $(x_1, y_1) = (3, 5)$ and $(x_2, y_2) = (6, -1)$.

FIND SLOPE
....
In Example 2, if you used two other points on the line, such as (4, 3) and (5, 1), in the slope formula, the slope would still be −2.

$m = \dfrac{y_2 - y_1}{x_2 - x_1}$ Write formula for slope.

$= \dfrac{-1 - 5}{6 - 3}$ Substitute.

$= \dfrac{-6}{3} = -2$ Simplify.

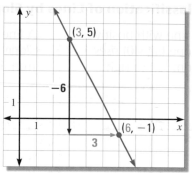

The line falls from left to right.
The slope is negative.

EXAMPLE 3 Find the slope of a horizontal line

Find the slope of the line shown.

Let $(x_1, y_1) = (-2, 4)$ and $(x_2, y_2) = (4, 4)$.

$m = \dfrac{y_2 - y_1}{x_2 - x_1}$ Write formula for slope.

$= \dfrac{4 - 4}{4 - (-2)}$ Substitute.

$= \dfrac{0}{6} = 0$ Simplify.

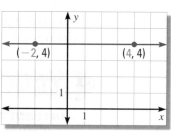

The line is horizontal.
The slope is zero.

EXAMPLE 4 Find the slope of a vertical line

Find the slope of the line shown.

Let $(x_1, y_1) = (3, 5)$ and $(x_2, y_2) = (3, 1)$.

$m = \dfrac{y_2 - y_1}{x_2 - x_1}$ Write formula for slope.

$= \dfrac{1 - 5}{3 - 3}$ Substitute.

$= \dfrac{-4}{0}$ Division by zero is undefined.

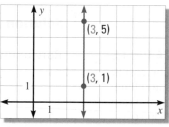

The line is vertical.
The slope is undefined.

▶ Because division by zero is undefined, the slope of a vertical line is undefined.

✓ **GUIDED PRACTICE**   for Examples 2, 3, and 4

Find the slope of the line that passes through the points.

  2. (5, 2) and (5, −2)   **3.** (0, 4) and (−3, 4)   **4.** (0, 6) and (5, −4)

Using ALTERNATIVE METHODS

Another Way to Solve Example 4, page 299

Standards
Preparation
Gr. 6 AF 2.0

In Example 4 on page 299, you saw how to solve the problem about how much sea salt to add to a saltwater fish tank by writing and using a direct variation equation. You can also solve the problem using a graph or a proportion.

PROBLEM

SALTWATER AQUARIUM The number s of tablespoons of sea salt needed in a saltwater fish tank varies directly with the number w of gallons of water in the tank. A pet shop owner recommends adding 100 tablespoons of sea salt to a 20 gallon tank. How many tablespoons of sea salt should be added to a 30 gallon saltwater fish tank?

METHOD 1

Using a Graph An alternative approach is to use a graph.

STEP 1 **Read** the problem. It tells you an amount of sea salt for a certain size fish tank. You can also assume that if a fish tank has no water, then no sea salt needs to be added. Write ordered pairs for this information.

Number of gallons	Tablespoons of sea salt
→ (20, 100) ←	
→ (0, 0) ←	

STEP 2 **Graph** the ordered pairs. Draw a line through the points.

The coordinates of points on the line give the amounts of sea salt that should be added to fish tanks of various sizes.

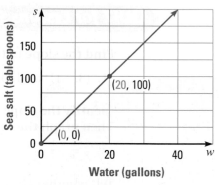

STEP 3 **Find** the point on the graph that has a w-coordinate of 30. The s-coordinate of this point is 150, so 150 tablespoons of sea salt should be added to a 30 gallon tank.

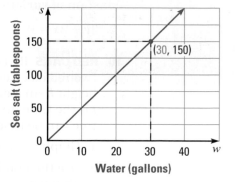

METHOD 2   **Writing a Proportion** Another alternative approach is to write and solve a proportion.

> **STEP 1** **Write** a proportion involving two ratios that each compare the amount of water (in gallons) to the amount of sea salt (in tablespoons).
>
> $$\frac{20}{100} = \frac{30}{s} \longleftarrow \text{amount of water (gallons)}$$
> $$\phantom{\frac{20}{100} = \frac{30}{s}} \longleftarrow \text{amount of sea salt (tablespoons)}$$
>
> **STEP 2** **Solve** the proportion.
>
> | | |
> |---|---|
> | $\dfrac{20}{100} = \dfrac{30}{s}$ | **Write proportion.** |
> | $20s = 100 \cdot 30$ | **Cross products property** |
> | $20s = 3000$ | **Simplify.** |
> | $s = 150$ | **Divide each side by 20.** |
>
> ▸ You should add 150 tablespoons of sea salt to a 30 gallon tank.
>
> **CHECK** Check your answer by writing each ratio in simplest form.
>
> $$\frac{20}{100} = \frac{1}{5} \text{ and } \frac{30}{150} = \frac{1}{5}$$
>
> Because each ratio simplifies to $\frac{1}{5}$, the answer is correct.

PRACTICE

1. **WHAT IF?** Suppose the fish tank in the problem above is a 22 gallon tank. How many tablespoons of sea salt should be added to the tank? *Describe* which method you used to solve this problem.

2. **ADVERTISING** A local newspaper charges by the word for printing classified ads. A 14 word ad costs $5.88. How much would a 21 word ad cost? Solve this problem using two different methods.

3. **REASONING** In Exercise 2, how can you quickly determine the cost of a 7 word ad? *Explain* how you could use the cost of a 7 word ad to solve the problem.

4. **NUTRITION** A company sells fruit smoothies in two sizes of bottles: 6 fluid ounces and 10 fluid ounces. You know that a 6 ounce bottle contains 96 milligrams of sodium. How many milligrams of sodium does a 10 ounce bottle contain?

5. **ERROR ANALYSIS** A student solved the problem in Exercise 4 as shown. *Describe* and correct the error made.

   > Let s = the number of milligrams of sodium in a 10 ounce bottle.
   >
   > $$\frac{6}{s} = \frac{10}{96}$$
   > $$576 = 10s$$
   > $$57.6 = s$$

6. **SLEEPING** You find an online calculator that calculates the number of calories you burn while sleeping. The results for various sleeping times are shown. About how many more calories would you burn by sleeping for 9.5 hours than for 8 hours? Choose any method for solving the problem.

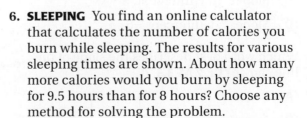

Hours of sleep	6.5	7	8.5	9
Calories burned	390	420	510	540

Multiple Choice Practice for Lessons 5.5–5.7

1. Which equation has the graph shown? **Alg. 6.0**

   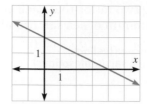

   (A) $y = -2x + 2$

   (B) $y = 2x - 2$

   (C) $y = -\frac{1}{2}x + 2$

   (D) $y = \frac{1}{2}x - 2$

2. A central observatory averages and then reports the number of sunspots recorded by various observatories. The table shows the average number of sunspots reported by the central observatory in years since 1995. The greatest increase in sunspots was from 1997 to 1999. What is the rate of change for this time period? **Gr. 7 AF 3.3**

Years since 1995	Average number of sunspots
0	17.5
2	21.0
4	93.2
6	110.9

   (A) 32 sunspots per year

   (B) 36.1 sunspots per year

   (C) 42.7 sunspots per year

   (D) 72.2 sunspots per year

3. What are the slope and the y-intercept of the graph of the line $y = 5x - 7$? **Alg. 6.0**

   (A) Slope: 5; y-intercept: 7

   (B) Slope: 5, y-intercept: -7

   (C) Slope: -7; y-intercept: 5

   (D) Slope: 7; y-intercept -5

4. Which word best describes the slope of the line shown? **Gr. 7 AF 3.3**

   (A) Positive

   (B) Negative

   (C) Zero

   (D) Undefined

   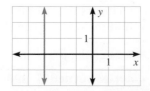

5. For each of three lines, two points on the line are listed. Which lines are parallel? **Alg. 6.0**

   Line 1: $(-4, 7)$ and $(-2, 3)$

   Line 2: $(-6, 2)$ and $(-4, 6)$

   Line 3: $(0, 1)$ and $(2, -3)$

   (A) Line 1 and line 2

   (B) Line 1 and line 3

   (C) Line 2 and line 3

   (D) No two lines are parallel.

6. The price for an adult ticket to a water park is shown. Let a be the amount (in dollars) the park receives from adult ticket sales, and let t be the number of adult tickets sold. Which equation relates a and t? **Gr. 7 AF 1.1**

   (A) $t = 25a$ (B) $a = t - 25$

   (C) $t = \frac{25}{a}$ (D) $a = 25t$

7. Which table does *not* represent direct variation? **Alg. 6.0**

   (A)

x	1	2	3	4
y	2	4	6	8

   (B)

x	−2	−1	0	2
y	3	5	7	11

   (C)

x	5	10	15	20
y	1	2	3	4

   (D)

x	−4	8	16	28
y	1	−2	−4	−7

Standards
Alg. 6.0, 16.0, 17.0
18.0

BIG IDEAS
For Your Notebook

Big Idea 1

Representing Functions as Verbal Rules, Equations, Ordered Pairs, and Graphs

You can use a verbal rule, an equation, a set of ordered pairs, or a graph to represent a function.

Words The output is one more than twice the input. The inputs are −1, 0, 1, 2.

Equation	Ordered Pairs	Graph
$y = 2x + 1$	(−1, −1)	
Domain: −1, 0, 1, 2	(0, 1)	
	(1, 3)	
	(2, 5)	

Big Idea 2

Graphing Linear Equations and Functions

You can graph a linear equation or function by making a table of ordered pairs, using intercepts, or using the slope and y-intercept.

A taxi company charges a $2 fee to pick up a customer plus $1 per mile to drive to the customer's destination. The total cost C (in dollars) that a customer pays to travel a distance d (in miles) is given by $C = d + 2$. Graph this function.

Method: Make a table.

d	C
0	2
1	3
2	4
3	5

Method: Use slope and C-intercept.

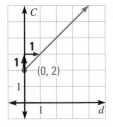

(0, 2)

Big Idea 3

Using Graphs to Solve Real-world Problems

Suppose the taxi company raises its rate to $1.50 per mile. The total amount that a customer pays is given by $C = 1.5d + 2$.

You can use the graphs of $C = d + 2$ and $C = 1.5d + 2$ to find out how much more a customer pays to travel 4 miles at the new rate than at the old rate.

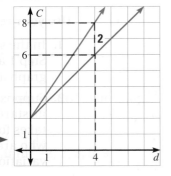

A customer pays $2 more to travel 4 miles at the new rate. ⋯⋯➤

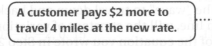

5.2 Represent Functions as Graphs
pp. 257–263

Alg. 17.0

EXAMPLE

Write a rule for the function represented by the graph. Identify the domain and the range of the function.

Make a table of ordered pairs for the graph.

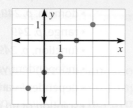

x	−1	0	1	2	3
y	−3	−2	−1	0	1

Each y-value is 2 less than the corresponding x-value. A rule for the function is $y = x - 2$. The domain is −1, 0, 1, 2, 3. The range is −3, −2, −1, 0, 1.

EXERCISES

**EXAMPLES
1 and 3**
....
on pp. 257–258
for Exs. 6–7

6. Graph the function $y = 4x - 3$ with domain 1, 2, 3, 4, 5.

7. Write a rule for the function represented by the graph. Identify the domain and the range of the function.

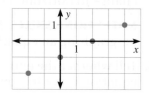

5.3 Graph Linear Equations and Functions
pp. 264–271

Alg. 6.0

EXAMPLE

Graph the equation $y + 3x = 1$.

STEP 1 **Solve** the equation for y.

$$y + 3x = 1$$
$$y = -3x + 1$$

STEP 2 **Make** a table of ordered pairs by choosing a few values for x and finding the values for y.

x	−1	0	1
y	4	1	−2

STEP 3 **Plot** the points.

STEP 4 **Connect** the points by drawing a line through them.

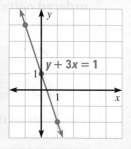

EXERCISES

**EXAMPLES
2 and 4**
....
on pp. 264–265
for Exs. 8–10

Graph the equation.

8. $y + 5x = -5$

9. $2x + 3y = 9$

10. $y = 9$

5.4 Graph Using Intercepts

pp. 273–279

Alg. 6.0 **EXAMPLE**

Graph the equation $-0.5x + 2y = 4$.

STEP 1 **Find** the intercepts.

$$-0.5x + 2y = 4$$
$$-0.5x + 2(0) = 4$$
$$x = -8 \leftarrow x\text{-intercept}$$

$$-0.5x + 2y = 4$$
$$-0.5(0) + 2y = 4$$
$$y = 2 \leftarrow y\text{-intercept}$$

STEP 2 **Plot** the points that correspond to the intercepts: $(-8, 0)$ and $(0, 2)$.

STEP 3 **Connect** the points by drawing a line through them.

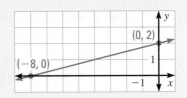

EXERCISES

EXAMPLES
2 and 4
on pp. 274–275
for Exs. 11–14

Graph the equation.

11. $-x + 5y = 15$

12. $4x + 4y = -16$

13. $2x - 6y = 18$

14. **CRAFT FAIR** You sell necklaces for $10 and bracelets for $5 at a craft fair. You want to earn $50. This situation is modeled by the equation $10n + 5b = 50$ where n is the number of necklaces you sell and b is the number of bracelets you sell. Find the intercepts of the graph of the equation. Then graph the equation. Give three possibilities for the number of bracelets and necklaces that you could sell.

5.5 Find Slope and Rate of Change

pp. 282–289

Gr. 7 AF 3.3 **EXAMPLE**

Find the slope of the line shown.

Let $(x_1, y_1) = (2, -3)$ and $(x_2, y_2) = (4, -4)$.

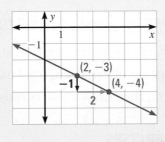

$$m = \frac{y_2 - y_1}{x_2 - x_1}$$ Write formula for slope.

$$= \frac{-4 - (-3)}{4 - 2}$$ Substitute values.

$$= -\frac{1}{2}$$ Simplify.

EXERCISES

EXAMPLES
1, 2, 3, and 4
on pp. 282–283
for Exs. 15–20

Find the slope of the line that passes through the points.

15. $(-1, 11)$ and $(2, 10)$

16. $(-2, 0)$ and $(4, 9)$

17. $(-5, 4)$ and $(1, -8)$

18. $(-5, 2)$ and $(-5, 7)$

19. $(4, 0)$ and $(-2, 0)$

20. $(-3, -5)$ and $(-1, -17)$

5.6 Graph Using Slope-Intercept Form

pp. 291–296

Alg. 6.0

EXAMPLE

Graph the equation $2x + y = -1$.

STEP 1 **Rewrite** the equation in slope-intercept form.

$$2x + y = -1 \rightarrow y = -2x - 1$$

STEP 2 **Identify** the slope and the y-intercept.

$$m = -2 \text{ and } b = -1$$

STEP 3 **Plot** the point that corresponds to the y-intercept, $(0, -1)$.

STEP 4 **Use** the slope to locate a second point on the line. Draw a line through the two points.

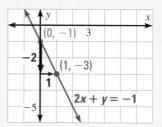

EXERCISES

Graph the equation.

EXAMPLES
2 and 3
on p. 292
for Exs. 21–24

21. $4x - y = 3$

22. $3x - 6y = 9$

23. $-3x + 4y - 12 = 0$

24. RUNNING Two athletes run a 60 meter race. The distance d (in meters) the athletes have left to run after t seconds is given by the following equations:

Athlete 1: $d = -6t + 60$ **Athlete 2:** $d = -5t + 60$

Graph both equations in the same coordinate plane. About how many seconds faster does the first athlete finish the race than the second athlete?

5.7 Recognize Direct Variation

pp. 297–303

Alg. 6.0

EXAMPLE

Graph the direct variation equation $y = -\frac{2}{3}x$.

Plot a point at the origin. The slope is equal to the constant of variation, $-\frac{2}{3}$. Find and plot a second point, then draw a line through the points.

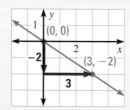

EXERCISES

EXAMPLES
1 and 2
on pp. 297–298
for Exs. 25–30

Tell whether the equation represents direct variation. If so, identify the constant of variation.

25. $x - y = 3$

26. $x + 2y = 0$

27. $8x - 2y = 0$

Graph the direct variation equation.

28. $y = 4x$

29. $-5y = 3x$

30. $4x + 3y = 0$

1. **VOCABULARY** Copy and complete: A relation is a(n) __?__ if for each domain element there is exactly one range element.

2. **VOCABULARY** Copy and complete: Two variables x and y show __?__ provided $y = kx$ and $k \neq 0$.

Determine whether the relation is a function.

3. $\{(-3, 5), (-1, 2), (-1, 4), (6, 0)\}$

4. $\{(-5, 1), (0, 1), (1, 1), (7, 1)\}$

Graph the function.

5. $y = x - 4$; domain: $-4, -2, 0, 2, 4, 6$

6. $y = 2x + 3$; domain: $-3, -1, 0, 5, 7$

Draw the line that has the given intercepts.

7. x-intercept: 2
y-intercept: -6

8. x-intercept: -1
y-intercept: 8

9. x-intercept: -3
y-intercept: -5

Find the slope of the line that passes through the points.

10. $(2, 1)$ and $(8, 4)$

11. $(-2, 7)$ and $(0, -1)$

12. $(3, 5)$ and $(3, 14)$

Identify the slope and y-intercept of the line with the given equation.

13. $y = -\frac{3}{2}x - 10$

14. $7x + 2y = -28$

15. $3x - 8y = 48$

Graph the equation.

16. $x = 3$

17. $y + x = 6$

18. $2x + 8y = -32$

Tell whether the equation represents direct variation. If so, identify the constant of variation.

19. $x + 4y = 4$

20. $-\frac{1}{3}x - y = 0$

21. $3x - 3y = 0$

22. **BUSINESS** To start a dog grooming business, you invest $300 in supplies. You charge $10 per hour for your services. Your profit P (in dollars) is given by $P = 10t - 300$ where t is the time (in hours) that you work. Graph the equation. You will break even when your profit is $0. Use the graph to find the number of hours you must work in order to break even.

23. **SHOE SIZES** A man's size 6 shoe is the same size as a woman's size $7\frac{1}{2}$.

The table shows other corresponding sizes of men's and women's shoes.

Men's size, x	6	$6\frac{1}{2}$	7	$7\frac{1}{2}$	8	$8\frac{1}{2}$	9
Women's size, y	$7\frac{1}{2}$	8	$8\frac{1}{2}$	9	$9\frac{1}{2}$	10	$10\frac{1}{2}$

a. Using the data in the table, write a rule for women's shoe size as a function of men's shoe size. Identify the domain and the range.

b. Graph the function.

5 ◆ MULTIPLE CHOICE STRATEGIES

STRATEGIES YOU'LL USE:
• SOLVE DIRECTLY
• ELIMINATE CHOICES

Standards
Alg. 6.0

If you have trouble solving a multiple choice problem directly, you may be able to use another approach to eliminate incorrect answer choices and obtain the correct answer.

PROBLEM 1

A recipe from a box of pancake mix states that 2 cups of pancake mix makes 16 pancakes. The number p of pancakes you can make varies directly with the number m of cups of mix you use. A full box of pancake mix contains 9 cups of mix. How many pancakes can you make using all of the mix in a box?

(A) 63 **(B)** 72 **(C)** 80 **(D)** 131

Strategy 1 SOLVE DIRECTLY

Write a direct variation equation. Then use the equation to find the number of pancakes you can make using the 9 cups of mix in a box.

STEP 1 **Write** a direct variation equation. Because the number p of pancakes you can make varies directly with the number m of cups of mix, you can use the equation $p = km$. Also, use the fact that $p = 16$ when $m = 2$.

$p = km$ **Write equation.**

$16 = k(2)$ **Substitute.**

$8 = k$ **Solve for k.**

A direct variation equation that relates p and m is $p = 8m$.

STEP 2 **Find** the number of pancakes you can make using 9 cups of pancake mix. Use the direct variation equation from Step 1.

$p = 8m$ **Write equation.**

$\quad = 8(9)$ **Substitute.**

$\quad = 72$ **Simplify.**

An entire box of pancake mix will make 72 pancakes.

The correct answer is B. (A) **(B)** (C) (D)

Strategy 2 ELIMINATE CHOICES

Write a ratio of cups of mix to number of pancakes made using the information given in the problem. Then compare the ratio with a ratio that uses each answer choice.

STEP 1 **Write** a ratio that compares the number m of cups of mix to the number p of pancakes you can make using the fact that $p = 16$ when $m = 2$.

$$\frac{m}{p} = \frac{2}{16} = \frac{1}{8}$$

STEP 2 **Compare** the ratio from Step 1 with a ratio written using 9 cups for m and the number of pancakes given in each answer choice for p.

Choice A: Use $m = 9$ and $p = 63$.

$$\frac{9}{63} \overset{?}{=} \frac{1}{8}$$

$$\frac{1}{7} = \frac{1}{8} \; ✗$$

You can eliminate choice A.

Choice B: Use $m = 9$ and $p = 72$.

$$\frac{9}{72} \overset{?}{=} \frac{1}{8}$$

$$\frac{1}{8} = \frac{1}{8} \; ✓$$

You can make 72 pancakes using 9 cups of pancake mix.

The correct answer is B. (A) **(B)** (C) (D)

PROBLEM 2

At a yard sale, Jack made $54 selling cassettes for $1 each and CDs for $3 each. This situation is modeled by the equation $x + 3y = 54$ where x is the number of cassettes and y is the number of CDs that Jack sold. The graph of the equation is shown. If Jack sold 18 cassettes, how many CDs did he sell?

(A) 4 **(B)** 12 **(C)** 18 **(D)** 20

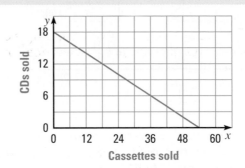

Strategy 1 SOLVE DIRECTLY

Use the graph to answer the question, then check the solution.

STEP 1 Use the graph. It shows that if Jack sold 18 cassettes, then he sold 12 CDs.

STEP 2 Check the solution from Step 1 using the given equation. Substitute 18 for x and 12 for y in the given equation.

$x + 3y = 54$ **Write original equation.**

$18 + 3(12) \stackrel{?}{=} 54$ **Substitute.**

$54 = 54$ **Simplify. Solution checks.**

So, Jack sold 12 CDs.

The correct answer is B. **(A)** **(B)** **(C)** **(D)**

Strategy 2 ELIMINATE CHOICES

Substitute 18 for x and each answer choice for y in the given equation.

Choice A: Substitute 18 for x and 4 for y.

$x + 3y = 54$ **Write original equation.**

$18 + 3(4) \stackrel{?}{=} 54$ **Substitute.**

$30 \neq 54$ **Simplify. Eliminate choice A.**

Choice B: Substitute 18 for x and 12 for y.

$x + 3y = 54$ **Write original equation.**

$18 + 3(12) \stackrel{?}{=} 54$ **Substitute.**

$54 = 54$ **Simplify. Choice B is correct.**

The correct answer is B. **(A)** **(B)** **(C)** **(D)**

STRATEGY PRACTICE

Explain why you can eliminate the highlighted answer choice.

1. The graph of $y = \frac{1}{3}x + 1$ is shown. Which ordered pair is *not* a solution of $y = \frac{1}{3}x + 1$?

   (A) (6, 3)   **(B)** (2, 5)

   (C) (3, 2)   **(D)** ✗ (0, 1)

   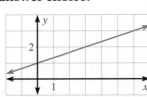

2. The table shows the total cost for admission to an ice skating rink. What is the cost per person?

   (A) $.20   **(B)** $1

   (C) $5   **(D)** ✗ $10

People	2	4	6
Cost (dollars)	10	20	30

In Exercises 1 and 2, use the graph below.

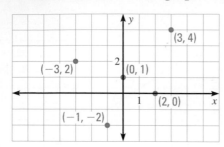

1. The graph represents a function. Which number is in the domain of the function? **Alg. 17.0**

   (A) −2

   (B) −1

   (C) 1

   (D) 4

2. The graph would no longer represent a function if which point were included? **Alg. 18.0**

   (A) (−4, −2)

   (B) (−2, 0)

   (C) (1, 3)

   (D) (3, −1)

3. Which equation has the graph shown? **Alg. 6.0**

   (A) $y = -\frac{3}{2}x + 4$

   (B) $y = \frac{2}{3}x - 4$

   (C) $y = \frac{3}{2}x - 4$

   (D) $y = -\frac{3}{2}x - 4$

4. The domain of the function $y = 3x + 6$ is 0, 1, 2, 3. What is the range of the function? **Alg. 17.0**

   (A) 6, 9, 12, 15

   (B) 0, 3, 6, 9

   (C) 2, 3, 4, 5

   (D) 2, 5, 8, 11

5. A humidifier is a device used to add moisture to the air by turning water into vapor as shown in the diagram. The amount w (in gallons) of water left in the humidifier is given by $w = 1.5 - 0.12t$ where t is the time (in hours) that the humidifier runs. What does the w-intercept of the graph of the equation represent? **Alg. 6.0**

   (A) The time when the tank is full

   (B) The time when the tank is empty

   (C) The initial amount of water in the tank

   (D) The amount of water in the tank after 2 hours

6. The graph below shows a traveler's movements through an airport to a terminal. The traveler has to walk and take a shuttle bus to the terminal.

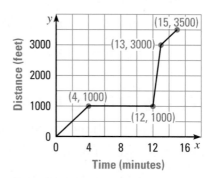

   For how many minutes does the traveler wait for the shuttle bus? **Gr. 7 AF 3.3**

   (A) 1 min

   (B) 2 min

   (C) 4 min

   (D) 8 min

7. The free throws attempted and made by a player in the first three games of a basketball season are shown below. For this player, the number *m* of free throws made varies directly with the number *a* of free throws attempted. What is the constant of variation of the direct variation equation? **Alg. 6.0**

	Free Throws	
Game	Attempts	Made
1	~~IIII~~ IIII	~~IIII~~ I
2	III	II
3	~~IIII~~ I	IIIII

- (A) $\frac{1}{3}$
- (B) $\frac{2}{5}$
- (C) $\frac{2}{3}$
- (D) $\frac{3}{2}$

8. The table shows the cost for work done by an electrician for a given amount of time. What is the cost per minute? **Gr. 7 AF 3.3**

Time (minutes)	30	45	60
Cost (dollars)	21.00	31.50	42.00

- (A) $.42
- (B) $.70
- (C) $1.40
- (D) $7.00

9. The total cost *C* (in dollars) of a certain fabric is given by $C = 30f$ where *f* is the number of yards purchased. A fashion designer orders up to 3 yards of fabric. What are the domain and range of the function? **Alg. 6.0**

- (A) Domain: $0 \le f \le 2$; range: $0 \le C \le 30$
- (B) Domain: $0 \le f \le 3$; range: $0 \le C \le 90$
- (C) Domain: $0 \le f \le 4$; range: $0 \le C \le 60$
- (D) Domain: $0 \le f \le 5$; range: $0 \le C \le 90$

10. What is a rule for the function? **Alg. 16.0**

x	8	10	12	14
y	5	7	9	11

- (A) $y = x - 3$
- (B) $y = x - 2$
- (C) $y = x + 3$
- (D) $y = x + 2$

11. What is the *y*-intercept of the graph of the line $y - x = 7$? **Alg. 6.0**

- (A) -7
- (B) -1
- (C) 1
- (D) 7

12. What is the slope of the line that passes through the points $(-3, 0)$ and $(0, 1)$? **Gr. 7 AF 3.3**

- (A) -3
- (B) $-\frac{1}{3}$
- (C) $\frac{1}{3}$
- (D) 3

13. When you prepare rice, the number *w* of cups of water needed varies directly with the number *r* of cups of uncooked rice. An example is given below. Which equation relates *r* and *w*? **Alg. 6.0**

- (A) $w = \frac{3}{2}r$
- (B) $w = \frac{2}{3}r$
- (C) $r = 2w$
- (D) $r = \frac{3}{2}w$

$\frac{3}{4}$ cup water

$\frac{1}{2}$ cup rice

6 Writing Linear Equations

Before

In previous chapters, you learned the following skills, which you'll use in Chapter 6:

- Graphing functions and identifying intercepts
- Identifying the slopes and *y*-intercepts of lines
- Calculating slopes of lines

Now

In Chapter 6 you'll study these **Big Ideas:**

1 Writing linear equations in a variety of forms

2 Using linear models to solve problems

3 Writing equations of parallel and perpendicular lines

Why?

So you can solve real-world problems about . . .

- Glaciers, p. 327
- Firefighting, p. 328
- Meteorology, p. 335
- Nutrition, p. 351
- Hockey, p. 359
- Biology, p. 359

Animated Algebra

at *classzone.com*

Get-Ready Games

NET GRAPH

California Standards

Review graphing linear equations. **Alg. 6.0**
Prepare for writing linear equations. **Alg. 7.0**

How to Play

Copy the graph shown. Then follow the steps below to find the year in which beach volleyball first became an Olympic sport.

1. Draw a square with vertices (1, 3) and (3, 5).
2. Draw a line segment with a slope of 1. One of its endpoints is (1, 1). The other endpoint is a vertex of the square from Step 1.
3. Draw a square with vertices (5, 1) and (7, 3).
4. Draw a line segment with a slope of 1. One of its endpoints is (7, 5). The other endpoint is a vertex of the square from Step 3.

CALIFORNIA STANDARDS

- **Alg. 7.0** Students verify that a point lies on a line, given an equation of the line. Students are able to derive linear equations by using the point-slope formula. *(Lesson 6.1, 6.2, 6.3, 6.4)*

- **Alg. 8.0** Students understand the concepts of parallel lines and perpendicular lines and how their slopes are related. Students are able to find the equation of a line perpendicular to a given line that passes through a given point. *(Lesson 6.5)*

Catch A Wave

California Standards

Review identifying the *y*-intercept. **Alg. 6.0**
Prepare for writing linear equations. **Alg. 7.0**

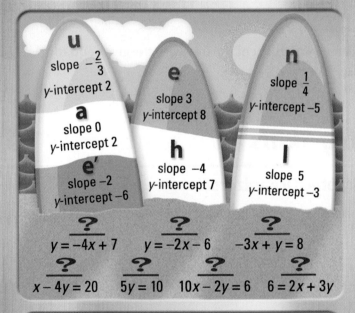

u slope $-\frac{2}{3}$, *y*-intercept 2

a slope 0, *y*-intercept 2

e' slope -2, *y*-intercept -6

e slope 3, *y*-intercept 8

h slope -4, *y*-intercept 7

n slope $\frac{1}{4}$, *y*-intercept -5

l slope 5, *y*-intercept -3

$$\frac{?}{y = -4x + 7} \qquad \frac{?}{y = -2x - 6} \qquad \frac{?}{-3x + y = 8}$$

$$\frac{?}{x - 4y = 20} \qquad \frac{?}{5y = 10} \qquad \frac{?}{10x - 2y = 6} \qquad \frac{?}{6 = 2x + 3y}$$

How to Play

Find the Hawaiian words for surfing.

- Match each equation with its slope and *y*-intercept.
- Copy and complete the blanks above with the appropriate letter.

Games Wrap-Up

Draw Conclusions

Complete these exercises after playing the games.

1. **WRITING** In what circumstances is the slope of the graph of $Ax + By = C$ zero? In what circumstances is the slope undefined?

2. **REASONING** Write a set of instructions for drawing the letter A in the coordinate plane. Your instructions should use slope.

Prerequisite Skills

California @HomeTutor
Prerequisite skills practice at classzone.com

REVIEW VOCABULARY

- *y*-intercept, *p. 273*
- slope, *p. 282*
- slope-intercept form, *p. 291*
- standard form, *p. 265*
- conditional statement, *p. 55*
- parallel, *p. 293*

VOCABULARY CHECK

Copy and complete the statement.

1. In the equation $y = mx + b$, the value of *m* is the __?__ of the graph of the equation.

2. In the equation $y = mx + b$, the value of *b* is the __?__ of the graph of the equation.

3. Two lines are __?__ if their slopes are equal.

SKILLS CHECK

Graph the equation. Label the points where the line crosses the axes.
(Review p. 273 for 6.1–6.5.)

4. $y = \frac{3}{2}x + 3$
5. $y = -\frac{1}{2}x + 4$
6. $2x - 3y = 6$

Find the slope of the line that passes through the points.
(Review p. 282 for 6.1–6.5.)

7. $(4, 5)$ and $(2, 3)$
8. $(0, -6)$ and $(8, 0)$
9. $(0, 0)$ and $(-1, 2)$

Identify the slope and *y*-intercept of the line with the given equation.
(Review p. 291 for 6.1–6.5.)

10. $y = x + 1$
11. $y = \frac{3}{4}x - 6$
12. $y = -\frac{2}{5}x - 2$

Notetaking Skills

NOW YOU TRY
Make a *four square diagram* for the slope-intercept form of a linear equation.

Focus on Graphic Organizers

You can make a *four square diagram* to organize what you know about a vocabulary term, such as *direct variation*.

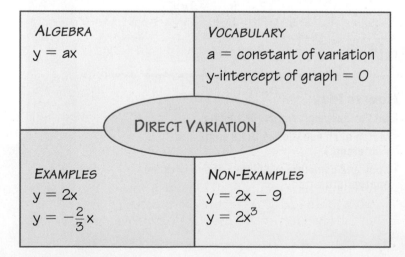

ALGEBRA	VOCABULARY
$y = ax$	a = constant of variation y-intercept of graph = 0

DIRECT VARIATION

EXAMPLES	NON-EXAMPLES
$y = 2x$ $y = -\frac{2}{3}x$	$y = 2x - 9$ $y = 2x^3$

6.1 Modeling Linear Relationships

Standards

Gr. 7 AF 1.1 **Use variables and appropriate operations to write** an expression, **an equation**, an inequality, or a system of equations or inequalities **that represents a verbal description** (e.g., **three less than a number**, **half as large as area** *A*).

MATERIALS · 8.5 inch by 11 inch piece of paper · inch ruler

QUESTION   **How can you model a linear relationship?**

You know that the perimeter of a rectangle is given by the formula $P = 2\ell + 2w$. In this activity, you will find a linear relationship using that formula.

EXPLORE   **Find perimeters of rectangles**

STEP 1 *Find perimeter*

Find the perimeter of a piece of paper that is 8.5 inches wide and 11 inches long. Record the result in a table like the one shown.

Fold number	Perimeter of rectangle (inches)
0	39
1	?
2	?
3	?
4	?

STEP 2 *Change paper size*

Measure 1 inch from a short edge of the paper. Fold over 1 inch of the paper. You now have a rectangle with the same width and a different length than the original piece of paper. Find the perimeter of this new rectangle and record it in your table.

STEP 3 *Find additional perimeters*

Unfold the paper and repeat Step 2, this time folding the paper 2 inches from a short edge. Find the perimeter of this rectangle and record the result in your table. Repeat with a fold of 3 inches and a fold of 4 inches.

DRAW CONCLUSIONS   **Use your observations to complete these exercises**

1. What were the length and the width of the piece of paper before it was folded? By how much did these dimensions change with each fold?

2. What was the perimeter of the piece of paper before it was folded? By how much did the perimeter change with each new fold?

3. Copy and complete the following statement: The perimeter of the piece of paper after a fold of 5 inches is equal to the difference between the original perimeter, __?__ inches, and the fold number, __?__ , times the change in perimeter with each fold, __?__ inches.

4. Use the statement from Exercise 3 to write a rule that you can use to find the perimeter of the piece of paper after a fold of *n* inches. Use the data in the table to show that this rule gives accurate results.

6.1 Write Linear Equations in Slope-Intercept Form

Standards **Alg. 7.0** Students verify that a point lies on a line, given an equation of the line. Students are able to derive linear equations by using the point-slope formula.

Connect *Before* you graphed equations of lines. *Now* you will write equations of lines in slope-intercept form to prepare for writing equations in point-slope form.

Math and **SPORTS**
Ex. 51, p. 328

Key Vocabulary
• **y-intercept**, *p. 273*
• **slope,** *p. 282*
• **slope-intercept form,** *p. 291*

Recall that the graph of an equation in slope-intercept form, $y = mx + b$, is a line with a slope of m and a y-intercept of b. You can use this form to write an equation of a line if you know its slope and y-intercept.

EXAMPLE 1   Use slope and *y*-intercept to write an equation

Write an equation of the line with a slope of −2 and a *y*-intercept of 5.

$y = mx + b$ Write slope-intercept form.

$y = -2x + 5$ Substitute −2 for *m* and 5 for *b*.

EXAMPLE 2   Write an equation of a line from a graph

Animated **Algebra**

For an interactive example of writing an equation of a line, go to **classzone.com**.

Write an equation of the line shown.

Solution

The slope of the line is $m = \dfrac{-2}{5} = -\dfrac{2}{5}$.

The line crosses the y-axis at $(0, 3)$.
So, the y-intercept is $b = 3$.

$y = mx + b$ Write slope-intercept form.

$y = -\dfrac{2}{5}x + 3$ Substitute $-\dfrac{2}{5}$ for *m* and 3 for *b*.

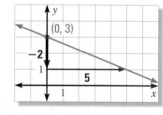

✓ GUIDED PRACTICE   for Examples 1 and 2

1. Write an equation of the line with a slope of 8 and a *y*-intercept of −7.

Write an equation of the line shown.

2.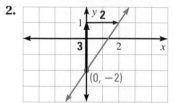

3.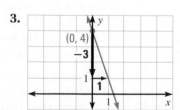

USING TWO POINTS If you know the point where a line crosses the *y*-axis and any other point on the line, you can write an equation of the line.

EXAMPLE 3 Write an equation of a line given two points

About the Standards

Slope-intercept form is a particular case of a more general form called point-slope form, which will be discussed in Lesson 6.3.

Write an equation of the line shown.

STEP 1 Calculate the slope.

$$m = \frac{y_2 - y_1}{x_2 - x_1} = \frac{-1 - (-5)}{3 - 0} = \frac{4}{3}$$

STEP 2 Write an equation of the line. The line crosses the *y*-axis at $(0, -5)$. So, the *y*-intercept is $b = -5$.

$y = mx + b$ Write slope-intercept form.

$y = \frac{4}{3}x - 5$ Substitute $\frac{4}{3}$ for *m* and -5 for *b*.

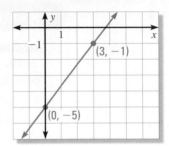

EXAMPLE 4 Find the slope or *y*-intercept given a point

Find the value of *m* or *b* if the given line passes through the given point.

a. $y = mx + 1; (3, -2)$ **b.** $y = 2x + b; (-1, -4)$

Solution

a. Substitute the coordinates of the given point into the equation and solve for *m*.

$y = mx + 1$ Write original equation.

$-2 = m(3) + 1$ Substitute 3 for *x* and -2 for *y*.

$-3 = 3m$ Subtract 1 from each side.

$-1 = m$ Divide each side by 3.

b. Substitute the coordinates of the given point into the equation and solve for *b*.

$y = 2x + b$ Write original equation.

$-4 = 2(-1) + b$ Substitute -1 for *x* and -4 for *y*.

$-4 = -2 + b$ Multiply.

$-2 = b$ Add 2 to each side.

✓ **GUIDED PRACTICE** for Examples 3 and 4

4. Write an equation of the line shown.

5. Find the value of *b* if the line $y = \frac{2}{3}x + b$ passes through the point $(-6, -9)$.

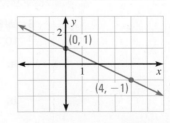

The number b is a starting value in a real-world situation modeled by $y = mx + b$, because when $x = 0$, the value of y is b.

MODELING REAL-WORLD SITUATIONS When a quantity y changes at a constant rate with respect to a quantity x, you can use the equation $y = mx + b$ to model the relationship. The value of m is the constant rate of change, and the value of b is an initial, or starting, value for y.

EXAMPLE 5   Solve a multi-step problem

RECORDING STUDIO A recording studio charges musicians an initial fee of $50 to record an album. Studio time costs an additional $35 per hour.

a. Write an equation that gives the total cost of an album as a function of studio time (in hours).

b. Find the total cost of recording an album that takes 10 hours of studio time.

Cost of studio time: $35 per hour

Solution

a. The cost changes at a constant rate, so you can write an equation in slope-intercept form to model the total cost.

STEP 1 **Identify** the rate of change and the starting value.

> **Rate of change, m:** cost per hour
> **Starting value, b:** initial fee

STEP 2 **Write** a verbal model. Then write the equation.

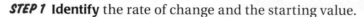

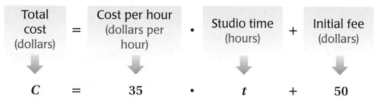

Total cost (dollars)	=	Cost per hour (dollars per hour)	·	Studio time (hours)	+	Initial fee (dollars)
C	=	35	·	t	+	50

CHECK Use unit analysis to check the equation.

$$\text{dollars} = \frac{\text{dollars}}{\text{hour}} \cdot \text{hours} + \text{dollars} \ \checkmark$$

▶ The total cost C is given by the function $C = 35t + 50$ where t is the studio time (in hours).

b. Evaluate the function for $t = 10$.

$C = 35(10) + 50 = 400$ **Substitute 10 for t and simplify.**

▶ The total cost for 10 hours of studio time is $400.

✓ **GUIDED PRACTICE**   for Example 5

6. WHAT IF? In Example 5, suppose the recording studio raises its initial fee to $75 and charges $40 per hour for studio time.

a. Write an equation that gives the total cost of an album as a function of studio time (in hours).

b. Find the total cost of recording an album that takes 10 hours of studio time.

6.1 **EXERCISES**

HOMEWORK KEY

◆ = **MULTIPLE CHOICE PRACTICE**
Exs. 9, 47, and 52–55

○ = **HINTS AND HOMEWORK HELP**
for Exs. 13, 19, and 47 at classzone.com

SKILLS · PROBLEM SOLVING · REASONING

1. **VOCABULARY** Copy and complete: The ratio of the rise to the run between any two points on a nonvertical line is called the __?__.

2. **WRITING** *Explain* how you can use slope-intercept form to write an equation of a line given its slope and *y*-intercept.

EXAMPLE 1
on p. 322
for Exs. 3–10

WRITING EQUATIONS Write an equation of the line with the given slope and *y*-intercept.

3. slope: 2
   y-intercept: 9

4. slope: 1
   y-intercept: 5

5. slope: −3
   y-intercept: 0

6. slope: −7
   y-intercept: 1

7. slope: $\frac{2}{3}$
   y-intercept: −9

8. slope: $\frac{3}{4}$
   y-intercept: −6

9. ◆ **MULTIPLE CHOICE** Which equation represents the line with a slope of −1 and a *y*-intercept of 2?

   A $y = -x + 2$ **B** $y = 2x - 1$ **C** $y = x - 2$ **D** $y = 2x + 1$

10. **ERROR ANALYSIS** *Describe* and correct the error in writing an equation of the line with a slope of 2 and a *y*-intercept of 7.

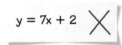

EXAMPLE 2
on p. 322
for Exs. 11–16

WRITING EQUATIONS Write an equation of the line shown.

11.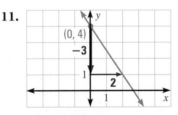

12.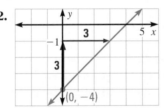

13.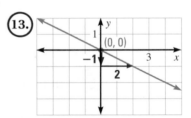

14.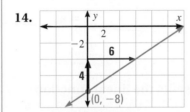

15.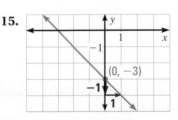

16.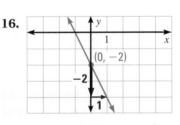

EXAMPLE 3
on p. 323
for Exs. 17–30

17. **ERROR ANALYSIS** *Describe* and correct the error in writing an equation of the line shown.

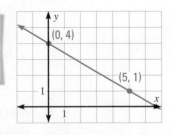

USING A GRAPH Write an equation of the line shown.

18.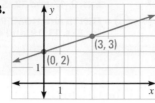

19.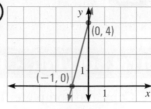

20.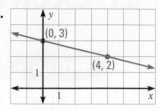

21.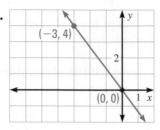

22.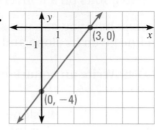

23.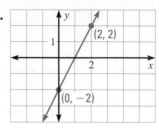

USING TWO POINTS Write an equation of the line that passes through the given points.

24. $(-3, 1), (0, -8)$

25. $(2, -7), (0, -5)$

26. $(2, -4), (0, -4)$

27. $(0, 4), \left(8, \frac{7}{2}\right)$

28. $(0, 5), \left(\frac{3}{2}, 1\right)$

29. $(-6, 0), (0, -24)$

30. **REASONING** *Explain* how to write an equation of a line in slope-intercept form given the *x*- and *y*-intercepts of the line.

EXAMPLE 4
on p. 323
for Exs. 31–37

FINDING THE SLOPE OR *y*-INTERCEPT Find the value of *m* or *b* if the given line passes through the given point.

31. $y = mx - 6;\ (-5, 9)$

32. $y = \frac{5}{4}x + b;\ (4, 8)$

33. $y = mx + 1;\ (2, -2)$

34. $y = 4x + b;\ \left(\frac{3}{2}, \frac{11}{2}\right)$

35. $y = mx + 8;\ (3, 7)$

36. $y = -2x + b;\ (1, -2)$

37. **ERROR ANALYSIS** *Describe* and correct the error in finding the value of *m* given that the line $y = mx - 2$ passes through the point $(-8, 2)$.

$$y = mx - 2$$
$$-8 = m(2) - 2$$
$$-6 = 2m$$
$$\frac{-6}{2} = m$$
$$m = -3$$

USING A TABLE Write an equation that represents the linear function represented by the table.

38.

x	y
1	−1
0	1
−1	3

39.

x	y
−4	−2
−2	−1
0	0

40.

x	y
−5	8
0	4
5	0

41. **WRITING** A line passes through the points $(3, 5)$ and $(3, -7)$. Is it possible to write an equation of the line in slope-intercept form? *Explain*.

◆ = **MULTIPLE CHOICE PRACTICE**   ◯ = **HINTS AND HOMEWORK HELP** at classzone.com

CONNECT SKILLS TO PROBLEM SOLVING Exercises 42–44 will help you prepare for problem solving.

Describe the starting value and the rate of change for the situation.

42. A car rental company charges a membership fee of $40 plus $10 per hour for renting a car.

43. A cell phone plan costs $37.80 per month. The plan requires an activation fee of $25.

44. You need an initial deposit of $50 to open a savings account. You deposit $150 each month in this account.

EXAMPLE 5
on p. 324
for Exs. 45–48

45. WEB SERVER The initial fee to have a website set up using a server is $48. It costs $44 per month to maintain the website.

   a. Write an equation that gives the total cost of setting up and maintaining a website as a function of the number of months it is maintained.

   b. Find the total cost of setting up and maintaining the website for 6 months.

California **@HomeTutor** for problem solving help at classzone.com

46. PHOTOGRAPHS A camera shop charges $3.99 for an enlargement of a photograph. There is a delivery charge of $1.49 per order, regardless of the number of enlargements ordered. Write an equation that gives the total cost of an order with delivery as a function of the number of enlargements. Find the total cost of ordering 8 enlargements with delivery.

California **@HomeTutor** for problem solving help at classzone.com

47. ◆ **MULTIPLE CHOICE** Your family spends $30 for tickets to an aquarium and $2.50 per hour for parking. Which equation gives the total cost C (in dollars) of your family's visit to the aquarium as a function of the time t (in hours) that you are there?

   (A) $C = 2.5t + 30$ **(B)** $C = 30t + 2.5$ **(C)** $C = 30t - 2.5$ **(D)** $C = 2.5t - 30$

48. GLACIERS The timeline shows the approximate total area of glaciers on Mount Kilimanjaro from 1970 to 2000.

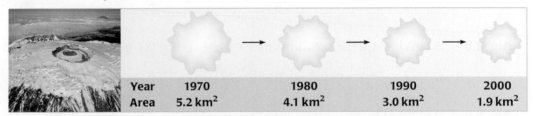

Year	1970	1980	1990	2000
Area	5.2 km²	4.1 km²	3.0 km²	1.9 km²

   a. Make a table for the data. Let x be the number of years since 1970 and y the area (in square kilometers) of the glaciers.

   b. Graph the data in the table. *Explain* how you know that the area of the glaciers changed at a constant rate.

   c. Write an equation that models the area of the glaciers as a function of the number of years since 1970. By how much did the area of the glaciers decrease each year from 1970 to 2000?

49. FIREFIGHTING The diagram shows the time a firefighting aircraft takes to scoop water from a lake, fly to a fire, and drop the water on the fire.

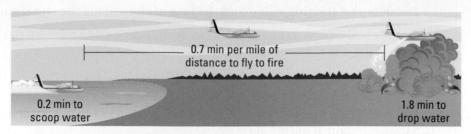

0.7 min per mile of distance to fly to fire

0.2 min to scoop water

1.8 min to drop water

a. **Model** Write an equation that gives the total time (in minutes) that the aircraft takes to scoop, fly, and drop as a function of the distance (in miles) flown from the lake to the fire.

b. **Predict** Find the time the aircraft takes to scoop, fly, and drop if it travels 20 miles from the lake to the fire.

50. CHALLENGE Show that the equation of the line that passes through the points $(0, b)$ and $(1, b + m)$ is $y = mx + b$. *Explain* how you can be sure that the point $(-1, b - m)$ also lies on the line.

51. CHALLENGE The elevation at which a baseball game is played affects the distance a ball travels when hit. For every increase of 1000 feet in elevation, the ball travels about 7 feet farther. Suppose a baseball travels 400 feet when hit in a ball park at sea level.

a. **Model** Write an equation that gives the distance (in feet) the baseball travels as a function of the elevation of the ball park in which it is hit.

b. **Justify** *Justify* the equation from part (a) using unit analysis.

c. **Predict** If the ball were hit in exactly the same way at a park with an elevation of 3500 feet, how far would it travel?

◆ CALIFORNIA STANDARDS SPIRAL REVIEW

Gr. 7 AF 3.3

52. What is the slope of the line that passes through the points $(3, -6)$ and $(9, -10)$? *(p. 282)*

Ⓐ $-\frac{8}{3}$ Ⓑ $-\frac{3}{2}$ Ⓒ $-\frac{2}{3}$ Ⓓ $\frac{2}{3}$

Alg. 3.0

53. What are the solutions of $3 + |4x - 15| = 13$? *(p. 220)*

Ⓐ $-\frac{25}{4}, -\frac{5}{4}$ Ⓑ $-\frac{1}{4}, \frac{25}{4}$ Ⓒ $\frac{1}{4}, \frac{25}{4}$ Ⓓ $\frac{5}{4}, \frac{25}{4}$

Alg. 5.0

54. What is the *x*-intercept of the graph of $3x + 4y = 24$? *(p. 273)*

Ⓐ $-\frac{3}{4}$ Ⓑ 4   Ⓒ 6   Ⓓ 8

Alg. 5.0

55. Karla uses a babysitting service that charges $8 per hour plus $16 if you are late picking up your child. Karla was late picking up her daughter and paid $48. How long was Karla's daughter with the babysitter? *(p. 132)*

Ⓐ 3 h   Ⓑ 4 h   Ⓒ 5 h   Ⓓ 6 h

6.2 Use Linear Equations in Slope-Intercept Form

Standards

Alg. 7.0 Students verify that a point lies on a line, given an equation of the line. Students are able to derive linear equations by using the point-slope formula.

Connect

Before you wrote an equation of a line using its slope and *y*-intercept.
Now you will write an equation of a line in slope-intercept form using points on the line to prepare for writing equations in point-slope form.

Math and **SPORTS**
Example 5, p. 332

Key Vocabulary
- **y-intercept,** *p. 273*
- **slope,** *p. 282*
- **slope-intercept form,** *p. 291*

KEY CONCEPT   *For Your Notebook*

Writing an Equation of a Line in Slope-Intercept Form

STEP 1 **Identify** the slope *m*. You can use the slope formula to calculate the slope if you know two points on the line.

STEP 2 **Find** the *y*-intercept. You can substitute the slope and the coordinates of a point (x, y) on the line in $y = mx + b$. Then solve for *b*.

STEP 3 **Write** an equation using $y = mx + b$.

EXAMPLE 1   ◆ Multiple Choice Practice

> **What is the equation of the line that passes through the point $(-1, 3)$ and has a slope of -4?**
>
> **(A)** $y = 4x + 2$ **(B)** $y = -4x + 7$ **(C)** $y = -4x - 1$ **(D)** $y = -4x + 11$

ELIMINATE CHOICES
The given slope is -4, so you can eliminate choice A.

Solution

The slope is -4. To find the *y*-intercept, substitute the slope and the coordinates of the given point in $y = mx + b$ and solve for *b*.

$3 = -4(-1) + b$ **Substitute -4 for *m*, -1 for *x*, and 3 for *y*.**

$-1 = b$ **Solve for *b*.**

Substitute -4 for *m* and -1 for *b* in $y = mx + b$.

$y = -4x - 1$ **Substitute -4 for *m* and -1 for *b*.**

▶ The correct answer is C. **(A) (B) (C) (D)**

✓ **GUIDED PRACTICE**   for Example 1

1. Write an equation of the line that passes through the point $(6, 3)$ and has a slope of 2.

EXAMPLE 2 **Write an equation of a line from a graph**

Write an equation of the line shown.

Solution

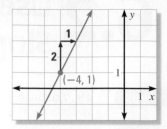

STEP 1 **Identify** the slope. The slope of the line is $m = \frac{2}{1} = 2$.

STEP 2 **Find** the y-intercept. Use the slope and the point $(-4, 1)$.

$y = mx + b$ Write slope-intercept form.

$1 = 2(-4) + b$ Substitute for *m, x,* and *y.*

$9 = b$ Solve for *b.*

STEP 3 **Write** an equation of the line.

$y = mx + b$ Write slope-intercept form.

$y = 2x + 9$ Substitute 2 for *m* and 9 for *b.*

EXAMPLE 3 **Write an equation given two points**

Write an equation of the line that passes through $(-2, 5)$ and $(2, -1)$.

Solution

STEP 1 **Calculate** the slope.

$$m = \frac{y_2 - y_1}{x_2 - x_1} = \frac{-1 - 5}{2 - (-2)} = \frac{-6}{4} = -\frac{3}{2}$$

ANOTHER WAY

You can also find the y-intercept using the coordinates of the other given point, $(2, -1)$:

$y = mx + b$

$-1 = -\frac{3}{2}(2) + b$

$2 = b$

STEP 2 **Find** the y-intercept. Use the slope and the point $(-2, 5)$.

$y = mx + b$ Write slope-intercept form.

$5 = -\frac{3}{2}(-2) + b$ Substitute $-\frac{3}{2}$ for *m*, −2 for *x*, and 5 for *y.*

$2 = b$ Solve for *b.*

STEP 3 **Write** an equation of the line.

$y = mx + b$ Write slope-intercept form.

$y = -\frac{3}{2}x + 2$ Substitute $-\frac{3}{2}$ for *m* and 2 for *b.*

✓ **GUIDED PRACTICE**   **for Examples 2 and 3**

2. Write an equation of the line shown.

Write an equation of the line that passes through the given points.

3. $(-2, 8), (8, 3)$

4. $(1, -2), (-5, 4)$

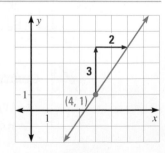

How to Write Equations in Slope-Intercept Form

Given slope m and y-intercept b	**Given** slope m and one point	**Given** two points
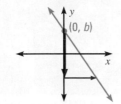	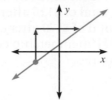	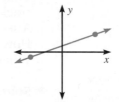
Substitute m and b in the equation $y = mx + b$.	Substitute m and the coordinates of the point in $y = mx + b$. Solve for b. Write the equation.	Use the points to find the slope m. Then choose one of the two points and follow the same steps described at the left.

MODELING REAL-WORLD SITUATIONS You can model a real-world situation that involves a constant rate of change with an equation in slope-intercept form.

EXAMPLE 4   Solve a multi-step problem

GYM MEMBERSHIP Your gym membership costs $33 per month after an initial membership fee. You paid a total of $228 after 6 months. Write an equation that gives the total cost as a function of the length of your gym membership (in months). Find the total cost after 9 months.

Cost for 6 months: $228

Solution

STEP 1 **Identify** the rate of change and starting value.

> **Rate of change, m:** monthly cost
> **Starting value, b:** initial membership fee

STEP 2 **Write** a verbal model. Then write an equation.

Total cost	=	Monthly cost	·	Number of months	+	Membership fee
C	=	33	·	t	+	b

STEP 3 **Find** the starting value b. Membership for 6 months costs $228, so substitute 6 for t and 228 for C in the equation $C = 33t + b$. Then use the value of b to write an equation for C as a function of t.

$228 = 33(6) + b$ **Substitute 6 for t and 228 for C.**

$30 = b$ **Solve for b, the starting value.**

$C = 33t + 30$ **Substitute 30 for b.**

STEP 4 **Evaluate** the function when $t = 9$.

$C = 33(9) + 30 = 327$ **Substitute 9 for t. Simplify.**

▶ Your total cost after 9 months is $327.

EXAMPLE 5 Solve a multi-step problem

BMX RACING In Bicycle Moto Cross (BMX) racing, racers purchase a one year membership to a track. They also pay an entry fee for each race at that track. One racer paid a total of $125 after 5 races. A second racer paid a total of $170 after 8 races. How much does the track membership cost? What is the entry fee per race?

A BMX racer paid $125 to compete in 5 races.

ANOTHER WAY

For alternative methods for solving the problem in Example 5, turn to page 337 for the **Problem Solving Workshop**.

Solution

STEP 1 **Identify** the rate of change and starting value.

Rate of change, m: entry fee per race
Starting value, b: track membership cost

STEP 2 **Write** a verbal model. Then write an equation.

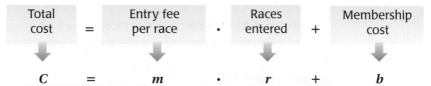

Total cost	=	Entry fee per race	·	Races entered	+	Membership cost

$$C = m \cdot r + b$$

STEP 3 **Calculate** the rate of change. This is the entry fee per race. Use the slope formula. Racer 1 is represented by $(r_1, C_1) = (5, 125)$. Racer 2 is represented by $(r_2, C_2) = (8, 170)$.

$$m = \frac{C_2 - C_1}{r_2 - r_1} = \frac{170 - 125}{8 - 5} = \frac{45}{3} = 15$$

STEP 4 **Find** the track membership cost b. Use the data pair $(5, 125)$ for racer 1 and the entry fee per race from Step 3.

$C = mr + b$	Write the equation from Step 2.
$125 = 15(5) + b$	Substitute 15 for m, 5 for r, and 125 for C.
$50 = b$	Solve for b.

▸ The track membership cost is $50. The entry fee per race is $15.

✓ **GUIDED PRACTICE** for Examples 4 and 5

5. **GYM MEMBERSHIP** A gym charges $35 per month after an initial membership fee. A member has paid a total of $250 after 6 months. Write an equation that gives the total cost of a gym membership as a function of the length of membership (in months). Find the total cost of membership after 10 months.

6. **BMX RACING** A BMX race track charges a membership fee and an entry fee per race. One racer paid a total of $76 after 3 races. Another racer paid a total of $124 after 7 races.

   a. What is the entry fee per race?

   b. Write an equation that gives the total cost as a function of the number of races entered.

   c. How much does the track membership cost?

6.2 EXERCISES

◆ = **MULTIPLE CHOICE PRACTICE**
Exs. 9, 23, 39, and 51–53

○ = **HINTS AND HOMEWORK HELP**
for Exs. 5, 17, and 39 at classzone.com

SKILLS · PROBLEM SOLVING · REASONING

1. **VOCABULARY** Copy and complete: The *y*-coordinate of a point where a graph crosses the *y*-axis is called the __?__ .

2. **WRITING** If the equation $y = mx + b$ is used to model a quantity *y* as a function of the quantity *x*, why is *b* considered to be the starting value?

EXAMPLE 1
on p. 329
for Exs. 3–10

WRITING EQUATIONS Write an equation of the line that passes through the given point and has the given slope *m*.

3. $(1, 1); m = 3$

4. $(5, 1); m = 2$

5. $(-4, 7); m = -5$

6. $(5, -5); m = -2$

7. $(8, -4); m = -\frac{3}{4}$

8. $(-3, -11); m = \frac{1}{2}$

9. ◆ **MULTIPLE CHOICE** What is an equation of the line that passes through the point (5, 3) and has a slope of 2?

   A $y = 2x + 2$

   B $y = 2x - 1$

   C $y = -2x + 13$

   D $y = 2x - 7$

10. **ERROR ANALYSIS** *Describe* and correct the error in finding the *y*-intercept of the line that passes through the point (6, −3) and has a slope of −2.

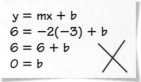

EXAMPLE 2
on p. 330
for Exs. 11–13

USING A GRAPH Write an equation of the line shown.

11.
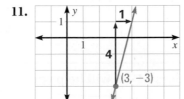

12.
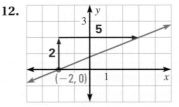

13.
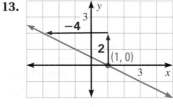

EXAMPLE 3
on p. 330
for Exs. 14–28

14.
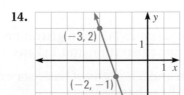

15.
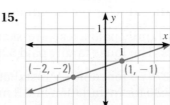

16.
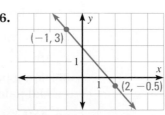

USING TWO POINTS Write an equation of the line that passes through the given points.

17. $(1, 4), (2, 7)$

18. $(3, 2), (4, 9)$

19. $(10, -5), (-5, 1)$

20. $(-2, 8), (-6, 0)$

21. $\left(-5, \frac{3}{4}\right), \left(-2, -\frac{3}{4}\right)$

22. $\left(\frac{9}{2}, 1\right), \left(-\frac{7}{2}, 7\right)$

23. ◆ **MULTIPLE CHOICE** What is an equation of the line that passes through the points (4, −15) and (7, 57)?

    Ⓐ $y = 14x - 71$ Ⓑ $y = 24x - 1361$ Ⓒ $y = 24x + 360$ Ⓓ $y = 24x - 111$

USING A TABLE Write an equation that represents the linear function represented by the table.

24.

x	y
−2	−16
−1	−10
1	2
2	8

25.

x	y
−4	−3
4	−1
8	0
12	1

26.

x	y
−3	8
3	4
6	2
9	0

27.

x	y
−6	6
−2	4
4	1
10	−2

28. ERROR ANALYSIS An appliance store uses a rule of thumb to determine how much refrigerator space (in cubic feet) a family will need. A salesperson suggests that a family of 5 buy a refrigerator with 16 cubic feet of space and that a family of 8 buy a refrigerator with 22 cubic feet of space. *Describe* and correct the error in finding the amount of refrigerator space per family member.

$$m = \frac{y_2 - y_1}{x_2 - x_1}$$
$$= \frac{8 - 5}{22 - 16}$$
$$= \frac{3}{6}$$
$$= \frac{1}{2} \ ft^3/person \quad \times$$

SHORT RESPONSE Tell whether the given information is enough to write an equation of a line. *Justify* your answer.

29. Two points on the line

30. The slope and a point on the line

31. The slope of the line

32. Both intercepts of the line

EXAMPLE 4
on p. 331
for Exs. 33
and 39

33. ERROR ANALYSIS An Internet service provider charges $18 per month plus an initial set-up fee. One customer paid a total of $81 after 2 months of service. *Describe* and correct the error in finding the set-up fee.

$$C = mt + b$$
$$81 = m(2) + 18$$
$$63 = m(2)$$
$$31.50 = m \quad \times$$

CONNECT SKILLS TO PROBLEM SOLVING Exercises 34–36 will help you prepare for problem solving.

Write the data pairs for the situation.

34. The Vasquez family paid a learn-to-skate program $745 for registration and 3 skaters. The Jones family paid $265 for registration and 1 skater.

35. Janet paid $276.50 for cable TV installation and 5 months of basic service. Ed paid $177.30 for installation and 3 months of basic service.

36. Mike spent $23.20 at a bowling alley to rent shoes and play 4 games. Erin spent $13.60 at the same bowling alley for shoe rental and 2 games.

EXAMPLE 5
on p. 332
for Exs. 37
and 38

37. BIOLOGY Four years after a tree was planted, its height was 9 feet. Eight years after it was planted, its height was 12 feet. What is the average growth rate of the tree? What was its height when it was planted?

    California @HomeTutor   for problem solving help at classzone.com

38. **ONLINE MAGAZINE** You have a subscription to an online magazine that allows you to view 25 articles from the magazine's archives. You are charged an additional fee for each article after the first 25 articles viewed. After viewing 28 archived articles, you paid a total of $34.80. After viewing 30 archived articles, you paid a total of $40.70.

   a. What is the cost per archived article after the first 25 articles viewed?

   b. What is the cost of the magazine subscription?

   California @HomeTutor for problem solving help at classzone.com

39. ◆ **MULTIPLE CHOICE** From 1990 to 2001, the number of airports in the United States increased at a relatively constant rate of 175 airports per year. There were 19,306 airports in the United States in 2001. Which equation gives the number of U.S. airports as a function of the number of years since 1990?

   (A) $y = 175x + 19,306$ (B) $y = 175x + 17,381$

   (C) $y = 175x + 16,521$ (D) $y = 19,306x + 175$

READING IN MATH   **Read the information below for Exercises 40–43.**

Newspapers Use the information in the article about the number of Sunday newspapers in circulation.

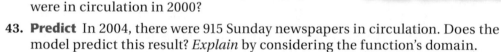

Sunday Edition C9

SUNDAY PAPERS INCREASE
From 1970 to 2000, the number of Sunday newspapers in circulation increased at a relatively constant rate of 11.8 newspapers per year. In 1997 there were 903 Sunday newspapers in circulation.

40. **Calculate** About how many Sunday newspapers were in circulation in 1970?

41. **Model** Write an equation that gives the number of Sunday newspapers in circulation as a function of the number of years since 1970.

42. **Calculate** About how many Sunday newspapers were in circulation in 2000?

43. **Predict** In 2004, there were 915 Sunday newspapers in circulation. Does the model predict this result? *Explain* by considering the function's domain.

44. **METEOROLOGY** A hurricane is traveling at a constant speed on a straight path toward a coastal town, as shown below.

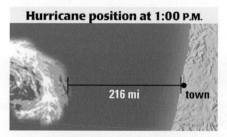

Hurricane position at 1:00 P.M.

216 mi   town

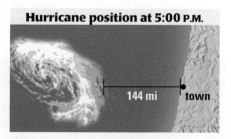

Hurricane position at 5:00 P.M.

144 mi   town

   a. **Write** Write an equation that gives the distance (in miles) of the hurricane from the town as a function of time (in hours) since 12:00 P.M.

   b. **Graph** Graph the equation from part (a). *Explain* what the slope and the y-intercept of the graph mean in this situation.

   c. **Predict** Predict the time at which the hurricane will reach the town.

REASONING Decide whether the three points lie on the same line. *Explain* how you know. If the points do lie on the same line, write an equation of the line that passes through all three points.

45. $(-4, -2)$, $(2, 2.5)$, $(8, 7)$

46. $(2, 2)$, $(-4, 5)$, $(6, 1)$

47. $(-10, 4)$, $(-3, 2.8)$, $(-17, 6.8)$

48. $(-5.5, 3)$, $(-7.5, 4)$, $(-4, 5)$

49. CHALLENGE A line passes through the points $(-2, 3)$, $(2, 5)$, and $(6, k)$. Find the value of k. *Explain* your steps.

50. CHALLENGE An in-line skater practices at a racetrack. In two trials, the skater travels the same distance going from a standstill to his top racing speed. He then travels at his top racing speed for different distances.

Trial number	Time at top racing speed (seconds)	Total distance traveled (meters)
1	24	300
2	29	350

a. **Model** Write an equation that gives the total distance traveled (in meters) as a function of the time (in seconds) at top racing speed.

b. **Justify** What do the rate of change and initial value in your equation represent? *Explain* your answer using unit analysis.

c. **Predict** One lap around the racetrack is 200 meters. The skater starts at a standstill and completes 3 laps. Predict the number of seconds the skater travels at his top racing speed. *Explain* your method.

◆ CALIFORNIA STANDARDS SPIRAL REVIEW

Alg. 3.0

51. Which number is a solution of $\left| \frac{1}{2}x - 6 \right| + 8 = 4$? *(p. 220)*

(**A**) -4 (**B**) 4 (**C**) 20 (**D**) No solution

Alg. 4.0

52. What is the solution of $8y - (8 + 6y) = 20$? *(p. 139)*

(**A**) -7 (**B**) 2 (**C**) 7 (**D**) 14

Alg. 5.0

53. The initial fee to join a club is $55. The monthly dues are $17. What is the total cost of a membership after 3 months? *(p. 132)*

(**A**) $72   (**B**) $89   (**C**) $106   (**D**) $182

QUIZ *for Lessons 6.1–6.2*

Write an equation in slope-intercept form of the line that passes through the given point and has the given slope *m*. *(p. 329)*

1. $(2, 5)$, $m = 3$

2. $(-1, 4)$, $m = -2$

3. $(0, -7)$, $m = 5$

Write an equation in slope-intercept form of the line that passes through the given points.

4. $(0, 2)$, $(9, 5)$ *(p. 322)*

5. $(-2, 3)$, $(0, 5)$ *(p. 322)*

6. $(-8, -4)$, $(0, -2)$ *(p. 322)*

7. $(5, 7)$, $(19, 14)$ *(p. 329)*

8. $(4, 24)$, $(12, 18)$ *(p. 329)*

9. $(-15, -10)$, $(-5, -6)$ *(p. 329)*

   EXTRA PRACTICE for Lesson 6.2, p. 815   ⚡ **ONLINE QUIZ** at classzone.com

Another Way to Solve Example 5, page 332

Standards
Gr. 7 AF 3.4

In Example 5 on page 332, you saw how to solve a problem about BMX racing using an equation. You can also solve this problem using a graph or a table.

PROBLEM

BMX RACING In Bicycle Moto Cross (BMX) racing, racers purchase a one year membership to a track. They also pay an entry fee for each race at that track. One racer paid a total of $125 after 5 races. A second racer paid a total of $170 after 8 races. How much does the track membership cost? What is the entry fee per race?

METHOD 1 **Using a Graph** One alternative approach is to use a graph.

STEP 1 **Read** the problem. It tells you the number of races and amount paid by each racer. Write this information as ordered pairs.

Racer 1: (5, 125)

Racer 2: (8, 170)

STEP 2 **Graph** the ordered pairs. Draw a line through the points.

The y-intercept is 50. So, the track membership is $50. · · · · · · · ·▶

STEP 3 **Find** the slope of the line. This is the entry fee per race.

$$\text{Fee} = \frac{45 \text{ dollars}}{3 \text{ races}} = \$15 \text{ per race}$$

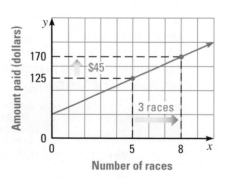

METHOD 2 **Using a Table** Another approach is to use a table showing the amount paid for various numbers of races.

STEP 1 **Calculate** the race entry fee.

Number of races	Amount paid
5	$125
6	?
7	?
8	$170

$+3$ $+$ $45

The number of races increased by 3, and the amount paid increased by $45, so the race entry fee is $45 ÷ 3 = $15.

STEP 2 **Find** the membership cost.

Number of races	Amount paid	
0	$50	− $15
1	$65	− $15
2	$80	− $15
3	$95	− $15
4	$110	− $15
5	$125	

The membership cost is the cost with no races. Use the race entry fee and work backwards to fill in the table. The membership cost is $50.

PRACTICE

1. **CALENDARS** A company makes calendars from personal photos. You pay a delivery fee for each order plus a cost per calendar. The cost of 2 calendars plus delivery is $43. The cost of 4 calendars plus delivery is $81. What is the delivery fee? What is the cost per calendar? Solve this problem using two different methods.

2. **BOOKSHELVES** A furniture maker offers bookshelves that have the same width and depth but that differ in height and price, as shown in the table. Find the cost of a bookshelf that is 72 inches high. Solve this problem using Method 2.

Height (inches)	Price (dollars)
36	56.54
48	77.42
60	98.30

3. **WHAT IF?** In Exercise 2, suppose the price of the 60 inch bookshelf is $99.30. Can you still solve the problem? *Explain*.

4. **CONCERT TICKETS** All tickets for a concert are the same price. The ticket agency adds a fixed fee to every order. A person who orders 5 tickets pays $80. A person who orders 3 tickets pays $50. How much will 4 tickets cost? Solve this problem using two different methods.

5. **ERROR ANALYSIS** A student solved the problem in Exercise 4 as shown below. *Describe* and correct the error.

Let p = price paid for 4 tickets.
$$\frac{57}{3} = \frac{p}{4}$$
$$228 = 3p$$
$$76 = p$$

MIXED REVIEW of Skills and Problem Solving

Multiple Choice Practice for Lessons 6.1–6.2

1. What is an equation for the linear function represented by the table? **Alg. 7.0**

x	−2	0	6
y	3	2	−1

Ⓐ $y = -2x + 2$ Ⓑ $y = -\frac{1}{2}x + 2$

Ⓒ $y = \frac{1}{2}x + 2$ Ⓓ $y = 2x + 2$

2. You use a garden hose to fill an empty swimming pool at a constant rate. After 5 minutes, there are 15 gallons of water in the pool. Which equation gives the volume V (in gallons) of water as a function of the time t (in minutes) since you began filling the pool? **Alg. 7.0**

Ⓐ $V = 5t$ Ⓑ $V = 15t + 5$

Ⓒ $V = 3t$ Ⓓ $V = 5t + 15$

3. What is an equation of the line shown? **Alg. 7.0**

Ⓐ $y = -\frac{5}{2}x - 6$

Ⓑ $y = -\frac{2}{5}x - \frac{9}{5}$

Ⓒ $y = -\frac{1}{2}x - 2$

Ⓓ $y = -\frac{5}{2}x + 4$

4. What is an equation of a line with a slope of −2 and a y-intercept of −5? **Alg. 7.0**

Ⓐ $y = -2x + 5$ Ⓑ $y = -5x + 2$

Ⓒ $y = -5x - 2$ Ⓓ $y = -2x - 5$

5. What is an equation of the line that passes through the points (−10, 6) and $\left(\frac{5}{2}, -4\right)$? **Alg. 7.0**

Ⓐ $y = -\frac{5}{4}x - \frac{13}{2}$ Ⓑ $y = -\frac{4}{5}x - 2$

Ⓒ $y = \frac{4}{5}x - 2$ Ⓓ $y = \frac{5}{4}x + 2$

6. You hike 5 miles before lunch. After lunch, you hike at an average rate of 3.5 miles per hour. If you use an equation in slope-intercept form to represent the total distance (in miles) that you hike as a function of time (in hours) since your break, what does the slope represent? **Alg. 7.0**

Ⓐ Miles hiked before your break

Ⓑ Miles hiked per hour before your break

Ⓒ Total number of miles hiked

Ⓓ Miles hiked per hour after your break

7. What is an equation of the line shown? **Alg. 7.0**

Ⓐ $y = x - 4$

Ⓑ $y = 3x + 4$

Ⓒ $y = 3x - 4$

Ⓓ $y = x + 4$

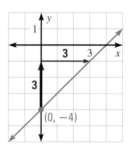

8. The sales ad for a satellite radio company is shown. What is the starting value in this situation? **Alg. 7.0**

SATELLITE RADIO
Equipment: $100
Service fee: $13 per month

Ⓐ $13 Ⓑ $100

Ⓒ $113 Ⓓ $87

9. What is an equation of the line that passes through the point (8, 3) and has a slope of $\frac{7}{8}$? **Alg. 7.0**

Ⓐ $y = \frac{7}{8}x - 4$ Ⓑ $y = -\frac{7}{8}x + 10$

Ⓒ $y = \frac{7}{8}x + 2$ Ⓓ $y = \frac{7}{8}x + \frac{43}{8}$

49. MARATHON The diagram below shows a marathon runner's speed at several outdoor temperatures. Write an equation in point-slope form that relates running speed (in feet per second) to temperature (in degrees Fahrenheit). Estimate the runner's speed when the temperature is 80°F.

Temperature	Running Speed
75°F	16.7 ft/sec
70°F	17.0 ft/sec
65°F	17.3 ft/sec
60°F	17.6 ft/sec

Not drawn to scale

CHALLENGE Find the value of k so that the line passing through the given points has slope m. Write an equation of the line in point-slope form.

50. $(k, 4k)$, $(k + 2, 3k)$, $m = -1$

51. $(-k + 1, 3)$, $(3, k + 3)$, $m = 3$

52. CHALLENGE The number of cans recycled per pound of aluminum recycled in the United States increased at a relatively constant rate from 1972 to 2002. In 1977 about 23.5 cans per pound of aluminum were recycled. In 2000, about 33.1 cans per pound of aluminum were recycled.

    a. Write an equation that gives the number of cans recycled per pound of aluminum recycled as a function of the number of years since 1972.

    b. In 2002, there were 53.8 billion aluminum cans collected for recycling. Approximately how many pounds of aluminum were collected? *Explain* how you found your answer.

◆ CALIFORNIA STANDARDS SPIRAL REVIEW

Alg. 7.0

53. What is an equation of the linear function represented by the table? *(p. 322)*

x	−10	−5	0	5
y	3	1	−1	−3

    Ⓐ $y = -5x + 1$ **Ⓑ** $y = -2x - 1$ **Ⓒ** $y = -\frac{2}{5}x - 1$ **Ⓓ** $y = \frac{1}{3}x - 1$

Alg. 5.0

54. What is the solution of $3(4 + 2x) = 4 - 2(8 - 7x)$? *(p. 146)*

    Ⓐ $-\frac{8}{3}$ **Ⓑ** $-\frac{6}{5}$ **Ⓒ** $\frac{1}{5}$ **Ⓓ** 3

Alg. 5.0

55. The total weight w (in pounds) of a truck loaded with b boxes is given by the equation $w = 75b + 13,050$. The total weight is 16,425 pounds. How many boxes are loaded on the truck? *(p. 132)*

    Ⓐ 45   **Ⓑ** 174   **Ⓒ** 219   **Ⓓ** 393

6.4 Write Linear Equations in Standard Form

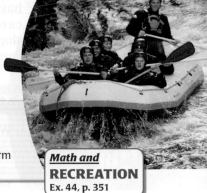

Standards Alg. 7.0 Students verify that a point lies on a line, given an equation of the line. **Students are able to derive linear equations by using the point-slope formula.**

Connect *Before* you wrote equations in point-slope form. *Now* you will use point-slope form to write equations in standard form.

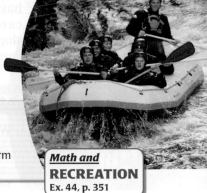

Math and
RECREATION
Ex. 44, p. 351

Key Vocabulary
• **standard form,**
  p. 265

Recall that the standard form of a linear equation is $Ax + By = C$ where A, B, and C are real numbers and A and B are not both zero. All linear equations can be written in standard form.

EXAMPLE 1 **Write equivalent equations in standard form**

Write two equations in standard form that are equivalent to $2x - 6y = 4$.

Solution

To write one equivalent equation, multiply each side by 2.

$$4x - 12y = 8$$

To write another equivalent equation, multiply each side by 0.5.

$$x - 3y = 2$$

EXAMPLE 2 **Write an equation from a graph**

Write an equation in standard form of the line shown.

Solution

STEP 1 **Calculate** the slope.

$$m = \frac{1 - (-2)}{1 - 2} = \frac{3}{-1} = -3$$

STEP 2 **Write** an equation in point-slope form. Use the point (1, 1).

$$y - y_1 = m(x - x_1) \quad \text{Write point-slope form.}$$
$$y - 1 = -3(x - 1) \quad \text{Substitute } -3 \text{ for } m, 1 \text{ for } x_1, \text{ and } 1 \text{ for } y_1.$$

STEP 3 **Rewrite** the equation in standard form.

$$3x + y = 4 \qquad \text{Simplify. Collect variable terms on one side, constants on the other.}$$

Algebra

For an interactive example of writing an equation in standard form, go to **classzone.com**.

About the Standards

Notice that point-slope form can be used to obtain an equation in standard form, as in Example 2. This is true for all lines except vertical lines.

✓ **GUIDED PRACTICE** for Examples 1 and 2

1. Write two equations in standard form that are equivalent to $x - y = 3$.

2. Write an equation in standard form of the line through $(3, -1)$ and $(2, -3)$.

---

45. TRANSPORTATION One bus ride costs $.75. One subway ride costs $1.00. A monthly pass can be used for unlimited subway and bus rides and costs the same as 36 subway rides plus 36 bus rides.

   a. Write an equation in standard form that models the possible combinations of bus and subway rides with the same value as the pass.

   b. You ride the bus 60 times in one month. How many times must you ride the subway in order for the cost of the rides to equal the value of the pass? *Explain* your answer.

46. **GEOMETRY** Write an equation in standard form that models the possible lengths and widths (in feet) of a rectangle having the same perimeter as a rectangle that is 10 feet wide and 20 feet long. Make a table that shows five possible lengths and widths of the rectangle.

47. CHALLENGE Given the equation $Ax + By = C$, suppose you know that y varies directly with x. What can you conclude about the values of A, B, and C? What is the constant of variation?

48. CHALLENGE Write an equation in standard form of the line that passes through $(0, a)$ and $(b, 0)$ where $a \neq 0$ and $b \neq 0$.

49. CHALLENGE You spend $92 on x T-shirts that cost $12 each and y sweatshirts that cost $22 each.

   a. Write an equation in standard form that models the possible combinations of T-shirts and sweatshirts that you buy.

   b. Graph the equation you wrote in part (a).

   c. Use your graph from part (b) to explain why there is only one solution for the number of T-shirts and the number of sweatshirts.

◆ CALIFORNIA STANDARDS SPIRAL REVIEW

Alg. 6.0

50. What is the y-intercept of the line $6x + 3y = 24$? *(p. 273)*

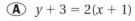

   (A) $-\dfrac{1}{2}$ **(B)** 4   **(C)** 8   **(D)** 24

Alg. 7.0

51. What is an equation of the line shown? *(p. 340)*

   (A) $y + 3 = 2(x + 1)$

   (B) $y - 1 = \dfrac{3}{4}(x - 4)$

   (C) $y - 1 = \dfrac{3}{4}(x + 3)$

   (D) $y - 4 = \dfrac{1}{2}(x + 1)$

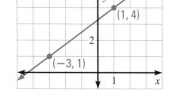

Alg. 3.0

52. An oral report for history class must last 10 minutes with an absolute deviation of 2 minutes. What are the minimum and maximum lengths (in seconds) of a report? *(p. 220)*

   (A) 320 sec, 570 sec   **(B)** 480 sec, 720 sec

   (C) 540 sec, 660 sec   **(D)** 720 sec, 840 sec

6.5 If-Then Statements and Their Converses

MATERIALS · index cards

Standards

Alg. 24.3 Students use counterexamples to **show that an assertion is false** and recognize that a single counterexample is sufficient to refute an assertion.

QUESTION Is the converse of a conditional statement true?

In Lesson 2.1, you learned that an if-then statement is a form of a conditional statement where the *if* part contains the hypothesis and the *then* part contains the conclusion. The *converse* of an if-then statement interchanges the hypothesis and conclusion of the original statement.

EXPLORE Write the converse

STEP 1 *Make cards*

Write each phrase below on a separate index card.

it swims	it is a tree	it flies	it needs water	it has wings
it is a duck	it grows	it is a bird	it is an airplane	it is a frog

STEP 2 *Write the conditional statement*

Place the cards face down. Select a card at random to be the hypothesis. Select another card at random to be the conclusion. Write the statement and determine whether it is true or false. If it is false, give a counterexample.

Hypothesis: **it is a duck**   Conclusion: **it has wings**

Statement: If it is a duck, then it has wings.

The statement is true. All ducks have wings.

it swims

STEP 3 *Write the converse*

Switch the order of the cards to create the converse statement. Determine whether the converse is true or false. If it is false, give a counterexample.

Hypothesis: **it has wings**   Conclusion: **it is a duck**

Statement: If it has wings, then it is a duck.

The statement is false. Airplanes have wings, but they are not ducks.

STEP 4 *Repeat*

Repeat Steps 2 and 3 ten times. Keep a record of your conditional statements and their converses.

DRAW CONCLUSIONS Use your observations to complete these exercises

1. **REASONING** If a conditional statement is true, can you be sure that its converse is true? *Justify* your answer.

2. **REASONING** If the converse of a statement is true, can you be sure that the original statement is true? *Justify* your answer.

6.5 Write Equations of Parallel and Perpendicular Lines

Math and NATURE
Ex. 36, p. 359

Standards Alg. 8.0 Students understand the concepts of parallel lines and perpendicular lines and how their slopes are related. Students are able to find the equation of a line perpendicular to a given line that passes through a given point.

Connect *Before* you used slope to determine whether lines are parallel. *Now* you will write equations of parallel and perpendicular lines.

Key Vocabulary
- converse
- perpendicular lines
- conditional statement, *p. 55*

The **converse** of a conditional statement interchanges the hypothesis and conclusion. The converse of a true statement is not necessarily true.

In Chapter 5, you learned that the statement "If two different nonvertical lines have the same slope, then they are parallel" is true. Its converse is also true.

KEY CONCEPT *For Your Notebook*

Parallel Lines

- If two different nonvertical lines in the same plane have the same slope, then they are parallel.

- If two different nonvertical lines in the same plane are parallel, then they have the same slope.

EXAMPLE 1 ◆ **Multiple Choice Practice**

> Which equation represents a line that is parallel to $y = \frac{4}{5}x + 2$?
>
> **A** $y = -\frac{4}{5}x + 2$ **B** $y = 1.5x - 1$ **C** $y = \frac{1}{3}x + 5$ **D** $y = \frac{4}{5}x - 3$

Solution

The given line has a slope of $\frac{4}{5}$. So, a line parallel to the given line has a slope of $\frac{4}{5}$.

▶ The line $y = \frac{4}{5}x - 3$ is parallel to the line $y = \frac{4}{5}x + 2$.

The correct answer is D. Ⓐ Ⓑ Ⓒ ●

✓ **GUIDED PRACTICE** for Example 1

1. Which line is parallel to the line $y = -2x + 4$?

   A $y = -2x - 5$ **B** $y = -2x + 4$ **C** $y = 2x + 4$ **D** $y = 2x - 3$

EXAMPLE 2 **Write an equation of a parallel line**

Write an equation of the line that passes through $(-3, -5)$ and is parallel to the line $y = 3x - 1$.

Solution

STEP 1 **Identify** the slope. The graph of the given equation has a slope of 3. So, the parallel line through $(-3, -5)$ has a slope of 3.

STEP 2 **Find** the y-intercept. Use the slope and the given point.

$$y = mx + b$$ Write slope-intercept form.

$$-5 = 3(-3) + b$$ Substitute 3 for m, -3 for x, and -5 for y.

$$4 = b$$ Solve for b.

STEP 3 **Write** an equation. Use $y = mx + b$.

$$y = 3x + 4$$ Substitute 3 for m and 4 for b.

CHECK REASONABLENESS
You can check that your answer is reasonable by graphing both equations.

GUIDED PRACTICE   **for Example 2**

Write an equation of the line that passes through the given point and is parallel to the given line.

2. $(-2, 11)$, $y = -x + 5$ **3.** $(4, -2)$, $y = -\frac{1}{2}x + 6$

PERPENDICULAR LINES Two lines in the same plane are **perpendicular** if they intersect to form a right angle. Horizontal and vertical lines are perpendicular to each other.

USE FRACTIONS
The product of a nonzero number m and its negative reciprocal is -1:
$$m\left(-\frac{1}{m}\right) = -1.$$

Compare the slopes of the perpendicular lines shown below. Notice that the slopes are negative reciprocals because $\left(-\frac{3}{2}\right)\left(\frac{2}{3}\right) = -1$.

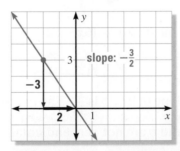

Rotate the line 90° in a clockwise direction about the origin to find a perpendicular line.

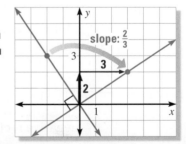

KEY CONCEPT   *For Your Notebook*

Perpendicular Lines

• If two nonvertical lines in the same plane have slopes that are negative reciprocals, then the lines are perpendicular.

• If two nonvertical lines in the same plane are perpendicular, then their slopes are negative reciprocals.

EXAMPLE 3 **Determine whether lines are parallel or perpendicular**

Determine which lines, if any, are parallel or perpendicular.

Line a: $y = 5x - 3$ **Line b:** $x + 5y = 2$ **Line c:** $-10y - 2x = 0$

Solution

Find the slopes of the lines.

Line a: The equation is in slope-intercept form. The slope is 5.

Write the equations for lines b and c in slope-intercept form.

Line b: $x + 5y = 2$	**Line c:** $-10y - 2x = 0$
$5y = -x + 2$	$-10y = 2x$
$y = -\frac{1}{5}x + \frac{2}{5}$	$y = -\frac{1}{5}x$

▶ Lines b and c have slopes of $-\frac{1}{5}$, so they are parallel. Line a has a slope

of 5, the negative reciprocal of $-\frac{1}{5}$, so it is perpendicular to lines b and c.

EXAMPLE 4 **Determine whether lines are perpendicular**

STATE FLAG The Arizona state flag is shown in a coordinate plane. Lines a and b appear to be perpendicular. Are they?

Line a: $17y = -9x + 122$

Line b: $11y = 16x - 52$

Solution

Find the slopes of the lines.
Write the equations in slope-intercept form.

Line a: $17y = -9x + 122$	**Line b:** $11y = 16x - 52$
$y = -\frac{9}{17}x + \frac{122}{17}$	$y = \frac{16}{11}x - \frac{52}{11}$

▶ The slope of line a is $-\frac{9}{17}$. The slope of line b is $\frac{16}{11}$. The two slopes are not

negative reciprocals, so lines a and b are not perpendicular.

✓ **GUIDED PRACTICE** for Examples 3 and 4

4. Determine which lines, if any, are parallel or perpendicular.

   Line a: $2x + 6y = -3$ **Line b:** $y = 3x - 8$ **Line c:** $-1.5y + 4.5x = 6$

5. Lines c and d are two other lines that appear to be perpendicular in the Arizona state flag from Example 4. Are the lines perpendicular? *Explain.*

   Line c: $2y + 5x = 38$ **Line d:** $4y = x + 10$

EXAMPLE 5 **Write an equation of a perpendicular line**

Write an equation of the line that passes through (4, −5) and is perpendicular to the line $y = 2x + 3$.

Solution

STEP 1 **Identify** the slope. The graph of the given equation has a slope of 2. Because the slopes of perpendicular lines are negative reciprocals, the slope of the perpendicular line through (4, −5) is $-\frac{1}{2}$.

ANOTHER WAY

Using point-slope form to find an equation of the perpendicular line gives:

$y + 5 = -\frac{1}{2}(x - 4)$

$y + 5 = -\frac{1}{2}x - 2$

$y = -\frac{1}{2}x - 3$

STEP 2 **Find** the y-intercept. Use the slope and the given point.

$y = mx + b$ Write slope-intercept form.

$-5 = -\frac{1}{2}(4) + b$ Substitute $-\frac{1}{2}$ for m, 4 for x, and −5 for y.

$-3 = b$ Solve for b.

STEP 3 **Write** an equation.

$y = mx + b$ Write slope-intercept form.

$y = -\frac{1}{2}x - 3$ Substitute $-\frac{1}{2}$ for m and −3 for b.

✓ **GUIDED PRACTICE** **for Example 5**

6. Write an equation of the line that passes through (4, 3) and is perpendicular to the line $y = 4x - 7$.

6.5 **EXERCISES**

HOMEWORK KEY

◆ = MULTIPLE CHOICE PRACTICE
Exs. 19, 31, 39, and 43−45

◯ = HINTS AND HOMEWORK HELP
for Exs. 13, 21, and 39 at classzone.com

SKILLS · PROBLEM SOLVING · REASONING

1. **VOCABULARY** Copy and complete: Two lines in a plane are ? if they intersect to form a right angle.

2. **WRITING** *Explain* how you can tell whether two nonvertical lines are perpendicular given the equations of the lines.

EXAMPLE 2
on p. 355
for Exs. 3–11

PARALLEL LINES Write an equation of the line that passes through the given point and is parallel to the given line.

3. (−1, 3), $y = 2x + 2$ 4. (6, 8), $y = -\frac{5}{2}x + 10$ 5. (5, −1), $y = -\frac{3}{5}x - 3$

6. (−1, 2), $y = 5x + 4$ 7. (1, 7), $-6x + y = -1$ 8. (18, 8), $3y = x - 12$

9. (−2, 5), $2y = 4x - 6$ 10. (9, 4), $y - x = 3$ 11. (−10, 0), $-y + 3x = 16$

EXAMPLES
1 and 3

on pp. 354, 356
for Exs. 12–20

PARALLEL OR PERPENDICULAR Determine which lines, if any, are parallel or perpendicular.

12. Line a: $y = 4x - 2$, line b: $y = -\frac{1}{4}x$

13. Line a: $y = \frac{1}{2}x - 14$, line b: $y = 2x + 2$

14. Line a: $y = \frac{2}{3}x - 1$, line b: $y = \frac{2}{3}x + 1$

15. Line a: $3y = x$, Line b: $y = -3x + 4$

16. Line a: $y = \frac{3}{5}x + 1$, line b: $5y = 3x - 2$, line c: $10x - 6y = -4$

17. Line a: $y = 3x + 6$, line b: $3x + y = 6$, line c: $3y = 2x + 18$

18. Line a: $4x - 3y = 2$, line b: $3x + 4y = -1$, line c: $4y - 3x = 20$

19. ◆ **MULTIPLE CHOICE** Which statement is true of the given lines?

Line a: $-2x + y = 4$ **Line b:** $2x + 5y = 2$ **Line c:** $x + 2y = 4$

(A) Lines a and b are parallel.   **(B)** Lines a and c are parallel.

(C) Lines a and b are perpendicular.   **(D)** Lines a and c are perpendicular.

20. SHORT RESPONSE Determine which of the lines shown, if any, are parallel or perpendicular. *Justify* your answer using slopes.

*Animated*Algebra at classzone.com

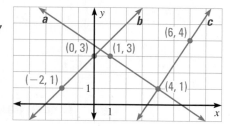

EXAMPLE 5

on p. 357
for Exs. 21–30

PERPENDICULAR LINES Write an equation of the line that passes through the given point and is perpendicular to the given line.

21. $(-9, 2)$, $y = 3x - 12$ **22.** $(3, -3)$, $y = x + 5$ **23.** $(5, 1)$, $y = 5x - 2$

24. $(7, 10)$, $y = 0.5x - 9$ **25.** $(-2, -4)$, $y = -\frac{2}{7}x + 1$ **26.** $(-4, -1)$, $y = \frac{4}{3}x + 6$

27. $(3, 3)$, $2y = 3x - 6$ **28.** $(-5, 2)$, $y + 3 = 2x$ **29.** $(8, -1)$, $4y + 2x = 12$

30. ERROR ANALYSIS *Describe* and correct the error in finding the y-intercept of the line that passes through $(2, 1)$ and is perpendicular to the line $y = -\frac{1}{2}x + 3$.

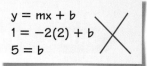

$$y = mx + b$$
$$1 = -2(2) + b$$
$$5 = b$$

31. ◆ **MULTIPLE CHOICE** What is an equation of the line that passes through $(0, 0)$ and is parallel to the line that passes through $(2, 3)$ and $(6, 1)$?

(A) $y = \frac{1}{2}x$ **(B)** $y = -\frac{1}{2}x$ **(C)** $y = -2x$ **(D)** $y = 2x$

32. REASONING Is the line through the points $(4, 3)$ and $(3, -1)$ perpendicular to the line through the points $(-3, 3)$ and $(1, 2)$? *Justify* your answer using slopes.

33. OPEN-ENDED Write equations of two lines that are parallel. Then write an equation of a line that is perpendicular to those lines.

34. REASONING Is the line through the points $(1, 3)$ and $(3, 7)$ parallel to the line through the points $(5, 9)$ and $(7, 13)$? *Justify* your answer using slopes.

CONNECT SKILLS TO PROBLEM SOLVING Exercises 35 and 36 will help you prepare for problem solving.

Use the following information: A nautical flag is shown in a coordinate plane. Equations of lines *a*, *b*, *c*, and *d* are:

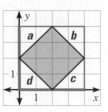

Line *a*: $y = x + 2$ Line *b*: $y = -x + 6$
Line *c*: $y = x - 2$ Line *d*: $y = -x + 2$

35. Which pairs of lines are parallel? *Explain* how you know.

36. Which pairs of lines are perpendicular? *Explain* how you know.

EXAMPLES
3, 4 and 5
on pp. 356–357
for Exs. 37–40

37. HOCKEY A hockey puck leaves the blade of a hockey stick, bounces off a wall, and travels in a new direction, as shown.

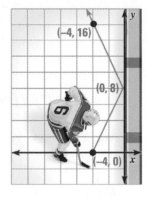

a. Write an equation that models the path of the puck from the blade of the hockey stick to the wall.

b. Write an equation that models the path of the puck after it bounces off the wall.

c. Does the path of the puck form a right angle? *Justify* your answer.

California@*HomeTutor* for problem solving help at classzone.com

38. BIOLOGY While nursing, blue whale calves can gain weight at a rate of 200 pounds per day. Two particular calves weigh 6000 pounds and 6250 pounds at birth.

a. Write equations that model the weight of each calf as a function of the number of days since birth.

b. How much is each calf expected to weigh 30 days after birth?

c. How are the graphs of the equations from part (a) related? *Justify* your answer.

California@*HomeTutor* for problem solving help at classzone.com

39. ◆ **MULTIPLE CHOICE** The streets on the map can be modeled by the equations given. Which of the streets are parallel?

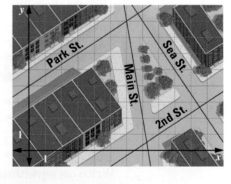

Park: $3y - 2x = 12$ **Main:** $y = -6x + 44$
Sea: $2y = -3x + 37$ **2nd:** $3y = 2x - 13$

Ⓐ Sea and Main   Ⓑ 2nd and Sea

Ⓒ 2nd and Main   Ⓓ Park and 2nd

40. MULTI-STEP PROBLEM If you are one of the first 100 people to join a new health club, you are charged a joining fee of $49. Otherwise, you are charged a joining fee of $149. The monthly membership cost is $38.75.

a. Write equations that give the total cost (in dollars) of membership as a function of the number of months of membership for each possibility: (1) you are one of the first 100 members to join, and (2) you are *not* one of the first 100 members to join.

b. How are the graphs of these functions related? How do you know?

c. After 6 months, what is the difference in total cost for a person who paid $149 to join and a person who paid $49 to join? after 12 months?

41. CHALLENGE Write a formula for the slope of a line that is perpendicular to the line through the points (x_1, y_1) and (x_2, y_2).

42. CHALLENGE You and your friend have gift cards to a shopping mall. Your card has a value of $50, and your friend's card has a value of $30. If neither of you uses the cards, the value begins to decrease at a rate of $2.50 per month after 6 months.

   a. Write two equations, one that gives the value of your card and another that gives the value of your friend's card as functions of the number of months after 6 months of non-use.

   b. How are the graphs of these functions related? How do you know?

   c. What are the x-intercepts of the graphs of the functions, and what do they mean in this situation?

◆ CALIFORNIA STANDARDS SPIRAL REVIEW

Alg. 2.0

43. Which number is between $\sqrt{14}$ and $\sqrt{19}$? *(p. 95)*

   (A) 3   **(B)** 4   **(C)** 5   **(D)** 6

Alg. 6.0

44. What are the x- and y-intercepts of the line $y = \frac{1}{2}x - 2$? *(p. 273)*

   (A) x-intercept: -2; y-intercept: 4   **(B)** x-intercept: -1; y-intercept: -2

   (C) x-intercept: 4; y-intercept: -2 **(D)** x-intercept: 1; y-intercept: -2

Alg. 5.0

45. You have a gift certificate to a bookstore worth C dollars. You buy a calendar for $11 and plan to spend the rest on paperback books that cost $8 each. Let b represent the number of books you can buy. Which equation models this situation? *(p. 146)*

   (A) $C = 8b + 11$ **(B)** $C = 8b$ **(C)** $C = 35b$ **(D)** $C = 8b - 11$

QUIZ *for Lessons 6.3–6.5*

Write an equation in (a) point–slope form and (b) standard form of the line that passes through the given points. *(pp. 340, 347)*

   1. $(-5, 2), (-4, 3)$ **2.** $(0, -1), (-6, -9)$ **3.** $(3, 9), (1, 1)$ **4.** $(-2, -5), (-1, -3)$

Write an equation of the line that passes through the given point and is (a) parallel to the given line and (b) perpendicular to the given line. *(p. 354)*

   5. $(2, 3), y = 2x + 5$ **6.** $(-2, 1), y = -3x - 2$ **7.** $(10, 5), y = -5x + 1$

8. DVDS The table shows the price per DVD for different numbers of DVDs purchased. Write an equation that models the price per DVD as a function of the number of DVDs purchased for up to 6 DVDs. *(p. 340)*

Number of DVDs purchased	1	2	3	4	5	6
Price per DVD (dollars)	20	18	16	14	12	10

MIXED REVIEW of Skills and Problem Solving

Multiple Choice Practice for Lessons 6.3–6.5

1. The table shows the cost of a catered lunch buffet for different numbers of people. Which of the following is an equation that relates the total cost C (in dollars) of a catered lunch buffet to the number p of people? **Alg. 7.0**

Number of people	12	18	24	30
Cost (dollars)	192	288	384	480

  (A) $C - 192 = 12(p - 12)$

  (B) $C - 192 = 16(p - 12)$

  (C) $C - 30 = 12(p - 480)$

  (D) $C - 2 = 16(p - 192)$

2. Which line passes through the point $(8, 2)$ and is perpendicular to the line $y = 2x + 10$? **Alg. 8.0**

  (A) $y = -2x + 18$ (B) $y = 2x - 14$

  (C) $y = \frac{1}{2}x - 2$ (D) $y = -\frac{1}{2}x + 6$

3. What is an equation in standard form of the line shown? **Alg. 7.0**

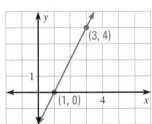

  (A) $2x + y = 10$ (B) $2x + y = 6$

  (C) $-2x + y = -2$ (D) $x - 2y = 2$

4. Which line passes through the point $(-6, 1)$ and is parallel to the line $y = \frac{5}{6}x - 3$? **Alg. 8.0**

  (A) $y = \frac{5}{6}x + 6$ (B) $y = -\frac{6}{5}x - 9$

  (C) $y = \frac{6}{5}x + 4$ (D) $y = \frac{5}{6}x - \frac{1}{3}$

5. Your city is paving the bike path shown. The same length of path is paved each day. After 4 days of paving, there are 8 miles of path left to be paved. Which equation gives the number y of miles of bike path left to be paved as a function of the number x of days since paving began? **Alg. 7.0**

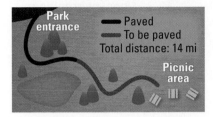

  (A) $y = -\frac{3}{2}x + 14$ (B) $y = 14x - \frac{3}{2}$

  (C) $y = -\frac{2}{3}x + 14$ (D) $y = 14x - \frac{2}{3}$

6. Which line passes through $(-5, 7)$ and has a slope of -3? **Alg. 7.0**

  (A) $y - 7 = -3(x - 5)$

  (B) $y - 7 = -5(x + 3)$

  (C) $y - 7 = -3(x + 5)$

  (D) $y + 7 = -3(x - 5)$

7. You have $10 to make copies. A copy store's ad below shows how much each copy costs. Which equation models the different combinations of the number b of black and white copies you can make and the number c of color copies you can make? **Alg. 7.0**

  (A) $b + 10c = 10$ (B) $c + 10b = 100$

  (C) $c - 10b = 0$ (D) $b + 10c = 100$

BIG IDEAS
For Your Notebook

Big Idea 1

Writing Linear Equations in a Variety of Forms

Using given information about a line, you can write an equation of the line in three different forms.

Form	Equation	Important information
Slope-intercept form	$y = mx + b$	• The slope of the line is m. • The y-intercept of the line is b.
Point-slope form	$y - y_1 = m(x - x_1)$	• The slope of the line is m. • The line passes through (x_1, y_1).
Standard form	$Ax + By = C$	• A, B, and C are real numbers. • A and B are not both zero.

Big Idea 2

Using Linear Models to Solve Problems

You can write a linear equation that models a situation involving a constant rate of change. Analyzing given information helps you choose a linear model.

Choosing a Linear Model	
If this is what you know . . .	**. . . then use this equation form**
constant rate of change and initial value	slope-intercept form
constant rate of change and one data pair	slope-intercept form or point-slope form
two data pairs and the fact that the rate of change is constant	slope-intercept form or point-slope form
the sum or difference of two variable quantities is constant	standard form

Big Idea 3

Writing Equations of Parallel and Perpendicular Lines

You can find an equation of a line that passes through a given point if you know that the line is parallel or perpendicular to a given line.

	Parallel to given line	Perpendicular to given line
STEP 1 Identify the slope.	The slope is the same as the slope of the given line.	The slope is the negative reciprocal of the slope of the given line.
STEP 2 Find the y-intercept.	Substitute the slope from Step 1 and the coordinates of the given point in $y = mx + b$ and solve for b.	
STEP 3 Write an equation.	Use the values for the slope and the y-intercept to write an equation.	

PROBLEM How can you use linear equations to describe a route for a scavenger hunt?

STEP 1 **Plan your route for a scavenger hunt.**

You are on a scavenger hunt at a historical park. You must photograph each monument in the park. The monuments are labeled with letters in the map below. Plan a route for visiting each monument by listing the letters of the monuments in the order you will visit them. Use the following rules:

• Each path between two monuments is a straight line.

• Any time you cross water you must use a bridge.

• At least two paths must be parallel. At least two must be perpendicular.

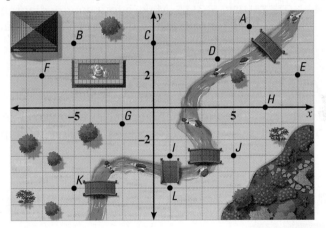

STEP 2 **Write equations for the paths.**

Write an equation of the line containing each path. Use each of the following forms at least once: slope-intercept form, point-slope form, and standard form. Identify which paths are parallel and which paths are perpendicular.

Extending the Problem

1. Is one form of a linear equation easier to write than another form for particular paths? *Explain.*

2. Suppose you earn points for each monument you photograph. Monuments *K*, *B*, and *H* are each worth 20 points, and all other monuments are worth 10 points. Once you reach exactly 100 points you have completed the scavenger hunt.

   a. Write a model for the number *m* of 20 point monuments and the number *n* of 10 point monuments you must photograph to reach 100 points. List several possible combinations.

   b. Determine where along the route you wrote in Step 1 you reach 100 points. If at any point along your route you go over 100 points, go back and revise your route so you earn exactly 100 points. Write equations of the lines containing any new paths on your route.

REVIEW KEY VOCABULARY

• point-slope form, *p. 340*   • converse, *p. 354*   • perpendicular, *p. 355*

VOCABULARY EXERCISES

1. Copy and complete: The __?__ of a conditional statement interchanges the hypothesis and conclusion.

2. Write the point-slope form of an equation of a line that passes through (x_1, y_1) and has a slope of m.

3. Copy and complete: If two lines are __?__, they intersect to form a right angle.

4. **NOTETAKING SKILLS** Make a four square diagram like the one on page 320 for the standard form of a linear equation.

REVIEW EXAMPLES AND EXERCISES

Use the review examples and exercises below to check your understanding of the concepts you have learned in each lesson of Chapter 6.

6.1 Write Linear Equations in Slope-Intercept Form   *pp. 322–328*

Alg. 7.0

EXAMPLE

Write an equation of the line shown.

$y = mx + b$ Write slope-intercept form.

$y = -\dfrac{2}{3}x + 4$ Substitute $-\dfrac{2}{3}$ for m and 4 for b.

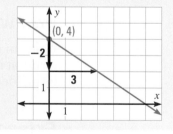

EXERCISES

EXAMPLES
1, 3, and 5
on pp. 322–324
for Exs. 5–11

Write an equation in slope-intercept form of the line with the given slope and y-intercept.

5. slope: 3
   y-intercept: -10

6. slope: $\dfrac{4}{9}$
   y-intercept: 5

7. slope: $-\dfrac{2}{11}$
   y-intercept: 7

Write an equation of the line that passes through the given points.

8. $(0, -3), (5, 8)$

9. $(-2, 4), (0, 6)$

10. $(-1, -9), (0, -7)$

11. **GIFT CARD** You have a $25 gift card for a bagel shop. A bagel costs $1.25. Write an equation that gives the amount (in dollars) that remains on the card as a function of the total number of bagels you have purchased so far. How much money is on the card after you buy 2 bagels?

6.2 Use Linear Equations in Slope-Intercept Form
pp. 329–336

Alg. 7.0 **EXAMPLE**

Write an equation of the line that passes through the point $(-2, -6)$ and has a slope of 2.

STEP 1 Find the y-intercept.

$y = mx + b$ Write slope-intercept form.

$-6 = 2(-2) + b$ Substitute 2 for m, -2 for x, and -6 for y.

$-2 = b$ Solve for b.

STEP 2 Write an equation of the line.

$y = mx + b$ Write slope-intercept form.

$y = 2x - 2$ Substitute 2 for m and -2 for b.

EXERCISES

Write an equation in slope-intercept form of the line that passes through the given point and has the given slope m.

12. $(-3, -1)$; $m = 4$ **13.** $(-2, 1)$; $m = 1$ **14.** $(8, -4)$; $m = -3$

6.3 Write Linear Equations in Point-Slope Form
pp. 340–346

Alg. 7.0 **EXAMPLE**

Write an equation in point-slope form of the line shown.

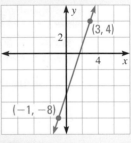

STEP 1 Find the slope of the line.

$$m = \frac{y_2 - y_1}{x_2 - x_1} = \frac{-8 - 4}{-1 - 3} = \frac{-12}{-4} = 3$$

STEP 2 Write an equation. Use $(3, 4)$.

$y - y_1 = m(x - x_1)$ Write point-slope form.

$y - 4 = 3(x - 3)$ Substitute 3 for m, 3 for x_1, and 4 for y_1.

EXERCISES

EXAMPLES
3 and 5
on pp. 341, 342
for Exs. 15–18

Write an equation in point-slope form of the line that passes through the given points.

15. $(4, 7), (5, 1)$ **16.** $(9, -2), (-3, 2)$ **17.** $(8, -8), (-3, -2)$

18. BUS TRIP A bus leaves at 10 A.M. to take students on a field trip to a historic site. At 10:25 A.M., the bus is 75 miles from the site. At 11:15 A.M., the bus is 25 miles from the site. The bus travels at a constant speed. Write an equation in point-slope form that relates the distance (in miles) from the site and the time (in minutes) after 10:00 A.M. How far is the bus from the site at 11:30 A.M.?

6.4 Write Linear Equations in Standard Form

pp. 347–352

Alg. 7.0 | **EXAMPLE**

Write an equation in standard form of the line shown.

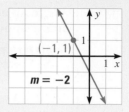

$y - y_1 = m(x - x_1)$ Write point-slope form.

$y - 1 = -2(x - (-1))$ Substitute 1 for y_1, −2 for m, and −1 for x_1.

$y - 1 = -2x - 2$ Distributive property

$2x + y = -1$ Collect variable terms on one side, constants on the other.

EXERCISES

Write an equation in standard form of the line that has the given characteristics.

EXAMPLES
2 and 5
on pp. 347, 349
for Exs. 19–21

19. Slope: −4; passes through $(-2, 7)$ **20.** Passes through $(-1, -5)$ and $(3, 7)$

21. COSTUMES You are buying ribbon to make costumes for a school play. Organza ribbon costs $.07 per yard. Satin ribbon costs $.04 per yard. Write an equation to model the possible combinations of yards of organza ribbon and yards of satin ribbon you can buy for $5. List several possible combinations.

6.5 Write Equations of Parallel and Perpendicular Lines

pp. 354–360

Alg. 8.0 | **EXAMPLE**

Write an equation of the line that passes through $(-4, -2)$ and is perpendicular to the line $y = 4x - 7$.

The slope of the line $y = 4x - 7$ is 4. The slope of the perpendicular line through $(-4, -2)$ is $-\frac{1}{4}$. Find the y-intercept of the perpendicular line.

$y = mx + b$ Write slope-intercept form.

$-2 = -\frac{1}{4}(-4) + b$ Substitute $-\frac{1}{4}$ for m, −4 for x, and −2 for y.

$-3 = b$ Solve for b.

An equation of the perpendicular line through $(-4, -2)$ is $y = -\frac{1}{4}x - 3$.

EXERCISES

Write an equation of the line that passes through the given point and is **(a)** parallel to the given line and **(b)** perpendicular to the given line.

EXAMPLES
2 and 5
on pp. 355, 357
for Exs. 22–24

22. $(0, 2)$, $y = -4x + 6$ **23.** $(2, -3)$, $y = -2x - 3$ **24.** $(6, 0)$, $y = \frac{3}{4}x - \frac{1}{4}$

1. **VOCABULARY** What kind of lines have slopes that are negative reciprocals?

2. **VOCABULARY** Write the standard form of an equation. State any restrictions on the constants in the equation.

3. **VOCABULARY** Name the following form of an equation of a line: $y = mx + b$. What does m represent? What does b represent?

Write an equation in slope-intercept form of the line with the given slope and y-intercept.

4. slope: 5
   y-intercept: -7

5. slope: $\frac{2}{5}$
   y-intercept: -2

6. slope: $-\frac{4}{3}$
   y-intercept: 1

Write an equation in slope-intercept form of the line that passes through the given point and has the given slope m.

7. $(-2, -8)$; $m = 3$

8. $(1, 1)$; $m = -4$

9. $(-1, 3)$; $m = -6$

Write an equation in point-slope form of the line that passes through the given points.

10. $(4, 5)$, $(2, 9)$

11. $(-2, 2)$, $(8, -3)$

12. $(3, 4)$, $(1, -6)$

Write an equation in standard form of the line with the given characteristics.

13. Slope: 10; passes through $(6, 2)$

14. Passes through $(-3, 2)$ and $(6, -1)$

Write an equation of the line that passes through the given point and is (a) parallel to the given line and (b) perpendicular to the given line.

15. $(2, 0)$, $y = -5x + 3$

16. $(-1, 4)$, $y = -x - 4$

17. $(4, -9)$, $y = \frac{1}{4}x + 2$

18. **FIELD TRIP** Your science class is taking a field trip to an observatory. The cost of a presentation and a tour of the telescope is $60 for the group plus an additional $3 per person. Write an equation that gives the total cost C as a function of the number p of people in the group.

19. **TELEPHONE SERVICE** The annual household cost of telephone service in the United States increased at a relatively constant rate of $27.80 per year from 1981 to 2001. In 2001 the annual household cost of telephone service was $914. Write an equation that gives the annual household cost of telephone service as a function of the number of years since 1981. Find the annual household cost of telephone service in 2000.

20. **SURFING** You have $250 to spend on learning to surf. The surfboard rental fee is $30 per day, and the surfing lessons cost $40 per hour. Write an equation that models the possible combinations of the number of days you can rent a surfboard and the number of hours you can take surfing lessons. Suppose you rent a surfboard for 3 days. How many hours of surfing lessons can you afford?

6 ◆ MULTIPLE CHOICE STRATEGIES

STRATEGIES YOU'LL USE:
- SOLVE DIRECTLY
- ELIMINATE CHOICES

Standards
Alg. 7.0, 8.0

If you have trouble solving a multiple choice problem directly, you may be able to use another approach to eliminate incorrect answer choices and obtain the correct answer.

PROBLEM 1

The average monthly cost of basic cable increased by about $1.47 each year from 1986 to 2003. In 1986 the average monthly cost of basic cable was $10.67. In what year was the average monthly cost of basic cable $31.25?

Ⓐ 1986　　　Ⓑ 1996　　　Ⓒ 2000　　　Ⓓ 2003

Strategy 1 — SOLVE DIRECTLY

Use a verbal model to write an equation. Then use the equation to find the year when the cost of basic cable was $31.25.

STEP 1 **Write** a verbal model.

Average monthly cost	=	Cost in 1986	+	Cost increase per year	·	Years since 1986

STEP 2 **Use** the verbal model to write an equation. Let y be the average monthly cost x years since 1986.

Average monthly cost	=	Cost in 1986	+	Cost increase per year	·	Years since 1986

$$y \quad = \quad 10.67 \quad + \quad 1.47 \quad · \quad x$$

STEP 3 **Find** the year when the monthly cost was $31.25 by substituting 31.25 for y. Then solve for x.

$$y = 10.67 + 1.47x$$
$$31.25 = 10.67 + 1.47x$$
$$14 = x$$

The monthly cost of basic cable was $31.25 fourteen years after 1986, or in 2000.

The correct answer is C. Ⓐ Ⓑ ⓒ Ⓓ

Strategy 2 — ELIMINATE CHOICES

You can eliminate choices that do not make sense in the context of the problem. Then test the remaining choices.

STEP 1 **Consider** choice A. It is reasonable to eliminate choice A because in 1986 the monthly cost of basic cable was $10.67.

STEP 2 **Test** choice B. Note that 1996 is 10 years after 1986, so multiply 1.47 by 10 and add the product to 10.67.

$$10.67 + (1.47)10 = 10.67 + 14.70$$
$$= 25.37$$

Eliminate choice B because $25.37 \neq 31.25$.

STEP 3 **Test** the next choice, C. Because the year 2000 is 14 years after 1986, multiply 1.47 by 14 and then add the product to 10.67.

$$10.67 + (1.47)14 = 10.67 + 20.58$$
$$= 31.25$$

The monthly cost of basic cable was $31.25 in the year 2000.

The correct answer is C. Ⓐ Ⓑ ⓒ Ⓓ

PROBLEM 2

What is an equation of the line that passes through $(-5, 2)$ and is parallel to $y = 2x + 4$?

A $y = -2x + 5$ **B** $y = 2x + 12$ **C** $y = \frac{1}{2}x - 4$ **D** $y = 2x + 2$

Strategy 1 SOLVE DIRECTLY

STEP 1 **Identify** the slope. The given line has a slope of 2. So, the parallel line through $(-5, 2)$ has a slope of 2.

STEP 2 **Find** the y-intercept. Use the slope and the given point.

$$y = mx + b$$
$$2 = 2(-5) + b$$
$$12 = b$$

STEP 3 **Write** an equation. Use $y = mx + b$.

$$y = 2x + 12$$

The correct answer is B. Ⓐ **Ⓑ** Ⓒ Ⓓ

Strategy 2 ELIMINATE CHOICES

The definition of parallel lines states that two lines are parallel if they have the same slope. Use this definition to eliminate choices.

Because the slope of the given line is 2, the slope of a line parallel to it is also 2. You can eliminate choice A and choice C.

Substitute the point $(-5, 2)$ into the remaining choices and check.

Choice B: $y = 2x + 12$

$$2 \stackrel{?}{=} 2(-5) + 12$$
$$2 \stackrel{?}{=} -10 + 12$$
$$2 = 2 \checkmark$$

The correct answer is B. Ⓐ **Ⓑ** Ⓒ Ⓓ

STRATEGY PRACTICE

Explain why you can eliminate the highlighted answer choice.

1. Which line passes through $(4, -1)$ and is perpendicular to $y = \frac{1}{2}x - 1$?

   Ⓐ $y = \frac{1}{2}x - 5$ **B** $y = -2x + 7$

   C $y = 2x + 2$ **D** $y = 2x + 5$

2. What is the y-intercept of the line $y = -3x - 13$?

   A -13 **B** -3 **C** 3 **D** 13

3. A club has $250 to go to a carnival. The carnival charges $6.75 per person and $.50 per ride ticket. Which equation models the possible combinations of the number x of club members who can go to the carnival and the number y of ride tickets the club can buy?

   Ⓐ $0.50x - 6.75y = 250$ **B** $6.75x + 0.50y = 250$

   C $6.75x + 0.50y = 100$ **D** $6x + 0.50y = 250$

1. The map below shows streets as lines on a coordinate grid. The city plans to construct a new road called Park Street that will be perpendicular to Reed Street. What will the slope of Park Street be when added to the map? **Alg. 8.0**

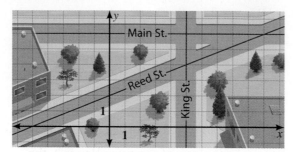

Ⓐ $-\dfrac{5}{2}$

Ⓑ $-\dfrac{2}{5}$

Ⓒ $\dfrac{2}{5}$

Ⓓ $\dfrac{5}{2}$

2. What is an equation of the line that passes through $(-3, 1)$ and has a slope of $\dfrac{2}{3}$? **Alg. 7.0**

Ⓐ $y = -3x + \dfrac{2}{3}$

Ⓑ $y = \dfrac{2}{3}x - \dfrac{11}{3}$

Ⓒ $y = \dfrac{2}{3}x - 3$

Ⓓ $y = \dfrac{2}{3}x + 3$

3. Which line is parallel to the line shown? **Alg. 8.0**

Ⓐ $y = -2x$

Ⓑ $y = -\dfrac{1}{2}x$

Ⓒ $y = \dfrac{1}{2}x$

Ⓓ $y = 2x$

4. What is an equation of the line that passes through $(2, -3)$ and $(-4, 9)$? **Alg. 7.0**

Ⓐ $2x + y = 1$

Ⓑ $2x + y = -1$

Ⓒ $x + 2y = -1$

Ⓓ $x + 2y = 1$

5. Your account summary for Internet service is shown below. What is the total cost after 9 months? **Alg. 5.0**

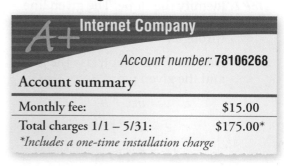

Ⓐ $135

Ⓑ $220

Ⓒ $235

Ⓓ $310

6. Which line passes through $(2, -1)$ and is parallel to the line $y = -2x - 5$? **Alg. 8.0**

Ⓐ $y = \dfrac{1}{2}x - 2$

Ⓑ $y = -\dfrac{1}{2}x$

Ⓒ $y = -2x + 3$

Ⓓ $y = -2x - 3$

7. Brenda claims that you can write an equation in point-slope form for any line. Which type of line is a counterexample to her claim? **Alg. 7.0**

Ⓐ A vertical line

Ⓑ A horizontal line

Ⓒ A line with a negative slope

Ⓓ A line with a fractional slope

8. What is an equation of the line that passes through $(1, -5)$ and $(3, 4)$? **Alg. 7.0**

Ⓐ $y - 5 = \frac{9}{2}(x - 1)$

Ⓑ $y - 4 = \frac{9}{2}(x - 3)$

Ⓒ $y + 4 = \frac{9}{2}(x + 3)$

Ⓓ $y + 5 = \frac{9}{2}(x + 1)$

9. What is an equation of the line shown? **Alg. 7.0**

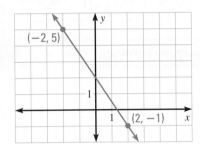

Ⓐ $2y + 3x = 4$

Ⓑ $2y + 3x = 11$

Ⓒ $2y + 3x = 16$

Ⓓ $3y + 2x = 11$

10. Fish farming increased at a relatively constant rate from 1991 to 2002. The table shows fish farmers' total crop in 1994 and 2000. Which equation gives the total crop c (in millions of metric tons) as a function of the time t (in years) since 1991? **Alg. 7.0**

Year	World aquaculture (million metric tons)
1994	20.8
2000	35.5

Ⓐ $c - 35.5 = 2.45(t - 8)$

Ⓑ $c - 20.8 = 2.45(t - 3)$

Ⓒ $c - 8 = 2.45(t - 35.5)$

Ⓓ $c - 3 = 2.45(t - 20.8)$

11. The equation $6p + 4b = 48$ gives the number p of paintbrushes and the number b of buckets that you can buy with $48. Which numbers of paintbrushes and buckets do *not* satisfy the equation? **Alg. 7.0**

Ⓐ 4 paintbrushes, 6 buckets

Ⓑ 5 paintbrushes, 4 buckets

Ⓒ 6 paintbrushes, 3 buckets

Ⓓ 8 paintbrushes, 0 buckets

12. Between 12:00 A.M. and 10:00 A.M. a certain dam releases 81 million gallons of water. Between 10:00 A.M. and 1:00 P.M. the dam releases water at a rate of 130 million gallons per hour. Which equation gives the total amount of water w (in millions of gallons) released as a function of the time t (in hours) since 10:00 A.M.? **Alg. 7.0**

Ⓐ $w = 130t + 81$

Ⓑ $w = 130t - 81$

Ⓒ $w = 81t + 130$

Ⓓ $w = 81t - 130$

13. What is an equation of the line that passes through $(-3, 4)$ and is perpendicular to the line $y = \frac{3}{2}x - 5$? **Alg. 8.0**

Ⓐ $y = -\frac{3}{2}x - \frac{1}{2}$

Ⓑ $y = -\frac{2}{3}x + 2$

Ⓒ $y = \frac{2}{3}x + 6$

Ⓓ $y = \frac{3}{2}x + \frac{17}{2}$

14. Which line passes through $(6, 0)$ and is parallel to the line $y = -\frac{1}{4}x - 5$? **Alg. 8.0**

Ⓐ $y = -\frac{1}{4}x - 6$

Ⓑ $y = -\frac{1}{4}x + 6$

Ⓒ $y = -\frac{1}{4}x + \frac{3}{2}$

Ⓓ $y = 4x - 5$

7 Systems of Equations and Inequalities

Before

In previous chapters, you learned the following skills, which you'll use in Chapter 7:

- Graphing linear equations
- Solving equations
- Determining whether lines are parallel
- Solving inequalities

Now

In Chapter 7 you'll study these **Big Ideas:**

1. Solving linear systems by graphing
2. Solving linear systems using algebra
3. Solving systems of linear inequalities

Why?

So you can solve real-world problems about . . .

- Television, p. 380
- Carnivals, p. 396
- Football, p. 403
- Photography, p. 410
- Speedboats, p. 415
- Bobsleds, p. 431

Animated Algebra
at *classzone.com*

Get-Ready Games

DECIPHERING NUMBERS

California Standards

Review using deductive reasoning. *Gr. 7 MR 2.4*

Prepare for solving a system of equations. *Alg. 9.0*

How to Play

Suppose the equations above are written using an ancient number system. Each symbol represents an integer from 1 to 10. Find the value of each symbol.

CALIFORNIA STANDARDS

• **Alg. 9.0** Students solve a system of two linear equations in two variables algebraically and are able to interpret the answer graphically. Students are able to solve a system of two linear inequalities in two variables and to sketch the solution sets. *(Lessons 7.1, 7.2, 7.3, 7.4, 7.5, 7.6, 7.7, 7.9)*

• **Alg. 15.0** Students apply algebraic techniques to solve rate problems, work problems, **and percent mixture problems.** *(Lessons 7.6, 7.7)*

STONE TABLET

California Standards

Review solving equations. **Alg. 5.0**

Prepare for solving a system of equations. **Alg. 9.0**

How to Play

Suppose an ancient stone tablet contains numbers arranged according to these rules:

• Each integer from 1 to 16 is used exactly once.

• The sum of each row, column, and diagonal is 34.

Find the missing numbers.

Games Wrap-Up

Draw Conclusions

Complete these exercises after playing the games.

1. **WRITING** Suppose you add 5 to each number on the *Stone Tablet*. *Describe* how this action changes the rules for the numbers' arrangement.

2. **REASONING** Write expressions that equal 20, 24, 36, and 150 using the symbols in *Deciphering Numbers*.

Prerequisite Skills

California @HomeTutor
Prerequisite skills practice
at classzone.com

REVIEW VOCABULARY

- **least common multiple,** *p. 783*
- **parallel,** *p. 293*
- **graph of an inequality,** *p. 189*
- **linear equation,** *p. 265*

VOCABULARY CHECK

Copy and complete the statement.

1. The least common multiple of 10 and 15 is __?__.

2. Two lines in the same plane are __?__ if they do not intersect.

3. The set of points that represents all solutions of an inequality in one variable is called the __?__.

SKILLS CHECK

Graph the equation. *(Review p. 264 for 7.1–7.5, 7.8–7.9.)*

4. $x - y = 4$ 5. $6x - y = -1$ 6. $4x + 5y = 20$ 7. $3x - 2y = -12$

Tell whether the graphs of the two equations are parallel lines. *Explain* **your reasoning.** *(Review p. 291 for 7.5.)*

8. $y = 2x - 3, y + 2x = -3$ 9. $y - 5x = -1, y - 5x = 1$

10. $y = x + 10, x - y = -9$ 11. $6x - y = 4, 4x - y = 6$

Solve the equation for y. *(Review p. 167 for 7.2–7.7.)*

12. $2x - 4y = 2$ 13. $-x + 2y = 10$ 14. $9x - 3y = -6$ 15. $20x = 5y - 25$

Notetaking Skills

NOW YOU TRY
Make a *case diagram* for the possible numbers of solutions of a linear equation in one variable.

Focus on Graphic Organizers

You can use a *case diagram* to organize information about possible results, such as the possible numbers of solutions of a compound inequality in one variable.

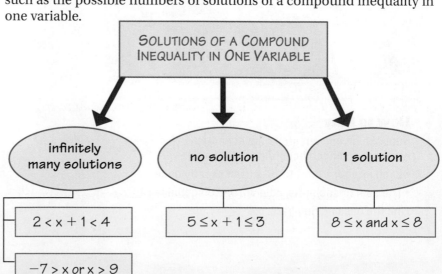

7.1 Solving Linear Systems

MATERIALS · pencil and paper

Standards

Alg. 9.0 Students solve a system of two linear equations in two variables algebraically and are able to interpret the answer graphically. Students are able to solve a system of two linear inequalities in two variables and to sketch the solution sets.

QUESTION How can you solve a linear system?

A *system of linear equations*, or *linear system*, consists of two or more linear equations in the same variables. A *solution of a linear system* is an ordered pair that satisfies each equation in the system.

EXPLORE Solve a linear system

Solve the linear system.

$y = x$ **Equation 1**

$y = -x + 4$ **Equation 2**

STEP 1 *Assign coordinates*

You and your classmates should be sitting at desks arranged in several straight rows. Your teacher will assign each of you a whole-number ordered pair representing a point in the coordinate plane, as shown.

STEP 2 *Represent Equation 1*

If your ordered pair is a solution of Equation 1, raise your right hand and keep it raised.

STEP 3 *Represent Equation 2*

If your ordered pair is a solution of Equation 2, raise your left hand and keep it raised.

STEP 4 *Find the solution*

Make a note of the ordered pair represented by the student with both hands raised.

DRAW CONCLUSIONS Use your observations to complete these exercises

1. *Explain* why the ordered pair represented by the student with both hands raised is the solution of the system.

2. *Explain* why the ordered pair represented by any student with only one hand raised is *not* a solution of the system.

Use the method described in the steps above to solve the linear system.

3. $y = \frac{1}{2}x$

   $y = x$

4. $y = -\frac{1}{2}x + 2$

   $y = x - 1$

5. $x - y = -1$

   $y - 3 = 0$

6. $x + y = 3$

   $y - 1 = 0$

7.1 Solve Linear Systems by Graphing

Standards Alg. 9.0 **Students solve a system of two linear equations in two variables** algebraically and are able to interpret the answer graphically. Students are able to solve a system of two linear inequalities in two variables and to sketch the solution sets.

Connect *Before* you graphed linear equations. *Now* you will solve a system of linear equations graphically to prepare for Algebra 1 Standard 9.0.

Math and **ART**
Ex. 35, p. 380

Key Vocabulary
• system of linear equations
• solution of a system of linear equations
• consistent independent system

A **system of linear equations**, or simply a *linear system*, consists of two or more linear equations in the same variables. An example is shown at the right.

$$x + 2y = 7 \quad \text{Equation 1}$$
$$3x - 2y = 5 \quad \text{Equation 2}$$

A **solution of a system of linear equations** in two variables is an ordered pair that is a solution of each equation in the system.

One way to find the solution of a linear system is by graphing. If the lines intersect in a single point, then the coordinates of the point form the solution of the linear system. A solution found using graphical methods should be checked algebraically.

EXAMPLE 1   Check the intersection point

Use the graph to solve the system. Then check your solution algebraically.

$$x + 2y = 7 \quad \text{Equation 1}$$
$$3x - 2y = 5 \quad \text{Equation 2}$$

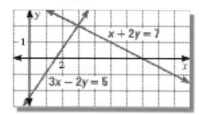

Solution

The lines appear to intersect at the point (3, 2).

CHECK Substitute 3 for x and 2 for y in each equation.

$x + 2y = 7$	$3x - 2y = 5$
$3 + 2(2) \stackrel{?}{=} 7$	$3(3) - 2(2) \stackrel{?}{=} 5$
$7 = 7 \checkmark$	$5 = 5 \checkmark$

▸ Because the ordered pair (3, 2) is a solution of each equation, it is a solution of the linear system.

TYPES OF LINEAR SYSTEMS A linear system that has exactly one solution, as in Example 1, is called a **consistent independent system** because the lines are distinct (are independent) and intersect (are consistent). You will consider other types of systems later in this chapter.

Solving a Linear System Using the Graph-and-Check Method

STEP 1   **Graph** both equations in the same coordinate plane. For
ease of graphing, you may want to write each equation in
slope-intercept form.

STEP 2   **Estimate** the coordinates of the point of intersection.

STEP 3   **Check** the coordinates algebraically by substituting into each
equation of the original linear system.

EXAMPLE 2   **Use the graph-and-check method**

Animated Algebra

For an interactive
example of solving a
linear system using the
graph-and-check method,
go to **classzone.com**.

Solve the linear system: $-x + y = -7$ **Equation 1**

$x + 4y = -8$ **Equation 2**

Solution

STEP 1   **Graph** both equations.

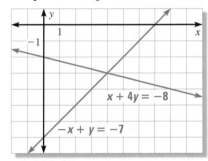

STEP 2   **Estimate** the point of intersection. The two lines appear to intersect
at $(4, -3)$.

STEP 3   **Check** whether $(4, -3)$ is a solution by substituting 4 for x and
-3 for y in each of the original equations.

Equation 1	**Equation 2**
$-x + y = -7$	$x + 4y = -8$
$-(4) + (-3) \stackrel{?}{=} -7$	$4 + 4(-3) \stackrel{?}{=} -8$
$-7 = -7 \checkmark$	$-8 = -8 \checkmark$

▶ Because $(4, -3)$ is a solution of each equation, it is a solution of
the linear system.

  GUIDED PRACTICE   for Examples 1 and 2

Solve the linear system by graphing. Check your solution.

1. $-5x + y = 0$
$5x + y = 10$

2. $-x + 2y = 3$
$2x + y = 4$

3. $x - y = 5$
$3x + y = 3$

EXAMPLE 3 **Solve a multi-step problem**

RENTAL BUSINESS A business rents in-line skates and bicycles. During one day, the business has a total of 25 rentals and collects $450 for the rentals. Find the number of pairs of skates rented and the number of bicycles rented.

RENTALS
In-line skates **$15** per day
Bicycles **$30** per day

Solution

STEP 1 **Write** a linear system. Let x be the number of pairs of skates rented, and let y be the number of bicycles rented.

$x + y = 25$ **Equation for number of rentals**

$15x + 30y = 450$ **Equation for money collected from rentals**

STEP 2 **Graph** both equations.

STEP 3 **Estimate** the point of intersection. The two lines appear to intersect at $(20, 5)$.

STEP 4 **Check** whether $(20, 5)$ is a solution.

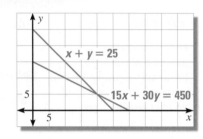

$x + y = 25$	$15x + 30y = 450$
$20 + 5 \overset{?}{=} 25$	$15(20) + 30(5) \overset{?}{=} 450$
$25 = 25$ ✓	$450 = 450$ ✓

▸ The business rented 20 pairs of skates and 5 bicycles.

✓ **GUIDED PRACTICE** **for Example 3**

4. **WHAT IF?** In Example 3, suppose the business has a total of 20 rentals and collects $420. Find the number of bicycles rented.

7.1 EXERCISES

HOMEWORK KEY

◆ = **MULTIPLE CHOICE PRACTICE**
Exs. 6, 7, 34, and 40–42

○ = **HINTS AND HOMEWORK HELP**
for Exs. 9, 15, and 35 at classzone.com

SKILLS · PROBLEM SOLVING · REASONING

1. **VOCABULARY** Copy and complete: A(n) _?_ of a system of linear equations in two variables is an ordered pair that satisfies each equation in the system.

2. **WRITING** *Explain* how to use the graph-and-check method to solve a linear system of two equations in two variables.

CHECKING SOLUTIONS Tell whether the ordered pair is a solution of the linear system.

3. $(-3, 1)$;
   $x + y = -2$
   $x + 5y = 2$

4. $(5, 2)$;
   $2x - 3y = 4$
   $2x + 8y = 11$

5. $(-2, 1)$;
   $6x + 5y = -7$
   $x - 2y = 0$

EXAMPLE 1
on p. 376
for Exs. 6–11

6. ◆ **MULTIPLE CHOICE** Which ordered pair is a solution of the linear system $x + y = -2$ and $7x - 4y = 8$?

(A) $(-2, 0)$ **(B)** $(0, -2)$ **(C)** $(2, 0)$ **(D)** $(0, 2)$

7. ◆ **MULTIPLE CHOICE** Which ordered pair is a solution of the linear system $2x + 3y = 12$ and $10x + 3y = -12$?

(A) $(-3, 3)$ **(B)** $(-3, 6)$ **(C)** $(3, 3)$ **(D)** $(3, 6)$

SOLVING SYSTEMS GRAPHICALLY Use the graph to solve the linear system. Check your solution.

8. $x - y = 4$
$4x + y = 1$

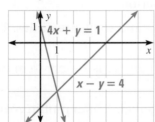

9. $-x + y = -2$
$2x - y = 6$

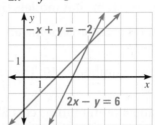

10. $x + y = 5$
$-2x + y = -4$

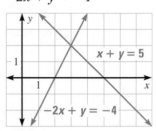

11. **ERROR ANALYSIS** *Describe* and correct the error in solving the linear system below.

$x - 3y = 6$ **Equation 1**
$2x - 3y = 3$ **Equation 2**

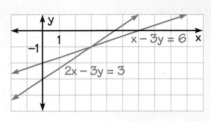

The solution is $(3, -1)$.

EXAMPLE 2
on p. 377
for Exs. 12–26

GRAPH-AND-CHECK METHOD Solve the linear system by graphing. Check your solution.

12. $y = -x + 3$
$y = x + 1$

13. $y = -x + 4$
$y = 2x - 8$

14. $y = 2x + 2$
$y = 4x + 6$

15. $x - y = 2$
$x + y = -8$

16. $x + 2y = 1$
$-2x + y = 8$

17. $3x + y = 15$
$y = -15$

18. $2x - 3y = -1$
$5x + 2y = 26$

19. $6x + y = 37$
$4x + 2y = 18$

20. $7x + 5y = -3$
$-9x + y = -11$

21. $6x + 12y = -6$
$2x + 5y = 0$

22. $2x + y = 9$
$2x + 3y = 15$

23. $-5x + 3y = 3$
$4x + 3y = 30$

24. $\frac{3}{4}x + \frac{1}{4}y = \frac{13}{2}$
$x - \frac{3}{4}y = \frac{13}{2}$

25. $\frac{1}{5}x - \frac{2}{5}y = -\frac{8}{5}$
$-\frac{3}{4}x + y = 3$

26. $-1.6x - 3.2y = -24$
$2.6x + 2.6y = 26$

27. **OPEN-ENDED** Find values for m and b so that the system $y = \frac{3}{5}x - 1$ and $y = mx + b$ has $(5, 2)$ as the only solution.

28. **REASONING** Suppose the graphs of the two equations of a linear system have the same slope but different y-intercepts. What conclusion can you make about the system? *Explain* your reasoning.

29. MULTI-STEP PROBLEM Consider the equation $-\frac{1}{4}x + 6 = \frac{1}{2}x + 3$.

   a. Solve the equation using algebra.

   b. Solve the linear system $y = -\frac{1}{4}x + 6$ and $y = \frac{1}{2}x + 3$ using a graph.

   c. How is the linear system in part (b) related to the original equation?

   d. *Explain* how to use a graph to solve the equation $-\frac{2}{5}x + 5 = \frac{1}{5}x + 2$.

CONNECT SKILLS TO PROBLEM SOLVING Exercises 30–32 will help you prepare for problem solving.

Write a linear system that models the situation.

30. You have a total of 5 coins. Some are nickels and some are dimes. The total value is 40 cents.

31. The sum of two numbers is 10. The greater number is 1 more than twice the lesser number.

32. Five bagels and 4 bran muffins cost $7 altogether. A bran muffin costs $.40 more than a bagel.

EXAMPLE 3
on pp. 378
for Exs. 33–35

33. TELEVISION The graph shows a projection, from 1990 on, of the percent of eighth graders who watch 1 hour or less of television on a weekday and the percent of eighth graders who watch more than 1 hour of television on a weekday. Use the graph to predict the year when the percent of eighth graders who watch 1 hour or less will equal the percent who watch more than 1 hour.

Graph: p (Percent of eighth graders) vs t (Years since 1990). Line labeled "1 hour or less" rising; line labeled "more than 1 hour" falling. Axes marked 0, 40, 80 on p; 0, 20, 40, 60, 80 on t.

California @HomeTutor for problem solving help at classzone.com

34. ◆ MULTIPLE CHOICE A car dealership is offering interest-free car loans for one day only. During this day, a salesperson at the dealership sells two cars. One of his clients decides to pay for his $17,424 car in 36 monthly payments of $484. His other client decides to pay for his $15,840 car in 48 monthly payments of $330. Which system of equations can be used to determine the number x of months after which both clients will have the same loan balance y?

(A) $y = -484x$
    $y = -330x$

(B) $y = -484x + 17{,}424$
    $y = -330x + 15{,}840$

(C) $y = -484x + 15{,}840$
    $y = -330x + 17{,}424$

(D) $y = 484x + 17{,}424$
    $y = 330x + 15{,}840$

California @HomeTutor for problem solving help at classzone.com

35.) CRAFTS Kirigami is the Japanese art of making paper designs by folding and cutting paper. A student sells small and large greeting cards decorated with kirigami at a craft fair. The small cards cost $3 per card, and the large cards cost $5 per card. The student collects $95 for selling a total of 25 cards. How many of each type of card did the student sell?

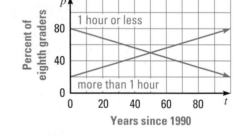

◆ = **MULTIPLE CHOICE PRACTICE**   ◯ = **HINTS AND HOMEWORK HELP** at classzone.com

36. FITNESS You want to burn 225 calories while exercising at a gym. The numbers of calories that you burn per minute on different machines at the gym are shown below.

Stair machine	Elliptical trainer	Stationary bike
You burn 5 Cal/min.	You burn 8 Cal/min.	You burn 6 Cal/min.

a. Suppose you have 40 minutes to exercise at the gym and you want to use the stair machine and stationary bike. How many minutes should you spend on each machine so that you burn 225 calories?

b. Suppose you have 30 minutes to exercise at the gym and you want to use the stair machine and the elliptical trainer. How many minutes should you spend on each machine so that you burn 225 calories?

37. MULTI-STEP PROBLEM A yearly membership to a movie club at a movie theater costs $15. A movie ticket costs $5 for club members and $8 for nonmembers. Write and graph a system of equations to find the number x of movies viewed for which the total cost y for a club member (including the membership fee) is the same as the cost for a nonmember. Under what circumstances does it make sense to become a club member? *Explain* your answer by using the graph.

38. CHALLENGE The three lines given below form a triangle. Find the coordinates of the vertices of the triangle.

Line 1: $-3x + 2y = 1$ **Line 2:** $2x + y = 11$ **Line 3:** $x + 4y = 9$

39. CHALLENGE With a minimum purchase of $25, Sally can open a credit account with a clothing store. The store is offering either $25 or 20% off of her purchase if she opens a credit account. She decides to open a credit account. Should Sally choose $25 or 20% off of her purchase? *Explain*.

◆ CALIFORNIA STANDARDS SPIRAL REVIEW

Alg. 1.0

40. Which set is *not* closed under multiplication? *(p. 74)*

   (A) Integers   **(B)** Positive whole numbers

   (C) $\{-2, -1, 0, 1, 2\}$ **(D)** $\{-1, 0, 1\}$

Alg. 17.0

41. What is the range of the function $\{(1, 9), (3, 9), (5, 6), (7, 6)\}$? *(p. 249)*

   (A) 6, 9   **(B)** 1, 3   **(C)** 3, 6, 9   **(D)** 1, 3, 5, 7

Alg. 5.0

42. You have $50 to spend on 4 bottles of sunscreen and some beach towels. A bottle of sunscreen costs $3, and a beach towel costs $8. What are the possible numbers b of beach towels that you can buy? *(p. 202)*

   (A) $b \le 3$ **(B)** $b \le 4$ **(C)** $b \le 5$ **(D)** $b \le 6$

7.1 Solving Linear Systems by Graphing

Standards

Alg. 9.0 Students solve a system of two linear equations in two variables algebraically and are able to interpret the answer graphically. Students are able to solve a system of two linear inequalities in two variables and to sketch the solution sets.

QUESTION How can you use a graphing calculator to solve a linear system?

EXAMPLE Solve a linear system

Solve the linear system using a graphing calculator.

$$5x + 2y = 6 \quad \text{Equation 1}$$
$$x - 3y = -5 \quad \text{Equation 2}$$

STEP 1 *Rewrite equations*

Solve each equation for y.

Equation 1	Equation 2
$5x + 2y = 6$	$x - 3y = -5$
$2y = -5x + 6$	$-3y = -x - 5$
$y = -\dfrac{5}{2}x + 3$	$y = \dfrac{1}{3}x + \dfrac{5}{3}$

STEP 2 *Enter equations*

Press [Y=] and enter the equations.

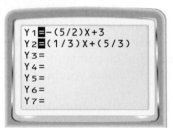

STEP 3 *Display graph*

Graph the equations using a standard viewing window.

STEP 4 *Find the point of intersection*

Use the *intersect* feature to find the point where the graphs intersect.

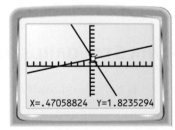

The solution is about (0.47, 1.8).

PRACTICE

Solve the linear system using a graphing calculator.

1. $y = x + 4$
$y = -3x - 2$

2. $5x + y = -4$
$x - y = -2$

3. $-0.45x - y = 1.35$
$-1.8x + y = -1.8$

4. $0.4x + 0.8y = 1.6$
$-1.2x + 0.4y = -2$

7.2 Solve Linear Systems by Substitution

Standards Alg. 9.0 **Students solve a system of two linear equations in two variables algebraically and are able to interpret the answer graphically.** Students are able to solve a system of two linear inequalities in two variables and to sketch the solution sets.

Connect *Before* you solved systems of linear equations by graphing. *Now* you will solve systems of linear equations by using substitution.

Math and **RECREATION**
Ex. 30, p. 387

Key Vocabulary
- **system of linear equations,** *p. 376*

KEY CONCEPT   *For Your Notebook*

Solving a Linear System Using the Substitution Method

STEP 1 **Solve** one of the equations for one of its variables. When possible, solve for a variable that has a coefficient of 1 or −1.

STEP 2 **Substitute** the expression from Step 1 into the other equation and solve for the other variable.

STEP 3 **Substitute** the value from Step 2 into the revised equation from Step 1 and solve.

EXAMPLE 1   Use the substitution method

Animated **Algebra**

For an interactive example of solving a linear system using substitution, go to **classzone.com**.

Solve the linear system: $y = 3x + 2$ **Equation 1**
                               $x + 2y = 11$ **Equation 2**

Solution

STEP 1 **Solve** for y. Equation 1 is already solved for y.

STEP 2 **Substitute** $3x + 2$ for y in Equation 2 and solve for x.

$$x + 2y = 11 \qquad \text{Write Equation 2.}$$
$$x + 2(\mathbf{3x + 2}) = 11 \qquad \text{Substitute } 3x + 2 \text{ for } y.$$
$$7x + 4 = 11 \qquad \text{Simplify.}$$
$$7x = 7 \qquad \text{Subtract 4 from each side.}$$
$$x = 1 \qquad \text{Divide each side by 7.}$$

STEP 3 **Substitute** 1 for x in Equation 1 to find the value of y.

$$y = 3x + 2 = 3(\mathbf{1}) + 2 = 3 + 2 = 5$$

▶ The solution is $(1, 5)$.

CHECK Substitute 1 for x and 5 for y in each of the original equations.

$$5 \overset{?}{=} 3(\mathbf{1}) + 2 \qquad \bigm| \qquad 1 + 2(5) \overset{?}{=} 11$$
$$5 = 5 ✓ \qquad \bigm| \qquad 11 = 11 ✓$$

EXAMPLE 2 Use the substitution method

Solve the linear system:

$$x - 2y = -6 \quad \textbf{Equation 1}$$
$$4x + 6y = 4 \quad \textbf{Equation 2}$$

**CHOOSE AN
EQUATION**
Equation 1 was chosen
in Step 1 because x has
a coefficient of 1. So,
only one step is needed
to solve Equation 1
for x.

Solution

STEP 1 **Solve** Equation 1 for x.

$x - 2y = -6$	**Write original Equation 1.**
$x = 2y - 6$	**Revised Equation 1**

STEP 2 **Substitute** $2y - 6$ for x in Equation 2 and solve for y.

$4x + 6y = 4$	**Write Equation 2.**
$4(2y - 6) + 6y = 4$	**Substitute 2y – 6 for x.**
$8y - 24 + 6y = 4$	**Distributive property**
$14y - 24 = 4$	**Simplify.**
$14y = 28$	**Add 24 to each side.**
$y = 2$	**Divide each side by 14.**

STEP 3 **Substitute** 2 for y in the original Equation 1 to find the value of x.

$x - 2y = -6$	**Write original Equation 1.**
$x - 2(2) = -6$	**Substitute 2 for y.**
$x = -2$	**Simplify.**

▶ The solution is $(-2, 2)$.

CHECK Substitute -2 for x and 2 for y in each of the original equations.

Equation 1	**Equation 2**
$x - 2y = -6$	$4x + 6y = 4$
$-2 - 2(2) \stackrel{?}{=} -6$	$4(-2) + 6(2) \stackrel{?}{=} 4$
$-6 = -6 \checkmark$	$4 = 4 \checkmark$

About the Standards

Algebra 1 Standard 9.0
refers both to
solving a linear
system algebraically
and interpreting the
answer graphically.
Here, you use a
graph to check the
reasonableness of an
algebraic solution.

CHECK REASONABLENESS When solving
a linear system using the substitution
method, you can use a graph to check
the reasonableness of your solution. For
example, the graph at the right verifies that
$(-2, 2)$ is a solution of the linear system in
Example 2.

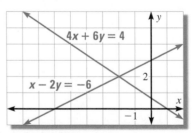

✓ **GUIDED PRACTICE** for Examples 1 and 2

Solve the linear system using the substitution method.

1. $y = 2x + 5$
$3x + y = 10$

2. $x - y = 3$
$x + 2y = -6$

3. $3x + y = -7$
$-2x + 4y = 0$

ANOTHER WAY

For an alternative method for solving the problem in Example 3, turn to page 389 for the **Problem Solving Workshop**.

EXAMPLE 3 **Solve a multi-step problem**

WEBSITES Many businesses pay website hosting companies to store and maintain the computer files that make up their websites. Internet service providers also offer website hosting. The costs for website hosting offered by a website hosting company and an Internet service provider are shown in the table. Find the number of months for which the total cost for website hosting will be the same for both companies.

Company	Set-up fee (dollars)	Cost per month (dollars)
Internet service provider	10	21.95
Website hosting company	None	22.45

Solution

STEP 1 **Write** a system of equations. Let y be the total cost after x months.

Equation 1: Internet service provider

Total cost	=	Set-up fee	+	Cost per month	·	Number of months
y	=	10	+	21.95	·	x

Equation 2: Website hosting company

Total cost	=	Cost per month	·	Number of months
y	=	22.45	·	x

The system of equations is: $y = 10 + 21.95x$ **Equation 1**
$$y = 22.45x \qquad \textbf{Equation 2}$$

STEP 2 **Substitute** $22.45x$ for y in Equation 1 and solve for x.

$y = 10 + 21.95x$ **Write Equation 1.**

$22.45x = 10 + 21.95x$ **Substitute 22.45x for y.**

$0.5x = 10$ **Subtract 21.95x from each side.**

$x = 20$ **Divide each side by 0.5.**

▸ The total cost will be the same for both companies in 20 months.

✓ **GUIDED PRACTICE** for Example 3

4. In Example 3, what is the total cost for website hosting for each company in 20 months?

5. **WHAT IF?** In Example 3, suppose the Internet service provider offers $5 off the set-up fee. In how many months will the total cost for website hosting be the same for both companies?

7.2 EXERCISES

HOMEWORK
KEY

◆ = **MULTIPLE CHOICE PRACTICE**
Exs. 21, 23, 29, and 37–39

◯ = **HINTS AND HOMEWORK HELP**
for Exs. 5, 15, and 31 at classzone.com

SKILLS • PROBLEM SOLVING • REASONING

1. **VOCABULARY** Copy and complete: A(n) __?__ consists of two or more linear equations in the same variables.

2. **WRITING** If you are solving the linear system shown using the substitution method, which equation would you solve for which variable? *Explain.*

$2x - 3y = 24$ **Equation 1**
$2x + y = 8$ **Equation 2**

EXAMPLE 1
on p. 383
for Exs. 3–11

SOLVING LINEAR SYSTEMS Solve the linear system using the substitution method.

3. $x = 17 - 4y$
$y = x - 2$

4. $y = 2x - 1$
$2x + y = 3$

5. $x = y + 3$
$2x - y = 5$

6. $4x - 7y = 10$
$y = x - 7$

7. $x = 16 - 4y$
$3x + 4y = 8$

8. $-5x + 3y = 51$
$y = 10x - 8$

9. $-4x + 3y = -5$
$x = 4 - 2y$

10. $x = 7 - 10y$
$10x - 4y = 18$

11. $3x - 2y = -1$
$y = -x - 7$

EXAMPLE 2
on p. 384
for Exs. 12–22

12. $2x = 12$
$x - 5y = -29$

13. $2x - y = 23$
$x - 9 = -1$

14. $x + y = 0$
$x - 2y = 6$

15. $5x + 2y = 9$
$x + y = -3$

16. $2x + y = 9$
$4x - y = -15$

17. $5x + 4y = 32$
$9x - y = 33$

18. $11x - 7y = -14$
$x - 2y = -4$

19. $20x - 30y = -50$
$x + 2y = 1$

20. $6x + y = 4$
$x - 4y = 19$

21. ◆ **MULTIPLE CHOICE** What is the solution of the linear system $4x - y = 17$ and $-9x + 8y = 2$?

  A $(6, 7)$ **B** $(7, 6)$ **C** $(7, 11)$ **D** $(11, 7)$

22. **ERROR ANALYSIS** *Describe* and correct the error in solving the linear system $4x + 2y = 6$ and $3x + y = 9$.

Step 1	Step 2	Step 3	The solution is (6, 1).
$3x + y = 9$	$4x + 2(9 - 3x) = 6$	$y = 9 - 3x$	
$y = 9 - 3x$	$4x + 18 - 6x = 6$	$6 = 9 - 3x$	
	$-2x = -12$	$-3 = -3x$	
	$x = 6$	$1 = x$	

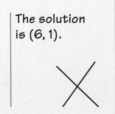

23. ◆ **MULTIPLE CHOICE** What is the *x*-coordinate of the solution of the linear system $15x - 16y = -34$ and $2x + y = 8$?

  A 0   **B** 2   **C** 4   **D** 6

24. **WRITING** Suppose you solve a linear system using substitution. *Explain* how you can use a graph to check your solution.

Write a linear system that models the situation.

25. The sum of two numbers x and y is 35. The value of x is 4 times the value of y.

26. The difference between two numbers y and x is 12. The value of y is 5 times the value of x.

27. The perimeter of a rectangle is 32 inches. The length is 3 times the width.

28. You have twice as many apples as oranges, and you have 12 apples and oranges altogether.

EXAMPLE 3
on p. 385
for Exs. 29–32

29. ◆ **MULTIPLE CHOICE** During a football game, students sell drinks and popcorn. They charge $2.50 for a bag of popcorn and $2 for a drink. The students collect $336 in sales. They sell twice as many bags of popcorn as drinks. How many bags of popcorn do they sell?

(**A**) 48 bags   (**B**) 52 bags   (**C**) 96 bags   (**D**) 104 bags

California **@HomeTutor**   for problem solving help at classzone.com

30. **TUBING COSTS** A group of friends take a day-long tubing trip. The rental shop charges $15 to rent a tube for a person and $7.50 to rent a "cooler" tube, which is used to carry food in a cooler. The friends spend $360 to rent a total of 26 tubes. How many of each type of tube do they rent?

California **@HomeTutor**   for problem solving help at classzone.com

31. **SHORT RESPONSE** In the mobile shown, objects are attached to each end of a wooden stick. For the wooden stick to balance, the following must be true:

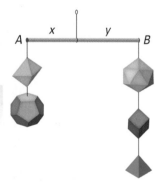

| Distance x (inches) | · | Weight hanging from point A | = | Distance y (inches) | · | Weight hanging from point B |

The weight of the objects hanging from point A is 1.5 pounds, and the weight of the objects hanging from point B is 1.2 pounds. The length of the wooden stick is 9 inches. How far from point A should the string be placed? *Explain.*

32. **MULTI-STEP PROBLEM** For a floral arrangement class, every student has to create an arrangement of daisies and irises that has a total of 15 flowers. Students have to pay for the daisies and irises that they use in their arrangements. Each daisy costs $1.15, and each iris costs $.75.

a. Writing a System Suppose a student spends $12.85 on the daisies and irises. Write and solve a linear system to find the number of daisies and the number of irises the student uses.

b. Making a Table Check your answer to part (a) by making a table that shows the number of irises in the arrangement and the total cost of the arrangement when the number of daisies purchased is 0, 1, 2, 3, 4, or 5.

Total flowers: 15

33. SHORT RESPONSE A gazelle can run 73 feet per second for several minutes. A cheetah can run 88 feet per second, but it can sustain this speed for only 20 seconds. A gazelle is 350 feet from a cheetah when both animals start running. Can the gazelle stay ahead of the cheetah? *Explain.*

 at classzone.com

Gazelle's speed: 73 ft/sec

34. REASONING Use the substitution method to show that the solution of the system of equations $y = ax + b$ and $y = cx + d$ is $x = \frac{d - b}{a - c}$ and $y = \frac{ad - bc}{a - c}$, where a, b, c, and d are nonzero real numbers and $a \neq c$.

35. CHALLENGE Find values of a and b so that the linear system shown has a solution of $(-9, 4)$.

$ax + by = -16$ **Equation 1**
$ax - by = -56$ **Equation 2**

36. CHALLENGE A group of students held a car wash to raise money. They charged $9 for each car and $12 for each van or SUV. Two teams worked continuously, one washing cars and the other washing vans and SUVs. The team washing cars required 25% less time per vehicle than the other team. Each team washed vehicles for 4 hours. The two teams together raised a total of $720. How long, on average, did each team take to wash a vehicle?

◆ CALIFORNIA STANDARDS SPIRAL REVIEW

Alg. 9.0

37. What is the solution of the linear system whose graph is shown? *(p. 376)*

Ⓐ (3, 2)

Ⓑ (0, 0)

Ⓒ (2, 3)

Ⓓ (2, 0)

$y = \frac{2}{3}x$

$y = 2x - 4$

Alg. 4.0

38. What is the solution of $2(2x - 0.1) + 2x = 28.6$? *(p. 139)*

Ⓐ 4.7   Ⓑ 4.8   Ⓒ 7.1   Ⓓ 7.2

Alg. 24.3

39. Rachel claims that one half of any number is less than the original number. Which number serves as a counterexample to her claim? *(p. 53)*

Ⓐ −4   Ⓑ 0.8   Ⓒ 1   Ⓓ 5

QUIZ *for Lessons 7.1–7.2*

Solve the linear system by graphing. Check your solution. *(p. 376)*

1. $x + y = -2$
$-x + y = 6$

2. $x - y = 0$
$5x + 2y = -7$

3. $x - 2y = 12$
$-3x + y = -1$

Solve the linear system using substitution. *(p. 383)*

4. $y = x - 4$
$-2x + y = 18$

5. $2y + x = -4$
$y - x = -5$

6. $3x - 5y = 13$
$x + 4y = 10$

EXTRA PRACTICE for Lesson 7.2, p. 816   ↗ **ONLINE QUIZ** at classzone.com

Using ALTERNATIVE METHODS

Another Way to Solve Example 3, page 385

Standards
Alg. 9.0

In Example 3 on page 385, you saw how to solve the problem about website hosting by solving a linear system algebraically. You can also solve the problem using a table.

PROBLEM

WEBSITES Many businesses pay website hosting companies to store and maintain the computer files that make up their websites. Internet service providers also offer website hosting. The costs for website hosting offered by a website hosting company and an Internet service provider are shown in the table. Find the number of months for which the total cost for website hosting will be the same for both companies.

Company	Set-up fee	Cost per month
Internet service provider	$10	$21.95
Website hosting company	None	$22.45

METHOD **Making a Table** An alternative approach is to make a table.

STEP 1 **Make** a table for the total cost of website hosting for both companies.

> Include the set-up fee in the cost for the first month.

STEP 2 **Look** for the month for which the total cost of the service from the Internet service provider and the website hosting company is the same. This happens in 20 months.

Months	Internet service provider	Website hosting company
1	$31.95	$22.45
2	$53.90	$44.90
3	$75.85	$67.35
⋮	⋮	⋮
19	$427.05	$426.55
20	$449.00	$449.00
21	$470.95	$471.45

PRACTICE

1. **TAXIS** A taxi company charges $2.80 for the first mile and $1.60 for each additional mile. Another taxi company charges $3.20 for the first mile and $1.50 for each additional mile. For what distance will each taxi cost the same? Use a table to solve the problem.

2. **SCHOOL PLAY** An adult ticket to a school play costs $5 and a student ticket costs $3. A total of $460 was collected from the sale of 120 tickets. How many student tickets were purchased? Solve the problem using algebra. Then use a table to check your answer.

7.3 Linear Systems and Elimination

MATERIALS · algebra tiles

Standards

Alg. 9.0 Students solve a system of two linear equations in two variables algebraically and are able to interpret the answer graphically. Students are able to solve a system of two linear inequalities in two variables and to sketch the solution sets.

QUESTION How can you solve a linear system using algebra tiles?

You can use the following algebra tiles to model equations.

1-tiles	x-tiles	y-tiles
+ −	+ −	+ −

EXPLORE Solve a linear system using algebra tiles.

Solve the linear system: $3x - y = 5$ Equation 1
$x + y = 3$ Equation 2

STEP 1 *Model equations*

Model each equation using algebra tiles. Arrange the algebra tiles so that one equation is directly below the other equation.

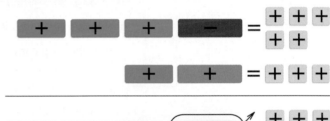

STEP 2 *Add equations*

Combine the two equations to form one equation. Notice that the new equation has one positive y-tile and one negative y-tile. The y-tiles can be removed because the pair of y-tiles has a value of 0.

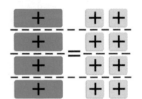

STEP 3 *Solve for x*

Divide the remaining tiles into four equal groups. Each x-tile is equal to two 1-tiles. So, $x = 2$.

STEP 4 *Solve for y*

To find the value of y, use the model for Equation 2. Because $x = 2$, you can replace the x-tile with two 1-tiles. Solve the new equation for y. So, $y = 1$. The solution of the system is (2, 1).

DRAW CONCLUSIONS Use your observations to complete these exercises

Use algebra tiles to model and solve the linear system.

1. $x + 3y = 8$
   $4x - 3y = 2$

2. $2x + y = 5$
   $-2x + 3y = 7$

3. $5x - 2y = -2$
   $x + 2y = 14$

4. $x + 2y = 3$
   $-x + 3y = 2$

5. REASONING Is it possible to solve the linear system $3x - 2y = 6$ and $2x + y = 11$ using the steps shown above? *Explain* your reasoning.

7.3 Solve Linear Systems by Adding or Subtracting

Standards Alg. 9.0 **Students solve a system of two linear equations in two variables algebraically** and are able to interpret the answer graphically. Students are able to solve a system of two linear inequalities in two variables and to sketch the solution sets.

Connect *Before* you solved linear systems by graphing and using substitution. *Now* you will solve linear systems using elimination.

Math and EDUCATION
Ex. 51, p. 397

Key Vocabulary
• like terms, *p. 82*
• system of linear equations, *p. 376*

You can sometimes add or subtract the equations in a linear system to obtain a new equation in one variable. This method is called *elimination*.

KEY CONCEPTS *For Your Notebook*

Solving a Linear System Using the Elimination Method

STEP 1 **Add or subtract** the equations to eliminate one variable.

STEP 2 **Solve** the resulting equation for the other variable.

STEP 3 **Substitute** in either original equation to find the value of the eliminated variable.

EXAMPLE 1 Use addition to eliminate a variable

Solve the linear system:
$2x + 3y = 11$ **Equation 1**
$-2x + 5y = 13$ **Equation 2**

Solution

ADD EQUATIONS
When the coefficients of one variable are opposites, add the equations to eliminate the variable.

STEP 1 **Add** the equations to eliminate one variable.

$$2x + 3y = 11$$
$$-2x + 5y = 13$$
$$\overline{\,8y = 24}$$

STEP 2 **Solve** for y. $y = 3$

STEP 3 **Substitute** 3 for y in either equation and solve for x.

$2x + 3y = 11$ **Write Equation 1.**

$2x + 3(\mathbf{3}) = 11$ **Substitute 3 for y.**

$x = 1$ **Solve for x.**

▶ The solution is $(1, 3)$.

CHECK Substitute 1 for x and 3 for y in each of the original equations.

$2(\mathbf{1}) + 3(3) \stackrel{?}{=} 11$ $-2(\mathbf{1}) + 5(3) \stackrel{?}{=} 13$

$11 = 11 ✓$ $13 = 13 ✓$

EXAMPLE 2 Use subtraction to eliminate a variable

Solve the linear system: $4x + 3y = 2$ **Equation 1**
$5x + 3y = -2$ **Equation 2**

Solution

SUBTRACT EQUATIONS
When the coefficients of one variable are the same, subtract the equations to eliminate the variable.

STEP 1 **Subtract** the equations to eliminate one variable.

$$4x + 3y = 2$$
$$5x + 3y = -2$$
$$\overline{\qquad -x \qquad = 4}$$

STEP 2 **Solve** for x. $x = -4$

STEP 3 **Substitute** -4 for x in either equation and solve for y.

$4x + 3y = 2$ **Write Equation 1.**

$4(-4) + 3y = 2$ **Substitute -4 for x.**

$y = 6$ **Solve for y.**

▶ The solution is $(-4, 6)$.

✓ **GUIDED PRACTICE**   for Examples 1 and 2

Solve the linear system using elimination.

1. $4x - 3y = 5$
$-2x + 3y = -7$

2. $-5x - 6y = 8$
$5x + 2y = 4$

3. $6x - 4y = 14$
$-3x + 4y = 1$

EXAMPLE 3 Arrange like terms

Solve the linear system $8x - 3y = 1$ and $3y = 2x + 11$.

Solution

STEP 1 **Rewrite** $3y = 2x + 11$ so that the like terms are arranged in columns.

AVOID ERRORS
Make sure that the equal signs are in the same column, just as the like terms are.

$8x - 3y = 1$ $8x - 3y = 1$
$3y = 2x + 11$ ⟶ $-2x + 3y = 11$

STEP 2 **Add** the equations. $\overline{6x \qquad = 12}$

STEP 3 **Solve** for x. $x = 2$

STEP 4 **Substitute** 2 for x in either equation and solve for y.

$3y = 2x + 11$ **Write Equation 2.**

$3y = 2(2) + 11$ **Substitute 2 for x.**

$y = 5$ **Solve for y.**

▶ The solution is $(2, 5)$.

 GUIDED PRACTICE   for Example 3

4. Solve the linear system $3x + 4y = -6$ and $2y = 3x + 6$.

EXAMPLE 4 **Write and solve a linear system**

HOCKEY A National Hockey League team receives 2 points for each win (in regulation time or overtime), 1 point for each loss in overtime, and no points for each loss in regulation. There are no ties. One season, the Los Angeles Kings lost 35 games in regulation. Use the table to find the number of games the Kings won and the number of games the Kings lost in overtime.

Hockey team	Number of games played	Total number of points
Los Angeles Kings	82	89
Anaheim Mighty Ducks	82	98

STEP 1 **Write** a system of equations. Let x represent the number of wins, and let y represent the number of games lost in overtime.

Equation 1: Number of games played

Number of games won (in regulation or overtime)	+	Number of games lost (in regulation)	+	Number of games lost (in overtime)	=	Number of games played
x	+	35	+	y	=	82

Equation 2: Total number of points

Points for each game won	·	Number of games won	+	Point for each overtime loss	·	Number of games lost (in overtime)	=	Total number of points
2	·	x	+	1	·	y	=	89

STEP 2 **Rewrite** Equation 1 so that the like terms are arranged in columns.

$$x + 35 + y = 82 \qquad\qquad x + y = 47$$
$$2x + y = 89 \qquad\qquad\qquad \underline{2x + y = 89}$$

STEP 3 **Subtract** the equations. $\qquad\qquad -x \quad\;\; = -42$

STEP 4 **Solve** for x. $\qquad\qquad\qquad\qquad\quad x = 42$

STEP 5 **Substitute** 42 for x in either equation and solve for y.

$x + y = 47$ **Write Equation 1.**

$42 + y = 47$ **Substitute 42 for x.**

$y = 5$ **Solve for y.**

▸ The Los Angeles Kings won 42 games and lost 5 games in overtime.

✓ **GUIDED PRACTICE**   **for Example 4**

5. HOCKEY In Example 4, the Anaheim Mighty Ducks lost 27 games in regulation. How many games did the Ducks win?

7.3 EXERCISES

HOMEWORK KEY

♦ = **MULTIPLE CHOICE PRACTICE**
Exs. 21, 31, 36, 45, and 54–56

◯ = **HINTS AND HOMEWORK HELP**
for Exs. 13, 23, and 47 at classzone.com

SKILLS · PROBLEM SOLVING · REASONING

1. **VOCABULARY** Give an example of a linear system in two variables that can be solved by first adding the equations to eliminate one variable.

2. **WRITING** *Explain* how to solve the linear system shown using the elimination method.

$2x - y = 2$ **Equation 1**
$2x + 3y = 22$ **Equation 2**

EXAMPLE 1
on p. 391
for Exs. 3–11

USING ADDITION Solve the linear system using elimination.

3. $x + 2y = 13$
$-x + y = 5$

4. $9x + y = 2$
$-4x - y = -17$

5. $-3x - y = 8$
$7x + y = -12$

6. $3x - y = 30$
$-3x + 7y = 6$

7. $-9x + 4y = -17$
$9x - 6y = 3$

8. $-3x - 5y = -7$
$-4x + 5y = 14$

9. $2x + 5y = 31$
$-2x + y = -1$

10. $-4x - 8y = -16$
$6x + 8y = -8$

11. $3x + y = 10$
$-3x - 4y = 23$

EXAMPLE 2
on p. 392
for Exs. 12–21

USING SUBTRACTION Solve the linear system using elimination.

12. $x + y = 1$
$-2x + y = 4$

13. $x - y = -4$
$x + 3y = 4$

14. $2x - y = 7$
$2x + 7y = 31$

15. $6x + y = -10$
$5x + y = -10$

16. $5x + 6y = 50$
$-x + 6y = 26$

17. $4x - 9y = -21$
$4x + 3y = -9$

18. $x + 5y = 35$
$-2x + 5y = -10$

19. $6x - y = -1$
$6x - 3y = -27$

20. $4x - 7y = 39$
$9x - 7y = 9$

21. ♦ **MULTIPLE CHOICE** What is the solution of the linear system $4x + 9y = -2$ and $11x + 9y = 26$?

Ⓐ $(-2, 4)$ Ⓑ $(2, -4)$ Ⓒ $(4, -2)$ Ⓓ $(4, 2)$

EXAMPLE 3
on p. 392
for Exs. 22–31

ARRANGING LIKE TERMS Solve the linear system using elimination.

22. $2x - y = 32$
$y - 5x = 13$

23. $-8y + 6x = 36$
$6x - y = 15$

24. $2x - y = -11$
$y = -2x - 13$

25. $-x - y = 14$
$x = 5y - 38$

26. $11y - 3x = 18$
$-3x = -16y + 33$

27. $-5x + y = -23$
$-y = 3x - 9$

28. $-2x = y - 9$
$2x - 5y = 15$

29. $5y - 7x = -13$
$-7x = -3y - 5$

30. $8x + 6y = -36$
$9y = -8x - 66$

31. ♦ **MULTIPLE CHOICE** Which system of equations has the solution (3, 1)?

Ⓐ $3x = 4 - y$
$3x + 5y = 18$

Ⓑ $2x + y = 6$
$3y = 14 - 2x$

Ⓒ $-12y = 16 - 7x$
$5x + 12y = 32$

Ⓓ $2x + 2y = 8$
$x = 5 - 2y$

ERROR ANALYSIS *Describe* and correct the error in finding the value of one of the variables in the given linear system.

32. $5x - 7y = 16$
$-x - 7y = 8$

$$5x - 7y = 16$$
$$-x - 7y = 8$$
$$\overline{}$$
$$4x = 24$$
$$x = 6$$ ✗

33. $3x - 2y = -3$
$5y = 60 - 3x$

$$3x - 2y = -3$$
$$-3x + 5y = 60$$
$$\overline{}$$
$$3y = 57$$
$$y = 19$$ ✗

34. WRITING AN EQUATION OF A LINE Use the following steps to write an equation of the line that passes through the points $(1, 2)$ and $(-4, 12)$.

  a. Write a system of linear equations by substituting 1 for x and 2 for y in $y = mx + b$ and -4 for x and 12 for y in $y = mx + b$.

  b. Solve the system of linear equations from part (a). What is the slope of the line? What is the y-intercept?

  c. Write an equation of the line that passes through $(1, 2)$ and $(-4, 12)$.

35. GEOMETRY The rectangle shown has a perimeter P of 14 feet, and twice its length ℓ is equal to 1 less than 4 times its width w. Write and solve a system of linear equations to find the length and the width of the rectangle.

$P = 14$ ft, w, ℓ

36. ◆ MULTIPLE CHOICE What is the solution of the linear system $\frac{2}{3}y = -3 - \frac{1}{2}x$ and $3x = 2 - \frac{2}{3}y$?

  Ⓐ $(-6, 2)$ **Ⓑ** $(2, -6)$ **Ⓒ** $\left(-\frac{2}{3}, -6\right)$ **Ⓓ** $\left(26, -\frac{2}{3}\right)$

37. SHORT RESPONSE Find the solution of the system of linear equations below. *Explain* your steps.

$$x + 3y = 8 \qquad \textbf{Equation 1}$$
$$x - 6y = -19 \qquad \textbf{Equation 2}$$
$$5x - 3y = -14 \qquad \textbf{Equation 3}$$

38. REASONING Prove that if (a, b) is a solution of the system shown, then (a, b) is also a solution of the equation $(A + D)x + (B + E)y = C + F$.

$$Ax + By = C$$
$$Dx + Ey = F$$

CONNECT SKILLS TO PROBLEM SOLVING Exercises 39–42 will help you prepare for problem solving.

Write a linear system that models the situation.

39. The sum of two numbers is 14. Their difference is 10.

40. The sum of x and 3 times y is -2. The difference of x and y is 6.

41. You buy two CDs for a total of $28. One CD costs $2 more than the other.

42. You buy 2 sandwiches for $8. One sandwich costs 3 times as much as the other sandwich.

EXAMPLE 4
on p. 393
for Exs. 43–50

43. CARNIVAL At a carnival, a ride on a roller coaster costs 5 tickets, and a ride on a Ferris wheel costs 1 ticket. You went on 6 rides and used 22 tickets. Find the number of times you rode the Ferris wheel.

(California **@HomeTutor**) for problem solving help at classzone.com

Ferris wheel

44. BOOK SALE A bookstore is having a sale of used books. All paperback books cost $1, and all hardcover books cost $3. You purchase 15 books for $25. How many paperback books did you buy?

(California **@HomeTutor**) for problem solving help at classzone.com

45. ◆ MULTIPLE CHOICE At a high school basketball game, a student ticket costs $1 and a non-student ticket costs $4. A total of 275 people attended, and $569 was collected. How many students attended the game?

(A) 75   (B) 98   (C) 142   (D) 177

46. OIL CHANGE Two cars get an oil change at the same service center. Each customer is charged a fee x (in dollars) for the oil change plus y dollars per quart of oil used. The first car required 5 quarts of oil, and the oil change cost $22.45. The second car required 7 quarts of oil, and the oil change cost $25.45. Find the fee and the cost per quart of oil.

47. PHONES Cell phone ring tones can be monophonic or polyphonic. Monophonic ring tones play one tone at a time, and polyphonic ring tones play multiple tones at a time. The table shows the ring tones downloaded from a website by two customers. Use the information to find the cost of a monophonic ring tone and the cost of a polyphonic ring tone, assuming that all monophonic ring tones cost the same and all polyphonic ring tones cost the same.

Customer	Monophonic ring tones	Polyphonic ring tones	Total cost (dollars)
Julie	3	2	12.85
Tate	1	2	8.95

48. WEBSITE Alicia is a member of a photo sharing website. She uploads a total of 76 photos to the site. Some of the photos are 5 megabyte (MB) files and some are 1 MB files. The total disk space used for the 76 photos is 156 MB. Write and solve a linear system to find the number of 5 MB photos and the number of 1 MB photos Alicia uploads.

49. FOOTBALL In football, a placekicker scores 3 points for every field goal attempt made and 1 point for every extra point attempt made. A high school placekicker successfully makes 30 kick attempts and scores a total of 66 points. How many field goals did the placekicker make?

50. MUSIC An online music store allows you to download an individual song for $1 or an entire album for $10. Suppose you download 25 items for $115. How many individual songs did you download?

51. SHORT RESPONSE The students in the graduating classes at the three high schools in a school district have to pay for their caps and gowns. A cap-and-gown set costs x dollars, and an extra tassel costs y dollars. The table shows the total cost and number of items ordered for each school. How much will students at the third high school pay? *Explain.*

High school	Total cost	Number of cap-and-gown sets	Number of extra tassels
North	$3262	215	72
Central	$3346	221	72
South	?	218	56

52. CHALLENGE Solve for x, y, and z in the system of equations below. *Explain* your steps.

$$x + 7y + 3z = 29 \qquad \textbf{Equation 1}$$
$$3z + x - 2y = -7 \qquad \textbf{Equation 2}$$
$$5y = 10 - 2x \qquad \textbf{Equation 3}$$

53. CHALLENGE A clothing manufacturer makes men's dress shirts. For the production process, an ideal sleeve length x (in centimeters) for each shirt size and an allowable deviation y (in centimeters) from the ideal length are established. The deviation is expressed as $\pm y$. For a specific shirt size, the minimum allowable sleeve length is 62.2 centimeters and the maximum allowable sleeve length is 64.8 centimeters. Find the ideal sleeve length and the allowable deviation.

◆ CALIFORNIA STANDARDS SPIRAL REVIEW

Alg. 9.0

54. What is the solution of the linear system $x = 9 - 6y$ and $y = 5x + 17$? *(p. 383)*

 (A) $(3, -2)$ **(B)** $(-2, 1)$ **(C)** $(2, -1)$ **(D)** $(-3, 2)$

Alg. 6.0

55. The graph of which equation is shown? *(p. 264)*

 (A) $y = x - 1$

 (B) $y = x$

 (C) $2x + 2y = 6$

 (D) $y + x = 0$

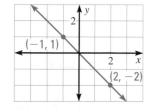

Alg. 17.0

56. The graph shows the total cost C (in dollars) of renting a kayak for t hours where $t = 1, 2, 3, 4,$ and 5. What is the range of the function represented by the graph? *(p. 257)*

 (A) 20, 40, 60, 80, 100

 (B) 1, 2, 3, 4, 5

 (C) 20, 40, 60

 (D) 1, 2, 3

7.4 Solve Linear Systems by Multiplying First

Standards Alg. 9.0 Students solve a system of two linear equations in two variables algebraically and are able to interpret the answer graphically. Students are able to solve a system of two linear inequalities in two variables and to sketch the solution sets.

Connect *Before* you solved linear systems by adding or subtracting. *Now* you will solve linear systems by multiplying first.

Math and **COOKING**
Ex. 38, p. 403

Key Vocabulary
• least common multiple, *p. 785*

In a linear system like the one below, neither variable can be eliminated by adding or subtracting the equations. For systems like these, you can multiply one or both of the equations by a nonzero constant so that adding or subtracting the equations will eliminate one variable.

$$5x + 2y = 16 \quad \times 2 \quad \longrightarrow \quad 10x + 4y = 32$$
$$3x - 4y = 20 \quad \longrightarrow \quad 3x - 4y = 20$$

The new system is equivalent to the original system.

EXAMPLE 1 Multiply one equation, then add

Solve the linear system: $\quad 6x + 5y = 19 \quad$ Equation 1
$\qquad\qquad\qquad\qquad\qquad\ 2x + 3y = 5 \quad\ $ Equation 2

Solution

STEP 1 **Multiply** Equation 2 by -3 so that the coefficients of x are opposites.

$$6x + 5y = 19 \qquad\qquad\qquad 6x + 5y = 19$$
$$2x + 3y = 5 \qquad \times (-3) \qquad \underline{-6x - 9y = -15}$$

ANOTHER WAY
You can also multiply Equation 2 by 3 and subtract the equations.

STEP 2 **Add** the equations. $\qquad\qquad\qquad\qquad -4y = 4$

STEP 3 **Solve** for y. $\qquad\qquad\qquad\qquad\qquad\quad y = -1$

STEP 4 **Substitute** -1 for y in either of the original equations and solve for x.

$$2x + 3y = 5 \qquad\qquad \text{Write Equation 2.}$$
$$2x + 3(-1) = 5 \qquad\quad \text{Substitute } -1 \text{ for } y.$$
$$2x + (-3) = 5 \qquad\qquad \text{Multiply.}$$
$$2x = 8 \qquad\qquad\qquad\ \text{Subtract } -3 \text{ from each side.}$$
$$x = 4 \qquad\qquad\qquad\ \text{Divide each side by 2.}$$

▶ The solution is $(4, -1)$.

CHECK Substitute 4 for x and -1 for y in each of the original equations.

Equation 1	**Equation 2**
$6x + 5y = 19$	$2x + 3y = 5$
$6(4) + 5(-1) \stackrel{?}{=} 19$	$2(4) + 3(-1) \stackrel{?}{=} 5$
$19 = 19 \checkmark$	$5 = 5 \checkmark$

MULTIPLYING BOTH EQUATIONS To eliminate one variable when adding or subtracting equations in a linear system, you may need to multiply both equations by nonzero constants. Use the least common multiple of the coefficients of one of the variables to determine the constants.

$$2x - 9y = 1 \qquad \times 4 \longrightarrow \qquad 8x - 36y = 4$$

$$7x - 12y = 23 \qquad \times 3 \longrightarrow \qquad 21x - 36y = 69$$

The least common multiple of −9 and −12 is −36.

EXAMPLE 2 Multiply both equations, then subtract

Solve the linear system: $4x + 5y = 35$ **Equation 1**
$\qquad\qquad\qquad\qquad\qquad\quad 2y = 3x - 9$ **Equation 2**

Solution

STEP 1 **Arrange** the equations so that like terms are in columns.

$\qquad 4x + 5y = 35$ **Write Equation 1.**

$\qquad -3x + 2y = -9$ **Rewrite Equation 2.**

ANOTHER WAY
You can also multiply Equation 1 by 3 and Equation 2 by 4. Then add the revised equations to eliminate x.

STEP 2 **Multiply** Equation 1 by 2 and Equation 2 by 5 so that the coeffcient of y in each equation is the least common multiple of 5 and 2, or 10.

$\qquad 4x + 5y = 35 \qquad \times 2 \longrightarrow \qquad 8x + 10y = 70$

$\qquad -3x + 2y = -9 \qquad \times 5 \longrightarrow \qquad \underline{-15x + 10y = -45}$

STEP 3 **Subtract** the equations. $\qquad\qquad\qquad 23x \qquad\quad = 115$

STEP 4 **Solve** for x. $\qquad\qquad\qquad\qquad\qquad\qquad x = 5$

STEP 5 **Substitute** 5 for x in either of the original equations and solve for y.

$\qquad 4x + 5y = 35$ **Write Equation 1.**

$\qquad 4(5) + 5y = 35$ **Substitute 5 for x.**

$\qquad\qquad\quad y = 3$ **Solve for y.**

▸ The solution is (5, 3).

CHECK Substitute 5 for x and 3 for y in each of the original equations.

Equation 1	**Equation 2**
$4x + 5y = 35$	$2y = 3x - 9$
$4(5) + 5(3) \stackrel{?}{=} 35$	$2(3) \stackrel{?}{=} 3(5) - 9$
$35 = 35 \checkmark$	$6 = 6 \checkmark$

✔ **GUIDED PRACTICE** for Examples 1 and 2

Solve the linear system using elimination.

1. $2x + 3y = 10$
$\quad 4x + 5y = 18$

2. $2x + 5y = 3$
$\quad 3x + 10y = -3$

3. $3x - 7y = 5$
$\quad 9y = 5x + 5$

4. $3x + 2y = 7$
$\quad 5x - y = 3$

5. $6x - 2y = 1$
$\quad -2x + 3y = -5$

6. $4x - 15y = -20$
$\quad -3x + 5y = 5$

EXAMPLE 3 **Write and solve a linear system**

SOCCER A sports equipment store is having a sale on soccer balls. A soccer coach purchases 10 soccer balls and 2 soccer ball bags for $155. Another soccer coach purchases 12 soccer balls and 3 soccer ball bags for $189. Find the cost of a soccer ball and the cost of a soccer ball bag.

10 soccer balls and 2 bags: $155

Solution

STEP 1 Write a system of equations. Let x represent the cost of a soccer ball, and let y represent the cost of a soccer ball bag.

Equation 1: Purchase by first soccer coach

Number of soccer balls purchased	·	Cost of a soccer ball	+	Number of soccer ball bags purchased	·	Cost of a soccer ball bag	=	Total cost
10	·	x	+	2	·	y	=	155

Equation 2: Purchase by second soccer coach

Number of soccer balls purchased	·	Cost of a soccer ball	+	Number of soccer ball bags purchased	·	Cost of a soccer ball bag	=	Total cost
12	·	x	+	3	·	y	=	189

STEP 2 Multiply Equation 1 by 3 and Equation 2 by 2 so that the coefficient of y in each equation is the least common multiple of 3 and 2, or 6.

$$10x + 2y = 155 \quad \times 3 \longrightarrow \quad 30x + 6y = 465$$
$$12x + 3y = 189 \quad \times 2 \longrightarrow \quad 24x + 6y = 378$$

STEP 3 Subtract the equations. $\quad 6x \quad = 87$

STEP 4 Solve for x. $\quad x = 14.5$

STEP 5 Substitute 14.5 for x in either of the original equations and solve for y.

$$10x + 2y = 155 \qquad \text{Write Equation 1.}$$
$$10(\mathbf{14.5}) + 2y = 155 \qquad \text{Substitute 14.5 for } x.$$
$$y = 5 \qquad \text{Solve for } y.$$

▸ A soccer ball costs $14.50, and a soccer ball bag costs $5.

✓ **GUIDED PRACTICE** for Example 3

7. **FABRIC** Dina makes a quilt that has alternating stripes of quilting fabric and sateen fabric. Quilting fabric costs $4 per yard, and sateen fabric costs $6 per yard. She spends $76 on a total of 16 yards of the two fabrics. Find the amounts of quilting fabric and sateen fabric that Dina purchases.

Methods for Solving Linear Systems

Method	Example	When to Use
Graphing (p. 376)	 $3x - 2y = 2$ $x + y = 4$	When you want to see the lines that the equations represent
Substitution (p. 383)	$y = 4 - 2x$ $4x + 3y = 8$	When one equation is already solved for x or y
Addition (p. 391)	$4x + 7y = 15$ $6x - 7y = 5$	When the coefficients of one variable are opposites
Subtraction (p. 392)	$3x + 5y = -13$ $3x + y = -5$	When the coefficients of one variable are the same
Multiplication (p. 398)	$9x + 2y = 38$ $3x - 5y = 7$	When no corresponding coefficients are the same or opposites

7.4 EXERCISES

HOMEWORK KEY

◆ = **MULTIPLE CHOICE PRACTICE**
Exs. 15, 16, 31, 36, and 46–48

○ = **HINTS AND HOMEWORK HELP**
for Exs. 7, 23, and 39 at classzone.com

SKILLS · PROBLEM SOLVING · REASONING

1. VOCABULARY What is the least common multiple of 12 and 18?

2. WRITING *Explain* how to solve the linear system using the elimination method.

     $2x - 3y = -4$ **Equation 1**
     $7x + 9y = -5$ **Equation 2**

EXAMPLE 1
on p. 398
for Exs. 3–16

SOLVING LINEAR SYSTEMS Solve the linear system using elimination.

3. $x + y = 2$
$2x + 7y = 9$

4. $3x - 2y = 3$
$-x + y = 1$

5. $4x + 3y = 8$
$x - 2y = 13$

6. $2x - 9y = 15$
$-x + 3y = -6$

7. $-4x + y = 5$
$11x - 9y = 5$

8. $2x + 5y = 18$
$3x - 10y = -8$

9. $2x - 10y = 6$
$-3x + 2y = -22$

10. $x + 3y = 13$
$-3x - 2y = -4$

11. $4x - y = 9$
$5x + 2y = 21$

12. $10x - 9y = 46$
$-2x + 3y = 10$

13. $8x - 5y = 11$
$4x - 3y = 5$

14. $11x - 20y = 28$
$3x + 4y = 36$

15. ◆ **MULTIPLE CHOICE** What is the solution of the linear system $3x - 4y = 1$ and $-x + 3y = -7$?

     Ⓐ $(-4, -5)$ **Ⓑ** $(-4, 5)$ **Ⓒ** $(-5, -4)$ **Ⓓ** $(5, -4)$

16. ◆ **MULTIPLE CHOICE** Which process will eliminate a variable in the given linear system?

$3x + 5y = -8$ **Equation 1**
$x - 2y = 1$ **Equation 2**

  Ⓐ Multiply Equation 2 by 8, then add the equations.

  Ⓑ Multiply Equation 1 by 2, then subtract the equations.

  Ⓒ Multiply Equation 2 by −3, then add the equations.

  Ⓓ Multiply Equation 1 by −1, then subtract the equations.

EXAMPLE 2
on p. 399 for
Exs. 17–31

SOLVING LINEAR SYSTEMS Solve the linear system using elimination.

17. $4x - 3y = 8$
$5x - 2y = -11$

18. $-2x - 5y = 9$
$3x + 11y = 4$

19. $7x - 6y = -1$
$5x - 4y = 1$

20. $5x + 9y = 2$
$6x + 8y = -6$

21. $9x + 2y = 5$
$7x + 3y = 14$

22. $5x + 4y = -23$
$3x - 7y = 5$

23. $7x + 3y = -12$
$2x + 5y = 38$

24. $9x - 8y = 4$
$2x - 3y = -4$

25. $12x - 7y = -2$
$-8x + 11y = 14$

26. $9x + 2y = 39$
$6x + 13y = -9$

27. $-7x + 10y = 11$
$-8x + 15y = 34$

28. $-14x + 15y = 15$
$21x - 20y = -10$

ERROR ANALYSIS *Describe* and correct the error when solving the linear system.

29.

$$
\begin{array}{l}
2x - 3y = -9 \xrightarrow{\times 2} 4x - 6y = -18 \\
5x - 6y = -9 \phantom{\xrightarrow{\times 2}} \underline{5x - 6y = -9} \\
\phantom{5x - 6y = -9 \xrightarrow{\times 2}} 9x = -27 \\
\phantom{5x - 6y = -9 \xrightarrow{\times 2}} x = -3
\end{array}
$$

30.

$$
\begin{array}{l}
9x + 8y = 11 \xrightarrow{\times 3} 27x + 24y = 11 \\
7x + 6y = 9 \xrightarrow{\times 4} 28x + 24y = 9 \\
\phantom{7x + 6y = 9 \xrightarrow{\times 4}} -x = 2 \\
\phantom{7x + 6y = 9 \xrightarrow{\times 4}} x = -2
\end{array}
$$

31. ◆ **MULTIPLE CHOICE** What is the solution of the linear system $15x + 8y = 6$ and $25x + 12y = 14$?

  Ⓐ $(-3, -2)$ Ⓑ $(-3, 2)$ Ⓒ $(-2, -3)$ Ⓓ $(2, -3)$

32. **WRITING** For which values of a can you solve the linear system

$ax + 3y = 2$ and $\frac{1}{2}x + 5y = 6$ without multiplying first? *Explain.*

CONNECT SKILLS TO PROBLEM SOLVING Exercises 33–35 will help you prepare for problem solving.

Write a linear system that models the situation.

33. You spend $22 for 17 flowers, all roses and carnations. Each rose costs $1.50, and each carnation costs $1. Let x represent the number of roses and y represent the number of carnations that you purchase.

34. The problems on a math test are worth either 2 points or 3 points. The test has 60 problems worth a total of 150 points. Let x represent the number of 2 point questions and y represent the number of 3 point questions.

35. A store is selling used DVDs for $10 and new DVDs for $18. You buy 12 DVDs for $208. Let x represent the number of new DVDs and y represent the number of used DVDs that you purchase.

◆ = **MULTIPLE CHOICE PRACTICE**   ◯ = **HINTS AND HOMEWORK HELP** at classzone.com

EXAMPLE 3
on p. 400
for Exs. 36–38

36. ◆ **MULTIPLE CHOICE** A clothing store is having a sale. Sweatshirts cost $24, and T-shirts cost $12. A customer spends $132 for 8 shirts. How many sweatshirts does the person purchase?

　　(A) 3　　　　　　**(B)** 4　　　　　　**(C)** 5　　　　　　**(D)** 6

California @HomeTutor for problem solving help at classzone.com

37. ENTERTAINMENT A website allows users to download television episodes and music videos. All television episodes cost the same to download, and all music videos cost the same to download. Ryan pays $5.95 to download 4 television episodes and 1 music video. Seth pays $6.95 to download 3 television episodes and 2 music videos. How much does the website charge to download a television episode? a music video?

California @HomeTutor for problem solving help at classzone.com

38. FARM PRODUCTS The table shows the numbers of tomatoes and avocados needed to make a batch of salsa and a batch of guacamole. You have harvested 22 tomatoes and 33 avocados in your home garden. How many batches of salsa and batches of guacamole can you make if you use every tomato and every avocado?

	Tomatoes	Avocados
Salsa	3	1
Guacamole	1	4

(39.) FOOTBALL Tickets for admission to a high school football game cost $3 for students and $5 for adults. During one game, $3000 was collected from the sale of 720 tickets.

　a. Writing a System Write and solve a system of linear equations to find the number of tickets sold to students and the number of tickets sold to adults.

　b. Drawing a Graph Graph the system of linear equations. Use the graph to determine whether your answer to part (a) is reasonable.

40. MULTI-STEP PROBLEM A local country club offers private tennis lessons and group tennis lessons. You take 5 private lessons and 2 group lessons. Your total cost is $190. Your friend takes 4 private lessons and 3 group lessons. Your friend's total cost is $180.

　a. How much does a private lesson cost?

　b. How much does a group lesson cost?

　c. What is the total cost of 6 private lessons and 2 group lessons?

41. OPEN-ENDED *Describe* a real-world problem that can be solved using a system of linear equations. Then solve the problem and explain what the solution means in this situation.

5 private lessons and
2 group lessons: $190

42. **REASONING** Use elimination to show that the solution of the system of equations $Ax + By = E$ and $Cx + Dy = F$ is $x = \dfrac{ED - BF}{AD - BC}$ and $y = \dfrac{AF - EC}{AD - BC}$, where $AD \neq BC$.

CHALLENGE Find the values of *a* and *b* so that the linear system has the given solution.

$ax - by = 4$ **Equation 1**
$bx - ay = 10$ **Equation 2**

43. $(4, 2)$

44. $(2, 1)$

45. **CHALLENGE** You drive a car 45 miles at an average speed *r* (in miles per hour) to reach your destination. Due to traffic, your average speed on the return trip is $\dfrac{3}{4}r$. The round trip takes a total of 1 hour 45 minutes. Find the average speed for each leg of your trip.

◆ CALIFORNIA STANDARDS SPIRAL REVIEW

Alg. 9.0

46. What is the solution of the linear system whose graph is shown? *(p. 376)*

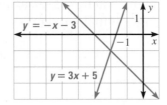

$y = -x - 3$
$y = 3x + 5$

ⓐ $(-3, 0)$

ⓑ $(-2, 1)$

ⓒ $(0, -3)$

ⓓ $(-2, -1)$

Alg. 8.0

47. What is an equation of the line that passes through $(-2, 6)$ and is perpendicular to $y = 2x + 5$? *(p. 354)*

ⓐ $y = \dfrac{1}{2}x + 6$

ⓑ $y = 2x + 3$

ⓒ $y = 2x - 2$

ⓓ $y = -\dfrac{1}{2}x + 5$

Alg. 5.0

48. The length of a rectangle is 4 feet more than the width. The perimeter is 12 times the width. What is the width of the rectangle? *(p. 146)*

ⓐ 1 ft
ⓑ 2 ft
ⓒ 3 ft
ⓓ 4 ft

QUIZ *for Lessons 7.3–7.4*

Solve the linear system using elimination. *(pp. 391, 398)*

1. $x + y = 4$
$-3x + y = -8$

2. $2x - y = 2$
$6x - y = -2$

3. $x + y = 5$
$-x + y = -3$

4. $x + 3y = -10$
$-x + 5y = -30$

5. $x + 3y = 10$
$3x - y = 13$

6. $x + 7y = 10$
$x + 2y = -8$

7. $4x - y = 2$
$3x + 2y = 7$

8. $x + 3y = 1$
$5x + 6y = 14$

9. $3x + y = 21$
$x + y = 1$

10. $2x - 3y = -5$
$5x + 2y = 16$

11. $7x + 2y = 13$
$4x + 3y = 13$

12. $3x - 5y = 23$
$2x + 9y = 3$

7.5 Solve Special Types of Linear Systems

Standards Alg. 9.0 **Students solve a system of two linear equations in two variables algebraically and are able to interpret the answer graphically.** Students are able to solve a system of two linear inequalities in two variables and to sketch the solution sets.

Connect *Before* you found the solution of a linear system. *Now* you will identify the number of solutions of a linear system.

Math and **CLIMBING**
Ex. 42, p. 411

Key Vocabulary
• **inconsistent system**
• **consistent dependent system**
• **system of linear equations,** *p. 376*
• **parallel,** *p. 293*

A linear system can have no solution or infinitely many solutions. A linear system has no solution when the graphs of the equations are parallel. A linear system with no solution is called an **inconsistent system**.

A linear system has infinitely many solutions when the graphs of the equations are the same line. A linear system with infinitely many solutions is called a **consistent dependent system**.

EXAMPLE 1 A linear system with no solution

Show that the linear system has no solution.

$3x + 2y = 10$ **Equation 1**
$3x + 2y = 2$ **Equation 2**

Solution

METHOD 1 Graphing

Graph the linear system.

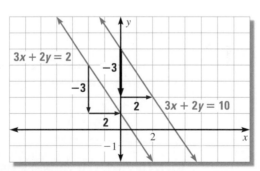

Animated **Algebra**

For an interactive example of identifying the number of solutions of a linear system, go to **classzone.com**.

▶ The lines are parallel because they have the same slope but different *y*-intercepts. Parallel lines do not intersect, so the system has no solution.

METHOD 2 Elimination

IDENTIFY TYPES OF SYSTEMS

The linear system in Example 1 is called an inconsistent system because the lines do not intersect (are not consistent).

Subtract the equations.

$$3x + 2y = 10$$
$$\underline{3x + 2y = 2}$$
$$0 = 8 \quad \longleftarrow \textbf{This is a false statement.}$$

▶ The variables are eliminated and you are left with a false statement regardless of the values of *x* and *y*. This tells you that the system has no solution.

EXAMPLE 2 A linear system with infinitely many solutions

Show that the linear system has infinitely many solutions.

$x - 2y = -4$ **Equation 1**

$y = \frac{1}{2}x + 2$ **Equation 2**

Solution

METHOD 1 Graphing

Graph the linear system.

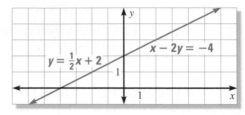

▸ The equations represent the same line, so any point on the line is a solution. So, the linear system has infinitely many solutions.

METHOD 2 Substitution

Substitute $\frac{1}{2}x + 2$ for y in Equation 1 and solve for x.

$x - 2y = -4$ **Write Equation 1.**

$x - 2\left(\frac{1}{2}x + 2\right) = -4$ **Substitute $\frac{1}{2}x + 2$ for y.**

$-4 = -4$ **Simplify.**

▸ The variables are eliminated and you are left with a statement that is true regardless of the values of x and y. This tells you that the system has infinitely many solutions.

IDENTIFY TYPES OF SYSTEMS

The linear system in Example 2 is called a consistent dependent system because the lines intersect (are consistent) and the equations are equivalent (are dependent).

 GUIDED PRACTICE for Examples 1 and 2

Tell whether the linear system has *no solution* or *infinitely many solutions*. *Explain* your answer.

1. $5x + 3y = 6$
  $-5x - 3y = 3$

2. $y = 2x - 4$
  $-6x + 3y = -12$

IDENTIFYING THE NUMBER OF SOLUTIONS When the equations of a linear system are written in slope-intercept form, you can identify the number of solutions of the system by looking at the slopes and y-intercepts of the lines.

Slopes and y-intercepts	Number of solutions
Different slopes	One solution
Same slope Different y-intercepts	No solution
Same slope Same y-intercept	Infinitely many solutions

EXAMPLE 3 ◆ **Multiple Choice Practice**

What is the solution to this system of equations?

$$6x + 2y = 4 \qquad \textbf{Equation 1}$$
$$6x + 2y = -8 \qquad \textbf{Equation 2}$$

(**A**) $(-3, 2)$

(**B**) No solution

(**C**) $(5, 7)$

(**D**) Infinitely many solutions

Solution

Write each equation in slope-intercept form.

$6x + 2y = 4 \quad \longrightarrow \quad y = -3x + 2$

$6x + 2y = -8 \quad \longrightarrow \quad y = -3x - 4$

Because the lines have the same slope but different y-intercepts, the system has no solution.

▶ The correct answer is B. (A) (B) (C) (D)

EXAMPLE 4 **Write and solve a system of linear equations**

ART An artist wants to sell prints of her paintings. She orders a set of prints for each of two of her paintings. Each set contains regular prints and glossy prints, as shown in the table. Find the cost of one glossy print.

Regular	Glossy	Cost
45	30	$465
15	10	$155

Solution

STEP 1 **Write** a linear system. Let x be the cost (in dollars) of a regular print, and let y be the cost (in dollars) of a glossy print.

$45x + 30y = 465$ **Cost of prints for one painting**
$15x + 10y = 155$ **Cost of prints for other painting**

STEP 2 **Solve** the linear system using elimination.

$45x + 30y = 465 \qquad\qquad 45x + 30y = 465$
$15x + 10y = 155 \quad \times (-3) \longrightarrow \quad -45x - 30y = -465$
$$\overline{\qquad\qquad\qquad 0 = 0}$$

▶ There are infinitely many solutions, so you cannot determine the cost of one glossy print. You need more information.

✔ **GUIDED PRACTICE**   **for Examples 3 and 4**

3. Without solving the linear system, tell whether it has *one solution, no solution,* or *infinitely many solutions.*

$5x + y = -2$ **Equation 1**
$-10x - 2y = 4$ **Equation 2**

4. **WHAT IF?** In Example 4, suppose a glossy print costs $3 more than a regular print. Find the cost of a glossy print.

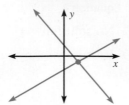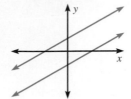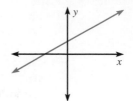
7.5 EXERCISES

SKILLS · PROBLEM SOLVING · REASONING

1. **VOCABULARY** Copy and complete: A linear system with no solution is called a(n) __?__ system.

2. **NOTETAKING SKILLS** Make a case diagram like the one on page 374 for the possible numbers of solutions of a system of equations.

3. **WRITING** *Describe* the graph of a linear system that has no solution.

4. **WRITING** *Describe* the graph of a linear system that has infinitely many solutions.

EXAMPLES 1 and 2
on pp. 405–406
for Exs. 5–7

INTERPRETING GRAPHS Match the linear system with its graph. Then use the graph to tell whether the linear system has *one solution*, *no solution*, or *infinitely many solutions*.

5. $x - 3y = -9$
   $x - y = -1$

6. $x - y = -4$
   $-3x + 3y = 2$

7. $x + 3y = -1$
   $-2x - 6y = 2$

A.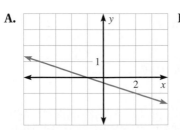

B.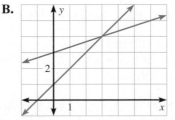

C.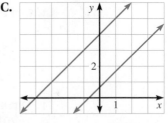

EXAMPLES
1 and 2
on pp. 405–406
for Exs. 8–25

INTERPRETING GRAPHS Graph the linear system. Then use the graph to tell whether the linear system has *one solution*, *no solution*, or *infinitely many solutions*.

8. $x + y = -2$
$y = -x + 5$

9. $3x - 4y = 12$
$y = \frac{3}{4}x - 3$

10. $3x - y = -9$
$3x + 5y = -15$

11. $-2x + 2y = -16$
$3x - 6y = 30$

12. $-9x + 6y = 18$
$6x - 4y = -12$

13. $-3x + 4y = 12$
$-3x + 4y = 24$

14. ERROR ANALYSIS *Describe* and correct the error in solving the linear system below.

$6x + y = 36$
$5x - y = 8$

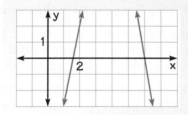

SOLVING LINEAR SYSTEMS Solve the linear system using substitution or elimination.

15. $2x + 5y = 14$
$6x + 7y = 10$

16. $-16x + 2y = -2$
$y = 8x - 1$

17. $3x - 2y = -5$
$4x + 5y = 47$

18. $5x - 5y = -3$
$y = x + 0.6$

19. $x - y = 0$
$5x - 2y = 6$

20. $x - 2y = 7$
$-x + 2y = 7$

21. $-18x + 6y = 24$
$3x - y = -2$

22. $4y + 5x = 15$
$x = 8y + 3$

23. $6x + 3y = 9$
$2x + 9y = 27$

24. ◆ MULTIPLE CHOICE Which linear system has *exactly* one solution?

Ⓐ $-x + y = 9$
$x - y = 9$

Ⓑ $-x + y = 9$
$x - y = -9$

Ⓒ $-x + y = 9$
$-x - y = 9$

Ⓓ $x - y = -9$
$-x + y = -9$

25. ◆ MULTIPLE CHOICE Which linear system has infinitely many solutions?

Ⓐ $15x + 5y = 20$
$6x - 2y = 8$

Ⓑ $15x - 5y = 20$
$6x - 2y = -8$

Ⓒ $15x - 5y = -20$
$6x - 2y = 8$

Ⓓ $15x - 5y = 20$
$6x - 2y = 8$

EXAMPLE 3
on p. 407
for Exs. 26–31

IDENTIFYING THE NUMBER OF SOLUTIONS Without solving the linear system, tell whether the linear system has *one solution*, *no solution*, or *infinitely many solutions*.

26. $y = -6x - 2$
$12x + 2y = -6$

27. $y = 7x + 13$
$-21x + 3y = 39$

28. $4x + 3y = 27$
$4x - 3y = -27$

29. $9x - 15y = 24$
$6x - 10y = 16$

30. $0.3x + 0.4y = 2.4$
$0.5x - 0.6y = 0.2$

31. $0.9x - 2.1y = 12.3$
$1.5x - 3.5y = 20.5$

32. REASONING What can you conclude about a, b, c, and d if the system $y = ax + b$ and $y = cx + d$ has infinitely many solutions? no solution?

33. OPEN-ENDED Write a linear system so that it has infinitely many solutions and one of the equations is $y = 3x + 2$.

34. REASONING Give a counterexample for the following statement:
If the graphs of the equations of a linear system have the same slope, then the linear system has no solution.

CONNECT SKILLS TO PROBLEM SOLVING Exercises 35–37 will help you prepare for problem solving.

Write a linear system that models the situation.

35. At a farmer's market, you purchase 6 apples and 8 pears for $6.40. Your friend purchases 4 apples and 5 pears for $4.10. Let a represent the cost of each apple, and let p represent the cost of each pear.

36. Tom spent $40 on 2 CDs and 2 DVDs. Gillian spent $90 on 3 CDs and 3 DVDs. Let c represent the cost of each CD, and let d represent the cost of each DVD.

37. You have x nickels and y dimes worth $1.50. Your friend has twice as many nickels and 8 times as many dimes, and the coins are worth $3.

EXAMPLE 4
on p. 407
for Exs. 38–40

38. RECREATION One admission to a roller skating rink costs x dollars, and renting a pair of skates costs y dollars. A group pays $243 for admission for 36 people and 21 skate rentals. Another group pays $81 for admission for 12 people and 7 skate rentals. Is there enough information to determine the cost of one admission to the roller skating rink? *Explain*.

California @HomeTutor for problem solving help at classzone.com

(39.) TRANSPORTATION A train travels from San Diego to Los Angeles, then back to San Diego. The table shows the number of coach tickets and business class tickets purchased for each leg of the trip. Is there enough information to determine the cost of one coach ticket? *Explain*.

Destination	Coach tickets	Business class tickets	Money collected (dollars)
Los Angeles	150	80	7480
San Diego	170	100	8860

California @HomeTutor for problem solving help at classzone.com

40. PHOTOGRAPHY In addition to taking pictures on your digital camera, you can record 30 second movies. All pictures use the same amount of memory, and all 30 second movies use the same amount of memory. The number of pictures and 30 second movies on 2 memory cards is shown.

a. Is there enough information to determine the amount of memory used by a 30 second movie? *Explain*.

b. Given that a 30 second movie uses 50 times the amount of memory that a digital picture uses, can you determine the amount of memory used by a 30 second movie? *Explain*.

Size of card (megabytes)	64	256
Pictures	450	1800
Movies	7	28

41. ◆ **MULTIPLE CHOICE** A clothing store sold 15 pairs of pants for $500. Which of the following facts does *not* give a unique solution for the number of jeans and number of dress pants sold?

Ⓐ Jeans cost $25, and dress pants cost $50.

Ⓑ Jeans cost $25, and dress pants cost $25.

Ⓒ Jeans cost $30, and dress pants cost $36.25.

Ⓓ Jeans cost $50, and dress pants cost $25.

42. **MULTI-STEP PROBLEM** Two people are training for a speed ice-climbing event. During a practice climb, one climber starts 15 seconds after the first climber. The rates that the climbers ascend are shown.

a. Let d be the distance (in feet) traveled by a climber t seconds after the first person starts climbing. Write a linear system that models the situation.

b. Graph the linear system from part (a). Does the second climber catch up to the first climber? *Explain.*

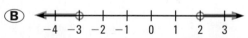
Climbs 10 feet every 30 seconds

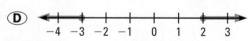
Climbs 5 feet every 15 seconds

43. **CHALLENGE** Find values of p, q, and r that produce a system with:

a. No solution.
b. Infinitely many solutions.
c. One solution, (4, 1).

$$px + qy = r \quad \text{Equation 1}$$
$$2x - 3y = 5 \quad \text{Equation 2}$$

44. **CHALLENGE** A group of 16 people attend a musical. Of the group, 12 people purchase balcony tickets and 4 people purchase floor tickets. The total cost is $280. Of the people who purchase balcony tickets, 6 people receive a 10% discount. Of the people who purchase floor tickets, 2 people receive a 10% discount. The total cost for the 8 people who receive a 10% discount is $126. Is there enough information to determine how much the group saves collectively? each individual saves? *Explain.*

◆ CALIFORNIA STANDARDS SPIRAL REVIEW

Alg. 3.0 | **45.** Which graph represents the solution of $|2x + 1| < 5$? *(p. 226)*

Ⓐ <-+--○--+--+--+--○--+->
     -4 -3 -2 -1 0 1 2 3

Ⓑ <-+--○--+--+--+--+--○--+->
     -4 -3 -2 -1 0 1 2 3

Ⓒ <-+--●--+--+--+--+--●--+->
     -4 -3 -2 -1 0 1 2 3

Ⓓ <-+--+--+--+--+--+--●--+->
     -4 -3 -2 -1 0 1 2 3

Alg. 7.0 | **46.** Which ordered pair is a solution of the equation $y = -3x - 2$? *(p. 322)*

Ⓐ (13, −5)   Ⓑ (2, −8)   Ⓒ (−11, 3)   Ⓓ (0, 0)

Alg. 5.0 | **47.** Admission to a concert costs $45. A vendor sells T-shirts for $12 each. You have $90. What is the maximum number of T-shirts you can buy? *(p. 146)*

Ⓐ 3   Ⓑ 4   Ⓒ 5   Ⓓ 6

Multiple Choice Practice for Lessons 7.1–7.5

1. What is the solution of the linear system whose graph is shown? **Alg. 9.0**

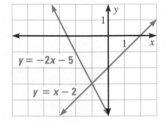

(A) $(-3, -1)$

(B) $(-1, -3)$

(C) $(-3, 1)$

(D) $(1, -3)$

$y = -2x - 5$

$y = x - 2$

2. At a grocery store, a customer pays a total of $8 for 2 pounds of potato salad and 1.5 pounds of coleslaw. Another customer pays a total of $6.50 for 1 pound of potato salad and 2 pounds of coleslaw. How much does 3 pounds of coleslaw cost? **Alg. 9.0**

(A) $2   (B) $4

(C) $6   (D) $8

3. What is the solution of the linear system $y = 3x + 9$ and $-9x + 3y = 36$? **Alg. 9.0**

(A) $(-2, 3)$

(B) $(0, 9)$

(C) No solution

(D) Infinitely many solutions

4. At a paint store, two people purchase the same brand of paint and paintbrushes. The amount of paint and number of brushes each person purchases is shown below. What is the cost of one can of paint? **Alg. 9.0**

2 cans of paint

2 paintbrushes

Total cost: $78

1 can of paint

1 paintbrush

Total cost: $39

(A) $10

(B) $20

(C) $30

(D) The cost cannot be determined.

5. During one day, two computers are sold at a computer store. The two customers each arrange payment plans with the salesperson. The graph shows the amount y of money (in dollars) paid for the computers after x months. In how many months will each customer have paid the same amount? **Alg. 9.0**

Months since purchase

(A) 2 months   (B) 3 months

(C) 4 months   (D) 5 months

6. A rectangle has a perimeter of 18 inches. A new rectangle is formed by doubling the width w and tripling the length ℓ, as shown. The new rectangle has a perimeter of 46 inches. What is the length of the new rectangle? **Alg. 9.0**

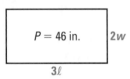

$P = 46$ in.

$2w$

3ℓ

(A) 4 in.   (B) 5 in.

(C) 8 in.   (D) 15 in.

7. Which linear system has *exactly* one solution? **Alg. 9.0**

(A) $y = -2x + 5$
    $y = -2x + 1$

(B) $x - y = 0$
    $5x - 2y = 6$

(C) $-x + 2y = -2$
    $-x + 2y = 21$

(D) $-2x + y = 3$
    $-4x + 2y = 6$

7.6 Solve Rate Problems

Standards Alg. 15.0 Students apply algebraic techniques to solve rate problems, work problems, and percent mixture problems.

Connect *Before* you solved linear systems. *Now* you will use linear systems to solve rate problems.

Math and MOTION
Example 1, p. 413

Key Vocabulary
• uniform motion

Recall that the formula for distance traveled is $d = rt$ where d is the distance traveled, r is the rate (constant or average speed), and t is the time. An object moving at a constant rate is said to be in **uniform motion**. Throughout this lesson, assume people or objects are in uniform motion.

When reading rate problems, look for rate, time, and distance relationships that can be used to solve the problem. An example of each is shown in the table below.

Relationship	Example
Rate relationship	Object A moves twice as fast as object B.
Time relationship	The total time is 30 minutes.
Distance relationship	Object A catches up with object B.

EXAMPLE 1 Write a system of equations

AIRCRAFT A helicopter leaves an airport and flies north at 180 miles per hour. An hour later, an airplane leaves the airport flying in the same direction at 330 miles per hour. Write a system of equations that can be used to determine how long it will take the airplane to overtake the helicopter.

Solution

STEP 1 **Identify** relationships.

Time: The airplane flies one hour less than the helicopter.

Distance: When the airplane overtakes the helicopter, they will have traveled the same distance.

STEP 2 **Write** a linear system. Let x be the helicopter's flying time, and let y be the airplane's flying time.

Airplane's time	=	Helicopter's time	−	One hour
y	=	x	−	1

Airplane's rate	·	Airplane's time	=	Helicopter's rate	·	Helicopter's time
330	·	y	=	180	·	x

7.6 Solve Rate Problems **413**

7.8 Linear Inequalities in Two Variables

MATERIALS • set of tangram pieces • 4 tangram puzzles • stopwatch

QUESTION How can you use inequalities to describe an overestimate or an underestimate?

EXPLORE Conduct an experiment

To solve a tangram puzzle, you use seven pieces to create a figure. Each piece must lie flat and touch at least one other piece, and the pieces cannot overlap.

> **Standards**
>
> **Alg. 6.0 Students** graph a linear equation and compute the *x*- and *y*-intercepts (e.g., graph 2*x* + 6*y* = 4). They **are also able to sketch the region defined by linear inequalities (e.g., they sketch the region defined by 2*x* + 6*y* < 4).**

STEP 1 *Predict a time*

Have your partner give you a tangram puzzle, such as the dog shown below. Predict how long it will take you to create the figure.

Predicted time:
50 seconds

STEP 2 *Create figure*

Use the tangrams to create the figure. Your partner will use a stopwatch to record the actual time it takes you to finish.

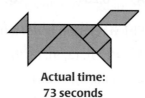

Actual time:
73 seconds

STEP 3 *Record times*

Record the actual time *x* and the predicted time *y* in a table, as below. Repeat Steps 1–3 for three more puzzles. Then switch roles with your partner.

Figure	Actual time x (sec)	Predicted time y (sec)
1	73	50
2	67	67
3	70	88
4	90	74

STEP 4 *Plot points*

Graph *y = x* in Quadrant I. Then plot the points (*x, y*) from the table.

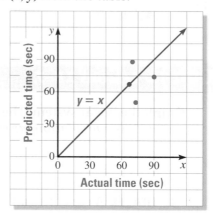

DRAW CONCLUSIONS Use your observations to complete these exercises

1. *Describe* the points that represent an *overestimate* of the actual finishing time. Then write an inequality that describes the region in the coordinate plane where these points are located.

2. *Describe* the points that represent an *underestimate* of the actual finishing time. Then write an inequality that describes the region in the coordinate plane where these points are located.

7.8 Graph Linear Inequalities in Two Variables

Standards Alg. 6.0 Students graph a linear equation and compute the *x*- and *y*-intercepts (e.g., graph $2x + 6y = 4$). They **are also able to sketch the region defined by linear inequalities** (e.g., **they sketch the region defined by** $2x + 6y < 4$).

Connect *Before* you graphed linear equations in two variables. *Now* you will graph linear inequalities in two variables.

Math and **MUSIC**
Ex. 64, p. 431

Key Vocabulary
- **linear inequality in two variables**
- **solution of an inequality in two variables**
- **graph of an inequality in two variables**
- **half-plane**

A **linear inequality in two variables**, such as $x - 3y < 6$, is the result of replacing the $=$ sign in a linear equation with $<$, $\leq$, $>$, or $\geq$. A **solution of an inequality in two variables** x and y is an ordered pair (x, y) that produces a true statement when the values of x and y are substituted into the inequality.

EXAMPLE 1 Check solutions of a linear inequality

Tell whether the ordered pair is a solution of $2x - 3y > 5$.

a. $(4, 1)$ **b.** $(2, -2)$

Solution

a. $2x - 3y > 5$ **Write inequality.**

     $2(4) - 3(1) \stackrel{?}{>} 5$ **Substitute 4 for *x* and 1 for *y*.**

            $5 > 5$ ✗   **Simplify.**

▶ So, $(4, 1)$ is not a solution of $2x - 3y > 5$.

b. $2x - 3y > 5$ **Write inequality.**

     $2(2) - 3(-2) \stackrel{?}{>} 5$ **Substitute 2 for *x* and −2 for *y*.**

           $10 > 5$ ✓   **Simplify.**

▶ So, $(2, -2)$ is a solution of $2x - 3y > 5$.

✓ **GUIDED PRACTICE**   for Example 1

   1. Tell whether $(-2, 5)$ and $(3, 1)$ are solutions of $-x + 2y < 8$.

INTERPRET GRAPHS
A dashed boundary line means that points on the line are *not* solutions. A solid boundary line means that points on the line are solutions.

GRAPH OF AN INEQUALITY In a coordinate plane, the **graph of an inequality in two variables** is the set of points that represent all solutions of the inequality. The *boundary line* of a linear inequality divides the coordinate plane into two **half-planes**. Only one half-plane contains the points that represent the solutions of the inequality.

Graph of $2x - 3y > 5$

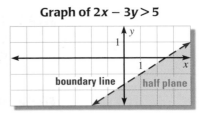

BIG IDEAS
For Your Notebook

Big Idea 1

Solving Linear Systems by Graphing

The graph of a linear system tells you how many solutions the system has.

Consistent independent system One solution	Inconsistent system No solution	Consistent dependent system Infinitely many solutions
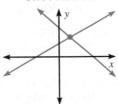	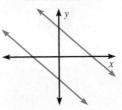	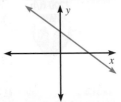
The lines intersect.	The lines are parallel.	The lines coincide.

Big Idea 2

Solving Linear Systems Using Algebra

You can use any of the following algebraic methods to solve a linear system. Sometimes it is easier to use one method instead of another.

Method	Procedure	When to use
Substitution	Solve one equation for *x* or *y*. Substitute the expression for *x* or *y* into the other equation.	When one equation is already solved for *x* or *y*
Addition	Add the equations to eliminate *x* or *y*.	When the coefficients of one variable are opposites
Subtraction	Subtract the equations to eliminate *x* or *y*.	When the coefficients of one variable are the same
Multiplication	Multiply one or both equations by a nonzero constant so that adding or subtracting the equations will eliminate *x* or *y*.	When no corresponding coefficients are the same or opposites

Big Idea 3

Solving Systems of Linear Inequalities

The graph of a system of linear inequalities is the intersection of the half-planes of each inequality in the system. For example, the graph of the system of inequalities below is the shaded region.

$x \le 6$ **Inequality 1**
$y < 2$ **Inequality 2**
$2x + 3y \ge 6$ **Inequality 3**

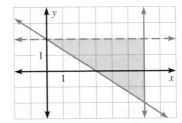

APPLYING THE
BIG IDEAS

Big Idea 1
You solve a linear system by graphing in **Step 3**.

Big Idea 2
You solve a linear system using algebra in **Step 4**.

Big Idea 3
You solve a system of linear inequalities in **Ex. 2**.

PROBLEM How can you use systems of equations and inequalities to plan a workout?

STEP 1 Choose a number of calories to burn and two exercises.

Suppose you are a personal fitness trainer who is planning a 45 minute workout for a client. The workout will consist of two different exercises. The table below shows the calories burned for various exercises.

Exercise	Calories burned (calories per minute)
Step aerobics	7
Rowing machine	8
Running	11
Swimming	10
Ski machine	9

Choose a number as the goal for the total number of calories your client should burn during the workout. Then choose two exercises.

STEP 2 Write a system of equations.

Let x be the number of minutes your client spends on the first exercise, and let y be the number of minutes your client spends on the second exercise. Write a system of equations that can be used to determine how many minutes your client should spend on each exercise in order to reach the goal.

STEP 3 Graph a system of equations.

Graph your system of equations to determine whether a solution exists. If no solution exists, go back to Step 1 and choose a new goal for your client.

STEP 4 Solve the system algebraically.

Solve your system of equations algebraically.

Extending the Problem

1. Use the graph from Step 3 to determine what range of total calories burned guarantees that the system will have a solution. Does that range work for *any* two exercises? *Explain*.

2. Suppose another client has a *maximum* of 40 minutes to work out. Choose a *minimum* goal for the total number of calories your client should burn during the workout. Then choose two exercises. Write and graph a system of inequalities that models the situation. Note that the number of minutes for each exercise cannot be negative. If a solution region exists, list several solutions. If a solution region does not exist, explain why not.

REVIEW KEY VOCABULARY

• system of linear equations, *p. 376*

• solution of a system of linear equations, *p. 376*

• consistent independent system, *p. 376*

• inconsistent system, *p. 405*

• consistent dependent system, *p. 405*

• uniform motion, *p. 413*

• linear inequality in two variables, *p. 425*

• solution of an inequality in two variables, *p. 425*

• graph of an inequality in two variables, *p. 425*

• half-plane, *p. 425*

• system of linear inequalities, *p. 433*

• solution of a system of linear inequalities, *p. 433*

• graph of a system of linear inequalities, *p. 433*

VOCABULARY EXERCISES

1. Copy and complete: A(n) __?__ consists of two or more linear inequalities in the same variables.

2. **NOTETAKING SKILLS** Make a case diagram like the one on page 374 for the possible numbers of solutions of a system of linear inequalities.

3. Give an example of a consistent dependent system. *Explain* why the system is a consistent dependent system.

REVIEW EXAMPLES AND EXERCISES

Use the review examples and exercises below to check your understanding of the concepts you have learned in each lesson of Chapter 7.

7.1 Solve Linear Systems by Graphing
pp. 376–381

Alg. 9.0

EXAMPLE

Solve the linear system by graphing. Check your solution.

$y = x - 2$ **Equation 1**
$y = -3x + 2$ **Equation 2**

Graph both equations. The lines appear to intersect at $(1, -1)$. Check the solution by substituting 1 for x and -1 for y in each equation.

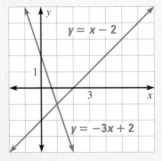

$y = x - 2$	$y = -3x + 2$
$-1 \stackrel{?}{=} 1 - 2$	$-1 \stackrel{?}{=} -3(1) + 2$
$-1 = -1 \checkmark$	$-1 = -1 \checkmark$

EXERCISES

Solve the linear system by graphing. Check your solution.

EXAMPLES
1 and 2
on pp. 376–377
for Exs. 4–6

4. $y = -3x + 1$
$y = x - 7$

5. $y = 3x + 4$
$y = -2x - 1$

6. $x + y = 3$
$x - y = 5$

7.2 Solve Linear Systems by Substitution
pp. 383–388

Alg. 9.0

EXAMPLE

Solve the linear system: $3x + y = -9$ **Equation 1**
                          $y = 5x + 7$ **Equation 2**

STEP 1   Substitute $5x + 7$ for y in Equation 1 and solve for x.

$$3x + y = -9 \qquad \text{Write Equation 1.}$$
$$3x + 5x + 7 = -9 \qquad \text{Substitute } 5x + 7 \text{ for } y.$$
$$x = -2 \qquad \text{Solve for } x.$$

STEP 2   Substitute -2 for x in Equation 2 to find the value of y.

$$y = 5x + 7 = 5(-2) + 7 = -10 + 7 = -3$$

▶ The solution is $(-2, -3)$. You can check the solution by substituting -2 for x and -3 for y in each of the original equations.

EXERCISES

**EXAMPLES
1 and 2**
on pp. 383–384
for Exs. 7–9

Solve the linear system using substitution.

7. $y = 2x - 7$
    $x + 2y = 1$

8. $x + 4y = 9$
    $x - y = 4$

9. $2x + y = -15$
    $y - 5x = 6$

7.3 Solve Linear Systems by Adding or Subtracting
pp. 391–397

Alg. 9.0

EXAMPLE

Solve the linear system: $5x - y = 8$ **Equation 1**
                           $-5x + 4y = -17$ **Equation 2**

STEP 1   **Add** the equations to eliminate one variable.

$$\begin{array}{r} 5x - y = 8 \\ -5x + 4y = -17 \\ \hline 3y = -9 \end{array}$$

STEP 2   **Solve** for y. $y = -3$

STEP 3   Substitute -3 for y in either equation and solve for x.

$$5x - y = 8 \qquad \text{Write Equation 1.}$$
$$5x - (-3) = 8 \qquad \text{Substitute } -3 \text{ for } y.$$
$$x = 1 \qquad \text{Solve for } x.$$

▶ The solution is $(1, -3)$. You can check the solution by substituting 1 for x and -3 for y in each of the original equations.

EXERCISES

**EXAMPLES
1, 2, and 3**
on pp. 391–392
for Exs. 10–12

Solve the linear system using elimination.

10. $4x - 5y = 14$
     $-4x + y = -6$

11. $x + 7y = 12$
     $-2x + 7y = 18$

12. $4y = 11 - 3x$
     $3x + 2y = -5$

Solve Linear Systems by Multiplying First

pp. 398–404

Alg. 9.0

EXAMPLE

Solve the linear system: $x - 2y = -7$ **Equation 1**
$3x - y = 4$ **Equation 2**

STEP 1 **Multiply** the first equation by -3.

$$x - 2y = -7 \quad \times (-3) \quad -3x + 6y = 21$$
$$3x - y = 4 \qquad\qquad\qquad \underline{3x - \ y = 4}$$

STEP 2 **Add** the equations. $5y = 25$

STEP 3 **Solve** for y. $y = 5$

STEP 4 **Substitute** 5 for y in either of the original equations and solve for x.

$x - 2y = -7$ **Write Equation 1.**

$x - 2(5) = -7$ **Substitute 5 for y.**

$x = 3$ **Solve for x.**

▶ The solution is $(3, 5)$. You can check the solution by substituting 3 for x and 5 for y in each of the original equations.

EXERCISES

Solve the linear system using elimination.

EXAMPLES
1 and 2
on pp. 398–399
for Exs. 13–15

13. $x + 6y = 28$
$2x - 3y = -19$

14. $3x - 5y = -7$
$-4x + 7y = 8$

15. $5x = 3y - 2$
$3x + 2y = 14$

Solve Special Types of Linear Systems

pp. 405–411

Alg. 9.0

EXAMPLE

Show that the linear system has no solution. $-2x + y = -3$ **Equation 1**
$y = 2x + 1$ **Equation 2**

Rewrite $-2x + y = -3$ as $y = 2x - 3$. Then graph the linear system.

The lines are parallel because they have the same slope but different y-intercepts. Parallel lines do not intersect, so the system has no solution.

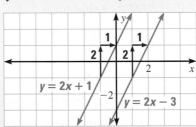

EXERCISES

Tell whether the linear system has *one solution, no solution,* or *infinitely many solutions. Explain.*

EXAMPLES
1, 2, and 3
on pp. 405–407
for Exs. 16–18

16. $x = 2y - 3$
$1.5x - 3y = 0$

17. $-x + y = 8$
$x + 8 = y$

18. $4x = 2y + 6$
$4x + 2y = 10$

7.6 Solve Rate Problems

pp. 413–417

Alg. 15.0

EXAMPLE

A car leaves a rest area on a highway traveling at a speed of 45 miles per hour. Two hours later, a motorcycle leaves the rest area traveling in the same direction at 55 miles per hour. Write a system of equations that can be used to determine how long it will take the motorcycle to overtake the car.

Let x be the car's traveling time, and let y be the motorcycle's traveling time.

The motorcycle travels two hours less than the car. So, $y = x - 2$.

When the motorcycle overtakes the car, the two vehicles will have traveled the same distance. So, $55y = 45x$.

▶ The system of equations is:
$$y = x - 2 \quad \text{Equation 1}$$
$$55y = 45x \quad \text{Equation 2}$$

EXERCISES

EXAMPLE 2
on p. 414
for Ex. 19

19. SKIING A ski lift carries Carlos up a slope at a rate of 5 miles per hour. Carlos skis down the slope, parallel to the lift, at a speed of 20 miles per hour. The round trip takes a half hour. Write and solve a system of equations to determine how far Carlos skis.

7.7 Solve Mixture Problems

pp. 418–423

Alg. 15.0

EXAMPLE

The owner of a food store wants to sell a 3 pound mixture of cashews and pecans for $19 per pound. The cashews sell for $5 per pound, and the pecans sell for $9 per pound. How many pounds of cashews should the owner use?

STEP 1 **Write** a system of equations. Let x be the number of pounds of cashews, and let y be the number of pounds of pecans.

Total amount of mixture: $x + y = 3$ **Equation 1**
Total cost of mixture: $5x + 9y = 19$ **Equation 2**

STEP 2 **Solve** the system for x. Multiply Equation 1 by -9.

$$x + y = 3 \qquad \times (-9) \qquad -9x - 9y = -27$$
$$5x + 9y = 19 \qquad\qquad\qquad \underline{ 5x + 9y = 19}$$

Add the equations. $\qquad\qquad -4x = -8$

Solve for x. $\qquad\qquad\qquad\qquad x = 2$

▶ The owner should use 2 pounds of cashews in the mixture.

EXERCISES

EXAMPLE 3
on p. 420
for Ex. 20

20. CHEMISTRY A chemist obtains 18 grams of a 10% saline solution from a mixture of a 5% saline solution and a 15% saline solution. How much of the 15% saline solution is used in the mixture?

7.8 Graph Linear Inequalities in Two Variables
pp. 425–432

Alg. 6.0

EXAMPLE

Graph the inequality $y < 3x - 1$.

STEP 1 **Graph** the equation $y = 3x - 1$. The inequality is <, so use a dashed line.

STEP 2 **Test** $(0, 0)$ in $y < 3x - 1$.

$$0 \overset{?}{<} 3(0) - 1$$

$$0 < -1 \; \textbf{✗}$$

STEP 3 **Shade** the half-plane that does not contain $(0, 0)$, because $(0, 0)$ is *not* a solution of the inequality.

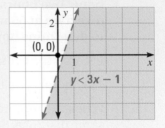

EXERCISES

EXAMPLES
1, 2, 3, and 4
on pp. 425–427
for Exs. 21–24

Graph the inequality.

21. $y > 2x + 3$ **22.** $y \le \frac{1}{2}x - 1$ **23.** $3x - 2y < 12$ **24.** $y \ge 3$

7.9 Solve Systems of Linear Inequalities
pp. 433–440

Alg. 9.0

EXAMPLE

Graph the system of inequalities.

$y < -2x + 3$ **Inequality 1**
$y \ge x - 3$ **Inequality 2**

The graph of $y < -2x + 3$ is the half-plane below the dashed line $y = -2x + 3$.

The graph of $y \ge x - 3$ is the half-plane on and above the solid line $y = x - 3$.

The graph of the system is the intersection of the two half-planes, which is the region shown in the darker shade of blue.

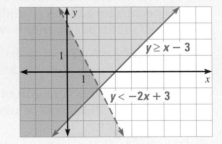

EXERCISES

EXAMPLES
1, 2, 3, 4, and 5
on pp. 433–436
for Exs. 25–28

Graph the system of inequalities.

25. $y < x + 3$
$y > -3x - 2$

26. $y \le -x - 2$
$y > 4x + 1$

27. $y \ge 0$
$x \le 2$
$y < x + 4$

28. MOVIE COSTS You receive a $40 gift card to a movie theater. A ticket to an afternoon movie costs $5, and a ticket to an evening movie costs $8. Write and graph a system of inequalities for the number of tickets you can purchase using the gift card.

1. **VOCABULARY** Copy and complete: The boundary line of a linear inequality divides the coordinate plane into two ___?___.

2. **VOCABULARY** Copy and complete: A(n) ___?___ of an inequality in two variables is the set of points that represent all solutions of the inequality.

Solve the linear system by graphing. Check your solution.

3. $3x - y = -6$
   $x + y = 2$

4. $-2x + y = 5$
   $x + y = -1$

5. $2x + 7y = 14$
   $5x + 7y = -7$

Solve the linear system using substitution.

6. $y = 5x - 7$
   $-4x + y = -1$

7. $3x + y = -19$
   $x - y = 7$

8. $3y + x = 17$
   $x + y = 8$

Solve the linear system using elimination.

9. $8x + 3y = -9$
   $-8x + y = 29$

10. $x - 5y = -3$
    $3x - 5y = 11$

11. $4x + y = 17$
    $7y = 4x - 9$

12. $3x + 2y = -5$
    $x - y = 10$

13. $3y = x + 5$
    $-3x + 8y = 8$

14. $6x - 5y = 9$
    $9x - 7y = 15$

Tell whether the linear system has *one solution*, *no solution*, or *infinitely many solutions*.

15. $15x - 3y = 12$
    $y = 5x - 4$

16. $4x - y = -4$
    $-8x + 2y = 2$

17. $-12x + 3y = 18$
    $4x + y = -6$

18. $6x - 7y = 5$
    $-12x + 14y = 10$

19. $3x - 4y = 24$
    $3x + 4y = 24$

20. $10x - 2y = 14$
    $15x - 3y = 21$

Graph the system of inequalities.

21. $y < 2x + 2$
    $y \geq -x - 1$

22. $y \leq 3x - 2$
    $y > x + 4$

23. $y \leq 3$
    $x > -1$
    $y > 3x - 3$

24. **TRAVEL** An airplane flies 4200 kilometers east (against the wind) in 6 hours. The airplane's return flight (with the wind) takes 5 hours. The speed of the wind remains constant. Find the speed of the plane in still air and the speed of the wind.

25. **SALINE** You obtain 15 grams of a 5% saline solution from a mixture of a 3% saline solution and an 8% saline solution. How much of the 3% saline solution is used in the mixture?

26. **COMMUNITY SERVICE** A town committee has a $75 spending limit on snacks for the volunteers participating in a clean-up day. The committee chairperson decides to purchase granola bars and at least 50 bottles of water. Granola bars cost $.50 each, and bottles of water cost $.75 each. Write and graph a system of linear inequalities for the number of bottles of water and the number of granola bars that can be purchased.

STRATEGIES YOU'LL USE:
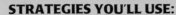
• SOLVE DIRECTLY
• ELIMINATE CHOICES

Standards
Alg. 6.0, 9.0

If you have difficulty solving a multiple choice problem directly, you may be able to use another approach to eliminate incorrect answer choices and obtain the correct answer.

PROBLEM 1

Which system of inequalities has the graph shown?

(A) $x > -1$
$y \leq 2$
$y \leq x - 2$

(B) $x > -1$
$y < 2$
$y > x - 2$

(C) $x > -1$
$y \leq 2$
$y < x - 2$

(D) $x > -1$
$y \leq 2$
$y > x - 2$

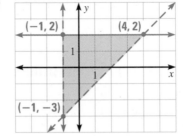

Strategy 1 SOLVE DIRECTLY

Use each boundary line to write an inequality.

STEP 1 **Write** the inequality that involves the vertical boundary line. The boundary line is $x = -1$. Because the line is dashed, the inequality is either > or <. Test the point $(0, 1)$ from the solution region. Because $0 > -1$, the inequality is $x > -1$.

STEP 2 **Write** the inequality that involves the horizontal boundary line. The boundary line is $y = 2$. Because the line is solid, the inequality is either $\leq$ or $\geq$. Test the point $(0, 1)$ from the solution region. Because $1 \leq 2$, the inequality is $y \leq 2$.

STEP 3 **Write** the last inequality. Using the points $(2, 0)$ and $(0, -2)$, you know the equation of the boundary line is $y = x - 2$. Because the line is dashed, the inequality is either > or <. Test the point $(0, 1)$. Because $1 > 0 - 2$, the inequality is $y > x - 2$.

The correct answer is D. Ⓐ Ⓑ Ⓒ **Ⓓ**

Strategy 2 ELIMINATE CHOICES

You can eliminate choices by observing boundary lines and testing points.

STEP 1 **Check** boundary lines.

You can see from the graph that the boundary line $y = 2$ is solid. So, you can eliminate any system in which the boundary line $y = 2$ would be dashed. You can eliminate choice B.

You can also see from the graph that the boundary line $y = x - 2$ is dashed. So, you can eliminate any system in which the boundary line $y = x - 2$ would be solid. You can eliminate choice A.

STEP 2 **Use** a test point.

From the graph, you can see that $(0, 0)$ is a solution of the system. The point $(0, 0)$ does not satisfy the inequality $y < x - 2$, so you can eliminate choice C.

The correct answer is D. Ⓐ Ⓑ Ⓒ **Ⓓ**

PROBLEM 2

What is the solution of the linear system $y = 2x - 1$ and $2x - 5y = -11$?

(A) $(0, 1)$ **(B)** $(2, 3)$ **(C)** $(3, 2)$ **(D)** $(1, 0)$

Strategy 1 SOLVE DIRECTLY	**Strategy 2** ELIMINATE CHOICES

Strategy 1   SOLVE DIRECTLY

STEP 1 **Write** the equations so that the like terms are arranged in columns.

$y = 2x - 1 \longrightarrow -2x + y = -1$

$2x - 5y = -11 \longrightarrow 2x - 5y = -11$

STEP 2 **Add** the equations. $-4y = -12$

STEP 3 **Solve** for y. $y = 3$

STEP 4 **Substitute** 3 for y in either equation and solve for x.

$2x - 5y = -11$ **Write equation.**

$2x - 5(3) = -11$ **Substitute 3 for y.**

$x = 2$ **Solve for x.**

So, the solution of the system is $(2, 3)$.

The correct answer is B. **(A)** **(B)** **(C)** **(D)**

Strategy 2   ELIMINATE CHOICES

Test each answer choice in the linear system.

Choice A: $(0, 1)$

$y = 2x - 1$ $2x - 5y = -11$

$1 \overset{?}{=} 2(0) - 1$ $2(0) - 5(1) \overset{?}{=} -11$

$1 = -1$ ✗ $-5 = -11$ ✗

Choice B: $(2, 3)$

$y = 2x - 1$ $2x - 5y = -11$

$3 \overset{?}{=} 2(2) - 1$ $2(2) - 5(3) \overset{?}{=} -11$

$3 = 3$ ✓ $-11 = -11$ ✓

The ordered pair $(2, 3)$ satisfies both equations in the linear system.

The correct answer is B. **(A)** **(B)** **(C)** **(D)**

STRATEGY PRACTICE

Explain why you can eliminate the highlighted answer choice.

1. The sum of two numbers is -27. One number is twice the other. What are the numbers?

   (A) ✗ **9 and 18**   **(B)** -3 and 24 **(C)** -18 and -9 **(D)** -14 and -13

2. Which ordered pair is a solution of the linear system $5x + 2y = -11$ and $2x = y + 8$?

   (A) $(18, -5)$ **(B)** $(-5, -18)$ **(C)** $(5, -18)$ **(D)** ✗ **(5, 18)**

3. A vendor at a concert sells long-sleeve and short-sleeve T-shirts. A long-sleeve T-shirt costs $25, and a short-sleeve T-shirt costs $15. During the concert, the vendor collects $8415 from the sale of 441 T-shirts. How many short-sleeve T-shirts are sold?

   (A) 100 **(B)** ✗ **180**   **(C)** 261 **(D)** 441

1. Your friend is making strawberry lemonade. The lemonade requires 3 times as many pounds of lemons as strawberries. Your friend spends $7 on lemons and strawberries. How many pounds of strawberries are used? **Alg. 9.0**

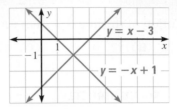

Lemons

Strawberries

$1.50 per pound

$2.50 per pound

Ⓐ 1 lb

Ⓑ 2 lb

Ⓒ 3 lb

Ⓓ 4 lb

2. What is the solution of the linear system $4x + y = 3$ and $2x - y = 3$? **Alg. 9.0**

Ⓐ $(-4, 2)$

Ⓑ $(1, -1)$

Ⓒ No solution

Ⓓ Infinitely many solutions

3. A store is having a sale on CDs and DVDs. All CDs cost the same, and all DVDs cost the same. Tyler buys 4 CDs and 2 DVDs for $78. The next day, while the sale is still in progress, Tyler goes back and buys 2 CDs and 1 DVD. What is the cost of his second purchase? **Alg. 9.0**

Ⓐ $26

Ⓑ $34

Ⓒ $39

Ⓓ $52

4. You mix 50 milligrams of a 7% saline solution with 30 milligrams of a 5% saline solution. About what percent of the mixture is salt? **Alg. 15.0**

Ⓐ 5.4%

Ⓑ 6.3%

Ⓒ 7.1%

Ⓓ 12%

5. Which ordered pair is the solution of the linear system shown? **Alg. 9.0**

Ⓐ $(2, 1)$

Ⓑ $(-2, -1)$

Ⓒ $(2, -1)$

Ⓓ $(1, -2)$

6. At a craft store, a customer pays a total of $10 for 5 candles and 2 candle holders. Another customer pays a total of $16 for 6 candles and 4 candle holders. How much do 4 candles cost? **Alg. 9.0**

Ⓐ $2

Ⓑ $3

Ⓒ $4

Ⓓ $5

7. A helicopter flying against the wind takes 15 minutes to travel between cities. The return flight (flying with the wind) takes 10 minutes. During the trip, the speed of the wind remains constant. Which system of equations can be used to determine the speed x of the helicopter in still air, and the speed y of the wind? **Alg. 15.0**

30 kilometers

Ⓐ $15x = 12y$
   $x + y = 30$

Ⓑ $x + y = 15$
   $x - y = 10$

Ⓒ $x + y = 2$
   $x - y = 3$

Ⓓ $x + y = 3$
   $x - y = 2$

8. The departure times for two buses are shown below. Bus A travels at a rate of 20 miles per hour, and bus B travels at a rate of 24 miles per hour. At what time will the buses have traveled the same distance? **Alg. 15.0**

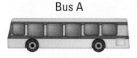

Bus A — Departs 9:00 A.M.   Bus B — Departs 9:15 A.M.

Ⓐ 9:45 A.M.

Ⓑ 10:30 A.M.

Ⓒ 10:45 A.M.

Ⓓ 11:30 A.M.

9. Which linear system has *no* solution? **Alg. 9.0**

Ⓐ $y = -2x + 5$
$y = -2x + 1$

Ⓑ $x - y = 0$
$5x - 2y = 6$

Ⓒ $-x + 2y = -2$
$2x + 3y = 21$

Ⓓ $-2x + y = 3$
$-4x + 2y = 6$

10. The graph of which system of inequalities is shown? **Alg. 9.0**

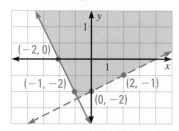

Ⓐ $2x + y < 4$
$-2x + y \le 4$

Ⓑ $2x + y \ge -4$
$x - 2y < 4$

Ⓒ $2x + y \le 4$
$2x + y \ge -4$

Ⓓ $3x + y > 6$
$-3x + y \ge 6$

11. A family is planning a vacation and can spend no more than $2000 for 4 airplane tickets and 5 nights at a hotel. Which graph describes the combinations of prices x (in dollars) of an airplane ticket and prices y (in dollars) of a night at a hotel? **Alg. 6.0**

Ⓐ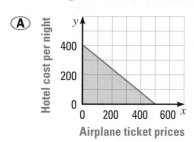

Ⓑ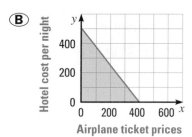

Ⓒ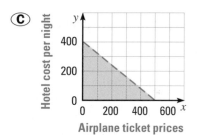

Ⓓ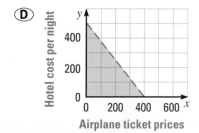

12. Which ordered pair is *not* a solution of the inequality $4x + 3y < 24$? **Alg. 6.0**

Ⓐ $(0, 2)$

Ⓑ $(0, 0)$

Ⓒ $(-2, 1)$

Ⓓ $(7, 1)$

Evaluate the expression.

1. $2^5 \cdot 2 - 4 \div 2$ *(p. 11)*

2. $24 \div 6 + (9 - 6)$ *(p. 11)*

3. $5[(6 - 2)^2 - 5]$ *(p. 11)*

4. $\sqrt{144}$ *(p. 95)*

5. $-\sqrt{2500}$ *(p. 95)*

6. $\pm\sqrt{400}$ *(p. 95)*

Check whether the given number is a solution of the equation or inequality. *(p. 26)*

7. $7 + 3x = 16; 3$

8. $21y + 1 = 1; 0$

9. $20 - 12h = 12; 1$

10. $g - 3 > 2; 5$

11. $10 \geq 4 - x; 0$

12. $30 - 4p \geq 5; 6$

Simplify the expression.

13. $5(y - 1) + 4$ *(p. 81)*

14. $12w + (w - 2)3$ *(p. 81)*

15. $(g - 1)(-4) + 3g$ *(p. 81)*

16. $\dfrac{10h - 25}{5}$ *(p. 88)*

17. $\dfrac{21 - 4x}{-7}$ *(p. 88)*

18. $\dfrac{32 - 20m}{2}$ *(p. 88)*

Solve the equation.

19. $x - 8 = 21$ *(p. 125)*

20. $-1 = x + 3$ *(p. 125)*

21. $6x = -42$ *(p. 125)*

22. $\dfrac{x}{3} = 8$ *(p. 125)*

23. $5 - 2x = 11$ *(p. 132)*

24. $\dfrac{2}{3}x - 3 = 17$ *(p. 132)*

25. $3(x - 2) = -15$ *(p. 139)*

26. $3(5x - 7) = 5x - 1$ *(p. 146)*

27. $-7(2x - 10) = 4x - 10$ *(p. 146)*

Solve the inequality. Then graph your solution.

28. $x - 9 < -13$ *(p. 189)*

29. $8 \leq x + 7$ *(p. 189)*

30. $8x \geq 56$ *(p. 196)*

31. $\dfrac{x}{-4} > 7$ *(p. 196)*

32. $1 - 2x < 11$ *(p. 202)*

33. $8 > -3x - 1$ *(p. 202)*

34. $4x - 10 \leq 7x + 8$ *(p. 202)*

35. $7x - 5 < 6x - 4$ *(p. 202)*

36. $-4 < 3x - 1 < 5$ *(p. 210)*

37. $3 \leq 9 - 2x \leq 15$ *(p. 210)*

38. $|3x| < 15$ *(p. 226)*

39. $|4x - 2| \geq 18$ *(p. 226)*

Graph the equation.

40. $x + 2y = -8$ *(p. 273)*

41. $-2x + 5y = -10$ *(p. 273)*

42. $3x - 4y = 12$ *(p. 273)*

43. $y = 3x - 7$ *(p. 291)*

44. $y = x + 6$ *(p. 291)*

45. $y = -\dfrac{1}{3}x$ *(p. 297)*

Write an equation in slope-intercept form of the line with the given slope and y-intercept. *(p. 322)*

46. slope: 5
 y-intercept: -1

47. slope: -1
 y-intercept: 3

48. slope: -7
 y-intercept: 0

Write an equation in point-slope form of the line that passes through the given points. *(p. 340)*

49. $(1, -10), (-5, 2)$

50. $(4, 7), (-4, 3)$

51. $(-9, -2), (-6, 8)$

52. $(-1, 1), (1, -3)$

53. $(2, 4), (8, 2)$

54. $(-6, 1), (3, -5)$

Solve the linear system using elimination. *(pp. 391, 398)*

55. $4x + y = 8$
$5x - 2y = -3$

56. $3x - 5y = 5$
$x - 5y = -4$

57. $12x + 7y = 3$
$8x + 5y = 1$

58. ART PROJECT You are making a tile mosaic on the rectangular tabletop shown. A bag of porcelain tiles costs $3.95 and covers 36 square inches. How much will it cost to buy enough tiles to cover the tabletop? *(p. 32)*

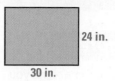

24 in.

30 in.

59. FOOD The table shows the changes in the price for a dozen grade A, large eggs over 4 years. Find the average yearly change, to the nearest tenth of a cent, in the price for a dozen grade A, large eggs during the period 2001–2004. *(p. 88)*

Year	2001	2002	2003	2004
Change in price for a dozen grade A, large eggs (dollars)	−0.03	0.25	0.38	−0.58

60. HONEY PRODUCTION Honeybees visit about 2,000,000 flowers to make 16 ounces of honey. About how many flowers do honeybees visit to make 6 ounces of honey? *(p. 161)*

61. THERMOMETERS A nanotube thermometer is the world's smallest thermometer. The thermometer can measure temperatures from 50°C to 500°C. Write and solve a compound inequality to find the temperatures (in degrees Fahrenheit) that the thermometer can measure. *(p. 210)*

62. MUSIC The table shows the prices for various lengths of speaker cable. *(p. 297)*

Length, ℓ (feet)	3	5	12	15
Price, p (dollars)	7.50	12.50	30.00	37.50

a. *Explain* why p varies directly with ℓ.

b. Write a direct variation equation that relates ℓ and p.

63. RIVERBOATS A riverboat traveling downstream (with the current) takes 2 hours to travel between cities. The return trip (against the current) takes 3 hours. The speed of the current remains constant during both trips. What is the speed of the current? *(p. 413)*

24 miles

8 Exponents and Radicals

Before

In previous chapters, you learned the following skills, which you'll use in Chapter 8:

- Evaluating powers
- Evaluating expressions involving exponents
- Evaluating square roots
- Using the distributive property

Now

In Chapter 8 you'll study these **Big Ideas:**

1 Applying properties of exponents to simplify expressions

2 Using definitions of exponents to simplify expressions

3 Applying properties of radicals to simplify expressions

Why?

So you can solve real-world problems about . . .

- Ice cream, p. 464
- Astronomy, p. 465
- Earthquakes, p. 472
- Architecture, p. 495
- Long jump, p. 502

Animated Algebra
at *classzone.com*

Get-Ready Games

THREE of a KIND

California Standards

Review evaluating expressions involving exponents. **Gr. 7 AF 2.1**

Prepare for using the rules of exponents. **Alg. 2.0**

Materials

- One deck of *Three of a Kind* cards

2 • 2 • 2

How to Play Play in groups of three or four. The dealer shuffles the cards and deals six cards to each player. Players do not show each other their cards.

The dealer places the remaining deck of cards face down. This is the *draw* pile. The dealer turns the top card face up and places it beside the draw pile. This is the *discard* pile. The player to the left of the dealer begins, following the steps on the next page.

CALIFORNIA STANDARDS

- **Alg. 2.0** Students understand and use such operations as taking the opposite, finding the reciprocal, **taking a root, and raising to a fractional power. They understand and use the rules of exponents.** *(Lessons 8.1, 8.2, 8.3, 8.6)*

2 • 2 • 2

30^2

30 • 30

900

1 **Draw** the top card from either the draw pile or the discard pile.

2 • 2 • 2

2 **Decide** whether you have a group of 3 cards with the same value in your hand. If you do, then place those cards face up in front of you.

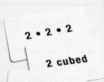

3 **Remove** one card from those remaining in your hand and place it face up on top of the discard pile.

How to Win Be the first player to put down 2 groups of 3 cards with the same value.

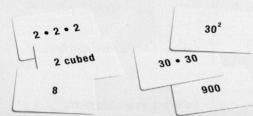

Games Wrap-Up

Draw Conclusions

Complete these exercises after playing the game.

1. **WRITING** Choose a card from the deck of *Three of a Kind* cards with a value other than 1. *Describe* how the value of the card can be written as the product of two different whole numbers.

2. **REASONING** For what values of n is $(-2)^n = 2^n$? *Explain* your reasoning.

Prerequisite Skills

California @HomeTutor

Prerequisite skills practice
at classzone.com

**REVIEW
VOCABULARY**

• **power,** *p. 6*
• **exponent,** *p. 6*
• **base,** *p. 6*
• **square root,** *p. 95*
• **reciprocal,** *p. 789*

VOCABULARY CHECK

1. Identify the exponent and the base in the expression 13^8.

2. Copy and complete: An expression that represents repeated multiplication of the same factor is called a(n) __?__ .

SKILLS CHECK

Evaluate the expression. *(Review p. 5 for 8.1–8.3, 8.5.)*

3. x^2 when $x = 10$ 4. a^3 when $a = 3$ 5. m^2 when $m = 1.2$

6. y^3 when $y = 0.4$ 7. r^2 when $r = \frac{5}{6}$ 8. z^3 when $z = \frac{1}{2}$

Evaluate the expression. *(Review p. 95 for 8.4.)*

9. $\sqrt{81}$ 10. $-\sqrt{64}$ 11. $\pm\sqrt{100}$ 12. $-\sqrt{121}$

Use the distributive property to write an equivalent expression.
(Review p. 81 for 8.4.)

13. $4(y - 3)$ 14. $2(x - 2)$ 15. $-x(x + 11)$ 16. $4x(x - 9)$

Notetaking Skills

NOW YOU TRY
Make a *property and examples* chart for dividing fractions. Illustrate division by a whole number, a fraction, and a mixed number. You may want to use colored pencils.

Focus on Graphic Organizers

You can use a *property and examples* chart to organize examples that illustrate different uses of a mathematical rule or property, such as the subtraction rule.

SUBTRACTION RULE
To subtract b from a, add the opposite of b to a.

$2 - 3 = 2 + (-3) = -1$ **Subtract a positive number.**

$4 - (-2) = 4 + 2 = 6$ **Subtract a negative number.**

$2x - 5x = 2x + (-5x) = -3x$ **Subtract a variable term.**

8.1 Products and Powers

MATERIALS · paper and pencil

Standards

Alg. 2.0 Students understand and use such operations as taking the opposite, finding the reciprocal, taking a root, and raising to a fractional power. They **understand and use the rules of exponents.**

QUESTION   How can you find a product of powers and a power of a power?

EXPLORE 1   Find products of powers

STEP 1 *Simplify expressions* Copy and complete the table.

Expression	Expression as repeated multiplication	Number of factors	Simplified expression
$7^4 \cdot 7^5$	$(7 \cdot 7 \cdot 7 \cdot 7) \cdot (7 \cdot 7 \cdot 7 \cdot 7 \cdot 7)$	9	7^9
$(-4)^2 \cdot (-4)^3$	$[(-4) \cdot (-4)] \cdot [(-4) \cdot (-4) \cdot (-4)]$	?	?
$x^1 \cdot x^5$	?	?	?

STEP 2 *Analyze results* Find a pattern that relates the exponents of the factors in the first column and the exponent of the expression in the last column.

EXPLORE 2   Find powers of powers

STEP 1 *Copy and complete* Copy and complete the table.

Expression	Expanded expression	Expression as repeated multiplication	Number of factors	Simplified expression
$(5^3)^2$	$(5^3) \cdot (5^3)$	$(5 \cdot 5 \cdot 5) \cdot (5 \cdot 5 \cdot 5)$	6	5^6
$[(-6)^2]^3$	$[(-6)^2] \cdot [(-6)^2] \cdot [(-6)^2]$	?	?	?
$(a^3)^3$	?	?	?	?

STEP 2 *Analyze results* Find a pattern that relates the exponents of the expression in the first column and the exponent of the expression in the last column.

DRAW CONCLUSIONS   Use your observations to complete these exercises

Simplify the expression. Write your answer using exponents.

1. $5^2 \cdot 5^3$ **2.** $(-6)^1 \cdot (-6)^4$ **3.** $(m^2)^5$ **4.** $[(-2)^3]^4$

In Exercises 5 and 6, copy and complete the statement.

5. If a is a real number and m and n are positive integers, then $a^m \cdot a^n = \underline{\ ?\ }$.

6. If a is a real number and m and n are positive integers, then $(a^m)^n = \underline{\ ?\ }$.

8.1 Apply Exponent Properties Involving Products

Standards **Alg. 2.0** **Students** understand and use such operations as taking the opposite, finding the reciprocal, taking a root, and raising to a fractional power. They **understand and use the rules of exponents.**

Connect *Before* you evaluated exponential expressions. *Now* you will use properties of exponents involving products.

Math and **AGRICULTURE**
Example 6, p. 463

Key Vocabulary
• **order of magnitude**
• **power,** *p. 6*
• **exponent,** *p. 6*
• **base,** *p. 6*

Notice what happens when you multiply two powers that have the same base.

5 factors

$$a^2 \cdot a^3 = \overbrace{(a \cdot a)} \cdot \overbrace{(a \cdot a \cdot a)} = a^5 = a^{2+3}$$

2 factors   3 factors

The example above suggests the following property of exponents, known as the product of powers property.

KEY CONCEPT *For Your Notebook*

Product of Powers Property

Let a be a real number, and let m and n be positive integers.

Words To multiply powers having the same base, add the exponents.

Algebra $a^m \cdot a^n = a^{m+n}$ **Example** $5^6 \cdot 5^3 = 5^{6+3} = 5^9$

EXAMPLE 1 **Use the product of powers property**

SIMPLIFY EXPRESSIONS
When simplifying powers with numerical bases only, write your answers using exponents, as in parts (a) and (c).

a. $(-2)^3 \cdot (-2)^5 = (-2)^{3+5}$
$= (-2)^8$

b. $x^4 \cdot x^3 = x^{4+3}$
$= x^7$

c. $7^6 \cdot 7 \cdot 7^8 = 7^6 \cdot 7^1 \cdot 7^8$
$= 7^{6+1+8}$
$= 7^{15}$

d. $y \cdot y^3 \cdot y^2 = y^1 \cdot y^3 \cdot y^2$
$= y^{1+3+2}$
$= y^6$

 GUIDED PRACTICE for Example 1

Simplify the expression.

1. $3^2 \cdot 3^7$ **2.** $(-5) \cdot (-5)^9$ **3.** $z^5 \cdot z^5$ **4.** $x^2 \cdot x^6 \cdot x$

EXAMPLE 2 ◆ Multiple Choice Practice

Which expression is equivalent to w^3w^2?

(A) w^3w^3 **(B)** w^4w **(C)** w^5w **(D)** w^9w^4

Solution

STEP 1 **Simplify** the given expression, w^3w^2.

$$w^3w^2 = w^{3+2} = w^5$$

STEP 2 **Determine** which expression equals w^5.

Choice A: $w^3w^3 = w^{3+3} = w^6$ ✗

Choice B: $w^4w = w^4w^1 = w^{4+1} = w^5$ ✓

▶ The correct answer is B. (A) **(B)** (C) (D)

AVOID ERRORS

Remember that variables raised to the first power are usually written without an exponent. For example, $w = w^1$.

POWER OF A POWER Notice what happens when you raise a power to a power.

$$(a^2)^3 = a^2 \cdot a^2 \cdot a^2 = (a \cdot a) \cdot (a \cdot a) \cdot (a \cdot a) = a^6 = a^{2 \cdot 3}$$

The example above suggests the following property of exponents, known as the power of a power property.

KEY CONCEPT *For Your Notebook*

Power of a Power Property

Let a be a real number, and let m and n be positive integers.

Words To find a power of a power, multiply exponents.

Algebra $(a^m)^n = a^{mn}$

Example $(3^4)^2 = 3^{4 \cdot 2} = 3^8$

EXAMPLE 3 Use the power of a power property

AVOID ERRORS

In part (d), notice that you can write $[(y + 2)^6]^2$ as $(y + 2)^{12}$, but you cannot write $(y + 2)^{12}$ as $y^{12} + 2^{12}$.

a. $(2^5)^3 = 2^{5 \cdot 3}$
     $= 2^{15}$

c. $(x^2)^4 = x^{2 \cdot 4}$
     $= x^8$

b. $[(-6)^2]^5 = (-6)^{2 \cdot 5}$
     $= (-6)^{10}$

d. $[(y + 2)^6]^2 = (y + 2)^{6 \cdot 2}$
     $= (y + 2)^{12}$

✓ **GUIDED PRACTICE** for Examples 2 and 3

Simplify the expression.

5. $m^8 \cdot m^9$ **6.** $(4^2)^2$ **7.** $[(-2)^4]^5$ **8.** $(x^5)^7$

POWER OF A PRODUCT Notice what happens when you raise a product to a power.

$$(ab)^3 = (ab) \cdot (ab) \cdot (ab) = (a \cdot a \cdot a) \cdot (b \cdot b \cdot b) = a^3 b^3$$

The example above suggests the following property of exponents, known as the power of a product property.

KEY CONCEPT *For Your Notebook*

Power of a Product Property

Let a and b be real numbers, and let m be a positive integer.

Words To find a power of a product, find the power of each factor and multiply.

Algebra $(ab)^m = a^m b^m$

Example $(23 \cdot 17)^5 = 23^5 \cdot 17^5$

EXAMPLE 4 Use the power of a product property

SIMPLIFY EXPRESSIONS
When simplifying powers with numerical *and* variable bases, be sure to evaluate the numerical power, as in parts (b), (c), and (d).

a. $(24 \cdot 13)^8 = 24^8 \cdot 13^8$

b. $(9xy)^2 = (9 \cdot x \cdot y)^2 = 9^2 \cdot x^2 \cdot y^2 = 81x^2 y^2$

c. $(-4z)^2 = (-4 \cdot z)^2 = (-4)^2 \cdot z^2 = 16z^2$

d. $-(4z)^2 = -(4 \cdot z)^2 = -(4^2 \cdot z^2) = -16z^2$

EXAMPLE 5 Use all three properties

Animated Algebra

For an interactive example of using properties of exponents, go to **classzone.com**.

Simplify $(2x^3)^2 \cdot x^4$.

$$
\begin{aligned}
(2x^3)^2 \cdot x^4 &= 2^2 \cdot (x^3)^2 \cdot x^4 && \text{Power of a product property} \\
&= 4 \cdot x^6 \cdot x^4 && \text{Power of a power property} \\
&= 4x^{10} && \text{Product of powers property}
\end{aligned}
$$

✓ **GUIDED PRACTICE** for Examples 4 and 5

Simplify the expression.

9. $(42 \cdot 12)^2$ **10.** $(-3n)^2$ **11.** $(9m^3 n)^4$ **12.** $5 \cdot (5x^2)^4$

ORDER OF MAGNITUDE The **order of magnitude** of a quantity can be defined as the power of 10 nearest the quantity. Order of magnitude can be used to estimate or perform rough calculations. For instance, there are about 91,000 species of insects in the United States. The power of 10 closest to 91,000 is 10^5, or 100,000. So, there are about 10^5 species of insects in the United States.

EXAMPLE 6 **Solve a real-world problem**

BEES In 2003 the U.S. Department of Agriculture (USDA) collected data on about 10^3 honeybee colonies. There are about 10^4 bees in an average colony during honey production season. About how many bees were in the USDA study?

Solution

To find the total number of bees, find the product of the number of colonies, 10^3, and the number of bees per colony, 10^4.

$$10^3 \cdot 10^4 = 10^{3+4} = 10^7$$

▶ The USDA studied about 10^7, or 10,000,000, bees.

Honeybee colony

✓ **GUIDED PRACTICE** for Example 6

13. WHAT IF? In Example 6, about 10^2 honeybee colonies in the study were located in Idaho. About how many bees were studied in Idaho?

8.1 EXERCISES

HOMEWORK KEY

◆ = MULTIPLE CHOICE PRACTICE
Exs. 41, 42, 43, 59, and 68–70

○ = HINTS AND HOMEWORK HELP
for Exs. 31 and 61 at classzone.com

SKILLS · PROBLEM SOLVING · REASONING

1. VOCABULARY Copy and complete: The __?__ of the quantity 93,534,004 people is the power of 10 nearest the quantity, or 10^8 people.

2. NOTETAKING SKILLS Make a property and examples chart like the one on page 458 for the product of powers property.

EXAMPLES
1, 2, 3, 4, and 5
on pp. 460–462
for Exs. 3–43

SIMPLIFYING EXPRESSIONS Simplify the expression. Write your answer using exponents.

3. $4^2 \cdot 4^6$

4. $8^5 \cdot 8^2$

5. $3^3 \cdot 3$

6. $9 \cdot 9^5$

7. $(-7)^4(-7)^5$

8. $(-6)^6(-6)$

9. $2^4 \cdot 2^9 \cdot 2$

10. $(-3)^2(-3)^{11}(-3)$

11. $\left(3^5\right)^2$

12. $\left(7^4\right)^3$

13. $\left[(-5)^3\right]^4$

14. $\left[(-8)^9\right]^2$

15. $(15 \cdot 29)^3$

16. $(17 \cdot 16)^4$

17. $(132 \cdot 9)^6$

18. $[(-14) \cdot 22]^5$

SIMPLIFYING EXPRESSIONS Simplify the expression.

19. $x^4 \cdot x^2$

20. $y^9 \cdot y$

21. $z^2 \cdot z \cdot z^3$

22. $a^4 \cdot a^3 \cdot a^{10}$

23. $\left(x^8\right)^2$

24. $\left(y^4\right)^6$

25. $\left[(b-2)^2\right]^6$

26. $\left[(d+9)^7\right]^3$

27. $(-5x)^2$

28. $-(5x)^2$

29. $(7xy)^2$

30. $(5pq)^3$

31. $\left(-10x^6\right)^2 \cdot x^2$

32. $\left(-8m^4\right)^2 \cdot m^3$

33. $6d^2 \cdot \left(2d^5\right)^4$

34. $\left(-20x^3\right)^2\left(-x^7\right)$

35. $-\left(2p^4\right)^3\left(-1.5p^7\right)$

36. $\left(\frac{1}{2}y^5\right)^3\left(2y^2\right)^4$

37. $\left(3x^5\right)^3\left(2x^7\right)^2$

38. $(-10n)^2\left(-4n^3\right)^3$

ERROR ANALYSIS *Describe* and correct the error in simplifying the expression.

39.
$$c \cdot c^4 \cdot c^5 = c^1 \cdot c^4 \cdot c^5$$
$$= c^{1 \cdot 4 \cdot 5}$$
$$= c^{20}$$

40.
$$(4d^2)^3 = 4d^{2 \cdot 3}$$
$$= 4d^6$$

41. ◆ **MULTIPLE CHOICE** Which expression is equivalent to $(-9)^6$?

  Ⓐ $(-9)^2(-9)^3$ Ⓑ $(-9)(-9)^5$ Ⓒ $[(-9)^4]^2$ Ⓓ $[(-9)^3]^3$

42. ◆ **MULTIPLE CHOICE** Which expression is equivalent to $2^a \cdot 3^a$?

  Ⓐ 5^a Ⓑ 5^{2a} Ⓒ 6^a Ⓓ 6^{2a}

43. ◆ **MULTIPLE CHOICE** Which expression is equivalent to $81x^6y^2$?

  Ⓐ $9^9 \cdot (x^3y)^2$ Ⓑ $(9x^2)^2 \cdot (9xy)^2$ Ⓒ $(3xy)^2 \cdot 9x^4$ Ⓓ $(9xy)^2 \cdot x^3$

SIMPLIFYING EXPRESSIONS Find the missing exponent.

44. $x^4 \cdot x^? = x^5$ **45.** $(y^8)^? = y^{16}$ **46.** $(2z^?)^3 = 8z^{15}$ **47.** $(3a^3)^? \cdot 2a^3 = 18a^9$

SIMPLIFYING EXPRESSIONS Simplify the expression.

48. $(-3x^2y)^3(11x^3y^5)^2$ **49.** $-(-xy^2z^3)^5(x^4yz)^2$ **50.** $(-2s)(-5r^3st)^3(-2r^4st^7)^2$

51. OPEN-ENDED Write three expressions involving products of powers, powers of powers, or powers of products that are equivalent to $12x^8$.

REASONING Prove the statement using the definition of a power given below. Assume that a is a real number and m and n are positive integers.

  For any real number a and any positive integer m, $a^m = a \cdot a \cdot \ldots \cdot a$ for m factors of a.

52. $a^m a^n = a^{m+n}$ **53.** $(a^m)^n = a^{mn}$

CONNECT SKILLS TO PROBLEM SOLVING Exercises 54–57 will help you prepare for problem solving.

Find the order of magnitude of the population.

54. The population of California in 2003 was about 35,484,000.

55. The population of New York in 2003 was about 19,190,000.

56. The population of Arkansas in 2003 was about 649,000.

57. The population of the United States in 2003 was about 290,810,000.

EXAMPLE 6
on p. 463
for Exs. 58–60

58. ICE CREAM COMPOSITION There are about 954,930 air bubbles in 1 cubic centimeter of ice cream. There are about 946 cubic centimeters in 1 quart. Use order of magnitude to find the approximate number of air bubbles in 1 quart of ice cream.

  California @HomeTutor for problem solving help at classzone.com

59. ◆ **MULTIPLE CHOICE** The order of magnitude of the radius of our solar system is 10^{13} meters. The order of magnitude of the radius of the visible universe is 10^{13} times as great. What is the approximate radius of the visible universe?

    (A) 10^{169} m   **(B)** 10^{29} m   **(C)** 10^{26} m   **(D)** 10^{1} m

    California *@HomeTutor*   for problem solving help at classzone.com

60. **COASTAL LANDSLIDE** There are about 1 billion grains of sand in 1 cubic foot of sand. In 1995 a stretch of beach at Sleeping Bear Dunes National Lakeshore in Michigan slid into Lake Michigan. Scientists believe that around 35 million cubic feet of sand fell into the lake. Use order of magnitude to find about how many grains of sand slid into the lake.

61. **GOLD** There are about 10^{23} atoms of gold in 1 ounce of gold.

    a. **Making a Table** Copy and complete the table by finding the number of atoms of gold for the given amounts of gold (in ounces).

Gold (ounces)	10	100	1000	10,000	100,000
Atoms	?	?	?	?	?

    b. **Writing an Expression** A particular mine in California extracted about 96,000 ounces of gold in 1 year. Use order of magnitude to write an expression you can use to find the approximate number of atoms of gold extracted in the mine that year. Simplify the expression. Verify your answer using the table.

READING IN MATH   **Read the information below for Exercises 62 and 63.**

Science A microscope has two types of lenses, the objective lens and the eyepiece, that work together to magnify an object. The total magnification of the microscope is the product of the magnification of the objective lens and the magnification of the eyepiece. Your microscope has three objective lenses that each have a different magnification. The eyepiece on your microscope magnifies an object 10 times.

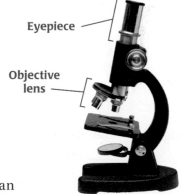

Eyepiece

Objective lens

62. **Calculate** You decide to use use the objective lens that magnifies an object 10^{2} times. What is the total magnification of your microscope?

63. **Calculate** You use the objective lens that magnifies an object 10^{2} times to magnify an object that is 10^{3} nanometers long. How long is the magnified image?

64. **VOLUME OF THE SUN** The radius of the sun is about 695,000,000 meters.

The formula for the volume of a sphere, such as the sun, is $V = \frac{4}{3}\pi r^{3}$.

Because the order of magnitude of $\frac{4}{3}\pi$ is 1, it does not contribute to the formula in a significant way. So, you can find the order of magnitude of the volume of the sun by cubing its radius. Find the order of magnitude of the volume of the sun.

65. **NATURAL RESOURCES** Rock salt can be mined from large deposits of salt called salt domes. A particular salt dome is roughly cylindrical in shape. The order of magnitude of the radius of the salt dome is 10^3 feet. The order of magnitude of the height of the salt dome is about 10 times that of its radius. The formula for the volume of a cylinder is $V = \pi r^2 h$.

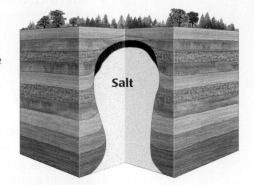

Salt

   a. **Calculate** What is the order of magnitude of the height of the salt dome?

   b. **Calculate** What is the order of magnitude of the volume of the salt dome?

   c. **Explain** The order of magnitude of the radius of a salt dome can be 10 times the radius of the salt dome described in this exercise. What effect does multiplying the order of magnitude of the radius of the salt dome by 10 have on the volume of the salt dome? *Explain*.

66. **CHALLENGE** Show that when a and b are real numbers and n is a positive integer, $(ab)^n = a^n b^n$.

67. **CHALLENGE** Your school is conducting a poll that has two parts. One part has 13 questions for which students answer "yes" or "no." The other part has 10 questions for which students answer "agree" or "disagree."

   a. What power of 2 represents the number of ways there are to answer the questions in the first part of the poll?

   b. What power of 2 represents the number of ways there are to answer the questions in the second part of the poll?

   c. What power of 2 represents the number of ways there are to answer all of the questions on the poll?

◆ CALIFORNIA STANDARDS SPIRAL REVIEW

Alg. 6.0

68. What is the x-intercept of the graph of $2x + 3y = 18$? *(p. 273)*

   (A) -6 (B) 3 (C) 0 (D) 9

Alg. 17.0

69. What is the domain of the function represented by the graph? *(p. 257)*

   (A) $-2, -4, -6, -8$

   (B) $2, 4, 6, 8$

   (C) $4, 6, 8, 10$

   (D) $6, 10, 14, 18$

Alg. 9.0

70. You have $2.75 in dimes and quarters, and you have a total of 17 dimes and quarters. How many of each type of coin do you have? *(p. 383)*

   (A) 10 dimes and 7 quarters   (B) 8 dimes and 9 quarters

   (C) 11 dimes and 6 quarters   (D) 15 dimes and 2 quarters

8.2 Apply Exponent Properties Involving Quotients

Standards Alg. 2.0 **Students** understand and use such operations as taking the opposite, finding the reciprocal, taking a root, and raising to a fractional power. They **understand and use the rules of exponents.**

Connect *Before* you used properties of exponents involving products. *Now* you will use properties of exponents involving quotients.

Math and GEOLOGY
Ex. 56, p. 472

Key Vocabulary
• **power,** *p. 6*
• **exponent,** *p. 6*
• **base,** *p. 6*

Notice what happens when you divide powers with the same base.

$$\frac{a^5}{a^3} = \frac{a \cdot a \cdot \cancel{a} \cdot \cancel{a} \cdot \cancel{a}}{\cancel{a} \cdot \cancel{a} \cdot \cancel{a}} = a \cdot a = a^2 = a^{5-3}$$

The example above suggests the following property of exponents, known as the quotient of powers property.

KEY CONCEPT *For Your Notebook*

Quotient of Powers Property

Let a be a nonzero real number, and let m and n be positive integers such that $m > n$.

Words To divide powers having the same base, subtract exponents.

Algebra $\dfrac{a^m}{a^n} = a^{m-n}, a \neq 0$ **Example** $\dfrac{4^7}{4^2} = 4^{7-2} = 4^5$

EXAMPLE 1   Use the quotient of powers property

SIMPLIFY EXPRESSIONS
When simplifying powers with numerical bases only, write your answers using exponents, as in parts (a) and (b).

a. $\dfrac{8^{10}}{8^4} = 8^{10-4}$

$= 8^6$

b. $\dfrac{1}{(-5)^4} \cdot (-5)^{11} = \dfrac{(-5)^{11}}{(-5)^4}$

$= (-5)^{11-4}$

$= (-5)^7$

c. $\dfrac{x^7}{x^3} = x^{7-3}$

$= x^4$

d. $\dfrac{x^3 y}{x^2} = \dfrac{x^3}{x^2} \cdot \dfrac{y}{1}$

$= x^{3-2} \cdot y$

$= xy$

 GUIDED PRACTICE   for Example 1

Simplify the expression.

1. $\dfrac{(-6)^{11}}{(-6)^5}$

2. $\dfrac{1}{4^5} \cdot 4^8$

3. $\dfrac{c^{12}}{c^5}$

4. $\dfrac{mn^9}{n^3}$

POWER OF A QUOTIENT Notice what happens when you raise a quotient to a power.

$$\left(\frac{a}{b}\right)^4 = \frac{a}{b} \cdot \frac{a}{b} \cdot \frac{a}{b} \cdot \frac{a}{b} = \frac{a \cdot a \cdot a \cdot a}{b \cdot b \cdot b \cdot b} = \frac{a^4}{b^4}$$

The example above suggests the following property of exponents, known as the power of a quotient property.

KEY CONCEPT   *For Your Notebook*

Power of a Quotient Property

Let a and b be real numbers with $b \neq 0$, and let m be a positive integer.

Words To find a power of a quotient, find the power of the numerator and the power of the denominator and divide.

Algebra $\left(\frac{a}{b}\right)^m = \frac{a^m}{b^m}, b \neq 0$ **Example** $\left(\frac{3}{2}\right)^7 = \frac{3^7}{2^7}$

EXAMPLE 2 **Use the power of a quotient property**

Simplify the expression.

a. $\left(\frac{5}{6}\right)^2$ **b.** $\left(-\frac{2}{3}\right)^3$ **c.** $\left(\frac{x}{y}\right)^5$ **d.** $\left(-\frac{7}{x}\right)^2$

Solution

a. $\left(\frac{5}{6}\right)^2 = \frac{5^2}{6^2}$ **Power of a quotient property**

b. $\left(-\frac{2}{3}\right)^3 = \left(\frac{-2}{3}\right)^3$ **Place negative sign in numerator.**

$= \frac{(-2)^3}{3^3}$ **Power of a quotient property**

c. $\left(\frac{x}{y}\right)^5 = \frac{x^5}{y^5}$ **Power of a quotient property**

SIMPLIFY EXPRESSIONS

When simplifying powers with numerical *and* variable bases, evaluate the numerical power, as in part (d).

d. $\left(-\frac{7}{x}\right)^2 = \left(\frac{-7}{x}\right)^2$ **Place negative sign in numerator.**

$= \frac{(-7)^2}{x^2}$ **Power of a quotient property**

$= \frac{49}{x^2}$ **Simplify.**

✔ **GUIDED PRACTICE** for Example 2

Simplify the expression.

5. $\left(\frac{9}{7}\right)^2$ **6.** $\left(-\frac{3}{4}\right)^3$ **7.** $\left(\frac{m}{n}\right)^2$ **8.** $\left(\frac{1}{y}\right)^3$

EXAMPLE 3 **Use properties of exponents**

a. $\left(\dfrac{4x^2}{5y}\right)^3 = \dfrac{(4x^2)^3}{(5y)^3}$ **Power of a quotient property**

$\qquad\quad = \dfrac{4^3 \cdot (x^2)^3}{5^3 y^3}$ **Power of a product property**

$\qquad\quad = \dfrac{64x^6}{125y^3}$ **Power of a power property**

b. $\left(\dfrac{a^2}{b}\right)^5 \cdot \dfrac{1}{2a^2} = \dfrac{(a^2)^5}{b^5} \cdot \dfrac{1}{2a^2}$ **Power of a quotient property**

$\qquad\qquad\quad = \dfrac{a^{10}}{b^5} \cdot \dfrac{1}{2a^2}$ **Power of a power property**

$\qquad\qquad\quad = \dfrac{a^{10}}{2a^2 b^5}$ **Multiply fractions.**

$\qquad\qquad\quad = \dfrac{a^8}{2b^5}$ **Quotient of powers property**

✓ **GUIDED PRACTICE** **for Example 3**

Simplify the expression.

9. $\left(\dfrac{x^2}{4y}\right)^2$ **10.** $\left(\dfrac{3h}{k^2}\right)^4$ **11.** $\left(\dfrac{2s}{3t}\right)^3 \cdot \dfrac{t^5}{16}$ **12.** $\dfrac{9c^5}{10d} \cdot \left(\dfrac{7}{11c^2}\right)^2$

EXAMPLE 4 **Solve a real-world problem**

ASTRONOMY Canopus is the second brightest star in the night sky. Its distance from Earth has an order of magnitude of 10^{15} kilometers. Suppose a spacecraft leaves Earth and travels at a speed that has an order of magnitude of 10^4 kilometers per hour. Use order of magnitude to approximate the number of hours that the spacecraft takes to reach Canopus.

Canopus

Solution

$$\dfrac{\text{Distance to Canopus (km)}}{\text{Speed (km/h)}} = \dfrac{10^{15}}{10^4} = 10^{15-4} = 10^{11}$$

▶ The spacecraft takes about 10^{11} hours to reach Canopus.

✓ **GUIDED PRACTICE** **for Example 4**

13. WHAT IF? In Example 4, suppose the spacecraft travels to the star Rigil Kent. The distance from Earth to this star has an order of magnitude of 10^{13} kilometers. Use order of magnitude to approximate the number of hours that the spacecraft takes to reach Rigil Kent.

SKILLS · PROBLEM SOLVING · REASONING

1. **VOCABULARY** Copy and complete: In the power 4^3, 4 is the __?__ and 3 is the __?__.

2. **WRITING** *Explain* when and how to use the quotient of powers property.

EXAMPLES 1 and 2
on pp. 467–468
for Exs. 3–19

SIMPLIFYING EXPRESSIONS Simplify the expression. Write your answer using exponents.

3. $\dfrac{5^6}{5^2}$

4. $\dfrac{2^{11}}{2^6}$

5. $\dfrac{3^9}{3^5}$

6. $\dfrac{(-6)^8}{(-6)^5}$

7. $\dfrac{(-4)^7}{(-4)^4}$

8. $\dfrac{(-12)^9}{(-12)^3}$

9. $\left(\dfrac{1}{3}\right)^5$

10. $\left(\dfrac{3}{2}\right)^4$

11. $\left(-\dfrac{5}{4}\right)^4$

12. $\left(-\dfrac{2}{5}\right)^5$

13. $7^9 \cdot \dfrac{1}{7^2}$

14. $\dfrac{1}{9^5} \cdot 9^{11}$

15. $\dfrac{9 \cdot 6^7}{6^4}$

16. $\dfrac{(-10)^5 \cdot 7}{(-10)^4}$

17. $\left(\dfrac{1}{3}\right)^4 \cdot 3^{12}$

18. $4^9 \cdot \left(-\dfrac{1}{4}\right)^5$

19. ◆ **MULTIPLE CHOICE** Which expression is equivalent to 16^6?

Ⓐ $\dfrac{16^4}{16^2}$ Ⓑ $\dfrac{16^{12}}{16^2}$ Ⓒ $\left(\dfrac{16^6}{16^3}\right)^2$ Ⓓ $\left(\dfrac{16^9}{16^6}\right)^3$

EXAMPLES 1, 2, and 3
on pp. 467–469
for Exs. 20–38

SIMPLIFYING EXPRESSIONS Simplify the expression.

20. $\dfrac{1}{y^8} \cdot y^{15}$

21. $\dfrac{z^8}{z^7}$

22. $\left(\dfrac{a}{y}\right)^9$

23. $\left(\dfrac{j}{k}\right)^{11}$

24. $\left(\dfrac{p}{q}\right)^4$

25. $\left(-\dfrac{1}{x}\right)^5$

26. $\left(-\dfrac{4}{x}\right)^3$

27. $\left(-\dfrac{a}{b}\right)^4$

28. $\left(\dfrac{4c}{d^2}\right)^3$

29. $\left(\dfrac{a^7}{2b}\right)^5$

30. $\left(\dfrac{x^2}{3y^3}\right)^2$

31. $\left(\dfrac{3x^5}{7y^2}\right)^3$

32. $\left(\dfrac{2x^3}{y}\right)^3 \cdot \dfrac{1}{6x^3}$

33. $\left(\dfrac{3x^3}{2y}\right)^2 \cdot \dfrac{1}{x^2}$

34. $\dfrac{3}{8m^5} \cdot \left(\dfrac{m^4}{n^2}\right)^3$

35. $\left(-\dfrac{5}{x}\right)^2 \cdot \left(\dfrac{2x^4}{y^3}\right)^2$

36. ◆ **MULTIPLE CHOICE** Which expression is equivalent to $\left(\dfrac{7x^3}{2y^4}\right)^2$?

Ⓐ $\dfrac{7x^5}{2y^6}$ Ⓑ $\dfrac{7x^6}{2y^8}$ Ⓒ $\dfrac{49x^5}{4y^6}$ Ⓓ $\dfrac{49x^6}{4y^8}$

ERROR ANALYSIS *Describe* and correct the error in simplifying the expression.

37.
$$\left(\dfrac{4x}{5}\right)^2 = \dfrac{4^2 \cdot x^2}{5}$$
$$= \dfrac{16x^2}{5} \quad ✗$$

38.
$$\left(\dfrac{x^3}{6}\right)^2 \cdot \dfrac{1}{x^2} = \dfrac{x^9}{36} \cdot \dfrac{1}{x^2}$$
$$= \dfrac{x^7}{36} \quad ✗$$

SIMPLIFYING EXPRESSIONS Find the missing exponent.

39. $\dfrac{(-8)^7}{(-8)^?} = (-8)^3$

40. $\dfrac{7^? \cdot 7^2}{7^4} = 7^6$

41. $\dfrac{1}{p^5} \cdot p^? = p^9$

42. $\left(\dfrac{2c^3}{d^2}\right)^? = \dfrac{16c^{12}}{d^8}$

SIMPLIFYING EXPRESSIONS Simplify the expression.

43. $\left(\dfrac{2f^2g^3}{3fg}\right)^4$

44. $\dfrac{2s^3t^3}{st^2} \cdot \dfrac{(3st)^3}{s^2t}$

45. $\left(\dfrac{2m^5n}{4m^2}\right)^2 \cdot \left(\dfrac{mn^4}{5n}\right)^2$

46. $\left(\dfrac{3x^3y}{x^2}\right)^3 \cdot \left(\dfrac{y^2x^4}{5y}\right)^2$

47. OPEN-ENDED Write three expressions involving quotients that are equivalent to 14^7.

48. REASONING Copy and complete the proof of $\dfrac{a^m}{a^n} = \dfrac{1}{a^{n-m}}$ where m and n are positive integers such that $m < n$ by choosing a reason for each step.

Let $m < n$.   **a.** ___?___

$\dfrac{a^m}{a^n} = \dfrac{a^m}{a^n}\left(\dfrac{\frac{1}{a^m}}{\frac{1}{a^m}}\right)$ **b.** ___?___

$= \dfrac{\frac{a^m}{a^m}}{\frac{a^n}{a^m}}$ **c.** ___?___

$= \dfrac{1}{\frac{a^n}{a^m}}$ **d.** ___?___

$= \dfrac{1}{a^{n-m}}$ **e.** ___?___

Reasons
Definition of fraction multiplication
Simplify numerator.
Quotient of powers property
Given
Muliplicative identity property

CONNECT SKILLS TO PROBLEM SOLVING Exercises 49–52 will help you prepare for problem solving.

Find the order of magnitude for the comparison using the table, which gives the orders of magnitude of the volumes of various objects.

49. Number of classrooms that could fit inside a school

50. Number of classrooms that could fit inside a skyscraper

51. Number of schools that could fit inside a skyscraper

52. Number of skyscrapers that could fit inside Earth

Location	Order of magnitude of volume (cubic meters)
Classroom	10^2
School	10^4
Skyscraper	10^6
Earth	10^{21}

EXAMPLE 4
on p. 469
for Exs. 53–56

53. ◆ **MULTIPLE CHOICE** In 2003 the gross domestic product (GDP) for the United States was about 11 trillion dollars, and the order of magnitude of the population of the United States was 10^8. What order of magnitude was the per capita (per person) GDP in 2003?

(A) 10^3 dollars   **(B)** 10^4 dollars   **(C)** 10^5 dollars   **(D)** 10^6 dollars

California @HomeTutor for problem solving help at classzone.com

54. PATTERNS Draw a square with a side length of 1 unit. Divide it into four new squares with a side length that is one half the side length of the original square, as shown in Step 1. Keep dividing the squares into new squares, as shown in Steps 2 and 3.

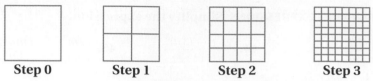

Step 0   Step 1   Step 2   Step 3

a. **Making a Table** Make a table showing the number of new squares and the side length of a new square at each step for Steps 1–4. Write the number of new squares as a power of 4. Write the side length of a new square as a power of $\frac{1}{2}$.

b. **Writing an Expression** Write and simplify an expression to find by how many times the number of new squares increased from Step 2 to Step 4.

California @*HomeTutor* for problem solving help at classzone.com

55.) ASTRONOMY The constellation Ursa Minor (the Little Dipper) is shown. The order of magnitude of the volume V of two stars in the constellation is given.

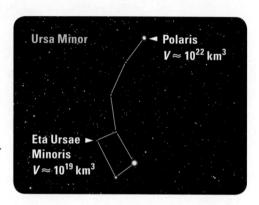

Ursa Minor   ◄ Polaris
$V \approx 10^{22}$ km³

Eta Ursae ►
Minoris
$V \approx 10^{19}$ km³

a. Based on order of magnitude, which star has a greater volume? How many times greater?

b. Polaris is 10^{15} kilometers from Earth. Suppose a spacecraft leaves Earth and travels at an average speed that has an order of magnitude of 10^5 kilometers per hour. Use order of magnitude to find the time the spacecraft takes to reach Polaris.

56. EARTHQUAKES The energy released by one earthquake relative to another earthquake can be measured by comparing the magnitudes (as determined by the Richter scale) of the earthquakes. For every increase of 1 in magnitude, the energy released is multiplied by a factor of about 31. How many times greater is the energy released by an earthquake of magnitude 7 than the energy released by an earthquake of magnitude 4?

57. COMPUTERS A byte is a unit used to measure computer memory. Other units are based on the number of bytes they represent. The table shows the number of bytes in certain units. For example, from the table you can calculate that 1 gigabyte is equivalent to 2^{10} megabytes.

a. **Calculate** How many kilobytes are there in 1 megabyte? in 1 gigabyte?

b. **CHALLENGE** Another unit used to measure computer memory is a bit. There are 8 bits in a byte. *Explain* how you can convert the number of bytes per unit given in the table to the number of bits per unit.

Unit	Number of bytes
Kilobyte	2^{10}
Megabyte	2^{20}
Gigabyte	2^{30}

58. CHALLENGE Find the values of x and y if you know that $\dfrac{b^x}{b^y} = b^9$ and

$\dfrac{b^x \cdot b^2}{b^{2y}} = b^5$. *Explain* how you found your answer.

59. CHALLENGE Simplify the expression $\dfrac{x^{3n+1} y^n}{(x^2 y)^n}$ where n is a positive integer.

◆ CALIFORNIA STANDARDS SPIRAL REVIEW

Alg. 3.0   **60.** Which number is a solution of $|x + 2| = 10$? *(p. 220)*

     (A) 4   (B) 8

     (C) 10   (D) 12

Alg. 2.0   **61.** Which expression is equivalent to $(10x^2 y^3)^2 (-3xy^2)^3$? *(p. 460)*

     (A) $27x^{18} y^{36}$ (B) $-2700x^7 y^{12}$

     (C) $-2700x^7 y^{10}$ (D) $-100x^7 y^{12}$

Alg. 8.0   **62.** The map shows several streets in a city. Which two streets are perpendicular? *(p. 354)*

     (A) State Street and Hill Street

     (B) Peach Street and Hill Street

     (C) State Street and Main Street

     (D) Peach Street and Main Street

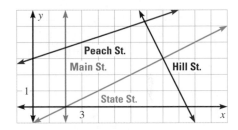

QUIZ *for Lessons 8.1–8.2*

Simplify the expression. Write your answer using exponents.

1. $3^2 \cdot 3^6$ *(p. 460)*   **2.** $(5^4)^3$ *(p. 460)*   **3.** $(32 \cdot 14)^7$ *(p. 460)*

4. $7^2 \cdot 7^6 \cdot 7$ *(p. 460)*   **5.** $(-4)(-4)^9$ *(p. 460)*   **6.** $\dfrac{7^{12}}{7^4}$ *(p. 467)*

7. $\dfrac{(-9)^9}{(-9)^7}$ *(p. 467)*   **8.** $\dfrac{3^7 \cdot 3^4}{3^6}$ *(p. 467)*   **9.** $\left(\dfrac{5}{4}\right)^4$ *(p. 467)*

Simplify the expression.

10. $x^2 \cdot x^5$ *(p. 460)*   **11.** $(3x^3)^2$ *(p. 460)*   **12.** $-(7x)^2$ *(p. 460)*

13. $(6x^5)^3 \cdot x$ *(p. 460)*   **14.** $(2x^5)^3 (7x^7)^2$ *(p. 460)*   **15.** $\dfrac{1}{x^9} \cdot x^{21}$ *(p. 467)*

16. $\left(-\dfrac{4}{x}\right)^3$ *(p. 467)*   **17.** $\left(\dfrac{w}{v}\right)^6$ *(p. 467)*   **18.** $\left(\dfrac{x^3}{4}\right)^2$ *(p. 467)*

19. AGRICULTURE In 2004 the order of magnitude of the number of pounds of oranges produced in the United States was 10^{10}. The order of magnitude of the number of acres used for growing oranges was 10^6. About how many pounds of oranges per acre were produced in the United States in 2004? *(p. 467)*

8.3 Zero and Negative Exponents

MATERIALS · paper and pencil

Standards

Alg. 2.0 Students understand and use such operations as taking the opposite, finding the reciprocal, taking a root, and raising to a fractional power. They **understand and use the rules of exponents**.

QUESTION How can you simplify expressions with zero or negative exponents?

EXPLORE Evaluate powers with zero and negative exponents

STEP 1 *Find a pattern*

Copy and complete the tables for the powers of 2 and 3.

Exponent, n	Value of 2^n
4	16
3	?
2	?
1	?

Exponent, n	Value of 3^n
4	81
3	?
2	?
1	?

As you read the tables from the *bottom up*, you see that each time the exponent is increased by 1, the value of the power is multiplied by the base. What can you say about the exponents and the values of the powers as you read the table from the *top down*?

STEP 2 *Extend the pattern*

Copy and complete the tables using the pattern you observed in Step 1.

Exponent, n	Power, 2^n
3	8
2	?
1	?
0	?
−1	?
−2	?

Exponent, n	Power, 3^n
3	27
2	?
1	?
0	?
−1	?
−2	?

DRAW CONCLUSIONS Use your observations to complete these exercises

1. Find 2^n and 3^n for $n = -3$, $n = -4$, and $n = -5$.

2. What appears to be the value of a^0 for any nonzero number a?

3. Write each power in the tables above as a power with a nonnegative exponent. For example, you can write 3^{-1} as $\dfrac{1}{3^1}$.

4. **REASONING** Write an equation that describes the relationship between a^n and a^{-n} for any nonzero number a.

8.3 Define and Use Zero and Negative Exponents

Standards Alg. 2.0 **Students** understand and use such operations as taking the opposite, finding the reciprocal, taking a root, and raising to a fractional power. They **understand and use the rules of exponents**.

Connect *Before* you used properties of exponents to simplify expressions.
Now you will use zero and negative exponents.

Math and **BOTANY**
Ex. 50, p. 479

Key Vocabulary
• reciprocal, *p. 789*

In the activity on page 474, you saw what happens when you raise a number to a zero or negative exponent. The activity suggests the following definitions.

KEY CONCEPT   *For Your Notebook*

Definition of Zero and Negative Exponents

Words	**Algebra**	**Example**
a to the zero power is 1.	$a^0 = 1, a \neq 0$	$5^0 = 1$
a^{-n} is the reciprocal of a^n.	$a^{-n} = \dfrac{1}{a^n}, a \neq 0$	$2^{-1} = \dfrac{1}{2}$
a^n is the reciprocal of a^{-n}.	$a^n = \dfrac{1}{a^{-n}}, a \neq 0$	$2 = \dfrac{1}{2^{-1}}$

EXAMPLE 1 Use definition of zero and negative exponents

SIMPLIFY POWERS
In this lesson, when simplifying powers with numerical bases, evaluate the power.

a. $3^{-2} = \dfrac{1}{3^2} = \dfrac{1}{9}$ **Definition of negative exponents**

b. $(-7)^0 = 1$ **Definition of zero exponent**

c. $\left(\dfrac{1}{5}\right)^{-2} = \dfrac{1}{\left(\dfrac{1}{5}\right)^2}$ **Definition of negative exponents**

$= \dfrac{1}{\dfrac{1}{25}}$ **Evaluate power.**

$= 25$ **Simplify by multiplying numerator and denominator by 25.**

d. $0^{-5} = \dfrac{1}{0^5}$ (Undefined) a^{-n} is defined only for a *nonzero* number a.

✓ **GUIDED PRACTICE** for Example 1

Evaluate the expression.

1. $\left(\dfrac{2}{3}\right)^0$ **2.** $(-8)^{-2}$ **3.** $\dfrac{1}{2^{-3}}$ **4.** $(-1)^0$

PROPERTIES OF EXPONENTS The properties of exponents you learned in Lessons 8.1 and 8.2 can be used with negative or zero exponents.

> **KEY CONCEPT**   *For Your Notebook*
>
> ### Properties of Exponents
>
> Let a and b be real numbers, and let m and n be integers.
>
> $a^m \cdot a^n = a^{m+n}$ **Product of powers property**
>
> $(a^m)^n = a^{mn}$ **Power of a power property**
>
> $(ab)^m = a^m b^m$ **Power of a product property**
>
> $\dfrac{a^m}{a^n} = a^{m-n}, a \neq 0$ **Quotient of powers property**
>
> $\left(\dfrac{a}{b}\right)^m = \dfrac{a^m}{b^m}, b \neq 0$ **Power of a quotient property**

READING

The quotient of powers property no longer has the restriction that $m > n$ because a^{m-n} is now defined even when $m = n$ and $m < n$.

EXAMPLE 2   **Evaluate exponential expressions**

a. $6^{-4} \cdot 6^4 = 6^{-4+4}$ **Product of powers property**

$\qquad\qquad = 6^0$ **Add exponents.**

$\qquad\qquad = 1$ **Definition of zero exponent**

b. $(4^{-2})^2 = 4^{-2 \cdot 2}$ **Power of a power property**

$\qquad\qquad = 4^{-4}$ **Multiply exponents.**

$\qquad\qquad = \dfrac{1}{4^4}$ **Definition of negative exponents**

$\qquad\qquad = \dfrac{1}{256}$ **Evaluate power.**

c. $\dfrac{1}{3^{-4}} = 3^4$ **Definition of negative exponents**

$\qquad\qquad = 81$ **Evaluate power.**

d. $\dfrac{5^{-1}}{5^2} = 5^{-1-2}$ **Quotient of powers property**

$\qquad\qquad = 5^{-3}$ **Subtract exponents.**

$\qquad\qquad = \dfrac{1}{5^3}$ **Definition of negative exponents**

$\qquad\qquad = \dfrac{1}{125}$ **Evaluate power.**

✓ **GUIDED PRACTICE**   **for Example 2**

Evaluate the expression.

5. $\dfrac{1}{4^{-3}}$ **6.** $(5^{-3})^{-1}$ **7.** $(-3)^5 \cdot (-3)^{-5}$ **8.** $\dfrac{6^{-2}}{6^2}$

Use properties of exponents

Animated Algebra

For an interactive example of using properties of exponents, go to **classzone.com**.

Simplify the expression. Write your answer using only positive exponents.

a. $(2xy^{-5})^3 = 2^3 \cdot x^3 \cdot (y^{-5})^3$ **Power of a product property**

$= 8 \cdot x^3 \cdot y^{-15}$ **Power of a power property**

$= \dfrac{8x^3}{y^{15}}$ **Definition of negative exponents**

b. $\dfrac{(2x)^{-2}y^5}{-4x^2y^2} = \dfrac{y^5}{(2x)^2(-4x^2y^2)}$ **Definition of negative exponents**

$= \dfrac{y^5}{(4x^2)(-4x^2y^2)}$ **Power of a product property**

$= \dfrac{y^5}{[4(-4)](x^2 \cdot x^2)y^2}$ **Regroup factors in denominator.**

$= \dfrac{y^5}{-16x^4y^2}$ **Simplify denominator.**

$= -\dfrac{y^3}{16x^4}$ **Quotient of powers property**

Solve a real-world problem

MOTHS The order of magnitude of the mass of a certain type of moth larva when it hatches is 10^{-3} gram. During the first 56 days of its life, the moth larva can eat about 10^5 times its own mass in food. Find the number of grams of food the moth larva can eat during its first 56 days.

Moth and larva

Solution

To find the amount of food the moth larva can eat in the first 56 days of its life, multiply its original mass, 10^{-3} gram, by 10^5.

$10^5 \cdot 10^{-3} = 10^{5+(-3)}$ **Product of powers property**

$= 10^2$ **Add exponents.**

$= 100$ **Evaluate power.**

The moth larva can eat about 100 grams of food in the first 56 days of its life.

✓ **GUIDED PRACTICE**   for Examples 3 and 4

Simplify the expression. Write your answer using only positive exponents.

9. $(3wz^2)^{-2}$ **10.** $(-7w^{-2}z^3)^2$ **11.** $\dfrac{w^{-2}z^7}{6w^2z^{-3}}$ **12.** $\dfrac{(3w)^{-3}z}{-3wz^2}$

13. ATOMS The order of magnitude of the mass of a proton is 10^4 times greater than the order of magnitude of the mass of an electron, which is 10^{-27} gram. Find the order of magnitude of the mass of a proton.

8.3 EXERCISES

HOMEWORK KEY

◆ = **MULTIPLE CHOICE PRACTICE**
Exs. 23, 40, 41, 48, and 58–60

○ = **HINTS AND HOMEWORK HELP**
for Exs. 9, 29, and 49 at classzone.com

SKILLS · PROBLEM SOLVING · REASONING

1. VOCABULARY Which definitions or properties would you use to simplify the expression $3^5 \cdot 3^{-5}$? *Explain.*

2. WRITING *Explain* why the expression 0^{-4} is undefined.

EXAMPLE 1
on p. 475
for Exs. 3–10

EVALUATING EXPRESSIONS Evaluate the expression.

3. 4^{-3} **4.** 7^{-3} **5.** $(-3)^{-1}$ **6.** $(-2)^{-6}$

7. 2^0 **8.** $\left(\dfrac{-9}{16}\right)^0$ **9.** $\left(\dfrac{2}{7}\right)^{-2}$ **10.** $\left(\dfrac{4}{3}\right)^{-3}$

EXAMPLE 2
on p. 476
for Exs. 11–23

11. $2^{-2} \cdot 2^{-3}$ **12.** $7^{-6} \cdot 7^4$ **13.** $(2^{-1})^5$ **14.** $(3^{-2})^2$

15. $\dfrac{1}{3^{-3}}$ **16.** $\dfrac{1}{6^{-2}}$ **17.** $\dfrac{3^{-3}}{3^2}$ **18.** $\dfrac{6^{-3}}{6^{-5}}$

19. $4\left(\dfrac{3}{2}\right)^{-1}$ **20.** $16\left(\dfrac{2^{-3}}{2^2}\right)$ **21.** $6^0 \cdot \left(\dfrac{1}{4^{-2}}\right)$ **22.** $3^{-2} \cdot \left(\dfrac{5}{7^0}\right)$

23. ◆ MULTIPLE CHOICE Which expression is equivalent to $10(2^3)^{-2}$?

   A $\dfrac{1}{64}$ **B** $\dfrac{5}{256}$ **C** $\dfrac{5}{32}$ **D** 640

EXAMPLE 3
on p. 477
for Exs. 24–41

SIMPLIFYING EXPRESSIONS Simplify the expression. Write your answer using only positive exponents.

24. x^{-4} **25.** $2y^{-3}$ **26.** $(4g)^{-3}$ **27.** $(-11h)^{-2}$

28. $x^2 y^{-3}$ **29.** $5m^{-3}n^{-4}$ **30.** $(6x^{-2}y^3)^{-3}$ **31.** $(-15fg^2)^0$

32. $\dfrac{r^{-2}}{s^{-4}}$ **33.** $\dfrac{x^{-5}}{y^2}$ **34.** $\dfrac{1}{8x^{-2}y^{-6}}$ **35.** $\dfrac{1}{15x^{10}y^{-8}}$

36. $\dfrac{1}{(-2z)^{-2}}$ **37.** $\dfrac{9}{(3d)^{-3}}$ **38.** $\dfrac{(3x)^{-3}y^4}{-x^2y^{-6}}$ **39.** $\dfrac{12x^8y^{-7}}{(4x^{-2}y^{-6})^2}$

40. ◆ MULTIPLE CHOICE Which expression is equivalent to $2x^4$?

   A $2x^{-4}$ **B** $\dfrac{32}{(2x)^{-4}}$ **C** $\dfrac{1}{2x^{-4}}$ **D** $\dfrac{8}{4x^{-4}}$

41. ◆ MULTIPLE CHOICE Which expression is equivalent to $(-4 \cdot 2^0 \cdot 3)^{-2}$?

   A -12 **B** $-\dfrac{1}{144}$ **C** 0 **D** $\dfrac{1}{144}$

ERROR ANALYSIS *Describe* and correct the error in evaluating or simplifying the expression.

42.
$$-6 \cdot 3^0 = -6 \cdot 0$$
$$= 0$$
(incorrect — marked with ✗)

43.
$$\frac{2x}{5x^{-3}} = (2x)(5x^3)$$
$$= 10x^4$$
(incorrect — marked with ✗)

CONNECT SKILLS TO PROBLEM SOLVING Exercises 44–46 will help you prepare for problem solving.

Write an expression that can be used to answer the question. Do not evaluate the expression.

44. An elephant has a mass of about 10^6 grams. An ant has a mass of about 10^{-5} gram. How many times greater is the mass of the elephant than the mass of the ant?

45. A human hair has a thickness of 10^{-5} meter. A sheet of gold leaf has a thickness of 10^{-7} meter. How many times greater is the thickness of the human hair than the thickness of the gold leaf?

46. A microsecond is 10^{-6} second long. A millisecond 10^{-3} second long. How many times longer is a millisecond than a microsecond?

EXAMPLE 4
on p. 477
for Exs. 47–50

47. **SALT** The mass of a grain of salt is about 10^{-4} gram. About how many grains of salt are in a box containing 100 grams of salt?

California @HomeTutor for problem solving help at classzone.com

48. ◆ **MULTIPLE CHOICE** The mass of a grain of a certain type of rice is about 10^{-2} gram. About how many grains of rice are in a box containing 10^3 grams of rice?

(A) 10^{-5} (B) 10^2 (C) 10^3 (D) 10^5

California @HomeTutor for problem solving help at classzone.com

49. **MEDICINE** A doctor collected about 10^{-2} liter of blood from a patient to run some tests. The doctor determined that a drop, or about 10^{-6} liter, of the patient's blood contained about 10^7 red blood cells. How many red blood cells did the entire sample contain?

50. **BOTANY** One of the smallest plant seeds comes from an orchid, and one of the largest plant seeds comes from a giant fan palm. A seed from the orchid has a mass of 10^{-9} gram, and a seed from the giant fan palm has 10^{13} times that mass. A student says that the seed from the giant fan palm has a mass of about 1 kilogram. Is the student correct? *Explain.*

Orchid   Giant fan palm

51. **PATTERNS** Consider folding a piece of paper in half a number of times.

a. **Making a Table** Each time the paper is folded, record the number of folds and the fraction of the original area in a table like the one shown.

Folds	0	1	2	3
Fraction of original area	1	?	?	?

b. **Writing an Expression** Write an exponential expression for the fraction of the original area of the paper using a base of $\frac{1}{2}$.

52. **SOUND** The intensity I of sound (in watts per square meter) can be modeled by $I = 0.08Pd^{-2}$ where P is the power (in watts) of the sound's source and d is your distance (in meters) from the source of the sound.

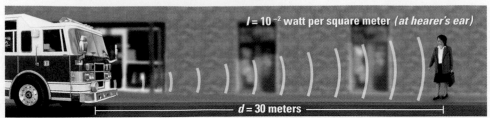

$I = 10^{-2}$ watt per square meter *(at hearer's ear)*

$d = 30$ meters

Not drawn to scale

  a. What is the power (in watts) of the siren of the firetruck shown in the diagram?

  b. Using the power of the siren you found in part (a), simplify the formula for the intensity of sound from the siren.

53. **REASONING** For $a > 0$, what happens to the value of a^{-n} as n increases?

CHALLENGE In Exercises 54–56, tell whether the statement is true for all nonzero values of a and b. If it is not true, give a counterexample.

54. $\dfrac{a^{-3}}{a^{-4}} = \dfrac{1}{a}$ 55. $\dfrac{a^{-1}}{b^{-1}} = \dfrac{b}{a}$ 56. $a^{-1} + b^{-1} = \dfrac{1}{a + b}$

57. **CHALLENGE** Coal can be burned to generate energy. The heat energy in 1 pound of coal is about 10^4 BTU (British Thermal Units). Suppose you have a stereo. It takes about 10 pounds of coal to create the energy needed to power the stereo for 1 year.

  a. About how many BTUs does your stereo use in 1 year?

  b. Suppose the power plant that delivers energy to your home produces 10^{-1} pound of sulfur dioxide for each 10^6 BTU of energy that it creates. How much sulfur dioxide is added to the air by generating the energy needed to power your stereo for 1 year?

◆ CALIFORNIA STANDARDS SPIRAL REVIEW

Alg. 7.0

58. What is an equation of the line that passes through the point $(3, -2)$ and has a slope of -2? *(p. 329)*

  (A) $y = -2x + 1$ **(B)** $y = -2x + 4$

  (C) $y = 2x - 4$ **(D)** $y = 2x + 1$

Alg. 2.0

59. Which expression is equivalent to $\left(\dfrac{2x^2y^3}{5x^3y}\right)^2$? *(p. 467)*

  (A) $\dfrac{4x^4y^5}{25x^5y^2}$ **(B)** $\dfrac{4y^4}{25x^2}$ **(C)** $\dfrac{2y^3}{5x}$ **(D)** $\dfrac{2y^4}{5x^2}$

Alg. 9.0

60. Dan drove a total of 27 miles. He drove x miles on Interstate 5 and y miles on Interstate 405. He drove twice as many miles on Interstate 5 as he did on Interstate 405. How many miles did Dan drive on Interstate 5? *(p. 383)*

  (A) 9   **(B)** 12   **(C)** 18   **(D)** 20

Multiple Choice Practice for Lessons 8.1–8.3

1. Which expression is equivalent to $(-2x^2)^3 \cdot x^5$? **Alg. 2.0**

   Ⓐ $-8x^{11}$ Ⓑ $-8x^{10}$

   Ⓒ $-2x^{11}$ Ⓓ $8x^{10}$

2. In 2004 the fastest computers could record about 10^9 bits per second. (A bit is the smallest unit of memory storage for computers.) Scientists believed that the speed limit at the time was about 10^{12} bits per second. About how many times more bits per second was the speed limit than the fastest computers? **Alg. 2.0**

   Ⓐ 10 times

   Ⓑ 100 times

   Ⓒ 1000 times

   Ⓓ 10,000 times

3. Which expression is equivalent to $\left(\dfrac{4x^5}{x \cdot y^2}\right)^3$? **Alg. 2.0**

   Ⓐ $\dfrac{4x^{12}}{y^6}$ Ⓑ $\dfrac{4x^{14}}{y^2}$

   Ⓒ $\dfrac{64x^5}{y^6}$ Ⓓ $\dfrac{64x^{12}}{y^6}$

4. Clouds contain millions of tiny spherical water droplets. The radius of one droplet is shown. Droplets combine to form raindrops. The radius of a spherical raindrop is about 10^2 times greater than the radius of a droplet. What is the radius of the raindrop? **Alg. 2.0**

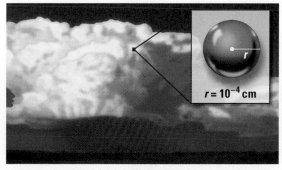

$r = 10^{-4}$ cm

   Ⓐ 10^{-8} cm   Ⓑ 10^{-2} cm

   Ⓒ 10^2 cm   Ⓓ 10^4 cm

5. Which expression is equivalent to $(w^0)^{-3}$? **Alg. 2.0**

   Ⓐ 0   Ⓑ 1

   Ⓒ $\dfrac{1}{w}$ Ⓓ $\dfrac{1}{w^3}$

6. A store sells cubical containers that can be used to hold office supplies. What is the volume of the cube? **Alg. 2.0**

   Ⓐ $\dfrac{7^3}{2}$ in.^{3}

   Ⓑ $\dfrac{7^3}{2^3}$ in.^{3}

   Ⓒ $\dfrac{7}{2}$ in.^{3}

   Ⓓ $\dfrac{7}{2^3}$ in.^{3}

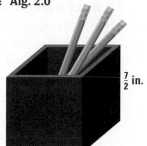

$\frac{7}{2}$ in.

7. Which expression is equivalent to $\dfrac{1}{36}$? **Alg. 2.0**

   Ⓐ $(-3 \cdot 2)^{-2}$ Ⓑ $(2^{-3})^2$

   Ⓒ 6^{-3} Ⓓ $6^{-2} \cdot 6^4$

In Exercises 8 and 9, use the table below, which shows units of measurement of time and the durations of each unit in seconds.

Name of unit	Duration (seconds)
Gigasecond	10^9
Megasecond	10^6
Millisecond	10^{-3}
Nanosecond	10^{-9}

8. How many milliseconds are in a gigasecond? **Alg. 2.0**

   Ⓐ 10^3 Ⓑ 10^6

   Ⓒ 10^{12} Ⓓ 10^{27}

9. How many nanoseconds are in a megasecond? **Alg. 2.0**

   Ⓐ 10^{-3} Ⓑ 10^3

   Ⓒ 10^9 Ⓓ 10^{15}

8.4 Properties of Radicals

MATERIALS · calculator

Standards

Alg. 24.1 Students explain the difference between inductive and deductive reasoning and identify and provide examples of each.

QUESTION What property does a product of square roots have?

EXPLORE Apply inductive and deductive reasoning to products of square roots

STEP 1 *Make a conjecture*

In the table below, a and b are perfect squares. Copy and complete the table without using a calculator. What conjecture can you make?

Values of a and b	Value of $\sqrt{a} \cdot \sqrt{b}$	Value of $\sqrt{ab}$
$a = 4, b = 9$	?	?
$a = 9, b = 16$	?	?
$a = 25, b = 4$	?	?
$a = 16, b = 36$	?	?

STEP 2 *Test your conjecture*

Use a calculator to copy and complete the table. Does your conjecture from Step 1 still hold?

Values of a and b	Value of $\sqrt{a} \cdot \sqrt{b}$	Value of $\sqrt{ab}$
$a = 2, b = 3$	?	?
$a = 10, b = 5$	?	?
$a = 7, b = 11$	?	?
$a = 13, b = 6$	?	?

STEP 3 *Begin a proof of your conjecture*

To prove the conjecture that you made in Steps 1 and 2, begin with two nonnegative numbers a and b, and consider the square of the product $\sqrt{a} \cdot \sqrt{b}$. Provide reasons for the following statements:

Statement	**Reason**
$(\sqrt{a} \cdot \sqrt{b})^2 = (\sqrt{a})^2 \cdot (\sqrt{b})^2$	?
$= ab$	?

STEP 4 *Complete the proof of your conjecture*

Copy and complete: In Step 3 you showed that the _?_ of $\sqrt{a} \cdot \sqrt{b}$ is ab. This means that $\sqrt{a} \cdot \sqrt{b}$ is the nonnegative _?_ of ab. In other words, $\sqrt{a} \cdot \sqrt{b} =$ _?_ .

DRAW CONCLUSIONS Use your observations to complete these exercises

1. **REASONING** Use inductive reasoning to determine what relationship exists between $\dfrac{\sqrt{a}}{\sqrt{b}}$ and $\sqrt{\dfrac{a}{b}}$ for $a \geq 0$ and $b > 0$. Then use deductive reasoning to prove the relationship.

2. **REASONING** Do you think that $\sqrt{a} + \sqrt{b} = \sqrt{a + b}$ for $a \geq 0$ and $b \geq 0$? If so, prove it. If not, give a counterexample.

8.4 Simplify Radical Expressions

Math and DISTANCES
Ex. 65, p. 489

Standards **Alg. 1.0** Students identify and use the arithmetic properties of subsets of integers and rational, **irrational**, and real **numbers, including closure properties for the four basic arithmetic operations where applicable.**

Alg. 25.1 Students use properties of numbers to construct simple, valid **arguments** (direct and **indirect**) for, or formulate counterexamples to, claimed assertions.

Connect *Before* you found square roots. *Now* you will simplify radical expressions to prepare for Algebra 1 Standards 19.0 and 20.0.

Key Vocabulary
- **radical expression**
- **simplest form of a radical expression**
- **rationalizing the denominator**

A **radical expression** is an expression that contains a radical, such as a square root, cube root, or other root. A radical expression containing a square root is in **simplest form** if the following conditions are true:

- No perfect square factors other than 1 are in the radicand.
- No fractions are in the radicand.
- No radicals appear in the denominator of a fraction.

You can use the following property to simplify radical expressions.

About the Standards

You will learn how to write square roots using fractional powers in Lesson 8.6 as part of Algebra 1 Standard 2.0.

KEY CONCEPT *For Your Notebook*

Product Property of Radicals

Words The square root of a product equals the product of the square roots of the factors.

Algebra $\sqrt{ab} = \sqrt{a} \cdot \sqrt{b}$ where $a \geq 0$ and $b \geq 0$

Example $\sqrt{4x} = \sqrt{4} \cdot \sqrt{x} = 2\sqrt{x}$

You can also use the fact that $\sqrt{a^2} = a$, where $a \geq 0$, to simplify radical expressions. In this book, whenever a variable appears in the radicand of a square root *assume that the variable has only nonnegative values.*

EXAMPLE 1 Use the product property of radicals

Animated Algebra

For an interactive example of simplifying a radical expression, go to **classzone.com**.

a. $\sqrt{32} = \sqrt{16 \cdot 2}$ **Factor using perfect square factor.**

$\phantom{\sqrt{32}} = \sqrt{16} \cdot \sqrt{2}$ **Product property of radicals**

$\phantom{\sqrt{32}} = 4\sqrt{2}$ **Simplify.**

b. $\sqrt{9x^3} = \sqrt{9 \cdot x^2 \cdot x}$ **Factor using perfect square factors.**

$\phantom{\sqrt{9x^3}} = \sqrt{9} \cdot \sqrt{x^2} \cdot \sqrt{x}$ **Product property of radicals**

$\phantom{\sqrt{9x^3}} = 3x\sqrt{x}$ **Simplify.**

EXAMPLE 2 Multiply radicals

a. $\sqrt{2} \cdot \sqrt{8} = \sqrt{2 \cdot 8}$ Product property of radicals

          $= \sqrt{16}$ Multiply.

          $= 4$ Simplify.

b. $\sqrt{3x} \cdot 4\sqrt{x} = 4\sqrt{3x \cdot x}$ Product property of radicals

          $= 4\sqrt{3x^2}$ Multiply.

          $= 4 \cdot \sqrt{3} \cdot \sqrt{x^2}$ Product property of radicals

          $= 4x\sqrt{3}$ Simplify.

c. $\sqrt{7xy^2} \cdot 3\sqrt{x} = 3\sqrt{7xy^2 \cdot x}$ Product property of radicals

          $= 3\sqrt{7x^2y^2}$ Multiply.

          $= 3 \cdot \sqrt{7} \cdot \sqrt{x^2} \cdot \sqrt{y^2}$ Product property of radicals

          $= 3xy\sqrt{7}$ Simplify.

WRITE RADICALS
When writing a product involving a radical, write the radical last to avoid confusion. For instance, if you write the product of x and $\sqrt{3}$ as $\sqrt{3}x$, it might be read as $\sqrt{3x}$.

KEY CONCEPT   *For Your Notebook*

Quotient Property of Radicals

Words The square root of a quotient equals the quotient of the square roots of the numerator and denominator.

Algebra $\sqrt{\dfrac{a}{b}} = \dfrac{\sqrt{a}}{\sqrt{b}}$ where $a \geq 0$ and $b > 0$ **Example** $\sqrt{\dfrac{16}{25}} = \dfrac{\sqrt{16}}{\sqrt{25}} = \dfrac{4}{5}$

EXAMPLE 3 Use the quotient property of radicals

a. $\sqrt{\dfrac{13}{100}} = \dfrac{\sqrt{13}}{\sqrt{100}}$ Quotient property of radicals

          $= \dfrac{\sqrt{13}}{10}$ Simplify.

b. $\sqrt{\dfrac{7}{x^2}} = \dfrac{\sqrt{7}}{\sqrt{x^2}}$ Quotient property of radicals

          $= \dfrac{\sqrt{7}}{x}$ Simplify.

✓ **GUIDED PRACTICE**   for Examples 1, 2, and 3

Simplify the expression.

1. $\sqrt{24}$ **2.** $\sqrt{25x^2}$ **3.** $\sqrt{2x^3} \cdot \sqrt{x}$ **4.** $\sqrt{\dfrac{1}{y^2}}$

RATIONALIZING THE DENOMINATOR Example 4 shows how to eliminate a radical from the denominator of a radical expression by multiplying the expression by an appropriate form of 1. The process of eliminating a radical from an expression's denominator is called **rationalizing the denominator.**

EXAMPLE 4 **Rationalize the denominator**

MULTIPLY BY 1
In part (a), notice that $\frac{\sqrt{7}}{\sqrt{7}}$ is equal to 1, so multiplying the expression by $\frac{\sqrt{7}}{\sqrt{7}}$ does not change the value of the expression.

a. $\dfrac{5}{\sqrt{7}} = \dfrac{5}{\sqrt{7}} \cdot \dfrac{\sqrt{7}}{\sqrt{7}}$ Multiply by $\dfrac{\sqrt{7}}{\sqrt{7}}$.

$= \dfrac{5\sqrt{7}}{\sqrt{49}}$ Product property of radicals

$= \dfrac{5\sqrt{7}}{7}$ Simplify.

b. $\dfrac{\sqrt{2}}{\sqrt{3b}} = \dfrac{\sqrt{2}}{\sqrt{3b}} \cdot \dfrac{\sqrt{3b}}{\sqrt{3b}}$ Multiply by $\dfrac{\sqrt{3b}}{\sqrt{3b}}$.

$= \dfrac{\sqrt{6b}}{\sqrt{9b^2}}$ Product property of radicals

$= \dfrac{\sqrt{6b}}{\sqrt{9} \cdot \sqrt{b^2}}$ Product property of radicals

$= \dfrac{\sqrt{6b}}{3b}$ Simplify.

SUMS AND DIFFERENCES You can use the distributive property to simplify sums and differences of radical expressions when the expressions have the same radicand.

EXAMPLE 5 **Add and subtract radicals**

a. $4\sqrt{10} + \sqrt{13} - 9\sqrt{10} = 4\sqrt{10} - 9\sqrt{10} + \sqrt{13}$ Commutative property

$= (4 - 9)\sqrt{10} + \sqrt{13}$ Distributive property

$= -5\sqrt{10} + \sqrt{13}$ Simplify.

b. $5\sqrt{3} + \sqrt{48} = 5\sqrt{3} + \sqrt{16 \cdot 3}$ Factor using perfect square factor.

$= 5\sqrt{3} + \sqrt{16} \cdot \sqrt{3}$ Product property of radicals

$= 5\sqrt{3} + 4\sqrt{3}$ Simplify.

$= (5 + 4)\sqrt{3}$ Distributive property

$= 9\sqrt{3}$ Simplify.

✔ **GUIDED PRACTICE**   for Examples 4 and 5

Simplify the expression.

5. $\dfrac{1}{\sqrt{3}}$ **6.** $\dfrac{1}{\sqrt{x}}$ **7.** $\dfrac{3}{\sqrt{2x}}$ **8.** $2\sqrt{7} + 3\sqrt{63}$

EXAMPLE 6 **Multiply radical expressions**

Animated Algebra

For an interactive example of multiplying radical expressions, go to **classzone.com**.

a. $\sqrt{5}(4 - \sqrt{20}) = 4\sqrt{5} - \sqrt{5} \cdot \sqrt{20}$ **Distributive property**

$\qquad\qquad = 4\sqrt{5} - \sqrt{100}$ **Product property of radicals**

$\qquad\qquad = 4\sqrt{5} - 10$ **Simplify.**

b. $(\sqrt{7} + \sqrt{2})(\sqrt{7} - 3\sqrt{2})$

$\qquad = \sqrt{7}(\sqrt{7} - 3\sqrt{2}) + \sqrt{2}(\sqrt{7} - 3\sqrt{2})$ **Distributive property**

$\qquad = (\sqrt{7})^2 + \sqrt{7}(-3\sqrt{2}) + \sqrt{2} \cdot \sqrt{7} + \sqrt{2}(-3\sqrt{2})$ **Distributive property**

$\qquad = 7 - 3\sqrt{7 \cdot 2} + \sqrt{7 \cdot 2} - 3(\sqrt{2})^2$ **Product property of radicals**

$\qquad = 7 - 3\sqrt{14} + \sqrt{14} - 6$ **Simplify.**

$\qquad = 1 - 2\sqrt{14}$ **Simplify.**

EXAMPLE 7 **Solve a real-world problem**

ASTRONOMY The orbital period of a planet is the time that it takes the planet to travel around the sun. You can find the orbital period P (in Earth years) using the formula $P = \sqrt{d^3}$ where d is the average distance (in astronomical units, abbreviated AU) of the planet from the sun.

a. Simplify the formula.

b. Jupiter's average distance from the sun is shown in the diagram. What is Jupiter's orbital period?

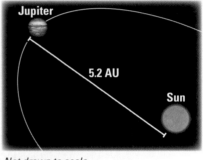

Not drawn to scale

READING

An astronomical unit is approximately the mean distance from Earth to the sun, or about 93 million miles.

Solution

a. $P = \sqrt{d^3}$ **Write formula.**

$\quad = \sqrt{d^2 \cdot d}$ **Factor using perfect square factor.**

$\quad = \sqrt{d^2} \cdot \sqrt{d}$ **Product property of radicals**

$\quad = d\sqrt{d}$ **Simplify.**

b. Substitute 5.2 for d in the simplified formula.

$\quad P = d\sqrt{d} = 5.2\sqrt{5.2} \approx 11.9$ **Use a calculator.**

▶ The orbital period of Jupiter is about 11.9 Earth years.

✓ **GUIDED PRACTICE** for Examples 6 and 7

9. Simplify the expression $(4 - \sqrt{5})(1 - \sqrt{5})$.

10. **ASTRONOMY** Neptune's average distance from the sun is about 6 times Jupiter's average distance from the sun. Is the orbital period of Neptune 6 times the orbital period of Jupiter? *Explain.*

8.4 EXERCISES

HOMEWORK KEY

◆ = **MULTIPLE CHOICE PRACTICE**
Exs. 23, 47, 65, and 70–72

○ = **HINTS** AND **HOMEWORK HELP**
for Ex. 9, 37, and 67 at classzone.com

SKILLS · PROBLEM SOLVING · REASONING

1. **VOCABULARY** Copy and complete: The process of eliminating a radical from the denominator of a radical expression is called __?__.

2. **WRITING** Is the expression $\sqrt{\frac{2x}{9}}$ written in simplest form? *Explain* why or why not.

EXAMPLES
1, 2, and 3
on pp. 483–484
for Exs. 3–26

USING PRODUCT AND QUOTIENT PROPERTIES Simplify the expression.

3. $\sqrt{20}$ 4. $\sqrt{48}$ 5. $\sqrt{96}$ 6. $\sqrt{72}$

7. $\sqrt{125b}$ 8. $\sqrt{4x^2}$ 9. $\sqrt{81m^3}$ 10. $\sqrt{32m^5}$

11. $\sqrt{5} \cdot \sqrt{30}$ 12. $\sqrt{50} \cdot \sqrt{18}$ 13. $\sqrt{14x} \cdot \sqrt{2x}$ 14. $\sqrt{3b^3} \cdot \sqrt{18b}$

15. $2\sqrt{a^4b^5}$ 16. $\sqrt{64s^4t^3}$ 17. $\sqrt{m^2n} \cdot \sqrt{n}$ 18. $\sqrt{75xy} \cdot \sqrt{2x^3}$

19. $\sqrt{\frac{4}{49}}$ 20. $\sqrt{\frac{7}{81}}$ 21. $\sqrt{\frac{a^3}{121}}$ 22. $\sqrt{\frac{100}{4x^2}}$

23. ◆ **MULTIPLE CHOICE** Which expression is equivalent to $\sqrt{\frac{9x}{16}}$?

(A) $\frac{\sqrt{3x}}{4}$ (B) $\frac{3\sqrt{x}}{4}$ (C) $\frac{3\sqrt{x}}{16}$ (D) $\frac{3x}{4}$

ERROR ANALYSIS *Describe* and correct the error in simplifying the expression.

24.
$$\sqrt{72} = \sqrt{4} \cdot \sqrt{18}$$
$$= 2\sqrt{18}$$ ✗

25.
$$\sqrt{\frac{4}{9}} = \frac{\sqrt{4}}{9} = \frac{2}{9}$$ ✗

26. **WRITING** *Describe* two different sequences of steps you could take to simplify the expression $\sqrt{45} \cdot \sqrt{5}$.

EXAMPLE 4
on p. 485
for Exs. 27–34

RATIONALIZING THE DENOMINATOR Simplify the expression.

27. $\frac{2}{\sqrt{2}}$ 28. $\frac{4}{\sqrt{3}}$ 29. $\sqrt{\frac{5}{48}}$ 30. $\sqrt{\frac{4}{52}}$

31. $\frac{3}{\sqrt{a}}$ 32. $\frac{1}{\sqrt{2x}}$ 33. $\sqrt{\frac{2x^2}{5}}$ 34. $\sqrt{\frac{8}{3n^3}}$

EXAMPLES
5 and 6
on pp. 485–486
for Exs. 35–47

PERFORMING OPERATIONS ON RADICALS Simplify the expression.

35. $2\sqrt{2} + 6\sqrt{2}$ 36. $\sqrt{5} - 6\sqrt{5}$ 37. $9\sqrt{32} + \sqrt{2}$

38. $2\sqrt{6} - 5\sqrt{54}$ 39. $\sqrt{12} + 6\sqrt{3} + 2\sqrt{6}$ 40. $3\sqrt{7} - 5\sqrt{14} + 2\sqrt{28}$

41. $\sqrt{5}(5 - \sqrt{5})$ 42. $\sqrt{6}(7\sqrt{3} + 6)$ 43. $\sqrt{3}(6\sqrt{2} - 4\sqrt{3})$

44. $(4 - \sqrt{2})(5 + \sqrt{2})$ 45. $(2\sqrt{5} + 7)^2$ 46. $(\sqrt{7} + \sqrt{3})(6 + \sqrt{8})$

47. ◆ **MULTIPLE CHOICE** Which expression is equivalent to $\sqrt{2}(\sqrt{8} - 4)$?

    Ⓐ $4 - 4\sqrt{2}$　　　Ⓑ $4 - 2\sqrt{2}$　　　Ⓒ $4 + 4\sqrt{2}$　　　Ⓓ $16 - 4\sqrt{2}$

SIMPLIFYING RADICAL EXPRESSIONS Simplify the expression.

48. $\sqrt{75m^2np^4}$

49. $\sqrt{512rs^6} \cdot \sqrt{t^3}$

50. $\sqrt{\dfrac{600a}{4b^3}}$

51. $\sqrt{\dfrac{50gh^2}{125f^3}}$

52. $\dfrac{4}{\sqrt{3}} + \dfrac{7}{\sqrt{12}}$

53. $\dfrac{2\sqrt{6}}{\sqrt{30}} - \dfrac{3}{\sqrt{20}}$

54. $\dfrac{7}{\sqrt{x}} + \dfrac{3}{2\sqrt{x}}$

55. $\dfrac{3}{\sqrt{x^3}} + \dfrac{4}{\sqrt{x}}$

56. $\dfrac{6m}{\sqrt{m^3}} - \dfrac{8}{\sqrt{m}}$

57. **REASONING** Multiply the expressions $a\sqrt{b} + c\sqrt{d}$ and $a\sqrt{b} - c\sqrt{d}$ to show that the product does not contain a radical.

58. **WRITING** According to the definition of square root, a square root of a nonnegative real number a is a real number b such that $b^2 = a$. How can you use the definition to show that $\sqrt{x^2} = x$ for $x \geq 0$? *Explain.*

INDIRECT PROOF In Exercises 59 and 60, use the example below to prove the statement.

EXAMPLE　**Writing an indirect proof**

Prove that $\sqrt{2}$ is irrational.

Solution

Rather than showing that $\sqrt{2}$ is irrational directly, assume that $\sqrt{2}$ is *rational* and show that this assumption leads to a contradiction. This approach is called an *indirect* proof.

    STEP 1　Assume that $\sqrt{2}$ is rational.

    STEP 2　If $\sqrt{2}$ is rational, then $\sqrt{2} = \dfrac{a}{b}$ where a and b are positive integers and $\dfrac{a}{b}$ is in simplest form.

    STEP 3　If $\sqrt{2} = \dfrac{a}{b}$, then $2 = \dfrac{a^2}{b^2}$ by the definition of square root.

    STEP 4　Multiply both sides of the equation $2 = \dfrac{a^2}{b^2}$ by b^2 to get $a^2 = 2b^2$. The square of a is even, so a must be even.

    STEP 5　Let $a = 2n$ where n is a positive integer, and substitute $2n$ for a in $a^2 = 2b^2$. Then $(2n)^2 = 2b^2$, or $4n^2 = 2b^2$.

    STEP 6　Divide each side of the equation $4n^2 = 2b^2$ by 2 to get $2n^2 = b^2$. The square of b is even, so b must be even.

    STEP 7　Because both a and b are even, both a and b have 2 as a factor. This contradicts the fact that $\dfrac{a}{b}$ is in simplest form.

    STEP 8　The assumption that $\sqrt{2}$ is rational is false because it leads to a contradiction. So, $\sqrt{2}$ is irrational.

---

59. Prove that $\sqrt{3}$ is irrational.

60. Prove that $\sqrt{p}$ is irrational for any prime number p.

　◆ = **MULTIPLE CHOICE PRACTICE**　　　◯ = **HINTS AND HOMEWORK HELP** at classzone.com

CONNECT SKILLS TO PROBLEM SOLVING Exercises 61–63 will help you prepare for problem solving.

Use the following information: **The formula for the side length s of a square is $s = \sqrt{A}$ where A is the area of the square.**

61. The area of a square dog run is $2x^2$ square feet. Find the side length of the dog run.

62. The area of a square quilt is $\dfrac{4x^2}{9}$ square centimeters. Find the side length of the quilt.

63. The area of a square garden is $\dfrac{16x^2}{7}$ square centimeters. Find the side length of the garden.

EXAMPLE 7
on p. 486
for Exs. 64, 65

64. FINANCE You invest $225 in a savings account for two years. You can find the average annual interest rate r that the account earned over two years using the formula $r = \sqrt{\dfrac{V_2}{V_0}} - 1$ where V_0 is the initial investment and V_2 is the amount in the account after two years. At the end of two years, you have $270 in the account. What was the average annual interest rate (written as a percent) the account earned over two years?

California @HomeTutor for problem solving help at classzone.com

65. ◆ MULTIPLE CHOICE The distance d (in miles) that a person can see to the horizon is given by the formula $d = \sqrt{\dfrac{3h}{2}}$ where h is the person's eye level (in feet) above the water. What is the distance, to the nearest mile, that the person shown standing on a sea cliff in Pacifica, California, can see to the horizon?

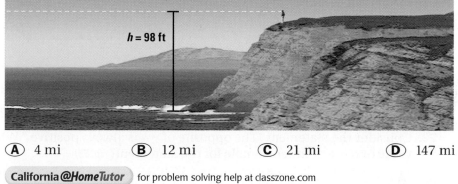

$h = 98$ ft

(A) 4 mi   **(B)** 12 mi   **(C)** 21 mi   **(D)** 147 mi

California @HomeTutor for problem solving help at classzone.com

66. MULTI-STEP PROBLEM You are making a cube-shaped footrest that will be covered with fabric. You have enough money to buy 5 square yards of the fabric that you want to cover the footrest.

a. The edge length s (in yards) of the largest footrest that you can cover can be found using the formula $s = \sqrt{\dfrac{S}{6}}$ where S is the surface area of the footrest (in square yards). Use unit analysis to check the units in the formula.

b. To the nearest tenth of a yard, find the edge length of the largest footrest that you can cover.

67. **PHYSICS** The velocity v (in feet per second) of an object that has been dropped is given by the equation $v = \sqrt{64d}$ where d is the distance (in feet) the object falls before hitting the ground. Write the equation in simplified form. Then use the simplified equation to find the exact value of v when the distance the object falls before hitting the ground is 20 feet.

68. **CHALLENGE** Decide whether the set of irrational numbers is closed under multiplication. *Explain* your reasoning. (To review the closure property of multiplication, see page 75.)

69. **CHALLENGE** The speed s (in miles per hour) at which a vehicle is traveling on a newly paved road before an accident is given by $s = \sqrt{24d}$ where d is the length of the skid mark (in feet).

Skid mark: 100 feet long

   a. A driver sees a hazard in the road and is forced to brake. The car skids to a halt leaving a skid mark that is 100 feet long. At what speed was the car traveling when the driver applied the brakes?

   b. The driver in part (a) applies the brakes 1.5 seconds after noticing the hazard. How many feet does the car travel before the driver applies the brakes? *Explain* how you found your answer.

   c. What is the total distance (in feet) traveled from the time the driver in part (a) sees the hazard until the time the car skids to a halt?

◆ CALIFORNIA STANDARDS SPIRAL REVIEW

Alg. 2.0

70. Which expression is equivalent to $4x^6$? *(p. 475)*

   (A) $\left(\dfrac{2}{x^{-4}}\right)^2$ **(B)** $\left(\dfrac{2}{x^{-3}}\right)^2$ **(C)** $4 \cdot \left(\dfrac{x^{-4}}{x^{-1}}\right)^2$ **(D)** $4 \cdot \left(\dfrac{x^2}{x^{-2}}\right)^3$

Alg. 16.0

71. Which relation is a function? *(p. 249)*

   (A) $\{(2, 1), (3, 1), (4, 1), (4, 5)\}$ **(B)** $\{(-4, 10), (-3, 9), (-2, 8), (-1, 7)\}$

   (C) $\{(3, -5), (3, -4), (3, 6), (3, 7)\}$ **(D)** $\{(7, 5), (8, 4), (8, 2), (2, 1)\}$

Alg. 25.1

72. Consider the statement "The opposite of $-a$ is always positive." Which value of a is a counterexample for the statement? *(p. 53)*

   (A) -3 **(B)** 1 **(C)** 2.5 **(D)** 7

QUIZ for Lessons 8.3–8.4

Simplify the expression. Write your answer using only positive exponents. *(p. 475)*

   1. $(-4x)^4 \cdot (-4)^{-6}$ **2.** $\left(-3x^7y^{-2}\right)^{-3}$ **3.** $\dfrac{1}{(5z)^{-3}}$ **4.** $\dfrac{6x^{-2}y^5}{-x^3y^{-7}}$

Simplify the expression. *(p. 483)*

   5. $\sqrt{150}$ **6.** $\sqrt{5}(2 - \sqrt{5})$ **7.** $\sqrt{2c^2} \cdot \sqrt{8c}$ **8.** $\sqrt{\dfrac{80x^3}{5y}}$

8.5 Apply the Pythagorean Theorem and Its Converse

Standards Preparation

Gr. 7 MG 3.3 Know and understand the Pythagorean theorem and its converse and use it to find the length of the missing side of a right triangle and the lengths of other line segments and, in some situations, empirically verify the Pythagorean theorem by direct measurement.

Connect   *Before* you simplified expressions with exponents and radicals. *Now* you will use the Pythagorean theorem and its converse to prepare for Geometry Standard 8.0.

Math and
ARCHITECTURE
Ex. 35, p. 496

Key Vocabulary
• hypotenuse
• legs of a right triangle
• Pythagorean theorem

The **hypotenuse** of a right triangle is the side opposite the right angle. It is the longest side of a right triangle. The **legs** are the two sides that form the right angle.

A *theorem* is a statement that can be proved true. The **Pythagorean theorem** states the relationship among the lengths of the sides of a right triangle.

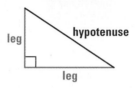

KEY CONCEPT   *For Your Notebook*

The Pythagorean Theorem

Words If a triangle is a right triangle, then the sum of the squares of the lengths of the legs equals the square of the length of the hypotenuse.

Algebra $a^2 + b^2 = c^2$

EXAMPLE 1   Use the Pythagorean theorem

Find the unknown length for the triangle shown.

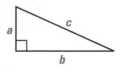

Solution

$a^2 + b^2 = c^2$	**Pythagorean theorem**
$a^2 + 6^2 = 7^2$	**Substitute 6 for b and 7 for c.**
$a^2 + 36 = 49$	**Simplify.**
$a^2 = 13$	**Subtract 36 from each side.**
$a = \sqrt{13}$	**Take positive square root of each side.**

▸ The side length a is $\sqrt{13}$.

Animated Algebra

For an interactive example of using the Pythagorean theorem, go to **classzone.com**.

✓ **GUIDED PRACTICE**   for Example 1

1. The lengths of the legs of a right triangle are $a = 5$ and $b = 12$. Find c.

EXAMPLE 2 ◆ **Multiple Choice Practice**

In the triangle shown, *D* is the midpoint of segment *AC*, and segment *BD* is perpendicular to segment *AC*. What is the length of segment *BD*?

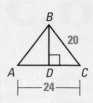

Ⓐ 12 cm   Ⓑ 14 cm

Ⓒ 16 cm   Ⓓ 23 cm

ELIMINATE CHOICES
The length of segment *BD* must be less than the length of the hypotenuse, 20. So, you can eliminate choice D.

Solution

Because *D* is the midpoint of segment *AC*, the length of segment *CD* is half of the length of segment *AC*. So, $CD = \frac{1}{2}AC = 12$ cm. Use the Pythagorean theorem to find the length of segment *BD*.

$a^2 + b^2 = c^2$ **Pythagorean theorem**

$a^2 + 12^2 = 20^2$ **Substitute 12 for *b* and 20 for *c*.**

$a^2 + 144 = 400$ **Simplify.**

$a^2 = 256$ **Subtract 144 from each side.**

$a = \sqrt{256} = 16$ **Take positive square root of each side.**

▶ The correct answer is C. Ⓐ Ⓑ Ⓒ Ⓓ

EXAMPLE 3   **Solve a real-world problem**

SOCCER A soccer player makes a corner kick to another player, as shown. Find the distance the player kicks the ball.

ANOTHER WAY
For an alternative method for solving Example 3, turn to page 497 for the **Problem Solving Workshop**.

Solution

The path of the kicked ball is the hypotenuse of a right triangle. The length of one leg is 12 yards, and the length of the other leg is 40 yards.

$c^2 = a^2 + b^2$ **Pythagorean theorem**

$c^2 = 12^2 + 40^2$ **Substitute 12 for *a* and 40 for *b*.**

$c^2 = 1744$ **Simplify.**

$c = \sqrt{1744} \approx 42$ **Take positive square root of each side.**

▶ The player kicks the ball about 42 yards.

✓   **GUIDED PRACTICE**   for Examples 2 and 3

2. **WHAT IF?** In Example 2, suppose the length of segment *BC* is 25 centimeters. Find the length of segment *BD*.

3. **SWIMMING** A rectangular pool is 30 feet wide and 60 feet long. You swim diagonally across the pool. To the nearest foot, how far do you swim?

REVIEW
REASONING
For help with if-then statements and converses, see pp. 55, 98, and 354.

CONVERSE OF THE PYTHAGOREAN THEOREM Recall that when you reverse the hypothesis and conclusion of an if-then statement, the new statement is called the converse. Although not all converses of true statements are true, the converse of the Pythagorean theorem is true.

KEY CONCEPT   *For Your Notebook*

Converse of the Pythagorean Theorem

If a triangle has side lengths a, b, and c such that $a^2 + b^2 = c^2$, then the triangle is a right triangle.

EXAMPLE 4   **Determine right triangles**

AVOID ERRORS
When using given side lengths to see whether $a^2 + b^2 = c^2$, substitute the longest side length for c.

Tell whether the triangle with the given side lengths is a right triangle.

a. 8, 15, 17

$$8^2 + 15^2 \stackrel{?}{=} 17^2$$

$$64 + 225 \stackrel{?}{=} 289$$

$$289 = 289 \checkmark$$

▸ The triangle is a right triangle.

b. 5, 8, 9

$$5^2 + 8^2 \stackrel{?}{=} 9^2$$

$$25 + 64 \stackrel{?}{=} 81$$

$$89 = 81 \ \textsf{✗}$$

▸ The triangle is *not* a right triangle.

EXAMPLE 5   **Use the converse of the Pythagorean theorem**

CONSTRUCTION A construction worker is making sure one corner of the foundation of a house is a right angle. To do this, the worker makes a mark 8 feet from the corner along one wall and another mark 6 feet from the same corner along the other wall. The worker then measures the distance between the two marks and finds the distance to be 10 feet. Is the corner a right angle?

Solution

$$8^2 + 6^2 \stackrel{?}{=} 10^2 \qquad \textsf{Check to see if } a^2 + b^2 = c^2 \textsf{ when } a = 8, b = 6, \textsf{ and } c = 10.$$

$$64 + 36 \stackrel{?}{=} 100 \qquad \textsf{Simplify.}$$

$$100 = 100 \checkmark \qquad \textsf{Add.}$$

▸ Because the sides that the construction worker measured form a right triangle, the corner of the foundation is a right angle.

 GUIDED PRACTICE   for Examples 4 and 5

Tell whether the triangle with the given side lengths is a right triangle.

4. 7, 11, 13   **5.** 15, 36, 39   **6.** 15, 112, 113

7. WINDOW DESIGN A window has the shape of a triangle with side lengths of 120 centimeters, 120 centimeters, and 180 centimeters. Is the window a right triangle? *Explain.*

8.5 EXERCISES

SKILLS · PROBLEM SOLVING · REASONING

1. **VOCABULARY** Copy and complete: In a right triangle, the side opposite the right angle is called the __?__ .

2. **WRITING** *Explain* how you can tell whether a triangle with side lengths of 9, 12, and 15 is a right triangle.

EXAMPLE 1
on p. 491
for Exs. 3–16

USING THE PYTHAGOREAN THEOREM Let *a* and *b* represent the lengths of the legs of a right triangle, and let *c* represent the length of the hypotenuse. Find the unknown length.

3. $a = 3, c = 5$ 4. $b = 3, c = 7$ 5. $a = 5, b = 6$

6. $b = 5, c = 10$ 7. $a = 8, b = 8$ 8. $a = 5, b = 12$

9. $a = 8, b = 12$ 10. $a = 7, c = 25$ 11. $b = 15, c = 17$

12. $a = 9, c = 41$ 13. $b = 3, c = 3.4$ 14. $a = 1.2, c = 3.7$

15. ◆ **MULTIPLE CHOICE** A rectangular tennis court is 36 feet by 78 feet. To the nearest tenth of a foot, what is the length of a diagonal?

     A 42.0 ft   **B** 69.2 ft   **C** 85.9 ft   **D** 114.0 ft

16. **ERROR ANALYSIS** *Describe* and correct the error in finding the unknown length.

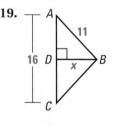

$$18^2 + 30^2 = x^2$$
$$1224 = x^2$$
$$6\sqrt{34} = x$$

EXAMPLE 2
on p. 492
for Exs. 17–19

USING THE PYTHAGOREAN THEOREM Given that *D* is the midpoint of segment *AC*, find the unknown length. Round your answer to the nearest tenth, if necessary.

17.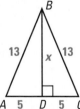

18.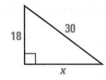

19.

EXAMPLE 4
on p. 493
for Exs. 20–25

DETERMINING RIGHT TRIANGLES Tell whether the triangle with the given side lengths is a right triangle.

20. 9, 12, 15   21. 2, 3, 4   22. 8, 16, 18

23. 9, 21, 24   24. 11, 60, 61   25. 24, 143, 145

26. **WRITING** The side lengths of a right triangle are 15, 39, and 36. *Explain* how you know which side is the hypotenuse.

27. ◆ **MULTIPLE CHOICE** What is the area of the largest square in the coordinate plane shown?

(A) 100 square units

(B) 64 square units

(C) 36 square units

(D) 25 square units

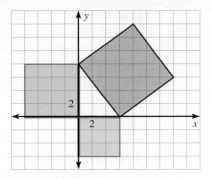

28. WRITING Given that two side lengths of a right triangle are 11 inches and 6 inches, is it possible to find the length of the third side? *Explain*.

CONNECT SKILLS TO PROBLEM SOLVING Exercises 29–32 will help you prepare for problem solving.

Tell whether the unknown measure is the length of a leg or of the hypotenuse of the right triangle in the situation described.

29. The length of the diagonal of a rectangular flag is 32 inches. The flag has a length of x inches and a width of 19 inches.

30. A square park has a side length of 800 feet. You walk x feet from one corner of the park to the opposite corner.

31. A ladder is leaning against the side of a house. The base of the ladder is 5 feet from the house, and the top of the ladder is 16 feet above the ground. The ladder is x feet in length.

32. The ramp to a lifeguard tower is 14 feet in length. The base of the ramp is 10 feet from the lifeguard tower, and the top of the ramp is x feet above the ground.

EXAMPLES
3 and 5
on pp. 492–493
for Exs. 33–36

33. ARCHITECTURE An earthquake-resistant building has dampers built into its structure to help minimize damage caused by an earthquake. A section of the structural frame of such a building is shown. What is the length of the damper? Round your answer to the nearest foot.

10 ft

Damper

12 ft

California @*HomeTutor* for problem solving help at classzone.com

34. SAILS A sail has the shape of a triangle. The side lengths are 146 inches, 131 inches, and 84 inches. Is the sail a right triangle? *Explain*.

California @*HomeTutor* for problem solving help at classzone.com

35. **FLATIRON BUILDING** A top view of the Flatiron Building in New York City is shown. The triangle indicates the basic shape of the building's roof. Is the triangle a right triangle? *Explain.*

36. ◆ **MULTIPLE CHOICE** The size of a television is indicated by the length of a diagonal of the television screen. The aspect ratio of a television screen is the ratio of the length of the screen to the width of the screen. The size of a particular television is 30 inches, and its aspect ratio is 4 : 3. What is the width of the television screen?

A 9 in.   **B** 12 in.   **C** 18 in.   **D** 20 in.

37. **CHALLENGE** The edge length of the cube is 7 inches.

a. Find the value of x.

b. Find the value of y.

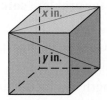

38. **CHALLENGE** During a baseball game, a base runner is running from first base to second base. To get the runner out, the catcher must throw the ball to second base before the runner reaches second base.

a. The catcher is 5 feet behind home plate. How far does the catcher have to throw the ball to reach second base? Round your answer to the nearest foot.

b. The catcher throws the ball at a rate of 90 feet per second when a base runner is 30 feet away from second base. Will the catcher get the runner out if the runner is running at a rate of 22 feet per second? *Explain.*

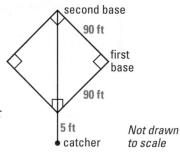

◆ CALIFORNIA STANDARDS SPIRAL REVIEW

Alg. 2.0   **39.** Which expression is equivalent to $2\sqrt{11}$? *(p. 483)*

A $\dfrac{2}{\sqrt{11}}$ **B** $\dfrac{\sqrt{11}}{2}$ **C** $\sqrt{22}$ **D** $\dfrac{22}{\sqrt{11}}$

Alg. 6.0   **40.** The graph of which inequality is shown? *(p. 425)*

A $x + 2y \le 2$ **B** $x + 2y \le 4$

C $x + 2y \ge 4$ **D** $x - 2y \ge 4$

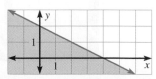

Alg. 5.0   **41.** Admission fees to an indoor skateboard park are $5 for members and $8 for nonmembers. During one afternoon, the park collected $699 in admission fees. There were 28 more members than nonmembers admitted to the park. How many nonmembers were admitted? *(p. 139)*

A 15   **B** 43   **C** 52   **D** 71

Using ALTERNATIVE METHODS

Another Way to Solve Example 3, page 492

Standards Preparation
Gr. 7 MG 3.3

In Example 3 on page 492, you saw how to solve a problem about finding the distance a soccer player kicks a ball by using the Pythagorean theorem. You can also solve the problem by making a scale drawing of the given right triangle.

PROBLEM

SOCCER A soccer player makes a corner kick to another player, as shown. Find the distance the player kicks the ball.

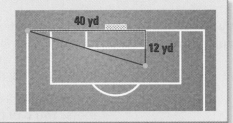

METHOD

MAKING A SCALE DRAWING An alternative approach is to make a scale drawing of the triangle on graph paper and measure the hypotenuse directly.

Let each square on the grid paper represent 4 yards. Use this scale to draw the triangle on graph paper. Then measure the length of the hypotenuse using another piece of the graph paper, as shown. The length of the hypotenuse is about 10.5 units.

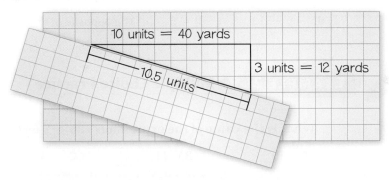

Because each square on the graph paper represents 4 yards, multiply 10.5 by 4 to find the number of yards the soccer ball was kicked: $10.5 \cdot 4 = 42$ yards.

▸ The player kicks the ball about 42 yards.

PRACTICE

1. **WHAT IF?** In the problem above, suppose the ball is kicked to a player who is 8 yards from the goal line instead of 12 yards. Use a scale drawing to find the distance that the ball is kicked.

2. **FOOTBALL** A football field is a rectangle with a length of 360 feet and a width of 160 feet. What is the length of a diagonal from one corner of the field to the opposite corner? Solve this problem using two methods.

8.6 Use Cube Roots and Fractional Exponents

Math and SPORTS
Ex. 45, p. 502

Standards **Alg. 2.0** Students understand and use such operations as taking the opposite, finding the reciprocal, **taking a root, and raising to a fractional power. They understand and use the rules of exponents.**

Connect *Before* you used the properties of exponents. *Now* you will simplify expressions with fractional exponents.

Key Vocabulary
• cube root

The **cube root** of a real number a is a real number b such that $b^3 = a$. For example, $2^3 = 8$, so 2 is the cube root of 8. The cube root of a can be written as $\sqrt[3]{a}$. Negative real numbers have cube roots because the cube of a negative number is negative.

The properties of radicals presented in Lesson 8.4 can also be applied to cube roots. You will prove the properties for cube roots in Exercise 47.

EXAMPLE 1 **Find cube roots**

Evaluate the expression.

a. $\sqrt[3]{27} = 3$ The cube root of 27 is 3.

b. $\sqrt[3]{-216} = -6$ The cube root of −216 is −6.

c. $-\sqrt[3]{8} = -2$ The opposite of the cube root of 8 is −2.

d. $-\sqrt[3]{-512} = -(-8) = 8$ The opposite of the cube root of −512 is 8.

EXAMPLE 2 ◆ **Multiple Choice Practice**

What is the value of the expression $\sqrt{36} + \sqrt[3]{64}$?

(A) 10   **(B)** 11   **(C)** 14   **(D)** 18

Solution

$\sqrt{36} + \sqrt[3]{64} = 6 + 4$ Evaluate $\sqrt{36}$ and $\sqrt[3]{64}$.

$= 10$ Add.

▶ The correct answer is A. **(A)** **(B)** **(C)** **(D)**

 GUIDED PRACTICE for Examples 1 and 2

Evaluate the expression.

1. $\sqrt[3]{125}$ **2.** $-\sqrt[3]{1000}$ **3.** $\sqrt[3]{729} - \sqrt{25}$

FRACTIONAL EXPONENTS You have so far written square roots and cube roots using a radical sign. You can also write square roots and cube roots using exponents.

For any $a \geq 0$, suppose you want to write $\sqrt{a}$ as a^k. Recall that a number b (in this case, a^k) is a square root of a number a provided $b^2 = a$. Use this definition to find a value for k as follows.

$b^2 = a$ **Definition of square root**

$(a^k)^2 = a$ **Substitute a^k for b.**

$a^{2k} = a^1$ **Product of powers property**

Because the bases are the same in the equation $a^{2k} = a^1$, the exponents must be equal:

$2k = 1$ **Set exponents equal.**

$k = \dfrac{1}{2}$ **Solve for k.**

So, for a nonnegative number a, $\sqrt{a} = a^{1/2}$. Similarly, for any number a, $\sqrt[3]{a} = a^{1/3}$. When working with fractional exponents, you can use the same properties of exponents that you used with integer exponents. In this lesson you will work with exponents of $\frac{1}{2}$, $\frac{1}{3}$, multiples of $\frac{1}{2}$, and multiples of $\frac{1}{3}$.

EXAMPLE 3   **Evaluate expressions involving square roots**

a. $16^{1/2} = \sqrt{16}$

$\qquad\quad = 4$

b. $25^{-1/2} = \dfrac{1}{25^{1/2}}$

$\qquad\qquad = \dfrac{1}{\sqrt{25}}$

$\qquad\qquad = \dfrac{1}{5}$

c. $9^{5/2} = 9^{(1/2) \cdot 5}$

$\qquad\quad = (9^{1/2})^5$

$\qquad\quad = (\sqrt{9})^5$

$\qquad\quad = 3^5$

$\qquad\quad = 243$

EXAMPLE 4   **Evaluate expressions involving cube roots**

a. $8^{-1/3} = \dfrac{1}{8^{1/3}}$

$\qquad\quad = \dfrac{1}{\sqrt[3]{8}}$

$\qquad\quad = \dfrac{1}{2}$

b. $64^{4/3} = 64^{(1/3) \cdot 4}$

$\qquad\quad = (64^{1/3})^4$

$\qquad\quad = (\sqrt[3]{64})^4$

$\qquad\quad = 4^4$

$\qquad\quad = 256$

c. $125^{-2/3} = 125^{(1/3) \cdot (-2)}$

$\qquad\qquad = (125^{1/3})^{-2}$

$\qquad\qquad = (\sqrt[3]{125})^{-2}$

$\qquad\qquad = 5^{-2}$

$\qquad\qquad = \dfrac{1}{5^2}$

$\qquad\qquad = \dfrac{1}{25}$

✓   **GUIDED PRACTICE**   **for Examples 3 and 4**

Evaluate the expression.

4. $81^{3/2}$ **5.** $121^{-1/2}$ **6.** $1000^{2/3}$ **7.** $27^{-4/3}$

EXAMPLE 5 Use properties of exponents

Simplify the expression. Write your answer using only positive exponents.

a. $\dfrac{6^{4/3} \cdot 6}{\sqrt[3]{6}} = \dfrac{6^{(4/3)+1}}{6^{1/3}}$

$= \dfrac{6^{7/3}}{6^{1/3}}$

$= 6^{(7/3)-(1/3)}$

$= 6^2$

$= 36$

b. $\left(x^{1/2}y^{1/3}\right)^2 y^{1/3} = x^{(1/2) \cdot 2} y^{(1/3) \cdot 2} y^{1/3}$

$= x^{2/2} y^{2/3} y^{1/3}$

$= xy^{(2/3)+(1/3)}$

$= xy^{3/3}$

$= xy$

✓ **GUIDED PRACTICE** for Example 5

Simplify the expression. Write your answer using only positive exponents.

8. $\left(27^{-1/3} x^{2/3}\right)^3$

9. $\sqrt[3]{8}(-8)^{-2/3}(-8)^{1/3}$

EXAMPLE 6 Solve a real world problem

TRAPEZE The velocity v (in meters per second) at which a trapeze performer swings can be modeled by the function $v = (19.6d)^{1/2}$ where d is the difference (in meters) between the highest and lowest position of the performer's center of gravity during the swing. Find the velocity of the performer when d is 1.5 meters.

Solution

$v = (19.6d)^{1/2}$ **Write original equation.**

$= (19.6 \cdot 1.5)^{1/2}$ **Substitute 1.5 for d.**

$= 29.4^{1/2}$ **Multiply.**

You can use a calculator to evaluate $29.4^{1/2}$, as shown at the right.

▸ The velocity of the trapeze performer is about 5.4 meters per second.

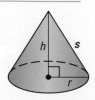

```
29.4^(1/2)
        5.422176685
```

✓ **GUIDED PRACTICE** for Example 6

10. **GEOMETRY** The formula for the slant height s (in inches) of a cone is $s = \left(h^2 + r^2\right)^{1/2}$ where h is the height of the cone (in inches) and r is the radius of its base (in inches). Find the slant height of a cone with a height of $2\sqrt{3}$ inches and a radius of 2 inches.

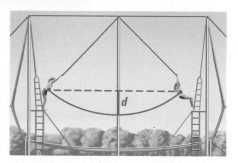

8.6 EXERCISES

HOMEWORK KEY

◆ = **MULTIPLE CHOICE PRACTICE**
Exs. 15, 24, 43, and 49–51

○ = **HINTS AND HOMEWORK HELP**
for Exs. 7, 25, and 45 at classzone.com

SKILLS · PROBLEM SOLVING · REASONING

1. **VOCABULARY** Copy and complete: The __?__ of a real number a is a real number b such that $b^3 = a$.

2. **WRITING** Are $(-8)^{1/3}$ and $-(8)^{1/3}$ equivalent expressions? *Explain.*

EXAMPLES 1 and 2
on p. 498
for Ex. 3–15

EVALUATING ROOTS Evaluate the expression.

3. $\sqrt[3]{1000}$
4. $\sqrt[3]{1}$
5. $-\sqrt[3]{27}$
6. $\sqrt[3]{-125}$

7. $\sqrt[3]{1331}$
8. $-\sqrt[3]{729}$
9. $\sqrt[3]{-512}$
10. $-\sqrt[3]{-343}$

11. $\sqrt[3]{64} + \sqrt{64}$
12. $\sqrt{81} + \sqrt[3]{-1000}$
13. $\sqrt{49} - \sqrt[3]{8}$
14. $-\sqrt[3]{125} + \sqrt{25}$

15. ◆ **MULTIPLE CHOICE** Which expression does *not* have a value of 6?

   (A) $-\sqrt[3]{-216}$
   (B) $\sqrt{16} + \sqrt[3]{8}$
   (C) $\sqrt[3]{343} + \sqrt[3]{-1}$
   (D) $\sqrt{144} - \sqrt[3]{-216}$

EXAMPLES 3 and 4
on p. 499
for Ex. 16–24

EVALUATING EXPRESSIONS Evaluate the expression.

16. $16^{1/2}$
17. $8^{1/3}$
18. $64^{-1/3}$
19. $25^{-3/2}$

20. $27^{4/3}$
21. $4^{5/2}$
22. $36^{-5/2}$
23. $125^{-2/3}$

24. ◆ **MULTIPLE CHOICE** What is the value of $36^{-1/2}$?

   (A) -6
   (B) $-\dfrac{1}{6}$
   (C) $\dfrac{1}{6}$
   (D) 6

EXAMPLE 5
on p. 500
for Ex. 25–34

SIMPLIFYING EXPRESSIONS Simplify the expression. Write your answer using only positive exponents.

25. $12^{-1/2} \cdot 12^{5/2}$
26. $x^{7/2} \cdot x^{-3/2}$
27. $8^{1/2} \cdot 8^{-5/2}$
28. $x^{4/3} \cdot x^{-2/3}$

29. $\left(\dfrac{1}{16}\right)^{1/2}\left(\dfrac{1}{16}\right)^{1/2}$
30. $\dfrac{(\sqrt[3]{3})^5 \cdot 3^0}{3^{2/3}}$
31. $(\sqrt{x})^3(x^{3/2})^2$
32. $36^{5/2} \cdot \dfrac{36^{-1/2}}{(36^{-1})^{-7/2}}$

ERROR ANALYSIS *Describe* and correct the error in simplifying the expression.

33.
$$27^{-2/3} \cdot 27^{1/3} = 27^{(-2/3)-(1/3)}$$
$$= 27^{-3/3}$$
$$= 27^{-1}$$
$$= \frac{1}{27}$$

34.
$$\left(4y^3\right)^{-1/2} = \frac{1}{\left(4 \cdot y^3\right)^{1/2}}$$
$$= \frac{1}{4 \cdot y^{3 \cdot (1/2)}}$$
$$= \frac{1}{4y^{3/2}}$$

SIMPLIFYING EXPRESSIONS Simplify the expression.

35. $\sqrt[3]{x^{30}} \cdot 4\sqrt[3]{x^9}$
36. $\sqrt[3]{27x^{15}} \cdot \sqrt[3]{x^3y^3}$
37. $\sqrt[3]{\dfrac{x^6}{8y^{12}}}$
38. $\sqrt[3]{\dfrac{1000x^{27}}{x^{24}y^{18}}}$

CONNECT SKILLS TO PROBLEM SOLVING Exercises 39–41 will help you prepare for problem solving.

Find the surface area of the cube described. Use the formula $S = 6V^{2/3}$ where S is the surface area of a cube with volume V.

39. An ice cube has a volume of 8 cubic inches.

40. A cubical audio speaker has a volume of 27 cubic centimeters.

41. A cubical box of tissues has a volume of 216 cubic inches.

 CALCULATOR In Exercises 42–45, you may wish to use a calculator.

EXAMPLE 6
on p. 500
for Exs. 42–45

42. **BRIDGES** The time t (in seconds) it takes an object dropped from a height h (in feet) to reach the ground is given by the function $t = \dfrac{h^{1/2}}{4}$. The Royal Gorge Bridge in Colorado is the world's highest suspension bridge. The height of the bridge is about 1024 feet. About how long does it take for a stone dropped from the bridge to reach the gorge below?

California@*HomeTutor* for problem solving help at classzone.com

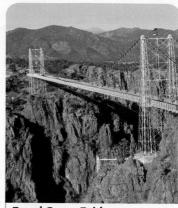

Royal Gorge Bridge

43. ◆ **MULTIPLE CHOICE** Ocean waves can be shallow water, intermediate depth, or deep water waves. The speed s (in meters per second) of a shallow water wave can be modeled by the function $s = 3.13d^{1/2}$ where d is the depth (in meters) of the water over which the wave is traveling. A tsunami is a type of shallow water wave. What is the approximate speed of a tsunami when it is traveling over water 1021 meters deep?

　(A) 32 m/s 　　　**(B)** 100 m/s 　　　**(C)** 150 m/s 　　　**(D)** 215 m/s

California@*HomeTutor* for problem solving help at classzone.com

44. **BIOLOGY** The northern pike, a type of fish, has a length ℓ (in inches) that can be modeled by the function $\ell = (3500w)^{1/3}$ where w is the weight (in pounds) of the fish. Find the approximate length of a northern pike that weighs 4 pounds.

45. **LONG JUMP** A function for the speed at which a long jumper is running before jumping is $s = 10.9h^{1/2}$ where s and h are defined in the diagram. During a jump, the jumper reaches a maximum height of 1.2 meters. To the nearest tenth of a meter per second, approximate her speed before jumping.

h = maximum height (in meters)

s = speed (in meters per second)

46. REASONING Show that $\sqrt[3]{a}$ can be written as $a^{1/3}$ using an argument similar to the one given for square roots on page 499.

47. CHALLENGE Prove that the properties of radicals apply to cube roots.

  a. Product property of radicals: $\sqrt[3]{ab} = \sqrt[3]{a} \cdot \sqrt[3]{b}$

  b. Quotient property of radicals: $\sqrt[3]{\dfrac{a}{b}} = \dfrac{\sqrt[3]{a}}{\sqrt[3]{b}}$ where $b \neq 0$

48. CHALLENGE The amount of time t (in seconds) a clock's pendulum takes to complete one full swing is called the period of the pendulum and is given by the function $t = 2\pi\left(\dfrac{\ell}{32}\right)^{1/2}$ where ℓ is the length (in feet) of the pendulum. Does increasing the length of a pendulum *increase* or *decrease* its period? Give examples to support your answer.

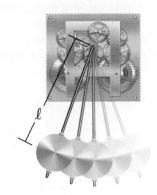

◆ CALIFORNIA STANDARDS SPIRAL REVIEW

Alg. 2.0

49. Which expression is equivalent to $\dfrac{5}{\sqrt{2}} + \dfrac{9}{\sqrt{8}}$? *(p. 483)*

  (A) $\dfrac{7\sqrt{2}}{4}$ **(B)** $\dfrac{19\sqrt{2}}{2}$ **(C)** $\dfrac{19\sqrt{2}}{4}$ **(D)** $\dfrac{29\sqrt{2}}{2}$

Alg. 4.0

50. What is the solution of the inequality $6(x + 2) > 3x - 2$? *(p. 202)*

  (A) $x > -\dfrac{14}{3}$ **(B)** $x < -\dfrac{10}{3}$ **(C)** $x > -7$ **(D)** $x > -\dfrac{1}{2}$

Alg. 15.0

51. A chemist mixes x grams of a 20% saline solution and y grams of a 5% saline solution to make 4.5 grams of a 10% saline solution. What are the values of x and y? *(p. 418)*

  (A) $x = 15$ **(B)** $x = 10$ **(C)** $x = 1.5$ **(D)** $x = 3$
          $y = 10$ $y = 15$ $y = 3$ $y = 1.5$

QUIZ *for Lessons 8.5–8.6*

Find the unknown length. *(p. 491)*

1. 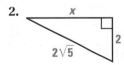   **2.** 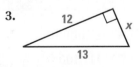   **3.**

Evaluate the expression. *(p. 498)*

4. $10{,}000^{3/2}$ **5.** $8^{-2/3}$ **6.** $64^{4/3}$

7. SAILING The hull speed s (in nautical miles per hour) of a sailboat can be estimated using the formula $s = 1.34\ell^{1/2}$ where ℓ is the length (in feet) of the sailboat's waterline (the line formed by the water along one side of the sailboat). Find the approximate hull speed s (in nautical miles per hour) of a sailboat that has a waterline of about 36 feet. *(p. 498)*

Multiple Choice Practice for Lessons 8.4–8.6

1. A side view of a staircase being built in a house is shown below. What is the approximate distance d between the edges of two consecutive steps? **Gr. 7 MG 3.3**

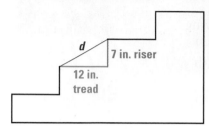

(**A**) 10 in. (**B**) 14 in.

(**C**) 19 in. (**D**) 25 in.

2. For the period 1999–2002, the number y of companies listed on the New York Stock Exchange can be modeled by the function $y = 3018 - 146x^{1/2}$ where x is the number of years since 1999. About how many more companies were listed on the New York Stock Exchange in 1999 than in 2001? **Alg. 2.0**

(**A**) 73 (**B**) 146

(**C**) 206 (**D**) 292

3. Three streets in the downtown area of a city form a right triangle with the lengths shown. What is the approximate area of the triangle? **Gr. 7 MG 3.3**

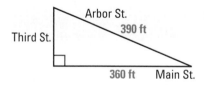

(**A**) 27,000 ft^2 (**B**) 95,500 ft^2

(**C**) 117,100 ft^2 (**D**) 152,100 ft^2

4. During a hiking trip, you walk 2 miles directly east and then 4 miles directly north. If you walk a straight path back to your starting point, about how far will you have to walk? **Gr. 7 MG 3.3**

(**A**) 3.5 mi (**B**) 4.5 mi

(**C**) 6 mi (**D**) 8 mi

5. For the period 1994–2001, the annual consumption y (in pounds per person) of corn products in the United States can be modeled by the function $y = 6.1\sqrt{x} + 158$ where x is the number of years since 1994. About how many pounds of corn products were consumed per person in 1996? **Alg. 2.0**

(**A**) 40 lb (**B**) 80 lb

(**C**) 100 lb (**D**) 240 lb

6. Which expression is equivalent to $\sqrt{3}(5\sqrt{2} + \sqrt{3})$? **Alg. 2.0**

(**A**) $5\sqrt{6} + \sqrt{3}$ (**B**) $5\sqrt{6} + 3$

(**C**) $15\sqrt{6} + \sqrt{3}$ (**D**) $15\sqrt{6} + 3$

7. At the start of a football game, the kicker on one team must kick the ball to the opposing team. To position himself for the starting kick, the kicker places a football on a tee, walks 8 yards behind the tee, then 6 yards to the left. What is the kicker's distance from the football? **Gr. 7 MG 3.3**

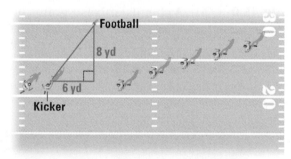

(**A**) 3.5 yd (**B**) 5.5 yd

(**C**) 10 yd (**D**) 14 yd

8. What is the value of $16^{1/2} \cdot 16^{-3/2}$? **Alg. 2.0**

(**A**) -16 (**B**) $-\dfrac{1}{16}$

(**C**) $\dfrac{1}{16}$ (**D**) $\dfrac{1}{8}$

9. Which expression is equivalent to $\sqrt{40x^3yz^2}$? **Alg. 2.0**

(**A**) $2xz\sqrt{10xy}$ (**B**) $2yz\sqrt{20xy}$

(**C**) $4xz\sqrt{10x^2yz}$ (**D**) $4x^2z^2\sqrt{10xy}$

BIG IDEAS
For Your Notebook

Big Idea 1

Applying Properties of Exponents to Simplify Expressions

You can use the properties of exponents to simplify expressions. For the properties listed below, a and b are real numbers, and m and n are rational numbers. (In cases where a fractional exponent has an even denominator, a and b are understood to be nonnegative.)

Property	Name
$a^m \cdot a^n = a^{m+n}$	Product of powers property
$(a^m)^n = a^{mn}$	Power of a power property
$(ab)^m = a^m b^m$	Power of a product property
$\dfrac{a^m}{a^n} = a^{m-n}, a \neq 0$	Quotient of powers property
$\left(\dfrac{a}{b}\right)^m = \dfrac{a^m}{b^m}, b \neq 0$	Power of a quotient property

Big Idea 2

Using Definitions of Exponents to Simplify Expressions

You can use definitions of exponents to simplify expressions.

Type of exponent	Definition	Algebra
Zero exponent	a to the zero power is 1.	$a^0 = 1, a \neq 0$
Negative exponent	a^{-n} is the reciprocal of a^n.	$a^{-n} = \dfrac{1}{a^n}, a \neq 0$
Fractional exponent	$a^{1/2}$ is the positive square root of a.	$a^{1/2} = \sqrt{a}, a \geq 0$
	$a^{1/3}$ is the cube root of a.	$a^{1/3} = \sqrt[3]{a}$

Big Idea 3

Applying Properties of Radicals to Simplify Expressions

You can use the properties of radicals to simplify radical expressions. You can also use radicals to solve problems involving the Pythagorean theorem and the converse of the Pythagorean theorem.

Property	Name
$\sqrt{ab} = \sqrt{a} \cdot \sqrt{b}, a \geq 0$ and $b \geq 0$	Product property of radicals
$\sqrt{\dfrac{a}{b}} = \dfrac{\sqrt{a}}{\sqrt{b}}, a \geq 0$ and $b > 0$	Quotient property of radicals

PROBLEM How can you apply properties of exponents and radicals to compare two stars?

STEP 1 Choose two stars.

Choose two stars from the table below.

Star	Sirius	Capella	Betelgeuse	Aldebaran
Approximate volume (km³)	10^{19}	10^{21}	10^{26}	10^{23}
Apparent magnitude	−1.46	0.08	0.5	0.85

STEP 2 Compare the diameters of the stars.

The diameter d (in kilometers) of a star is given by the formula $d = \sqrt[3]{\dfrac{6V}{\pi}}$

where V is the volume (in cubic kilometers) of the star. Approximate the diameters of the two stars you chose in Step 1 using the volumes of the stars given in the table. How many times greater is the diameter of the bigger star than the diameter of the smaller star?

STEP 3 Compare the apparent magnitudes of the stars.

The *apparent magnitude* of a star is a measure of how bright it looks from Earth. Brightness decreases with an increase in apparent magnitude. A star with magnitude a is 2.5 times brighter than a star with magnitude $a + 1$.

The ratio $\dfrac{2.5^a}{2.5^b}$ compares a star with apparent magnitude a to a star with apparent magnitude b. Rewrite the ratio as a single power of 2.5. Then evaluate the power using the apparent magnitudes of the two stars you chose in Step 1. In the statements below, x represents the value of the power. Use the statements to compare the apparent magnitudes of your chosen stars.

Betelgeuse

Constellation of Orion

- If $a > b$, then the star with apparent magnitude b is x times brighter than the star with apparent magnitude a.

- If $a < b$, then the star with apparent magnitude b is $\dfrac{1}{x}$ times brighter than the star with apparent magnitude a.

Extending the Problem

1. Suppose a star has volume V_1 and another star has volume V_2. Show that the ratio of the diameters of the stars is equal to the cube root of the ratio of the volumes. Use the formula $d = \sqrt[3]{\dfrac{6V}{\pi}}$, but treat $\dfrac{6}{\pi}$ as a constant c and write the formula as $d = \sqrt[3]{cV}$.

California @HomeTutor
classzone.com
• Multi-Language Visual Glossary
• Vocabulary practice

REVIEW KEY VOCABULARY

• order of magnitude, *p. 462*
• zero exponent, *p. 475*
• negative exponent, *p. 475*
• radical expression, *p. 483*

• simplest form of a radical expression, *p. 483*
• rationalizing the denominator, *p. 485*

• hypotenuse, *p. 491*
• legs of a right triangle, *p. 491*
• Pythagorean theorem, *p. 491*
• cube root, *p. 498*

VOCABULARY EXERCISES

1. Which definitions or properties of exponents can be used to simplify $2^{-4} \cdot 2^4$? *Explain.*

2. *Describe* the steps you would take to rationalize the denominator of a radical expression.

3. **NOTETAKING SKILLS** Make a property and examples chart like the one on page 458 for the power of a power property.

REVIEW EXAMPLES AND EXERCISES

Use the review examples and exercises below to check your understanding of the concepts you have learned in each lesson of Chapter 8.

8.1 Apply Exponent Properties Involving Products
pp. 460–466

Alg. 2.0

EXAMPLE

Simplify $(3y^3)^4 \cdot y^5$.

$$(3y^3)^4 \cdot y^5 = 3^4 \cdot (y^3)^4 \cdot y^5 \qquad \text{Power of a product property}$$

$$= 81 \cdot y^{12} \cdot y^5 \qquad \text{Power of a power property}$$

$$= 81y^{17} \qquad \text{Product of powers property}$$

EXERCISES

EXAMPLES
1, 2, 3, 4, 5, and 6
on pp. 460–463
for Exs. 4–13

Simplify the expression.

4. $4^4 \cdot 4^3$

5. $(-3)^7(-3)$

6. $z^3 \cdot z^5 \cdot z^5$

7. $(y^4)^5$

8. $[(-7)^4]^4$

9. $[(b+2)^8]^3$

10. $(6^4 \cdot 31)^5$

11. $-(8xy)^2$

12. $(2x^2)^4 \cdot x^5$

13. **EARTH SCIENCE** The order of magnitude of the mass of Earth's atmosphere is 10^{18} kilograms. The order of magnitude of the mass of Earth's oceans is 10^3 times greater. What is the order of magnitude of the mass of Earth's oceans?

8.2 Apply Exponent Properties Involving Quotients

pp. 467–473

Alg. 2.0

EXAMPLE

Simplify $\left(\dfrac{x^3}{y}\right)^4 \cdot \dfrac{2}{x^5}$.

$$\left(\frac{x^3}{y}\right)^4 \cdot \frac{2}{x^5} = \frac{(x^3)^4}{y^4} \cdot \frac{2}{x^5} \qquad \text{Power of a quotient property}$$

$$= \frac{x^{12}}{y^4} \cdot \frac{2}{x^5} \qquad \text{Power of a power property}$$

$$= \frac{2x^{12}}{y^4 x^5} \qquad \text{Multiply fractions.}$$

$$= \frac{2x^7}{y^4} \qquad \text{Quotient of powers property}$$

EXERCISES

EXAMPLES
1, 2, 3, and 4
on pp. 467–469
for Exs. 14–22

Simplify the expression.

14. $\dfrac{(-3)^7}{(-3)^3}$

15. $\dfrac{5^2 \cdot 5^4}{5^3}$

16. $\left(\dfrac{m}{n}\right)^3$

17. $\dfrac{17^{12}}{17^8}$

18. $\left(-\dfrac{1}{x}\right)^4$

19. $\left(\dfrac{7x^5}{y^2}\right)^2$

20. $\dfrac{1}{p^2} \cdot p^6$

21. $\dfrac{6}{7r^{10}} \cdot \left(\dfrac{r^5}{s}\right)^5$

22. INCOME The order of magnitude of the population of Montana in 2003 was 10^6 people. The order of magnitude of the total personal income (in dollars) for Montana in 2003 was 10^{10}. What was the order of magnitude of the mean personal income in Montana in 2003?

8.3 Define and Use Zero and Negative Exponents

pp. 475–480

Alg. 2.0

EXAMPLE

Evaluate $(4^{-3})^{-1}$.

$$(4^{-3})^{-1} = 4^{-3 \cdot (-1)} \qquad \text{Power of a power property}$$

$$= 4^3 \qquad \text{Multiply exponents.}$$

$$= 64 \qquad \text{Evaluate power.}$$

EXAMPLE

Simplify $(2x^0 y^{-5})^3$.

$$(2x^0 y^{-5})^3 = 2^3 \cdot x^0 \cdot y^{-15} \qquad \text{Power of a power property}$$

$$= 8 \cdot 1 \cdot y^{-15} \qquad \text{Definition of zero exponent}$$

$$= \frac{8}{y^{15}} \qquad \text{Definition of negative exponents}$$

EXERCISES

Evaluate the expression.

23. 14^0

24. 3^{-4}

25. $\left(\dfrac{2}{3}\right)^{-3}$

26. $7^{-5} \cdot 7^5$

Simplify the expression. Write your answer using only positive exponents.

27. $\left(5c^{-3}d\right)^2$

28. $7n^{-2} \cdot 9n^5$

29. $\dfrac{(3m^{-3})^2}{m^{-4}}$

30. $\dfrac{x^2 y}{(2x)^{-3}}$

31. UNITS OF MEASURE Use the fact that 1 femtogram $= 10^{-18}$ kilogram and 1 nanogram $= 10^{-12}$ kilogram to complete the following statement: 1 nanogram $= \underline{?}$ femtogram(s).

8.4 Simplify Radical Expressions

pp. 483–490

Alg. 1.0

EXAMPLE

Simplify $7\sqrt{5} - \sqrt{45}$.

$$7\sqrt{5} - \sqrt{45} = 7\sqrt{5} - \sqrt{9 \cdot 5} \qquad \text{Factor using perfect square factor.}$$

$$= 7\sqrt{5} - \sqrt{9} \cdot \sqrt{5} \qquad \text{Product property of radicals}$$

$$= 7\sqrt{5} - 3\sqrt{5} \qquad \text{Simplify.}$$

$$= (7 - 3)\sqrt{5} \qquad \text{Distributive property}$$

$$= 4\sqrt{5} \qquad \text{Simplify.}$$

EXAMPLE

Simplify $\sqrt{\dfrac{17}{4y^2}}$.

$$\sqrt{\dfrac{17}{4y^2}} = \dfrac{\sqrt{17}}{\sqrt{4y^2}} \qquad \text{Quotient property of radicals}$$

$$= \dfrac{\sqrt{17}}{2y} \qquad \text{Simplify.}$$

EXERCISES

Simplify the expression.

32. $\sqrt{60}$

33. $\sqrt{98}$

34. $\sqrt{121x^3}$

35. $\sqrt{2} \cdot \sqrt{21}$

36. $\sqrt{7x} \cdot 7\sqrt{x}$

37. $\sqrt{x} \cdot 14x\sqrt{x}$

38. $\sqrt{\dfrac{7}{36}}$

39. $\sqrt{\dfrac{5}{x^2}}$

40. $\sqrt{\dfrac{x^4}{25}}$

41. $\dfrac{2}{\sqrt{5}}$

42. $\dfrac{6}{\sqrt{7}}$

43. $\dfrac{x}{\sqrt{3}}$

44. $3\sqrt{2} - \sqrt{128}$

45. $5\sqrt{27} + 4\sqrt{3}$

46. $\sqrt{2}\left(7 - \sqrt{6}\right)$

47. $\sqrt{5}\left(\sqrt{5} + \sqrt{10}\right)$

Apply the Pythagorean Theorem and Its Converse

pp. 491–496

Gr. 7 MG 3.3

EXAMPLE

Find the unknown length for the triangle shown.

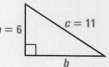

$a^2 + b^2 = c^2$	Pythagorean theorem
$6^2 + b^2 = 11^2$	Substitute 6 for a and 11 for c.
$36 + b^2 = 121$	Simplify.
$b^2 = 85$	Subtract 36 from each side.
$b = \sqrt{85}$	Take positive square root of each side.

EXERCISES

EXAMPLES
1 and 3
on pp. 491–492
for Exs. 48–54

Let a and b represent the lengths of the legs of a right triangle, and let c represent the length of the hypotenuse. Find the unknown length.

48. $a = 7$, $b = 13$ **49.** $a = 10$, $c = 21$ **50.** $a = 8$, $c = 11$

51. $a = 9$, $b = 17$ **52.** $b = 4$, $c = 15$ **53.** $b = 6$, $c = 6.5$

54. REFLECTING POOL The Reflecting Pool in front of the Lincoln Memorial in Washington, D.C., is rectangular with a length of 2029 feet and a width of 167 feet. To the nearest foot, what is the length of a diagonal of the Reflecting Pool?

Use Cube Roots and Fractional Exponents

pp. 498–503

Alg. 2.0

EXAMPLE

Simplify $\dfrac{\sqrt[3]{4} \cdot 4^{2/3}}{4}$.

$\dfrac{\sqrt[3]{4} \cdot 4^{2/3}}{4} = \dfrac{4^{1/3} \cdot 4^{2/3}}{4}$	Rewrite $\sqrt[3]{4}$ as $4^{1/3}$.
$= \dfrac{4}{4}$	Product of powers property
$= 1$	Simplify.

EXERCISES

EXAMPLES
1, 3, 4, 5, and 6
on pp. 498–500
for Exs. 55–59

Simplify the expression.

55. $\sqrt[3]{1728}$ **56.** $9^{-3/2}$ **57.** $y^{7/2} \cdot y^{-7/2}$ **58.** $\left(\dfrac{1}{8}\right)^{1/3}\left(\dfrac{1}{36}\right)^{1/2}$

59. FOOD The amount of consumption y (in pounds per person) of mozzarella cheese in the United States for the period 1980–2001 can be modeled by $y = 2(x + 1)^{1/2}$ where x is the number of years since 1980. About how many pounds of mozzarella cheese were consumed per person in 1996?

1. **VOCABULARY** Copy and complete: In a right triangle, the side opposite the right angle is called the __?__.

2. **VOCABULARY** Copy and complete: The process of eliminating a radical from the denominator of a radical expression is called __?__.

Simplify the expression. Write your answer using exponents.

3. $(-3)(-3)^6$

4. $(8^4)^3$

5. $[(-4)^3]^2$

6. $\dfrac{2^{15}}{2^8}$

Simplify the expression.

7. $t^2 \cdot t^6$

8. $\left(\dfrac{s}{t}\right)^6$

9. $\dfrac{1}{9^{-2}}$

10. $-(6p)^2$

11. $(5xy)^2$

12. $\dfrac{1}{z^7} \cdot z^9$

13. $(x^5)^3$

14. $\left(-\dfrac{4}{c}\right)^2$

Simplify the expression. Write your answer using only positive exponents.

15. $\left(\dfrac{a^{-3}}{3b}\right)^4$

16. $\dfrac{3}{4d} \cdot \dfrac{(2d)^4}{c^3}$

17. $y^0 \cdot (8x^6y^{-3})^{-2}$

18. $(5r^5)^3 \cdot r^{-2}$

Simplify the expression.

19. $2\sqrt{5} + \sqrt{45}$

20. $7\sqrt{6} - 2\sqrt{2} + \sqrt{24}$

21. $\sqrt{3}(7 - \sqrt{15})$

22. $(8 - \sqrt{7})(1 + \sqrt{7})$

23. $\sqrt[3]{8} + \sqrt[3]{-512}$

24. $64^{4/3} \cdot 64^{-3/2}$

25. $(72m^6)^{-1/2}$

26. $(8z^3)^{1/2} \cdot (6z^3)^{1/2}$

27. $\dfrac{\sqrt{20}}{(27n^3)^{1/3}}$

Find the unknown length. Round your answer to the nearest tenth, if necessary.

28.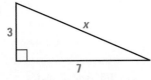

29.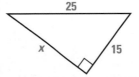

30.

Tell whether the triangle with the given side lengths is a right triangle.

31. 8, 16, 20

32. 11, 60, 61

33. 7.5, 10, 12.5

34. **BIRD HOUSES** The front view of a bird house is shown. Find the height of the bird house to the nearest tenth of an inch.

35. **LIFE EXPECTANCY** For the period 1900–2000, the life expectancy at birth e (in years) for people born in the United States can be modeled by the function $e = 3.66t^{1/2} + 40.6$ where t is the number of years since 1900. Find the life expectancy at birth to the nearest year for a person born in 1994.

STRATEGIES YOU'LL USE:
- SOLVE DIRECTLY
- ELIMINATE CHOICES

Standards
Alg. 2.0

If you have difficulty solving a multiple choice problem directly, you may be able to use another approach to eliminate incorrect answer choices and obtain the correct answer.

PROBLEM 1

The order of magnitude of the distance from the sun to Earth is 10^8 kilometers. The order of magnitude of the speed of light is 10^9 kilometers per hour. About how long does light from the sun take to travel to Earth?

(A) 10^{17} h   (B) 10 h   (C) 1 h   (D) 10^{-1} h

Strategy 1 SOLVE DIRECTLY

To find the time light from the sun takes to travel to Earth, divide the distance from the sun to Earth by the speed of light.

$$\frac{\text{Distance (km)}}{\text{Speed (km/h)}} = \frac{10^8}{10^9} = 10^{-1}$$

The time is about 10^{-1} hour.

The correct answer is D. (A) (B) (C) (D)

Strategy 2 ELIMINATE CHOICES

You can eliminate answer choices by using number sense and reasoning.

The speed of light is 10^9 kilometers per hour. Because light travels more than 10^8 kilometers in one hour, the time light takes to travel 10^8 kilometers is *less* than one hour. The only answer choice that is less than 1 hour is choice D.

The correct answer is D. (A) (B) (C) (D)

PROBLEM 2

The edge length s of a cube with a volume of V is given by $s = V^{1/3}$. What is the edge length of a cube with a volume of 729 cubic feet?

(A) 3 ft   (B) 9 ft   (C) 27 ft   (D) 30 ft

Strategy 1 SOLVE DIRECTLY

Substitute 729 for V in the given formula.

$$s = V^{1/3} = 729^{1/3} = \left(9^3\right)^{1/3} = 9$$

The edge length is 9 feet.

The correct answer is B. (A) (B) (C) (D)

Strategy 2 ELIMINATE CHOICES

Because the edge length is the cube root of the volume, the volume is the cube of the edge length. Compare the cube of each edge length with the volume.

Choice A, 3 ft: $3^3 = 27$ ✗

Choice B, 9 ft: $9^3 = 729$ ✓

The correct answer is B. (A) (B) (C) (D)

PROBLEM 3

Which expression is equivalent to $(10a^2)^2 \cdot a^2$?

(A) $100a^6$ **(B)** $10a^8$ **(C)** $10a^6$ **(D)** $100a^4$

Strategy 1   SOLVE DIRECTLY

Simplify the expression using properties of exponents.

$$(10a^2)^2 \cdot a^2 = 10^2 \cdot (a^2)^2 \cdot a^2$$
$$= 100 \cdot a^4 \cdot a^2$$
$$= 100a^6$$

The correct answer is A. **(A)** (B) (C) (D)

Strategy 2   ELIMINATE CHOICES

You can compare values to eliminate some choices.

STEP 1 **Assign** a value to a, such as $a = 2$, and evaluate the given expression:

$$(10a^2)^2 \cdot a^2 = (10 \cdot 2^2)^2 \cdot 2^2$$
$$= (10 \cdot 4)^2 \cdot 2^2$$
$$= 40^2 \cdot 2^2$$
$$= 6400$$

STEP 2 **Evaluate** the expression in each answer choice when $a = 2$. Compare each answer with 6400.

Choice A: $100a^6 = 100 \cdot 2^6$
$$= 100 \cdot 64$$
$$= 6400$$

The correct answer is A. **(A)** (B) (C) (D)

STRATEGY PRACTICE

Explain why you can eliminate the highlighted answer choice.

1. What is the value of $\left(\frac{4}{5}\right)^0$?

    (A) $-\frac{4}{5}$ **(B)** 0 **(C)** $\frac{4}{5}$ **(D)** 1

2. Which expression is equivalent to $\sqrt{20} + 6\sqrt{5}$?

    (A) $8\sqrt{5}$ **(B)** $10\sqrt{5}$ **(C)** ✗ 30 **(D)** $8\sqrt{15}$

3. What is the length of the hypotenuse of the right triangle shown?

    (A) 12 **(B)** 18

    (C) 24 **(D)** 30

1. Which expression is *not* equivalent to $\left(\dfrac{4x^6}{x^5}\right)^3$?

Alg. 2.0

Ⓐ $x(4x)^3$

Ⓑ $8x \cdot 8x^2$

Ⓒ $\left(\dfrac{4x^8}{x^7}\right)^3$

Ⓓ $\left(\dfrac{4x^6}{x^5}\right)^2 \cdot \dfrac{4x^4}{x^3}$

2. The order of magnitude of the mass and the volume of Europa, one of Jupiter's moons, is shown below.

Europa

Mass ≈ 10^{22} kg
Volume ≈ 10^{19} m³

The density d (in kilograms per cubic meter) of an object is given by the formula $d = \dfrac{m}{V}$ where m is the mass (in kilograms) and V is the volume (in cubic meters). What is the approximate density of Europa? **Alg. 2.0**

Ⓐ $10\,\text{kg/m}^3$

Ⓑ $10^3\,\text{kg/m}^3$

Ⓒ $10^6\,\text{kg/m}^3$

Ⓓ $10^{41}\,\text{kg/m}^3$

3. Which expression is equivalent to $\sqrt{\dfrac{11}{81y^2}}$?

Alg. 2.0

Ⓐ $\dfrac{y\sqrt{11}}{81}$

Ⓑ $\dfrac{\sqrt{11}}{9y^2}$

Ⓒ $9y$

Ⓓ $\dfrac{\sqrt{11}}{9y}$

4. A ferry travels from Shore City to Tern Island and then to Gull Island before returning to Shore City, as shown. The distance between consecutive grid lines represents 1 mile. What is the distance from Gull Island to Shore City? **Gr. 7 MG 3.3**

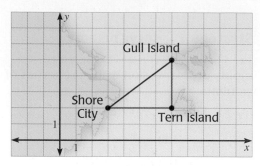

Ⓐ 4 mi

Ⓑ 5 mi

Ⓒ 6 mi

Ⓓ 7 mi

5. Which expression serves as a counterexample to the statement "The set of irrational numbers is closed under division"? **Alg. 1.0**

Ⓐ $\sqrt{3} \div \sqrt{2}$

Ⓑ $\sqrt{14} \div \sqrt{7}$

Ⓒ $4\sqrt{3} \div \sqrt{3}$

Ⓓ $5\sqrt{10} \div 5\sqrt{2}$

6. For the period 1920–2000, the annual banana consumption y (in pounds per person) in the United States can be modeled by the function

$$y = (18x + 272)^{1/2}$$

where x is the number of years since 1970. About how many pounds of bananas were consumed per person in 1977? **Alg. 2.0**

Ⓐ 10

Ⓑ 15

Ⓒ 20

Ⓓ 25

7. For an experiment, a scientist dropped a spoonful, or about 10^{-1} cubic inch, of biodegradable olive oil into a pond to see how the oil would spread over the surface of the pond. The scientist found that the oil spread until it covered an area of about 10^5 square inches. About how deep was the layer of oil that spread across the pond? **Alg. 2.0**

(A) 10^{-6} in.

(B) 10^{-4} in.

(C) 10^4 in.

(D) 10^6 in.

8. Which expression is equivalent to $\dfrac{1}{(6x^{-3})^3}$?

Alg. 2.0

(A) $216x^9$

(B) $\dfrac{x^9}{216}$

(C) $6x^9$

(D) $\dfrac{216}{x^9}$

9. A map of a town is shown. The distance between consecutive grid lines is 1 mile. A student rides his bike from the school to the theater. From the theater, the student rides his bike to the library. The student decides to ride his bike back to school. About how far does he ride his bike altogether?

Gr. 7 MG 3.3

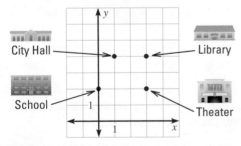

(A) 7.2 mi

(B) 8.6 mi

(C) 10 mi

(D) 18 mi

In Exercises 10–12, use the table below, which shows units of length and the number of meters in each unit.

Unit	Meters
Kilometer	10^3
Centimeter	10^{-2}
Millimeter	10^{-3}
Nanometer	10^{-9}

10. How many millimeters are in 1 kilometer? **Alg. 2.0**

(A) 1 mm

(B) 20 mm

(C) 10^3 mm

(D) 10^6 mm

11. How many nanometers (nm) are in 1 centimeter? **Alg. 2.0**

(A) 10^{-11} nm

(B) 10^{-7} nm

(C) 10^7 nm

(D) 10^{18} nm

12. A micrometer is 10^3 times greater than a nanometer. How many meters are in a micrometer? **Alg. 2.0**

(A) 10^{-27} m

(B) 10^{-12} m

(C) 10^{-6} m

(D) 10^6 m

13. The voltage V (in volts) of an amplifier is given by the function $V = (PR)^{1/2}$ where P is the power (in watts) and R is the resistance (in ohms). Your amplifier produces 25 watts and has a resistance of 4 ohms. What is the voltage of your amplifier? **Alg. 2.0**

(A) 5 volts

(B) 10 volts

(C) 15 volts

(D) 20 volts

Polynomials and Factoring

Before

In previous chapters, you learned the following skills, which you'll use in Chapter 9:
- Using the distributive property
- Combining like terms
- Using the properties of exponents

Now

In Chapter 9 you'll study these **Big Ideas:**

1 Adding, subtracting, multiplying, and dividing polynomials

2 Factoring polynomials

3 Writing and solving polynomial equations to solve problems

Why?

So you can solve real-world problems about . . .

- Baseball, p. 525
- Video games, p. 538
- DVD rentals, p. 546
- Penguins, p. 553
- Construction, p. 561
- Jumping robots, p. 585

 **Algebra** at *classzone.com*

Get-Ready Games

PAIRING *for* PRODUCTS

California Standards

Review using the rules of exponents. **Alg 2.0**
Prepare for multiplying polynomials. **Alg 10.0**

Materials

- One deck of factor cards
- One deck of product cards

Product Cards xy^2 x^5 xy^3 y^6 x^2y^2

Factor Cards x^3

How to Play Play in pairs. Shuffle the factor cards and deal three cards to each player. Players do not show each other their cards.

Place the remaining factor cards face down in a *draw* pile that both players can reach. Turn over the top card and place it face up next to the draw pile to start a *discard* pile.

Place one set of five product cards face up so that both players can read them. Players should take turns following the steps on the next page.

CALIFORNIA STANDARDS

- **Alg. 10.0** Students add, subtract, multiply, and divide monomials and polynomials. Students solve multistep problems, including word problems, by using these techniques. *(Lessons 9.1, 9.2, 9.3, 9.4)*

- **Alg. 14.0** Students solve a quadratic equation by factoring or completing the square. *(Lessons 9.5, 9.6, 9.7, 9.8, 9.9)*

1 **Draw** the top card from either the draw pile or the discard pile.

2 **Decide** whether you can multiply exactly two of your factor cards to form a displayed product. If so, take the displayed product card and place it in front of you with the correct pair of factors.

3 **Discard** a card from your hand if you were unable to form a displayed product. If you were able to form a displayed product, then draw one card so that you have three in your hand. Also, replace the product card that you took with one from the deck.

Games Wrap-Up

How To Win Be the first player to collect three product cards.

Draw Conclusions

Complete these exercises after playing the game.

1. **WRITING** Based on the factor cards you saw as you played *Pairing for Products*, which product card do you think is easier to find a factor pair for, xy^3 or xy^4? *Explain* your reasoning.

2. **REASONING** *Explain* how you decided which cards to discard in *Pairing for Products*.

Prerequisite Skills

California @HomeTutor
Prerequisite skills practice
at classzone.com

REVIEW VOCABULARY

- exponent, *p. 6*
- distributive property, *p. 81*
- like terms, *p. 82*
- quotient, *p. 783*
- remainder, *p. 783*
- greatest common factor, *p. 785*

VOCABULARY CHECK

Copy and complete the statement.

1. Terms that have identical variable parts with corresponding variables raised to the same power are called __?__.

2. A whole number that has a(n) __?__ of 0 when divided by 2 is called even.

SKILLS CHECK

Find the quotient and remainder. Check your answer. *(Review p. 783 for 9.4.)*

3. $518 \div 4$ 4. $213 \div 7$ 5. $891 \div 8$ 6. $649 \div 5$

Find the greatest common factor of the pair of numbers. *(Review p. 784 for 9.5.)*

7. $121, 77$ 8. $96, 32$ 9. $81, 42$ 10. $12, 56$

Simplify the expression. *(Review p. 81 for 9.1–9.9.)*

11. $3x + (-6x)$ 12. $5 + 4x + 2$ 13. $4(2x - 1) + x$ 14. $-(x + 4) - 6x$

Simplify the expression. *(Review p. 460 for 9.2–9.9.)*

15. $(3xy)^3$ 16. $xy^2 \cdot xy^3$ 17. $(x^5)^3$ 18. $(-x)^3$

Tell whether the number is even or odd. Then write it in the form $2q$ or $2q + 1$. *(Review p. 783 for 9.9.)*

19. 79 20. 241 21. 52 22. 138

Notetaking Skills

NOW YOU TRY
Make an *information wheel* for the methods of solving a system of linear equations. You may want to use colored pencils.

Focus on Graphic Organizers

You can use an *information wheel* to organize ideas that relate to the same topic, such as methods of graphing linear equations.

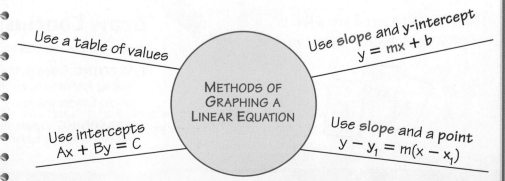

Use a table of values

Use slope and y-intercept
$y = mx + b$

METHODS OF GRAPHING A LINEAR EQUATION

Use intercepts
$Ax + By = C$

Use slope and a point
$y - y_1 = m(x - x_1)$

9.1 Addition with Algebra Tiles

MATERIALS • algebra tiles

Standards

Alg. 10.0 Students add, subtract, multiply, and divide monomials and **polynomials.** Students solve multistep problems, including word problems, by using these techniques.

QUESTION How can you add polynomials using algebra tiles?

A *monomial* is a number, a variable with a positive integer exponent, or the product of a number and one or more variables with positive integer exponents. A *polynomial* is a monomial or a sum of monomials. You can use the following algebra tiles to model polynomials.

Positive 1-tile	Negative 1-tile	Positive x-tile	Negative x-tile	Positive x^2-tile
+	−	+	−	+

EXPLORE Add polynomials

Find the sum of $2x^2 + x + 5$ and $x^2 + 3x - 4$ using algebra tiles.

STEP 1 *Model the polynomials*

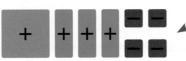

$2x^2 + x + 5$ $x^2 + 3x - 4$

> Think of $x^2 + 3x - 4$ as $x^2 + 3x + (-4)$, so you need 4 negative 1-tiles.

STEP 2 *Add the polynomials*

To add the polynomials, combine like terms. Group the x^2-tiles, the x-tiles, and the 1-tiles.

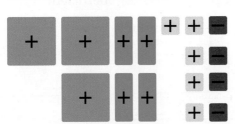

STEP 3 *Simplify the sum*

Remove all pairs of positive and negative tiles. The sum is $3x^2 + 4x + 1$.

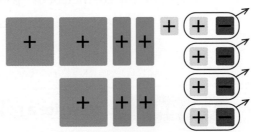

DRAW CONCLUSIONS Use your observations to complete these exercises

Find the sum using algebra tiles.

1. $(x + 2) + (3x - 1)$ 2. $(x^2 + 4x + 1) + (x^2 + x + 2)$

3. $(x^2 - 6x - 8) + (2x^2 + 7x + 2)$ 4. $(3x^2 + 4) + (2x^2 - 4x)$

5. **REASONING** Use what you know about the distributive property to explain how to use algebra tiles to find the *difference* of $x^2 - x + 1$ and $-3x^2 + 5x - 1$. Then check your answer using addition.

9.1 Add and Subtract Polynomials

Standards **Alg. 10.0** Students add, subtract, multiply, and divide **monomials and polynomials. Students solve multistep problems, including word problems, by using these techniques.**

Connect *Before* you added and subtracted integers. *Now* you will add and subtract polynomials.

Math and **RECREATION**
Ex. 44, p. 524

Key Vocabulary
• **monomial**
• **degree**
• **polynomial**
• **leading coefficient**
• **binomial**
• **trinomial**

A **monomial** is a number, a variable with a positive integer exponent, or the product of a number and one or more variables with positive integer exponents. The **degree of a monomial** is the sum of the exponents of the variables in the monomial. The degree of a nonzero constant term is 0. The constant 0 does not have a degree.

Monomial	Degree
10	0
$3x$	1
$\frac{1}{2}ab^2$	$1 + 2 = 3$
$-1.8m^5$	5

Not a monomial	Reason
$5 + x$	A sum is not a monomial.
$\frac{2}{n}$	A monomial cannot have a variable in the denominator.
4^a	A monomial cannot have a variable exponent.
x^{-1}	The variable must have a positive integer exponent.

A **polynomial** is a monomial or a sum of monomials, each called a *term* of the polynomial. The **degree of a polynomial** is the greatest degree of its terms.

When a polynomial is written so that the exponents of a variable decrease from left to right, the coefficient of the first term is called the **leading coefficient**.

leading coefficient ⟶ degree ⟶ constant term

$$2x^3 + x^2 - 5x + 12$$

EXAMPLE 1 Rewrite a polynomial

Write $15x - x^3 + 3$ so that the exponents decrease from left to right. Identify the degree and leading coefficient of the polynomial.

Solution

The polynomial can be written as $-x^3 + 15x + 3$. The table shows the degree of each term. The greatest degree is 3, so the degree of the polynomial is 3, and the leading coefficient is -1.

Term	$-x^3$	$15x$	3
Degree	3	1	0

BINOMIALS AND TRINOMIALS A polynomial with two terms is called a **binomial**. A polynomial with three terms is called a **trinomial**.

EXAMPLE 2 Identify and classify polynomials

Tell whether the expression is a polynomial. If it is a polynomial, find its degree and classify it by the number of its terms. Otherwise, tell why it is not a polynomial.

	Expression	Is it a polynomial?	Classify by degree and number of terms
a.	9	Yes	0 degree monomial
b.	$2x^2 + x - 5$	Yes	2nd degree trinomial
c.	$6n^4 - 8^n$	No; variable exponent	
d.	$n^{-2} - 3$	No; negative exponent	
e.	$7bc^3 + 4b^4c$	Yes	5th degree binomial

EXAMPLE 3 Add and subtract monomials

Find the sum or difference.

a. $-3b^2 + 7b^2 = 4b^2$ **Combine like terms.**

b. $2xy - 5xy = 2xy + (-5xy)$ **Rewrite as a sum.**

$\qquad\qquad = -3xy$ **Combine like terms.**

EXAMPLE 4 Add polynomials

Animated Algebra

For an interactive example of adding polynomials, go to **classzone.com**.

Find the sum $(3x^2 + x - 6) + (x^2 + 4x + 10)$.

Solution

Group like terms and simplify.

$$(3x^2 + x - 6) + (x^2 + 4x + 10) = (3x^2 + x^2) + (x + 4x) + (-6 + 10)$$
$$= 4x^2 + 5x + 4$$

✓ **GUIDED PRACTICE** for Examples 1, 2, 3, and 4

1. Write $5y - 2y^2 + 9$ so that the exponents decrease from left to right. Identify the degree and leading coefficient of the polynomial.

2. Tell whether $y^3 - 4y + 3$ is a polynomial. If it is a polynomial, find its degree and classify it by the number of its terms. Otherwise, tell why it is not a polynomial.

Find the sum or difference.

3. $2x^2 + 4x^2$ 4. $2ab^2 - 7ab^2$ 5. $(5x^3 + 4x - 2x) + (4x^2 + 3x^3 - 6)$

SUBTRACTING POLYNOMIALS To subtract a polynomial, add its opposite. To find the opposite of a polynomial, multiply each of its terms by -1.

EXAMPLE 5 ◆ **Multiple Choice Practice**

ANOTHER WAY
You can also use a vertical format:
$$4x^2 - 3x + 5$$
$$- (3x^2 - x - 8)$$
Rewrite as a sum and add:
$$4x^2 - 3x + 5$$
$$+ (-3x^2 + x + 8)$$
$$\overline{\quad x^2 - 2x + 13}$$

$(4x^2 - 3x + 5) - (3x^2 - x - 8) =$

Ⓐ $x^2 - 4x - 3$ Ⓑ $x^2 - 2x - 3$ Ⓒ $x^2 - 2x + 13$ Ⓓ $x^2 - 4x + 13$

Solution

$(4x^2 - 3x + 5) - (3x^2 - x - 8) = 4x^2 - 3x + 5 - 3x^2 + x + 8$
$$= (4x^2 - 3x^2) + (-3x + x) + (5 + 8)$$
$$= x^2 - 2x + 13$$

▶ The correct answer is C. Ⓐ Ⓑ ● Ⓓ

EXAMPLE 6 **Solve a multi-step problem**

BASEBALL ATTENDANCE Major League Baseball teams are divided into two leagues. During the period 1995–2001, the attendance N and A (in thousands) at National and American League baseball games, respectively, can be modeled by

$N = -488t^2 + 5430t + 24{,}700$ and

$A = -318t^2 + 3040t + 25{,}600$

where t is the number of years since 1995. About how many people attended Major League Baseball games in 2001?

Dodger Stadium, Los Angeles

Solution

STEP 1 **Add** the models for the attendance in each league to find a model for M, the total attendance (in thousands).

$$M = (-488t^2 + 5430t + 24{,}700) + (-318t^2 + 3040t + 25{,}600)$$
$$= (-488t^2 - 318t^2) + (5430t + 3040t) + (24{,}700 + 25{,}600)$$
$$= -806t^2 + 8470t + 50{,}300$$

STEP 2 **Substitute** 6 for t in the model, because 2001 is 6 years after 1995.

$$M = -806(6)^2 + 8470(6) + 50{,}300 \approx 72{,}100$$

▶ About 72,100,000 people attended Major League Baseball games in 2001.

AVOID ERRORS
Because a value of M represents *thousands* of people, $M \approx 72{,}100$ represents about 72,100,000 people.

✓ **GUIDED PRACTICE** for Examples 5 and 6

6. Find the difference $(4x^2 - 7x) - (5x^2 + 4x - 9)$.

7. BASEBALL ATTENDANCE Look back at Example 6. Find the difference in attendance at National and American League baseball games in 2001.

9.1 EXERCISES

SKILLS • PROBLEM SOLVING • REASONING

1. **VOCABULARY** Copy and complete: A(n) __?__ is a number, a variable with a positive integer exponent, or the product of one or more variables with positive integer exponents.

2. **WRITING** Is 6 a polynomial? *Explain* why or why not.

EXAMPLE 1
on p. 520
for Exs. 3–9

REWRITING POLYNOMIALS Write the polynomial so that the exponents decrease from left to right. Identify the degree and leading coefficient of the polynomial.

3. $9m^5$

4. $2 - 6y$

5. $2x^2y^2 - 8xy$

6. $5n^3 + 2n - 7$

7. $5z + 2z^3 - z^2 + 3z^4$

8. $-2h^2 + 2h^4 - h^6$

9. ◆ **MULTIPLE CHOICE** What is the degree of $-4x^3 + 6x^4 - 1$?

Ⓐ -4 Ⓑ 3 Ⓒ 4 Ⓓ 6

EXAMPLE 2
on p. 521
for Exs. 10–16

10. ◆ **MULTIPLE CHOICE** Which expression is *not* a monomial?

Ⓐ $-5x^2$ Ⓑ $0.2y^4$ Ⓒ $3mn$ Ⓓ $3s^{-2}$

IDENTIFYING AND CLASSIFYING POLYNOMIALS Tell whether the expression is a polynomial. If it is a polynomial, find its degree and classify it by the number of its terms. Otherwise, tell why it is not a polynomial.

11. -4^x

12. $w^{-3} + 1$

13. $3x - 5$

14. $\frac{4}{5}f^2 - \frac{1}{2}f + \frac{2}{3}$

15. $6 - n^2 + 5n^3$

16. $10y^4 - 3y^2 + 11$

EXAMPLES 3, 4, and 5
on pp. 521–522
for Exs. 17–32

ADDING AND SUBTRACTING POLYNOMIALS Find the sum or difference.

17. $8b - 5b$

18. $14cd - 23cd$

19. $4z^5 + 9z^5$

20. $-2x^2y + 5x^2y$

21. $(5a^2 - 3) + (8a^2 - 1)$

22. $(h^2 + 4h - 4) + (5h^2 - 8h + 2)$

23. $(4m^2 - m + 2) + (-3m^2 + 10m + 7)$

24. $(7k^2 + 2k - 6) + (3k^2 - 11k - 8)$

25. $(6c^2 + 3c + 9) - (3c - 5)$

26. $(3x^2 - 8) - (4x^3 + x^2 - 15x + 1)$

27. $(-n^2 + 2n) - (2n^3 - n^2 + n + 12)$

28. $(9b^3 - 13b^2 + b) - (-13b^2 - 5b + 14)$

29. $(4d - 6d^3 + 3d^2) - (9d^3 + 7d - 2)$

30. $(9p^2 - 6p^3 + 3 - 11p) + (7p^3 - 3p^2 + 4)$

ERROR ANALYSIS *Describe* and correct the error in finding the sum or difference of the polynomials.

31.
$$x^3 - 4x^2 + 3$$
$$+ \ (-3x^3 + 8x - 2)$$
$$\overline{-2x^3 + 4x^2 + 1}$$

32.
$$(6x^2 - 5x) - (2x^2 + 3x - 2)$$
$$= (6x^2 - 2x^2) + (-5x + 3x) - 2$$
$$= 4x^2 - 2x - 2$$

33. REASONING Suppose the degree of each of two polynomials is *d*. Can you conclude that the degree of the sum or difference of the polynomials is also *d*? *Explain.*

GEOMETRY **Write a polynomial that represents the perimeter of the figure.**

34.
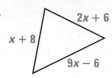

35.
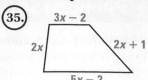

ADDING AND SUBTRACTING POLYNOMIALS **Find the sum or difference.**

36. $(3r^2s + 5rs + 3) + (-8rs^2 - 9rs - 12)$

37. $(x^2 + 11xy - 3y^2) + (-2x^2 - xy + 4y^2)$

38. $(5mn + 3m - 9n) - (13mn + 2m)$

39. $(8a^2b - 6a) - (2a^2b - 4b + 19)$

CONNECT SKILLS TO PROBLEM SOLVING **Exercises 40–43 will help you prepare for problem solving.**

Use the following information: The population of a city is 50,000 and is growing at a rate of 1200 people per year. The population of the city's suburbs is 30,000 and is growing at a rate of 800 people per year.

40. Write an expression for the population of the city *t* years from now.

41. Write an expression for the population of the city's suburbs *t* years from now.

42. Write an expression for the sum of the combined population of the city and its suburbs *t* years from now.

43. Write an expression for the difference of the populations of the city and its suburbs *t* years from now.

EXAMPLE 6
on p. 522
for Exs. 44–45

44. BACKPACKING AND CAMPING During the period 1992–2002, the participation *B* (in millions of people) in backpacking and the participation *C* (in millions of people) in camping can be modeled by

$$B = -0.0262t^3 + 0.376t^2 - 0.574t + 9.67 \text{ and}$$
$$C = -0.0182t^3 + 0.522t^2 - 2.59t + 47$$

where *t* is the number of years since 1992. About how many more people camped than backpacked in 2002?

California **@HomeTutor** for problem solving help at classzone.com

About 55.1 million
people camped in 2002.

45. ◆ **MULTIPLE CHOICE** During the period 1990–2002, the average costs *D* (in dollars) for a new domestic car and the average costs *I* (in dollars) for a new imported car can be modeled by

$$D = 442.14t + 14{,}433 \quad \text{and} \quad I = -137.63t^2 + 2705.2t + 15{,}111$$

where *t* is the number of years since 1990. What is the difference in average costs for a new imported car and a new domestic car in 2002?

A −$8016   **B** $8016   **C** $36,882   **D** $47,493

California **@HomeTutor** for problem solving help at classzone.com

46. **BASEBALL** The award for the best pitchers in baseball is named after the pitcher Cy Young. During the period 1890–1911, the total number of Cy Young's wins W and losses L can be modeled by

$$W = -0.44t^2 + 34t + 4.7 \quad \text{and} \quad L = 15t + 15$$

where t is the number of years since 1890.

Eric Gagne with the Cy Young Award

a. A game credited to a pitcher as a win or a loss is called a decision. Write an equation that models the number of decisions for Cy Young as a function of the number of years since 1890.

b. Cy Young's career in Major League Baseball lasted from 1890 to 1911. Approximately how many total decisions did Cy Young have during his career?

c. About what percent of the decisions in Cy Young's career were wins? *Explain* how you found your answer.

47. **CHALLENGE** Consider any integer x. The next consecutive integer can be represented by the binomial $(x + 1)$.

a. Write a polynomial for the sum of any two consecutive integers.

b. *Explain* how you can be sure that the sum of two consecutive integers is always odd. Use the polynomial from part (a) in your explanation.

48. **CHALLENGE** During the period 1985–2012, the projected enrollment B (in thousands of students) in public schools and the projected enrollment R (in thousands of students) in private schools can be modeled by

$$B = -18.53t^2 + 975.8t + 48{,}140 \quad \text{and} \quad R = 80.8t + 8049$$

where t is the number of years since 1985. Write an equation that models the *percent* of the total projected enrollment that is expected to enroll in public schools as a function of the number of years since 1985.

◆ CALIFORNIA STANDARDS SPIRAL REVIEW

Alg. 1.1

49. Which set of numbers is closed under multiplication? *(p. 74)*

   Ⓐ Negative real numbers   Ⓑ Negative integers

   Ⓒ Irrational numbers   Ⓓ Integers

Alg. 2.0

50. What is the value of $36^{1/2}$? *(p. 498)*

   Ⓐ 6   Ⓑ 12   Ⓒ 18   Ⓓ 54

Alg. 15.0

51. Flying against the wind, a plane takes 6 hours to travel 4200 kilometers. The return flight takes 5 hours. The speed of the wind remains constant during the entire trip. What is the speed of the wind? *(p. 413)*

   Ⓐ 70 km/h   Ⓑ 700 km/h

   Ⓒ 770 km/h   Ⓓ 840 km/h

Alg. 4.0

52. Which equation is equivalent to $3(6 - 4x) = 5 - 8(1 - 2x)$? *(p. 146)*

   Ⓐ $6x = 21$ Ⓑ $6x = 31$ Ⓒ $28x = 21$ Ⓓ $28x = 31$

9.1 Graph Polynomial Functions

Standards

Alg. 10.0 Students **add**, **subtract**, multiply, and divide monomials and **polynomials**. Students solve multistep problems, including word problems, by using these techniques.

QUESTION How can you use a graph to check your work with polynomials?

EXAMPLE Check a sum or difference of polynomials

Tell whether the sum or difference is correct.

a. $(x^2 - 2x + 3) + (2x^2 + 4x - 5) \overset{?}{=} 3x^2 + 2x - 2$

b. $(x^3 + x + 1) - (5x^3 - 2x + 7) \overset{?}{=} -4x^3 - x - 6$

STEP 1 *Enter expressions*

Let y_1 equal the original expression.
Let y_2 equal the sum.

STEP 2 *Graph expressions*

For y_1, choose a normal graph style.
For y_2, choose a thicker graph style.

a.

a.

b.

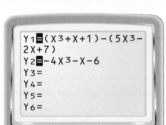

b.

STEP 3 *Analyze graphs*

a. The thick curve coincides with the thin curve, so the sum is correct.

b. The thick curve deviates from the thin curve, so the difference is incorrect.

PRACTICE

Find the sum or difference. Use a graphing calculator to check your answer.

1. $(6x^2 + 4x - 1) + (x^2 - 2x + 2)$ **2.** $(3x^2 - 2x + 1) - (4x^2 - 5x + 1)$

Tell whether the sum or difference is correct. Correct any incorrect answers.

3. $(3x^2 - 2x + 4) + (-x^2 + 3x + 2) \overset{?}{=} 2x^2 + x + 6$

4. $(-4x^2 - 5x - 1) - (-5x^2 + 6x + 3) \overset{?}{=} -9x^2 + x + 2$

9.2 Multiplication with Algebra Tiles

MATERIALS · algebra tiles

Standards

Alg. 10.0 Students add, subtract, **multiply**, and divide monomials and **polynomials.** Students solve multistep problems, including word problems, by using these techniques.

QUESTION How can you multiply binomials using algebra tiles?

You can use the following algebra tiles to model polynomials with positive coefficients.

1-tile
1
1

x-tile
1
x

x^2-tile
x
x

EXPLORE Multiply binomials

Find the product $(x + 3)(2x + 1)$.

STEP 1 Model the rectangle's dimensions

Model each binomial with algebra tiles. Arrange the first binomial vertically and the second horizontally, as shown. These polynomials model the length and width of a rectangle.

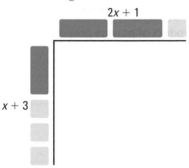

STEP 2 Fill in the area

Fill in the rectangle with the appropriate algebra tiles.

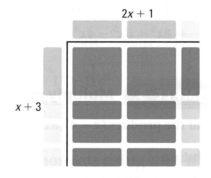

STEP 3 Find the product

The rectangle you created represents the polynomial $2x^2 + 7x + 3$.
So, $(x + 3)(2x + 1) = 2x^2 + 7x + 3$.

DRAW CONCLUSIONS Use your observations to complete these exercises

Use algebra tiles to find the product. Include a drawing of your model.

1. $(x + 1)(x + 3)$
2. $(x + 5)(x + 4)$
3. $(2x + 1)(x + 2)$

4. $(3x + 2)(x + 1)$
5. $(3x + 2)(2x + 1)$
6. $(4x + 1)(2x + 3)$

7. **REASONING** Find the product $x(2x + 1)$ and the product $3(2x + 1)$. What is the sum of these two products? What do your answers suggest you can do to find the product $(x + 3)(2x + 1)$?

51. ⬢ **GEOMETRY** The diagram shows a small square with side length d inside a large square with side length c.

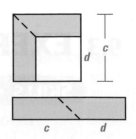

  a. Using the areas of the squares, determine the area of the shaded region.

  b. Suppose you cut out the shaded region and reassemble its parts as shown. What are the dimensions of the resulting rectangle?

  c. What pattern do parts (a) and (b) establish?

CONNECT SKILLS TO PROBLEM SOLVING Exercises 52–54 will help you prepare for problem solving.

Use the following information to tell which lettered parts of the diagram represent the outcome: The area model shows the possible outcomes when the weather forecast calls for a 30% chance of rain on both Monday and Tuesday.

52. Rain on both Monday and Tuesday

53. Rain on either Monday or Tuesday, but not both

54. No rain on either day

Monday forecast

	No rain: 70%	Rain: 30%
Tuesday forecast No rain: 70%	A	B
Rain: 30%	C	D

EXAMPLES 4 and 5 on p. 536 for Exs. 55–57

55. **VIDEO GAMES** You reach the last level of a video game in 45% of all the games you play. Make an area model that shows the possible outcomes of playing the game twice. What percent of the possible outcomes involve reaching the last level exactly once?

California *@HomeTutor* for problem solving help at classzone.com

56. ◆ **MULTIPLE CHOICE** You have a 20% chance of winning a prize each time you purchase a meal at your favorite restaurant. You purchase two meals at the restaurant. What percent of the possible outcomes involve winning a prize at least once?

  (A) 4%   **(B)** 6%   **(C)** 32%   **(D)** 36%

California *@HomeTutor* for problem solving help at classzone.com

Meal 1

	No win: 80%	Win: 20%
Meal 2 No win: 80%	No prize	1 prize
Win: 20%	1 prize	2 prizes

57. **FOOTBALL STATISTICS** During the 2004 regular season, the San Diego Chargers' quarterback Drew Brees completed 65.5% of the passes he attempted. The area model shows the possible outcomes of two attempted passes.

  a. What percent of the possible outcomes involve throwing at least one complete pass? *Explain* how you found your answer using the area model.

  b. Show how you could use a polynomial to model the possible results of two attempted passes.

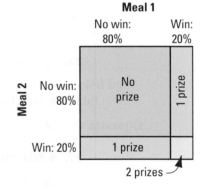

First Pass Attempt

	Complete: 65.5%	Incomplete: 34.5%
Second Pass Attempt Complete: 65.5%	2 complete	1 complete 1 incomplete
Incomplete: 34.5%	1 complete 1 incomplete	2 incomplete

Read the passage below for Exercises 58–60. Leave
your answers in terms of π.

Vision The iris of an eye surrounds the pupil. It regulates the amount of light
entering the eye by opening and closing the pupil. The iris of a human eye has
a width w that varies from 0.5 millimeter to 4 millimeters.

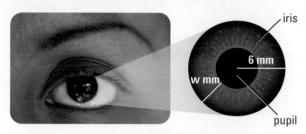

58. **Represent** Write a polynomial that represents the pupil's radius.

59. **Represent** Write a polynomial that represents the pupil's area.

60. **Explain** What are the least possible area and the greatest possible area of
the pupil? *Explain* how you found your answers.

61. **CHALLENGE** Write a pattern for the cube of a binomial, $(a + b)^3$.

62. **CHALLENGE** You use 100 feet of fencing to form a square with a side
length of 25 feet. You want to change the dimensions of the enclosed
region. For every 1 foot you increase the width, you must decrease the
length by 1 foot. Write a polynomial that gives the area of the rectangle
after you increase the width by x feet and decrease the length by x feet.
Explain why *any* change in dimensions results in an area less than that of
the original square.

◆ CALIFORNIA STANDARDS SPIRAL REVIEW

Alg. 10.0

63. What is the difference of $(5x^2 - x + 1)$ and $(4x^2 - 1)$? *(p. 520)*

   (A) $x^2 - x$ (B) $x^2 - x + 2$ (C) $9x^2 - x$ (D) $9x^2 - x + 2$

Alg. 17.0

64. What is the range of the function represented
by the graph? *(p. 257)*

   (A) $-1\ 2$

   (B) $-1, 1, 2$

   (C) $-1, 0, 1, 2$

   (D) $-2, -1, 0, 1, 2$

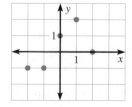

Alg. 24.2

65. What is the conclusion of the statement "If a binomial is multiplied by a
monomial, then the result is a binomial"? *(p. 53)*

   (A) The result is a binomial.

   (B) The result is a monomial.

   (C) A binomial is multiplied by a binomial.

   (D) A binomial is multiplied by a monomial.

9.4 Division with Algebra Tiles

MATERIALS · algebra tiles

Standards

Alg. 10.0 Students add, subtract, multiply, and **divide** monomials and **polynomials**. Students solve multistep problems, including word problems, by using these techniques.

QUESTION How can you divide polynomials using algebra tiles?

In the equation $36 \div 5 = 7\frac{1}{5}$, the dividend is 36, the divisor is 5, the quotient is 7, and the remainder is 1. This equation illustrates the following rule:

$$\text{Dividend} \div \text{Divisor} = \text{Quotient} + \frac{\text{Remainder}}{\text{Divisor}}$$

This rule can also be applied when dividing polynomials.

EXPLORE Divide polynomials

Divide $2x^2 + 3x + 5$ by $x + 1$.

STEP 1 *Model using algebra tiles*

Think of $2x^2 + 3x + 5$ as the area of a figure. Try to arrange the tiles to form a rectangle with $x + 1$ as one of the side lengths.

Notice that the other side length is $2x + 1$, but there are four 1-tiles remaining.

STEP 2 *Write equation*

The divisor is $x + 1$, the quotient is $2x + 1$, and the remainder is 4.

So, $(2x^2 + 3x + 5) \div (x + 1) = 2x + 1 + \dfrac{4}{x + 1}$.

DRAW CONCLUSIONS Use your observations to complete these exercises

1. To check that $36 \div 5 = 7\frac{1}{5}$, you can evaluate $5 \cdot 7 + 1$ to obtain 36.

   Use this method to check the division equation in Step 2 above.

Use algebra tiles to divide the polynomials. Include a drawing of your model.

2. $(2x^2 + 7x + 6) \div (x + 2)$ 3. $(2x^2 + 9x + 10) \div (x + 3)$

4. $(4x^2 + 4x + 5) \div (2x + 1)$ 5. $(2x^2 + 5x + 7) \div (2x + 3)$

6. $(3x^2 + 7x + 3) \div (x + 2)$ 7. $(4x^2 + 6x + 5) \div (x + 1)$

8. **REASONING** For which of the division problems in Exercises 2–7 is the divisor a factor of the dividend? How do you know?

9.4 Divide Polynomials

Math and RECREATION
Ex. 37, p. 546

Standards Alg. 10.0 Students add, subtract, multiply, and **divide monomials and polynomials. Students solve multistep problems, including word problems, by using these techniques.**

Connect *Before* you multiplied polynomials. *Now* you will divide monomials and polynomials.

Key Vocabulary
• **monomial,** *p. 520*
• **polynomial,** *p. 520*
• **binomial,** *p. 521*

When dividing polynomials, remember that you can always check your work using multiplication.

EXAMPLE 1   Divide monomials

Divide $-8x^5$ by $2x^2$.

Solution

Write the division as a fraction and use the quotient of powers property.

$$-8x^5 \div (2x^2) = \frac{-8x^5}{2x^2} \qquad \text{Write as fraction.}$$

$$= \frac{-8}{2} \cdot \frac{x^5}{x^2} \qquad \text{Rewrite using product rule for fractions.}$$

$$= \frac{-8}{2} \cdot x^{5-2} \qquad \text{Quotient of powers property}$$

$$= -4x^3 \qquad \text{Simplify.}$$

EXAMPLE 2   ◆ Multiple Choice Practice

$$\frac{4x^3}{16x^8} =$$

(A) $4x^5$ **(B)** $\dfrac{1}{4x^5}$ **(C)** $\dfrac{x^5}{12}$ **(D)** $\dfrac{1}{12x^5}$

$$\frac{4x^3}{16x^8} = \frac{4}{16} \cdot \frac{x^3}{x^8} \qquad \text{Rewrite using product rule for fractions.}$$

$$= \frac{1}{4} \cdot x^{-5} \qquad \text{Quotient of powers property}$$

$$= \frac{1}{4} \cdot \frac{1}{x^5} \qquad \text{Definition of negative exponents}$$

$$= \frac{1}{4x^5} \qquad \text{Simplify.}$$

▶ The correct answer is B. Ⓐ **Ⓑ** Ⓒ Ⓓ

Multiple Choice Practice for Lessons 9.1–9.4

1. Students in an environmental club are planning a rectangular garden with stone paths along two sides, as shown. The stone paths will have the same width. Which polynomial represents the area of the garden? **Alg. 10.0**

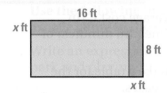

A $x^2 - 24x + 128$

B $x^2 + 12x - 130$

C $x^2 + 24x - 110$

D $x^2 - 36x + 128$

2. What is the sum of $x - 4$ and $2x^2 + x + 2$? **Alg. 10.0**

A $x^2 - 2$

B $2x^2 + 2x - 2$

C $3x^2 + 4x + 18$

D $6x^2 + 2x - 10$

3. During the period 1992–2000, the number C (in millions) of people participating in cross-country skiing and the number S (in millions) of people participating in snowboarding can be modeled by

$$C = 0.067t^3 - 0.107t^2 + 0.27t + 3.5$$

$$S = 0.416t + 1.24$$

where t is the number of years since 1992. Which equation models the total number T (in millions) of people participating in cross-country skiing and snowboarding as a function of the number of years since 1992? **Alg. 10.0**

A $T = 0.067t^3 - 0.107t^2 + 0.686t + 4.74$

B $T = 0.067t^3 - 0.523t^2 + 0.27t + 4.74$

C $T = 0.483t^3 - 1.331t^2 + 0.27t + 3.5$

D $T = 0.483t^3 + 1.133t^2 + 0.27t + 3.5$

4. What is the quotient of $x^2 + 4x + 4$ and $x + 2$? **Alg. 10.0**

A $x + 2$

B $x - 4$

C $x + 3$

D $x - 5$

5. Which polynomial represents the area of the shaded region of the diagram? **Alg. 10.0**

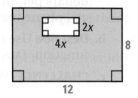

A $96 - 6x^2$

B $96 - 8x^2$

C $8x^2 - 96$

D $96 - 56x + 8x^2$

6. What is the degree of the polynomial $-3x^4 + 8x^2 - 6x$? **Alg. 10.0**

A 1   B 2   C 3   D 4

7. Dana hits the bull's-eye 70% of the time when playing darts. The area model shows the possible outcomes when Dana throws a dart two times. What percent of the possible outcomes involve making exactly one bull's-eye? **Alg. 10.0**

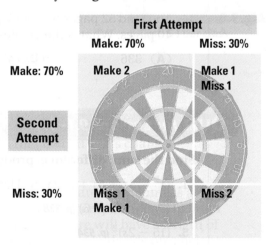

A 35%

B 42%

C 51%

D 57%

9.5 Solve Polynomial Equations in Factored Form

Standards

Alg. 11.0 Students apply basic factoring techniques to second- and simple third-degree polynomials. These techniques include finding a common factor for all terms in a polynomial, recognizing the difference of two squares, and recognizing perfect squares of binomials.

Alg. 14.0 Students solve a quadratic equation by factoring or completing the square.

Alg. 23.0 Students apply quadratic equations to physical problems, such as the motion of an object under the force of gravity.

Connect *Before* you solved linear equations. *Now* you will solve polynomial equations.

Math and **NATURE**
Ex. 52, p. 553

Key Vocabulary
- root
- vertical motion model

In Lesson 2.4, you learned the multiplicative property of zero: For any real number a, $a \cdot 0 = 0$. This is equivalent to saying:

For real numbers a and b, if $a = 0$ or $b = 0$, then $ab = 0$.

The converse of this statement is also true (as you will show in Exercise 58), and it is called the zero-product property.

KEY CONCEPT *For Your Notebook*

Zero-Product Property

Let a and b be real numbers. If $ab = 0$, then $a = 0$ or $b = 0$.

EXAMPLE 1 Use the zero-product property

Solve $(x - 4)(x + 2) = 0$.

$(x - 4)(x + 2) = 0$ **Write original equation.**

$x - 4 = 0$ *or* $x + 2 = 0$ **Zero-product property**

$x = 4$ *or* $x = -2$ **Solve for x.**

▶ The solutions of the equation are 4 and -2.

CHECK Substitute each solution into the original equation to check.

$(4 - 4)(4 + 2) \overset{?}{=} 0$ $(-2 - 4)(-2 + 2) \overset{?}{=} 0$

$0 \cdot 6 \overset{?}{=} 0$ $-6 \cdot 0 \overset{?}{=} 0$

$0 = 0 ✓$ $0 = 0 ✓$

 GUIDED PRACTICE for Example 1

1. Solve the equation $(x - 5)(x - 1) = 0$.

REVIEW GCF

For help with finding the GCF, see p. 784.

FACTORING To solve a polynomial equation using the zero-product property, you may need to *factor* the polynomial, which involves writing it as a product of other polynomials. One step in factoring is to look for the *greatest common monomial factor* of the polynomial's terms.

EXAMPLE 2 Find the greatest common monomial factor

Factor out the greatest common monomial factor.

a. $12x + 42y$ **b.** $4x^4 + 24x^3$

Solution

FIND THE GCF OF x^m AND x^n

In part (b), the common factors of x^4 and x^3 are 1, x, x^2, and x^3. The *greatest* common factor is x^3.

a. The GCF of 12 and 42 is 6. The variables x and y have no common factor. So, the greatest common monomial factor of the terms is 6.

▸ $12x + 42y = 6(2x + 7y)$

b. The GCF of 4 and 24 is 4. The GCF of x^4 and x^3 is x^3. So, the greatest common monomial factor of the terms is $4x^3$.

▸ $4x^4 + 24x^3 = 4x^3(x + 6)$

EXAMPLE 3 Solve an equation by factoring

Solve $2x^2 = -8x$.

About the Standards

You will learn to solve a quadratic equation by completing the square as part of Algebra 1 Standard 14.0 in Lesson 10.6 on page 643.

$2x^2 = -8x$	Write original equation.
$2x^2 + 8x = 0$	Add 8x to each side.
$2x(x + 4) = 0$	Factor left side.
$2x = 0 \quad or \quad x + 4 = 0$	Zero-product property
$x = 0 \quad or \qquad x = -4$	Solve for x.

▸ The solutions of the equation are 0 and -4.

ROOTS A **root** of a polynomial involving x is a value of x for which the corresponding value of the polynomial is 0.

EXAMPLE 4 Find the roots of a polynomial

Find the roots of $6x^2 - 15x$.

$6x^2 - 15x = 0$	Set polynomial equal to 0.
$3x(2x - 5) = 0$	Factor the polynomial.
$3x = 0 \quad or \quad 2x - 5 = 0$	Zero-product property
$x = 0 \quad or \qquad x = \dfrac{5}{2}$	Solve for x.

▸ The roots of the polynomial are 0 and $\dfrac{5}{2}$.

2. Factor out the greatest common monomial factor from $14m + 35n$.

3. Solve the equation $3s^2 - 9s = 0$.

4. Find the roots of $a^2 + 5a$.

VERTICAL MOTION   A *projectile* is an object that is propelled into the air but has no power to keep itself in the air. A thrown ball is a projectile, but an airplane is not. The height of a projectile can be described by the **vertical motion model**.

About the Standards

The vertical motion model accounts for the effect of the force of gravity mentioned in Algebra 1 Standard 23.0. The model ignores other, less significant, factors such as air resistance.

KEY CONCEPT   *For Your Notebook*

Vertical Motion Model

The height h (in feet) of a projectile can be modeled by

$$h = -16t^2 + vt + s$$

where t is the time (in seconds) the object has been in the air, v is the initial vertical velocity (in feet per second), and s is the initial height (in feet).

EXAMPLE 5   **Solve a multi-step problem**

SALMON   As a salmon swims upstream, it leaps into the air with an initial vertical velocity of 10 feet per second. After how many seconds does the salmon return to the water?

Solution

STEP 1   **Write** a model for the salmon's height above the surface of the water.

$h = -16t^2 + vt + s$	**Vertical motion model**
$h = -16t^2 + 10t + 0$	**Substitute 10 for v and 0 for s.**
$h = -16t^2 + 10t$	**Simplify.**

STEP 2   **Substitute** 0 for h. When the salmon returns to the water, its height above the surface is 0 feet. Solve for t.

$0 = -16t^2 + 10t$	**Substitute 0 for h.**
$0 = 2t(-8t + 5)$	**Factor right side.**
$2t = 0$ *or* $-8t + 5 = 0$	**Zero-product property**
$t = 0$ *or* $t = 0.625$	**Solve for t.**

▶ The salmon returns to the water 0.625 second after leaping.

Salmon swimming upstream

INTERPRET SOLUTIONS

The solution $t = 0$ means that just before the salmon leaps, its height above the surface of the water is 0 feet.

✓ **GUIDED PRACTICE**   for Example 5

5. **WHAT IF?**   In Example 5, suppose the salmon's initial vertical velocity is 12 feet per second. After how many seconds does the salmon return to the water?

9.5 EXERCISES

HOMEWORK KEY

◆ = **MULTIPLE CHOICE PRACTICE**
Exs. 12, 39, 55, and 60–62

○ = **HINTS AND HOMEWORK HELP**
for Exs. 3, 27, and 53 at classzone.com

SKILLS · PROBLEM SOLVING · REASONING

1. **VOCABULARY** What is the vertical motion model and what does each variable in the model represent?

2. **WRITING** *Explain* how to use the zero-product property to find the solutions of the equation $3x(x - 7) = 0$.

EXAMPLE 1
on p. 549
for Exs. 3–13

ZERO-PRODUCT PROPERTY Solve the equation.

3. $(x - 5)(x + 3) = 0$

4. $(y + 9)(y - 1) = 0$

5. $(z - 13)(z - 14) = 0$

6. $(c + 6)(c + 8) = 0$

7. $(d - 7)\left(d + \frac{4}{3}\right) = 0$

8. $\left(g - \frac{1}{8}\right)(g + 18) = 0$

9. $(3x + 1)(x + 6) = 0$

10. $(2y + 5)(7y - 5) = 0$

11. $(8z - 6)(12z + 14) = 0$

12. ◆ **MULTIPLE CHOICE** What are the solutions of $(y - 12)(y + 6) = 0$?

(A) −12 and −6   (B) −12 and 6   (C) −6 and 12   (D) 6 and 12

13. **ERROR ANALYSIS** *Describe* and correct the error in solving $(z - 15)(z + 21) = 0$.

$(z - 15)(z + 21) = 0$
$z = -15$ *or* $z = 21$

EXAMPLE 2
on p. 550
for Exs. 14–23

FACTORING EXPRESSIONS Factor out the greatest common monomial factor.

14. $2x + 2y$

15. $6x^2 - 15y$

16. $3s^4 + 16s$

17. $5d^6 + 2d^5$

18. $7w^5 - 35w^2$

19. $9m^7 - 3m^2$

20. $15n^3 + 25n$

21. $12a^5 + 8a$

22. $21x^6 - 33x^4$

23. **ERROR ANALYSIS** *Describe* and correct the error in factoring out the greatest common monomial factor of $9x^4 - 6x^3$.

$9x^4 - 6x^3 = 3x(3x^3 - 2x^2)$

EXAMPLES 3 and 4
on p. 550
for Exs. 24–39

SOLVING EQUATIONS Solve the equation.

24. $b^2 + 6b = 0$

25. $5w^2 - 5w = 0$

26. $-10n^2 + 35n = 0$

27. $2x^2 + 15x = 0$

28. $18c^2 + 6c = 0$

29. $-32y^2 - 24y = 0$

30. $-42z^2 = 14z$

31. $28m^2 = -8m$

32. $-12p^2 = -30p$

FINDING ROOTS Find the roots of the polynomial.

33. $3k^2 - 6k$

34. $6h^2 - 3h$

35. $4s^2 - 10s$

36. $4x^2 - 2x$

37. $4t^2 + 16t$

38. $z^2 + z$

39. ◆ **MULTIPLE CHOICE** What are the roots of $4x^2 - x$?

(A) −4 and 0   (B) $-\frac{1}{4}$ and 0   (C) 0 and $\frac{1}{4}$ (D) 0 and 4

FACTORING EXPRESSIONS Factor out the greatest common monomial factor.

40. $20x^2y^2 - 4xy$ **41.** $8a^2b - 6ab^2$ **42.** $18s^2t^5 - 2s^3t$

43. $v^3 - 5v^2 + 9v$ **44.** $-2g^4 + 14g^2 + 6g$ **45.** $6q^5 - 21q^4 - 15q^2$

46. REASONING Consider the equation $z = x^2 - xy$. For what values of x and y does $z = 0$?

CONNECT SKILLS TO PROBLEM SOLVING Exercises 47–49 will help you prepare for problem solving.

Write a vertical motion model for the given situation.

47. You kick a ball from the ground into the air with an initial vertical velocity of 3 feet per second.

48. A steelhead trout leaps from the sea with an initial vertical velocity of 5.5 feet per second.

49. A dog jumps into the air off of a deck that is 2 feet above the ground. The dog's initial vertical velocity is 5 feet per second.

EXAMPLE 5
on p. 551
for Exs. 50–52

50. CATS A cat leaps from the ground into the air with an initial vertical velocity of 11 feet per second. After how many seconds does the cat land on the ground?

California @*HomeTutor*   for problem solving help at classzone.com

51. JUMPING SPIDERS While hunting, a jumping spider leaps from the ground with an initial vertical velocity of 2.4 feet per second.

   a. Write an equation that gives the height of the spider as a function of the time (in seconds) since it left the ground.

   b. The spider reaches its maximum height after 0.075 second. How high can it jump?

California @*HomeTutor*   for problem solving help at classzone.com

Jumping spider

52. PENGUINS A penguin leaps out of the water while swimming. The height h (in feet) of the penguin can be modeled by $h = -16t^2 + 4.5t$ where t is the time (in seconds) since the penguin leaped out of the water. How long is the penguin in the air?

VERTICAL MOTION In Exercises 53 and 54, use the information below.

The height h (in meters) of a projectile can be modeled by $h = -4.9t^2 + vt + s$ where t is the time (in seconds) the object has been in the air, v is the initial vertical velocity (in meters per second), and s is the initial height (in meters).

53. SOCCER A soccer ball is kicked upward from the ground with an initial vertical velocity of 3.6 meters per second. How long is the ball in the air?

54. FIELD HOCKEY A field hockey ball is hit into the air from the ground with a field hockey stick. The initial vertical velocity is 4.9 meters per second.

   a. Write an equation that gives the height of the ball as a function of the time (in seconds) since the ball left the ground.

   b. What is a reasonable domain for the function? *Explain* your answer.

55. ◆ **MULTIPLE CHOICE** Two rectangular rooms in a building's floor plan have different dimensions but the same area. The dimensions (in meters) are shown. What is the value of w?

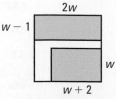

A 3   **B** 4   **C** 6   **D** 8

56. **TABLETOP AREAS** A display in your school library sits on top of two rectangular tables arranged in an L shape, as shown. The tabletops have the same area.

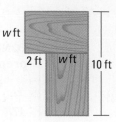

  a. Write an equation that relates the areas of the tabletops.

  b. Find the value of w.

  c. What is the combined area of the tabletops?

57. **ARCHES** An arch frames the entrance to a garden. The shape of the arch is modeled by the graph of the equation $y = -2x^2 + 8x$ where x and y are measured in feet. On a coordinate plane, the ground is represented by the x-axis.

  a. **Making a Table** Make a table of values that shows the height of the arch for $x = 0, 1, 2, 3,$ and 4 feet.

  b. **Drawing a Graph** Plot the ordered pairs in the table as points in a coordinate plane. Connect the points with a smooth curve that represents the arch.

  c. **Interpreting a Graph** How wide is the base of the arch?

58. **CHALLENGE** Consider the equation $ab = 0$. Assume that $a \neq 0$ and solve the equation for b. Then assume that $b \neq 0$ and solve the equation for a. What conclusion can you draw about the values of a and b?

59. **CHALLENGE** The shape of an arched doorway is modeled by the graph of the function $y = -0.5x(x - 8)$ where x and y are measured in feet. On a coordinate plane, the floor is represented by the x-axis.

  a. How wide is the doorway at its base? *Justify* your answer.

  b. The doorway's highest point occurs above the center of its base. How high is the highest point of the arched doorway? *Explain*.

◆ CALIFORNIA STANDARDS SPIRAL REVIEW

Alg. 25.1

60. Benjamin claims that when two polynomials of degree n are multiplied, the degree of the product is n^2. Which product is a counterexample to his claim? *(p. 528)*

  A $x^2(4x + 9)$ **B** $(x^2 + 9)(x^2 - 1)$

  C $(x^2 + x + 9)(x^2 - 1)$ **D** $(x^4 - 9)(x^4 + 2x^2 + 1)$

Alg. 10.0

61. What is the sum of $3n^2 + 2n - 7$ and $n^2 - n - 2$? *(p. 520)*

  A $4n^2 + n - 9$ **B** $n^2 + n + 9$ **C** $3n^2 - n + 2$ **D** $n^2 - n - 2$

Alg. 15.0

62. You mix 40 grams of a 6% saline solution with 20 grams of a 4% saline solution. Approximately what percent of the mixture is salt? *(p. 418)*

  A 3%   **B** 4.5%   **C** 5.3%   **D** 6.1%

9.6 Factorization with Algebra Tiles

MATERIALS · algebra tiles

Standards

Alg. 11.0 Students apply basic factoring techniques to second- and simple third-degree polynomials. These techniques include finding a common factor for all terms in a polynomial, recognizing the difference of two squares, and recognizing perfect squares of binomials.

QUESTION How can you factor a trinomial using algebra tiles?

You have seen that algebra tiles can be used to add polynomials and to multiply binomials. Now, you will use algebra tiles to factor trinomials.

EXPLORE Factor the trinomial $x^2 + 6x + 8$

STEP 1 *Make a rectangle*

Model the trinomial with algebra tiles. You will need one x^2-tile, six x-tiles, and eight 1-tiles. Arrange all of the tiles to form a rectangle. There can be no gaps or leftover tiles. The area of the rectangle represents the trinomial.

There is a gap. Try again.

Correct arrangement

STEP 2 *Find the side lengths*

The side lengths of the rectangle represent the polynomials $x + 2$ and $x + 4$. So, $x^2 + 6x + 8 = (x + 2)(x + 4)$.

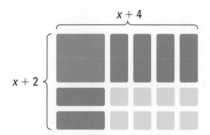

$x + 4$

$x + 2$

DRAW CONCLUSIONS Use your observations to complete these exercises

1. Use multiplication to show that $x + 4$ and $x + 2$ are factors of the polynomial $x^2 + 6x + 8$.

Use algebra tiles to factor the trinomial. Include a drawing of your model.

2. $x^2 + 6x + 5$ 3. $x^2 + 9x + 14$ 4. $x^2 + 5x + 6$

5. $x^2 + 8x + 16$ 6. $x^2 + 5x + 4$ 7. $x^2 + 8x + 12$

8. **REASONING** The factors of the trinomial $x^2 + 6x + 8$ have the form $x + p$ and $x + q$, as shown above. How are p and q related to 6 and 8?

9.6 Factor $x^2 + bx + c$

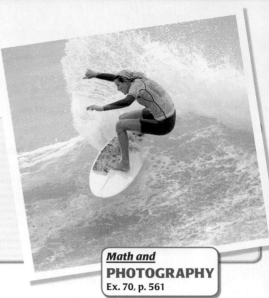

Standards

Alg. 11.0 Students apply basic factoring techniques to second- and simple third-**degree polynomials.** These techniques include finding a common factor for all terms in a polynomial, recognizing the difference of two squares, and recognizing perfect squares of binomials.

Alg. 14.0 Students solve a quadratic equation by **factoring** or completing the square.

Connect *Before* you factored out the greatest monomial factor. *Now* you will factor trinomials of the form $x^2 + bx + c$.

Math and
PHOTOGRAPHY
Ex. 70, p. 561

Key Vocabulary
• **root,** *p. 550*

From Lesson 9.2, you know that

$$(x + 3)(x + 4) = x^2 + (4 + 3)x + 4 \cdot 3 = x^2 + 7x + 12.$$

You will reverse this process to factor trinomials of the form $x^2 + bx + c$.

KEY CONCEPT   *For Your Notebook*

Factoring $x^2 + bx + c$

Algebra $x^2 + bx + c = (x + p)(x + q)$ provided $p + q = b$ and $pq = c$.

Example $x^2 + 5x + 6 = (x + 3)(x + 2)$ because $3 + 2 = 5$ and $3 \cdot 2 = 6$.

EXAMPLE 1   **Factor when b and c are positive**

Factor $x^2 + 11x + 18$.

Find two positive factors of 18 whose sum is 11. Make an organized list.

Factors of 18	Sum of factors	
18, 1	$18 + 1 = 19$	✗
9, 2	$9 + 2 = \mathbf{11}$	← Correct sum
6, 3	$6 + 3 = 9$	✗

The factors 9 and 2 have a sum of 11, so they are the correct values of p and q.

▶ $x^2 + 11x + 18 = (x + \mathbf{9})(x + \mathbf{2})$

✓ **GUIDED PRACTICE**   for Example 1

Factor the trinomial.

    1. $x^2 + 3x + 2$ **2.** $a^2 + 7a + 10$ **3.** $t^2 + 9t + 14$

FACTORING When factoring a trinomial, first consider the signs of p and q.

$(x + p)(x + q)$	$x^2 + bx + c$	Signs of b and c
$(x + 2)(x + 3)$	$x^2 + 5x + 6$	b is positive; c is positive.
$(x + 2)(x + (-3))$	$x^2 - x - 6$	b is negative; c is negative.
$(x + (-2))(x + 3)$	$x^2 + x - 6$	b is positive; c is negative.
$(x + (-2))(x + (-3))$	$x^2 - 5x + 6$	b is negative; c is positive.

By observing the signs of b and c in the table, you can see that:

- b and c are positive when both p and q are positive.
- b is negative and c is positive when both p and q are negative.
- c is negative when p and q have different signs.

EXAMPLE 2 Factor when b is negative and c is positive

Factor $n^2 - 6n + 8$.

Because b is negative and c is positive, p and q must both be negative.

Factors of 8	Sum of factors	
$-8, -1$	$-8 + (-1) = -9$	✗
$-4, -2$	$-4 + (-2) = -6$	← Correct sum

▶ $n^2 - 6n + 8 = (n - 4)(n - 2)$

EXAMPLE 3 Factor when b is positive and c is negative

Factor $y^2 + 2y - 15$.

Because c is negative, p and q must have different signs.

Factors of -15	Sum of factors	
$-15, 1$	$-15 + 1 = -14$	✗
$15, -1$	$15 + (-1) = 14$	✗
$-5, 3$	$-5 + 3 = -2$	✗
$5, -3$	$5 + (-3) = 2$	← Correct sum

▶ $y^2 + 2y - 15 = (y + 5)(y - 3)$

✓ **GUIDED PRACTICE** for Examples 2 and 3

Factor the trinomial.

4. $x^2 - 4x + 3$ **5.** $t^2 - 8t + 12$ **6.** $m^2 + m - 20$ **7.** $w^2 + 6w - 16$

EXAMPLE 4 ◆ Multiple Choice Practice

What are the solutions for the quadratic equation $x^2 - 3x = 18$?

(A) $-3, -6$ **(B)** $3, -6$ **(C)** $-3, 6$ **(D)** $3, 6$

Solution

$x^2 - 3x = 18$	Write original equation.
$x^2 - 3x - 18 = 0$	Subtract 18 from each side.
$(x - 6)(x + 3) = 0$	Factor left side.
$x - 6 = 0$ *or* $x + 3 = 0$	Zero-product property
$x = 6$ *or* $x = -3$	Solve for x.

▶ The correct answer is C. (A) (B) (C) (D)

EXAMPLE 5 Solve a multi-step problem

BANNER DIMENSIONS You are making banners to hang during school spirit week. Each banner requires 16.5 square feet of felt and will be cut as shown. Find the width of one banner.

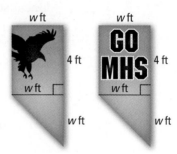

Solution

ANOTHER WAY

For alternative methods for solving Example 5, turn to page 563 for the **Problem Solving Workshop**.

STEP 1 **Draw** a diagram of two banners together.

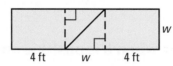

4 ft w 4 ft

REVIEW AREA

For help with area, see p. 796.

STEP 2 **Write** an equation using the fact that the area of 2 banners is $2(16.5) = 33$ square feet. Solve the equation for w.

$A = \ell \cdot w$	Formula for area of a rectangle
$33 = (4 + w + 4) \cdot w$	Substitute 33 for A and $(4 + w + 4)$ for ℓ.
$0 = w^2 + 8w - 33$	Simplify and subtract 33 from each side.
$0 = (w + 11)(w - 3)$	Factor right side.
$w + 11 = 0$ *or* $w - 3 = 0$	Zero-product property
$w = -11$ *or* $w = 3$	Solve for w.

▶ The banner cannot have a negative width, so the width is 3 feet.

✓ **GUIDED PRACTICE** for Examples 4 and 5

8. Solve the equation $s^2 - 2s = 24$.

9. **WHAT IF?** In Example 5, suppose the area of a banner is to be 10 square feet. What is the width of one banner?

9.6 EXERCISES

HOMEWORK
KEY

◆ = **MULTIPLE CHOICE PRACTICE**
Exs. 18, 21, 46, 71, and 77–79

○ = **HINTS AND HOMEWORK HELP**
for Exs. 7, 51, and 71 at classzone.com

SKILLS · PROBLEM SOLVING · REASONING

1. **VOCABULARY** Copy and complete: The __?__ of $t^2 + 3t + 2$ are $t + 2$ and $t + 1$.

2. **WRITING** If $x^2 - 8x + 12 = (x + p)(x + q)$, what are the signs of p and q? *Justify* your answer.

**EXAMPLES
1, 2, and 3**
on pp. 556–557
for Exs. 3–21

FACTORING TRINOMIALS Factor the trinomial.

3. $x^2 + 4x + 3$ 4. $a^2 + 6a + 8$ 5. $b^2 - 17b + 72$

6. $s^2 - 10s + 16$ 7. $z^2 + 8z - 48$ 8. $w^2 + 18w + 56$

9. $y^2 - 7y - 18$ 10. $n^2 - 9n + 14$ 11. $x^2 + 3x - 70$

12. $f^2 + 4f - 32$ 13. $m^2 - 7m - 120$ 14. $d^2 - 20d + 99$

15. $p^2 + 20p + 64$ 16. $x^2 + 6x - 72$ 17. $c^2 + 15c + 44$

18. ◆ **MULTIPLE CHOICE** Which binomial is a factor of $x^2 - 5x - 24$?

ⓐ $x - 3$ ⓑ $x - 8$ ⓒ $x + 5$ ⓓ $x + 8$

ERROR ANALYSIS *Describe* and correct the error in factoring the trinomial.

19.
$$s^2 - 17s - 60 = (s - 5)(s - 12)$$
✗

20.
$$m^2 - 10m + 24 = (m - 12)(m + 2)$$
✗

21. ◆ **MULTIPLE CHOICE** What is the factored form of $x^2 + 10x - 39$?

ⓐ $(x - 3)(x + 13)$ ⓑ $(x - 4)(x + 15)$

ⓒ $(x - 4)(x - 12)$ ⓓ $(x + 3)(x - 13)$

EXAMPLE 4
on p. 558
for Exs. 22–46

SOLVING EQUATIONS Solve the equation.

22. $x^2 - 10x + 21 = 0$ 23. $n^2 - 7n - 30 = 0$ 24. $w^2 - 15w + 44 = 0$

25. $a^2 + 5a = 50$ 26. $r^2 + 2r = 24$ 27. $t^2 + 9t = -20$

28. $y^2 - 2y - 8 = 7$ 29. $m^2 + 22 = -23m$ 30. $b^2 + 5 = 8b - 10$

FINDING ROOTS Find the roots of the polynomial.

31. $x^2 + 11x + 18$ 32. $x^2 + 5x + 6$ 33. $x^2 - 18x + 32$

34. $x^2 - 14x + 45$ 35. $x^2 - 5x - 24$ 36. $x^2 - 16x + 28$

SOLVING EQUATIONS Solve the equation.

37. $s(s + 1) = 72$ 38. $t(t - 13) = 30$ 39. $q(q + 19) = -34$

40. $a^2 + 3(a - 7) = 33$ 41. $b^2 - 6(b + 8) = 7$ 42. $x^2 - 10(x - 1) = -11$

43. $p^2 - 14(p + 2) = 23$ 44. $2t\left(\frac{1}{2}t + 5\right) = 39$ 45. $-m(m - 24) = -180$

46. ◆ **MULTIPLE CHOICE** What are the solutions of the equation $x^2 - 8x = 240$?

  Ⓐ   −20 and −12   Ⓑ   −20 and 12

  Ⓒ   20 and −12   Ⓓ   12 and 20

47. REASONING Write an equation of the form $x^2 + bx + c = 0$ that has the solutions −4 and 6. *Explain* how you found your answer.

🅖 GEOMETRY **Find the dimensions of the rectangle or triangle that has the given area.**

48. Area = 100 in.^{2} **49.** Area = 34 m^2

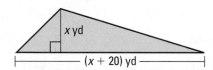

x in.

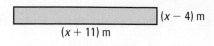

50. Area = 78 yd^2 **51.** Area = 119 ft^2

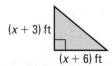

FACTORING TRINOMIALS **In Exercises 52–63, use the example below to factor the trinomial.**

EXAMPLE   **Factor a trinomial in two variables**

Factor $x^2 + 9xy + 14y^2$.

Solution

To factor the trinomial, you must find factors of the form $x + py$ and $x + qy$.

First, consider the signs of the factors needed. In this example, b is 9, and c is 14. Because both b and c are positive, you must find two positive factors of 14 that have a sum of 9.

Factors of 14	Sum of factors	
14, 1	14 + 1 = 15	✗
7, 2	7 + 2 = 9	← Correct sum

The factors 7 and 2 have a sum of 9, so 7 and 2 are the correct values of p and q.

▶ $x^2 + 9xy + 14y^2 = (x + 7y)(x + 2y)$

---

52. $x^2 - 4xy + 4y^2$ **53.** $y^2 - 6yz + 5z^2$ **54.** $c^2 + 13cd + 36d^2$

55. $r^2 + 15rs + 50s^2$ **56.** $a^2 + 2ab - 15b^2$ **57.** $x^2 + 8xy - 65y^2$

58. $m^2 - mn - 42n^2$ **59.** $u^2 - 3uv - 108v^2$ **60.** $g^2 + 4gh - 60h^2$

61. $s^2 + 2st - 35t^2$ **62.** $b^2 - 10bc - 24c^2$ **63.** $w^2 + 6wx - 91x^2$

Use the diagram. Segments in the diagram intersect at right angles.

64. Write an expression for the length of the green segment.

65. Extend the red segment so that it divides the figure into two rectangles. Write an expression for the area of each rectangle.

66. The combined area of the rectangles is 1200 square feet. Use your answer from Exercise 65 to write an equation representing the combined area of the rectangles.

67. Use your equation to find the area of each rectangle.

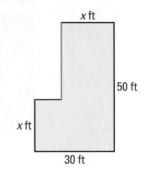

x ft

50 ft

x ft

30 ft

EXAMPLE 5
on p. 558
for Exs. 68–71

68. **CARD DESIGN** You are designing a gift card that has a border along one side, as shown. The area of the white part of the card is 30 square centimeters. What is the area of the border?

California @HomeTutor for problem solving help at classzone.com

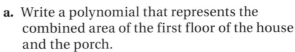

s cm

(s + 1) cm   2 cm

69. **CONSTRUCTION** A contractor is building a porch along two sides of a house. The house is rectangular with a width of 32 feet and a length of 50 feet. The porch will have the same width on each side of the house.

a. Write a polynomial that represents the combined area of the first floor of the house and the porch.

b. The owners want the combined area of the first floor and the porch to be 2320 square feet. How wide should the contractor build the porch?

California @HomeTutor for problem solving help at classzone.com

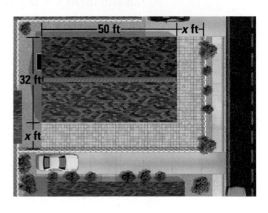

50 ft   x ft

32 ft

x ft

70. **SHORT RESPONSE** You trimmed a large square picture so that you could fit it into a frame. You trimmed 3 inches from the length and 2 inches from the width. The area of the resulting picture is 56 square inches. What was the perimeter of the original large square picture? *Explain* how you found your answer.

2 in.

x in.

3 in.

x in.

71. ◆ **MULTIPLE CHOICE** A rectangular garden is 15 feet wide and 20 feet long. When you increase both the width and length by x feet, the area of the garden increases by 200 square feet. Which equation represents this situation?

(A) $(15 + x)(20 + x) = 200$ (B) $(15 + x)(20 + x) = 500$

(C) $(15 - x)(20 - x) = 200$ (D) $(15 - x)(20 - x) = 500$

72. PARK PATHS A town has a rectangular park. The parks department is planning to install two brick paths that will intersect at right angles. One path will be 130 feet long, and the other path will be 500 feet long. The paths will have the same width.

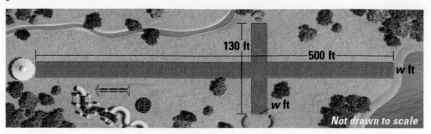

130 ft   500 ft   w ft   w ft   Not drawn to scale

HINT
Add the path areas, but subtract the overlap, so that it is not counted twice.

a. Write a polynomial that represents the combined area of the two paths.

b. The parks department can afford brick for 3125 square feet of path. Write and solve an equation to find the width of the paths.

c. In part (b) you used one solution of the equation to find your answer. *Explain* how you chose which solution to use.

CHALLENGE Find all integer values of *b* for which the trinomial has factors of the form $x + p$ and $x + q$ where p and q are integers.

73. $x^2 + bx + 15$　　　　**74.** $x^2 - bx + 21$　　　　**75.** $x^2 + bx - 42$

76. CHALLENGE A rectangular stage is positioned in the center of a rectangular room, as shown. The area of the stage is 120 square feet.

a. Use the dimensions given in the diagram to find the length and width of the stage.

b. The combined area of the stage and the surrounding floor is 360 square feet. Find the length and width of the room.

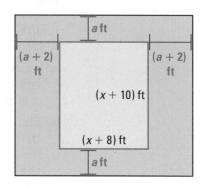

a ft
(a + 2) ft   (a + 2) ft
(x + 10) ft
(x + 8) ft
a ft

◆ CALIFORNIA STANDARDS SPIRAL REVIEW

Alg. 2.0

77. If $x = 81$, the value of which expression is a perfect square? *(p. 95)*

　A $16 - \sqrt{x}$　　　**B** $17 \cdot \sqrt{x}$　　　**C** $27 + \sqrt{x}$　　　**D** $15 + \sqrt{x}$

Alg. 3.0

78. Which numbers are solutions of $|x - 3| = 7$? *(p. 220)*

　A -4 and 10　　**B** -4 and 4　　**C** 7 and 10　　**D** -3 and 7

Gr. 7 AF 1.1

79. Your school's theater department charged $5 per person for admission to a performance. During intermission, the department sold refreshments. The profit from refreshment sales was $150. The department's total profit from the performance was $1000. Which equation represents this situation? *(p. 132)*

　A $5x - 150 = 1000$　　　　　　**B** $150x - 5 = 1000$

　C $150x - 5 = 1000$　　　　　　**D** $5x + 150 = 1000$

Using ALTERNATIVE METHODS

Another Way to Solve Example 5, page 558

Standards
Alg. 10.0

In Example 5 on page 558, you saw how to solve the problem about a school banner by solving an equation. You can also solve the problem using a table or a graph.

PROBLEM

BANNER DIMENSIONS You are making banners to hang during school spirit week. Each banner requires 16.5 square feet of felt and will be cut as shown. Find the width of one banner.

METHOD 1

Using a Table Consider the separate geometric figures that form one banner and find their areas in terms of w. Then find the total area of the banner for different values of w until you find a value that gives a total area of 16.5 square feet. Use a table to organize your work.

STEP 1 Write equations for the area of the pieces and the total area.

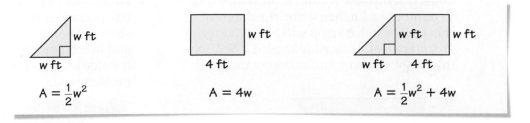

$$A = \frac{1}{2}w^2 \qquad A = 4w \qquad A = \frac{1}{2}w^2 + 4w$$

STEP 2 Organize your work in a table.

w	Triangle's area $\left(\frac{1}{2}w^2\right)$	Rectangle's area $(4w)$	Total area $\left(\frac{1}{2}w^2 + 4w\right)$	
1	0.5	4	4.5	4.5 < 16.5, so try a greater value of w.
2	2	8	10	10 < 16.5, so try a greater value of w.
3	4.5	12	16.5	Correct area

▶ The width of the banner is 3 feet.

Using a Graph Another approach is to use a graph.

STEP 1 **Write** an equation for the area of the banner. The area of the banner can be thought of as the area of a triangle plus the area of a rectangle.

> Area of banner = Area of triangle + Area of rectangle
>
> $$A = \frac{1}{2}w^2 + 4w$$

STEP 2 **Graph** the equation for the area of the banner using a graphing calculator. Graph $y_1 = 0.5x^2 + 4x$. Because you are looking for the value of x that gives an area of 16.5 square feet, you should display the graph of $y_2 = 16.5$ in the same viewing window.

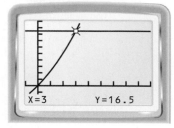

X=3   Y=16.5

STEP 3 **Find** the intersection of the graphs by using the *intersect* feature on your calculator. The graphs intersect at (3, 16.5).

▶ The width of the banner is 3 feet.

PRACTICE

1. **COUNTER DESIGN** A contractor is building a counter in a kitchen using the diagram shown. The countertop will have an area of 12 square feet. How wide should it be? Solve this problem using two different methods.

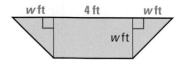

w ft   4 ft   *w* ft

w ft

2. **ERROR ANALYSIS** *Describe* and correct the error in using an equation to solve the problem in Exercise 1.

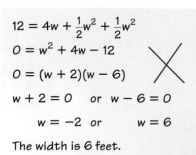

$12 = 4w + \frac{1}{2}w^2 + \frac{1}{2}w^2$

$0 = w^2 + 4w - 12$

$0 = (w + 2)(w - 6)$

$w + 2 = 0$ or $w - 6 = 0$

$w = -2$ or $w = 6$

The width is 6 feet.

3. **FOUNTAIN DESIGN** A square fountain in a city plaza is surrounded by brick patios as shown. The combined area of the fountain and brick patios is 205 square feet. What is the side length of the fountain? Solve this problem using two different methods.

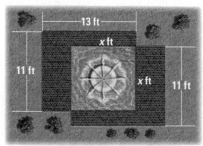

13 ft

x ft

11 ft

x ft

11 ft

4. **WHAT IF?** You want to make a larger banner using the same pattern shown in the problem on page 563. The new banner will have an area of 24 square feet. Find the width of the new banner. *Describe* the method you used to find your answer.

9.7 More Factorization with Algebra Tiles

MATERIALS · algebra tiles

Standards

Alg. 11.0 Students apply basic factoring techniques to second- and simple third-**degree polynomials**. These techniques include finding a common factor for all terms in a polynomial, recognizing the difference of two squares, and recognizing perfect squares of binomials.

QUESTION How can you factor a trinomial using algebra tiles?

EXPLORE Factor the trinomial $2x^2 + 7x + 3$

STEP 1 *Make a rectangle*

Model the trinomial with algebra tiles. Arrange all of the tiles to form a rectangle. You may have to try a few arrangements to make the rectangle. There can be no gaps or leftover tiles.

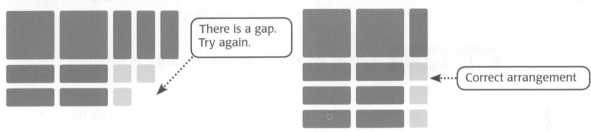

There is a gap. Try again.

Correct arrangement

STEP 2 *Find the side lengths*

The side lengths of the rectangle represent the polynomials $x + 3$ and $2x + 1$. So $2x^2 + 7x + 3 = (x + 3)(2x + 1)$.

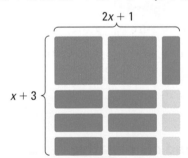

$2x + 1$

$x + 3$

DRAW CONCLUSIONS Use your observations to complete these exercises

1. Use multiplication to show that $x + 3$ and $2x + 1$ are factors of the polynomial $2x^2 + 7x + 3$.

Use algebra tiles to factor the trinomial. Include a drawing of your model.

2. $2x^2 + 5x + 3$ 3. $3x^2 + 5x + 2$ 4. $4x^2 + 9x + 2$

5. $3x^2 + 13x + 4$ 6. $4x^2 + 11x + 6$ 7. $4x^2 + 8x + 3$

8. **REASONING** Factor the trinomial $2x^2 + 11x + 5$ as the product of two binomials. How is the leading coefficient of the trinomial related to the leading coefficients of its binomial factors?

9.7 Factor $ax^2 + bx + c$

Math and ARCHITECTURE
Ex. 59, p. 572

Standards

Alg. 11.0 Students apply basic factoring techniques to second- and simple third-**degree polynomials**. These techniques include finding a common factor for all terms in a polynomial, recognizing the difference of two squares, and recognizing perfect squares of binomials.

Alg. 14.0 Students solve a quadratic equation by factoring or completing the square.

Connect

Before you factored trinomials of the form $x^2 + bx + c$. *Now* you will factor trinomials of the form $ax^2 + bx + c$ where a is not 1.

Key Vocabulary
• **trinomial,** *p. 521*

When factoring a trinomial of the form $ax^2 + bx + c$, first consider the signs of b and c, as in Lesson 9.6. This approach works when a is positive.

EXAMPLE 1   Factor when *b* is negative and *c* is positive

Factor $2x^2 - 7x + 3$.

Because b is negative and c is positive, both factors of c must be negative.

REVIEW FACTORING
For help with determining the signs of the factors of a trinomial, see p. 557.

You must consider the order of the factors of 3, because the x-terms of the possible factorizations are different.

Factors of 2	Factors of 3	Possible factorization	Middle term when multiplied	
1, 2	−1, −3	$(x - 1)(2x - 3)$	$-3x - 2x = -5x$	✗
1, 2	−3, −1	$(x - 3)(2x - 1)$	$-x - 6x = -7x$	← Correct

▶ $2x^2 - 7x + 3 = (x - 3)(2x - 1)$

EXAMPLE 2   Factor when *b* is positive and *c* is negative

Factor $3n^2 + 14n - 5$.

Because b is positive and c is negative, the factors of c have different signs.

Factors of 3	Factors of −5	Possible factorization	Middle term when multiplied	
1, 3	1, −5	$(n + 1)(3n - 5)$	$-5n + 3n = -2n$	✗
1, 3	−1, 5	$(n - 1)(3n + 5)$	$5n - 3n = 2n$	✗
1, 3	5, −1	$(n + 5)(3n - 1)$	$-n + 15n = 14n$	← Correct
1, 3	−5, 1	$(n - 5)(3n + 1)$	$n - 15n = -14n$	✗

▶ $3n^2 + 14n - 5 = (n + 5)(3n - 1)$

GUIDED PRACTICE for Examples 1 and 2

Factor the trinomial.

1. $3t^2 + 8t + 4$ **2.** $4s^2 - 9s + 5$ **3.** $2h^2 + 13h - 7$

FACTORING WHEN *a* IS NEGATIVE To factor a trinomial of the form $ax^2 + bx + c$ when *a* is negative, first factor −1 from each term of the trinomial. For instance:

$$-5x^2 + 3x - 2 = -1(5x^2 - 3x + 2)$$

Then factor the resulting trinomial as in the previous examples.

EXAMPLE 3 Factor when *a* is negative

Factor $-4x^2 + 12x + 7$.

Solution

STEP 1 Factor −1 from each term of the trinomial.

$$-4x^2 + 12x + 7 = -(4x^2 - 12x - 7)$$

STEP 2 Factor the trinomial $4x^2 - 12x - 7$. Because *b* and *c* are both negative, the factors of *c* must have different signs. As in the previous examples, use a table to organize information about the factors of *a* and *c*.

Factors of 4	Factors of −7	Possible factorization	Middle term when multiplied	
1, 4	1, −7	$(x + 1)(4x - 7)$	$-7x + 4x = -3x$	✗
1, 4	7, −1	$(x + 7)(4x - 1)$	$-x + 28x = 27x$	✗
1, 4	−1, 7	$(x - 1)(4x + 7)$	$7x - 4x = 3x$	✗
1, 4	−7, 1	$(x - 7)(4x + 1)$	$x - 28x = -27x$	✗
2, 2	**1, −7**	$\mathbf{(2x + 1)(2x - 7)}$	$-14x + 2x = -12x$	← Correct
2, 2	7, −1	$(2x + 7)(2x - 1)$	$14x - 2x = 12x$	✗

AVOID ERRORS
Remember to include the −1 that you factored out in Step 1.

▶ $-4x^2 + 12x + 7 = -(2x + 1)(2x - 7)$

CHECK You can check your factorization using a graphing calculator. Graph $y_1 = -4x^2 + 12x + 7$ and $y_2 = -(2x + 1)(2x - 7)$. Because the graphs coincide, you know that your factorization is correct.

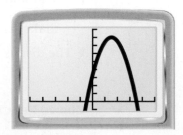

 GUIDED PRACTICE for Example 3

Factor the trinomial.

4. $-2y^2 - 5y - 3$ **5.** $-5m^2 + 6m - 1$ **6.** $-3x^2 - x + 2$

FINDING A COMMON FACTOR In Lesson 9.5, you learned to factor out the greatest common monomial factor from the terms of a polynomial. Sometimes you may need to do this before finding two binomial factors of a trinomial.

EXAMPLE 4 Write and solve a polynomial equation

DISCUS An athlete throws a discus from an initial height of 6 feet and with an initial vertical velocity of 46 feet per second.

a. Write an equation that gives the height (in feet) of the discus as a function of the time (in seconds) since it left the athlete's hand.

b. After how many seconds does the discus hit the ground?

An athlete throws a discus.

Solution

USE VERTICAL MOTION MODEL
For help with using the vertical motion model, see p. 551.

a. Use the vertical motion model to write an equation for the height h (in feet) of the discus. In this case, $v = 46$ and $s = 6$.

$$h = -16t^2 + vt + s \qquad \text{Vertical motion model}$$

$$h = -16t^2 + \mathbf{46}t + \mathbf{6} \qquad \text{Substitute 46 for } v \text{ and 6 for } s.$$

b. To find the number of seconds that pass before the discus lands, find the value of t for which the height of the discus is 0. Substitute 0 for h and solve the equation for t.

$$0 = -16t^2 + 46t + 6 \qquad \text{Substitute 0 for } h.$$

$$0 = -2(8t^2 - 23t - 3) \qquad \text{Factor out } -2.$$

$$0 = -2(8t + 1)(t - 3) \qquad \text{Factor the trinomial. Find factors of 8 and } -3 \text{ that produce a middle term with a coefficient of } -23.$$

$$8t + 1 = 0 \quad or \ t - 3 = 0 \qquad \text{Zero-product property}$$

$$t = -\frac{1}{8} \ or \qquad t = 3 \qquad \text{Solve for } t.$$

The solutions of the equation are $-\frac{1}{8}$ and 3. A negative solution does not make sense in this situation, so disregard $-\frac{1}{8}$.

▶ The discus hits the ground after 3 seconds.

✓ **GUIDED PRACTICE** for Example 4

7. WHAT IF? In Example 4, suppose an athlete throws the discus from an initial height of 5 feet and with an initial vertical velocity of 38 feet per second. After how many seconds does the discus hit the ground?

8. SHOT PUT In a shot put event, an athlete throws the shot put from an initial height of 6 feet and with an initial vertical velocity of 29 feet per second. After how many seconds does the shot put hit the ground?

EXAMPLE 5 ◆ **Multiple Choice Practice**

> The height of a triangle is 6 inches less than 4 times the base. The area of the triangle is 54 square inches. What is the base of the triangle?
>
> **(A)** 4 in.　　　**(B)** 4.5 in.　　　**(C)** 6 in.　　　**(D)** 54 in.

REVIEW AREA
For help finding area, see p. 796.

Use the area formula $A = \frac{1}{2}bh$ with $h = 4b - 6$ and $A = 54$.

$$\frac{1}{2}b(4b - 6) = 54 \qquad \text{Write an equation to model area.}$$

$$2b^2 - 3b - 54 = 0 \qquad \text{Simplify and subtract 54 from each side.}$$

$$(2b + 9)(b - 6) = 0 \qquad \text{Factor left side.}$$

$$2b + 9 = 0 \quad or \quad b - 6 = 0 \qquad \text{Zero-product property}$$

$$b = -\frac{9}{2} \quad or \qquad b = 6 \qquad \text{Solve for } b.$$

Disregard the negative value of b.

▸ The correct answer is C. Ⓐ Ⓑ ⬤ Ⓓ

 GUIDED PRACTICE　for Example 5

9. A rectangle's length is 1 inch more than twice its width. The area is 6 square inches. What is the width?

(A) $\frac{1}{2}$ in.　　　**(B)** $\frac{3}{2}$ in.　　　**(C)** 2 in.　　　**(D)** $\frac{5}{2}$ in.

9.7 **EXERCISES**

HOMEWORK KEY

◆ = **MULTIPLE CHOICE PRACTICE**
　Exs. 23, 49, 57, and 65–67

○ = **HINTS AND HOMEWORK HELP**
　for Exs. 3, 25, and 59 at classzone.com

SKILLS · PROBLEM SOLVING · REASONING

1. **VOCABULARY** Copy and complete: A polynomial with three terms is called a(n) __?__.

2. **WRITING** *Compare* factoring $6x^2 - x - 2$ with factoring $x^2 - x - 2$.

EXAMPLES 1, 2, and 3
on pp. 566–567
for Exs. 3–23

FACTORING TRINOMIALS Factor the trinomial.

3. $-y^2 + 2y + 8$ 　　　**4.** $-x^2 + x + 20$　　　**5.** $-a^2 + 12a - 27$

6. $5w^2 - 6w + 1$　　　**7.** $-3p^2 - 10p - 3$　　　**8.** $6s^2 - s - 5$

9. $2t^2 + 5t - 63$　　　**10.** $2c^2 - 7c + 3$　　　**11.** $3n^2 - 17n + 10$

12. $-2h^2 + 5h + 3$　　　**13.** $-6k^2 - 13k - 6$　　　**14.** $10x^2 - 3x - 27$

15. $4m^2 + 9m + 5$　　　**16.** $3z^2 + z - 14$　　　**17.** $4a^2 + 9a - 9$

18. $4n^2 + 16n + 15$　　　**19.** $-5b^2 + 7b - 2$　　　**20.** $6y^2 - 5y - 4$

ERROR ANALYSIS *Describe* and correct the error in factoring the trinomial.

21.

$$2x^2 + 7x - 15 = (2x + 3)(x - 5)$$ ✗

22.

$$6x^2 - 5x - 4 = (3x + 2)(2x - 3)$$ ✗

23. ◆ **MULTIPLE CHOICE** What is the factored form of $8x^2 - 10x + 3$?

  A $(2x - 3)(4x - 1)$ **B** $(2x - 1)(4x - 3)$

  C $(4x + 1)(2x - 3)$ **D** $(8x - 3)(x - 1)$

EXAMPLES 4 and 5
on pp. 568–569
for Exs. 24–43

SOLVING EQUATIONS Solve the equation.

24. $2x^2 - 3x - 35 = 0$ **25.** $3w^2 + 22w + 7 = 0$ **26.** $4s^2 + 11s - 3 = 0$

27. $b(20b - 3) - 2 = 0$ **28.** $4(3y^2 - 7y + 4) = 1$ **29.** $p(3p + 14) = 5$

30. $6r^2 - 15r = 99$ **31.** $56z^2 + 2 = 22z$ **32.** $30x^2 + 25x = 20$

FINDING ROOTS Find the roots of the polynomial.

33. $7a^2 + 2a - 5$ **34.** $8t^2 - 2t - 3$ **35.** $6m^2 - 5m - 14$

36. $4n^2 - 2n - 90$ **37.** $10c^2 - 14c + 4$ **38.** $-16k^2 + 8k + 24$

39. $5r^2 - 6r - 8$ **40.** $-12x^2 - 5x + 3$ **41.** $w(2w - 19) + 42$

ERROR ANALYSIS *Describe* and correct the error in solving the equation.

42.

$$5x^2 + x = 4$$
$$x(5x + 1) = 4$$
$$x = 4 \text{ or } 5x + 1 = 4$$
$$x = 4 \text{ or } \qquad x = \frac{3}{5}$$
✗

43.

$$12x^2 + 5x - 2 = 0$$
$$(3x - 1)(4x + 2) = 0$$
$$3x - 1 = 0 \text{ or } 4x + 2 = 0$$
$$x = \frac{1}{3} \text{ or } \qquad x = -\frac{1}{2}$$
✗

44. ⊕ **GEOMETRY** The length of a rectangle is 7 inches more than 5 times its width. The area of the rectangle is 6 square inches. What is the width?

45. **SHORT RESPONSE** The length of a rectangle is 1 inch more than 4 times its width. The area of the rectangle is 3 square inches. What is the perimeter of the rectangle? *Explain* how you found your answer.

SOLVING EQUATIONS Multiply each side of the equation by an appropriate power of 10 to obtain integer coefficients. Then solve the equation.

46. $0.3x^2 - 0.7x - 4.0 = 0$ **47.** $0.8x^2 - 1.8x - 0.5 = 0$ **48.** $0.4x^2 - 0.4x = 9.9$

49. ◆ **MULTIPLE CHOICE** What are the solutions of the equation $0.4x^2 - 1.1x = 2$?

  A -12.5 and 40 **B** -4 and 1.25 **C** -1.25 and 4 **D** -0.125 and 0.4

WRITING EQUATIONS Write a polynomial equation that has the given solutions. The equation must have integer coefficients. *Explain* your reasoning.

50. -3 and 2 **51.** $-\frac{1}{2}$ and 5 **52.** $-\frac{3}{4}$ and $-\frac{1}{3}$

◆ = **MULTIPLE CHOICE PRACTICE**   ◯ = **HINTS AND HOMEWORK HELP** at classzone.com

CONNECT SKILLS TO PROBLEM SOLVING Exercise 53–55 will help you prepare for problem solving.

Match the situation with the correct vertical motion model.

53. A kicked ball leaves the ground with an initial vertical velocity of 6 feet per second.

54. A ball is dropped from an initial height of 12 feet.

55. A ball is thrown from an initial height of 12 feet and with an initial vertical velocity of 6 feet per second.

$\quad$ **A.** $h = -16t^2 + 6t + 12$ $\quad$ **B.** $h = -16t^2 + 6t$ $\qquad$ **C.** $h = -16t^2 + 12$

EXAMPLES 4 and 5
on pp. 568–569 for Exs. 56–60

56. SCRAPBOOK DESIGN You plan to make a scrapbook. On the cover, you want to display three pictures with space between them, as shown. Each of the pictures is twice as long as it is wide.

a. Write a polynomial that represents the area of the scrapbook cover.

b. The area of the cover will be 96 square inches. Find the length and width of the pictures you will use.

California@HomeTutor for problem solving help at classzone.com

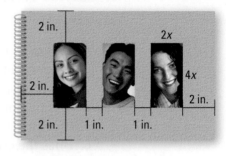

57. ◆ **MULTIPLE CHOICE** A diver dives from a cliff when her center of gravity is 46 feet above the surface of the water. Her initial vertical velocity leaving the cliff is 9 feet per second. After how many seconds does her center of gravity enter the water?

$\quad$ **(A)** 1.5 sec $\qquad$ **(B)** 2 sec $\qquad$ **(C)** 8 sec $\qquad$ **(D)** 23 sec

California@HomeTutor for problem solving help at classzone.com

58. SERVALS An African cat called a serval leaps from the ground in an attempt to catch a bird. The serval's initial vertical velocity is 24 feet per second.

a. Writing an Equation Write an equation that gives the serval's height (in feet) as a function of the time (in seconds) since it left the ground.

b. Making a Table Use the equation from part (a) to make a table that shows the height of the serval for $t = 0, 0.3, 0.6, 0.9, 1.2$, and 1.5 seconds.

c. Drawing a Graph Plot the ordered pairs in the table as points in a coordinate plane. Connect the points with a smooth curve. After how many seconds does the serval reach a height of 9 feet? *Justify* your answer using the equation from part (a).

Animated Algebra at classzone.com

The serval's initial vertical velocity is 24 ft/sec.

59. **PARTHENON** The Parthenon in Athens, Greece, is an ancient structure that has a rectangular base. The length of the Parthenon's base is 8 meters more than twice its width. The area of the base is about 2170 square meters. Find the length and width of the Parthenon's base.

60. **SHORT RESPONSE** You throw a ball into the air with an initial vertical velocity of 31 feet per second. The ball leaves your hand when it is 6 feet above the ground. You catch the ball when it reaches a height of 4 feet. After how many seconds do you catch the ball? *Explain* how you can use the solutions of an equation to find your answer.

CHALLENGE Factor the trinomial.

61. $2x^2 - 11xy + 5y^2$ **62.** $3x^2 + 2xy - 8y^2$ **63.** $6x^3 - 10x^2y - 56xy^2$

64. **CHALLENGE** A bush cricket jumps from the ground into the air with an initial vertical velocity of 4 feet per second.

     a. Write an equation that gives the cricket's height (in feet) as a function of the time (in seconds) since it left the ground. After how many seconds is the cricket 3 inches off the ground?

     b. Does the cricket jump higher than 3 inches? *Explain* your reasoning.

◆ CALIFORNIA STANDARDS SPIRAL REVIEW

Alg. 11.0   **65.** What is the greatest common monomial factor of $3xy^2 + 15x^3yz$? *(p. 549)*

     (A) $3xy$ **(B)** $3x^2yz$ **(C)** $4x^2y^2$ **(D)** $3x^3y^2$

Alg. 10.0   **66.** Find the product $(2x^2 - 5)(-4x)$. *(p. 528)*

     (A) $6x^2 + 10x$ **(B)** $-8x^3 + 20x$ **(C)** $-6x^2 + 20$ **(D)** $8x^3 - 9x$

Alg. 5.0   **67.** You spend $40 on beads and $12 on thread to make necklaces. You sell the necklaces for $9 each. What is the least number of necklaces that you must sell to make a profit? *(p. 202)*

     (A) 5   **(B)** 6   **(C)** 7   **(D)** 8

QUIZ for Lessons 9.5–9.7

Factor out the greatest common monomial factor. *(p. 549)*

   1. $16a^2 - 40b$ **2.** $12abc^2 - 6a^2c$ **3.** $-36s^3 + 18s^2 - 54s$

Factor the trinomial.

   4. $r^2 + 15r + 56$ *(p. 556)*   **5.** $-a^2 + 9a + 22$ *(p. 566)*   **6.** $18c^2 + 12c - 6$ *(p. 566)*

Solve the equation.

   7. $-8u^2 + 28u = 0$ *(p. 549)*   **8.** $m^2 + 12m = -35$ *(p. 556)*   **9.** $4y^2 + 31y = 8$ *(p. 566)*

10. **BASEBALL** A baseball player hits a baseball into the air from a height of 3 feet with an initial vertical velocity of 72 feet per second. After how many seconds is the baseball 84 feet above the ground? *(p. 566)*

9.8 Factor Special Products

Standards

Alg. 11.0 Students apply basic factoring techniques to second- and simple third-degree polynomials. These techniques include finding a common factor for all terms in a polynomial, recognizing the difference of two squares, and recognizing perfect squares of binomials.

Alg. 14.0 Students solve a quadratic equation by factoring or completing the square.

Alg. 25.2 Students judge the validity of an argument according to whether the properties of the real number system and the order of operations have been applied correctly at each step.

Math and **NATURE**
Ex. 45, p. 577

Connect   *Before* you factored polynomials of the form $ax^2 + bx + c$. *Now* you will factor special products.

Key Vocabulary
• **perfect square trinomial**

You can use the special product patterns you studied in Lesson 9.3 to factor polynomials, such as a difference of two squares.

KEY CONCEPT   *For Your Notebook*

Difference of Two Squares Pattern

Algebra   **Example**

$a^2 - b^2 = (a + b)(a - b)$ $y^2 - 16 = y^2 - 4^2 = (y + 4)(y - 4)$

EXAMPLE 1   Factor the difference of two squares

Factor the polynomial.

a. $25m^2 - 36 = (5m)^2 - 6^2$ Write as $a^2 - b^2$.

$\quad\quad\quad\quad = (5m + 6)(5m - 6)$ Difference of two squares pattern

b. $x^2 - 49y^2 = x^2 - (7y)^2$ Write as $a^2 - b^2$.

$\quad\quad\quad\quad = (x + 7y)(x - 7y)$ Difference of two squares pattern

c. $8 - 18n^2 = 2(4 - 9n^2)$ Factor out common factor.

$\quad\quad\quad\quad = 2[2^2 - (3n)^2]$ Write $4 - 9n^2$ as $a^2 - b^2$.

$\quad\quad\quad\quad = 2(2 + 3n)(2 - 3n)$ Difference of two squares pattern

d. $-9 + 4x^2 = 4x^2 - 9$ Rewrite as difference.

$\quad\quad\quad\quad = (2x)^2 - 3^2$ Write as $a^2 - b^2$.

$\quad\quad\quad\quad = (2x + 3)(2x - 3)$ Difference of two squares pattern

---

 GUIDED PRACTICE   for Example 1

1. Factor the polynomial $4y^2 - 64$.

PERFECT SQUARE TRINOMIALS The pattern for finding the square of a binomial gives you the pattern for factoring trinomials of the form $a^2 + 2ab + b^2$ and $a^2 - 2ab + b^2$. These are called **perfect square trinomials**.

KEY CONCEPT   *For Your Notebook*

Perfect Square Trinomial Pattern

Algebra   **Example**

$a^2 + 2ab + b^2 = (a + b)^2$ $x^2 + 6x + 9 = x^2 + 2(x \cdot 3) + 3^2 = (x + 3)^2$

$a^2 - 2ab + b^2 = (a - b)^2$ $x^2 - 10x + 25 = x^2 - 2(x \cdot 5) + 5^2 = (x - 5)^2$

EXAMPLE 2   **Factor perfect square trinomials**

Animated Algebra

For an interactive example of factoring perfect square trinomials, go to **classzone.com**.

Factor the polynomial.

a. $n^2 - 12n + 36 = n^2 - 2(n \cdot 6) + 6^2$ Write as $a^2 - 2ab + b^2$.

$= (n - 6)^2$ Perfect square trinomial pattern

b. $9x^2 - 12x + 4 = (3x)^2 - 2(3x \cdot 2) + 2^2$ Write as $a^2 - 2ab + b^2$.

$= (3x - 2)^2$ Perfect square trinomial pattern

c. $4s^2 + 4st + t^2 = (2s)^2 + 2(2s \cdot t) + t^2$ Write as $a^2 + 2ab + b^2$.

$= (2s + t)^2$ Perfect square trinomial pattern

EXAMPLE 3   ◆ **Multiple Choice Practice**

> **What is the factored form of $-3x^2 + 36xy - 108y^2$?**
>
> **(A)** $(-3x - 6y)^2$ **(B)** $-3(x + 6y)^2$ **(C)** $(3x - 6y)^2$ **(D)** $-3(x - 6y)^2$

Solution

$-3x^2 + 36xy - 108y^2 = -3(x^2 - 12xy + 36y^2)$ Factor out -3.

$= -3[x^2 - 2(x \cdot 6y) + (6y)^2]$ Write $x^2 - 12xy + 36y^2$ as $a^2 - 2ab + b^2$.

$= -3(x - 6y)^2$ Perfect square trinomial pattern

▶ The correct answer is D. Ⓐ Ⓑ Ⓒ ●

✓   **GUIDED PRACTICE**   for Examples 2 and 3

Factor the polynomial.

2. $h^2 + 4h + 4$ **3.** $2y^2 - 20y + 50$ **4.** $18z^2 + 12z + 2$

5. $4t^2 - 24t + 36$ **6.** $3x^2 + 6xy + 3y^2$ **7.** $x^2 + 12xy + 36y^2$

EXAMPLE 4 Solve a polynomial equation

Solve the equation $x^2 + \frac{2}{3}x + \frac{1}{9} = 0$.

$$x^2 + \frac{2}{3}x + \frac{1}{9} = 0 \qquad \text{Write original equation.}$$

$$9x^2 + 6x + 1 = 0 \qquad \text{Multiply each side by 9.}$$

$$(3x)^2 + 2(3x \cdot 1) + (1)^2 = 0 \qquad \text{Write left side as } a^2 + 2ab + b^2.$$

FIND SOLUTIONS
This equation has two identical solutions, because it has two identical factors.

$$\longrightarrow \quad (3x + 1)^2 = 0 \qquad \text{Perfect square trinomial pattern}$$

$$3x + 1 = 0 \qquad \text{Zero-product property}$$

$$x = -\frac{1}{3} \qquad \text{Solve for } x.$$

▶ The solution of the equation is $-\frac{1}{3}$.

EXAMPLE 5 Solve a vertical motion problem

FALLING OBJECT A window washer drops a wet sponge from a height of 64 feet. After how many seconds does the sponge land on the ground?

Solution

Use the vertical motion model to write an equation for the height h (in feet) of the sponge as a function of the time t (in seconds) after it is dropped.

Because the sponge was dropped, it has no initial vertical velocity. To determine when the sponge lands on the ground, find the value of t for which the height is 0.

Height: 64 feet

$$h = -16t^2 + vt + s \qquad \text{Vertical motion model}$$

$$0 = -16t^2 + (0)t + 64 \qquad \text{Substitute 0 for } h, \text{ 0 for } v, \text{ and 64 for } s.$$

$$0 = -16(t^2 - 4) \qquad \text{Factor out } -16.$$

$$0 = -16(t + 2)(t - 2) \qquad \text{Difference of two squares pattern}$$

$$t + 2 = 0 \quad or \quad t - 2 = 0 \qquad \text{Zero-product property}$$

$$t = -2 \quad or \qquad t = 2 \qquad \text{Solve for } t.$$

Disregard the negative solution of the equation.

▶ The sponge lands on the ground 2 seconds after it is dropped.

✓ **GUIDED PRACTICE** for Examples 4 and 5

Solve the equation.

8. $a^2 + 6a + 9 = 0$ **9.** $w^2 - 14w + 49 = 0$ **10.** $n^2 - 81 = 0$

11. WHAT IF? In Example 5, suppose the sponge is dropped from a height of 16 feet. After how many seconds does it land on the ground?

9.8 **EXERCISES**

HOMEWORK
KEY

◆ = MULTIPLE CHOICE PRACTICE
  Exs. 23, 24, 44, and 50–52

○ = HINTS AND HOMEWORK HELP
  for Exs. 11, 25, and 45 at classzone.com

SKILLS • PROBLEM SOLVING • REASONING

1. **VOCABULARY** Copy and complete: The polynomial $9n^2 + 6n + 1$ is called a(n) __?__ trinomial.

2. **WRITING** *Explain* how to factor the difference of two squares.

**EXAMPLES
1, 2, and 3**
on pp. 573–574
for Exs. 3–24

DIFFERENCE OF TWO SQUARES Factor the polynomial.

3. $x^2 - 25$

4. $n^2 - 64$

5. $81c^2 - 4$

6. $49 - 121p^2$

7. $-3m^2 + 48n^2$

8. $225x^2 - 144y^2$

PERFECT SQUARE TRINOMIALS Factor the polynomial.

9. $x^2 - 4x + 4$

10. $y^2 - 10y + 25$

11. $49a^2 + 14a + 1$

12. $9t^2 - 12t + 4$

13. $m^2 + m + \frac{1}{4}$

14. $2x^2 + 12xy + 18y^2$

FACTORING POLYNOMIALS Factor the polynomial.

15. $4c^2 - 400$

16. $4f^2 - 36f + 81$

17. $-9r^2 + 4s^2$

18. $z^2 + 12z + 36$

19. $72 - 32y^2$

20. $45r^2 - 120rs + 80s^2$

ERROR ANALYSIS *Describe* and correct the error in factoring.

21.
$$36x^2 - 81 = 9(4x^2 - 9)$$
$$= 9((2x)^2 - 3^2)$$
$$= 9(2x - 3)^2$$ ✗

22.
$$y^2 - 6y + 9 = y^2 - 2(y \cdot 3) + 3^2$$
$$= (y - 3)(y + 3)$$ ✗

23. ◆ **MULTIPLE CHOICE** What is the factored form of $-45x^2 + 20y^2$?

  Ⓐ $-5(3x + 2y)^2$

  Ⓑ $5(3x - 2y)^2$

  Ⓒ $-5(3x + 2y)(3x - 2y)$

  Ⓓ $5(3x + 2y)(3x - 2y)$

24. ◆ **MULTIPLE CHOICE** What is the factored form of $16m^2 - 8mn + n^2$?

  Ⓐ $(4m - n)^2$ Ⓑ $(4m + n)^2$ Ⓒ $(8m - n)^2$ Ⓓ $(4m - n)(4m + n)$

EXAMPLE 4
on p. 575
for Exs. 25–39

SOLVING EQUATIONS Solve the equation.

25. $x^2 + 8x + 16 = 0$

26. $16a^2 - 8a + 1 = 0$

27. $4w^2 - 36 = 0$

28. $-\frac{4}{3}x + \frac{4}{9} = -x^2$

29. $y^2 - \frac{5}{3}y = -\frac{25}{36}$

30. $\frac{2}{9} = 8n^2$

31. $-9c^2 = -16$

32. $-20s - 3 = 25s^2 + 1$

33. $y^4 - 2y^3 + y^2 = 0$

FINDING ROOTS Find the roots of the polynomial.

34. $36p^2 - 900$

35. $27c^2 + 108c + 108$

36. $8k^2 - 98$

37. $32 - 18m^2$

38. $-2h^2 - 28h - 98$

39. $-3t^2 + 108$

CONNECT SKILLS TO PROBLEM SOLVING Exercises 40–42 will help you prepare for problem solving.

Match the situation with the correct vertical motion model.

40. While bouncing a tennis ball before a serve, you throw the ball downward from a height of 4 feet with an initial vertical velocity of −36 feet per second.

41. A pine cone drops from a height of 36 feet.

42. A softball is hit from an initial height of 4 feet and with an initial vertical velocity of 36 feet per second.

    A. $h = -16t^2 + 36$ **B.** $h = -16t^2 + 36t + 4$ **C.** $h = -16t^2 - 36t + 4$

EXAMPLE 5
on p. 575
for Exs. 43–45

43. FALLING BRUSH While standing on a ladder, you drop a paintbrush from a height of 25 feet. After how many seconds does the paintbrush land on the ground?

    California @HomeTutor for problem solving help at classzone.com

44. ◆ MULTIPLE CHOICE A hickory nut falls from a branch that is 100 feet above the ground. After how many seconds does the hickory nut land on the ground?

    (A) 2 sec   **(B)** 2.5 sec   **(C)** 3 sec   **(D)** 3.5 sec

    California @HomeTutor for problem solving help at classzone.com

45. GRASSHOPPER A grasshopper jumps from the ground with an initial vertical velocity of 8 feet per second.

  a. Write an equation that gives the height (in feet) of the grasshopper as a function of the time (in seconds) since it leaves the ground.

  b. After how many seconds is the grasshopper 1 foot off the ground?

46. GRADUATION An arch of balloons decorates the stage at a high school graduation. The balloons are tied to a frame. The shape of the frame can be modeled by the graph of the equation $y = -\frac{1}{4}x^2 + 3x$ where x and y are measured in feet.

  a. Make a table of values that shows the height of the balloon arch for $x = 0, 2, 5, 8,$ and 11 feet.

  b. For what additional values of x does the equation make sense? *Explain.*

  c. Use your table from part (a) to approximate the distance from the left end at which the arch reaches a height of 9 feet. Check your answer algebraically.

47. FRAMING A square mirror is framed with stained glass as shown. Each corner of the frame began as a square with a side length of d inches before it was cut to fit the mirror. The mirror has a side length of 3 inches. The area of the stained glass frame is 91 square inches.

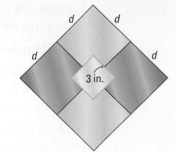

a. Write a polynomial that represents the area of the stained glass frame.

b. What is the side length of the frame?

48. REASONING Nick used the following argument to show that $2 = 0$. *Explain* where in his argument an error occurs.

Let $a = 1$ and $b = 1$.	Given
$a = b$	Transitive property of equality
$a^2 = b^2$	Square each side.
$a^2 - b^2 = 0$	Subtraction property of equality
$(a + b)(a - b) = 0$	Difference of squares
$\dfrac{(a + b)(a - b)}{a - b} = \dfrac{0}{a - b}$	Division property of equality
$a + b = 0$	Simplify each side.
$1 + 1 = 0$	Substitute 1 for a and 1 for b.
$2 = 0$	Add.

49. CHALLENGE Michelle used the following argument to show that $-1 = 1$. *Explain* where in her argument an error occurs.

Suppose a and b are two nonzero numbers such that $a = -2b$. Multiplying each side by a gives $a^2 = -2ab$. Adding $2ab + b^2$ to each side gives $a^2 + 2ab + b^2 = b^2$. Factoring the left side gives $(a + b)^2 = b^2$. Taking the positive square root of each side gives $a + b = b$. Substituting $-2b$ for a and simplifying the left side gives $-b = b$. Finally, dividing each side by b gives $-1 = 1$.

◆ CALIFORNIA STANDARDS SPIRAL REVIEW

Alg. 7.0

50. What is an equation of the line that passes through $(1, 1)$ and $(3, 5)$? *(p. 340)*

(A) $y - 5 = 2(x - 3)$ **(B)** $y + 1 = 2(x - 5)$

(C) $y - 3 = 2(x + 1)$ **(D)** $y + 1 = 2(x + 1)$

Alg. 9.0

51. What is the solution of the linear system $-x + 2y = 10$ and $3x + y = 5$? *(p. 383)*

(A) $(4, 7)$ **(B)** $(0, 5)$ **(C)** $(-8, 1)$ **(D)** $(3, -4)$

Alg. 15.0

52. You mix 14 grams of a solution that is 40% acid with 6 grams of a solution that is 60% acid. What percent of the mixture is acid? *(p. 418)*

(A) 44%   **(B)** 46%   **(C)** 50%   **(D)** 54 %

9.9 Factor Polynomials Completely

Standards Alg. 11.0 Students apply basic factoring techniques to second- and simple third-degree polynomials. These techniques include finding a common factor for all terms in a polynomial, recognizing the difference of two squares, and recognizing perfect squares of binomials.

Alg. 14.0 Students solve a quadratic equation by factoring or completing the square.

Alg. 25.1 Students use properties of numbers to construct simple, valid arguments (direct and indirect) for, or formulate counterexamples to, claimed assertions.

Math and **RECREATION**
Ex. 73, p. 585

Connect *Before* you used various factoring methods. *Now* you will combine methods to factor more complicated polynomials completely.

Key Vocabulary
• factor by grouping
• factor completely

You have used the distributive property to factor the greatest common monomial from the terms of a polynomial. Sometimes, you can factor out a common binomial.

EXAMPLE 1 **Factor out a common binomial**

Factor the expression.

a. $2x(x + 4) - 3(x + 4)$ 　　　　　　**b.** $3y^2(y - 2) + 5(2 - y)$

Solution

a. $2x(x + 4) - 3(x + 4) = (2x - 3)(x + 4)$ 　　**Distributive property**

b. The binomials $y - 2$ and $2 - y$ are opposites. Factor -1 from $2 - y$ to obtain $y - 2$ as a common binomial factor.

$3y^2(y - 2) + 5(2 - y) = 3y^2(y - 2) - 5(y - 2)$ 　　**Factor -1 from $(2 - y)$.**

$= (3y^2 - 5)(y - 2)$ 　　**Distributive property**

GROUPING You may be able to use the distributive property to factor polynomials with four terms. Factor a common monomial from pairs of terms, then look for a common binomial factor. This is called **factor by grouping**.

EXAMPLE 2 **Factor by grouping**

Factor $x^3 + 3x^2 + x + 3$.

:**CHECK WORK**
Remember that you can check a factorization by multiplying the factors.

$x^3 + 3x^2 + x + 3 = (x^3 + 3x^2) + (x + 3)$ 　　**Group terms.**

$= x^2(x + 3) + 1(x + 3)$ 　　**Factor each group; write $x + 3$ as $1(x + 3)$.**

$= (x^2 + 1)(x + 3)$ 　　**Distributive property**

9.9 Factor Polynomials Completely 　**579**

EXAMPLE 3 **Factor by grouping**

Factor $x^3 - 6 + 2x - 3x^2$.

Solution

The terms x^3 and -6 have no common factor. Use the commutative property to rearrange the terms so that you can group terms with a common factor.

$$x^3 - 6 + 2x - 3x^2 = x^3 - 3x^2 + 2x - 6 \qquad \text{Rearrange terms.}$$
$$= (x^3 - 3x^2) + (2x - 6) \qquad \text{Group terms.}$$
$$= x^2(\mathbf{x - 3}) + 2(\mathbf{x - 3}) \qquad \text{Factor each group.}$$
$$= (x^2 + 2)(\mathbf{x - 3}) \qquad \text{Distributive property}$$

CHECK   Check your factorization using a graphing calculator. Graph $y_1 = x^3 - 6 + 2x - 3x^2$ and $y_2 = (x - 3)(x^2 + 2)$. Because the graphs coincide, you know that your factorization is correct.

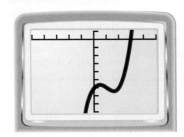

 GUIDED PRACTICE   for Examples 1, 2, and 3

Factor the expression.

1. $x(x - 2) + (x - 2)$ **2.** $a^3 + 3a^2 + a + 3$ **3.** $y^2 + 2x + yx + 2y$

READING
....
If a polynomial has two or more terms and is unfactorable, it is called a *prime polynomial*.

FACTORING COMPLETELY   You have seen that the polynomial $x^2 - 1$ can be factored as $(x + 1)(x - 1)$. This polynomial is factorable. Notice that the polynomial $x^2 + 1$ cannot be written as the product of polynomials with integer coefficients. This polynomial is unfactorable. A factorable polynomial with integer coefficients is **factored completely** if it is written as a product of unfactorable polynomials with integer coefficients.

CONCEPT SUMMARY   *For Your Notebook*

Guidelines for Factoring Polynomials Completely

To factor a polynomial completely, you should try each of these steps.

1. Factor out the greatest common monomial factor. $3x^2 + 6x = 3x(x + 2)$
  (Lesson 9.5)

2. Look for a difference of two squares or a perfect $x^2 + 4x + 4 = (x + 2)^2$
  square trinomial. *(Lesson 9.8)*

3. Factor a trinomial of the form $ax^2 + bx + c$ into a product $3x^2 - 5x - 2 = (3x + 1)(x - 2)$
  of binomial factors. *(Lessons 9.6 and 9.7)*

4. Factor a polynomial with four terms by grouping. $x^3 + x - 4x^2 - 4 = (x - 4)(x^2 + 1)$
  (Lesson 9.9)

EXAMPLE 4 ◆ Multiple Choice Practice

Which is the completely factored form of $12n^2 + 10n - 8$?

(A) $2(3n - 4)(2n + 1)$ **(B)** $2(3n + 4)(2n - 1)$

(C) $3(3n - 2)(2n + 2)$ **(C)** $3(6n - 2)(n + 4)$

Solution

$$12n^2 + 10n - 8 = 2(6n^2 + 5n - 4) \quad \text{Factor out 2.}$$
$$= 2(3n + 4)(2n - 1) \quad \text{Factor trinomial.}$$

▸ The correct answer is B. Ⓐ **Ⓑ** Ⓒ Ⓓ

✓ **GUIDED PRACTICE**   for Example 4

If possible, factor the polynomial completely.

4. $3x^3 - 12x$ **5.** $2y^3 - 12y^2 + 18y$ **6.** $m^3 - 2m^2 - 8m$

7. $n^2 + 2n - 1$ **8.** $4x^3 - 44x^2 + 96x$ **9.** $50h^4 - 2h^2$

EXAMPLE 5   Solve a polynomial equation

Solve $3x^3 + 18x^2 = -24x$.

Solution

$$3x^3 + 18x^2 = -24x \qquad \text{Write original equation.}$$
$$3x^3 + 18x^2 + 24x = 0 \qquad \text{Add 24x to each side.}$$
$$3x(x^2 + 6x + 8) = 0 \qquad \text{Factor out 3x.}$$
$$3x(x + 2)(x + 4) = 0 \qquad \text{Factor trinomial.}$$
$$3x = 0 \ \text{ or } \ x + 2 = 0 \quad \text{ or } \ x + 4 = 0 \qquad \text{Zero-product property}$$
$$x = 0 \ \text{ or } \quad x = -2 \ \text{ or } \quad x = -4 \qquad \text{Solve for x.}$$

▸ The solutions of the equation are 0, -2, and -4.

CHECK   Check each solution by substituting it for x in the equation. One check is shown here.

$$3(-2)^3 + 18(-2)^2 \overset{?}{=} -24(-2)$$
$$-24 + 72 \overset{?}{=} 48$$
$$48 = 48 \ ✓$$

✓ **GUIDED PRACTICE**   for Example 5

Solve the equation.

10. $w^3 - 8w^2 + 16w = 0$ **11.** $x^3 - 25x = 0$ **12.** $c^3 - 7c^2 + 12c = 0$

EXAMPLE 6 **Solve a multi-step problem**

TERRARIUM A large terrarium is used to display a box turtle in a pet store. The terrarium has the shape of a rectangular prism with a volume of 8748 cubic inches. The dimensions of the terrarium are shown. Find the length, width, and height of the terrarium.

$(w - 9)$ in.

w in.

$(w + 36)$ in.

Solution

STEP 1 **Write** a verbal model. Then write an equation.

Volume (cubic inches)	=	Length (inches)	·	Width (inches)	·	Height (inches)

$$8748 = (w + 36) \cdot w \cdot (w - 9)$$

STEP 2 **Solve** the equation for w.

$8748 = (w + 36)(w)(w - 9)$	**Write equation.**
$0 = w^3 + 27w^2 - 324w - 8748$	**Multiply. Subtract 8748 from each side.**
$0 = (w^3 + 27w^2) - (324w + 8748)$	**Group terms.**
$0 = w^2(w + 27) - 324(w + 27)$	**Factor each group.**
$0 = (w^2 - 324)(w + 27)$	**Distributive property**
$0 = (w + 18)(w - 18)(w + 27)$	**Difference of two squares pattern**
$w + 18 = 0$ or $w - 18 = 0$ or $w + 27 = 0$	**Zero-product property**
$w = -18$ or $w = 18$ or $w = -27$	**Solve for w.**

Because the width cannot be negative, the only solution is $w = 18$.

STEP 3 **Find** the length and height.

Length $= w + 36 = 18 + 36 = 54$

Height $= w - 9 = 18 - 9 = 9$

▶ The length is 54 inches, the width is 18 inches, and the height is 9 inches.

✓ **GUIDED PRACTICE** **for Example 6**

13. **DIMENSIONS OF A BOX** A box in the shape of a rectangular prism has a volume of 72 cubic feet. The box has a length of x feet, a width of $(x - 1)$ feet, and a height of $(x + 9)$ feet. Find the dimensions of the box.

9.9 EXERCISES

HOMEWORK KEY

◆ = MULTIPLE CHOICE PRACTICE
Exs. 12, 41, 72, and 79–81

◯ = HINTS AND HOMEWORK HELP
for Exs. 13, 23, and 73 at classzone.com

SKILLS · PROBLEM SOLVING · REASONING

1. **VOCABULARY** What does it mean for a polynomial with integer coefficients to be factored completely?

2. **WRITING** *Explain* how you know if a polynomial with integer coefficients is unfactorable.

EXAMPLE 1
on p. 579
for Exs. 3–12

BINOMIAL FACTORS **Factor the expression.**

3. $x(x - 8) + (x - 8)$

4. $5y(y + 3) - 2(y + 3)$

5. $6z(z - 4) - 7(z - 4)$

6. $10(a - 6) - 3a(a - 6)$

7. $b^2(b + 5) - 3(b + 5)$

8. $7c^2(c + 9) + 2(c + 9)$

9. $x(13 + x) - (x + 13)$

10. $y^2(y - 4) + 5(4 - y)$

11. $12(z - 1) - 5z^2(1 - z)$

12. ◆ **MULTIPLE CHOICE** What is the factored form of $x^2(x - 8) + 5(8 - x)$?

Ⓐ $(x^2 + 5)(x - 8)$

Ⓑ $(x^2 + 5)(8 - x)$

Ⓒ $(x^2 - 5)(x - 8)$

Ⓓ $(x^2 - 5)(8 - x)$

EXAMPLES 2 and 3
on pp. 579–580
for Exs. 13–22

FACTORING BY GROUPING **Factor the polynomial.**

13. $x^3 + x^2 + 2x + 2$

14. $y^3 - 9y^2 + y - 9$

15. $z^3 - 4z^2 + 3z - 12$

16. $c^3 + 7c^2 + 5c + 35$

17. $a^3 + 13a^2 - 5a - 65$

18. $2s^3 - 3s^2 + 18s - 27$

19. $5n^3 - 4n^2 + 25n - 20$

20. $x^2 + 8x - xy - 8y$

21. $y^2 + y + 5xy + 5x$

22. **ERROR ANALYSIS** *Describe* and correct the error in factoring.

$$a^3 + 8a^2 - 6a - 48 = a^2(a + 8) + 6(a + 8)$$
$$= (a^2 + 6)(a + 8)$$

EXAMPLE 4
on p. 581
for Exs. 23–42

FACTORING COMPLETELY **If possible, factor the polynomial completely.**

23. $x^4 - x^2$

24. $36a^4 - 4a^2$

25. $3n^5 - 48n^3$

26. $4y^6 - 16y^4$

27. $75c^9 - 3c^7$

28. $72p - 2p^3$

29. $32s^4 - 8s^2$

30. $80z^8 - 45z^6$

31. $m^2 - 5m - 35$

32. $6g^3 - 24g^2 + 24g$

33. $3w^4 + 24w^3 + 48w^2$

34. $3r^5 + 3r^4 - 90r^3$

35. $b^3 - 5b^2 - 4b + 20$

36. $h^3 + 4h^2 - 25h - 100$

37. $9t^3 + 18t - t^2 - 2$

38. $2x^5y - 162x^3y$

39. $7a^3b^3 - 63ab^3$

40. $-4s^3t^3 + 24s^2t^2 - 36st$

41. ◆ **MULTIPLE CHOICE** What is the completely factored form of $3x^6 - 75x^4$?

Ⓐ $3x^4(x^2 - 25)$

Ⓑ $3x^4(x - 5)^2$

Ⓒ $3x^4(x + 5)^2$

Ⓓ $3x^4(x + 5)(x - 5)$

42. **ERROR ANALYSIS** *Describe* and correct the error in factoring the polynomial completely.

$$x^3 - 6x^2 - 9x + 54 = x^2(x - 6) - 9(x - 6)$$
$$= (x^2 - 9)(x - 6)$$

EXAMPLE 5
on p. 581
for Exs. 43–54

SOLVING EQUATIONS Solve the equation.

43. $x^3 + x^2 - 4x - 4 = 0$

44. $a^3 - 11a^2 - 9a + 99 = 0$

45. $4y^3 - 7y^2 - 16y + 28 = 0$

46. $5n^3 - 30n^2 + 40n = 0$

47. $3b^3 + 24b^2 + 45b = 0$

48. $2t^5 + 2t^4 - 144t^3 = 0$

49. $z^3 - 81z = 0$

50. $c^4 - 100c^2 = 0$

51. $12s - 3s^3 = 0$

52. $2x^3 - 10x^2 + 40 = 8x$

53. $3p + 1 = p^2 + 3p^3$

54. $m^3 - 3m^2 = 4m - 12$

FINDING ROOTS Find the roots of the polynomial.

55. $h^3 - 2h^2 - 4h + 8$

56. $3t^3 - 15t^2 + 18t$

57. $p^3 - 36p$

58. $c^3 + 5c^2 - 4c - 20$

59. $5y^3 - y^2 - 45y + 9$

60. $2z^3 + z^2 - 2z - 1$

61. WRITING Is it possible to find three solutions of the equation $x^3 + 2x^2 + 3x + 6 = 0$? *Explain* why or why not.

GEOMETRY Find the length, width, and height of the rectangular prism with the given volume.

62. Volume = 12 in.^{3}

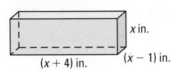

x in.

$(x + 4)$ in. $(x - 1)$ in.

63. Volume = 96 ft^3

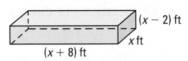

$(x - 2)$ ft

x ft

$(x + 8)$ ft

REASONING In Exercises 64–66, refer to the example to make a conjecture and write a proof.

EXAMPLE   **Make a conjecture, then prove it**

Make a conjecture about the product of an even integer and an odd integer. Then prove it.

Solution

Examples: $2 \cdot 3 = 6$ $4 \cdot 7 = 28$ $8 \cdot 5 = 40$

Conjecture: The product of an even integer and an odd integer is even.

Proof:

For any integers a and b, $2a$ is even and $2b + 1$ is odd.	**Definitions of even and odd integers** (See page 783.)
$2a(2b + 1) = 4ab + 2a$	**Distributive property**
$= 2(2ab + a)$	**Factor out 2.**
$= 2c$	**Substitute c for $2ab + a$. Because the set of integers is closed under addition and multiplication, c is an integer, and so is $2c$.**
$2c$ is an even integer, so $2a(2b + 1)$ is an even integer.	**Definition of even integer**

---

64. Make a conjecture about the square of an odd integer. Then prove it.

65. Make a conjecture about the product of two odd integers. Then prove it.

66. Make a conjecture about the cube of an odd integer. Then prove it.

◆ = **MULTIPLE CHOICE PRACTICE**   ◯ = **HINTS AND HOMEWORK HELP** at classzone.com

Find the dimensions of the rug given that it has an area of 24 square feet.

ℓ ft

w ft

67. $w = x, \ell = x + 5$

68. $w = x, \ell = 2x - 2$

69. $w = x, \ell = 6x$

EXAMPLE 6
on p. 582
for Exs. 70–72

70. **CYLINDRICAL VASE** A vase in the shape of a cylinder has a height of 6 inches and a volume of 24π cubic inches. What is the radius of the vase?

California @*HomeTutor* for problem solving help at classzone.com

71. **CARPENTRY** You are building a birdhouse that will have a volume of 128 cubic inches. The birdhouse will have the dimensions shown.

   a. Write a polynomial that represents the volume of the birdhouse.

   b. What are the dimensions of the birdhouse?

   California @*HomeTutor* for problem solving help at classzone.com

$(w + 4)$ in.

w in.   4 in.

72. ◆ **MULTIPLE CHOICE** A gift bag is shaped like a rectangular prism and has a volume of 1152 cubic inches. The dimensions of the gift bag are shown. The height is greater than the width. What is the height of the gift bag?

   (A) 2 in.   (B) 6 in.

   (C) 8 in.   (D) 12 in.

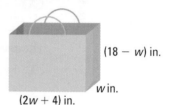

$(18 - w)$ in.

w in.

$(2w + 4)$ in.

73. **BOCCE** A pallino is the small target ball that is tossed in the air at the beginning of a game of bocce. The height h (in meters) of the pallino after you throw it can be modeled by $h = -4.9t^2 + 3.9t + 1$ where t is the time (in seconds) since you released it.

   a. For what values of t is $h = 0$?

   b. What meaning, if any, do the values of t found in part (a) have in this situation? *Explain* your reasoning.

74. **JUMPING ROBOT** The path of a jumping robot can be modeled by the graph of the equation $y = -10x^2 + 30x$ where x and y are both measured in feet. On a coordinate plane, the ground is represented by the x-axis, and the robot's starting position is the origin.

   a. The robot's maximum height is 22.5 feet. What is the robot's horizontal distance from its starting point when its height is 22.5 feet?

   b. How far has the robot traveled horizontally when when it lands on the ground? *Explain* your answer.

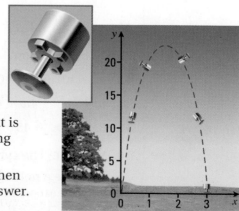

CHALLENGE Factor the polynomial completely.

75. $x^3 + 2x^2y - x - 2y$ **76.** $8b^3 - 4b^2a - 18b + 9a$ **77.** $4s^2 - s + 12st - 3t$

78. CHALLENGE A plastic cube is used to display an autographed baseball. The cube has an outer surface area of 54 square inches.

     a. Write a formula for the surface area of a cube with edge length s. Then use this formula to write and solve a polynomial equation to find the length of an outer edge of the plastic cube.

     b. What is the greatest volume the cube can possibly have? *Explain* why the actual volume inside of the cube may be less than the greatest possible volume.

◆ CALIFORNIA STANDARDS SPIRAL REVIEW

Alg. 8.0   **79.** What is an equation of the line that passes through $(6, 3)$ and is perpendicular to $y = -\frac{3}{5}x + 1$? *(p. 354)*

     (A) $y = \frac{3}{5}x + 1$ **(B)** $y = -\frac{5}{3}x - 13$ **(C)** $y = \frac{5}{3}x - 7$ **(D)** $y = \frac{5}{3}x + 1$

Alg. 4.0   **80.** What is the solution of $3(x + 3) + 2(2 - x) = 10$? *(p. 139)*

     (A) -3 **(B)** 0 **(C)** 2 **(D)** 5

Alg. 23.0   **81.** The height of a triangle is 6 inches greater than twice its base. The area of the triangle is 270 square inches. What is the base of the triangle? *(p. 566)*

     (A) 9 in.   **(B)** 10 in.   **(C)** 15 in.   **(D)** 18 in.

QUIZ *for Lessons 9.8–9.9*

Factor the polynomial. *(p. 573)*

   1. $x^2 - 400$ **2.** $18 - 32z^2$ **3.** $169x^2 - 25y^2$

   4. $n^2 - 6n + 9$ **5.** $100a^2 + 20a + 1$ **6.** $8r^2 - 40rs + 50s^2$

Factor the polynomial completely. *(p. 579)*

   7. $3x^5 - 75x^3$ **8.** $72s^4 - 8s^2$ **9.** $3x^4y - 300x^2y$

  10. $a^3 - 4a^2 - 21a$ **11.** $2h^4 + 28h^3 + 98h^2$ **12.** $z^3 - 4z^2 - 16z + 64$

Solve the equation.

  13. $x^2 + 10x + 25 = 0$ *(p. 573)*   **14.** $48 - 27m^2 = 0$ *(p. 573)*

  15. $w^3 - w^2 - 4w + 4 = 0$ *(p. 579)*   **16.** $4x^3 - 28x^2 + 40x = 0$ *(p. 579)*

  17. $3x^5 - 6x^4 - 45x^3 = 0$ *(p. 579)*   **18.** $x^3 - 121x = 0$ *(p. 579)*

  19. VOLUME The cylinder shown has a volume of 72π cubic inches. *(p. 573)*

     a. Write a polynomial equation that represents the situation. Leave your answer in terms of π.

     b. Find the radius of the cylinder.

r
8 in.

Multiple Choice Practice for Lessons 9.5–9.9

1. A tennis player hits a ball from an initial height of 4 feet and with an initial vertical velocity of 63 feet per second. After how many seconds does the tennis ball hit the ground? **Alg. 23.0**

   (A) 1 sec   (B) 4 sec

   (C) 6 sec   (D) 7 sec

2. A rectangular room has the dimensions shown. Which polynomial represents the area of the room? **Alg. 10.0**

   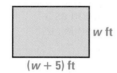

   w ft

   $(w + 5)$ ft

   (A) $w + 5w$ (B) $w^2 + 5w$

   (C) $w + 5$ (D) $w^2 + 5$

3. What is the completely factored form of $w^3 - w^2 - 4w + 4$? **Alg. 11.0**

   (A) $(w + 1)(w^2 - 4)$

   (B) $(w - 1)(w^2 - 4)$

   (C) $(w - 1)(w - 2)(w + 2)$

   (D) $(w + 1)(w - 2)(w + 2)$

4. You are making a wooden game board. You cut a square piece of wood, as shown. The area of the game board is 100 square inches. What equation can you use to find the side length of the original piece of wood? **Alg. 11.0**

   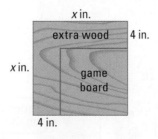

   x in.

   extra wood   4 in.

   x in.   game board

   4 in.

   (A) $x^2 - 16 = 100$

   (B) $x^2 + 16 = 100$

   (C) $(x - 4)^2 = 100$

   (D) $(x + 4)^2 = 100$

5. What are the solutions of the equation $-6x^2 - 18x = -60$? **Alg. 14.0**

   (A) 1 and 0   (B) 5 and -1

   (C) -8 and 3   (D) 2 and -5

6. What is the factored form of $4y^4 - 49$? **Alg. 11.0**

   (A) $(2y^2 + 7)(2y^2 - 7)$

   (B) $(2y^2 + 7)^2$

   (C) $(2y^2 - 7)^2$

   (D) $(2y - 7)(2y + 7)$

7. What are the solutions of the equation $(t + 4)(t - 7) = 0$? **Alg. 14.0**

   (A) 4 and -7 (B) -3 and 11

   (C) -4 and 7   (D) 3 and -3

8. What is the greatest common monomial factor of $7x^2y + 21xz - 42y^2z^2$? **Alg. 11.0**

   (A) xyz (B) $x^2y^2z^2$

   (C) 7   (D) $7x^2yz$

9. You hit a volleyball into the air. The diagram gives the initial vertical velocity v and initial height s of the volleyball. After how many seconds does the ball *first* reach a height of 13 feet? **Alg. 23.0**

   $v = 28$ ft/sec

   $s = 1$ ft

   (A) 0.3 sec   (B) 0.75 sec

   (C) 1 sec   (D) 1.3 sec

BIG IDEAS
For Your Notebook

Big Idea 1

Adding, Subtracting, Multiplying, and Dividing Polynomials

You can perform operations with polynomials using the steps below.

Operation	Steps
Add	Group like terms and add.
Subtract	First, rewrite subtraction as addition. Second, group like terms and add.
Multiply	First, multiply terms using the distributive property. Second, combine like terms.
Divide	To divide by a monomial, write the division as a fraction and simplify. To divide by a binomial, use long division.

Big Idea 2

Factoring Polynomials

When factoring a polynomial, you should use the following checklist so that you can be sure that you have factored the polynomial completely.

1. Factor out the greatest common monomial factor.

2. Look for special products to factor.

3. Factor a trinomial into a pair of binomials, if possible.

4. Factor a polynomial with four terms by grouping, if possible.

Big Idea 3

Writing and Solving Polynomial Equations to Solve Problems

You can write polynomials that model real-world situations in order to solve problems. For example, you can use the vertical motion model, $h = -16t^2 + vt + s$ (see page 551).

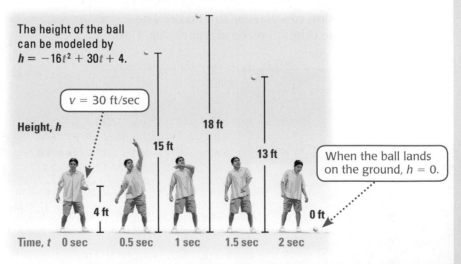

The height of the ball can be modeled by $h = -16t^2 + 30t + 4$.

$v = 30$ ft/sec

Height, h

18 ft

15 ft

13 ft

When the ball lands on the ground, $h = 0$.

4 ft

0 ft

Time, t 0 sec   0.5 sec   1 sec   1.5 sec   2 sec

APPLYING THE
BIG IDEAS

Big Idea 1
You use polynomial operations in **Step 2**.

Big Idea 2
You factor a polynomial in **Step 3**.

Big Idea 3
You write and solve a polynomial equation to solve a real-world problem in **Step 3**.

PROBLEM How can you use the volume of a box of detergent and the relationships among its dimensions to find the actual dimensions and surface area of the box?

STEP 1 Draw a diagram of a box.

You want to design a box for laundry detergent. The box should be a rectangular prism that holds 200 ounces of detergent. You determine that the volume of the box should be 768 cubic inches to hold this amount of detergent. You want the length of the box to be 4 inches greater than its height, and the width to be 16 inches less the height. Draw a diagram of the box and label the length and width in terms of the height h.

STEP 2 Write an expression for the volume of the box.

Use the formula $V = \ell wh$ to write a polynomial that represents the volume of the box of detergent.

STEP 3 Find the dimensions of the box.

Write an equation that relates the volume of the box given in Step 1 and the polynomial you wrote in Step 2. Use factoring to solve the equation. Then find the *two* sets of possible dimensions of the box.

STEP 4 Sketch or make the boxes.

Sketch both boxes or use construction paper or cardboard to make the boxes.

STEP 5 Find the surface area of the boxes.

Find the surface areas of the boxes with the dimensions you found in Step 3. Which box of detergent would be cheaper to make? *Explain*.

Extending the Problem

1. Use your results from the problem to complete parts (a) through (c).

   a. Find the dimensions of other rectangular prisms with a volume of 768 cubic inches. Include a cubic box with a volume of 768 cubic inches. (Approximate the edge length to be 9.15 inches.) Find the surface area of each box.

   b. Find the ratio of surface area to volume for each of the boxes.

   c. Compare the ratios of the boxes. Make a conjecture about the ratio of surface area to volume of the box and the cost of making that box.

2. Choose one of the sets of dimensions from Exercise 1 for the design of the laundry detergent box. *Explain* how you made your decision.

CHAPTER REVIEW

California @HomeTutor
classzone.com
• Multi-Language Visual Glossary
• Vocabulary practice

REVIEW KEY VOCABULARY

- monomial, *p. 520*
- degree of a monomial, *p. 520*
- polynomial, *p. 520*
- degree of a polynomial, *p. 520*

- leading coefficient, *p. 520*
- binomial, *p. 521*
- trinomial, *p. 521*
- root, *p. 550*

- vertical motion model, *p. 551*
- perfect square trinomial, *p. 574*
- factor by grouping, *p. 579*
- factor completely, *p. 580*

VOCABULARY EXERCISES

1. Copy and complete: The greatest degree of the terms in a polynomial is called the __?__ .

2. **WRITING** Is $2x^{-1}$ a monomial? *Explain* why or why not.

3. **NOTETAKING SKILLS** Make an information wheel like the one on page 518 for methods of factoring a polynomial.

In Exercises 4–6, match the polynomial with its classification.

4. $5x - 22$

5. $-11x^3$

6. $x^2 + x + 1$

A. Monomial

B. Binomial

C. Trinomial

REVIEW EXAMPLES AND EXERCISES

Use the review examples and exercises below to check your understanding of the concepts you have learned in each lesson of Chapter 9.

9.1 Add and Subtract Polynomials

pp. 520–525

Alg. 10.0

EXAMPLE

Find the difference $(3x^2 + 2) - (4x^2 - x - 9)$.

Use a vertical format.

$$
\begin{array}{r}
3x^2 + 2 \\
- \quad (4x^2 - x - 9) \\
\hline
\end{array}
\quad\Longrightarrow\quad
\begin{array}{r}
3x^2 + 2 \\
+ \quad -4x^2 + x + 9 \\
\hline
-x^2 + x + 11
\end{array}
$$

EXERCISES

EXAMPLES 4 and 5
on pp. 521–522
for Exs. 7–12

Find the sum or difference.

7. $(9x + 6x^3 - 8x^2) + (-5x^3 + 6x)$

8. $(7a^3 - 4a^2 - 2a + 1) + (a^3 - 1)$

9. $(11y^5 + 3y^2 - 4) + (y^2 - y + 1)$

10. $(3n^2 - 4n + 1) - (8n^2 - 4n + 17)$

11. $(2s^3 + 8) - (-3s^3 + 7s - 5)$

12. $(-k^2 + 7k + 5) - (2k^4 - 3k^3 - 6)$

9.2 Multiply Polynomials

pp. 528–533

Alg. 10.0

EXAMPLE

Find the product.

  a. $(x^2 + 4x - 5)(2x - 1)$ **b.** $(5y + 6)(y - 3)$

Solution

  a. Use a horizontal format.

$$(x^2 + 4x - 5)(2x - 1) \quad\quad \text{Write product.}$$
$$= x^2(2x - 1) + 4x(2x - 1) - 5(2x - 1) \quad\quad \text{Distributive property}$$
$$= 2x^3 - x^2 + 8x^2 - 4x - 10x + 5 \quad\quad \text{Distributive property}$$
$$= 2x^3 + 7x^2 - 14x + 5 \quad\quad \text{Combine like terms.}$$

  b. Use a vertical format.

STEP 1 Multiply by −3.	**STEP 2** Multiply by y.	**STEP 3** Add products.
$\begin{array}{r} 5y + 6 \\ \times \quad y - 3 \\ \hline -15y - 18 \end{array}$	$\begin{array}{r} 5y + 6 \\ \times \quad y - 3 \\ \hline -15y - 18 \\ 5y^2 + 6y \end{array}$	$\begin{array}{r} 5y + 6 \\ \times \quad y - 3 \\ \hline -15y - 18 \\ 5y^2 + 6y \\ \hline 5y^2 - 9y - 18 \end{array}$

EXERCISES

Find the product.

EXAMPLES 3, 4, 5, and 6 on pp. 528–529 for Exs. 13–21

13. $(x^2 - 2x + 1)(x - 3)$ **14.** $(y^2 + 5y + 4)(3y + 2)$ **15.** $(x - 4)(x + 2)$

16. $(5b^2 - b - 7)(b + 6)$ **17.** $(z + 8)(z - 11)$ **18.** $(2a - 1)(a - 3)$

19. $(6n + 7)(3n + 1)$ **20.** $(4n - 5)(7n - 3)$ **21.** $(3x - 2)(x + 4)$

9.3 Find Special Products of Polynomials

pp. 534–539

Alg. 10.0

EXAMPLE

Find the product $(3x + 2)(3x - 2)$.

$$(3x + 2)(3x - 2) = (3x)^2 - 2^2 \quad\quad \text{Sum and difference pattern}$$
$$= 9x^2 - 4 \quad\quad \text{Simplify.}$$

EXERCISES

Find the product.

EXAMPLES 1 and 2 on pp. 534–535 for Exs. 22–27

22. $(x + 11)^2$ **23.** $(6y + 1)^2$ **24.** $(2x - y)^2$

25. $(4a - 3)^2$ **26.** $(k + 7)(k - 7)$ **27.** $(3s + 5)(3s - 5)$

9.4 Divide Polynomials

pp. 541–547

Alg. 10.0

EXAMPLE

Divide $x^2 + 7x - 2$ by $x - 2$.

$$
\begin{array}{r}
x + 9 \\
x - 2 \overline{)\, x^2 + 7x - 2} \\
\end{array}
$$

$x^2 - 2x$ Multiply $x - 2$ and x.

$9x - 2$ Subtract $x^2 - 2x$. Bring down -2.

$9x - 18$ Multiply $x - 2$ and 9.

16 Subtract $9x - 18$.

▶ $(x^2 + 7x - 2) \div (x - 2) = x + 9 + \dfrac{16}{x - 2}$

EXERCISES

Divide.

EXAMPLES
4, 5, 6, 7, and 8
on pp. 542–544
for Exs. 28–32

28. $(x^2 + 12x + 35) \div (x + 7)$

29. $(y^2 - 5y - 8) \div (y - 3)$

30. $(4z + z^2 - 1) \div (5 + z)$

31. $(3a^2 - 2) \div (3 + 3a)$

32. CHARITY DONATIONS Sean intends to collect $500 in individual donations for a charity. His company will contribute $2 for every donation collected. Write an equation that gives the average amount a (including the company contribution) that the charity will receive per individual donation as a function of the number d of donations. Then make a table for the function. What do you notice as d increases?

9.5 Solve Polynomial Equations in Factored Form

pp. 549–554

Alg. 14.0

EXAMPLE

Solve $6x^2 + 42x = 0$.

$6x^2 + 42x = 0$ Write original equation.

$6x(x + 7) = 0$ Factor left side.

$6x = 0 \quad or \quad x + 7 = 0$ Zero-product property

$x = 0 \quad or \quad x = -7$ Solve for x.

▶ The solutions of the equation are 0 and -7.

EXERCISES

Solve the equation.

EXAMPLES
3 and 4
on p. 550
for Exs. 33–38

33. $2a^2 + 26a = 0$

34. $3t^2 - 33t = 0$

35. $8x^2 - 4x = 0$

36. $m^2 = 9m$

37. $5y^2 = -50y$

38. $21h^2 = 7h$

9.6 Factor $x^2 + bx + c$

pp. 556–562

Alg. 11.0

EXAMPLE

Factor $x^2 + 2x - 8$.

Find two factors of -8 whose sum is 2. One factor will be positive, and the other will be negative. Make an organized list of factors.

Factors of -8	Sum of factors	
1, -8	$1 + (-8) = -7$	✗
-1, 8	$-1 + 8 = 7$	✗
2, -4	$2 + (-4) = -2$	✗
-2, 4	$-2 + 4 = 2$	← Correct sum

▶ $x^2 + 2x - 8 = (x - 2)(x + 4)$

EXERCISES

EXAMPLES
1, 2, and 3
on pp. 556–557
for Exs. 39–47

Factor the trinomial.

39. $n^2 + 15n + 26$ **40.** $s^2 + 10s - 11$ **41.** $b^2 - 5b - 14$

42. $a^2 + 5a - 84$ **43.** $t^2 - 24t + 135$ **44.** $x^2 + 4x - 32$

45. $p^2 + 9p + 14$ **46.** $c^2 + 8c + 15$ **47.** $y^2 - 10y + 21$

9.7 Factor $ax^2 + bx + c$

pp. 566–572

Alg. 11.0

EXAMPLE

Factor $5x^2 + 14x - 3$.

Because b is positive and c is negative, the factors of c have different signs.

Factors of 5	Factors of -3	Possible factorization	Middle term when multiplied	
1, 5	1, -3	$(x + 1)(5x - 3)$	$-3x + 5x = 2x$	✗
1, 5	-1, 3	$(x - 1)(5x + 3)$	$3x - 5x = -2x$	✗
1, 5	3, -1	$(x + 3)(5x - 1)$	$-x + 15x = 14x$	← Correct sum
1, 5	-3, 1	$(x - 3)(5x + 1)$	$x - 15x = -14x$	✗

▶ $5x^2 + 14x - 3 = (x + 3)(5x - 1)$

EXERCISES

EXAMPLES
1 and 2
on pp. 566
for Exs. 48–53

Factor the trinomial.

48. $3s^2 + 4s - 4$ **49.** $2r^2 + 9r + 9$ **50.** $7x^2 - 8x + 1$

51. $4n^2 - 7n + 3$ **52.** $6z^2 + 13z - 5$ **53.** $3a^2 - 2a - 8$

9.8 Factor Special Products

pp. 573–578

Alg. 11.0   **EXAMPLE**

Factor the polynomial.

 a. $100x^2 - y^2$ **b.** $4x^2 - 36x + 81$

Solution

 a. $100x^2 - y^2 = (10x)^2 - y^2$ Write as $a^2 - b^2$.

              $= (10x + y)(10x - y)$ Difference of two squares pattern

 b. $4x^2 - 36x + 81 = (2x)^2 - 2(2x \cdot 9) + 9^2$ Write as $a^2 - 2ab + b^2$.

              $= (2x - 9)^2$ Perfect square trinomial pattern

EXERCISES

EXAMPLES
1, 2, 3, and 5
on pp. 573–575
for Exs. 54–60

Factor the polynomial.

54. $z^2 - 225$ **55.** $a^2 - 16y^2$ **56.** $12 - 48n^2$

57. $x^2 + 20x + 100$ **58.** $16p^2 - 8p + 1$ **59.** $-2y^2 + 32y - 128$

60. DROPPED OBJECT You drop a penny from a height of 16 feet. After how many seconds does the penny land on the ground?

9.9 Factor Polynomials Completely

pp. 579–586

Alg. 11.0   **EXAMPLE**

Factor the polynomial completely.

 a. $y^3 - 4y^2 + 8y - 32$ **b.** $5x^3 - 40x^2 + 80x$

Solution

 a. $y^3 - 4y^2 + 8y - 32 = (y^3 - 4y^2) + (8y - 32)$ Group terms.

              $= y^2(y - 4) + 8(y - 4)$ Factor each group.

              $= (y^2 + 8)(y - 4)$ Distributive property

 b. $5x^3 - 40x^2 + 80x = 5x(x^2 - 8x + 16)$ Factor out 5x.

              $= 5x(x - 4)^2$ Perfect square trinomial pattern

EXERCISES

EXAMPLES
2 and 4
on pp. 579–581
for Exs. 61–69

Factor the polynomial completely.

61. $a^3 + 6a - 5a^2 - 30$ **62.** $y^2 + 3y + yx + 3x$ **63.** $x^3 - 11x^2 - x + 11$

64. $5s^4 - 125s^2$ **65.** $147n^5 - 3n^3$ **66.** $2z^3 + 2z^2 - 60z$

67. $x^3 + 5x^2 - x - 5$ **68.** $2b^3 + 3b^2 - 8b - 12$ **69.** $x^3 + x^2 - 6x - 6$

1. **VOCABULARY** Copy and complete: A polynomial with two terms is called a(n) __?__ .

2. **VOCABULARY** Copy and complete: A polynomial having the form $a^2 + 2ab + b^2$ is called a(n) __?__ trinomial.

Find the sum or difference.

3. $(a^2 - 4a + 6) + (-3a^2 + 13a + 1)$

4. $(5x^2 - 2) + (8x^3 + 2x^2 - x + 9)$

5. $(15n^2 + 7n - 1) - (4n^2 - 3n - 8)$

6. $(9c^3 - 11c^2 + 2c) - (-6c^2 - 3c + 11)$

Find the product.

7. $(2z + 9)(z - 7)$

8. $(5m - 8)(5m - 7)$

9. $(b + 2)(-b^2 + 4b - 3)$

10. $(5 + 7y)(1 - 9y)$

11. $(2x^2 - 3x + 5)(x - 4)$

12. $(5p - 6)(5p + 6)$

13. $(12 - 3g)^2$

14. $(2s + 9t)^2$

15. $(11a - 4b)(11a + 4b)$

Divide.

16. $(8w - 2w^2 - 6) \div (w - 1)$

17. $(v^2 - 16v + 49) \div (v - 8)$

18. $(6x^2 + x) \div (2x + 1)$

Factor the polynomial.

19. $x^2 + 8x + 7$

20. $2n^2 - 11n + 15$

21. $-12r^2 + 5r + 3$

22. $t^2 - 10t + 25$

23. $-3n^2 + 75$

24. $3x^2 + 29x - 44$

25. $x^2 - 49$

26. $2a^4 + 21a^3 + 49a^2$

27. $y^3 + 2y^2 - 81y - 162$

Solve the equation.

28. $25a = 10a^2$

29. $21z^2 + 85z - 26 = 0$

30. $x^2 - 22x = -121$

31. $56b^2 + b = 1$

32. $n^3 - 121n = 0$

33. $a^3 + a^2 = 64a + 64$

34. **POSTER AREA** Two posters have the lengths and widths shown. The posters have the same area.

    a. Write an equation that relates the areas of the two posters.

    b. Find the length and width of each poster.

w ft
$3w$ ft

$(w + 2)$ ft
$2w$ ft

35. **VERTICAL MOTION** A cricket jumps off the ground with an initial vertical velocity of 4 feet per second. Write an equation that gives the height (in feet) of the cricket as a function of the time (in seconds) since it jumps. After how many seconds does the cricket land on the ground?

36. **BOX DIMENSIONS** A cardboard box that is a rectangular prism has the dimensions shown. The volume of the box is 72 cubic inches. What are the length, width, and height of the box?

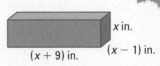
x in.
$(x + 9)$ in.
$(x - 1)$ in.

STRATEGIES YOU'LL USE:
- SOLVE DIRECTLY
- ELIMINATE CHOICES

Standards
Alg. 11.0, 14.0, 23.0

If you have difficulty solving a multiple choice problem directly, you may be able to use another approach to eliminate incorrect answer choices and obtain the correct answer.

PROBLEM 1

A rectangular photo has an area of 24 square inches. You trim the photo so that it fits into a square frame. You trim 3 inches from the length and 1 inch from the width of the photo. What is the side length of the resulting square photo?

(A) 0 in.   **(B)** 2 in.   **(C)** 3 in.   **(D)** 7 in.

Strategy 1 — SOLVE DIRECTLY

Use the formula for the area of a rectangle with length $\ell = x + 3$ and width $w = x + 1$.

$$A = \ell w$$
$$= (x + 3)(x + 1)$$
$$= x^2 + 4x + 3$$

Substitute 24 for A and solve.

$$24 = x^2 + 4x + 3$$
$$0 = x^2 + 4x - 21$$
$$0 = (x - 3)(x + 7)$$
$$0 = x - 3 \quad or \quad 0 = x + 7$$
$$x = 3 \quad or \quad x = -7$$

Disregard the negative value of x. The side length is 3 inches.

The correct answer is C. (A) (B) **(C)** (D)

Strategy 2 — ELIMINATE CHOICES

You can eliminate choices that do not make sense in the context of the problem.

Because the side length of the square photo cannot be 0 in., you can eliminate choice A.

Test the remaining choices.

Use the formula for the area of a rectangle, $A = \ell w$. Make a table of lengths, widths, and areas.

Answer choice	Length	Width	Area	
B	2 + 3 = 10	2 + 1 = 3	15	✗
C	3 + 3 = 6	3 + 1 = 4	24	✓
D	7 + 3 = 10	7 + 1 = 8	80	✗

The correct answer is C. (A) (B) **(C)** (D)

PROBLEM 2

What is the factored form of $x^2 + 3x - 4$?

(A) $(x - 2)(x - 2)$

(B) $(x - 2)(x + 2)$

(C) $(x + 4)(x + 1)$

(D) $(x + 4)(x - 1)$

| **Strategy 1** | SOLVE DIRECTLY |

Find two factors of -4 whose sum is 3.

Factors of −4	Sum of factors	
−4, 1	−4 + 1 = −3	✗
4, −1	4 + (−1) = 3	Correct sum
2, −2	2 + (−2) = 0	✗
−2, 2	−2 + 2 = 0	✗

The factors 4 and -1 have a sum of 3.

$x^2 + 3x - 4 = (x + 4)(x - 1)$

The correct answer is D. (A) (B) (C) **(D)**

| **Strategy 2** | ELIMINATE CHOICES |

When factoring trinomials of the form $x^2 + bx + c$, you can use the signs of b and c to eliminate choices.

Recall that $x^2 + bx + c = (x + p)(x + q)$.

Because c is negative, you know that p and q have different signs. So, you can eliminate choice A and choice C.

You can use the FOIL method to test choice B.

$(x - 2)(x + 2) = x^2 + 2x - 2x - 4$

$\qquad\qquad\quad = x^2 - 4$

So, you can eliminate choice B.

The correct answer is D. (A) (B) (C) **(D)**

STRATEGY PRACTICE

Explain why you can eliminate the highlighted answer choice.

1. What are the solutions of the equation $(x + 4)(x - 12) = 0$?

   (A) ✗ **4 and −12**   (B) 4 and 12   (C) −4 and −12   (D) −4 and 12

2. What is the factored form of $25x^2 - 144$?

   (A) $(5x + 9)(5x - 16)$

   (B) ✗ $(5x - 12)^2$

   (C) $(5x + 18)(5x - 18)$

   (D) $(5x - 12)(5x + 12)$

3. A fish tank is a rectangular prism with a volume of 576 cubic inches. Its length is greater than 10 inches. The dimensions of the tank are shown in the diagram. What is the height of the fish tank?

   (A) ✗ **2 in.**   (B) 4 in.

   (C) 6 in.   (D) 8 in.

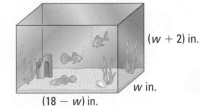

$(w + 2)$ in.

w in.

$(18 - w)$ in.

1. What is the sum of $x^2 - 4x + 3$ and $3x^2 - 3x - 5$? **Alg. 10.0**

   (A) $2x^2 + x - 8$

   (B) $4x^2 - 7x - 2$

   (C) $-2x^2 - x + 8$

   (D) $-4x^2 + 7x + 2$

2. What is the product of $6 - 5n$ and $6 + 5n$? **Alg. 10.0**

   (A) $25n^2 - 36$

   (B) $-25n^2 + 60n + 36$

   (C) $36 - 25n^2$

   (D) $25n^2 - 60n - 36$

3. A rectangle's length is 13 meters more than 3 times its width. The area is 10 square meters. What is the width? **Alg. 23.0**

   (A) $\frac{2}{3}$ m

   (B) 3 m

   (C) 5 m

   (D) 10 m

4. You hit a baseball straight up into the air. The diagram gives the initial vertical velocity v and the initial height s of the baseball. How many times does the baseball reach a height of 99 feet? **Alg. 23.0**

   (A) 0

   (B) 1

   (C) 2

   (D) 3

$v = 80$ ft/sec

$s = 3$ ft

5. What is the quotient of $x^2 + x - 17$ and $x - 4$? **Alg. 10.0**

   (A) $x + 5 + \dfrac{3}{x - 4}$

   (B) $x + 5$

   (C) $x + 3 + \dfrac{2}{x - 4}$

   (D) $x - 2$

6. What is the greatest common monomial factor of $-2x^3y + 10x^2z - 4xy^4z + 8yz^3$? **Alg. 11.0**

   (A) $2x^3y^4z^3$

   (B) 2

   (C) $2xyz^3$

   (D) xyz

7. A block of clay in the shape of a rectangular prism has the dimensions shown. The clay has a volume of 180 cubic inches. What are the length, width, and height of the block? **Alg. 23.0**

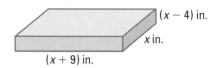

$(x - 4)$ in.

x in.

$(x + 9)$ in.

   (A) 10 in., 3 in., 2 in.

   (B) 9 in., 7 in., 3 in.

   (C) 12 in., 9 in., 4 in.

   (D) 15 in., 6 in., 2 in.

8. A triangle's height is 4 less than 2 times the base. The area of the triangle is 15 square inches. What is the height of the triangle? **Alg. 23.0**

   (A) 3 in.

   (B) 5 in.

   (C) 6 in.

   (D) 8 in.

9. You are designing a postcard that has a border along the bottom, as shown. The area of the picture part of the postcard is 54 square centimeters. What is the area of the border? **Alg. 23.0**

r cm

2 cm

(*r* + 3) cm

  A   10 cm²

  B   14 cm²

  C   18 cm²

  D   22 cm²

10. During the period 1996–2000, the total value *T* (in millions of dollars) of toys imported to the United States can be modeled by

$$T = 82.9t^3 - 848t^2 + 3030t + 9610$$

where *t* is the number of years since 1996. What is the degree of the polynomial that represents *T*? **Alg. 10.0**

  A   1

  B   2

  C   3

  D   4

11. What are the solutions of the equation $4x^2 - 8x = -3$? **Alg. 14.0**

  A $\frac{1}{2}$ and $\frac{3}{2}$

  B   2 and 1

  C $\frac{1}{3}$ and $\frac{2}{3}$

  D   0 and −4

12. What is the factored form of $6x^2 + x - 35$? **Alg. 11.0**

  A $(3x - 5)(2x + 7)$

  B $(2x + 7)(3x + 5)$

  C $(3x - 7)(2x + 5)$

  D $(2x + 5)(3x + 7)$

13. The dimensions of a rectangular box are shown. Which polynomial represents the volume of the box? **Alg. 10.0**

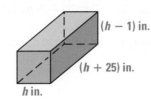

(*h* − 1) in.

(*h* + 25) in.

h in.

  A $h^3 - 25h^2 - h$

  B $h^3 + h^2 - h$

  C $h^3 - 20h^2 + 24h$

  D $h^3 + 24h^2 - 25h$

14. What is the difference of $3x^3 - 2x^2 + 5$ and $x^3 - 5x^2 + x$? **Alg. 10.0**

  A $2x^3 + 3x^2 - x + 5$

  B $2x^3 + 3x^2 + x + 5$

  C $2x^3 - 7x^2 - x + 5$

  D $2x^3 - 7x^2 + x + 5$

15. A circular rug has an interior circle and two rings around the circle, as shown. Which polynomial represents the area of the rug? **Alg. 10.0**

  A $\pi r^2 + \pi r + \pi$

  B $\pi(r + 2)$

  C $\pi r + 4\pi$

  D $\pi r^2 + 4\pi r + 4\pi$

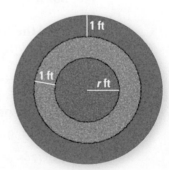

1 ft

1 ft

r ft

Evaluate the expression for the given value of x. (p. 53)

1. $-|x| + 9$ when $x = -6$

2. $|-x| + 2.6$ when $x = 2$

3. $0.7 - |x|$ when $x = -0.5$

Solve the equation.

4. $9x + 4 = -14$ **(p. 132)**

5. $5 - 2a = 13$ **(p. 132)**

6. $13y + 16 - y = 4$ **(p. 139)**

7. $6d + 11 - 8d = 5$ **(p. 139)**

8. $7n + 3 = n - 15$ **(p. 146)**

9. $-(w + 1) = w + 3$ **(p. 146)**

Solve the inequality. Then graph the solution.

10. $m - 8 < -15$ **(p. 189)**

11. $\dfrac{x}{-3} > 12$ **(p. 196)**

12. $1 - 4n < -11$ **(p. 202)**

13. $5b - 7 \le 7b - 5$ **(p. 202)**

14. $12 < z + 9 \le 16$ **(p. 210)**

15. $4 \le 2c + 7 \le 21$ **(p. 210)**

Graph the equation. (pp. 264, 273, 291, 297)

16. $x = -6$

17. $y = -3x$

18. $y = 6.5x$

19. $y = \dfrac{4}{3}x - 8$

20. $y = -3x + 9$

21. $y + x = 8$

22. $2y - x = 2$

23. $2x + 5y = -40$

Write an equation of the line that passes through the given point and is perpendicular to the given line. (p. 354)

24. $(0, 3)$, $y = -5x + 2$

25. $(2, 2)$, $y = -x - 7$

26. $(8, 3)$, $y = \dfrac{1}{2}x + 2$

Solve the linear system. (pp. 376, 383, 391, 398, 405)

27. $y = 5x - 4$
$-4x + y = -2$

28. $x - 4y = -44$
$-3x + 12y = 132$

29. $-4x + 7y = -33$
$-3x + 2y = -15$

Simplify the expression. Write your answer using only positive exponents.

30. $(-9r)^3$ **(p. 460)**

31. $(2p^4)^3 \cdot p^7$ **(p. 460)**

32. $\dfrac{(3x)^4 y}{xy^3}$ **(p. 467)**

33. $(2x^3)^{-4} \cdot 4x^9$ **(p. 475)**

34. $\dfrac{(3x)^{-3} y^3}{x^2 y^0}$ **(p. 475)**

35. $(9x^2)^{-3/2} \cdot \sqrt[3]{8y^6}$ **(p. 498)**

Let a and b represent the lengths of the legs of a right triangle, and let c represent the length of the hypotenuse. Find the unknown length. (p. 491)

36. $a = 10$, $b = 24$

37. $b = 8$, $c = 10$

38. $a = 2$, $b = 8$

Find the sum or difference. (p. 520)

39. $(x^2 - 3x + 8) + (-2x^2 + 15x + 4)$

40. $(7 - 3a^3 + 9a) + (a^3 - 2a + 5)$

41. $(4b^2 - 10b + 13) - (-3b^2 + 7b + 1)$

42. $(5m^2 - 6) - (8m^3 + m^2 - 2m + 11)$

Find the product or quotient.

43. $(z + 9)(2z - 7)$ **(p. 528)**

44. $(5b - 2)(8b - 7)$ **(p. 528)**

45. $(7 + y)^2$ **(p. 534)**

46. $(12w - 5)(12w + 5)$ **(p. 534)**

47. $(x^2 + x - 17) \div (x - 4)$ **(p. 541)**

48. $(3a^2 - 11a - 26) \div (a - 5)$ **(p. 541)**

Factor the expression.

49. $x^2 + 6x - 72$ *(p. 556)*

50. $2m^2 - 5mn - 3n^2$ *(p. 566)*

51. $25d^2 + 60d + 36$ *(p. 573)*

52. $-2a^2 + 50b^2$ *(p. 573)*

53. $z^2(z - 6) + 4(6 - z)$ *(p. 579)*

54. $y^3 + 8y^2 - 9y - 72$ *(p. 579)*

55. BIKING You ride 18 miles on a bike in 2 hours. At this rate, how long will it take you to bike 49.5 miles? *(p. 19)*

56. SPORTS The Pan American Games is a sports event that is held every four years. Athletes from countries in North America, Central America, and South America compete in the games. The table shows the number *c* of countries that participated in each Pan American Games as a function of the time *t* (in years) since 1951. Graph the function. *(p. 257)*

Years since 1951, t	0	4	8	12	16	20	24	28	32
Countries, c	21	22	25	22	29	32	33	34	36

57. HORSEBACK RIDING The members of a family are horseback riding and they want to avoid using steep trails. The steepest part of trail A rises 15 feet over a horizontal distance of 50 feet. The steepest part of trail B rises 30 feet over a horizontal distance of 75 feet. Which trail should the family use? *Explain.* *(p. 282)*

58. CUSTOM PRINTING You create a design for a T-shirt. The table shows the cost for printing your design on T-shirts at a printing company. The printing company requires that your design be printed on a minimum of 6 T-shirts. *(p. 340)*

T-shirts	6	7	8	9	10
Cost (dollars)	78	81	84	87	90

    a. *Explain* why the situation can be modeled by a linear equation.

    b. Write an equation that gives the cost of the T-shirts as a function of the number of T-shirts printed. What is the domain of the function?

59. GEOMETRY A rectangle has a perimeter of 54 inches. Its length is 3 more than twice its width. Find the dimensions of the rectangle. *(p. 383)*

60. GUY WIRE A guy wire supports an antenna tower, as shown at the right. The bottom of the wire is secured in the ground 30 feet from the base of the tower. The top of the wire is secured to the tower at a height of 30 feet above the ground. How long is the wire? Round your answer to the nearest tenth of a foot. *(p. 491)*

30 ft   guy wire

30 ft

10 Quadratic Equations and Functions

Before

In previous chapters, you learned the following skills, which you'll use in Chapter 10:

- Evaluating and simplifying square roots
- Graphing equations by making a table of values
- Factoring a perfect square trinomial

Now

In Chapter 10 you'll study these **Big Ideas:**

① Graphing quadratic functions

② Solving quadratic equations

③ Finding numbers of roots, solutions, x-intercepts, and zeros

Why?

So you can solve real-world problems about . . .

- Sailing, p. 610
- Spiders, p. 617
- Football, p. 622
- Snowboarding, p. 648
- Advertising, p. 654
- Camping, p. 661

Animated Algebra
at *classzone.com*

Get-Ready Games

FOUR IN A ROW

California Standards

Review finding *x*- and *y*-intercepts. **Alg. 6.0**
Prepare for graphing quadratic functions. **Alg. 21.0**

Materials

- One deck of *Four in a Row* cards
- One *Four in a Row* game board
- 48 markers, 24 each of two colors

How to Play Play in pairs. Divide the markers so that each player has 24 markers of the same color. Shuffle the deck of cards and place the deck face down next to the game board. On each turn, each player should follow the steps on the next page.

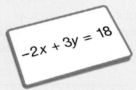

$$-2x + 3y = 18$$

1 **Draw** the top card from the deck.

$$-2x + 3y = 18$$

2 **Find** the intercepts of the graph of the equation.

$$-2(0) + 3y = 18; y = 6$$
y-intercept 6

$$-2x + 3(0) = 18; x = -9$$
x-intercept −9

3 **Place** a marker on *one* space of the game board that contains a fact about the graph of the equation. If there are no available spaces, your turn ends.

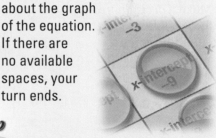

How to Win Be the first player to have four markers in a row on the game board. Markers can be aligned vertically, horizontally, or diagonally.

Games Wrap-Up

Draw Conclusions

Complete these exercises after playing the game.

1. **WRITING** Suppose you identify two *x*-intercepts of a given line. What can you say about the line? *Explain* your reasoning.

2. **REASONING** Suppose the first card that you draw has the equation $y = 3$. Where could you put your marker? *Explain* your reasoning.

Prerequisite Skills

California @HomeTutor
Prerequisite skills practice
at classzone.com

REVIEW VOCABULARY

- **root,** *p. 550*
- **x-intercept,** *p. 273*
- **square root,** *p. 95*
- **perfect square,** *p. 96*
- **perfect square trinomial,** *p. 574*

VOCABULARY CHECK

Copy and complete the statement.

1. The x-coordinate of a point where a graph crosses the x-axis is a(n) __?__ .

2. Polynomials of the form $a^2 + 2ab + b^2$ and $a^2 - 2ab + b^2$ are called __?__ .

SKILLS CHECK

Draw the blue figure. Then draw its image after a reflection in the red line.
(Review p. 801 for 10.1–10.4.)

3.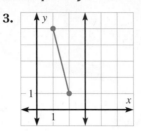

4.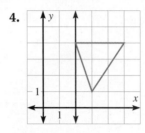

5.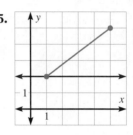

Simplify the expression. *(Review p. 483 for 10.5–10.7.)*

6. $\sqrt{12}$ 7. $-\sqrt{50}$ 8. $\sqrt{28}$ 9. $\pm\sqrt{45}$

Notetaking Skills

NOW YOU TRY
Make a *decision tree* for graphing a linear equation. You may want to use colored pencils.

Focus on Graphic Organizers

You can use a *decision tree* to organize the steps of a process, such as factoring a polynomial. In a decision tree, each box represents a possible step that you can take in a process. Arrows branching from one box indicate a choice that you must make.

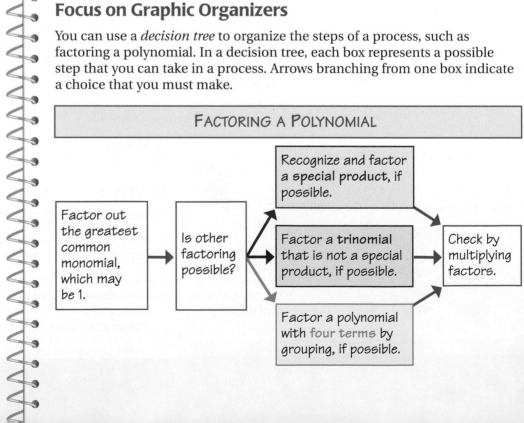

10.1 Graph $y = ax^2 + c$

Standards — **Alg. 21.0** Students graph quadratic functions and know that their roots are the *x*-intercepts.

Connect — *Before* you graphed linear functions. *Now* you will graph simple quadratic functions.

Math and ASTRONOMY
Example 5, p. 608

Key Vocabulary
- quadratic function
- standard form
- parabola
- vertex
- axis of symmetry

A **quadratic function** is a nonlinear function that can be written in the **standard form** $y = ax^2 + bx + c$ where $a \neq 0$. Every quadratic function has a U-shaped graph called a **parabola**. In this lesson, you will graph quadratic functions where $b = 0$. The graph of the basic function $y = x^2$ is shown below.

KEY CONCEPT   *For Your Notebook*

Graph of $y = x^2$

The lowest or highest point on a parabola is the **vertex**. The vertex of the graph of $y = x^2$ is $(0, 0)$.

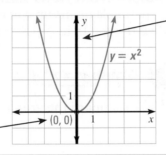

The line that passes through the vertex and divides the parabola into two symmetric parts is called the **axis of symmetry**. The axis of symmetry for the graph of $y = x^2$ is the *y*-axis, $x = 0$.

REVIEW SYMMETRY
For help with symmetry, see p. 801.

EXAMPLE 1   **Graph $y = ax^2$ where $|a| > 1$**

Graph $y = 3x^2$. Compare the graph with the graph of $y = x^2$.

Solution

STEP 1 **Make** a table of values for $y = 3x^2$.

x	−2	−1	0	1	2
y	12	3	0	3	12

STEP 2 **Plot** the points from the table.

STEP 3 **Draw** a smooth curve through the points.

STEP 4 **Compare** the graphs of $y = 3x^2$ and $y = x^2$. Both graphs open up and have the same vertex, $(0, 0)$, and axis of symmetry, $x = 0$. The graph of $y = 3x^2$ is narrower than the graph of $y = x^2$.

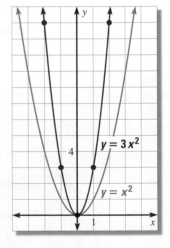

PLOT ADDITIONAL POINTS
If you are having difficulty seeing the shape of the parabola, plot additional points.

EXAMPLE 2 Graph $y = ax^2$ where $|a| < 1$

Graph $y = -\frac{1}{4}x^2$. Compare the graph with the graph of $y = x^2$.

Solution

STEP 1 Make a table of values for $y = -\frac{1}{4}x^2$.

MAKE A TABLE
To make the calculations easier, choose values of x that are multiples of 2.

x	−4	−2	0	2	4
y	−4	−1	0	−1	−4

STEP 2 Plot the points from the table.

STEP 3 Draw a smooth curve through the points.

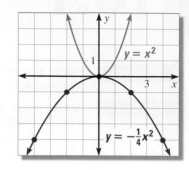

STEP 4 Compare the graphs of $y = -\frac{1}{4}x^2$ and $y = x^2$. Both graphs have the same vertex, $(0, 0)$, and the same axis of symmetry, $x = 0$. However, the graph of $y = -\frac{1}{4}x^2$ is a reflection in the x-axis of the graph of $y = \frac{1}{4}x^2$ and is wider than the graph of $y = x^2$.

REVIEW REFLECTIONS
For help with reflections, see p. 801.

GRAPHING QUADRATIC FUNCTIONS Examples 1 and 2 suggest the following general result: a parabola opens up when the coefficient of x^2 is positive and opens down when the coefficient of x^2 is negative.

EXAMPLE 3 Graph $y = x^2 + c$

Graph $y = x^2 + 5$. Compare the graph with the graph of $y = x^2$.

Solution

STEP 1 Make a table of values for $y = x^2 + 5$.

x	−2	−1	0	1	2
y	9	6	5	6	9

STEP 2 Plot the points from the table.

STEP 3 Draw a smooth curve through the points.

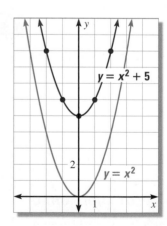

STEP 4 Compare the graphs of $y = x^2 + 5$ and $y = x^2$. Both graphs open up and have the same axis of symmetry, $x = 0$. However, the vertex of the graph of $y = x^2 + 5$, $(0, 5)$, is different than the vertex of the graph of $y = x^2$, $(0, 0)$, because the graph of $y = x^2 + 5$ is a vertical translation (of 5 units up) of the graph of $y = x^2$.

REVIEW TRANSLATIONS
For help with translations, see p. 801.

✓ **GUIDED PRACTICE** for Examples 1, 2, and 3

Graph the function. Compare the graph with the graph of $y = x^2$.

1. $y = -4x^2$ **2.** $y = \frac{1}{3}x^2$ **3.** $y = x^2 + 2$

EXAMPLE 4 Graph $y = ax^2 + c$

Graph $y = \frac{1}{2}x^2 - 4$. Compare the graph with the graph of $y = x^2$.

Solution

STEP 1 Make a table of values for $y = \frac{1}{2}x^2 - 4$.

x	−4	−2	0	2	4
y	4	−2	−4	−2	4

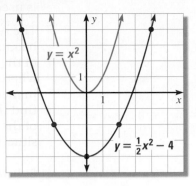

STEP 2 Plot the points from the table.

STEP 3 Draw a smooth curve through the points.

STEP 4 Compare the graphs of $y = \frac{1}{2}x^2 - 4$ and $y = x^2$. Both graphs open up and have the same axis of symmetry, $x = 0$. However, the graph of $y = \frac{1}{2}x^2 - 4$ is a vertical translation (of 4 units down) of the graph of $y = \frac{1}{2}x^2$ and is wider than the graph of $y = x^2$.

✓ **GUIDED PRACTICE** for Example 4

Graph the function. Compare the graph with the graph of $y = x^2$.

4. $y = 3x^2 - 6$ **5.** $y = -5x^2 + 1$ **6.** $y = \frac{3}{4}x^2 - 2$

KEY CONCEPT   *For Your Notebook*

Comparing Graphs of Quadratic Functions

$y = ax^2, a > 0$	$y = ax^2, a < 0$	$y = x^2 + c$
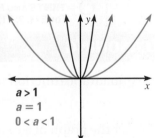	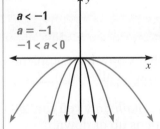	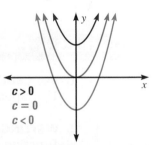
$a > 1$ $a = 1$ $0 < a < 1$	$a < -1$ $a = -1$ $-1 < a < 0$	$c > 0$ $c = 0$ $c < 0$
Compared with the graph of $y = x^2$, the graph of $y = ax^2$ is: • narrower if $a > 1$, • wider if $0 < a < 1$.	Compared with the graph of $y = x^2$, the graph of $y = ax^2$ is: • narrower with a reflection in the x-axis if $a < -1$, • wider with a reflection in the x-axis if $-1 < a < 0$.	Compared with the graph of $y = x^2$, the graph of $y = x^2 + c$ is: • an upward vertical translation if $c > 0$, • a downward vertical translation if $c < 0$.

EXAMPLE 5 Use a graph

SOLAR ENERGY A solar trough has a parabolic surface that reflects light and is used to collect solar energy.

The reflective surface can be modeled by the graph of the function $y = 0.09x^2$ where x and y are measured in meters. Use the graph to find the domain and range of the function in this situation.

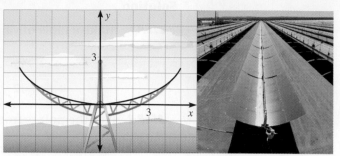

Solution

STEP 1 Find the domain. In the graph, the reflective surface extends 5 meters on either side of the origin. So, the domain is $-5 \le x \le 5$.

STEP 2 Find the range using the fact that the lowest point on the reflective surface is $(0, 0)$ and the highest point occurs at each end. The ends are each 5 meters from the lowest point.

$$y = 0.09(5)^2 = 2.25 \qquad \text{Substitute 5 for } x. \text{ Then simplify.}$$

The range is $0 \le y \le 2.25$.

✓ **GUIDED PRACTICE** for Example 5

7. **WHAT IF?** In Example 5, suppose the reflective surface extends 4 meters on either side of the origin. Find the domain and range.

10.1 EXERCISES

HOMEWORK KEY

◆ = **MULTIPLE CHOICE PRACTICE**
Exs. 23, 37, 46, and 54–56

○ = **HINTS AND HOMEWORK HELP**
for Exs. 7, 31, and 45 at classzone.com

SKILLS · PROBLEM SOLVING · REASONING

1. **VOCABULARY** Copy and complete: Every quadratic function has a U-shaped graph called a(n) __?__.

2. **WRITING** *Explain* how you can tell whether the graph of a quadratic function opens up or down.

MATCHING Match the quadratic function with its graph.

3. $y = \frac{1}{2}x^2 - 3$

4. $y = \frac{1}{2}x^2 - 2$

5. $y = -\frac{1}{2}x^2 + 2$

A.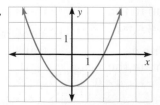

B.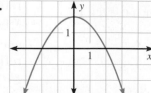

C.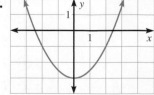

EXAMPLES
1, 2, and 3
on pp. 605–606
for Exs. 6–22

GRAPHING QUADRATIC FUNCTIONS Graph the function. Compare the graph with the graph of $y = x^2$.

6. $y = 2x^2$
7. $y = -2x^2$
8. $y = -3x^2$
9. $y = 5x^2$

10. $y = \frac{11}{2}x^2$
11. $y = \frac{2}{3}x^2$
12. $y = -\frac{3}{4}x^2$
13. $y = -\frac{1}{9}x^2$

14. $y = \frac{3}{8}x^2$
15. $y = -\frac{1}{5}x^2$
16. $y = x^2 - 7$
17. $y = x^2 + 9$

18. $y = x^2 + 6$
19. $y = x^2 - 4$
20. $y = x^2 - 1$
21. $y = x^2 + \frac{7}{4}$

22. **ERROR ANALYSIS** *Describe* and correct the error in drawing and comparing the graphs of $y = x^2$ and $y = x^2 - 2$.

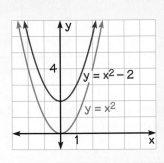

Both graphs open up and have the same axis of symmetry. However, the graph of $y = x^2 - 2$ is a vertical translation (of 2 units up) of the graph of $y = x^2$.

EXAMPLE 4
on p. 607
for Exs. 23–36

23. ◆ **MULTIPLE CHOICE** What is the vertex of the graph of the function $y = -\frac{3}{4}x^2 + 7$?

Ⓐ $(-7, 0)$ Ⓑ $(0, -7)$ Ⓒ $(0, 7)$ Ⓓ $(7, 0)$

24. **ERROR ANALYSIS** *Describe* and correct the error in finding the vertex of the graph of $y = \frac{2}{3}x^2 - 5$.

The vertex of the graph of $y = \frac{2}{3}x^2 - 5$ is $(-5, 0)$.

GRAPHING QUADRATIC FUNCTIONS Graph the function. Compare the graph with the graph of $y = x^2$.

25. $y = 3x^2 + 7$
26. $y = -x^2 + 5$
27. $y = 2x^2 - 12$

28. $y = -2x^2 - 1$
29. $y = -3x^2 - 2$
30. $y = 4x^2 + 3$

31. $y = \frac{3}{4}x^2 - 3$
32. $y = \frac{1}{5}x^2 + 10$
33. $y = \frac{1}{2}x^2 - 5$

34. $y = -\frac{2}{3}x^2 + 9$
35. $y = \frac{5}{2}x^2 - 3$
36. $y = -\frac{7}{2}x^2 - 1$

37. ◆ **MULTIPLE CHOICE** How does the graph of $y = x^2 + 3$ compare with the graph of $y = x^2 + 9$?

Ⓐ The graph of $y = x^2 + 3$ is a vertical translation (of 6 units down) of the graph of $y = x^2 + 9$.

Ⓑ The graph of $y = x^2 + 3$ is a vertical translation (of 6 units up) of the graph of $y = x^2 + 9$.

Ⓒ The graph of $y = x^2 + 3$ is narrower than the graph of $y = x^2 + 9$.

Ⓓ The graph of $y = x^2 + 3$ is wider than the graph of $y = x^2 + 9$.

COMPARING GRAPHS Compare the graphs of the functions.

38. $y = x^2 - 5$
$y = x^2 + 8$

39. $y = 3x^2 - 11$
$y = 3x^2 - 16$

40. $y = 4x^2$
$y = 2x^2$

41. REASONING Consider the graph of $y = ax^2 + c$. What can you say about the point $(0, c)$? If (p, q) is a point on the graph, what can you say about the point $(-p, q)$? *Explain* your reasoning.

CONNECT SKILLS TO PROBLEM SOLVING Exercises 42–44 will help you prepare for problem solving.

Use the following information: A fireplace opening includes a parabolic arch as shown. The graph of the function $y = -\frac{1}{4}x^2 + 3$ where x and y are measured in feet models this arch.

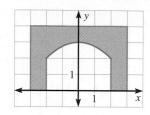

42. What is the domain of the function?

43. What is the height of the arch at its highest point (the middle of the arch)? at its lowest points (the ends of the arch)?

44. What is the range of the function?

GRAPHING CALCULATOR You may wish to use a graphing calculator to complete Exercises 45–53.

EXAMPLE 5
on p. 608
for Exs. 45–46

45. SAILING Sailors need to consider the speed of the wind when adjusting the sails on their boats. The force F (in pounds per square foot) on a sail when the wind is blowing perpendicular to the sail can be modeled by the function $F = 0.004v^2$ where v is the wind speed (in knots).

a. Graph the function for wind speeds from 0 knots to 50 knots.

b. Use the graph to estimate the wind speed that will produce a force of 1 pound per square foot on a sail.

c. Estimate the wind speed that will produce a force of 5 pounds per square foot on a sail.

California @*HomeTutor* for problem solving help at classzone.com

46. ◆ MULTIPLE CHOICE A cross section of the parabolic surface of the antenna shown can be modeled by the graph of the function $y = 0.012x^2$ where x and y are measured in meters. What is the domain of the function in this situation?

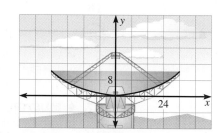

Ⓐ $-32 \le x \le 32$

Ⓑ $-24 \le x \le 24$

Ⓒ $0 \le x \le 32$

Ⓓ $0 \le x \le 12.288$

California @*HomeTutor* for problem solving help at classzone.com

REVIEW
VERTICAL
MOTION
For help with
the vertical
motion model,
see p. 551.

47. FALLING OBJECTS Two acorns drop from an oak tree. One falls 45 feet, while the other falls 32 feet. For each acorn, write an equation that gives the height h (in feet) of the acorn as a function of the time t (in seconds) it has fallen. *Describe* how the graphs of the two equations are related.

48. SHORT RESPONSE The breaking strength w (in pounds) of a manila rope can be modeled by the function $w = 8900d^2$ where d is the diameter (in inches) of the rope.

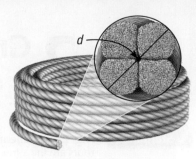

   a. Graph the function.

   b. If a manila rope has 4 times the breaking strength of another manila rope, does the rope have 4 times the diameter of the other rope? *Explain.*

49. MULTI-STEP PROBLEM For an engineering contest, you have to create a container for an egg so that the container can be dropped from a height of 30 feet without breaking the egg.

   a. The distance y (in feet) that the container falls is given by the function $y = 16t^2$ where t is the time (in seconds) the container has fallen. Graph the function.

   b. The height y (in feet) of the dropped container is given by the function $y = -16t^2 + 30$ where t is the time (in seconds) since the container is dropped. Graph the function.

   c. How are the graphs from part (a) and part (b) related? *Explain* how you can use each graph to find the number of seconds after which the container has fallen 10 feet.

   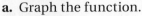 at classzone.com

CHALLENGE **Write a function of the form $y = ax^2 + c$ whose graph passes through the two given points.**

50. $(-1, 9)$, $(0, 3)$ **51.** $(2, 1)$, $(5, -20)$ **52.** $(-2, -16.5)$, $(1, 4.5)$

53. CHALLENGE The kinetic energy E (in joules) of an object in motion is given by $E = \frac{1}{2}mv^2$ where m is the object's mass (in kilograms) and v is the object's velocity (in meters per second). Suppose a baseball has 918.75 joules of energy when traveling 35 meters per second. Use this information to write and graph an equation that gives the energy E of the baseball as a function of its velocity v.

◆ CALIFORNIA STANDARDS SPIRAL REVIEW

Alg. 6.0   **54.** Which linear inequality's graph includes points in Quadrant IV? *(p. 425)*

     A $2x + 1 < 3y$ **B** $y \geq 6x + 3$ **C** $x + y \leq -3$ **D** $x < -\frac{5}{2}$

Alg. 14.0   **55.** What are the solutions of the equation $x^2 + 2x - 24 = 0$? *(p. 556)*

     A -6 and -4 **B** -6 and 4 **C** -4 and 6 **D** 4 and 6

Alg. 10.0   **56.** You order T-shirts for a club at school. Each shirt costs \$14. The shipping cost is \$12 regardless of the number of T-shirts ordered. Write an equation that gives the average cost C (in dollars per T-shirt) as a function of the number t of T-shirts that you order. *(p. 541)*

     A $C = 12t + 14$ **B** $C = 14t + 12$ **C** $C = 14 + \frac{12}{t}$ **D** $C = 14t^2 + 12t$

10.2 Graph $y = ax^2 + bx + c$

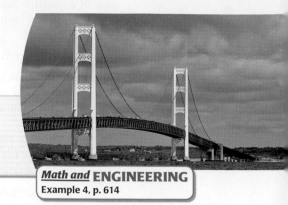

Standards   **Alg. 21.0** **Students graph quadratic functions** and know that their roots are the *x*-intercepts.

Connect   *Before* you graphed simple quadratic functions. *Now* you will graph general quadratic functions.

Math and **ENGINEERING**
Example 4, p. 614

Key Vocabulary
• **minimum value**
• **maximum value**

You can use the properties below to graph any quadratic function. You will justify the formula for the axis of symmetry in Exercise 38 on page 616.

KEY CONCEPT   *For Your Notebook*

Properties of the Graph of a Quadratic Function

The graph of $y = ax^2 + bx + c$ is a parabola that:

• opens up if $a > 0$ and opens down if $a < 0$.

• is narrower than the graph of $y = x^2$ if $|a| > 1$ and wider if $|a| < 1$.

• has an axis of symmetry of $x = -\dfrac{b}{2a}$.

• has a vertex with an *x*-coordinate of $-\dfrac{b}{2a}$.

• has a *y*-intercept of *c*. So, the point $(0, c)$ is on the parabola.

$y = ax^2 + bx + c, a > 0$

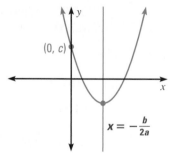

EXAMPLE 1   Find the axis of symmetry and the vertex

Consider the graph of the function $y = -2x^2 + 12x - 7$.

   a. Find the axis of symmetry.   **b.** Find the vertex.

Solution

   a. For the function $y = -2x^2 + 12x - 7$, $a = -2$ and $b = 12$.

$$x = -\frac{b}{2a} = -\frac{12}{2(-2)} = 3 \quad \text{Substitute } -2 \text{ for } a \text{ and } 12 \text{ for } b. \text{ Then simplify.}$$

     ▶ The axis of symmetry is the vertical line $x = 3$.

> **IDENTIFY THE VERTEX**
> Because the vertex lies on the axis of symmetry, $x = 3$, the *x*-coordinate of the vertex is 3.

   b. The *x*-coordinate of the vertex is $-\dfrac{b}{2a}$, or 3.

     To find the *y*-coordinate, substitute 3 for *x* in the function and simplify.

$$y = -2(3)^2 + 12(3) - 7 = 11 \quad \text{Substitute 3 for } x. \text{ Then simplify.}$$

     ▶ The vertex is $(3, 11)$.

EXAMPLE 2 **Graph** $y = ax^2 + bx + c$

Graph $y = 3x^2 - 6x + 2$.

STEP 1 **Determine** whether the parabola opens up or down. Because $a > 0$, the parabola opens up.

AVOID ERRORS
Be sure to include the negative sign before the fraction when finding the axis of symmetry.

STEP 2 **Find** and draw the axis of symmetry:

$$x = -\frac{b}{2a} = -\frac{-6}{2(3)} = 1$$

STEP 3 **Find** and plot the vertex.

The x-coordinate of the vertex is $-\frac{b}{2a}$, or 1.

To find the y-coordinate, substitute 1 for x in the function and simplify.

$$y = 3(1)^2 - 6(1) + 2 = -1$$

So, the vertex is $(1, -1)$.

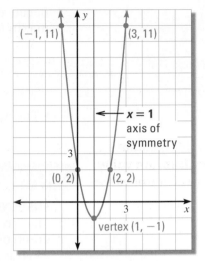

Animated Algebra

For an interactive example of graphing a quadratic function, go to **classzone.com**.

STEP 4 **Plot** two points. Choose two x-values less than the x-coordinate of the vertex. Then find the corresponding y-values.

x	0	−1
y	2	11

REVIEW REFLECTIONS
For help with reflections, see p. 801.

STEP 5 **Reflect** the points plotted in Step 4 in the axis of symmetry.

STEP 6 **Draw** a parabola through the plotted points.

✓ **GUIDED PRACTICE** for Examples 1 and 2

1. Find the axis of symmetry and the vertex of the graph of the function $y = x^2 - 2x - 3$.

2. Graph the function $y = 3x^2 + 12x - 1$. Label the vertex and axis of symmetry.

KEY CONCEPT *For Your Notebook*

Minimum and Maximum Values

For $y = ax^2 + bx + c$, the y-coordinate of the vertex is the **minimum value** of the function if $a > 0$ or the **maximum value** of the function if $a < 0$.

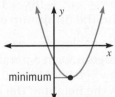

$y = ax^2 + bx + c, a > 0$

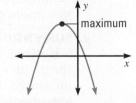

$y = ax^2 + bx + c, a < 0$

EXAMPLE 3 Find the minimum or maximum value

Tell whether the function $y = -3x^2 - 12x + 10$ has a *minimum value* or a *maximum value*. Then find the minimum or maximum value.

Solution

Because $a = -3$ and $-3 < 0$, the parabola opens down and the function has a maximum value. To find the maximum value, find the vertex.

$$x = -\frac{b}{2a} = -\frac{-12}{2(-3)} = -2 \qquad \text{The } x\text{-coordinate is } -\frac{b}{2a}.$$

$$y = -3(-2)^2 - 12(-2) + 10 = 22 \qquad \text{Substitute } -2 \text{ for } x. \text{ Then simplify.}$$

▶ The maximum value of the function is 22.

EXAMPLE 4 Find the minimum value of a function

SUSPENSION BRIDGES The suspension cables between the two towers of the Mackinac Bridge in Michigan form a parabola that can be modeled by the graph of $y = 0.000097x^2 - 0.37x + 549$ where x and y are measured in feet. What is the height of the cable above the water at its lowest point?

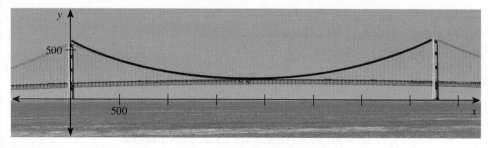

Solution

The lowest point of the cable is at the vertex of the parabola. Find the x-coordinate of the vertex. Use $a = 0.000097$ and $b = -0.37$.

$$x = -\frac{b}{2a} = -\frac{-0.37}{2(0.000097)} \approx 1910 \qquad \text{Use a calculator.}$$

Substitute 1910 for x in the equation to find the y-coordinate of the vertex.

$$y \approx 0.000097(1910)^2 - 0.37(1910) + 549 \approx 196$$

▶ The cable is about 196 feet above the water at its lowest point.

✓ **GUIDED PRACTICE** for Examples 3 and 4

3. Tell whether the function $y = 6x^2 + 18x + 13$ has a *minimum value* or a *maximum value*. Then find the minimum or maximum value.

4. **SUSPENSION BRIDGES** The cables between the two towers of the Tacoma Narrows Bridge in Washington form a parabola that can be modeled by the graph of the equation $y = 0.00014x^2 - 0.4x + 507$ where x and y are measured in feet. What is the height of the cable above the water at its lowest point? Round your answer to the nearest foot.

10.2 EXERCISES

HOMEWORK KEY

◆ = MULTIPLE CHOICE PRACTICE
Exs. 12, 27, 37, and 48–51

○ = HINTS AND HOMEWORK HELP
for Exs. 9, 21, and 43 at classzone.com

SKILLS · PROBLEM SOLVING · REASONING

1. **VOCABULARY** *Explain* how you can tell whether a quadratic function has a maximum value or minimum value without graphing the function.

2. **WRITING** *Describe* the steps you would take to graph a quadratic function in standard form.

EXAMPLE 1
on p. 612
for Exs. 3–14

FINDING AXIS OF SYMMETRY AND VERTEX Find the axis of symmetry and the vertex of the graph of the function.

3. $y = 2x^2 - 8x + 6$　　　4. $y = x^2 - 6x + 11$　　　5. $y = -3x^2 + 24x - 22$

6. $y = -x^2 - 10x$　　　7. $y = 6x^2 + 6x$　　　8. $y = 4x^2 + 7$

9. $y = -\frac{2}{3}x^2 - 1$　　　10. $y = \frac{1}{2}x^2 + 8x - 9$　　　11. $y = -\frac{1}{4}x^2 + 3x - 2$

12. ◆ **MULTIPLE CHOICE** What is the vertex of the graph of the function $y = -3x^2 + 18x - 13$?

　Ⓐ $(-3, -94)$　　Ⓑ $(-3, -14)$　　Ⓒ $(3, -13)$　　Ⓓ $(3, 14)$

ERROR ANALYSIS *Describe* and correct the error in finding the axis of symmetry of the graph of the given function.

13. $y = 2x^2 + 16x - 1$

14. $y = -\frac{3}{2}x^2 + 18x - 5$

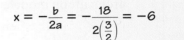
$$x = \frac{b}{2a} = \frac{16}{2(2)} = 4$$
The axis of symmetry is x = 4.

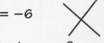
$$x = -\frac{b}{2a} = -\frac{18}{2\left(\frac{3}{2}\right)} = -6$$
The axis of symmetry is x = −6.

EXAMPLE 2
on p. 613
for Exs. 15–27

GRAPHING QUADRATIC FUNCTIONS Graph the function. Label the vertex and axis of symmetry.

15. $y = x^2 + 6x + 2$　　　16. $y = x^2 + 4x + 8$　　　17. $y = 2x^2 - 12x + 20$

18. $y = 5x^2 + 10x - 3$　　　19. $y = 9x^2 + 6x - 3$　　　20. $y = -4x^2 + 4x + 8$

21. $y = -3x^2 - 2x - 5$　　　22. $y = -8x^2 - 12x + 1$　　　23. $y = -x^2 + \frac{1}{2}x + \frac{7}{16}$

24. $y = \frac{1}{3}x^2 + 6x - 9$　　　25. $y = -\frac{1}{2}x^2 + 6x + 3$　　　26. $y = -\frac{1}{4}x^2 - x + 1$

27. ◆ **MULTIPLE CHOICE** Which function has the graph shown?

　Ⓐ $y = -2x^2 + 8x + 3$

　Ⓑ $y = -\frac{1}{2}x^2 + 2x + 3$

　Ⓒ $y = \frac{1}{2}x^2 + 2x + 3$

　Ⓓ $y = 2x^2 + 8x + 3$

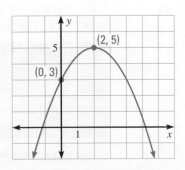

EXAMPLE 3
on p. 614
for Exs. 28–37

MAXIMUM AND MINIMUM VALUES Tell whether the function has a *minimum value* or a *maximum value*. Then find the minimum or maximum value.

28. $y = x^2 - 6$ **29.** $y = -5x^2 + 7$ **30.** $y = 4x^2 + 32x$

31. $y = -3x^2 + 12x - 20$ **32.** $y = x^2 + 7x + 8$ **33.** $y = -2x^2 - x + 10$

34. $y = \frac{1}{2}x^2 - 2x + 5$ **35.** $y = -\frac{3}{8}x^2 + 9x$ **36.** $y = \frac{1}{4}x^2 + 7x + 11$

37. ◆ **MULTIPLE CHOICE** What is the minimum value of the function
$y = x^2 - 5$?

(**A**) −5   (**B**) −1   (**C**) 0   (**D**) 5

38. **REASONING** Follow the steps below to justify the equation of the axis of symmetry for the graph of $y = ax^2 + bx + c$. Because the graph of $y = ax^2 + bx + c$ is a vertical translation of the graph of $y = ax^2 + bx$, the two graphs have the same axis of symmetry. Use the function $y = ax^2 + bx$ in place of $y = ax^2 + bx + c$.

   a. Find the x-intercepts of the graph of $y = ax^2 + bx$. (You can do this by finding the roots of the polynomial $ax^2 + bx$.)

   b. Because a parabola is symmetric about its axis of symmetry, the axis of symmetry passes through a point halfway between the x-intercepts of the parabola. Find the x-coordinate of this point. What is an equation of the vertical line through this point?

CONNECT SKILLS TO PROBLEM SOLVING Exercises 39–41 will help you prepare for problem solving.

Use the following information: You are growing roses on an arch at the entrance to a garden. The arch can be modeled by the graph of the equation $y = -\frac{2}{3}x^2 + 4x$ where x and y are measured in feet.

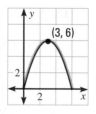

39. What does the x-coordinate of the plotted point tell you about the arch?

40. What does the y-coordinate of the plotted point tell you about the arch?

41. If you were given the height of the arch and the width of the arch at its base, how could you find the coordinates of the vertex?

■ **GRAPHING CALCULATOR** You may wish to use a graphing calculator to complete Exercises 42–47.

EXAMPLE 4
on p. 614
for Exs. 42–43

42. **ARCHITECTURE** The parabolic arches that support the roof of the convention center below can be modeled by the graph of the equation $y = -0.0019x^2 + 0.71x$ where x and y are measured in feet. What is the height h at the highest point of the arch as shown in the diagram?

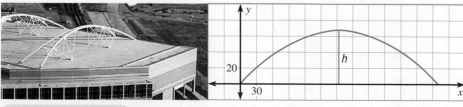

California *@HomeTutor*   for problem solving help at classzone.com

43. **SPIDERS** Fishing spiders can propel themselves across water and leap vertically from the surface of the water. During a vertical jump, the height of the body of the spider can be modeled by the function $y = -4500x^2 + 820x + 43$ where x is the duration (in seconds) of the jump and y is the height (in millimeters) of the spider above the surface of the water. After how many seconds does the spider's body reach its maximum height? What is the maximum height?

California @HomeTutor for problem solving help at classzone.com

44. **AIRCRAFT** An aircraft hangar is a large building where planes are stored. The opening of one airport hangar is a parabolic arch that can be modeled by the graph of the equation $y = -0.007x^2 + 1.7x$ where x and y are measured in feet. Graph the function. Use the graph to determine how wide the hangar is at its base.

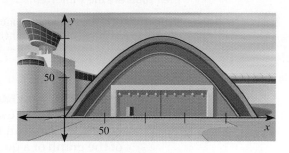

45. **SHORT RESPONSE** The casts of some Broadway shows go on tour, performing their shows in cities across the United States. For the period 1990–2001, the number of tickets sold S (in millions) for Broadway road tours can be modeled by the function $S = 332 + 132t - 10.4t^2$ where t is the number of years since 1990. Was the greatest number of tickets for Broadway road tours sold in 1995? *Explain*.

46. **CHALLENGE** Write a function of the form $y = ax^2 + bx$ whose graph contains the points (1, 6) and (3, 6).

47. **CHALLENGE** During an archery competition, an archer shoots an arrow from a height of 1.5 meters above the ground. The arrow follows the parabolic path shown and hits the ground 90 meters away. Use the y-intercept and the points on the graph to write an equation for the graph that models the path of the arrow.

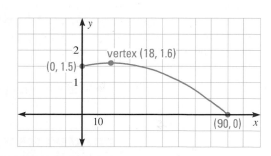

◆ CALIFORNIA STANDARDS SPIRAL REVIEW

Alg. 7.0   **48.** Which equation's graph is a horizontal line whose y-intercept is 4? *(p. 264)*

     A $x = 4$ **B** $y = 4$ **C** $y = x - 4$ **D** $y = x + 4$

Alg. 17.0   **49.** What is the range of the function $y = 3$? *(p. 264)*

     A -3 **B** 0   **C** 3   **D** All real numbers

Alg. 11.0   **50.** Which binomial is a factor of $2x^2 - 7x + 3$? *(p. 566)*

     A $2x + 1$ **B** $x - 3$ **C** $2x - 3$ **D** $x + 3$

Alg. 9.0   **51.** You buy x keychains for $2 each and y snow globes for $3 each. You spend $22 for 9 items. How many keychains do you buy? *(p. 398)*

     A 4   **B** 5   **C** 6   **D** 9

10.3 Graph $y = a(x - p)(x - q)$

Standards **Alg. 21.0** Students graph quadratic functions and know that their roots are the *x*-intercepts.

Connect *Before* you graphed quadratic functions in standard form.
Now you will graph quadratic functions in intercept form.

Math and **GEOGRAPHY**
Ex. 40, p. 622

Key Vocabulary
• intercept form
• root, *p. 550*

FACTORING POLYNOMIALS In Chapter 9, you learned how to factor polynomials and used the zero-product property to solve polynomial equations. You can use the zero-product property to find the *x*-intercepts of the graph of a quadratic function that is factored completely.

EXAMPLE 1 Find *x*-intercepts

Find the *x*-intercepts of the graph of $y = -(x + 1)(x - 5)$.

Solution

To find the *x*-intercepts, you need to find the values of *x* when $y = 0$.

$y = -(x + 1)(x - 5)$	**Write original function.**
$0 = -(x + 1)(x - 5)$	**Substitute 0 for *y*.**
$x + 1 = 0$ *or* $x - 5 = 0$	**Zero-product property**
$x = -1$ *or* $x = 5$	**Solve for *x*.**

▶ The *x*-intercepts are −1 and 5.

RELATE ROOTS AND *x*-INTERCEPTS

Notice that finding the *x*-intercepts of the graph of $y = a(x - p)(x - q)$ is the same procedure as finding the roots of the related polynomial, $a(x - p)(x - q)$.

INTERCEPT FORM In Example 1, the quadratic function $y = -(x + 1)(x - 5)$ is written in *intercept form*. The general form $y = a(x - p)(x - q)$ where $a \neq 0$ is called **intercept form** because the *x*-intercepts of the graph are *p* and *q*.

KEY CONCEPT *For Your Notebook*

Graph of Intercept Form $y = a(x - p)(x - q)$

Characteristics of the graph of $y = a(x - p)(x - q)$:

• The *x*-intercepts are *p* and *q*.

• The axis of symmetry is halfway between $(p, 0)$ and $(q, 0)$. So, the axis of symmetry is $x = \dfrac{p + q}{2}$.

• The parabola opens up if $a > 0$ and opens down if $a < 0$.

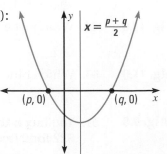

EXAMPLE 2 **Graph a quadratic function in intercept form**

Graph $y = -2(x - 1)(x + 3)$.

STEP 1 **Identify** the x-intercepts. The x-intercepts are $p = 1$ and $q = -3$. Plot $(1, 0)$ and $(-3, 0)$.

STEP 2 **Find** and draw the axis of symmetry: $x = \dfrac{p + q}{2} = \dfrac{1 + (-3)}{2} = -1$.

STEP 3 **Find** and plot the vertex. The axis of symmetry is $x = -1$, so the x-coordinate of the vertex is -1. To find the y-coordinate of the vertex, substitute -1 for x and simplify.

$$y = -2(-1 - 1)(-1 + 3) = 8$$

So, the vertex is $(-1, 8)$.

STEP 4 **Draw** a parabola through the vertex and the points where the x-intercepts occur.

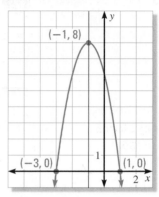

EXAMPLE 3 **Graph a quadratic function in standard form**

Graph $y = 3x^2 - 12x + 12$.

STEP 1 **Rewrite** the quadratic function in intercept form.

$y = 3x^2 - 12x + 12$ **Write the function.**

$= 3(x^2 - 4x + 4)$ **Factor out 3.**

$= 3(x - 2)^2$ **Factor the trinomial.**

$= 3(x - 2)(x - 2)$ **Write in intercept form.**

STEP 2 **Identify** the x-intercepts. There is one x-intercept, 2. Plot $(2, 0)$.

STEP 3 **Find** and draw the axis of symmetry: $x = \dfrac{p + q}{2} = \dfrac{2 + 2}{2} = 2$.

STEP 4 **Find** and plot the vertex. The axis of symmetry is $x = 2$, so the x-coordinate of the vertex is 2, which is also the x-intercept. So, the vertex is $(2, 0)$.

STEP 5 **Plot** a point and its reflection. Choose a value for x, say $x = 1$. When $x = 1$, $y = 3$. Plot $(1, 3)$. By reflecting the point in the axis of symmetry, you can also plot $(3, 3)$.

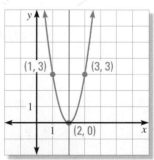

STEP 6 **Draw** a parabola through the points.

✔ **GUIDED PRACTICE** for Examples 1, 2, and 3

Graph the quadratic function. Label the vertex, axis of symmetry, and x-intercept(s).

1. $y = 3(x - 6)(x - 4)$ **2.** $y = -(x + 1)^2$ **3.** $y = 2x^2 - 2x - 12$

WRITING QUADRATIC FUNCTIONS You can write an equation of a parabola using the x-intercepts and the coordinates of a point on the parabola.

EXAMPLE 4 **Write a quadratic function in intercept form**

Write a quadratic function in intercept form whose graph has x-intercepts -1 and 3 and passes through the point $(0, -12)$.

> **STEP 1** **Substitute** the x-intercepts into $y = a(x - p)(x - q)$. The x-intercepts are $p = -1$ and $q = 3$.
>
> $$y = a(x - (-1))(x - 3)$$ Substitute -1 for p and 3 for q.
>
> $$y = a(x + 1)(x - 3)$$ Simplify.
>
> **STEP 2** **Find** the value of a in $y = a(x + 1)(x - 3)$ using the given point $(0, -12)$.
>
> $$-12 = a(0 + 1)(0 - 3)$$ Substitute 0 for x and -12 for y.
>
> $$-12 = -3a$$ Simplify.
>
> $$4 = a$$ Divide each side by -3.

▶ The function in intercept form is $y = 4(x + 1)(x - 3)$.

EXAMPLE 5 **Model a parabolic path using intercept form**

BIOLOGY When a dolphin leaps out of the water, its body follows a parabolic path through the air. Write a function whose graph is the path of the dolphin in the air.

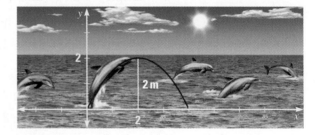

Solution

> **STEP 1** **Identify** the x-intercepts. The dolphin leaves the water at $(0, 0)$ and re-enters at $(4, 0)$, so the x-intercepts of the path are $p = 0$ and $q = 4$. The function is of the form $y = a(x - 0)(x - 4)$, or $y = ax(x - 4)$.
>
> **STEP 2** **Find** the axis of symmetry and the vertex. The axis of symmetry is $x = \dfrac{0 + 4}{2} = 2$. The maximum height of 2 meters occurs on the axis of symmetry, so the vertex of the graph is $(2, 2)$.
>
> **STEP 3** **Find** the value of a. Substitute the coordinates of the vertex into the function. The vertex is $(2, 2)$, so $2 = a(2 - 0)(2 - 4)$, or $a = -\dfrac{1}{2}$.

▶ The graph of the function $y = -\dfrac{1}{2}x(x - 4)$ is the dolphin's path.

✓ GUIDED PRACTICE   for Examples 4 and 5

4. Write a quadratic function in intercept form whose graph has x-intercepts 1 and -1 and passes through the point $(2, -3)$.

5. **WHAT IF?** In Example 5, suppose the maximum height of the jump is 3 meters. Write a function whose graph is the dolphin's path.

10.3 EXERCISES

HOMEWORK KEY

◆ = **MULTIPLE CHOICE PRACTICE**
Exs. 24, 33, 41, and 46–48

◯ = **HINTS AND HOMEWORK HELP**
for Exs. 11, 29, and 39 at classzone.com

SKILLS · PROBLEM SOLVING · REASONING

1. **VOCABULARY** Copy and complete: The __?__ of the graph of the function $y = a(x - p)(x - q)$ are p and q.

2. **NOTETAKING SKILLS** Make a decision tree like the one on page 604 for graphing a quadratic function.

EXAMPLE 1
on p. 618
for Exs. 3–8

FINDING x-INTERCEPTS Find the x-intercepts of the graph of the quadratic function.

3. $y = (x + 5)(x + 2)$

4. $y = -2(x - 5)(x + 1)$

5. $y = -5(x + 7)(x + 2)$

6. $y = 2(x + 10)(x - 3)$

7. $y = -\frac{1}{2}(x + 4)(x - 2)$

8. $y = (x - 7)(2x - 3)$

EXAMPLES 2 and 3
on p. 619
for Exs. 9–26

GRAPHING QUADRATIC FUNCTIONS Graph the quadratic function. Label the vertex, axis of symmetry, and x-intercept(s).

9. $y = (x - 5)(x - 3)$

10. $y = (x + 3)(x - 4)$

11. $y = -(x - 1)(x + 7)$

12. $y = -3(x + 1)(x + 2)$

13. $y = 4(x + 5)(x - 4)$

14. $y = 0.5(x - 6)(x - 8)$

15. $y = (x + 9)^2$

16. $y = -2(x - 3)^2$

17. $y = -\frac{1}{5}(x - 10)^2$

18. $y = x^2 - 10x + 25$

19. $y = x^2 - 6x + 9$

20. $y = -x^2 + 8x - 16$

21. $y = 12x^2 - 48$

22. $y = 3x^2 - 24x + 36$

23. $y = 8x^2 - 16x - 10$

24. ◆ **MULTIPLE CHOICE** What is the vertex of the graph of $y = -(x - 1)(x + 4)$?

   (A) $\left(-\frac{3}{2}, \frac{25}{4}\right)$

   (B) $\left(\frac{3}{2}, -\frac{11}{2}\right)$

   (C) $\left(\frac{3}{2}, -\frac{25}{4}\right)$

   (D) $\left(-\frac{3}{2}, \frac{11}{2}\right)$

ERROR ANALYSIS *Describe* and correct the error in finding the indicated characteristic of the graph of $y = (x + 2)(x - 6)$.

25. Find the x-intercepts.

$y = (x + 2)(x - 6)$
$y = (x + 2)[x + (-6)]$
The x-intercepts are 2 and −6. ✗

26. Find the axis of symmetry.

$y = [x - (-2)](x - 6)$, so $p = -2$ and $q = 6$.
$y = \frac{p + q}{2} = \frac{-2 + 6}{2} = 2$
The axis of symmetry is y = 2. ✗

EXAMPLE 4
on p. 620
for Exs. 27–33

WRITING QUADRATIC FUNCTIONS Write a quadratic function in intercept form whose graph has the given x-intercept(s) and passes through the given point.

27. x-intercepts: −3 and 3
point: (0, −9)

28. x-intercepts: −6 and 2
point: (−2, 8)

29. x-intercepts: 3 and 5
point: (6, −6)

30. x-intercepts: −9 and −1
point: (−3, −18)

31. only x-intercept: −7
point: (0, 49)

32. only x-intercept: 4
point: (6, −1)

33. ◆ **MULTIPLE CHOICE** Which function has the graph shown?

(A) $y = (x - 2)^2$

(B) $y = -(x - 2)^2$

(C) $y = -(x + 2)^2$

(D) $y = -\frac{3}{4}(x - 2)^2$

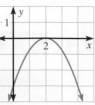

34. **OPEN-ENDED** Write a second-degree polynomial that has **(a)** two roots, **(b)** exactly one root, and **(c)** no real roots. For each polynomial, graph the related quadratic function to show the number of *x*-intercepts.

35. **REASONING** Can you write a second-degree polynomial that has three roots? *Explain* why or why not.

CONNECT SKILLS TO PROBLEM SOLVING Exercises 36 and 37 will help you prepare for problem solving.

Use the following information: You have a decorative parabolic bridge in your backyard. The arch of the bridge is shown where *x* and *y* are in feet.

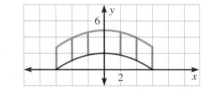

36. a. What are the *x*-intercepts of the graph?

b. What is the width of the bridge at its base?

37. a. What is the vertex of the graph?

b. What is the maximum height of the bridge's surface?

EXAMPLE 5
on p. 620
for Exs. 38–40

38. **FOOTBALL** The path of a football that you kicked is given by $y = -0.05x(x - 30)$. The path of a football that your friend kicked is given by $y = -0.1x(x - 25)$. For both functions, *x* is the horizontal distance (in yards) and *y* is the vertical distance (in yards) from the point where the ball was kicked. Graph each function. Who kicked the ball higher? Who kicked the ball farther?

California @*HomeTutor* for problem solving help at classzone.com

39. **ARCHITECTURE** The arch of a restaurant at Los Angeles International Airport can be modeled by a parabola. The maximum height of the arch is 135 feet. The arch measures 340 feet at its base. Write a function whose graph follows the shape of the arch.

California @*HomeTutor* for problem solving help at classzone.com

Los Angeles International Airport

40. **GEOGRAPHY** The maximum height of Telephone Arch in Inyo County, California, is 15 feet. The arch measures 25 feet at its base. Write a function whose graph follows the shape of the arch.

15 ft

41. ◆ **MULTIPLE CHOICE** The path of water sprayed by a lawn sprinkler is given by $y = -0.4x(x - 10)$ where x is the horizontal distance (in feet) and y is the vertical distance (in feet) from the sprinkler. The sprinkler rotates in a circle. What is the area of the lawn covered by the spray?

Ⓐ 10 ft^2 Ⓑ $10\pi \text{ ft}^2$ Ⓒ 100 ft^2 Ⓓ $100\pi \text{ ft}^2$

CHALLENGE In Exercises 42 and 43, write an equation in intercept form of the quadratic function whose graph has the given characteristics.

42. The vertex is $(-2, 5)$, and one of the x-intercepts is 3.

43. The graph passes through the points $(-5, -6)$, $(-2, 0)$, and $(-1, -6)$.

44. **CHALLENGE** Show how to write $y = a(x - p)(x - q)$ in standard form.

45. **CHALLENGE** The functions below give the horizontal position x and vertical position y of an object t seconds after it is thrown into the air.

$$x = 4t \text{ and } y = -16t^2 + 48t + 45$$

Write an equation in intercept form for the path of the object (where y is a function of x and t is eliminated).

◆ CALIFORNIA STANDARDS SPIRAL REVIEW

Alg. 11.0
46. Which of the following shows $8x^2 - 2x - 3$ factored completely? *(p. 566)*

Ⓐ $(2x - 3)(4x + 1)$ Ⓑ $(4x - 3)(2x + 1)$

Ⓒ $(4x + 3)(2x - 1)$ Ⓓ $2(2x - 3)(x + 1)$

Alg. 25.3
47. Gwen claims that the graph of $y = ax^2 + bx + c$ opens upward. When is her statement true? *(p. 612)*

Ⓐ Always   Ⓑ When $a < 0$ Ⓒ Never   Ⓓ When $a > 0$

Alg. 14.0
48. The base of a triangle is 3 inches less than 3 times its height. The area of the triangle is 63 square inches. What is the triangle's height? *(p. 556)*

Ⓐ 6 in.   Ⓑ 7 in.   Ⓒ 18 in.   Ⓓ 21 in.

QUIZ *for Lessons 10.1-10.3*

Graph the function. Compare the graph with the graph of $y = x^2$. *(p. 605)*

1. $y = -\dfrac{1}{2}x^2$ 2. $y = 2x^2 - 5$ 3. $y = -x^2 + 3$

Graph the function. Label the vertex and axis of symmetry.

4. $y = x^2 + 5$ *(p. 605)*   5. $y = x^2 + 4x - 2$ *(p. 612)*   6. $y = 2x^2 - 12x + 5$ *(p. 612)*

Graph the function. Label the vertex, axis of symmetry, and x-intercept(s).
(p. 618)

7. $y = (x - 2)(x - 4)$ 8. $y = -(x + 2)^2$ 9. $y = 2(x + 5)(x - 3)$

10. $y = 2x^2 - 11x + 5$ 11. $y = 3x^2 + 6x - 9$ 12. $y = 4x^2 - 16x + 16$

10.4 Solve Quadratic Equations by Graphing

Math and SPORTS
Example 6, p. 627

Connect *Before* you solved quadratic equations by factoring. *Now* you will solve quadratic equations by graphing.

Key Vocabulary
• quadratic equation
• zero of a function
• *x*-intercept, *p. 273*
• root, *p. 550*

A **quadratic equation** is an equation that can be written in the **standard form** $ax^2 + bx + c = 0$ where $a \neq 0$.

In Chapter 9, you used factoring to solve a quadratic equation. You can also use graphing to solve a quadratic equation. Notice that the solutions of the equation $ax^2 + bx + c = 0$, which are the roots of $ax^2 + bx + c$, are the *x*-intercepts of the graph of the related function $y = ax^2 + bx + c$.

Solve by Factoring	Solve by Graphing
$x^2 - 6x + 5 = 0$	To solve $x^2 - 6x + 5 = 0$, graph $y = x^2 - 6x + 5$. From the graph you can see that the *x*-intercepts are 1 and 5.
$(x - 1)(x - 5) = 0$	
$x = 1 \ or \ x = 5$	

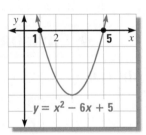

$y = x^2 - 6x + 5$

READING
In this course, *solutions* refers to real-number solutions.

To solve a quadratic equation by graphing, first write the equation in standard form. Then graph the related function. The *x*-intercepts of the graph are the solutions of the equation.

EXAMPLE 1 Solve a quadratic equation having two solutions

Solve $x^2 - 2x = 3$ by graphing.

Solution

STEP 1 Write the equation in standard form.

$$x^2 - 2x = 3 \qquad \text{Write original equation.}$$
$$x^2 - 2x - 3 = 0 \qquad \text{Subtract 3 from each side.}$$

STEP 2 Graph the related function $y = x^2 - 2x - 3$. The *x*-intercepts are −1 and 3.

▶ The solutions of the equation $x^2 - 2x = 3$ are −1 and 3.

$y = x^2 - 2x - 3$

CHECK You can check −1 and 3 in the original equation.

$x^2 - 2x = 3$	$x^2 - 2x = 3$	Write original equation.
$(-1)^2 - 2(-1) \stackrel{?}{=} 3$	$(3)^2 - 2(3) \stackrel{?}{=} 3$	Substitute for *x*.
$3 = 3 ✓$	$3 = 3 ✓$	Simplify. Each solution checks.

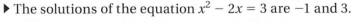

EXAMPLE 2   Solve a quadratic equation having one solution

Solve $-x^2 + 2x = 1$ by graphing.

Solution

STEP 1   **Write** the equation in standard form.

$$-x^2 + 2x = 1 \qquad \text{Write original equation.}$$

$$-x^2 + 2x - 1 = 0 \qquad \text{Subtract 1 from each side.}$$

STEP 2   **Graph** the related function $y = -x^2 + 2x - 1$. The x-intercept is 1.

▶ The solution of the equation $-x^2 + 2x = 1$ is 1.

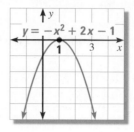

EXAMPLE 3   Solve a quadratic equation having no solution

Solve $x^2 + 7 = 4x$ by graphing.

Solution

STEP 1   **Write** the equation in standard form.

$$x^2 + 7 = 4x \qquad \text{Write original equation.}$$

$$x^2 - 4x + 7 = 0 \qquad \text{Subtract 4x from each side.}$$

STEP 2   **Graph** the related function $y = x^2 - 4x + 7$. The graph has no x-intercepts.

▶ The equation $x^2 + 7 = 4x$ has no solution.

AVOID ERRORS

Do not confuse y-intercepts and x-intercepts. Although the graph has a y-intercept, it does not have any x-intercepts.

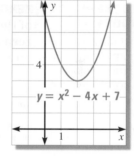

✓ **GUIDED PRACTICE**   for Examples 1, 2, and 3

Solve the equation by graphing.

1. $x^2 - 6x + 8 = 0$ **2.** $x^2 + x = -1$ **3.** $-x^2 + 6x = 9$

KEY CONCEPT   *For Your Notebook*

Number of Solutions of a Quadratic Equation

Two solutions	One solution	No solution
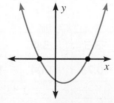	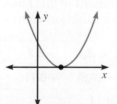	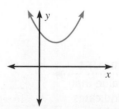
A quadratic equation has **two solutions** if the graph of its related function has **two x-intercepts**.	A quadratic equation has **one solution** if the graph of its related function has **one x-intercept**.	A quadratic equation has **no real solution** if the graph of its related function has **no x-intercepts**.

EXAMPLE 4 ◆ **Multiple Choice Practice**

The graph of the equation $y = x^2 + 6x - 7$ is shown. For what value or values of x is $y = 0$?

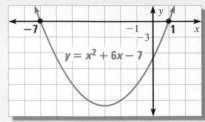

(A) $x = -7$ only

(B) $x = 1$ only

(C) $x = -7$ and $x = 1$

(D) $x = -1$ and $x = 7$

Solution

You can see from the graph that the x-intercepts are -7 and 1. So, $y = 0$ when $x = -7$ and $x = 1$.

▶ The correct answer is C. (A) (B) (C) (D)

RELATE ZEROS AND ROOTS
Note that the zero(s) of a polynomial function and the root(s) of the related polynomial are the same.

ZEROS AND GRAPHS In Example 4, the numbers -7 and 1 are called the *zeros* of the function $y = x^2 + 6x - 7$. Given an equation where y is a function of x, a **zero** of the function is an x-value for which $y = 0$. A zero of a function is also an x-intercept of the function's graph because $y = 0$.

APPROXIMATING ZEROS The zeros of a function are not necessarily integers. To approximate zeros, look at the signs of the function values. If two function values have opposite signs, then a zero falls between the x-values that correspond to the function values.

EXAMPLE 5 **Approximate the zeros of a quadratic function**

Approximate the zeros of $y = x^2 + 4x + 1$ to the nearest tenth.

Solution

STEP 1 **Graph** the function $y = x^2 + 4x + 1$. There are two x-intercepts: one between -4 and -3 and another between -1 and 0.

STEP 2 **Make** a table of values for x-values between -4 and -3 and between -1 and 0 using an increment of 0.1. Look for a change in the signs of the function values.

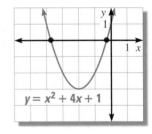

INTERPRET FUNCTION VALUES
The function value that is closest to 0 indicates the x-value that best approximates a zero of the function.

x	-3.9	-3.8	**-3.7**	-3.6	-3.5	-3.4	-3.3	-3.2	-3.1
y	0.61	0.24	**-0.11**	-0.44	-0.75	-1.04	-1.31	-1.56	-1.79

x	-0.9	-0.8	-0.7	-0.6	-0.5	-0.4	**-0.3**	-0.2	-0.1
y	-1.79	-1.56	-1.31	-1.04	-0.75	-0.44	**-0.11**	0.24	0.61

▶ In each table, the function value closest to 0 is -0.11. So, the zeros of $y = x^2 + 4x + 1$ are about -3.7 and about -0.3.

EXAMPLE 6 **Solve a multi-step problem**

SPORTS An athlete throws a shot put with an initial vertical velocity of 40 feet per second.

a. Write an equation that models the height h (in feet) of the shot put as a function of the time t (in seconds) after it is thrown.

b. Use the equation to find the time that the shot put is in the air.

6.5 ft

Solution

a. Use the initial vertical velocity and height to write a vertical motion model.

$$h = -16t^2 + vt + s \qquad \text{Vertical motion model}$$

$$h = -16t^2 + 40t + 6.5 \qquad \text{Substitute 40 for } v \text{ and 6.5 for } s.$$

b. The shot put lands when $h = 0$. To find the time t when $h = 0$, solve $0 = -16t^2 + 40t + 6.5$ for t.

To solve the equation, graph the related function $h = -16t^2 + 40t + 6.5$ on a graphing calculator. Use the *trace* feature to find the t-intercepts.

▸ There is only one positive t-intercept. The shot put is in the air for about 2.6 seconds.

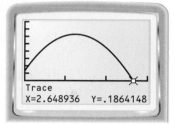

Trace
X=2.648936   Y=.1864148

USE A GRAPHING CALCULATOR

When entering $h = -16t^2 + 40t + 6.5$ in a graphing calculator, use y in place of h and x in place of t.

✔ **GUIDED PRACTICE** for Examples 4, 5, and 6

4. Find the zeros of $y = x^2 + x - 6$.

5. Approximate the zeros of $y = -x^2 + 2x + 2$ to the nearest tenth.

6. **WHAT IF?** In Example 6, suppose the initial vertical velocity is 30 feet per second. Find the time that the shot put is in the air.

CONCEPT SUMMARY   *For Your Notebook*

Relating Roots of Polynomials, Solutions of Equations, x-Intercepts of Graphs, and Zeros of Functions

Roots of a Polynomial
The roots of the polynomial $-x^2 + 8x - 12$ are 2 and 6.

Solutions of an Equation
The solutions of the equation $-x^2 + 8x - 12 = 0$ are 2 and 6.

x-Intercepts of a Graph
The x-intercepts of the graph of $y = -x^2 + 8x - 12$ occur where $y = 0$, so the x-intercepts are 2 and 6, as shown.

Zeros of a Function
The zeros of the function $y = -x^2 + 8x - 12$ are the values of x for which $y = 0$, so the zeros are 2 and 6.

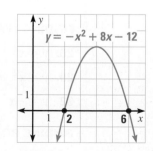

$y = -x^2 + 8x - 12$

10.4 EXERCISES

HOMEWORK
KEY

◆ = MULTIPLE CHOICE PRACTICE
Exs. 21, 50, 51, 56, and 64–66

○ = HINTS AND HOMEWORK HELP
for Exs. 5, 37, and 55 at classzone.com

SKILLS · PROBLEM SOLVING · REASONING

1. **VOCABULARY** Write $2x^2 + 11 = 9x$ in standard form.

2. **WRITING** Is $3x^2 - 2 = 0$ a quadratic equation? *Explain.*

EXAMPLES
1, 2, and 3
on pp. 624–625
for Exs. 3–22

SOLVING EQUATIONS Solve the equation by graphing.

3. $x^2 - 5x + 4 = 0$
4. $x^2 + 5x + 6 = 0$
5. $x^2 + 6x = -8$

6. $x^2 - 4x = 5$
7. $x^2 - 16 = 6x$
8. $x^2 - 12x = -35$

9. $x^2 - 6x + 9 = 0$
10. $x^2 + 8x + 16 = 0$
11. $x^2 + 10x = -25$

12. $x^2 + 81 = 18x$
13. $-x^2 - 14x = 49$
14. $-x^2 + 16x = 64$

15. $x^2 - 5x + 7 = 0$
16. $x^2 - 2x + 3 = 0$
17. $x^2 + x = -2$

18. $\frac{1}{5}x^2 - 5 = 0$
19. $\frac{1}{2}x^2 + 2x = 6$
20. $-\frac{1}{4}x^2 - 8 = x$

21. ◆ **MULTIPLE CHOICE** What are the solutions of $x^2 - 12x = -36$?

Ⓐ $-9, -4$ Ⓑ $6, -6$ Ⓒ 6 Ⓓ No solution

22. **ERROR ANALYSIS** The graph of the function related to the equation $0 = x^2 - 4x + 4$ is shown. *Describe* and correct the error in solving the equation.

The only solution of the equation
$0 = x^2 - 4x + 4$ is 4. ✗

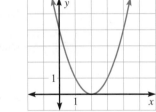

EXAMPLE 4
on p. 626
for Exs. 23–40

FINDING ZEROS Find the zeros of the function represented by the graph.

23.
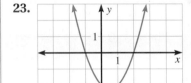

24.
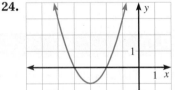

25.
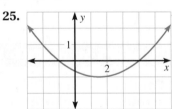

FINDING ZEROS Find the zeros of the function.

26. $y = x^2 + 4x - 5$
27. $y = x^2 - x - 12$
28. $y = x^2 - 5x - 6$

29. $y = x^2 + 3x - 10$
30. $y = -x^2 + 8x + 9$
31. $y = x^2 + x - 20$

32. $y = -x^2 - 7x + 8$
33. $y = x^2 - 12x + 11$
34. $y = -x^2 + 4x + 12$

FINDING ROOTS Find the roots of the polynomial.

35. $2x^2 + x - 3$
36. $4x^2 - 8x - 5$
37. $4x^2 - 4x + 1$

38. $x^2 + x + \frac{1}{4}$
39. $3x^2 - 2x + 1$
40. $5x^2 + x + 3$

EXAMPLE 5
on p. 626
for Exs. 41–51

APPROXIMATING ZEROS Approximate the zeros of the function to the nearest tenth.

41. $y = x^2 + 4x + 2$ **42.** $y = x^2 - 5x + 3$ **43.** $y = x^2 - 2x - 5$

44. $y = -x^2 - 3x + 3$ **45.** $y = -x^2 + 7x - 5$ **46.** $y = -x^2 - 5x - 2$

47. $y = 2x^2 + x - 2$ **48.** $y = -3x^2 + 8x - 2$ **49.** $y = 5x^2 + 30x + 30$

50. ◆ **MULTIPLE CHOICE** Which function has a zero between −3 and −2?

Ⓐ $y = -3x^2 + 4x + 11$ Ⓑ $y = 4x^2 - 3x - 11$

Ⓒ $y = 3x^2 + 4x - 11$ Ⓓ $y = 3x^2 + 11$

51. ◆ **MULTIPLE CHOICE** Between which two integers is there a zero of $y = 2x^2 - 5x - 13$?

Ⓐ −5 and −4 Ⓑ −3 and −2 Ⓒ 4 and 5 Ⓓ 5 and 6

CONNECT SKILLS TO PROBLEM SOLVING Exercises 52–54 will help you prepare for problem solving.

Describe what the *t*-intercepts or *x*-intercepts of the graph of the function represent for the given situation.

52. The height *h* (in meters) of a golf ball *t* seconds after it is hit can be modeled by $h = -4.9t^2 + 15t$.

53. The arch of a bridge can be modeled by $y = -\frac{1}{16}x^2 + x$ where *x* and *y* are measured in feet.

54. The path of a ball that is kicked is given by $y = -0.5x^2 + 2x$ where *x* is the horizontal distance (in feet) and *y* is the vertical distance (in feet) from where the ball is kicked.

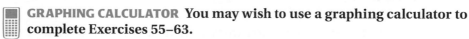

GRAPHING CALCULATOR You may wish to use a graphing calculator to complete Exercises 55–63.

EXAMPLE 6
on p. 627
for Exs. 55–56

55. **SURVEYING** To keep water off a road, the road's surface is shaped like a parabola as in the cross section below. The surface of the road can be modeled by the graph of $y = -0.0017x^2 + 0.041x$ where *x* and *y* are measured in feet. Find the width of the road to the nearest tenth of a foot.

California @*HomeTutor*** for problem solving help at classzone.com

56. ◆ **MULTIPLE CHOICE** The height *y* (in feet) of a soccer ball after it is kicked can be modeled by the graph of $y = -0.04x^2 + 1.2x$ where *x* is the horizontal distance (in feet) that the ball travels. The ball is not touched, and it lands on the ground. Find the distance that the ball is kicked.

Ⓐ 0 ft Ⓑ 3 ft Ⓒ 9 ft Ⓓ 30 ft

California @*HomeTutor*** for problem solving help at classzone.com

57. SHORT RESPONSE An arc of water sprayed from the nozzle of a fountain can be modeled by the graph of $y = -0.75x^2 + 6x$ where x is the horizontal distance (in feet) and y is the vertical distance (in feet) from the nozzle. The diameter of the circle formed by the arcs on the surface of the water is called the display diameter. Find the display diameter of the fountain. *Explain* your reasoning.

Display diameter

58. MULTI-STEP PROBLEM Two softball players are practicing catching fly balls. Sarah throws the ball upward from an initial height of 5.5 feet with an initial vertical velocity of 40 feet per second for her teammate to catch.

   a. Write an equation that models the height h (in feet) of the ball as a function of the time t (in seconds) after it is thrown.

   b. If Sarah's teammate misses the ball and it lands on the ground, how long was the ball in the air? If her teammate catches the ball at a height of 5.5 feet, how long was the ball in the air? *Explain*.

59. CHALLENGE For what values of c does the quadratic equation $x^2 + 10x + c = 0$ have two solutions? one solution? no solution?

CHALLENGE Use the given surface area S of the cylinder to find the radius r to the nearest tenth. (Use 3.14 for π.)

60. $S = 251 \text{ ft}^2$

6 ft

61. $S = 716 \text{ m}^2$

13 m

62. $S = 1074 \text{ cm}^2$

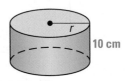
10 cm

63. CHALLENGE A stream of water from a fire hose can be modeled by the graph of $y = -0.003x^2 + 0.58x + 3$ where x and y are measured in feet. A firefighter is holding the hose 3 feet above the ground and 137 feet from a building. Will the stream of water pass through a window if the top of the window is 26 feet above the ground? *Explain*.

◆ CALIFORNIA STANDARDS SPIRAL REVIEW

Alg. 11.0

64. Which binomial is a factor of $x^2 - 5x + 6$? *(p. 556)*

   Ⓐ $x - 3$ **Ⓑ** $x + 2$ **Ⓒ** $x - 6$ **Ⓓ** $x + 1$

Alg. 24.3

65. Which set of dimensions for a rectangle is a counterexample to the statement "If a rectangle's area is a perfect square, then the rectangle is a square"? *(p. 95)*

   Ⓐ 9 in. by 4 in.   **Ⓑ** 6 in. by 6 in.   **Ⓒ** 3 in. by 6 in.   **Ⓓ** 10 in. by 10 in.

Alg. 5.0

66. You have $50 to spend at the mall. Candles cost $4 each. You want to buy several candles and still have $12 left for lunch. What is the maximum number of candles that you can buy? *(p. 202)*

   Ⓐ 7   **Ⓑ** 8   **Ⓒ** 9   **Ⓓ** 10

10.4 Find Zeros of a Function

Standards

Alg. 21.0 Students graph quadratic functions and know that their roots are the *x*-intercepts.

QUESTION How can you find the zeros of a quadratic function using a graphing calculator?

EXAMPLE Approximate the zeros of a function

Approximate the zeros of the function $y = 3x^2 + 2x - 4$.

STEP 1 *Enter the function*
Press **Y=** and enter the function $y = 3x^2 + 2x - 4$.

STEP 2 *Adjust the window*
Display the graph. Adjust the viewing window as needed so that the *x*-intercepts of the parabola are visible.

STEP 3 *Use the zero feature*
The *zero* feature is in the CALCULATE menu.

STEP 4 *Find the zeros*
Follow the graphing calculator's procedure to find a zero of the function. Then repeat the process to find the other zero.

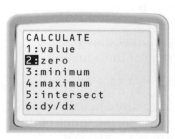

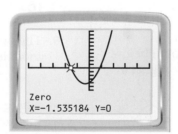

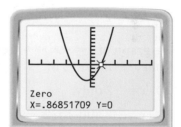

▶ The zeros are about −1.54 and about 0.87.

DRAW CONCLUSIONS

Approximate the zeros of the quadratic function to the nearest hundredth.

1. $y = 2x^2 - 5x - 8$ **2.** $y = -3x^2 + 6x - 2$ **3.** $y = -x^2 + 4x + 9$

4. $y = 4x^2 - 7x + 1$ **5.** $y = -2x^2 - 6x + 7$ **6.** $y = 5x^2 - 5.19x - 2.25$

7. REASONING If a quadratic function has only one zero, what is the maximum or minimum value of the function? *Explain.*

MIXED REVIEW of Skills and Problem Solving

Multiple Choice Practice for Lessons 10.1–10.4

1. The area of the triangle shown is 5 square inches. Which function's graph has x-intercepts that you can use to find the height x (in inches) of the triangle? **Alg. 23.0**

   A $y = x^2 - 5$

   B $y = x^2 - 4x + 5$

   C $y = x^2 - 4x$

   D $y = x^2 - 4x - 5$

   x in.

   $(2x - 8)$ in.

2. An apple falls from the height shown in the diagram. Which equation would you graph to find the elapsed time t (in seconds) when the apple hits the ground? **Alg. 23.0**

   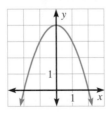

   A $h = -16(t^2 + 1)$

   B $h = -16t^2 + 16$

   C $h = -16t^2 + 1$

   D $h = -16(t - 4)(t + 4)$

   16 ft

3. What is the axis of symmetry of the graph of the function $y = -\frac{1}{4}x^2 - 6x + 3$? **Alg. 21.0**

   A $x = -12$ **B** $x = -3$

   C $x = -\frac{1}{2}$ **D** $x = 12$

4. The graph of $y = -x^2 + 4$ is shown below. What are the roots of $-x^2 + 4$? **Alg. 21.0**

   A $x = -2$ only

   B $x = -2$ and $x = 2$

   C $x = 2$ only

   D $x = -2$ and $x = 1$

   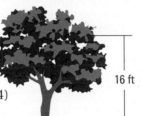

5. What are the x-intercepts of the graph of $y = -\frac{2}{3}(x + 5)(x - 3)$? **Alg. 21.0**

   A $-5, -3$ **B** $-5, 3$

   C $5, -3$ **D** $5, 3$

6. A company's yearly profits from 2001 to 2006 can be modeled by the function

   $$y = x^2 - 5x + 4$$

   where x is the number of years since 2001 and y is the yearly profit (in millions of dollars). The function's graph is shown below. In what year(s) did the company have a yearly profit of \$0? **Alg. 21.0**

   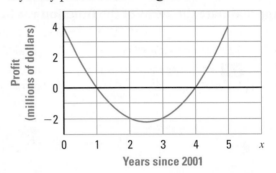

   A 2001   **B** 2001 and 2004

   C 2004   **D** 2002 and 2005

7. How many times does the graph of the function $y = (x + 2)(x + 2)$ intersect the x-axis? **Alg. 22.0**

   A 0   **B** 1

   C 2   **D** 3

8. The opening of the tunnel shown can be modeled by the graph of the equation

   $$y = -0.18x^2 + 4.4x - 12$$

   where x and y are measured in feet. Which inequality best represents the range of the function in this situation? **Alg. 17.0**

   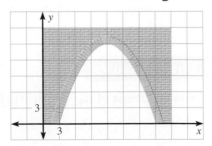

   A $0 \le y \le 5$ **B** $0 \le y \le 14.89$

   C $0 \le y \le 12$ **D** $3 \le y \le 21$

10.5 Use Square Roots to Solve Quadratic Equations

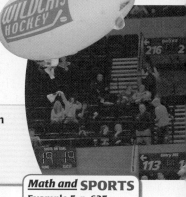

Standards Alg. 23.0 Students apply quadratic equations to physical problems, such as the motion of an object under the force of gravity.

Connect *Before* you solved a quadratic equation by graphing. *Now* you will solve a quadratic equation by finding square roots.

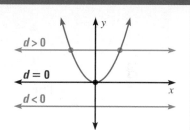

Math and SPORTS
Example 5, p. 635

Key Vocabulary
- square root,
  p. 95
- perfect square,
  p. 96

To use square roots to solve a quadratic equation of the form $ax^2 + c = 0$, first isolate x^2 on one side of the equation to obtain $x^2 = d$. Then use the following information about the solutions of $x^2 = d$ to solve the equation.

KEY CONCEPT *For Your Notebook*

Solving $x^2 = d$ by Taking Square Roots

- If $d > 0$, then $x^2 = d$ has two solutions:
  $x = \pm\sqrt{d}$.
- If $d = 0$, then $x^2 = d$ has one solution: $x = 0$.
- If $d < 0$, then $x^2 = d$ has no solution.

READING
Recall that in this course, *solutions* refers to real-number solutions.

EXAMPLE 1 Solve quadratic equations

Solve the equation.

a. $2x^2 = 8$ **b.** $m^2 - 18 = -18$ **c.** $b^2 + 12 = 5$

ANOTHER WAY
You can also use factoring to solve $2x^2 = 8$:
$$2x^2 = 8$$
$$2x^2 - 8 = 0$$
$$2(x^2 - 4) = 0$$
$$2(x - 2)(x + 2) = 0$$
$$x = 2 \ or \ x = -2$$

a. $2x^2 = 8$ Write original equation.

$\quad x^2 = 4$ Divide each side by 2.

$\quad x = \pm\sqrt{4}$ Take square roots of each side.

$\quad x = \pm 2$ Simplify.

▶ The solutions are -2 and 2.

b. $m^2 - 18 = -18$ Write original equation.

$\quad m^2 = 0$ Add 18 to each side.

$\quad m = 0$ The square root of 0 is 0.

▶ The solution is 0.

c. $b^2 + 12 = 5$ Write original equation.

$\quad b^2 = -7$ Subtract 12 from each side.

▶ Negative real numbers do not have real square roots. So, there is no solution.

1. Solve $4c^2 - 100 = 0$.

FRACTIONAL RADICANDS In cases where d in the equation $x^2 = d$ is a fraction whose numerator and denominator are perfect squares, you can simplify the radical by using the quotient property of radicals. For example, $\sqrt{\dfrac{16}{25}} = \dfrac{\sqrt{16}}{\sqrt{25}} = \dfrac{4}{5}$.

EXAMPLE 2 Take square roots of a fraction

Solve $4z^2 = 9$.

Solution

$4z^2 = 9$	**Write original equation.**
$z^2 = \dfrac{9}{4}$	**Divide each side by 4.**
$z = \pm\sqrt{\dfrac{9}{4}}$	**Take square roots of each side.**
$z = \pm\dfrac{3}{2}$	**Simplify.**

▶ The solutions are $-\dfrac{3}{2}$ and $\dfrac{3}{2}$.

RADICALS IN SOLUTIONS In cases where d in the equation $x^2 = d$ is not a perfect square or d is a fraction whose numerator and denominator are not perfect squares, leave the solution as a radical expression in simplest form.

EXAMPLE 3 Solve a quadratic equation

Solve $3x^2 - 11 = 13$.

Solution

$3x^2 - 11 = 13$	**Write original equation.**
$3x^2 = 24$	**Add 11 to each side.**
$x^2 = 8$	**Divide each side by 3.**
$x = \pm\sqrt{8}$	**Take square roots of each side.**
$x = \pm 2\sqrt{2}$	**Simplify.**

▶ The solutions are $-2\sqrt{2}$ and $2\sqrt{2}$.

REVIEW RADICALS
For help with simplifying radicals, see page 483.

 GUIDED PRACTICE for Examples 2 and 3

Solve the equation.

2. $25x^2 = 16$　　　**3.** $49b^2 + 64 = 0$　　　**4.** $x^2 + 4 = 31$　　　**5.** $2p^2 - 7 = 2$

EXAMPLE 4 Solve a quadratic equation

Solve $6(x - 4)^2 = 42$.

$6(x - 4)^2 = 42$ **Write original equation.**

$(x - 4)^2 = 7$ **Divide each side by 6.**

$x - 4 = \pm\sqrt{7}$ **Take square roots of each side.**

$x = 4 \pm\sqrt{7}$ **Add 4 to each side.**

▶ The solutions are $4 + \sqrt{7}$ and $4 - \sqrt{7}$.

EXAMPLE 5 Solve a multi-step problem

ANOTHER WAY

For alternative methods for solving the problem in Example 5, turn to page 640 for the **Problem Solving Workshop**.

SPORTS EVENT During an ice hockey game, a remote-controlled blimp flies above the crowd and drops a numbered table-tennis ball. The number on the ball corresponds to a prize. Use the information in the diagram to find the amount of time that the ball is in the air.

45 ft

17 ft

Not drawn to scale

Solution

DETERMINE VELOCITY

When an object is dropped, it has an initial vertical velocity of 0 feet per second.

STEP 1 **Use** the vertical motion model to write an equation for the height h (in feet) of the ball as a function of the time t (in seconds) after it is dropped.

$h = -16t^2 + vt + s$ **Vertical motion model**

$h = -16t^2 + 0t + 45$ **Substitute for v and s.**

STEP 2 **Find** the amount of time the ball is in the air by substituting 17 for h and solving for t.

$17 = -16t^2 + 45$ **Substitute 17 for h in model.**

$-28 = -16t^2$ **Subtract 45 from each side.**

$\dfrac{28}{16} = t^2$ **Divide each side by -16.**

INTERPRET SOLUTION

Because the time cannot be a negative number, ignore the negative square root.

$\sqrt{\dfrac{28}{16}} = \dfrac{\sqrt{7}}{2} = t$ **Take positive square root.**

$1.32 \approx t$ **Use a calculator.**

▶ The ball is in the air for about 1.32 seconds.

 GUIDED PRACTICE   **for Examples 4 and 5**

6. Solve $4(q - 3)^2 = 28$.

7. **WHAT IF?** In Example 5, suppose the table-tennis ball is dropped 58 feet above the ground and is caught 12 feet above the ground. Find the amount of time that the ball is in the air to the nearest hundredth of a second.

10.5 EXERCISES

SKILLS · PROBLEM SOLVING · REASONING

1. **VOCABULARY** Copy and complete: If $b^2 = a$, then b is a(n) __?__ of a.

2. **WRITING** *Describe* two methods for solving a quadratic equation of the form $ax^2 + c = 0$.

EXAMPLES 1 and 2
on pp. 633–634
for Exs. 3–16

SOLVING EQUATIONS Solve the equation.

3. $3x^2 - 3 = 0$

4. $2x^2 - 32 = 0$

5. $4x^2 - 400 = 0$

6. $2m^2 - 42 = 8$

7. $15d^2 = 0$

8. $a^2 + 8 = 3$

9. $4g^2 + 10 = 11$

10. $2w^2 + 13 = 11$

11. $9q^2 - 35 = 14$

12. $25b^2 + 11 = 15$

13. $3z^2 - 18 = -18$

14. $5n^2 - 17 = -19$

15. ◆ **MULTIPLE CHOICE** Which of the following is a solution of the equation $61 - 3n^2 = -14$?

   (A) 5   (B) 10   (C) 25   (D) 625

16. ◆ **MULTIPLE CHOICE** For which value of c does the equation $13 - 36x^2 = c$ have only one solution?

   (A) −13   (B) −12   (C) 12   (D) 13

EXAMPLE 3
on p. 634
for Exs. 17–31

EQUATIONS WITH RADICALS IN SOLUTIONS Solve the equation.

17. $x^2 + 6 = 13$

18. $x^2 + 11 = 24$

19. $14 - x^2 = 17$

20. $2a^2 - 9 = 11$

21. $4 - k^2 = 4$

22. $5 + 3p^2 = 38$

23. $53 = 8 + 9m^2$

24. $-21 = 15 - 2z^2$

25. $7c^2 = 100$

26. $5d^2 + 2 = 6$

27. $4b^2 - 5 = 2$

28. $9n^2 - 14 = -3$

29. ◆ **MULTIPLE CHOICE** The equation $17 - \frac{1}{4}x^2 = 12$ has a solution between which two integers?

   (A) 1 and 2   (B) 2 and 3   (C) 3 and 4   (D) 4 and 5

ERROR ANALYSIS *Describe* and correct the error in solving the equation.

30. $2x^2 - 54 = 18$

$$2x^2 - 54 = 18$$
$$2x^2 = 72$$
$$x^2 = 36$$
$$x = \sqrt{36}$$
$$x = 6$$

The solution is 6.

31. $7d^2 - 6 = -20$

$$7d^2 - 6 = -20$$
$$7d^2 = -14$$
$$d^2 = -2$$
$$d = \pm\sqrt{2}$$

The solutions are $-\sqrt{2}$ and $\sqrt{2}$.

EXAMPLE 4
on p. 635
for Exs. 32–40

SOLVING EQUATIONS Solve the equation.

32. $(x - 7)^2 = 6$

33. $7(x - 3)^2 = 35$

34. $6(x + 4)^2 = 18$

35. $20 = 2(m + 5)^2$

36. $5(a - 2)^2 = 70$

37. $21 = 3(z + 14)^2$

38. $\frac{1}{2}(c - 8)^2 = 3$

39. $\frac{3}{2}(n + 1)^2 = 33$

40. $\frac{4}{3}(k - 6)^2 = 20$

 GEOMETRY Use the given area A of the circle to find the radius r or the diameter d to the nearest hundredth.

41. $A = 144\pi$ in.^{2}

42. $A = 21\pi$ m^2

43. $A = 34\pi$ ft^2

SOLVING EQUATIONS Solve the equation.

44. $3x^2 - 35 = 45 - 2x^2$

45. $42 = 3(x^2 + 5)$

46. $11x^2 + 3 = 5(4x^2 - 3)$

47. $\left(\frac{t - 5}{3}\right)^2 = 49$

48. $11\left(\frac{w - 7}{2}\right)^2 - 20 = 101$

49. $(4m^2 - 6)^2 = 81$

50. REASONING An equation of the graph shown is $y = \frac{1}{2}(x - 2)^2 + 1$. Two points on the parabola have y-coordinates of 9. Find the x-coordinates of these points.

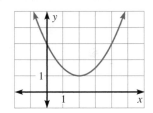

51. OPEN-ENDED Give values for a and c so that $ax^2 + c = 0$ has **(a)** two solutions, **(b)** one solution, and **(c)** no solution.

CONNECT SKILLS TO PROBLEM SOLVING Exercises 52–54 will help you prepare for problem solving.

Explain how you would use the following information to answer the question: An object falls from a height of 100 feet. Its height h (in feet) is given by $h = -16t^2 + 100$ where t is the time (in seconds) since the object fell.

52. What is the height of the object after falling for 2 seconds?

53. How long does it take the object to reach a height of 20 feet?

54. How long does it take the object to reach the ground?

EXAMPLE 5
on p. 635
for Exs. 55–56

55. FALLING OBJECT Fenway Park is a Major League Baseball park in Boston, Massachusetts. The park offers seats on top of the left field wall. A person sitting in one of these seats accidentally drops his sunglasses on the field. The height h (in feet) of the sunglasses can be modeled by the function $h = -16t^2 + 38$ where t is the time (in seconds) since the sunglasses were dropped. Find the time it takes the sunglasses to reach the field. Round your answer to the nearest hundredth of a second.

California @HomeTutor for problem solving help at classzone.com

56. ◆ MULTIPLE CHOICE Which equation can be used to find the time
t (in seconds) that it takes an object to hit the ground after it is dropped
from a height of 68 feet?

(A) $-16t^2 = 0$ **(B)** $-16t^2 = 68$ **(C)** $-16t^2 + 68 = 0$ **(D)** $-16t^2 - 68 = 0$

California @*HomeTutor*   for problem solving help at classzone.com

57. MULTI-STEP PROBLEM An object is dropped from a height of 256 feet
above the ground.

a. Write an equation for the height h (in feet) of the object as a function
of the time t (in seconds) since the object was dropped.

b. Copy and complete the table.

Time, t (sec)	0	1	2	3	4
Height, h (ft)	?	?	?	?	?
Change in height after each second	–	?	?	?	?

c. Use the table from part (b) to explain how the object's height
decreases as time increases.

58. OCEANOGRAPHY In deep water, the speed s (in meters per second) of a
series of waves and the wavelength L (in meters) of the waves are related
by the equation $2\pi s^2 = 9.8L$.

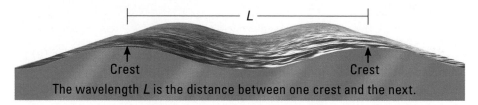

The wavelength L is the distance between one crest and the next.

a. Find the speed to the nearest hundredth of a meter per second of a
series of waves with the following wavelengths: 6 meters, 10 meters,
and 25 meters. (Use 3.14 for π.)

b. Does the speed of a series of waves increase or decrease as the
wavelength of the waves increases? *Explain.*

59. MULTI-STEP PROBLEM A ride at an amusement park lifts seated
riders 250 feet above the ground. Then the riders are dropped.
They experience free fall until the brakes are activated at 105 feet
above the ground.

a. Writing an Equation Use the vertical motion model to write an
equation for the height h (in feet) of the riders as a function of
the time t (in seconds) since the riders were dropped.

b. Making a Table Make a table that shows the height of the
riders after 0, 1, 2, and 3 seconds. Use the table to estimate
the amount of time the riders experience free fall.

c. Solving an Equation Use the equation to find the amount of
time, to the nearest tenth of a second, that the riders experience
free fall.

**Riders are lifted
250 feet.**

60. LUMBER The Doyle log rule is a formula used to estimate the amount of lumber that can be sawn from logs of various sizes. The amount of lumber V (in board feet) is given by $V = \dfrac{L(D - 4)^2}{16}$ where L is the length (in feet) of a log and D is the small-end diameter (in inches) of the log.

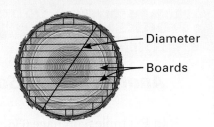

Diameter

Boards

a. Solve the formula for D.

b. Find the diameters, to the nearest tenth of an inch, of logs that will yield 50 board feet and have these lengths: 16 ft, 18 ft, and 20 ft.

CHALLENGE Solve the equation without graphing.

61. $x^2 - 12x + 36 = 31$ **62.** $x^2 + 14x + 49 = 24$ **63.** $x^2 + 18x + 81 = 45$

64. CHALLENGE The height h (in feet) of a dropped object on any planet can be modeled by $h = -\dfrac{g}{2}t^2 + s$ where g is the acceleration (in feet per second per second) due to the planet's gravity, t is the time (in seconds) after the object is dropped, and s is the initial height (in feet) of the object. Suppose the same object is dropped from the same height on Earth and Mars. Given that g is 32 feet per second per second on Earth and 12 feet per second per second on Mars, on which planet will the object hit the ground first? *Explain.*

◆ CALIFORNIA STANDARDS SPIRAL REVIEW

Alg. 6.0

65. The graph of which equation has a y-intercept of -7? *(p. 273)*

   A $3x + 7y = 49$ **B** $3x - 7y = 49$

   C $3x - 7y = 21$ **D** $3x + 7y = 21$

Alg. 25.2

66. A student claims that $2(x + 3)$ is equivalent to $2x + 3$. Which property did the student use incorrectly? *(p. 81)*

   A Commutative property   **B** Distributive property

   C Closure property of addition   **D** Addition property of equality

Alg. 11.0

67. What is the factored form of $12s^2 + 17st - 5t^2$? *(p. 556)*

   A $(4s - 5t)(3s + t)$ **B** $(2s - t)(6s + 5t)$

   C $(2s - 5t)(6s + t)$ **D** $(4s - t)(3s + 5t)$

QUIZ *for Lessons 10.4–10.5*

Find the zeros of the function. *(p. 624)*

1. $y = x^2 + 3x - 10$ **2.** $y = x^2 - 8x + 12$ **3.** $y = -x^2 + 5x + 14$

Solve the equation using square roots. *(p. 633)*

4. $3x^2 - 48 = 0$ **5.** $-6x^2 = -24$ **6.** $x^2 + 5 = 16$

Using ALTERNATIVE METHODS

Another Way to Solve Example 5, page 635

Standards
Alg. 23.0

In Example 5 on page 635, you saw how to solve a problem about a dropped table-tennis ball by using a square root. You can also solve the problem by using factoring or by using a table.

PROBLEM

SPORTS EVENT During an ice hockey game, a remote-controlled blimp flies above the crowd and drops a numbered table-tennis ball. The number on the ball corresponds to a prize. Use the information in the diagram to find the amount of time that the ball is in the air.

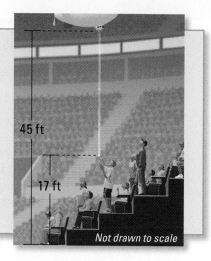

45 ft

17 ft

Not drawn to scale

METHOD 1 **Using Factoring** One alternative approach is to use factoring.

STEP 1 **Write** an equation for the ball's height h (in feet) as a function of the time t (in seconds) after it is dropped using the vertical motion model.

$$h = -16t^2 + vt + s$$ **Vertical motion model**

$$h = -16t^2 + 0t + 45$$ **Substitute 0 for v and 45 for s.**

STEP 2 **Substitute** 17 for h to find the time it takes the ball to reach a height of 17 feet. Then rewrite the equation so that 0 is on one side.

$$17 = -16t^2 + 45$$ **Substitute 17 for h.**

$$0 = -16t^2 + 28$$ **Subtract 17 from each side.**

STEP 3 **Solve** the equation by factoring. Replace 28 with the closest perfect square, 25, so that the right side of the equation is factorable as a difference of two squares.

USE AN APPROXIMATION
By replacing 28 with 25, you will obtain an answer that is an approximation of the amount of time that the ball is in the air.

$$0 = -16t^2 + \mathbf{25}$$ **Use 25 as an approximation for 28.**

$$0 = -(16t^2 - 25)$$ **Factor out -1.**

$$0 = -(4t - 5)(4t + 5)$$ **Difference of two squares pattern**

$$4t - 5 = 0 \ \ or \ \ 4t + 5 = 0$$ **Zero-product property**

$$t = \frac{5}{4} \ \ or \ \ \ \ \ \ \ \ t = -\frac{5}{4}$$ **Solve for t.**

▶ The ball is in the air about $\frac{5}{4}$, or 1.25, seconds.

METHOD 2 **Using a Table** Another approach is to make and use a table.

STEP 1 **Make** a table that shows the height h (in feet) of the ball by substituting values for time t (in seconds) in the function $h = -16t^2 + 45$. Use increments of 1 second.

Time t (seconds)	Height h (feet)
0	45
1	29
2	−19

STEP 2 **Identify** the time interval in which the height of the ball is 17 feet. This happens between 1 and 2 seconds.

STEP 3 **Make** a second table using increments of 0.1 second to get a closer approximation.

▶ The ball is in the air about 1.3 seconds.

Time t (seconds)	Height h (feet)
1.0	29.00
1.1	25.64
1.2	21.96
1.3	**17.96**
1.4	13.64

PRACTICE

1. **WHAT IF?** In the problem on page 640, suppose the ball is caught at a height of 10 feet. For how many seconds is the ball in the air? Solve this problem using two different methods.

2. **OPEN-ENDED** *Describe* a problem about a dropped object. Then solve the problem and explain what your solution means in this situation.

3. 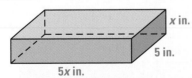 **GEOMETRY** The box below is a rectangular prism with the dimensions shown.

   x in.
   5 in.
   5x in.

   a. Write an equation that gives the volume V (in cubic inches) of the box as a function of x.

   b. The volume of the box is 83 cubic inches. Find the dimensions of the box. Use factoring to solve the problem.

   c. Make a table to check your answer from part (b).

4. **TRAPEZE** You are learning how to perform on a trapeze. While hanging from a still trapeze bar, your shoe comes loose and falls to a safety net that is 6 feet off the ground. If your shoe falls from a height of 54 feet, how long does it take your shoe to hit the net? Choose any method for solving the problem. Show your steps.

5. **ERROR ANALYSIS** A student solved the problem in Exercise 4 as shown below. *Describe* and correct the error.

   Let t be the time (in seconds) that the shoe is in the air.

   $6 = -16t^2 + 54$

   $0 = -16t^2 + 60$

   Replace 60 with the closest perfect square, 64.

   $0 = -16t^2 + 64$

   $0 = -16(t - 2)(t + 2)$

   $t = 2$ or $t = -2$

   It takes about 2 seconds.

10.6 Completing the Square Using Algebra Tiles

Standards

Alg. 14.0 Students solve a quadratic equation by factoring or **completing the square.**

QUESTION   How can you use algebra tiles to complete the square?

For an expression of the form $x^2 + bx$, you can add a constant c to the expression so that the expression $x^2 + bx + c$ is a perfect square trinomial. This process is called *completing the square*.

EXPLORE   Complete the square

Find the value of c that makes $x^2 + 4x + c$ a perfect square trinomial.

STEP 1 *Model expression*	STEP 2 *Rearrange tiles*	STEP 3 *Complete the square*
Use algebra tiles to model the expression $x^2 + 4x$. You will need one x^2-tile and four x-tiles for this expression.	Arrange the tiles to form a square. The arrangement will be incomplete in one of the corners.	Determine the number of 1-tiles needed to complete the square. The number of 1-tiles is the value of c. So, the perfect square trinomial is $x^2 + 4x + 4$, which you can write as $(x + 2)^2$.

      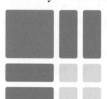

DRAW CONCLUSIONS   Use your observations to complete these exercises

1. Copy and complete the table using algebra tiles.

Expression	Number of 1-tiles needed to complete the square	Expression written as a square
$x^2 + 4x$	4	$x^2 + 4x + 4 = (x + 2)^2$
$x^2 + 6x$	?	?
$x^2 + 8x$	?	?
$x^2 + 10x$	?	?

2. In the statement $x^2 + bx + c = (x + d)^2$, how are b and d related? How are c and d related?

3. You can solve an equation like $x^2 + 18x = 4$ by completing the square. You begin by adding a constant c to each side: $x^2 + 18x + c = 4 + c$. Find the value of c for which $x^2 + 18x + c$ is a perfect square trinomial, then finish solving the equation.

10.6 Solve Quadratic Equations by Completing the Square

Standards Alg. 14.0 **Students solve a quadratic equation by** factoring or **completing the square.**

Connect *Before* you solved a quadratic equation by finding square roots. *Now* you will solve a quadratic equation by completing the square.

Math and **SPORTS**
Ex. 52, p. 648

Key Vocabulary
• **completing the square**
• **perfect square trinomial**, *p. 574*

For an expression of the form $x^2 + bx$, you can add a constant c to the expression so that the expression $x^2 + bx + c$ is a perfect square trinomial. This process is called **completing the square**.

KEY CONCEPT *For Your Notebook*

Completing the Square

Words To complete the square for the expression $x^2 + bx$, add the square of half of the coefficient of x.

Algebra $x^2 + bx + \left(\dfrac{b}{2}\right)^2 = \left(x + \dfrac{b}{2}\right)^2$

EXAMPLE 1 **Complete the square**

Find the value of c that makes the expression $x^2 + 5x + c$ a perfect square trinomial. Then write the expression as the square of a binomial.

Solution

STEP 1 **Find** the value of c.

$$c = \left(\frac{5}{2}\right)^2 = \frac{25}{4} \qquad \text{Find the square of half of the coefficient of } x, 5.$$

STEP 2 **Write** the expression as a perfect square trinomial. Then write the expression as the square of a binomial.

$$x^2 + 5x + c = x^2 + 5x + \frac{25}{4} \qquad \text{Substitute } \frac{25}{4} \text{ for c.}$$

$$= \left(x + \frac{5}{2}\right)^2 \qquad \text{Square of a binomial}$$

 GUIDED PRACTICE for Example 1

Find the value of c that makes the expression a perfect square trinomial. Then write the expression as the square of a binomial.

1. $x^2 + 8x + c$ **2.** $x^2 - 12x + c$ **3.** $x^2 + 3x + c$

SOLVING EQUATIONS The method of completing the square can be used to solve any quadratic equation. To use completing the square to solve a quadratic equation, you must write the equation in the form $x^2 + bx = d$.

EXAMPLE 2 ◆ **Multiple Choice Practice**

> What quantity should be added to both sides of this equation to complete the square?
>
> $$x^2 - 6x = 3$$
>
> **(A)** −9   **(B)** −3   **(C)** 3   **(D)** 9

ELIMINATE CHOICES
Because the *square* of half of the coefficient of x is added to each side, the number must be positive. You can eliminate choices A and B.

Solution

Find the square of half of the coefficient of x: $\left(\dfrac{-6}{2}\right)^2 = (-3)^2 = 9$.

▶ The correct answer is D. (A) (B) (C) **(D)**

EXAMPLE 3 **Solve a quadratic equation**

Solve $2x^2 + 12x + 14 = 0$ by completing the square.

Solution

$2x^2 + 12x + 14 = 0$	Write original equation.
$2x^2 + 12x = -14$	Subtract 14 from each side.
$x^2 + 6x = -7$	Divide each side by 2.
$x^2 + 6x + 3^2 = -7 + 3^2$	Add $\left(\dfrac{6}{2}\right)^2$, or 3^2, to each side.
$(x + 3)^2 = 2$	Write left side as the square of a binomial.
$x + 3 = \pm\sqrt{2}$	Take square roots of each side.
$x = -3 \pm \sqrt{2}$	Subtract 3 from each side.

AVOID ERRORS
Be sure that the coefficient of x^2 is 1 before you complete the square.

▶ The solutions are $-3 + \sqrt{2}$ and $-3 - \sqrt{2}$.

CHECK To check the solutions of $2x^2 + 12x + 14 = 0$, graph the related function $y = 2x^2 + 12x + 14$.

The x-intercepts are approximately −4.4 and −1.6. Compare these values with the solutions:

$-3 - \sqrt{2} \approx -4.41$ ✓

$-3 + \sqrt{2} \approx -1.59$ ✓

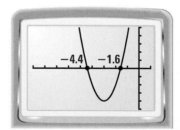

 GUIDED PRACTICE for Examples 2 and 3

Solve the equation by completing the square.

4. $x^2 - 2x = 3$ **5.** $m^2 + 10m = -8$ **6.** $3g^2 - 24g + 27 = 0$

EXAMPLE 4 **Solve a multi-step problem**

CRAFTS You decide to use chalkboard paint to create a chalkboard on a door. You want the chalkboard to have a uniform border as shown. You have enough chalkboard paint to cover 6 square feet. Find the width of the border to the nearest inch.

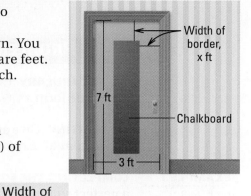
Width of border, x ft

7 ft

Chalkboard

3 ft

Solution

STEP 1 **Write** a verbal model. Then write an equation. Let x be the width (in feet) of the border.

Area of chalkboard (square feet)	=	Length of chalkboard (feet)	·	Width of chalkboard (feet)
6	=	$(7 - 2x)$	·	$(3 - 2x)$

WRITE EQUATION
The width of the border is subtracted twice because it is at the top and the bottom of the door, as well as at the left and the right.

STEP 2 **Solve** the equation.

$$6 = (7 - 2x)(3 - 2x) \qquad \text{Write equation.}$$

$$6 = 21 - 20x + 4x^2 \qquad \text{Multiply binomials.}$$

$$-15 = 4x^2 - 20x \qquad \text{Subtract 21 from each side.}$$

$$-\frac{15}{4} = x^2 - 5x \qquad \text{Divide each side by 4.}$$

$$-\frac{15}{4} + \frac{25}{4} = x^2 - 5x + \frac{25}{4} \qquad \text{Add } \left(-\frac{5}{2}\right)^2, \text{ or } \frac{25}{4}, \text{ to each side.}$$

$$-\frac{15}{4} + \frac{25}{4} = \left(x - \frac{5}{2}\right)^2 \qquad \text{Write right side as the square of a binomial.}$$

$$\frac{5}{2} = \left(x - \frac{5}{2}\right)^2 \qquad \text{Simplify left side.}$$

$$\pm\sqrt{\frac{5}{2}} = x - \frac{5}{2} \qquad \text{Take square roots of each side.}$$

$$\frac{5}{2} \pm \frac{\sqrt{10}}{2} = x \qquad \text{Rationalize denominator and add } \frac{5}{2} \text{ to each side.}$$

REVIEW RATIONALIZING
For help with rationalizing the denominator, see p. 483.

The solutions of the equation are $\frac{5}{2} + \frac{\sqrt{10}}{2} \approx 4.08$ and $\frac{5}{2} - \frac{\sqrt{10}}{2} \approx 0.92$.

It is not possible for the width of the border to be 4.08 feet because the width of the door is 3 feet. So, the width of the border is 0.92 foot. Convert 0.92 foot to inches.

$$0.92 \ \cancel{\text{ft}} \cdot \frac{12 \text{ in.}}{1 \ \cancel{\text{ft}}} = 11.04 \text{ in.} \qquad \text{Multiply by conversion factor.}$$

▶ The width of the border should be about 11 inches.

✓ **GUIDED PRACTICE** **for Example 4**

7. **WHAT IF?** In Example 4, suppose you have enough chalkboard paint to cover 4 square feet. Find the width of the border to the nearest inch.

10.6 EXERCISES

SKILLS • PROBLEM SOLVING • REASONING

1. **VOCABULARY** Copy and complete: The process of writing an expression of the form $x^2 + bx$ as a perfect square trinomial is called __?__.

2. **WRITING** Give an example of an expression that is a perfect square trinomial. *Explain* why the expression is a perfect square trinomial.

EXAMPLE 1
on p. 643
for Exs. 3–14

COMPLETING THE SQUARE Find the value of c that makes the expression a perfect square trinomial. Then write the expression as the square of a binomial.

3. $x^2 + 6x + c$

4. $x^2 + 12x + c$

5. $x^2 - 4x + c$

6. $x^2 - 8x + c$

7. $x^2 - 3x + c$

8. $x^2 + 5x + c$

9. $x^2 + 2.4x + c$

10. $x^2 - \frac{1}{2}x + c$

11. $x^2 - \frac{4}{3}x + c$

12. $x^2 + 3.6x + c$

13. $x^2 - \frac{3}{4}x + c$

14. $x^2 + \frac{6}{5}x + c$

EXAMPLES 2 and 3
on p. 644
for Exs. 15–42

15. ◆ **MULTIPLE CHOICE** What number should be added to each side of $x^2 + 4x = \frac{9}{4}$ when solving the equation by completing the square?

(A) 1   (B) 2   (C) 4   (D) 16

SOLVING EQUATIONS Solve the equation by completing the square.

16. $x^2 + 2x = 3$

17. $x^2 + 10x = 24$

18. $c^2 - 14c = 15$

19. $n^2 - 6n = 72$

20. $a^2 - 8a + 15 = 0$

21. $y^2 + 4y - 21 = 0$

22. $w^2 - 5w = \frac{11}{4}$

(23.) $z^2 + 11z = -\frac{21}{4}$

24. $g^2 - \frac{2}{3}g = 7$

25. $k^2 - 8k - 7 = 0$

26. $v^2 - 7v + 1 = 0$

27. $m^2 + 3m + \frac{5}{4} = 0$

28. ◆ **MULTIPLE CHOICE** What are the solutions of $x^2 + 12x + 10 = 0$?

(A) $-6 \pm \sqrt{46}$ (B) $-6 \pm \sqrt{26}$ (C) $6 \pm \sqrt{26}$ (D) $6 \pm \sqrt{46}$

ERROR ANALYSIS *Describe* and correct the error in solving the equation.

29. $x^2 - 14x = 11$

$$x^2 - 14x = 11$$
$$x^2 - 14x + 49 = 11$$
$$(x - 7)^2 = 11$$
$$✗ \quad x - 7 = \pm\sqrt{11}$$
$$x = 7 \pm \sqrt{11}$$

30. $x^2 - 2x - 4 = 0$

$$x^2 - 2x - 4 = 0$$
$$x^2 - 2x = 4$$
$$x^2 - 2x + 1 = 4 + 1$$
$$(x + 1)^2 = 5$$
$$✗ \quad x + 1 = \pm\sqrt{5}$$
$$x = -1 \pm \sqrt{5}$$

SOLVING EQUATIONS Solve the equation by completing the square.

31. $2x^2 - 8x - 14 = 0$

32. $2x^2 + 24x + 10 = 0$

33. $3x^2 - 48x + 39 = 0$

34. $4y^2 + 4y - 7 = 0$

35. $9n^2 + 36n + 11 = 0$

36. $3w^2 - 18w - 20 = 0$

37. $3p^2 - 30p - 11 = 6p$

38. $3a^2 - 12a + 3 = -a^2 - 4$

39. $15c^2 - 51c - 30 = 9c + 15$

40. $7m^2 + 24m - 2 = m^2 - 9$

41. $g^2 + 2g + 0.4 = 0.9g^2 + g$

42. $11z^2 - 10z - 3 = -9z^2 + \frac{3}{4}$

 GEOMETRY Find the value of x. Round your answer to the nearest hundredth, if necessary.

43. Area of triangle = 108 m²

x m

$(x + 6)$ m

44. Area of rectangle = 288 in.²

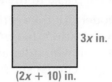

$3x$ in.

$(2x + 10)$ in.

45. REASONING Consider the equation $x^2 - 4x = 7$.

  a. Show that $2 + \sqrt{11}$ is a solution of the equation.

  b. Make a conjecture about the other solution of the equation. *Explain* how you can test your conjecture, then determine whether your conjecture is correct.

CONNECT SKILLS TO PROBLEM SOLVING Exercises 46–48 will help you prepare for problem solving.

46. The area of a triangular garden with a height of x feet and a base of $(x + 3)$ feet is 88 square feet. Write an equation to find the height.

47. The area of a rectangular garden with a length of x yards and a width of $(x - 4)$ yards is 45 square yards. Write an equation to find the length.

48. A rectangular garden is x feet long and $(x + 2)$ feet wide. In one corner of the garden is a shed that is 6 feet long and 4 feet wide. The area of the garden not including the shed is 120 square feet. Write an equation to find the length of the garden.

EXAMPLE 4
on p. 645
for Exs. 49–50

49. LANDSCAPING You are building a rectangular brick patio surrounded by crushed stone in a rectangular courtyard as shown. The crushed stone border has a uniform width of x feet. You have enough money in your budget to purchase patio bricks to cover 140 square feet. Solve the equation $140 = (20 - 2x)(16 - 2x)$ to find the width of the border.

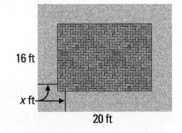

16 ft

x ft

20 ft

California @HomeTutor for problem solving help at classzone.com

50. ◆ MULTIPLE CHOICE The distance d (in feet) that it takes a car to come to a complete stop on dry asphalt can be modeled by $d = 0.05s^2 + 1.1s$ where s is the speed of the car (in miles per hour). A car has 78 feet to come to a complete stop. What is the maximum speed at which the car can travel?

  A 30 mi/h

  B 41 mi/h

  C 52 mi/h

  D 166 mi/h

California @HomeTutor for problem solving help at classzone.com

51. **MULTI-STEP PROBLEM** You have 80 feet of fencing to make a rectangular horse pasture that covers 750 square feet. A barn will be used as one side of the pasture as shown.

  a. Write equations for the length of fencing and the area of the pasture.

  b. Use substitution to solve the system of equations from part (a). What are the possible dimensions of the pasture?

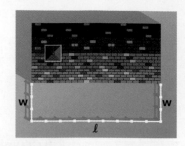

52. **SNOWBOARDING** During a "big air" competition, snowboarders launch themselves from a half pipe, perform tricks in the air, and land in the half pipe.

  a. **Model** Use the vertical motion model to write an equation that models the height h (in feet) of a snowboarder as a function of the time t (in seconds) she is in the air.

  b. **Apply** To the nearest tenth of a second, how long is the snowboarder in the air if she lands 13.2 feet above the base of the half pipe?

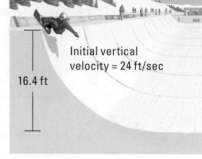

Initial vertical velocity = 24 ft/sec

16.4 ft

Cross section of a half pipe

Animated **Algebra** at classzone.com

CHALLENGE In Exercises 53 and 54, use the given information to find the integers.

53. The product of two consecutive negative integers is 210.

54. The product of two consecutive positive even integers is 288.

55. **CHALLENGE** You are knitting a rectangular scarf. The pattern you have created will result in a scarf that has a length of 60 inches and a width of 4 inches. However, you happen to have enough yarn to cover an area of 480 square inches. You decide to increase the dimensions of the scarf so that all of your yarn will be used. If the increase in the length is 10 times the increase in the width, what will the dimensions of the scarf be?

◆ CALIFORNIA STANDARDS SPIRAL REVIEW

Alg. 1.0
56. Which set is closed under multiplication? *(p. 74)*

    Ⓐ Integers   **Ⓑ** {0, 1, 4}   **Ⓒ** {−3, 0, 1}   **Ⓓ** Prime numbers

Alg. 11.0
57. What is the completely factored form of $x^3 - x^2$? *(p. 579)*

    Ⓐ $x^2(x - 1)$ **Ⓑ** $x^2(x + 1)$ **Ⓒ** $x(x^2 + x)$ **Ⓓ** $x(x + 1)(x - 1)$

Alg. 23.0
58. An object is dropped from a height of 52 feet. The height h (in feet) of the object can be modeled by the function $h = -16t^2 + 52$ where t is the time (in seconds) since the object is dropped. Find the time it takes the object to reach the ground. Round your answer to the nearest hundredth of a second. *(p. 633)*

    Ⓐ −1.80 sec   **Ⓑ** 1.80 sec   **Ⓒ** 0.45 sec   **Ⓓ** 3.25 sec

10.7 Solve Quadratic Equations by the Quadratic Formula

Standards　Alg. 19.0 Students know the quadratic formula and are familiar with its proof by completing the square.

Alg. 20.0 Students use the quadratic formula to find the roots of a second-degree polynomial and to solve quadratic equations.

Connect　*Before* you solved a quadratic equation by completing the square.
Now you will solve a quadratic equation by using the quadratic formula.

Math and **FILM**
Example 3, p. 651

Key Vocabulary
• quadratic formula

By completing the square for the quadratic equation $ax^2 + bx + c = 0$, you can develop a formula that gives the solutions of any quadratic equation in standard form. This formula is called the **quadratic formula**.

KEY CONCEPT　　　　　　　　　　　　　*For Your Notebook*

The Quadratic Formula

The roots of the polynomial $ax^2 + bx + c$ and the solutions of the quadratic equation $ax^2 + bx + c = 0$ are $x = \dfrac{-b \pm \sqrt{b^2 - 4ac}}{2a}$ where $a \neq 0$ and $b^2 - 4ac \geq 0$.

About the Standards

This derivation constitutes a proof of the quadratic formula.

DERIVING THE QUADRATIC FORMULA You can use the method of completing the square and a property of radicals to derive the quadratic formula.

$$ax^2 + bx + c = 0 \qquad \text{Write standard form of a quadratic equation.}$$

$$ax^2 + bx = -c \qquad \text{Subtract } c \text{ from each side.}$$

$$x^2 + \frac{b}{a}x = -\frac{c}{a} \qquad \text{Divide each side by } a,\ a \neq 0.$$

$$x^2 + \frac{b}{a}x + \left(\frac{b}{2a}\right)^2 = -\frac{c}{a} + \left(\frac{b}{2a}\right)^2 \qquad \text{Add } \left(\frac{b}{2a}\right)^2 \text{ to each side to complete the square.}$$

$$\left(x + \frac{b}{2a}\right)^2 = -\frac{c}{a} + \frac{b^2}{4a^2} \qquad \text{Write left side as the square of a binomial.}$$

COMBINE FRACTIONS

A common denominator for $-\frac{c}{a}$ and $\frac{b^2}{4a^2}$ is $4a^2$. An equivalent form of $-\frac{c}{a}$ is $-\frac{c \cdot 4a}{a \cdot 4a} = -\frac{4ac}{4a^2}$.

$$\left(x + \frac{b}{2a}\right)^2 = \frac{b^2 - 4ac}{4a^2} \qquad \text{Combine fractions on right side.}$$

$$x + \frac{b}{2a} = \pm\sqrt{\frac{b^2 - 4ac}{4a^2}} \qquad \text{Take square roots of each side.}$$

$$x + \frac{b}{2a} = \frac{\pm\sqrt{b^2 - 4ac}}{2a} \qquad \text{Quotient property of radicals}$$

$$x = \frac{-b \pm \sqrt{b^2 - 4ac}}{2a} \qquad \text{Subtract } \frac{b}{2a} \text{ from each side.}$$

USING THE QUADRATIC FORMULA You can use the quadratic formula and properties of radicals to find the roots of second-degree polynomials and to solve quadratic equations.

EXAMPLE 1   Find the roots of a polynomial

Find the roots of $x^2 - 6x + 3$.

Solution

The roots of $x^2 - 6x + 3$ are the values of x for which $x^2 - 6x + 3 = 0$.

$$x = \frac{-b \pm \sqrt{b^2 - 4ac}}{2a}$$ **Quadratic formula**

$$x = \frac{-(-6) \pm \sqrt{(-6)^2 - 4(1)(3)}}{2(1)}$$ **Substitute values in the quadratic formula:** $a = 1$, $b = -6$, and $c = 3$.

$$= \frac{6 \pm \sqrt{24}}{2}$$ **Simplify.**

$$= \frac{6 \pm 2\sqrt{6}}{2}$$ **Simplify radical.**

$$= \frac{\cancel{2}(3 \pm \sqrt{6})}{\cancel{2}} = 3 \pm \sqrt{6}$$ **Divide out factor of 2.**

▶ The roots of $x^2 - 6x + 3$ are $3 + \sqrt{6}$ and $3 - \sqrt{6}$.

CHECK Substitute each root for x. The polynomial should simplify to 0.

$$(3 + \sqrt{6})^2 - 6(3 + \sqrt{6}) + 3 \qquad\qquad (3 - \sqrt{6})^2 - 6(3 - \sqrt{6}) + 3$$
$$= 9 + 6\sqrt{6} + 6 - 18 - 6\sqrt{6} + 3 \qquad\qquad = 9 - 6\sqrt{6} + 6 - 18 + 6\sqrt{6} + 3$$
$$= 0 \checkmark \qquad\qquad\qquad\qquad\qquad\qquad = 0 \checkmark$$

EXAMPLE 2   ◆ Multiple Choice Practice

Which is one of the solutions to the equation $2x^2 - 7 = x$?

Ⓐ $\frac{1}{4} - \sqrt{57}$ Ⓑ $\frac{1}{4} + \sqrt{57}$ Ⓒ $\frac{-1 + \sqrt{57}}{4}$ Ⓓ $\frac{1 + \sqrt{57}}{4}$

Solution

$$2x^2 - 7 = x$$ **Write original equation.**

$$2x^2 - x - 7 = 0$$ **Write in standard form.**

$$x = \frac{-b \pm \sqrt{b^2 - 4ac}}{2a}$$ **Quadratic formula**

$$= \frac{-(-1) \pm \sqrt{(-1)^2 - 4(2)(-7)}}{2(2)}$$ **Substitute values in the quadratic formula:** $a = 2$, $b = -1$, and $c = -7$.

$$= \frac{1 \pm \sqrt{57}}{4}$$ **Simplify.**

▶ One solution is $\frac{1 + \sqrt{57}}{4}$. The correct answer is D. Ⓐ Ⓑ Ⓒ Ⓓ

EXAMPLE 3 **Use the quadratic formula**

FILM PRODUCTION For the period 1971–2001, the number y of films produced in the world can be modeled by the function $y = 10x^2 - 94x + 3900$ where x is the number of years since 1971. In what year were 4200 films produced?

Solution

$$y = 10x^2 - 94x + 3900$$ **Write function.**

$$4200 = 10x^2 - 94x + 3900$$ **Substitute 4200 for y.**

$$0 = 10x^2 - 94x - 300$$ **Write in standard form.**

$$x = \frac{-(-94) \pm \sqrt{(-94)^2 - 4(10)(-300)}}{2(10)}$$ **Substitute values in the quadratic formula: $a = 10$, $b = -94$, and $c = -300$.**

$$= \frac{94 \pm \sqrt{20{,}836}}{20}$$ **Simplify.**

INTERPRET SOLUTIONS
The solution -3 can be ignored because -3 represents the year 1968, which is not in the given time period.

The solutions of the equation are $\dfrac{94 + \sqrt{20{,}836}}{20} \approx 12$ and $\dfrac{94 - \sqrt{20{,}836}}{20} \approx -3$.

▸ There were 4200 films produced about 12 years after 1971, or in 1983.

 GUIDED PRACTICE   **for Examples 1, 2, and 3**

  1. Find the roots of $x^2 + 4x - 1$.

Use the quadratic formula to solve the equation.

  2. $x^2 - 8x + 16 = 0$ **3.** $x^2 - 5x = -21$ **4.** $4z^2 = 7z + 2$

  5. FILM PRODUCTION In Example 3, find the year when 4750 films were produced.

CONCEPT SUMMARY   *For Your Notebook*

Methods for Solving Quadratic Equations

Method	Lesson(s)	When to Use
Factoring	9.5–9.9	Use when a quadratic equation can be factored easily.
Graphing	10.4	Use when approximate solutions are adequate.
Finding square roots	10.5	Use when solving an equation that can be written in the form $x^2 = d$.
Completing the square	10.6	Can be used for *any* quadratic equation $ax^2 + bx + c = 0$ but is simplest to apply when $a = 1$ and b is an even number.
Quadratic formula	10.7	Can be used for *any* quadratic equation. Equation must be in standard form before reading the values of a, b, and c needed for the formula.

EXAMPLE 4 **Choose a solution method**

Tell what method(s) you would use to solve the quadratic equation. *Explain your choice(s).*

    a. $10x^2 - 7 = 0$ **b.** $x^2 + 4x = 0$ **c.** $5x^2 + 9x - 4 = 0$

Solution

    a. The quadratic equation can be solved using square roots because the equation can be written in the form $x^2 = d$.

    b. The quadratic equation can be solved by factoring because the expression $x^2 + 4x$ can be factored easily. Also, the equation can be solved by completing the square because the equation is of the form $ax^2 + bx + c = 0$ where $a = 1$ and b is an even number.

    c. The quadratic equation cannot be factored easily, and completing the square will result in many fractions. So, the equation should be solved using the quadratic formula.

✓ **GUIDED PRACTICE**   for Example 4

Tell what method(s) you would use to solve the quadratic equation. *Explain your choice(s).*

    6. $x^2 + x - 6 = 0$ **7.** $x^2 - 9 = 0$ **8.** $x^2 + 6x = 5$

10.7 EXERCISES

HOMEWORK KEY

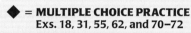 = **MULTIPLE CHOICE PRACTICE**
Exs. 18, 31, 55, 62, and 70–72

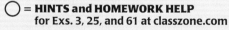 = **HINTS and HOMEWORK HELP**
for Exs. 3, 25, and 61 at classzone.com

SKILLS · PROBLEM SOLVING · REASONING

    1. VOCABULARY What formula can be used to solve any quadratic equation?

    2. WRITING What method(s) would you use to solve $-x^2 + 8x = 1$? *Explain your choice(s).*

EXAMPLE 1
on p. 650
for Exs. 3–8

FINDING ROOTS Use the quadratic formula to find the roots of the polynomial.

     3. $-x^2 + 3x - 1$ **4.** $x^2 + 5x - 5$ **5.** $2x^2 - 3x - 5$

    6. $6x^2 + 11x + 4$ **7.** $3x^2 - x - 3$ **8.** $-5x^2 + 3x + 7$

EXAMPLE 2
on p. 650
for Exs. 9–33

SOLVING QUADRATIC EQUATIONS Use the quadratic formula to solve the equation.

    9. $x^2 + 5x - 104 = 0$ **10.** $4x^2 - x - 18 = 0$ **11.** $6x^2 - 2x - 28 = 0$

    12. $m^2 + 3m + 1 = 0$ **13.** $-z^2 + z + 14 = 0$ **14.** $-2n^2 - 5n + 16 = 0$

    15. $4w^2 + 20w + 25 = 0$ **16.** $2t^2 + 3t - 11 = 0$ **17.** $-6g^2 + 9g + 8 = 0$

18. ◆ MULTIPLE CHOICE What are the solutions of $10x^2 - 3x - 1 = 0$?

(A) $-\frac{1}{5}$ and $-\frac{1}{2}$ **(B)** $-\frac{1}{5}$ and $\frac{1}{2}$ **(C)** $\frac{1}{5}$ and $-\frac{1}{2}$ **(D)** $\frac{1}{5}$ and $\frac{1}{2}$

SOLVING QUADRATIC EQUATIONS Use the quadratic formula to solve the equation.

19. $x^2 - 5x = 14$

20. $3x^2 - 4 = 11x$

21. $9 = 7x^2 - 2x$

22. $2m^2 + 9m + 7 = 3$

23. $-10 = r^2 - 10r + 12$

24. $3g^2 - 6g - 14 = 3g$

25. $6z^2 = 2z^2 + 7z + 5$

26. $8h^2 + 8 = 6 - 9h$

27. $4t^2 - 3t = 5 - 3t^2$

28. $-4y^2 - 3y + 3 = 2y + 4$

29. $7n + 5 = -3n^2 + 2$

30. $5w^2 + 4 = w + 6$

31. ◆ MULTIPLE CHOICE What are the solutions of $x^2 + 14x = 2x - 11$?

(A) -2 and -22 **(B)** -1 and -11 **(C)** 1 and 11 **(D)** 2 and 22

ERROR ANALYSIS *Describe* and correct the error in solving the equation.

32. $7x^2 - 5x - 1 = 0$

$$x = \frac{-5 \pm \sqrt{(-5)^2 - 4(7)(-1)}}{2(7)}$$

$$= \frac{-5 \pm \sqrt{53}}{14}$$

33. $-2x^2 + 3x = 1$

$$x = \frac{-3 \pm \sqrt{3^2 - 4(-2)(1)}}{2(-2)}$$

$$= \frac{-3 \pm \sqrt{17}}{-4}$$

EXAMPLE 4
on p. 652
for Exs. 34–42

CHOOSING A METHOD Tell what method(s) you would use to solve the quadratic equation. *Explain* your choice(s).

34. $3x^2 - 27 = 0$

35. $5x^2 = 25$

36. $2x^2 - 12x = 0$

37. $m^2 + 5m + 6 = 0$

38. $z^2 - 4z + 1 = 0$

39. $-10g^2 + 13g = 4$

40. $3r^2 + 2r - 7 = 0$

41. $2t^2 - 8t = 5$

42. $-6y^2 + 2 = 7y$

SOLVING QUADRATIC EQUATIONS Solve the quadratic equation using any method.

43. $-2x^2 = -32$

44. $x^2 - 8x = -16$

45. $x^2 + 2x - 6 = 0$

46. $x^2 = 12x - 36$

47. $x^2 + 4x = 9$

48. $-4x^2 + x = -17$

49. $2x^2 - 8 = -20x$

50. $(x + 13)^2 = 25$

51. $x^2 + x + 4 = x - 8$

52. $11x^2 - 1 = 6x^2 + 2$

53. $-2x^2 + 5 = 3x^2 - 10x$

54. $8x^2 + 2x - 21 = 2x^2 + 7x$

55. ◆ MULTIPLE CHOICE You are solving $ax^2 + bx + c = 0$ (where $a \neq 0$) by completing the square as shown below. How should you proceed to Step 3?

Step 1 $ax^2 + bx = -c$

Step 2 $x^2 + \frac{b}{a}x = -\frac{c}{a}$

Step 3 _____?_____

(A) Divide each side by x.

(B) Divide each side by x^2.

(C) Add $\frac{b}{2a}$ to each side.

(D) Add $\left(\frac{b}{2a}\right)^2$ to each side.

56. REASONING Use the quadratic formula to find the solutions of $ax^2 + bx + c = 0$ when $a \neq 0$ and $c = 0$. Then show how this equation can be solved without using the quadratic formula.

57. REASONING Suppose $b^2 - 4ac < 0$ for the equation $ax^2 + bx + c = 0$. Does the graph of the related function cross the x-axis? *Explain.*

CONNECT SKILLS TO PROBLEM SOLVING Exercises 58–60 will help you prepare for problem solving.

Use the following information: For the period 1997–2002, the total value y (in billions of dollars) of shipments of U.S. sound recordings can be modeled by the function $y = -0.336x^2 + 1.73x + 12.3$ where x is the number of years since 1997.

58. What value of y must you substitute into the model if you want to know the year(s) for which the total value of shipments was $13,700,000,000?

59. What equation do you get when you make the substitution in Exercise 58? Write the equation in standard form.

60. Suppose you solve the equation in Exercise 59 using the quadratic formula. You get the solutions $x \approx 1$ and $x \approx 4$. What do these solutions mean in this situation?

EXAMPLE 3
on p. 651
for Exs. 61–62

61. CELL PHONES For the period 1985–2001, the number y (in millions) of cell phone service subscribers in the U.S. can be modeled by the function $y = 0.7x^2 - 4.3x + 5.5$ where x is the number of years since 1985. In what year were there 16,000,000 cell phone service subscribers?

California @HomeTutor for problem solving help at classzone.com

62. ◆ MULTIPLE CHOICE For the period 1990–2000, the amount of money y (in billions of dollars) spent on advertising in the U.S. can be modeled by the function $y = 0.93x^2 + 2.2x + 130$ where x is the number of years since 1990. In what year was 164 billion dollars spent on advertising?

(A) 1993 **(B)** 1994 **(C)** 1995 **(D)** 1996

California @HomeTutor for problem solving help at classzone.com

63. MULTI-STEP PROBLEM A football is punted from an initial height of 2.5 feet with an initial vertical velocity of 45 feet per second.

Not drawn to scale
2.5 ft
5.5 ft

a. Use the vertical motion model to write an equation that gives the height h (in feet) of the football as a function of the time t (in seconds) since it is punted.

b. The football is caught 5.5 feet above the ground as shown in the diagram. Find the amount of time that the football is in the air.

Aeronautics NASA creates a weightless environment by flying a plane in a series of parabolic paths. The height h (in feet) of a plane t seconds after entering a parabolic flight path can be modeled by the graph of $h = -11t^2 + 700t + 21,000$. The passengers experience a weightless environment for less than 30 seconds when the height of the plane is greater than or equal to 30,800 feet.

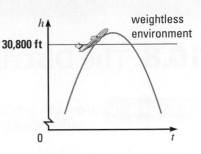

64. **Write** Write and solve an equation to find the times at which the plane enters and exits the weightless environment.

65. **Calculate** What is the duration of the period of weightlessness on a flight?

66. **Explain** *Explain* how the solutions of the equation can be used to determine the time when the plane reaches its maximum height.

67. **REASONING** A derivation of the quadratic formula is started below.

$ax^2 + bx + c = 0$	**Write equation.**
$4a^2x^2 + 4abx + 4ac = 0$	**Multiply each side by 4a.**
$4a^2x^2 + 4abx + 4ac + b^2 = b^2$	**Add b^2 to each side.**
$4a^2x^2 + 4abx + b^2 = b^2 - 4ac$	**Subtract 4ac from each side.**

The left side of the equation is now a perfect square trinomial. Use this fact to complete the derivation.

68. **CHALLENGE** The solutions of the quadratic equation $ax^2 + bx + c = 0$ are $x = \dfrac{-b + \sqrt{b^2 - 4ac}}{2a}$ and $x = \dfrac{-b - \sqrt{b^2 - 4ac}}{2a}$. Find the mean of the solutions. How is the mean related to the graph of $y = ax^2 + bx + c$? *Explain.*

69. **CHALLENGE** Mineral deposits have formed a uniform coating that is 4 millimeters thick on the inside of a water pipe. The cross-sectional area of the pipe has decreased by 10%. What was the original diameter of the pipe (to the nearest tenth of a millimeter)?

◆ CALIFORNIA STANDARDS SPIRAL REVIEW

Alg. 2.0 70. Which expression is equivalent to x^4x^8? *(p. 460)*

    (A) x^4 **(B)** x^{32} **(C)** $x^{11}x$ **(D)** $x^{12}x^2$

Alg. 14.0 71. Which of the following is a solution of $x^2 - 6x = 3$? *(p. 643)*

    (A) $-3 - 2\sqrt{3}$ **(B)** $2 - 3\sqrt{3}$ **(C)** $-3 + 2\sqrt{3}$ **(D)** $3 + 2\sqrt{3}$

Alg. 15.0 72. A truck leaves a garage and travels east at a rate of 55 miles per hour. A car leaves the same garage 15 minutes later and travels east at a rate of 66 miles per hour. After how many minutes from the time the car leaves does the car overtake the truck? *(p. 413)*

    (A) 1.25 min   **(B)** 1.5 min   **(C)** 75 min   **(D)** 90 min

10.8 The Discriminant

Standards

Alg. 22.0 Students use the quadratic formula or factoring techniques or both to determine whether the graph of a quadratic function will intersect the x-axis in zero, one, or two points.

QUESTION How can you determine the number of solutions of a quadratic equation?

In the quadratic formula, $x = \dfrac{-b \pm \sqrt{b^2 - 4ac}}{2a}$, the expression $b^2 - 4ac$ is called the *discriminant*.

EXPLORE Determine how the discriminant is related to the number of solutions of a quadratic equation

STEP 1 *Find the number of solutions*

Find the number of solutions of the equations below by finding the number of x-intercepts of the graphs of the related functions (shown at the right).

$0 = x^2 - 6x - 7$

$0 = x^2 - 6x + 9$

$0 = x^2 - 6x + 12$

STEP 2 *Find the value of $b^2 - 4ac$*

For each equation in Step 1, determine whether the value of $b^2 - 4ac$ is positive, negative, or zero.

STEP 3 *Make a table*

Organize your results from Steps 1 and 2 in a table as shown.

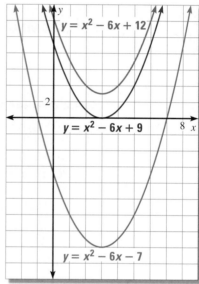

Equation	Number of solutions	Value of $b^2 - 4ac$
$0 = x^2 - 6x - 7$	?	?
$0 = x^2 - 6x + 9$	?	?
$0 = x^2 - 6x + 12$	?	?

STEP 4 *Make a conjecture*

Make a conjecture about the value of the discriminant and the number of solutions of a quadratic equation.

DRAW CONCLUSIONS Use your observations to complete these exercises

1. Repeat Steps 1–3 using the following equations: $x^2 + 4x - 5 = 0$, $x^2 + 4x + 4 = 0$, and $x^2 + 4x + 6 = 0$. Is your conjecture still true?

2. Notice that the expression $b^2 - 4ac$ is under the radical sign in the quadratic formula. Use this observation to explain why the value of $b^2 - 4ac$ determines the number of solutions of a quadratic equation.

10.8 Interpret the Discriminant

Math and CAMPING
Ex. 43, p. 661

Standards
Alg. 20.0 Students use the quadratic formula to find the roots of a second-degree polynomial and to solve quadratic equations.

Alg. 22.0 Students use the quadratic formula or factoring techniques or both to determine whether the graph of a quadratic function will intersect the *x*-axis in zero, one, or two points.

Connect
Before you used the quadratic formula. *Now* you will use the value of the discriminant to determine the number of times the graph of a quadratic function intersects the *x*-axis.

Key Vocabulary
• discriminant

In the quadratic formula, the expression $b^2 - 4ac$ is called the **discriminant** of the associated equation $ax^2 + bx + c = 0$.

$$x = \frac{-b \pm \sqrt{b^2 - 4ac}}{2a} \quad \longleftarrow \quad \text{discriminant}$$

The value of the discriminant can be used to determine the number of solutions of a quadratic equation and the number of *x*-intercepts of the graph of the related function.

KEY CONCEPT   *For Your Notebook*

Using the Discriminant of $ax^2 + bx + c = 0$

Discriminant	$b^2 - 4ac > 0$	$b^2 - 4ac = 0$	$b^2 - 4ac < 0$
Solutions	Two solutions	One solution	No solution
Graph of $y = ax^2 + bx + c$			
x-intercepts	Two *x*-intercepts	One *x*-intercept	No *x*-intercept

READING
Recall that in this course, *solutions* refers to real-number solutions.

EXAMPLE 1   **Use the discriminant**

Equation	Discriminant	Number of solutions
a. $2x^2 + 6x + 5 = 0$	$6^2 - 4(2)(5) = -4$	No solution
b. $x^2 - 7 = 0$	$0^2 - 4(1)(-7) = 28$	Two solutions
c. $4x^2 - 12x + 9 = 0$	$(-12)^2 - 4(4)(9) = 0$	One solution

EXAMPLE 2 ◆ **Multiple Choice Practice**

Which statement *best* explains why there is only one real solution to the quadratic equation $9x^2 + 6x + 1 = 0$?

A The value of $(6)^2 - 4 \cdot 9 \cdot 1$ is positive.

B The value of $(6)^2 - 4 \cdot 9 \cdot 1$ is equal to 0.

C The value of $(6)^2 - 4 \cdot 9 \cdot 1$ is negative.

D The value of $(6)^2 - 4 \cdot 9 \cdot 1$ is not a perfect square.

Solution

Find the value of the discriminant.

$$b^2 - 4 \cdot a \cdot c = (6)^2 - 4 \cdot 9 \cdot 1 = 36 - 36 = 0$$

The discriminant is zero, so the equation has one real solution.

▸ The correct answer is B. Ⓐ **Ⓑ** Ⓒ Ⓓ

EXAMPLE 3 **Find the number of *x*-intercepts**

Find the number of *x*-intercepts of the graph of $y = x^2 - 3x - 10$.

Solution

Find the number of solutions of the equation $0 = x^2 - 3x - 10$.

$$b^2 - 4ac = (-3)^2 - 4(1)(-10) \qquad \text{Substitute 1 for } a, -3 \text{ for } b, \text{ and } -10 \text{ for } c.$$

$$= 49 \qquad \text{Simplify.}$$

▸ The discriminant is positive, so the equation has two solutions. This means that the graph of $y = x^2 - 3x - 10$ has two *x*-intercepts.

CHECK You can use a graphing calculator to check the answer. Notice that the graph of $y = x^2 - 3x - 10$ has two *x*-intercepts.

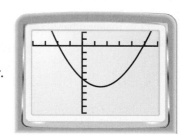

You can also use factoring to check the answer. Because $x^2 - 3x - 10 = (x - 5)(x + 2)$, the graph of $y = x^2 - 3x - 10$ crosses the *x*-axis at $x - 5 = 0$, or $x = 5$, and at $x + 2 = 0$, or $x = -2$.

AVOID ERRORS
Note that an unfactorable polynomial does not tell you anything about the *x*-intercepts of the graph of the related function.

✓ **GUIDED PRACTICE** for Examples 1, 2, and 3

Tell whether the equation has *two solutions*, *one solution*, or *no solution*.

1. $x^2 + 4x + 3 = 0$ **2.** $2x^2 - 5x + 6 = 0$ **3.** $-x^2 + 2x = 1$

Find the number of *x*-intercepts of the graph of the function.

4. $y = x^2 + 10x + 25$ **5.** $y = x^2 - 9x$ **6.** $y = -x^2 + 2x - 4$

EXAMPLE 4 **Solve a multi-step problem**

FOUNTAINS The Centennial Fountain in Chicago shoots a water arc that can be modeled by the graph of the equation $y = -0.006x^2 + 1.2x + 10$ where x is the horizontal distance (in feet) from the river's north shore and y is the height (in feet) above the river. Does the water arc reach a height of 50 feet? If so, about how far from the north shore is the water arc 50 feet above the water?

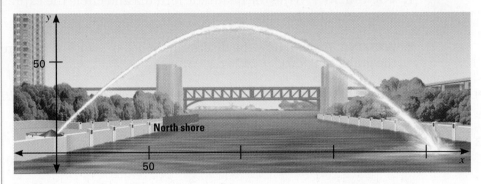

Solution

STEP 1 **Write** a quadratic equation. You want to know whether the water arc reaches a height of 50 feet, so let $y = 50$. Then write the quadratic equation in standard form.

$$y = -0.006x^2 + 1.2x + 10 \qquad \text{Write given equation.}$$
$$50 = -0.006x^2 + 1.2x + 10 \qquad \text{Substitute 50 for } y.$$
$$0 = -0.006x^2 + 1.2x - 40 \qquad \text{Subtract 50 from each side.}$$

STEP 2 **Find** the value of the discriminant of $0 = -0.006x^2 + 1.2x - 40$.

$$b^2 - 4ac = (1.2)^2 - 4(-0.006)(-40) \qquad a = -0.006, b = 1.2, c = -40$$
$$= 0.48 \qquad \text{Simplify.}$$

STEP 3 **Interpret** the discriminant. Because the discriminant is positive, the equation has two solutions. So, the water arc reaches a height of 50 feet at two points on the water arc.

STEP 4 **Solve** the equation $0 = -0.006x^2 + 1.2x - 40$ to find the distance from the north shore where the water arc is 50 feet above the water.

$$x = \frac{-b \pm \sqrt{b^2 - 4ac}}{2a} \qquad \text{Quadratic formula}$$

$$= \frac{-1.2 \pm \sqrt{0.48}}{2(-0.006)} \qquad \text{Substitute values in the quadratic formula.}$$

$$x \approx 42 \ or \ 158 \qquad \text{Use a calculator.}$$

▶ The water arc is 50 feet above the water about 42 feet from the north shore and about 158 feet from the north shore.

USE A SHORTCUT
Because the value of $b^2 - 4ac$ was calculated in Step 2, you can substitute 0.48 for $b^2 - 4ac$.

✓ **GUIDED PRACTICE** **for Example 4**

7. **WHAT IF?** In Example 4, does the water arc reach a height of 70 feet? If so, about how far from the north shore is the water arc 70 feet above the water?

SKILLS · PROBLEM SOLVING · REASONING

1. VOCABULARY Write the quadratic formula and circle the expression that represents the discriminant.

2. WRITING *Explain* how the discriminant of $ax^2 + bx + c = 0$ is related to the graph of $y = ax^2 + bx + c$.

**EXAMPLES
1 and 2**
on pp. 657–658
for Exs. 3–13

USING THE DISCRIMINANT Tell whether the equation has *two solutions, one solution,* or *no solution.*

3. $x^2 + x + 1 = 0$

4. $2x^2 - 5x - 6 = 0$

5. $-2x^2 + 8x - 4 = 0$

6. $3m^2 - 6m + 7 = 0$

7. $25p^2 - 16p = 0$

8. $10 = x^2 - 5x$

9. $\frac{1}{4}z^2 + 2 = z$

10. $3n^2 + 3 = 10n - 3n^2$

11. $8x^2 + 9 = 4x^2 - 4x + 8$

12. ◆ MULTIPLE CHOICE What is the value of the discriminant of the equation $5x^2 - 7x - 2 = 0$?

(A) -9 **(B)** 9 **(C)** 59 **(D)** 89

13. ◆ MULTIPLE CHOICE How many solutions does $-x^2 + 4x = 8$ have?

(A) None   **(B)** One   **(C)** Two   **(D)** Three

ERROR ANALYSIS *Describe* and correct the error in finding the number of *x*-intercepts of the the graph of the function.

14. $y = x^2 + 6x - 16$

15. $y = 2x^2 + 3x - 4$

$$y = x^2 + 6x - 16$$
$$= (x - 4)(x - 4)$$

The graph has only one
x-intercept because only
x = 4 makes y = 0.

$y = 0$ when

$$x = \frac{-3 \pm \sqrt{3^2 - 4(2)(4)}}{2(2)}$$

$$= \frac{-3 \pm \sqrt{-23}}{4}$$

The graph has no x-intercepts because
the discriminant is negative.

EXAMPLE 3
on p. 658
for Exs. 16–30

FINDING THE NUMBER OF *x*-INTERCEPTS Find the number of *x*-intercepts of the graph of the function by using the discriminant or by factoring.

16. $y = x^2 - 3x - 4$

17. $y = 2x^2 - x - 1$

18. $y = 4x^2 + 4x + 1$

19. $y = 2x^2 - 7x + 5$

20. $y = x^2 - 6x + 9$

21. $y = 6x^2 + 11x - 2$

22. $y = -13x^2 + 2x + 6$

23. $y = \frac{1}{4}x^2 - 3x + 9$

24. $y = \frac{2}{3}x^2 - 5x + 12$

FINDING ROOTS Find the number of roots of the polynomial.

25. $4x^2 + 4x + 1$

26. $2x^2 - 2x - 3$

27. $-2x^2 + 5x - 3$

28. $8x^2 - x + 7$

29. $2x^2 - 5x + 9$

30. $-9x^2 + 12x - 4$

REASONING Give a value of *c* for which the equation has (a) two solutions, (b) one solution, and (c) no solution.

31. $x^2 - 2x + c = 0$ **32.** $x^2 - 8x + c = 0$ **33.** $4x^2 + 12x + c = 0$

USING THE DISCRIMINANT Tell whether the vertex of the graph of the function lies above, below, or on the *x*-axis. *Explain* your reasoning.

34. $y = x^2 - 3x + 2$ **35.** $y = 3x^2 - 6x + 3$ **36.** $y = -15x^2 + 10x - 25$

37. REASONING Evan says that if a polynomial cannot be factored, then the graph of the related function has no *x*-intercepts. Give a counterexample to show that Evan's statement is false.

CONNECT SKILLS TO PROBLEM SOLVING Exercises 38–40 will help you prepare for problem solving.

Use the following information: A ball is kicked from an initial height of 2 feet with an initial vertical velocity of *v* feet per second.

38. If $v = 30$, does the object reach a height of 20 feet? *Explain.*

39. If $v = 40$, does the object reach a height of 27 feet? *Explain.*

40. If $v = 50$, does the object reach a height of 40 feet? *Explain.*

EXAMPLE 4
on p. 659
for Exs. 41–42

41. BIOLOGY The amount *y* (in milliliters per gram of body mass per hour) of oxygen consumed by a parakeet during flight can be modeled by the function $y = 0.06x^2 - 4x + 87$ where *x* is the speed (in kilometers per hour) of the parakeet.

 a. Use the discriminant to show that it is possible for a parakeet to consume 25 milliliters of oxygen per gram of body mass per hour.

 b. Find the speed(s) at which the parakeet consumes 25 milliliters of oxygen per gram of body mass per hour. Round your solution(s) to the nearest tenth.

 California @HomeTutor for problem solving help at classzone.com

42. ◆ MULTIPLE CHOICE For the period 1950–1999, the average amount *y* (in pounds per person per year) of butter consumed in the U.S. can be modeled by $y = 0.0051x^2 - 0.37x + 11$ where *x* is the number of years since 1950. According to the model, in what year(s) did butter consumption in the U.S. reach 5 pounds per person per year?

 (A) 1974 only **(B)** 1998 only **(C)** 1974, 1998 **(D)** No year

 California @HomeTutor for problem solving help at classzone.com

43. CAMPING The frame of the tent shown has a rectangular base and two parabolic arches that connect the opposite corners of the base. The graph of the equation $y = -0.18x^2 + 1.6x$ models the height *y* (in feet) of one of the arches *x* feet along the diagonal of the base. Can a child that is 4 feet tall walk under one of the arches without having to bend over? *Explain.*

Tent's frame is parabolic.

44. MULTI-STEP PROBLEM During a trampoline competition, a trampolinist leaves the mat when her center of gravity is 6 feet above the ground. She has an initial vertical velocity of 32 feet per second.

h ft

a. Use the vertical motion model to write an equation that models the height h (in feet) of the center of gravity of the trampolinist as a function of the time t (in seconds) into her jump.

b. Does her center of gravity reach a height of 24 feet during the jump? If so, at what time(s)?

CHALLENGE Find all values of k for which the equation has (a) two solutions, (b) one solution, and (c) no solution.

45. $2x^2 + x + 3k = 0$ **46.** $x^2 - 4kx + 36 = 0$ **47.** $kx^2 + 5x - 16 = 0$

48. CHALLENGE Last year, a company sold backpacks for $24 each. At this price, the company sold about 1000 backpacks per week. A marketing analyst predicts that for every $1 reduction in the price of the backpack, the company will sell 100 more backpacks per week.

a. Write an equation for the company's weekly revenue (in dollars) as a function of the number of $1 reductions in the price of the backpack.

b. Can the company have a weekly revenue of $28,000? $30,000? *Explain.*

◆ CALIFORNIA STANDARDS SPIRAL REVIEW

Alg. 3.0

49. What is the solution of $|2x + 5| \leq 7$? *(p. 226)*

  A $-6 \leq x \leq 1$ **B** $-1 \leq x \leq 6$ **C** $1 \leq x \leq 6$ **D** $x \leq -6$ or $x \geq 1$

Alg. 25.3

50. When does the equation $x^2 = d$ have two solutions? *(p. 633)*

  A Always   **B** Never   **C** When $d < 0$ **D** When $d > 0$

Alg. 10.0

51. The cost of going to x exhibits at a museum is $8x$ dollars for nonmembers and $15 + 5x$ dollars for members. Which polynomial expresses the difference of the cost for nonmembers and the cost for members? *(p. 520)*

  A $3x - 15$ **B** $3x + 15$ **C** $13x - 15$ **D** $13x + 15$

QUIZ *for Lessons 10.6–10.8*

Solve the equation by completing the square. *(p. 643)*

1. $x^2 + 2x - 6 = 0$ **2.** $x^2 - 8x = -6$ **3.** $x^2 + x = -7.75$

Solve the equation using the quadratic formula. *(p. 649)*

4. $x^2 + 4x + 1 = 0$ **5.** $-3x^2 + 3x = -1$ **6.** $4x^2 - 11x = 3$

Find the number of x-intercepts of the graph of the function by using the discriminant or by factoring. *(p. 657)*

7. $y = x^2 + x + 5$ **8.** $y = 5x^2 + 4x - 1$ **9.** $y = 4x^2 - 20x + 25$

MIXED REVIEW of Skills and Problem Solving

Multiple Choice Practice for Lessons 10.5–10.8

1. In slow-pitch softball, the ball is pitched in an underhand motion. During warm-up, a pitch is released from an initial height of 4 feet with an initial vertical velocity of 35 feet per second. About how long after the ball is pitched does the ball hit the ground? **Alg. 23.0**

- (A) 0.11 sec
- (B) 0.12 sec
- (C) 2.07 sec
- (D) 2.30 sec

2. Four steps in deriving the quadratic formula are shown below. What is the correct order for these steps? **Alg. 19.0**

$$\text{I} \quad x = \frac{\pm\sqrt{b^2 - 4ac}}{2a} - \frac{b}{2a}$$

$$\text{II} \quad \left(x + \frac{b}{2a}\right)^2 = \frac{b^2 - 4ac}{4a^2}$$

$$\text{III} \quad x = \frac{-b \pm \sqrt{b^2 - 4ac}}{2a}$$

$$\text{IV} \quad x + \frac{b}{2a} = \pm\sqrt{\frac{b^2 - 4ac}{4a^2}}$$

- (A) I, II, IV, III
- (B) III, I, IV, II
- (C) II, IV, I, III
- (D) IV, II, I, III

3. A worker accidentally drops a measuring tape from the roof of the taller building shown onto the roof of the building beside it. For about how long is the measuring tape in the air? **Alg. 23.0**

- (A) 1.1 sec
- (B) 1.4 sec
- (C) 1.8 sec
- (D) 2.2 sec

30 ft

80 ft

4. What quantity should be added to each side of $x^2 + 10x = 6$ when solving the equation by completing the square? **Alg. 14.0**

- (A) 5
- (B) 10
- (C) 25
- (D) 100

5. Which quadratic function has a graph that does *not* cross the x-axis? **Alg. 22.0**

- (A) $y = -2x^2 + x - 4$
- (B) $y = -3x^2 - 10x + 1$
- (C) $y = 6x^2 - 2x - 8$
- (D) $y = x^2 + 5x + 3$

6. The trapezoid below has an area of 54 square inches. What is the value of x? **Alg. 23.0**

- (A) −7
- (B) 5
- (C) 5.42
- (D) 6

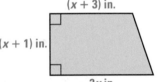
$(x + 3)$ in.
$(x + 1)$ in.
$2x$ in.

7. You are making a tabletop with a tiled border as shown. You have enough border tiles to cover 130 square inches. To the nearest inch, what should the width of the border be so that all the border tiles are used? **Alg. 20.0**

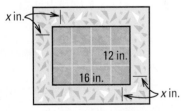
x in.
12 in.
16 in.
x in.

- (A) 2 in.
- (B) 6 in.
- (C) 16 in.
- (D) 20 in.

8. Which value of c makes the expression $x^2 - 8x + c$ a perfect square trinomial? **Alg. 14.0**

- (A) −16
- (B) 4
- (C) 16
- (D) 64

BIG IDEAS
For Your Notebook

Big Idea ①

Graphing Quadratic Functions

The graph of $y = ax^2 + bx + c$ is a parabola that:

- opens up if $a > 0$ and opens down if $a < 0$.
- is narrower than the graph of $y = x^2$ if $|a| > 1$ and wider if $|a| < 1$.
- has an axis of symmetry of $x = -\dfrac{b}{2a}$.
- has a vertex with an x-coordinate of $-\dfrac{b}{2a}$..
- has a y-intercept of c. So, the point $(0, c)$ is on the parabola.

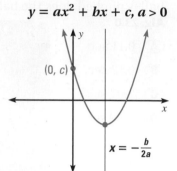

$y = ax^2 + bx + c, a > 0$

$(0, c)$

$x = -\dfrac{b}{2a}$

Big Idea ②

Solving Quadratic Equations

Method	Lesson	When to use
Graphing	10.4	Use when approximate solutions are adequate.
Finding square roots	10.5	Use when solving an equation that can be written in the form $x^2 = d$.
Completing the square	10.6	Can be used for *any* quadratic equation $y = ax^2 + bx + c$ but is simplest to apply when $a = 1$ and b is an even number.
Quadratic formula	10.7	Can be used for *any* quadratic equation.

Big Idea ③

Finding Numbers of Roots, Solutions, x-intercepts, and Zeros

If the discriminant $b^2 - 4ac$ is:	Positive	Zero	Negative
The polynomial $ax^2 + bx + c$ has:	2 roots	1 root	No roots
The equation $ax^2 + bx + c = 0$ has:	2 solutions	1 solution	No solutions
The function $y = ax^2 + bx + c$ has:	2 zeros	1 zero	No zeros
The graph of the function $y = ax^2 + bx + c$ has:	2 x-intercepts	1 x-intercept	No x-intercepts

APPLYING THE
BIG IDEAS

Big Idea 1
You graph quadratic functions in **Step 2**.

Big Idea 2
You solve quadratic equations in **Step 1**.

Big Idea 3
You find the number of solutions of a quadratic equation in **Step 3**.

PROBLEM How can you use quadratic functions to model the path of a ball in an electronic game?

STEP 1 Use a model.

The screen for an electronic volleyball game is shown below. The ceiling is 30 feet high, and the net is 8 feet high. The path of the ball after being served is parabolic as illustrated by the sample serve.

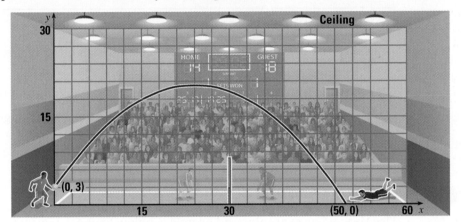

The graph of the function $y = \left(\dfrac{-16}{a^2}\right)x^2 + \left(\dfrac{b}{a}\right)x + s$ where x and y are in feet models the path of the volleyball where a is the initial horizontal velocity (in feet per second), b is the initial vertical velocity (in feet per second), and s is the initial height (in feet).

Choose an initial horizontal velocity and an initial vertical velocity for the ball. The ball's initial height is 3 feet. Using algebra, determine where the ball lands.

STEP 2 Graph the paths of three serves.

Three pairs of values for a and b are given. Write a function to model the path of each serve. Use a graphing calculator to graph each function, then make a sketch of the graph. Check that each serve lands at or near (50, 0).

Serve 1:	Serve 2:	Serve 3:
$a = 20, b = 38.8$	$a = 40, b = 17.6$	$a = 16, b = 49.0$

STEP 3 Check each path.

For each serve in Step 2, use algebra to determine if the ball hits the ceiling or the net. Which serve clears the net and does not hit the ceiling?

Extending the Problem

1. Write a different function whose graph models the path of a volleyball that is served from (0, 3), lands at or near (50, 0), clears the net, and does not hit the ceiling.

California @HomeTutor
classzone.com
• Multi-Language Visual Glossary
• Vocabulary practice

REVIEW KEY VOCABULARY

- quadratic function, *p. 605*
- standard form of a quadratic function, *p. 605*
- parabola, *p. 605*
- vertex of a parabola, *p. 605*
- axis of symmetry, *p. 605*

- minimum value, *p. 613*
- maximum value, *p. 613*
- intercept form of a quadratic function, *p. 618*
- quadratic equation, *p. 624*

- standard form of a quadratic equation, *p. 624*
- zero of a function, *p. 626*
- completing the square, *p. 643*
- quadratic formula, *p. 649*
- discriminant, *p. 657*

VOCABULARY EXERCISES

1. Copy and complete: The line that passes through the vertex and divides a parabola into two symmetric parts is called the __?__.

2. Does the function $y = 5x^2 - 4x$ have a *minimum value* or a *maximum value*?

3. **NOTETAKING SKILLS** Use a decision tree like the one on page 604 to determine the number of solutions of a quadratic equation.

REVIEW EXAMPLES AND EXERCISES

Use the review examples and exercises below to check your understanding of the concepts you have learned in each lesson of Chapter 10.

10.1 Graph $y = ax^2 + c$
pp. 605–611

Alg. 21.0   **EXAMPLE**

Graph $y = -x^2 + 3$. Compare the graph with the graph of $y = x^2$.

Make a table of values for $y = -x^2 + 3$. Then plot the points from the table and draw a smooth curve through the points.

x	−2	−1	0	1	2
y	−1	2	3	2	−1

Both graphs have the same axis of symmetry, $x = 0$. However, the graph of $y = -x^2 + 3$ has a different vertex than the graph of $y = x^2$, and it opens down. This is because the graph of $y = -x^2 + 3$ is a vertical translation (of 3 units up) of the graph of $y = -x^2$ and a reflection in the *x*-axis of the graph of $y = x^2$.

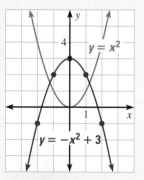

EXERCISES

EXAMPLES
1, 2, 3, and 4
on pp. 605–607
for Exs. 4–7

Graph the function. Compare the graph with the graph of $y = x^2$.

4. $y = -4x^2$

5. $y = 2x^2$

6. $y = x^2 - 2$

7. $y = \frac{1}{4}x^2 + 2$

Graph $y = ax^2 + bx + c$ *pp. 612–617*

Alg. 21.0 **EXAMPLE**

Graph $y = -x^2 + 2x + 1$.

> **STEP 1** **Determine** whether the parabola opens up or down. Because $a < 0$, the parabola opens down.
>
> **STEP 2** **Find** and draw the axis of symmetry:
>
> $$x = -\frac{b}{2a} = -\frac{2}{2(-1)} = 1$$
>
> **STEP 3** **Find** and plot the vertex. The x-coordinate of the vertex is $-\frac{b}{2a}$, or 1. To find the y-coordinate, substitute 1 for x in the function and simplify.
>
> $$y = -(1)^2 + 2(1) + 1 = 2$$
>
> **STEP 4** **Plot** four more points. Evaluating the function for $x = 0$ and $x = -1$ gives the points $(0, 1)$ and $(-1, -2)$. Plot these points and their reflections in the axis of symmetry.
>
> **STEP 5** **Draw** a parabola through the plotted points.

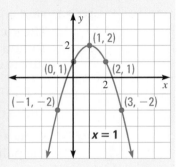

EXAMPLE

Tell whether the function $y = x^2 + 2x - 5$ has a *minimum value* or a *maximum value*. Then find the minimum or maximum value.

Because $a = 1$ and $1 > 0$, the parabola opens up and the function has a minimum value. To find the minimum value, find the vertex.

$$x = -\frac{b}{2a} = -\frac{2}{2(1)} = -1 \qquad \text{The } x\text{-coordinate is } -\frac{b}{2a}.$$

$$y = (-1)^2 + 2(-1) - 5 = -6 \qquad \text{Substitute } -1 \text{ for } x. \text{ Then simplify.}$$

▸ The minimum value of the function is -6.

EXERCISES

EXAMPLES
1, 2, and 3
on pp. 612–614
for Exs. 8–19

Find the axis of symmetry and the vertex of the graph of the function.

8. $y = x^2 - 7x + 10$ **9.** $y = -3x^2 + 14x - 8$ **10.** $y = \frac{1}{4}x^2 + x - 3$

Graph the function. Label the vertex and axis of symmetry.

11. $y = x^2 + 4x + 1$ **12.** $y = 2x^2 - 4x - 3$ **13.** $y = -2x^2 + 8x + 5$

Tell whether the function has a *minimum value* or a *maximum value*. Then find the minimum or maximum value.

14. $y = -x^2 + 7$ **15.** $y = 3x^2 + 6x$ **16.** $y = x^2 - 8x - 1$

17. $y = -2x^2 + 2x - 9$ **18.** $y = -\frac{1}{2}x^2 + x + 5$ **19.** $y = \frac{5}{4}x^2 - 8x + 3$

10.3 Graph $y = a(x - p)(x - q)$

pp. 618–623

Alg. 21.0 **EXAMPLE**

Graph $y = -(x + 4)(x - 2)$.

STEP 1 **Identify** the x-intercepts. The x-intercepts are $p = -4$ and $q = 2$. Plot $(-4, 0)$ and $(2, 0)$.

STEP 2 **Find** and draw the axis of symmetry:

$$x = \frac{p + q}{2} = \frac{-4 + 2}{2} = -1$$

STEP 3 **Find** and plot the vertex. The x-coordinate of the vertex is -1. To find the y-coordinate of the vertex, substitute -1 for x and simplify.

$$y = -(-1 + 4)(-1 - 2) = 9$$

The vertex is $(-1, 9)$.

STEP 4 **Draw** a parabola through the vertex and the points where the x-intercepts occur.

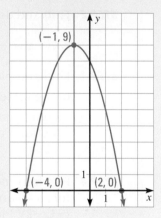

EXERCISES

EXAMPLES 2 and 3 on p. 619 for Exs. 20–22

Graph the quadratic function. Label the vertex, axis of symmetry, and x-intercepts.

20. $y = (x - 2)(x - 4)$

21. $y = \frac{1}{2}(x + 1)(x - 2)$

22. $y = -x^2 - 8x - 15$

10.4 Solve Quadratic Equations by Graphing

pp. 624–630

Alg. 21.0 **EXAMPLE**

Solve $x^2 - 7x = -12$ by graphing.

STEP 1 **Write** the equation in standard form.

$$x^2 - 7x = -12 \qquad \text{Write original equation.}$$
$$x^2 - 7x + 12 = 0 \qquad \text{Add 12 to each side.}$$

STEP 2 **Graph** the related function $y = x^2 - 7x + 12$. The x-intercepts of the graph are 3 and 4.

▶ The solutions of the equation $x^2 - 7x + 12 = 0$ are 3 and 4.

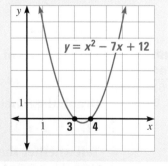

EXERCISES

EXAMPLES 1, 2, and 3 on pp. 624–625 for Exs. 23–25

Solve the equation by graphing.

23. $4x^2 + x + 3 = 0$

24. $x^2 + 2x = -1$

25. $-x^2 + 8 = 7x$

10.5 Use Square Roots to Solve Quadratic Equations

pp. 633–639

Alg. 23.0

EXAMPLE

Find the time it takes an object to hit the ground after it is dropped from a height of 75 feet.

$h = -16t^2 + vt + s$	**Vertical motion model**
$0 = -16t^2 + 0t + 75$	**Substitute 0 for v, 75 for s, and 0 for h.**
$-75 = -16t^2$	**Simplify and subtract 75 from each side.**
$\dfrac{75}{16} = t^2$	**Divide each side by -16.**
$\sqrt{\dfrac{75}{16}} = t$	**Take positive square root of each side.**
$2.17 \approx t$	**Use a calculator.**

▶ The object is in the air for about 2.17 seconds.

EXERCISES

Solve the equation.

EXAMPLES
1, 2, 3, and 5
on p. 633–635
for Exs. 26–29

26. $5x^2 = 40$

27. $25n^2 = 16$

28. $g^2 + 11 = 24$

29. FALLING OBJECT Find the time it takes an object to hit the ground after it is dropped from a height of 60 feet.

10.6 Solve Quadratic Equations by Completing the Square

pp. 643–648

Alg. 14.0

EXAMPLE

Solve $3x^2 + 12x = 18$ by completing the square.

$3x^2 + 12x = 18$	**Write original equation.**
$x^2 + 4x = 6$	**Divide each side by 3.**
$x^2 + 4x + 2^2 = 6 + 2^2$	**Add $\left(\dfrac{4}{2}\right)^2$, or 2^2, to each side.**
$(x + 2)^2 = 10$	**Write left side as the square of a binomial.**
$x + 2 = \pm\sqrt{10}$	**Take square roots of each side.**
$x = -2 \pm \sqrt{10}$	**Subtract 2 from each side.**

▶ The solutions of the equation are $-2 + \sqrt{10}$ and $-2 - \sqrt{10}$.

EXERCISES

Solve the equation by completing the square.

EXAMPLE 3
on pp. 644–645
for Exs. 30–33

30. $x^2 - 14x = 51$

31. $2a^2 + 12a - 4 = 0$

32. $2n^2 + 4n + 1 = 10n + 9$

33. $5g^2 - 3g + 6 = 2g^2 + 9$

10.7 Solve Quadratic Equations by the Quadratic Formula *pp. 649–655*

Alg. 20.0 **EXAMPLE**

Solve $4x^2 + 3x = 1$.

$$4x^2 + 3x = 1$$ Write original equation.

$$4x^2 + 3x - 1 = 0$$ Write in standard form.

$$x = \frac{-b \pm \sqrt{b^2 - 4ac}}{2a}$$ Quadratic formula

$$= \frac{-3 \pm \sqrt{3^2 - 4(4)(-1)}}{2(4)}$$ Substitute values in the quadratic formula: $a = 4$, $b = 3$, and $c = -1$.

$$= \frac{-3 \pm \sqrt{25}}{8}$$ Simplify.

$$= \frac{-3 \pm 5}{8}$$ Simplify the square root.

▸ The solutions of the equation are $\dfrac{-3 + 5}{8} = \dfrac{1}{4}$ and $\dfrac{-3 - 5}{8} = -1$.

EXERCISES

EXAMPLES
1 and 2
on pp. 650–651
for Exs. 34–42

Use the quadratic formula to solve the equation.

34. $x^2 - 2x - 15 = 0$ **35.** $2m^2 + 7m - 3 = 0$ **36.** $-w^2 + 5w = 3$

37. $5n^2 - 7n = -1$ **38.** $t^2 - 4 = 6t + 8$ **39.** $2h - 1 = 10 - 9h^2$

Use the quadratic formula to find the roots of the polynomial.

40. $3x^2 - 4x - 12$ **41.** $-7x^2 + 3x + 5$ **42.** $4x^2 + 6x + 15$

10.8 Interpret the Discriminant *pp. 657–662*

Alg. 22.0 **EXAMPLE**

Equation $ax^2 + bx + c = 0$	Discriminant $b^2 - 4ac$	Number of solutions
a. $-16x^2 + 8x - 1 = 0$	$8^2 - 4(-16)(-1) = 0$	One solution
b. $4x^2 - 5x + 2 = 0$	$(-5)^2 - 4(4)(2) = -7$	No solution
c. $x^2 + 3x = 0$	$3^2 - 4(1)(0) = 9$	Two solutions

EXERCISES

EXAMPLES
1 and 2
on pp. 657–658
for Exs. 43–48

Tell whether the equation has *two solutions, one solution,* or *no solution.*

43. $x^2 - 2x + 2 = 0$ **44.** $4g^2 + 12g + 9 = 0$ **45.** $5w^2 - 4w - 1 = 0$

46. $\frac{1}{8}v^2 - 6 = 0$ **47.** $n^2 - 3n = 4 - 2n^2$ **48.** $2q^2 + 1 = 3q - 5$

1. **VOCABULARY** Copy and complete: A nonlinear function that can be written in the form $y = ax^2 + bx + c$ where $a \neq 0$ is called a(n) __?__ .

2. **VOCABULARY** Copy and complete: Given an equation where y is a function of x, a(n) __?__ of the function is an x-value for which $y = 0$.

Match the quadratic function with its graph.

3. $y = x^2 - 2$

4. $y = x^2 + 2$

5. $y = -2x^2$

A.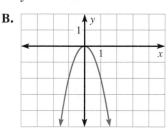

B.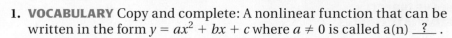

C.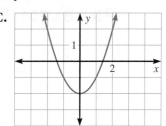

Graph the function. Label the vertex and axis of symmetry.

6. $y = 2x^2 + 6x - 5$

7. $y = -4x^2 - 8x + 25$

8. $y = \frac{1}{4}x^2 - x - 7$

Graph the quadratic function. Label the vertex, axis of symmetry, and x-intercept(s).

9. $y = (x + 2)(x + 3)$

10. $y = -2(x - 2)^2$

11. $y = \frac{1}{2}(x + 1)(x - 7)$

12. $y = x^2 - 4x + 21$

13. $y = 2x^2 - x - 15$

14. $y = 7x^2 - 7x + 3$

Solve the equation.

15. $0 = x^2 + 5x + 1$

16. $0 = x^2 - 8x + 3$

17. $0 = -3x^2 - 2x + 5$

18. $3x^2 = 108$

19. $-5w^2 + 51 = 6$

20. $-p^2 + 2p + 3 = 0$

21. $-2t^2 + 6t + 9 = 0$

22. $5m^2 - m = 5$

23. $2x^2 - 12x - 1 = -7x + 6$

Tell whether the equation has *two solutions*, *one solution*, or *no solution*.

24. $3x^2 - 4x + 9 = 0$

25. $4g^2 - 12g + 11 = 0$

26. $-2n^2 + 7n - 1 = 0$

27. $-m^2 - 17m = 0$

28. $-6x^2 - x - 5 = 0$

29. $10x^2 - 13 = 0$

30. **TENNIS** You are playing tennis with a friend. The path of the tennis ball after you hit it can be modeled by the graph of the equation $y = -0.005x^2 + 0.17x + 3$ where x is the horizontal distance (in feet) from where you hit the ball and y is the height of the ball (in feet) above the court.

   a. What is the maximum height reached by the tennis ball? Round your answer to the nearest tenth of a foot.

   b. Suppose you are standing 30 feet from the net, which has a height of 3 feet. Will the ball clear the net? *Explain* your reasoning.

   c. If your friend does not hit the ball back to you, how far from you does the ball strike the ground?

10 ◆ MULTIPLE CHOICE STRATEGIES

STRATEGIES YOU'LL USE:
- SOLVE DIRECTLY
- ELIMINATE CHOICES

Standards
Alg. 20.0, 23.0

If you have difficulty solving a multiple choice problem directly, you may be able to use another approach to eliminate incorrect answer choices and obtain the correct answer.

PROBLEM 1

What are the solutions of $-7 = x^2 + 6x$?

(A) $-7, -1$ **(B)** $-7, 1$ **(C)** $-3 \pm 2\sqrt{2}$ **(D)** $-3 \pm \sqrt{2}$

Strategy 1 — SOLVE DIRECTLY

Write the equation in standard form.

$-7 = x^2 + 6x$	**Write original equation.**
$0 = x^2 + 6x + 7$	**Write in standard form.**

Use the quadratic formula where $a = 1$, $b = 6$, and $c = 7$ to find the solutions.

$x = \dfrac{-b \pm \sqrt{b^2 - 4ac}}{2a}$	**Quadratic formula**
$= \dfrac{-6 \pm \sqrt{6^2 - 4(1)(7)}}{2(1)}$	**Substitute 1 for a, 6 for b, and 7 for c.**
$= \dfrac{-6 \pm \sqrt{8}}{2}$	**Simplify.**
$= \dfrac{-6 \pm 2\sqrt{2}}{2}$	**Simplify radical.**
$= \dfrac{2(-3 \pm \sqrt{2})}{2}$	**Factor out 2 from the numerator.**
$= -3 \pm \sqrt{2}$	**Divide out factor of 2.**

The correct answer is D. (A) (B) (C) **(D)**

Strategy 2 — ELIMINATE CHOICES

Before substituting values to eliminate choices, try analyzing the equation.

STEP 1 **Rewrite** the equation in standard form:
$0 = x^2 + 6x + 7$

You can see that for $x \geq 0$, the value of the polynomial in the equation, $x^2 + 6x + 7$, is greater than 0. So, both solutions of the equation must be negative. You can eliminate choice B.

STEP 2 **Substitute** values.

Test one of the numbers in choice A. Substitute -7 for x.

$-7 = x^2 + 6x$	**Write equation.**
$-7 \stackrel{?}{=} (-7)^2 + 6(-7)$	**Substitute.**
$-7 \stackrel{?}{=} 49 - 42$	**Simplify.**
$-7 \neq 7$	**Subtract.**

You can eliminate choice A.

Test one of the numbers in choice C. Substitute $-3 + 2\sqrt{2}$ for x.

$-7 \stackrel{?}{=} (-3 + 2\sqrt{2})^2 + 6(-3 + 2\sqrt{2})$

$-7 \stackrel{?}{=} 9 - 12\sqrt{2} + 8 - 18 + 12\sqrt{2}$

$-7 \neq -1$

You can eliminate choice C.

The correct answer is D. (A) (B) (C) **(D)**

PROBLEM 2

A volleyball player serves the ball from an initial height of 6.5 feet with an initial vertical velocity of 24 feet per second. The height h (in feet) of the ball t seconds after it is served can be modeled by the function $h = -16t^2 + 24t + 6.5$. What is the maximum height reached by the volleyball?

A 12.7 ft   **B** 15.5 ft   **C** 24 ft   **D** 6.5 ft

Strategy 1 SOLVE DIRECTLY

The maximum height occurs at the vertex of the graph of the function.

Find the t-coordinate of the vertex, $t = -\dfrac{b}{2a}$.

$t = -\dfrac{24}{2(-16)}$ **Substitute −16 for a and 24 for b.**

$= \dfrac{24}{32} = 0.75$ **Simplify.**

Find the height when $t = 0.75$ second.

$h = -16t^2 + 24t + 6.5$ **Write equation.**

$= -16(0.75)^2 + 24(0.75) + 6.5$ **Substitute.**

$= 15.5$ **Simplify.**

The maximum height reached by the volleyball is 15.5 feet.

The correct answer is B. **A** **B** **C** **D**

Strategy 2 ELIMINATE CHOICES

The volleyball reaches a maximum height only once, so when the correct height is substituted into the equation, the discriminant must be 0.

Choice A: Substitute the height in choice A into the equation. Rewrite the equation $12.7 = -16t^2 + 24t + 6.5$ in standard form.

$0 = -16t^2 + 24t - 6.2$

The discriminant is $24^2 - 4(-16)(-6.2) = 179.2$. Because the discriminant is not 0, you can eliminate choice A.

Choice B: Substitute the height in choice B into the equation. Rewrite the equation $15.5 = -16t^2 + 24t + 6.5$ in standard form.

$0 = -16t^2 + 24t - 9$

The discriminant is $24^2 - 4(-16)(-9) = 0$.

The correct answer is B. **A** **B** **C** **D**

STRATEGY PRACTICE

Explain why you can eliminate the highlighted answer choice.

1. What are the solutions of $x^2 + 3x = -4$?

   A −4, 1   **B** −1, 4   **C** $\dfrac{-3 \pm \sqrt{7}}{2}$ **D** No solution

2. The value of the discriminant of the equation $7x^2 - 8x + c = 6$ is −20. What is the value of c?

   A −3   **B** 3   **C**✕6   **D** 9

3. In Problem 2, no one touches the ball before it hits the floor. To the nearest hundredth of a second, how long is the volleyball in the air?

   A 0.50 sec   **B** 0.81 sec   **C** 1.57 sec   **D**✕20.26 sec

1. The force F (in newtons) that a passenger feels when a subway train goes around a curve is given by $F = \dfrac{mv^2}{r}$ where m is the mass (in kilograms) of the passenger, v is the velocity (in meters per second) of the train, and r is the radius (in meters) of the curve. A passenger who has a mass of 75 kilograms experiences a force of 18,150 newtons while going around a curve that has a radius of 8 meters. What is the velocity of the train? **Alg. 23.0**

   A 15.6 m/sec

   B 44 m/sec

   C 75 m/sec

   D 1936 m/sec

2. The graph of $y = 3x^2 - 3$ is shown below. What are the roots of $3x^2 - 3$? **Alg. 21.0**

   A $x = -1$ only

   B $x = 1$ only

   C $x = -1$ and $x = 1$

   D No roots

   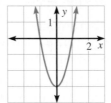

3. Which value of c makes the expression $x^2 + 7x + c$ a perfect square trinomial? **Alg. 14.0**

   A $-\dfrac{49}{2}$

   B $-\dfrac{49}{4}$

   C $\dfrac{49}{4}$

   D $\dfrac{49}{2}$

4. The parallelogram below has an area of 384 square centimeters. What is the height of the parallelogram? **Alg. 23.0**

   A 8 cm

   B 16 cm

   C 24 cm

   D 64 cm

   2x cm
   3x cm

5. During a game of lacrosse, Al throws a ball twice using a lacrosse stick. In the diagrams below, s is the height at which the ball is released, and v is the initial vertical velocity. Which statement correctly compares the two throws if neither is caught? **Alg. 23.0**

   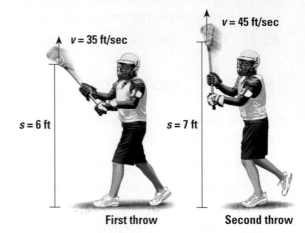

   First throw   **Second throw**

   A The first throw is in the air longer.

   B The second throw is in the air longer.

   C The first throw reaches a greater height.

   D The two throws have the same maximum height.

6. In which point(s) does the graph of $y = -2(x + 4)^2$ intersect the x-axis? **Alg. 22.0**

   A $(-4, 0)$

   B $(4, 0)$

   C $(-4, 0), (4, 0)$

   D Does not intersect the x-axis

7. The function $h = -16t^2 + vt + 4$ gives the height h (in feet) of a ball t seconds after it is thrown with an initial vertical velocity of v feet per second. The ball reaches a maximum height of 8 feet. What is the initial vertical velocity v? **Alg. 23.0**

   A -32 ft/sec

   B -4 ft/sec

   C 0.5 ft/sec

   D 16 ft/sec

8. A skateboarder in a half pipe launches himself from the top of the half pipe with an initial vertical velocity of 17 feet per second, performs a trick in the air, and lands back in the half pipe. The skateboarder lands 5 feet above the base of the half pipe. About how long is he in the air? **Alg. 23.0**

12 ft

Ⓐ −0.32 sec

Ⓑ 0.14 sec

Ⓒ 0.32 sec

Ⓓ 1.38 sec

9. What number should be added to each side of the equation $x^2 - x = 1$ when solving the equation by completing the square? **Alg. 14.0**

Ⓐ −1

Ⓑ $\frac{1}{4}$

Ⓒ $\frac{1}{2}$

Ⓓ 1

10. The area of the rectangle below is 170 square meters. The solutions of which equation can be used to find the value of x? **Alg. 23.0**

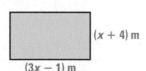

$(x + 4)$ m

$(3x - 1)$ m

Ⓐ $0 = 3x^2 + 11x - 174$

Ⓑ $0 = 3x^2 + 11x - 4$

Ⓒ $0 = 3x^2 + 11x + 166$

Ⓓ $0 = 3x^2 + 11x + 170$

11. The graph of which quadratic function has only one x-intercept? **Alg. 22.0**

Ⓐ $y = -4x^2 - x + 1$

Ⓑ $y = x^2 - 6x + 9$

Ⓒ $y = 2x^2 + 3x + 5$

Ⓓ $y = 3x^2 + 8x - 5$

12. A company uses a quadratic function to model its monthly profit. When the profit is $10,000, the discriminant of the resulting equation is 0. If the graph of the function opens up, which statement about the profit is true? **Alg. 22.0**

Ⓐ The maximum profit is $10,000.

Ⓑ The profit is always increasing.

Ⓒ The minimum profit is $10,000.

Ⓓ The profit is always decreasing.

13. Suppose the graph of $y = ax^2 + 3x + 1$ has two x-intercepts. Which is a possible value of a? **Alg. 20.0**

Ⓐ −1

Ⓑ 0

Ⓒ $\frac{9}{4}$

Ⓓ 3

14. A cross section of the glass lamp shade below can be modeled by the graph of the equation $y = -0.625x^2 + 5x$ where x and y are measured in inches. How tall is the lamp shade? **Alg. 23.0**

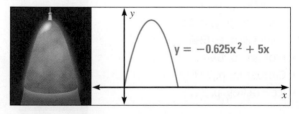

$y = -0.625x^2 + 5x$

Ⓐ 4 in.

Ⓑ 5 in.

Ⓒ 8 in.

Ⓓ 10 in.

11 Rational Expressions and Equations

Before

In previous courses and chapters, you learned the following skills, which you'll use in Chapter 11:

- Performing operations with fractions
- Solving equations
- Performing operations with polynomials
- Factoring polynomials

Now

In Chapter 11 you'll study these **Big Ideas:**

1. Performing operations with rational expressions
2. Solving rational equations
3. Solving work problems

Why?

So you can solve real-world problems about . . .

- Bicycles, p. 685
- Photography, p. 686
- Television, p. 693
- Biology, p. 694
- Canoeing, p. 711
- Ice hockey, p. 717

Animated Algebra at *classzone.com*

MATCHING EXPRESSIONS

California Standards

Review factoring polynomials. **Alg. 11.0**

Prepare for simplifying fractions with polynomials. **Alg. 12.0**

Materials

- One deck of *Matching Expression* cards

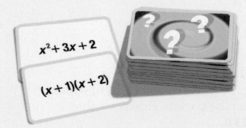

$$x^2 + 3x + 2$$

$$(x + 1)(x + 2)$$

How to Play There are 18 *Matching Expression* cards. Nine of these cards show trinomials. The other nine cards show two binomial factors. Shuffle the cards. Arrange the cards face down in three rows of six cards each. Players should take turns following the steps on the next page.

$$(x+1)(x+2)$$

$$x^2 + 3x + 2$$

1 **Turn** over two cards so that all players can see the expressions on the cards.

2 **Decide** whether the expressions on the cards are equivalent. If they are, then place them in front of you and take another turn. If they are not, then return them, face down, to their original positions.

3 **Remember** where the cards are placed, so that you can find equivalent expressions on future turns.

How to Win Be the player with the most cards when all pairs of equivalent expressions have been found.

Games Wrap-Up

Draw Conclusions

Complete these exercises after playing the game.

1. **WRITING** One player claims that $(2x - 3)^2$ and $4x^2 - 9$ are equivalent. *Describe* and correct the player's error.

2. **REASONING** Suppose you turn over a card with a trinomial that has a leading coefficient of 1. What can you predict about the binomial factors of this trinomial? *Explain* your reasoning.

Getting Ready

Prerequisite Skills

California @HomeTutor

Prerequisite skills practice
at classzone.com

**REVIEW
VOCABULARY**

• **multiplicative
  inverse,** *p. 88*

• **cross product,** *p. 161*

• **direct variation,**
  p. 297

• **polynomial,** *p. 520*

• **least common
  denominator,** *p. 788*

VOCABULARY CHECK

1. What is the least common denominator of $\frac{3}{8}$ and $\frac{7}{10}$?

2. Which equation is a direct variation equation, $\frac{y}{5} = x$ or $\frac{5}{y} = x$?

3. What is the degree of the polynomial $4x - 2 + 5x^2$?

4. What are the like terms in the expression $6x - 9x^2 + 6 + x^2$?

SKILLS CHECK

Factor the polynomial. *(Review pp. 555, 565, 573 for 11.2–11.4.)*

5. $x^2 - 2x - 15$ 6. $2x^2 - 8x + 6$ 7. $9x^2 - 25$ 8. $3x^3 - 48x$

Perform the indicated operation. *(Review pp. 788, 789 for 11.3–11.4.)*

9. $\frac{1}{3} + \frac{3}{4}$ 10. $\frac{7}{8} - \frac{2}{5}$ 11. $\frac{5}{9} \times \frac{3}{5}$ 12. $\frac{3}{10} \div \frac{6}{25}$

Solve the equation or proportion. *(Review pp. 125, 155, 548, 555 for 11.4.)*

13. $4x = 9$ 14. $\frac{x}{10} = \frac{3}{5}$ 15. $x^2 + x = 6$ 16. $5x^2 - 40x = 0$

Notetaking Skills

NOW YOU TRY
Make a *parallel
processes diagram*
that compares long
division of numbers
with long division of
polynomials.

Focus on Graphic Organizers

You can use a *parallel processes diagram* to compare two similar
mathematical processes, such as multiplication of numbers and
multiplication of polynomials.

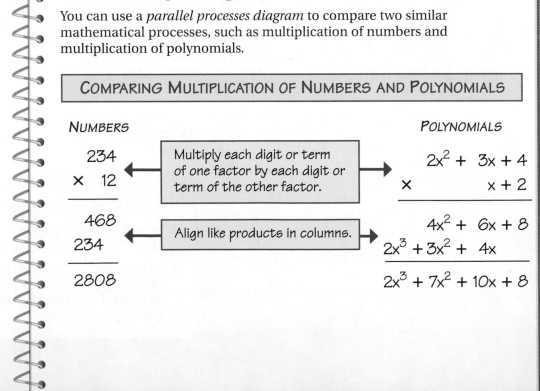

COMPARING MULTIPLICATION OF NUMBERS AND POLYNOMIALS

NUMBERS

$$\begin{array}{r} 234 \\ \times\ 12 \\ \hline 468 \\ 234 \\ \hline 2808 \end{array}$$

Multiply each digit or term
of one factor by each digit or
term of the other factor.

Align like products in columns.

POLYNOMIALS

$$\begin{array}{r} 2x^2 + 3x + 4 \\ \times\qquad x + 2 \\ \hline 4x^2 + 6x + 8 \\ 2x^3 + 3x^2 + 4x \\ \hline 2x^3 + 7x^2 + 10x + 8 \end{array}$$

11.1 Relationships Between Dimensions of a Rectangle

Standards Preparation

Gr. 7 AF 1.5 Represent quantitative relationships graphically and interpret the meaning of a specific part of a graph in the situation represented by the graph.

MATERIALS · 12 square tiles

QUESTION Given a rectangle with a fixed area, how is one dimension related to the other?

EXPLORE Graph the relationship between the dimensions of a rectangle

STEP 1 *Form rectangle*

Draw *x*- and *y*-axes on a sheet of paper as shown. Use 12 square tiles to form a rectangle in Quadrant I with the lower left vertex on the origin. Then label the upper right vertex with the coordinates (*x*, *y*) where *x* is the horizontal length of the rectangle and *y* is the vertical length.

STEP 2 *Draw curve*

Repeat Step 1 for all possible rectangles that can be formed with the tiles. Then connect the points by drawing a smooth curve through them.

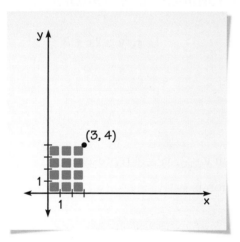

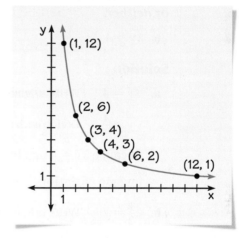

DRAW CONCLUSIONS Use your observations to complete these exercises

1. *Describe* how the vertical length changes as the horizontal length increases. *Describe* how the vertical length changes as the horizontal length decreases.

2. Does the graph cross the axes? *Explain* your reasoning.

3. Write an equation that gives the vertical length *y* as a function of the horizontal length *x*.

4. Let *A* represent the area of a rectangle with side lengths *x* and *y*. For *A* = 40, write an equation that gives *y* as a function of *x*. Then graph the equation.

5. *Compare* the graph of the equation that you wrote in Exercise 4 with the graph of the equation that you wrote in Exercise 3.

11.1 Recognize Inverse Variation

Standards Alg. 15.0 **Students apply algebraic techniques to solve** rate problems, **work problems,** and percent mixture problems.

Connect *Before* you wrote and graphed direct variation equations. *Now* you will write and graph inverse variation equations to solve problems such as work problems.

Math and **THEATER**
Example 6, p. 683

Key Vocabulary
- inverse variation
- constant of variation
- hyperbola
- branches of a hyperbola
- asymptotes of a hyperbola

Recall that two variables x and y show direct variation if $y = kx$ and $k \neq 0$. The variables x and y show **inverse variation** if $y = \frac{k}{x}$ and $k \neq 0$. The nonzero number k is the **constant of variation**, and y is said to *vary inversely* with x.

EXAMPLE 1 Identify direct and inverse variation

Tell whether the equation represents *direct variation*, *inverse variation*, or *neither*.

a. $xy = 4$　　　　**b.** $\dfrac{y}{2} = x$　　　　**c.** $y = 2x + 3$

Solution

a. $xy = 4$　　**Write original equation.**

$y = \dfrac{4}{x}$　　**Divide each side by x.**

Because $xy = 4$ can be written in the form $y = \dfrac{k}{x}$, $xy = 4$ represents inverse variation. The constant of variation is 4.

b. $\dfrac{y}{2} = x$　　**Write original equation.**

$y = 2x$　　**Multiply each side by 2.**

Because $\dfrac{y}{2} = x$ can be written in the form $y = kx$, $\dfrac{y}{2} = x$ represents direct variation.

c. Because $y = 2x + 3$ cannot be written in the form $y = \dfrac{k}{x}$ or $y = kx$, $y = 2x + 3$ does not represent either direct variation or inverse variation.

 GUIDED PRACTICE for Example 1

Tell whether the equation represents *direct variation*, *inverse variation*, or *neither*.

1. $y = \dfrac{2}{x}$　　　　**2.** $4y = 3x$　　　　**3.** $5x - y = 3$　　　　**4.** $xy = \dfrac{1}{2}$

EXAMPLE 2 **Graph an inverse variation equation**

Graph $y = \dfrac{4}{x}$.

Solution

STEP 1 **Make** a table by choosing several integer values of x and finding the values of y. Make a second table to see what happens to the values of y for values of x close to 0 and far from 0. Then plot the points.

x	y
-4	-1
-2	-2
-1	-4
0	undefined
1	4
2	2
4	1

x	y
-10	-0.4
-5	-0.8
-0.5	-8
-0.4	-10
0.4	10
0.5	8
5	0.8
10	0.4

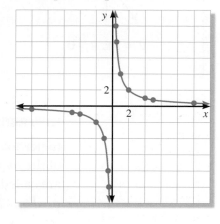

AVOID ERRORS
Note that y is undefined when $x = 0$. There is no point $(0, y)$ on the graph of $y = \dfrac{4}{x}$.

STEP 2 **Connect** the points in Quadrant I by drawing a smooth curve through them. Repeat for the points in Quadrant III.

GRAPHS OF INVERSE VARIATION As shown in Example 2, as you move away from the origin along the x-axis, the graph of an inverse variation equation approaches the x-axis without crossing it. As you move away from the origin along the y-axis, the graph approaches the y-axis without crossing it.

EXAMPLE 3 **Graph an inverse variation equation**

Animated Algebra

For an interactive example of graphing inverse variation equations, go to **classzone.com**.

Graph $y = \dfrac{-4}{x}$.

Solution

Notice that $y = \dfrac{-4}{x} = -1 \cdot \dfrac{4}{x}$. So, for every nonzero value of x, the value of y in $y = \dfrac{-4}{x}$ is the opposite of the value of y in $y = \dfrac{4}{x}$. You can graph $y = \dfrac{-4}{x}$ by reflecting the graph of $y = \dfrac{4}{x}$ (see Example 2) in the x-axis.

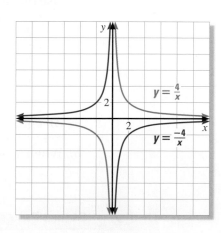

✓ GUIDED PRACTICE for Examples 2 and 3

5. Graph **(a)** $y = \dfrac{3}{x}$ and **(b)** $y = \dfrac{-3}{x}$.

Graphs of Direct Variation and Inverse Variation Equations

Direct variation | Inverse variation

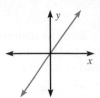 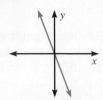 |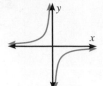

$y = kx, k > 0$ $\quad$ $y = kx, k < 0$ $\quad\quad$ $y = \dfrac{k}{x}, k > 0$ $\quad$ $y = \dfrac{k}{x}, k < 0$

HYPERBOLAS The graph of the inverse variation equation $y = \dfrac{k}{x}$ $(k \neq 0)$ is a **hyperbola**. The two symmetrical parts of a hyperbola are called the **branches of the hyperbola**. The lines that the hyperbola approaches but doesn't intersect are called the **asymptotes of the hyperbola**. The asymptotes of the graph of $y = \dfrac{k}{x}$ are the x-axis and the y-axis.

EXAMPLE 4 **Use an inverse variation equation**

The variables x and y vary inversely, and $y = 6$ when $x = -3$.

a. Write an inverse variation equation that relates x and y.

b. Find the value of y when $x = 4$.

Solution

a. Because y varies inversely with x, the equation has the form $y = \dfrac{k}{x}$.

Use the fact that $x = -3$ and $y = 6$ to find the value of k.

$y = \dfrac{k}{x}$ $\quad$ Write inverse variation equation.

$6 = \dfrac{k}{-3}$ $\quad$ Substitute −3 for x and 6 for y.

$-18 = k$ $\quad$ Multiply each side by −3.

An equation that relates x and y is $y = \dfrac{-18}{x}$.

b. When $x = 4$, $y = \dfrac{-18}{4} = -\dfrac{9}{2}$.

✓ GUIDED PRACTICE for Example 4

Given that y varies inversely with x, use the specified values to write an inverse variation equation that relates x and y. Then find the value of y when $x = -3$.

6. $x = 12, y = -2$ $\quad$ **7.** $x = 8, y = 20$ $\quad$ **8.** $x = -6, y = -4$

PRODUCTS By multiplying both sides of $y = \frac{k}{x}$ by x, you can write the equation as $xy = k$. This means that a set of ordered pairs (x, y) shows inverse variation if all the products xy are constant.

EXAMPLE 5 Write an inverse variation equation

Tell whether the table represents inverse variation. If so, write the inverse variation equation.

x	−5	−3	4	8	24
y	2.4	4	−3	−1.5	−0.5

Solution

Find the products xy for all ordered pairs (x, y):

$-5(2.4) = -12 \quad -3(4) = -12 \quad 4(-3) = -12 \quad 8(-1.5) = -12 \quad 24(-0.5) = -12$

The products are equal to the same number, −12. So, y varies inversely with x.

▶ The inverse variation equation is $xy = -12$, or $y = \frac{-12}{x}$.

CHECK PRODUCTS
For real-world data, the products may not be exactly equal. You may still be able to use an inverse variation model when the products are approximately equal.

EXAMPLE 6 Solve a work problem

THEATER A theater company plans to hire people to build a stage set. The work time t (in hours per person) varies inversely with the number p of people hired. The company estimates that 10 people working for 70 hours each can complete the job. Find the work time per person if the company hires 14 people.

Set takes 10 people 70 hours to build.

Solution

STEP 1 **Write** the inverse variation equation that relates p and t.

$t = \dfrac{k}{p}$ **Write inverse variation equation.**

$70 = \dfrac{k}{10}$ **Substitute 10 for p and 70 for t.**

$700 = k$ **Multiply each side by 10.**

The inverse variation equation is $t = \dfrac{700}{p}$.

STEP 2 **Find** t when $p = 14$: $t = \dfrac{700}{p} = \dfrac{700}{14} = 50$.

▶ If 14 people are hired, the work time per person is 50 hours.

About the Standards

Example 6 illustrates a special type of work problem (Algebra 1 Standard 15.0) in which all people are assumed to work at the same rate. In Lesson 11.6, you will consider more general work problems.

✓ **GUIDED PRACTICE** for Examples 5 and 6

9. Tell whether the ordered pairs $(-5, 2)$, $(-4, 2.5)$, $(8, -1.25)$, and $(20, -0.5)$ represent inverse variation. If so, write the inverse variation equation.

10. **WHAT IF?** In Example 6, suppose the theater company estimates that 8 people working for 80 hours each can complete the job. Find the work time per person if the company hires 10 people.

11.1 EXERCISES

HOMEWORK KEY

◆ = **MULTIPLE CHOICE PRACTICE**
Exs. 15, 44, 60, and 70–72

◯ = **HINTS AND HOMEWORK HELP**
for Exs. 29, 45, and 61 at classzone.com

SKILLS · PROBLEM SOLVING · REASONING

1. **VOCABULARY** Identify the constant of variation in the equation $y = \frac{-3}{x}$.

2. **WRITING** *Describe* the difference between a direct variation equation and an inverse variation equation.

EXAMPLE 1
on p. 680
for Exs. 3–15

DESCRIBING EQUATIONS Tell whether the equation represents *direct variation, inverse variation,* or *neither.*

3. $y = -2x$

4. $\frac{y}{x} = 4$

5. $y = x + 5$

6. $x = \frac{-1}{y}$

7. $xy = 5$

8. $xy = 1$

9. $x = 7y$

10. $2x + y = 6$

11. $2x = \frac{8}{y}$

12. $x = -7$

13. $3x - 3y = 0$

14. $3xy = 20$

15. ◆ **MULTIPLE CHOICE** Which equation represents inverse variation?

    (A) $x = 2$ (B) $y = x - 5$ (C) $y = -7x$ (D) $y = \frac{4}{x}$

EXAMPLES 2 and 3
on p. 681
for Exs. 16–27

GRAPHING EQUATIONS Graph the inverse variation equation.

16. $y = \frac{2}{x}$

17. $y = \frac{-1}{x}$

18. $y = \frac{-7}{x}$

19. $y = \frac{10}{x}$

20. $y = \frac{-5}{x}$

21. $y = \frac{18}{x}$

22. $y = \frac{9}{x}$

23. $y = \frac{-2}{x}$

24. $y = \frac{15}{x}$

25. $y = \frac{6}{x}$

26. $y = \frac{-12}{x}$

27. $y = \frac{-8}{x}$

EXAMPLE 4
on p. 682
for Exs. 28–44

28. **ERROR ANALYSIS** The variables x and y vary inversely, and $y = 8$ when $x = 2$. *Describe* and correct the error in writing an inverse variation equation that relates x and y.

$$y = kx$$
$$8 = k(2)$$
$$4 = k$$
$$\text{So, } y = 4x.$$

USE INVERSE VARIATION Given that y varies inversely with x, use the specified values to write an inverse variation equation that relates x and y. Then find the value of y when $x = 2$.

29. $x = 5, y = 2$

30. $x = 3, y = 7$

31. $x = -5, y = 4$

32. $x = 13, y = -1$

33. $x = -15, y = -15$

34. $x = -22, y = -6$

35. $x = 8, y = 3$

36. $x = 9, y = -2$

37. $x = 3, y = 3$

38. $x = -2, y = -10$

39. $x = -3, y = 40$

40. $x = -7, y = -10$

41. $x = -17, y = 8$

42. $x = 6, y = 11$

43. $x = -12, y = -13$

44. ◆ **MULTIPLE CHOICE** The variables x and y vary inversely, and $y = 6$ when $x = 4$. What is the constant of variation?

    (A) 1.5   (B) 4   (C) 6   (D) 24

EXAMPLE 5
on p. 683
for Exs. 45–48

WRITING EQUATIONS Tell whether the table represents inverse variation. If so, write the inverse variation equation.

(45.)

x	4	8	12	16	20
y	1	2	3	4	5

46.

x	−20	−5	14	32	50
y	−80	−20	56	128	200

47.

x	−10	−5	15	20	40
y	−30	−60	20	15	7.5

48.

x	−12	−10	−8	−5	−4
y	2	2.4	3	4.8	6

49. **WRITING** *Compare* the graph of an inverse variation equation with $k > 0$ and the graph of an inverse variation equation with $k < 0$.

50. **REASONING** The variables x and y vary inversely. How does the value of y change if the value of x is doubled? tripled? Give examples.

GEOMETRY Translate the verbal sentence into an equation using the appropriate geometric formula. Then tell whether the equation represents *direct variation*, *inverse variation*, or *neither*.

51. The circumference of a circle with radius r units is C units.

52. The area of a triangle with base b and height h units is 27 square units.

53. The volume of a rectangular prism with base B square units and height h units is 400 cubic units.

54. **REASONING** Let y vary inversely with x with a constant of variation a, and let z vary inversely with y with a constant of variation b. Write an equation that gives z as a function of x. Then tell whether z varies *directly* or *inversely* with x.

CONNECT SKILLS TO PROBLEM SOLVING Exercises 55–57 will help you prepare for problem solving.

Write an inverse variation equation that relates the two given quantities. Use k as the constant of variation.

55. The time t (in minutes) that you spend walking to school varies inversely with the speed s (in feet per minute) at which you walk.

56. The number s of slices of pizza that a person can eat varies inversely with the total number p of people eating pizza.

57. The number p of people needed to do a job varies inversely with the time t available to get the job done.

EXAMPLE 5
on p. 683
for Ex. 58

58. **BICYCLES** The table shows the bicycle speed s (in miles per hour) for various pedaling speeds p (in pedal rotations per mile). Tell whether the table represents inverse variation. If so, write the inverse variation equation that relates p and s.

Pedal

Pedaling speed, p (pedal rotations/mi)	831	612	420	305
Bicycle speed, s (mi/h)	4.33	5.88	8.57	11.8

California @HomeTutor for problem solving help at classzone.com

EXAMPLE 6
on p. 683
for Exs. 59–61

59. ECONOMICS The owner of an electronics store determines that the monthly demand d (in units) for a computer varies inversely with the price p (in dollars) of the computer. When the price is $700, the monthly demand is 250 units. Write the inverse variation equation that relates p and d. Then find the monthly demand when the price is $500.

California @*HomeTutor*   for problem solving help at classzone.com

60. ◆ MULTIPLE CHOICE A 25 person work crew takes 20 hours to set up booths for a home show. The work time t (in hours per person) varies inversely with the number p of people in the work crew. What is the approximate work time per person if the crew is expanded to 30 people?

(**A**) 16.7 h   (**B**) 24.0 h   (**C**) 25.0 h   (**D**) 37.5 h

61. CAR WASH Three students are raising money for a club by washing cars. They can wash, rinse, and dry a car in 6 minutes. The work time t (in minutes per student) varies inversely with the number s of students working. Find the work time per student if 2 more students help.

READING *IN* MATH   Read the information below for Exercises 62–64.

Photography The focal length f (in millimeters) of a camera lens is the distance between the lens and the point at which light rays meet after passing through the opening in the lens. The f-stop s is the ratio of the focal length f to the diameter d (in millimeters) of the opening.

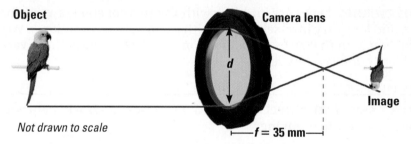

Object   Camera lens

d

Image

Not drawn to scale $f = 35$ mm

62. Model Write an equation that relates d and s for the lens in the diagram. Tell whether the equation represents inverse variation.

63. Calculate Find the diameter d when the f-stop is 4.

64. Compare The greater the diameter of the opening, the more light that passes through the opening. For the lens in the diagram, does more light pass through the opening when the f-stop is 4 or when it is 8? *Explain.*

65. SPORTS An athlete is running a 200 meter dash. Write and graph an equation that relates the athlete's average running speed r (in meters per second) and the time t (in seconds) that the athlete will take to finish the race. Is the equation an inverse variation equation? *Explain.*

66. SNOWSHOES Denise walks in deep snow wearing boots with a sole area of 29 square inches each and a pressure on each sole of 2 pounds per square inch (psi). The pressure P (in psi) on each boot sole varies inversely with the area A of the sole. Write an inverse variation equation that relates P and A. If Denise changes into snowshoes, each with a sole area of 319 square inches, what is the pressure on each snowshoe?

67. MULTI-STEP PROBLEM The photo below shows a replica of an airplane designed by Orville and Wilbur Wright, who were aviation pioneers in the early 20th century. The aspect ratio r of a wing from similar airplanes is given by the formula $r = \dfrac{s^2}{A}$ where s is the span, or the distance (in feet) between the wing tips, and A is the area (in square feet) of the wing.

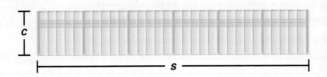

a. Model The length c of the chord of a wing is the distance (in feet) between the front and the back of the wing. For the rectangular wing shown, rewrite the formula for r in terms of c and s.

b. Analyze How does the value of r change when s is constant and c increases? when c is constant and s increases?

68. CHALLENGE The points $(3, c^2 - 7c + 10)$ and $(3c + 1, c + 2)$ lie on the graph of an inverse variation equation. Find the coordinates of the points.

69. CHALLENGE A fulcrum is placed under the center of a board. In order for two objects to balance on the board, the distance (in feet) of each object from the center of the board must vary inversely with the object's weight (in pounds). In the diagram shown, what is the distance of each animal from the center of the board?

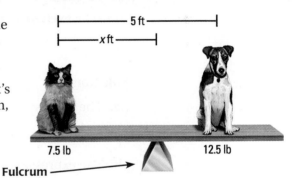

◆ CALIFORNIA STANDARDS SPIRAL REVIEW

Alg. 14.0

70. What are the solutions of $x^2 + 9x + 14 = 0$? *(p. 556)*

　Ⓐ　-2 and -7 　　Ⓑ　2 and 7 　　Ⓒ　-3 and 5 　　Ⓓ　-5 and 3

Alg. 11.0

71. What is the factored form of $25n^2 - 20n + 4$? *(p. 573)*

　Ⓐ　$(25n - 4)^2$ 　　Ⓑ　$2(2n - 1)^2$ 　　Ⓒ　$5(4n - 1)^2$ 　　Ⓓ　$(5n - 2)^2$

Alg. 10.0

72. The diagram shows the dimensions of a picture inside a frame having a uniform width of 2 inches. What is a polynomial expression that represents the total area of the picture, including the frame? *(p. 528)*

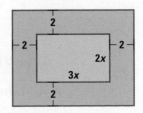

　Ⓐ　$(3x + 2)(2x)$ 　　Ⓑ　$6x^2 + 20x + 16$

　Ⓒ　$(2x + 2)(3x)$ 　　Ⓓ　$2x^2 - 4x + 5$

11.2 Simplify Rational Expressions

Math and COMMUNICATION
Example 5, p. 691

Standards Alg. 12.0 Students simplify fractions with polynomials in the numerator and denominator by factoring both and reducing them to the lowest terms.

Connect *Before* you factored polynomials. *Now* you will simplify rational expressions.

Key Vocabulary
• rational expression
• excluded value
• simplest form of a rational expression
• rational function

A **rational expression** is an expression that can be written as a ratio of two polynomials where the denominator is not 0. A rational expression is undefined when the denominator is 0. A number that makes a rational expression undefined is called an **excluded value**. For example, $\frac{2}{x-3}$ is undefined when $x = 3$. So, 3 is an excluded value.

EXAMPLE 1 Find excluded values

Find the excluded values, if any, of the expression.

a. $\frac{x+8}{10x}$ **b.** $\frac{5}{2y+14}$ **c.** $\frac{4v}{v^2-9}$ **d.** $\frac{7w+2}{8w^2+w+5}$

Solution

a. The expression $\frac{x+8}{10x}$ is undefined when $10x = 0$, or $x = 0$.

▸ The excluded value is 0.

b. The expression $\frac{5}{2y+14}$ is undefined when $2y + 14 = 0$, or $y = -7$.

▸ The excluded value is −7.

c. The expression $\frac{4v}{v^2-9}$ is undefined when $v^2 - 9 = 0$, or $(v+3)(v-3) = 0$. The solutions of the equation are −3 and 3.

▸ The excluded values are −3 and 3.

d. The expression $\frac{7w+2}{8w^2+w+5}$ is undefined when $8w^2 + w + 5 = 0$.

REVIEW DISCRIMINANT
For help with finding the discriminant of a quadratic equation, see p. 657.

The discriminant is $b^2 - 4ac = 1^2 - 4(8)(5) < 0$. So, the quadratic equation has no real roots.

▸ There are no excluded values.

✓ GUIDED PRACTICE for Example 1

Find the excluded values, if any, of the expression.

1. $\frac{x+2}{3x-5}$ **2.** $\frac{2}{5y^2+2y+3}$ **3.** $\frac{n-6}{2n^2-5n-12}$ **4.** $\frac{2m}{m^2-4}$

SIMPLIFYING A RATIONAL EXPRESSION To simplify a rational expression, you factor the numerator and denominator and then divide out any common factors. A rational expression is in **simplest form** if the numerator and denominator have no factors in common other than 1.

KEY CONCEPT *For Your Notebook*

Simplifying Rational Expressions

Let a, b, and c be polynomials where $b \neq 0$ and $c \neq 0$.

Algebra $\dfrac{ac}{bc} = \dfrac{a \cdot \cancel{c}}{b \cdot \cancel{c}} = \dfrac{a}{b}$

Example $\dfrac{2x + 4}{3x + 6} = \dfrac{2\cancel{(x + 2)}}{3\cancel{(x + 2)}} = \dfrac{2}{3}$

EXAMPLE 2 **Simplify expressions by dividing out monomials**

Simplify the rational expression, if possible. State the excluded values.

a. $\dfrac{r}{2r}$

b. $\dfrac{5x}{5(x + 2)}$

c. $\dfrac{6m^3 - 12m^2}{18m^2}$

d. $\dfrac{y}{7 - y}$

Solution

a. $\dfrac{r}{2r} = \dfrac{\cancel{r}}{2\cancel{r}}$ **Divide out common factor.**

$\phantom{\dfrac{r}{2r}} = \dfrac{1}{2}$ **Simplify.**

▸ The excluded value is 0.

b. $\dfrac{5x}{5(x + 2)} = \dfrac{\cancel{5} \cdot x}{\cancel{5} \cdot (x + 2)}$ **Divide out common factor.**

$\phantom{\dfrac{5x}{5(x + 2)}} = \dfrac{x}{x + 2}$ **Simplify.**

▸ The excluded value is −2.

c. $\dfrac{6m^3 - 12m^2}{18m^2} = \dfrac{6m^2(m - 2)}{6 \cdot 3 \cdot m^2}$ **Factor numerator and denominator.**

$\phantom{\dfrac{6m^3 - 12m^2}{18m^2}} = \dfrac{\cancel{6m^2}(m - 2)}{\cancel{6} \cdot 3 \cdot \cancel{m^2}}$ **Divide out common factors.**

$\phantom{\dfrac{6m^3 - 12m^2}{18m^2}} = \dfrac{m - 2}{3}$ **Simplify.**

▸ The excluded value is 0.

d. The expression $\dfrac{y}{7 - y}$ is already in simplest form.

▸ The excluded value is 7.

✓ **GUIDED PRACTICE** for Example 2

Simplify the rational expression, if possible. State the excluded values.

5. $\dfrac{4a^3}{22a^6}$

6. $\dfrac{2c}{c + 5}$

7. $\dfrac{2s^2 + 8s}{3s + 12}$

8. $\dfrac{8x}{8x^3 + 16x^2}$

EXAMPLE 3 ◆ Multiple Choice Practice

Simplify $\dfrac{6x^2 + 32x + 10}{9x^2 - 1}$ to lowest terms.

(A) $\dfrac{2(3x + 5)}{3x - 1}$ (B) $\dfrac{2(x + 5)}{3x - 1}$ (C) $\dfrac{2(x + 1)}{9(x - 1)}$ (D) $\dfrac{2(x + 5)}{3x + 1}$

Solution

$$\dfrac{6x^2 + 32x + 10}{9x^2 - 1} = \dfrac{2(x + 5)(3x + 1)}{(3x - 1)(3x + 1)} \qquad \text{Factor numerator and denominator.}$$

$$= \dfrac{2(x + 5)\cancel{(3x + 1)}}{(3x - 1)\cancel{(3x + 1)}} \qquad \text{Divide out common factor.}$$

$$= \dfrac{2(x + 5)}{3x - 1} \qquad \text{Simplify.}$$

▶ The correct answer is B. Ⓐ Ⓑ Ⓒ Ⓓ

OPPOSITES When simplifying a rational expression, look for factors that are opposites of each other. For example, $x - 1$ and $1 - x$ are opposites, because $x - 1 = -(1 - x)$.

EXAMPLE 4 Recognize opposites

Simplify $\dfrac{x^2 - 7x + 12}{16 - x^2}$. State the excluded values.

$$\dfrac{x^2 - 7x + 12}{16 - x^2} = \dfrac{(x - 3)(x - 4)}{(4 - x)(4 + x)} \qquad \text{Factor numerator and denominator.}$$

$$= \dfrac{(x - 3)(x - 4)}{-(x - 4)(4 + x)} \qquad \text{Rewrite } 4 - x \text{ as } -(x - 4).$$

$$= \dfrac{(x - 3)\cancel{(x - 4)}}{-\cancel{(x - 4)}(4 + x)} \qquad \text{Divide out common factor.}$$

$$= \dfrac{x - 3}{-(4 + x)} \qquad \text{Simplify.}$$

$$= -\dfrac{x - 3}{x + 4} \qquad \text{Write } \dfrac{a}{-b} \text{ as } -\dfrac{a}{b}.$$

▶ The excluded values are -4 and 4.

✓ **GUIDED PRACTICE** for Examples 3 and 4

Simplify the rational expression. State the excluded values.

9. $\dfrac{x^2 + 3x + 2}{x^2 + 7x + 10}$ 10. $\dfrac{y^2 - 64}{y^2 - 16y + 64}$ 11. $\dfrac{5 + 4z - z^2}{z^2 - 3z - 10}$

RATIONAL FUNCTIONS A **rational function** has a rule given by a fraction whose numerator and denominator are polynomials and whose denominator is not 0.

EXAMPLE 5 **Simplify a rational model**

CELL PHONE COSTS The average cost C (in dollars per minute) for cell phone service in the United States during the period 1991–2000 can be modeled by the rational function

$$C = \frac{46 - 2.2x}{100 - 18x + 2.2x^2}$$

where x is the number of years since 1991. Rewrite the model so that it has only whole number coefficients. Then simplify the model.

1991 cell phone

Solution

$$C = \frac{46 - 2.2x}{100 - 18x + 2.2x^2} \qquad \text{Write model.}$$

$$= \frac{460 - 22x}{1000 - 180x + 22x^2} \qquad \text{Multiply numerator and denominator by 10.}$$

$$= \frac{2(230 - 11x)}{2(500 - 90x + 11x^2)} \qquad \text{Factor numerator and denominator.}$$

$$= \frac{\cancel{2}(230 - 11x)}{\cancel{2}(500 - 90x + 11x^2)} \qquad \text{Divide out common factor.}$$

$$= \frac{230 - 11x}{500 - 90x + 11x^2} \qquad \text{Simplify.}$$

✓ **GUIDED PRACTICE** for Example 5

12. In Example 5, approximate the average cost per minute for cell phone service in 2000.

11.2 EXERCISES

HOMEWORK KEY

◆ = **MULTIPLE CHOICE PRACTICE**
Exs. 33, 34, 46, and 50–52

○ = **HINTS AND HOMEWORK HELP**
for Exs. 9, 23, and 45 at classzone.com

SKILLS · PROBLEM SOLVING · REASONING

1. VOCABULARY Copy and complete: A value that makes a rational expression undefined is called a(n) ? .

2. WRITING Is the expression $\dfrac{(x + 3)(x - 6)}{(x - 3)(6 - x)}$ in simplest form? *Explain.*

EXAMPLE 1
on p. 688
for Exs. 3–10

FINDING EXCLUDED VALUES Find the excluded values, if any, of the expression.

3. $\dfrac{4x}{20}$

4. $\dfrac{13}{2y}$

5. $\dfrac{5}{r + 1}$

6. $\dfrac{-s}{3s + 4}$

7. $\dfrac{-m}{4m^2 - 3m + 9}$

8. $\dfrac{n + 2}{n^2 - 64}$

9. $\dfrac{-3}{2p^2 - p}$

10. $\dfrac{5q}{q^2 - 6q + 9}$

EXAMPLES
2, 3, and 4
on pp. 689–690
for Exs. 11–33

ERROR ANALYSIS *Describe* and correct the error in simplifying the rational expression or in stating the excluded values.

11. $\dfrac{2x^2 - x - 3}{2x^2 - 11x + 12}$

$$\dfrac{2x^2 - x - 3}{2x^2 - 11x + 12} = \dfrac{(x + 1)(2x - 3)}{(2x - 3)(x - 4)}$$

$$= \dfrac{(x + 1)(2x - 3)}{(2x - 3)(x - 4)}$$

$$= \dfrac{x + 1}{x - 4}$$

The excluded value is 4. ✕

12. $\dfrac{2(x - 5)}{(x - 5)(x + 2)}$

$$\dfrac{2(x - 5)}{(x - 5)(x + 2)} = \dfrac{2(x - 5)}{(x - 5)(x + 2)}$$

$$= \dfrac{2}{x + 2}$$

$$= \dfrac{2}{x + 2}$$

$$= \dfrac{1}{x + 1}$$

The excluded values are −2 and 5. ✕

SIMPLIFYING EXPRESSIONS Simplify the rational expression, if possible. State the excluded values.

13. $\dfrac{10x}{25}$

14. $\dfrac{63}{18y}$

15. $\dfrac{-48a^2}{16a}$

16. $\dfrac{27b^2}{30b^5}$

17. $\dfrac{3c + 33}{c + 11}$

18. $\dfrac{d + 8}{d - 8}$

19. $\dfrac{2u - 6}{3 - u}$

20. $\dfrac{v + 2}{v^2 - 4}$

21. $\dfrac{2}{f^2 - 9}$

22. $\dfrac{g + 4}{g^2 - 16}$

㉓. $\dfrac{h + 3}{h^2 - h - 12}$

24. $\dfrac{j - 2}{j^2 - 6j + 8}$

25. $\dfrac{-48w}{16w^2 - 40w}$

26. $\dfrac{12y^4}{12y^2 + 18y}$

27. $\dfrac{6z^2 - 24z}{2z^2 - 8z}$

28. $\dfrac{14x^2 + 21x}{2x^2 + x - 3}$

29. $\dfrac{s^2 + 16s + 64}{s^2 + 7s - 8}$

30. $\dfrac{t^2 - 4t - 45}{2t^2 - 21t + 27}$

31. $\dfrac{m + 5}{m^3 + 10m^2 + 25m}$

32. $\dfrac{-n^2 - 3n + 28}{3n^3 + 9n^2 - 84n}$

33. ◆ **MULTIPLE CHOICE** What is the simplified form of $\dfrac{x^2 - 3x - 10}{x^2 + 6x + 8}$?

Ⓐ $\dfrac{x - 5}{x + 4}$
Ⓑ $\dfrac{x}{x + 3}$
Ⓒ $\dfrac{x + 2}{x + 3}$
Ⓓ $\dfrac{x - 4}{x + 2}$

34. ◆ **MULTIPLE CHOICE** The expression $\dfrac{a}{x^2 + 5x - 6}$ simplifies to $\dfrac{2x + 5}{x + 6}$. What is a?

Ⓐ $2x^2 + 7x + 5$
Ⓑ $2x^2 + 5x - 1$
Ⓒ $2x^2 + 3x - 5$
Ⓓ $2x^2 + 7x - 5$

GEOMETRY Write and simplify a rational expression for the ratio of the perimeter of the given figure to its area.

35. Square

5x

36. Rectangle

2x
x + 6

37. Triangle
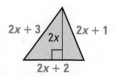
2x + 3   2x   2x + 1
2x + 2

38. **OPEN-ENDED** Write a rational expression whose excluded values are −3 and −5.

◆ = **MULTIPLE CHOICE PRACTICE**   ◯ = **HINTS AND HOMEWORK HELP** at classzone.com

SIMPLIFYING EXPRESSIONS In Exercises 39–41, use the example below to simplify the rational expression. State the restrictions on the variables.

EXAMPLE **Simplify a rational expression in two variables**

Simplify $\dfrac{x^2 + 5xy - 6y^2}{4x^2 + 24xy}$. State the restrictions on the variables.

$\dfrac{x^2 + 5xy - 6y^2}{4x^2 + 24xy} = \dfrac{(x + 6y)(x - y)}{4x(x + 6y)}$　　Factor numerator and denominator.

$= \dfrac{\cancel{(x + 6y)}(x - y)}{4x\cancel{(x + 6y)}}$　　Divide out common factor.

$= \dfrac{x - y}{4x}$　　Simplify.

▶ The restrictions on the variables are $x \neq 0$ and $x \neq -6y$.

---

39. $\dfrac{x^2 - 9x + 14}{2xy - 14y}$

40. $\dfrac{8x^2 - 20xy + 8y^2}{4x^2 + 18xy - 10y^2}$

41. $\dfrac{25x^2 - 5xy - 2y^2}{20x^2 - 3xy - 2y^2}$

CONNECT SKILLS TO PROBLEM SOLVING Exercises 42 and 43 will help you prepare for problem solving.

Rewrite the given model using only whole number coefficients.

42. A salesperson earns $450 plus 15% of her weekly sales s. The percent p (in decimal form) of her pay that is commission is $p = \dfrac{0.15s}{450 + 0.15s}$.

43. A printer charges $150 to set up the presses and $.62 per copy for printing c copies of a brochure. The percent p (in decimal form) of the total cost that is the set-up fee is $p = \dfrac{150}{150 + 0.62c}$.

EXAMPLE 5
on p. 691
for Exs. 44–46

44. CREDIT CARD FEES The average late payment fee F (in dollars) on a credit card account during the period 1994–2003 can be modeled by

$$F = \dfrac{12 + 1.6x^2}{1 + 0.04x^2}$$

where x is the number of years since 1994. Rewrite the model with only whole number coefficients. Then simplify the model and approximate the average late payment fee in 2003.

California **@HomeTutor**　for problem solving help at classzone.com

45. TELEVISION For the period 1980–2003, the percent p of non-network television commercials in the United States that lasted 15 seconds can be modeled by

$$p = \dfrac{0.12x^2 - 0.48}{0.88x^2 + 100}$$

where x is the number of years since 1980. Rewrite the model with only whole number coefficients. Then simplify the model and approximate the percent of non-network commercials in 2003 that lasted 15 seconds.

California **@HomeTutor**　for problem solving help at classzone.com

About 9% of commercials in 1995 were 15 seconds.

46. ◆ MULTIPLE CHOICE The revenue R (in millions of dollars) from sales of printed music in the United States during the period 1988–2002 can be modeled by the rational function

$$R = \frac{300 + 20x}{1 + 0.008x}$$

where x is the number of years since 1988. Which rational expression is an equivalent model for R?

(A) $\dfrac{30,000 + 2000x}{1000 + 8x}$ **(B)** $\dfrac{37,500 + 2500x}{125 + x}$ **(C)** $\dfrac{2500 + 1000x}{25 + x}$ **(D)** $\dfrac{3000 + 200x}{x}$

47. BIOLOGY Suppose a microorganism is shaped like a cylinder and grows by increasing its length ℓ and not its radius r. The surface area S (in square micrometers) and the volume V (in cubic micrometers) of the microorganism can be modeled by

$$S = 2\pi r^2 + 2\pi r\ell \quad \text{and} \quad V = \pi r^2 \ell.$$

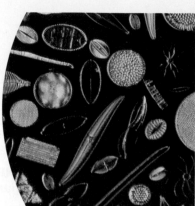

a. Write an equation that models the ratio y of the surface area of the microorganism to its volume.

b. Suppose the microorganism has a radius of 50 micrometers. Incorporate this information into the model from part (a).

c. *Describe* how the ratio changes as the length of the microorganism increases.

Microorganisms magnified 36 times

48. CHALLENGE Find two polynomials whose ratio is $\dfrac{3x - 1}{2x + 1}$ in simplified form and whose sum is $5x^2 + 20x$. *Describe* your steps.

49. CHALLENGE The average annual expenses E (in dollars) of a middle income family and the average annual amount T (in dollars) spent on telephone service during the period 1992–2001 can be modeled by

$$E = 1240x + 24,800 \quad \text{and} \quad T = 31x + 620$$

where x is the number of years since 1992. Write and simplify a model to show that the average annual amount spent on telephone service was 2.5% of the average annual expenses during the period.

◆ CALIFORNIA STANDARDS SPIRAL REVIEW

Alg. 8.0

50. Which line passes through $(5, 14)$ and is parallel to $y = 2x - 2$? *(p. 354)*

   (A) $y = -2x + 4$ **(B)** $y = 2x + 2$

   (C) $y = 2x - 1$ **(D)** $y = 2x + 4$

Alg. 14.0

51. What are the solutions of $x^2 + 14x = -13$? *(p. 556)*

   (A) 2 and 12   **(B)** 1 and 13   **(C)** −2 and −12   **(D)** −1 and −13

Alg. 15.0

52. A company plans to publish two comic books. The work time t (in hours per person) varies inversely with the number p of people hired. The company estimates that 15 people working for 200 hours each can complete the comic books. What is the work time per person if 12 people are hired? *(p. 680)*

   (A) 200 h   **(B)** 225 h   **(C)** 250 h   **(D)** 300 h

11.2 Graph Rational Functions

MATERIALS · Graphing calculator

Standards

Gr. 7 AF 1.5 Represent quantitative relationships **graphically** and interpret the meaning of a specific part of a graph in the situation represented by the graph.

QUESTION How can you use a graph to check your work with a rational function?

EXPLORE Compare graphs of rational expressions

Verify the simplification of $\dfrac{x+2}{x^2-4}$ **using a graph.**

$$\frac{x+2}{x^2-4} = \frac{\cancel{x+2}}{\cancel{(x+2)}(x-2)} = \frac{1}{x-2} \qquad \text{The excluded values are } -2 \text{ and } 2.$$

STEP 1 *Graph the original expression*

Enter $y_1 = \dfrac{x+2}{x^2-4}$ into your graphing calculator. Press [MODE] and select

either connected mode or dot mode. Then graph the function. In connected mode the screen appears to show the line $x = 2$. This line is *not* part of the graph. The calculator is instead connecting the two branches of the hyperbola. In dot mode, the screen does not show the line.

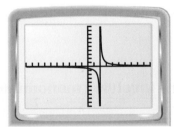

Connected mode

Dot mode

STEP 2 *Graph the simplified expression*

Enter $y_2 = \dfrac{1}{x-2}$ into your graphing calculator.

Because the graphs coincide, the expressions are equivalent for all values of x other than the excluded values -2 and 2.

DRAW CONCLUSIONS

1. Enter $y_1 = \dfrac{x+2}{x^2-4}$ and $y_2 = \dfrac{1}{x-2}$ on your graphing calculator and select [TABLE]. *Explain* why y_2 is defined for $x = -2$ but y_1 is not.

2. Simplify **(a)** $\dfrac{3x-6}{x^2+2x-8}$ and **(b)** $\dfrac{5x^2-15x}{15x^4}$. Check your work with a graph.

11.3 Multiply and Divide Rational Expressions

Standards Alg. 13.0 Students add, subtract, multiply, and divide rational expressions and functions. Students solve both computationally and conceptually challenging problems by using these techniques.

Connect *Before* you multiplied and divided polynomials. *Now* you will multiply and divide rational expressions.

Math and SPORTS
Ex. 33, p. 702

Key Vocabulary
• **multiplicative inverse,** *p. 88*
• **polynomial,** *p. 520*
• **rational expression,** *p. 688*

Multiplying and dividing rational expressions is similar to multiplying and dividing numerical fractions.

KEY CONCEPT   *For Your Notebook*

Multiplying and Dividing Rational Expressions

Let a, b, c, and d be polynomials.

Algebra $\dfrac{a}{b} \cdot \dfrac{c}{d} = \dfrac{ac}{bd}$ where $b \neq 0$ and $d \neq 0$

$\dfrac{a}{b} \div \dfrac{c}{d} = \dfrac{a}{b} \cdot \dfrac{d}{c} = \dfrac{ad}{bc}$ where $b \neq 0$, $c \neq 0$, and $d \neq 0$

Examples $\dfrac{x+2}{x} \cdot \dfrac{3}{x^2} = \dfrac{3(x+2)}{x^3}$ $\dfrac{x}{x-1} \div \dfrac{4}{x} = \dfrac{x}{x-1} \cdot \dfrac{x}{4} = \dfrac{x^2}{4(x-1)}$

EXAMPLE 1 Multiply rational expressions involving monomials

Find the product $\dfrac{2x^2}{3x} \cdot \dfrac{6x^2}{12x^4}$.

IDENTIFY EXCLUDED VALUES
When performing operations with rational expressions, remember that the answer may have excluded values. In Example 1, the excluded value is 0.

$\dfrac{2x^2}{3x} \cdot \dfrac{6x^2}{12x^4} = \dfrac{(2x^2)(6x^2)}{(3x)(12x^4)}$ **Multiply numerators and denominators.**

$= \dfrac{12x^4}{36x^5}$ **Product of powers property**

$= \dfrac{\cancel{12} \cdot \cancel{x^4}}{3 \cdot \cancel{12} \cdot \cancel{x^4} \cdot x}$ **Factor and divide out common factors.**

$= \dfrac{1}{3x}$ **Simplify.**

CHECK Check your simplification using a graphing calculator.

Graph $y_1 = \dfrac{2x^2}{3x} \cdot \dfrac{6x^2}{12x^4}$ and $y_2 = \dfrac{1}{3x}$.

The graphs coincide. So, the expressions are equivalent for all values of x other than 0.

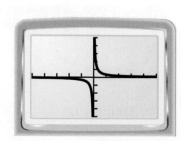

EXAMPLE 2 ♦ **Multiple Choice Practice**

What is the product of $\dfrac{3x^2 + 3x}{4x^2 - 24x + 36}$ and $\dfrac{x^2 - 4x + 3}{x^2 - x}$?

(A) $\dfrac{3x}{x - 3}$ **(B)** $\dfrac{3(x - 1)}{4(x + 3)}$ **(C)** $\dfrac{3(x + 1)}{4(x - 3)}$ **(D)** $\dfrac{x + 1}{x + 3}$

Solution

$\dfrac{3x^2 + 3x}{4x^2 - 24x + 36} \cdot \dfrac{x^2 - 4x + 3}{x^2 - x}$

$= \dfrac{(3x^2 + 3x)(x^2 - 4x + 3)}{(4x^2 - 24x + 36)(x^2 - x)}$ **Multiply numerators and denominators.**

$= \dfrac{3x(x + 1)(x - 3)(x - 1)}{4x(x - 3)(x - 3)(x - 1)}$ **Factor and divide out common factors.**

$= \dfrac{3(x + 1)}{4(x - 3)}$ **Simplify.**

▸ The correct answer is C. Ⓐ Ⓑ ⓒ Ⓓ

MULTIPLYING BY A POLYNOMIAL When you multiply a rational expression by a polynomial, first write the polynomial as a fraction with a denominator of 1.

EXAMPLE 3   **Multiply a rational expression by a polynomial**

Find the product $\dfrac{5x}{x^2 + 5x + 6} \cdot (x + 3)$.

$\dfrac{5x}{x^2 + 5x + 6} \cdot (x + 3)$

$= \dfrac{5x}{x^2 + 5x + 6} \cdot \dfrac{x + 3}{1}$ **Rewrite polynomial as a fraction.**

$= \dfrac{5x(x + 3)}{x^2 + 5x + 6}$ **Multiply numerators and denominators.**

$= \dfrac{5x(x + 3)}{(x + 2)(x + 3)}$ **Factor and divide out common factor.**

$= \dfrac{5x}{x + 2}$ **Simplify.**

✓ **GUIDED PRACTICE**   **for Examples 1, 2, and 3**

Find the product.

1. $\dfrac{2y^3}{5y} \cdot \dfrac{15y^3}{8y^5}$

2. $\dfrac{7z^2}{4z^3} \cdot \dfrac{z^3}{14z}$

3. $\dfrac{x^2 + x - 2}{x^2 + 2x} \cdot \dfrac{2x^2 + 2x}{5x^2 - 15x + 10}$

4. $\dfrac{2w^2}{w^2 - 7w + 12} \cdot (w - 4)$

DIVIDING RATIONAL EXPRESSIONS To divide by a rational expression, multiply by its multiplicative inverse.

EXAMPLE 4   Divide rational expressions involving polynomials

Find the quotient $\dfrac{7x^2 - 7x}{x^2 + 2x - 3} \div \dfrac{x + 1}{x^2 - 7x - 8}$.

$$\dfrac{7x^2 - 7x}{x^2 + 2x - 3} \div \dfrac{x + 1}{x^2 - 7x - 8}$$

$$= \dfrac{7x^2 - 7x}{x^2 + 2x - 3} \cdot \dfrac{x^2 - 7x - 8}{x + 1} \qquad \textbf{Multiply by multiplicative inverse.}$$

$$= \dfrac{(7x^2 - 7x)(x^2 - 7x - 8)}{(x^2 + 2x - 3)(x + 1)} \qquad \textbf{Multiply numerators and denominators.}$$

$$= \dfrac{7x(x - 1)(x - 8)(x + 1)}{(x + 3)(x - 1)(x + 1)} \qquad \textbf{Factor and divide out common factors.}$$

$$= \dfrac{7x(x - 8)}{x + 3} \qquad \textbf{Simplify.}$$

DIVIDING BY A POLYNOMIAL When you divide a rational expression by a polynomial, first write the polynomial as a fraction with a denominator of 1. Then multiply by the multiplicative inverse of the polynomial.

EXAMPLE 5   Divide a rational expression by a polynomial

Animated Algebra

For an interactive example of dividing rational expressions, go to **classzone.com**.

Find the quotient $\dfrac{2x^2 + 16x + 24}{3x^2} \div (x + 6)$.

$$\dfrac{2x^2 + 16x + 24}{3x^2} \div (x + 6)$$

$$= \dfrac{2x^2 + 16x + 24}{3x^2} \div \dfrac{x + 6}{1} \qquad \textbf{Rewrite polynomial as fraction.}$$

$$= \dfrac{2x^2 + 16x + 24}{3x^2} \cdot \dfrac{1}{x + 6} \qquad \textbf{Multiply by multiplicative inverse.}$$

$$= \dfrac{2x^2 + 16x + 24}{3x^2(x + 6)} \qquad \textbf{Multiply numerators and denominators.}$$

$$= \dfrac{2(x + 2)(x + 6)}{3x^2(x + 6)} \qquad \textbf{Factor and divide out common factor.}$$

$$= \dfrac{2(x + 2)}{3x^2} \qquad \textbf{Simplify.}$$

✓ **GUIDED PRACTICE**   for Examples 4 and 5

Find the quotient.

5. $\dfrac{m^2 - 4}{2m^2 + 4m} \div \dfrac{6m - 3m^2}{4m + 44}$

6. $\dfrac{4x}{5x - 20} \div \dfrac{x^2 - 2x}{x^2 - 6x + 8}$

7. $\dfrac{n^2 - 6n + 9}{12n} \div (n - 3)$

8. $\dfrac{2b^2 - 3b - 5}{6b} \div (2b^2 - 5b)$

EXAMPLE 6 Solve a multi-step problem

BASEBALL Hank Aaron's career number B of times at bat and career number H of hits through each year of the period 1954–1976 can be modeled by

$$B = \frac{300 + 700x}{1 + 0.01x} \quad \text{and} \quad H = \frac{62 + 240x}{1 + 0.017x}$$

where x is the number of years since 1954. A baseball player's batting average is the number of hits divided by the number of times at bat.

Hank Aaron

• Write a model that gives Hank Aaron's career batting average A as a function of x.

• Approximate his career batting average in 1959.

Solution

STEP 1 **Write** a verbal model. Then write an equation.

Aaron's career batting average	=	Number of hits	÷	Number of times at bat
A	=	H	÷	B

STEP 2 **Find** the quotient.

$$A = H \div B \qquad \text{Write equation.}$$

$$= \frac{62 + 240x}{1 + 0.017x} \div \frac{300 + 700x}{1 + 0.01x} \qquad \text{Substitute for } H \text{ and } B.$$

$$= \frac{62 + 240x}{1 + 0.017x} \cdot \frac{1 + 0.01x}{300 + 700x} \qquad \text{Multiply by multiplicative inverse.}$$

$$= \frac{(62 + 240x)(1 + 0.01x)}{(1 + 0.017x)(300 + 700x)} \qquad \text{Multiply numerators and denominators.}$$

$$= \frac{\cancel{(2)}(31 + 120x)(1 + 0.01x)}{(1 + 0.017x)\cancel{(2)}(150 + 350x)} \qquad \text{Factor and divide out common factor.}$$

$$= \frac{(31 + 120x)(1 + 0.01x)}{(1 + 0.017x)(150 + 350x)} \qquad \text{Simplify.}$$

STEP 3 **Approximate** Aaron's career batting average in 1959. Substitute 5 for x in the model and use a calculator to evaluate.

$$A = \frac{(31 + 120 \cdot \mathbf{5})(1 + 0.01 \cdot \mathbf{5})}{(1 + 0.017 \cdot \mathbf{5})(150 + 350 \cdot \mathbf{5})} \approx .321$$

▸ According to the model, Hank Aaron's career batting average in 1959 was approximately .321.

✓ **GUIDED PRACTICE** for Example 6

9. In Example 6, find Aaron's approximate career batting average in 1976 (at the end of his career).

11.3 EXERCISES

SKILLS · PROBLEM SOLVING · REASONING

1. **VOCABULARY** Copy and complete: To divide by a rational expression, multiply by its ___?___.

2. **NOTETAKING SKILLS** Make a process diagram like the one on page 678 to compare multiplying numerical fractions and multiplying rational expressions.

EXAMPLES 1, 2, and 3
on pp. 696–697
for Exs. 3–11, 13

MULTIPLYING EXPRESSIONS Find the product.

3. $\dfrac{9p^2}{7} \cdot \dfrac{5}{6p^4}$

4. $\dfrac{5}{8q^6} \cdot \dfrac{4q^5}{3}$

5. $\dfrac{v^2 + v - 12}{5v + 10} \cdot \dfrac{-v - 2}{v^2 + 5v + 4}$

6. $\dfrac{y - 2}{-2y^2 - 10y} \cdot \dfrac{4y^2 + 20y}{y^2 - 4}$

7. $\dfrac{5x}{2x^3 - 17x^2 - 9x} \cdot \dfrac{4x^2 - 20x - 144}{20}$

8. $\dfrac{r^5}{7r^3 + 56r} \cdot (r^2 + 8)$

9. $\dfrac{-3m}{m^2 - 7m + 10} \cdot (m - 5)$

10. $\dfrac{2n - 6}{3n^2 - 7n - 6} \cdot (3n^2 + 14n + 8)$

11. ◆ **MULTIPLE CHOICE** What is the product $\dfrac{x + 2}{4x - 2} \cdot \dfrac{3x - 7}{x - 3}$?

Ⓐ $\dfrac{x^2 - x - 6}{12x^2 - 34x + 14}$
Ⓑ $\dfrac{3x^2 - 14}{4x^2 + 6}$
Ⓒ $\dfrac{3x^2 - 19x - 14}{4x^2 - 11x + 6}$
Ⓓ $\dfrac{3x^2 - x - 14}{4x^2 - 14x + 6}$

EXAMPLES 4 and 5
on p. 698
for Exs. 12, 14–23

ERROR ANALYSIS *Describe* and correct the error in finding the product or quotient.

12. $\dfrac{x^3}{5} \div \dfrac{15x^3}{2}$

$$\dfrac{x^3}{5} \div \dfrac{15x^3}{2} = \dfrac{5}{x^3} \cdot \dfrac{15x^3}{2}$$
$$= \dfrac{75x^3}{2x^3}$$
$$= \dfrac{75}{2}$$

13. $\dfrac{x - 2}{x + 5} \cdot \dfrac{x}{2 - x}$

$$\dfrac{x - 2}{x + 5} \cdot \dfrac{x}{2 - x} = \dfrac{(x - 2)x}{(x + 5)(2 - x)}$$
$$= \dfrac{(x - 2)x}{(x + 5)(2 - x)}$$
$$= \dfrac{x}{x + 5}$$

DIVIDING EXPRESSIONS Find the quotient.

14. $\dfrac{16r^2}{3} \div \dfrac{12}{5r}$

15. $\dfrac{25s^{12}}{18} \div \dfrac{5s^6}{2}$

16. $\dfrac{2w^2 + 5w}{w^2 - 81} \div \dfrac{w^2}{w + 9}$

17. $\dfrac{c^2 + c}{c^2 + c - 30} \div \dfrac{c - 6}{c^2 - 11c + 30}$

18. $\dfrac{a^2 + 3a - 10}{a^2 + 6a - 7} \div \dfrac{9a^3 - 18a^2}{3a^2 + 18a - 21}$

19. $\dfrac{2x^2 - 9x + 9}{35x + 14} \div \dfrac{-3x^2 + 13x - 12}{15x^2 - 14x - 8}$

20. $\dfrac{4k^2 + 4k - 15}{2k - 3} \div (2k + 5)$

21. $\dfrac{t^2 - 9t - 22}{5t - 1} \div (5t^2 + 9t - 2)$

22. ◆ **MULTIPLE CHOICE** What common factor do you divide out when finding

the quotient $\dfrac{x^2 - 3x + 2}{x^2 - 2x - 3} \div \dfrac{x^2 + 4x + 3}{x^2 - 7x + 12}$?

   (A) $x - 1$ **(B)** $x - 3$ **(C)** $x + 1$ **(D)** $x + 3$

23. ◆ **MULTIPLE CHOICE** What is the quotient $\dfrac{x^2 - 1}{-(x + 1)} \div (x - 1)$?

   (A) -1 **(B)** 0 **(C)** 1 **(D)** $x^2 - 1$

REASONING Let a, b, c, and d be different polynomials. Find two rational expressions $\dfrac{a}{b}$ and $\dfrac{c}{d}$ that satisfy the given conditions.

24. The product of the rational expressions is $\dfrac{x - 3}{x + 2}$, and the excluded values are -2, -1, 4, and 5.

25. The quotient of the rational expressions is $\dfrac{x - 6}{x + 4}$, and the excluded values are -4, -2, 3, and 6.

⬡ GEOMETRY Write an expression for the area of the figure. Find a value of x less than 5 for which the given dimensions and the area are positive.

26. Rectangle

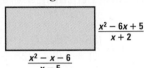

$\dfrac{x^2 - 6x + 5}{x + 2}$

$\dfrac{x^2 - x - 6}{x - 5}$

27. Triangle

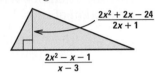

$\dfrac{2x^2 + 2x - 24}{2x + 1}$

$\dfrac{2x^2 - x - 1}{x - 3}$

CONNECT SKILLS TO PROBLEM SOLVING Exercises 28–30 will help you prepare for problem solving.

Use the following information: The total cost T (in millions of dollars) of a construction project for a city and its population P (in thousands of people), where x is the number of years since 2000, can be modeled by

$$T = \dfrac{49 + 14x}{1 - 0.05x} \quad \text{and} \quad P = 630 + 7x$$

28. Which equation gives the cost per person C of the project in terms of T and P: $C = T \cdot P$, $C = T \div P$, or $C = P \div T$? *Explain* your reasoning.

29. Use your answer from Exercise 28 to write C as a function of x.

30. What are the units associated with the values of C?

EXAMPLE 6
on p. 699
for Exs. 31–33

31. VEHICLES The total distance M (in billions of miles) traveled by all motor vehicles and the distance T (in billions of miles) traveled by trucks in the United States during the period 1980–2002 can be modeled by

$$M = 1500 + 63x \quad \text{and} \quad T = \dfrac{100 + 2.2x}{1 - 0.014x}$$

where x is the number of years since 1980. Write a model that gives the percent p (in decimal form) of the total motor vehicle distance that was traveled by trucks as a function of x. Then approximate the percent traveled by trucks in 2002.

U.S. vehicles now travel over 3 trillion miles annually.

California @HomeTutor for problem solving help at classzone.com

32. CONSUMER SPENDING The average annual amount T (in dollars) spent on reading and entertainment and the average annual amount E (in dollars) spent only on entertainment by consumers in the United States during the period 1985–2002 can be modeled by the functions

$$T = \frac{1300 + 84x}{1 + 0.015x} \qquad \text{and} \qquad E = \frac{1100 + 64x}{1 + 0.0062x}$$

where x is the number of years since 1985. Let p be the percent (in decimal form) of the amount spent on reading and entertainment that was spent only on entertainment. Write a model that gives p as a function of x. Then approximate the percent spent on entertainment in 2000.

California @HomeTutor for problem solving help at classzone.com

33. ◆ MULTIPLE CHOICE Football player Emmitt Smith's career number Y of rushing yards gained and his career number A of rushing attempts for the 1990–2002 football seasons can be modeled by the functions

$$Y = \frac{860 + 1800x}{1 + 0.024x} \qquad \text{and} \qquad A = \frac{230 + 380x}{1 + 0.014x}$$

where x is the number of years since 1990. A football player's rushing average is the number of rushing yards gained divided by the number of rushing attempts. Which model gives Smith's career rushing average R as a function of x for the period 1990–2002?

(A) $R = \dfrac{(1 + 0.024x)(23 + 38x)}{(86 + 180x)(1 + 0.014x)}$ 　　　 **(B)** $R = \dfrac{(86 + 180x)(1 + 0.014x)}{(1 + 0.024x)(23 + 38x)}$

(C) $R = \dfrac{(86 + 180x)(1 + 0.024x)}{(1 + 0.014x)(23 + 38x)}$ 　　　 **(D)** $R = \dfrac{(860 + 180x)(1 + 0.014x)}{(1 + 0.024x)(230 + 38x)}$

34. MULTI-STEP PROBLEM The gross revenue R (in millions of dollars) from movie tickets sold and the average movie ticket price P (in dollars) in the United States during the period 1991–2002 can be modeled by the functions

$$R = \frac{4700 - 74x}{1 - 0.053x} \qquad \text{and} \qquad P = 0.015x^2 + 4.1$$

where x is the number of years since 1991.

Average movie ticket price in 1993: $4.14

a. Model Write a model that gives the number T of movie tickets sold (in millions) as a function of x.

b. Describe Graph the model on a graphing calculator and describe how the number of tickets sold changed over time. Can you use the graph to describe how the gross revenue and ticket prices changed over time? *Explain* your reasoning.

35. ADVERTISING The amount A (in millions of dollars) spent on advertising and the amount T (in millions of dollars) spent on television advertising in the United States during the period 1970–2003 can be modeled by

$$A = \frac{13{,}000 + 3700x}{1 - 0.015x} \qquad \text{and} \qquad T = \frac{1800 + 860x}{1 - 0.016x}$$

where x is the number of years since 1970. Let p be the percent (in decimal form) of the amount spent on all advertising that was spent on television advertising. Write a model that gives p as a function of x. Then approximate the percent spent on television advertising in 2003.

 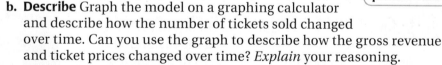 **◆ = MULTIPLE CHOICE PRACTICE** 　　　 **○ = HINTS AND HOMEWORK HELP** at classzone.com

CHALLENGE Let a be a polynomial in the given equation. Find a.

36. $\dfrac{a}{x+2} \cdot \dfrac{3x^2 + 5x - 2}{x - 4} = 6x^2 + 7x - 3$

37. $\dfrac{8x^2 - 2x - 3}{x - 5} \div \dfrac{2x + 1}{a} = 12x^2 - x - 6$

38. CHALLENGE The total amount F (in billions of dollars) spent on food other than groceries and the amount E (in billions of dollars) spent at restaurants in the United States during the period 1977–2003 can be modeled by the functions

$$F = \dfrac{88 + 9.2x}{1 - 0.0097x} \qquad \text{and} \qquad E = \dfrac{54 + 6.5x}{1 - 0.012x}$$

where x is the number of years since 1977. Let p be the percent (in decimal form) of the amount spent on food other than groceries that was spent at restaurants. Write a model that gives p as a function of x. Approximate the percent that was spent at locations *other* than restaurants in 2002.

◆ CALIFORNIA STANDARDS SPIRAL REVIEW

Alg. 2.0

39. What is the approximate value of $\sqrt{37}$? *(p. 95)*

(A) 3   **(B)** 4   **(C)** 5   **(D)** 6

Alg. 5.0

40. What is the solution of $2(3x + 6) - 4 = 12$? *(p. 139)*

(A) $\dfrac{2}{3}$ **(B)** 2   **(C)** 3   **(D)** 6

Alg. 12.0

41. The total number A of airports and the number P of private airports in the United States during the period 1989–2002 can be modeled by $A = 0.18x^3 + 140x + 17{,}000$ and $P = 0.16x^3 + 120x + 12{,}000$ where x is the number of years since 1989. Which model (in simplest form) gives the percent p of airports that were private airports as a function of x? *(p. 688)*

(A) $p = \dfrac{8x^3 + 6000x + 600{,}000}{9x^3 + 7000x + 850{,}000}$

(B) $p = \dfrac{9x^3 + 7000x + 850{,}000}{8x^3 + 6000x + 600{,}000}$

(C) $p = \dfrac{16x^3 + 120x + 12{,}000}{18x^3 + 140x + 17{,}000}$

(D) $p = \dfrac{18x^3 + 140x + 17{,}000}{16x^3 + 120x + 12{,}000}$

QUIZ *for Lessons 11.1–11.3*

Tell whether the equation represents *direct variation*, *inverse variation*, or *neither*. *(p. 680)*

1. $\dfrac{1}{5}xy = 1$ **2.** $y = -9x$ **3.** $5x + y = 3$

Simplify the rational expression, if possible. State the excluded values.
(p. 688)

4. $\dfrac{w + 10}{w^2 - 100}$ **5.** $\dfrac{250x^3}{14x}$ **6.** $\dfrac{y + 7}{y - 7}$ **7.** $\dfrac{z^2 - 4z - 45}{3z^2 + 25z + 50}$

Find the product or quotient. *(p. 696)*

8. $\dfrac{5}{8x^2} \cdot \dfrac{4x^3}{15}$ **9.** $\dfrac{3y^2 + 6y}{y^2 - 16} \div \dfrac{y^2}{y - 4}$ **10.** $\dfrac{m^2}{(n+1)^4} \div \dfrac{m^5}{(n+1)^6}$ **11.** $\dfrac{2x - 1}{x + 3} \cdot \dfrac{(x + 3)^2}{x - 4}$

Multiple Choice Practice for Lessons 11.1–11.3

1. For the period 1991–2002, the average total revenue T (in dollars per admission) that a movie theater earned and the average revenue C (in dollars per admission) earned from concessions in the United States can be modeled by the functions

$$T = \frac{0.018x^2 + 5.4}{1 - 0.001x^2} \text{ and } C = \frac{0.013x^2 + 1.1}{0.001x^2 + 1}$$

where x is the number of years since 1991. Which model gives the percent p (in decimal form) of the average total revenue per admission that came from concessions as a function of x? **Alg. 13.0**

(A) $p = \dfrac{(0.013x^2 + 1.1)(1 - 0.001x^2)}{(0.001x^2 + 1)(0.018x^2 + 5.4)}$

(B) $p = \dfrac{(0.001x^2 + 1)(0.018x^2 + 5.4)}{(0.013x^2 + 1.1)(1 - 0.001x^2)}$

(C) $p = \dfrac{(0.013x^2 + 1.1)(0.018x^2 + 5.4)}{(0.001x^2 + 1)(1 - 0.001x^2)}$

(D) $p = \dfrac{0.001x^2 + 1}{1 - 0.001x^2}$

2. What is the simplified form of $\dfrac{4 - x^2}{x^2 - x - 2}$? **Alg. 12.0**

(A) $-\dfrac{x + 2}{x + 1}$

(B) $\dfrac{x + 1}{x + 2}$

(C) $-x - 2$

(D) $\dfrac{x + 2}{x + 1}$

3. The average amount A (in pounds per person) of fish and shellfish consumed in the United States during the period 1992–2001 can be modeled by the function

$$A = \frac{52x + 3800}{3.2x + 260}$$

where x is the number of years since 1992. What is the simplified form of this model? **Alg. 12.0**

(A) $A = \dfrac{65x + 4750}{4x + 325}$

(B) $A = \dfrac{52x + 38,000}{32x + 2600}$

(C) $A = \dfrac{x + 750}{2x + 35}$

(D) $A = \dfrac{650x + 47,500}{40x + 3250}$

4. The table shows the inverse relationship between the time t (in hours) it takes p people to stuff all of the envelopes for a promotion. How much time do 25 people take to stuff all of the envelopes? **Alg. 15.0**

People, p	Time, t (hours)
1	20
4	5
8	2.5
16	1.25
50	0.4

(A) 0.6 h (B) 0.8 h

(C) 1 h (D) 1.25 h

5. What is the quotient of $\dfrac{y - 12}{2y + 3}$ and $y^2 - 14y + 24$? **Alg. 13.0**

(A) $\dfrac{2y + 3}{y - 2}$

(B) $(2y + 3)(y - 2)$

(C) $2y + 3$

(D) $\dfrac{1}{(2y + 3)(y - 2)}$

6. A bookseller uses shipping cartons in the shape of rectangular prisms. The cartons have the same size base but vary in height.

What is a rational function that gives the ratio r of the surface area to volume as a function of the height h? **Alg. 12.0**

(A) $r = \dfrac{1248 + 100h}{156h}$

(B) $r = \dfrac{312 + 25h}{156h}$

(C) $r = \dfrac{312 + 25h}{312h}$

(D) $r = \dfrac{312 + 25h}{624h}$

11.4 Add and Subtract Rational Expressions

Standards Alg. 13.0 Students add, subtract, multiply, and divide **rational expressions and functions. Students solve both computationally and conceptually challenging problems by using these techniques.**

Connect *Before* you multiplied and divided rational expressions. *Now* you will add and subtract rational expressions.

Math and **RECREATION**
Ex. 48, p. 711

Key Vocabulary
• least common denominator (LCD) of rational expressions

Adding and subtracting rational expressions with the same denominator is similar to adding and subtracting numerical fractions with the same denominator.

KEY CONCEPT
For Your Notebook

Adding and Subtracting Rational Expressions with the Same Denominator

Let a, b, and c be polynomials where $c \neq 0$.

Algebra $\dfrac{a}{c} + \dfrac{b}{c} = \dfrac{a+b}{c}$ $\qquad \dfrac{a}{c} - \dfrac{b}{c} = \dfrac{a-b}{c}$

Examples $\dfrac{2}{x} + \dfrac{3}{x} = \dfrac{2+3}{x} = \dfrac{5}{x}$ $\qquad \dfrac{5}{4x} - \dfrac{2}{4x} = \dfrac{5-2}{4x} = \dfrac{3}{4x}$

EXAMPLE 1 Add and subtract with the same denominator

a. $\dfrac{5}{3x} + \dfrac{7}{3x} = \dfrac{12}{3x}$ Add numerators.

$= \dfrac{\cancel{3} \cdot 4}{\cancel{3} \cdot x}$ Factor and divide out common factor.

$= \dfrac{4}{x}$ Simplify.

b. $\dfrac{3x}{x-1} - \dfrac{x+5}{x-1} = \dfrac{3x-(x+5)}{x-1}$ Subtract numerators.

$= \dfrac{2x-5}{x-1}$ Simplify.

 GUIDED PRACTICE for Example 1

Find the sum or difference.

1. $\dfrac{2}{y} + \dfrac{y+1}{y}$

2. $\dfrac{4x+1}{2x-1} - \dfrac{2x-3}{2x-1}$

REVIEW LEAST COMMON MULTIPLE
For help with finding least common multiples of numbers, see p. 785.

LEAST COMMON DENOMINATOR The **least common denominator (LCD)** of two or more rational expressions is the same as the least common multiple of the denominators of the rational expressions.

EXAMPLE 2   **Find the LCD of rational expressions**

Find the LCD of the rational expressions.

a. $\dfrac{1}{4r}, \dfrac{r+3}{10r^2}$ **b.** $\dfrac{5}{(x-3)^2}, \dfrac{3x+4}{x^2-x-6}$ **c.** $\dfrac{3}{c-2}, \dfrac{c+8}{2c+7}$

Solution

a. Find the least common multiple (LCM) of $4r$ and $10r^2$.

$4r = 2^2 \cdot r$

$10r^2 = 2 \cdot 5 \cdot r^2$

$\text{LCM} = 2^2 \cdot 5 \cdot r^2 = 20r^2$

▶ The LCD of $\dfrac{1}{4r}$ and $\dfrac{r+3}{10r^2}$ is $20r^2$.

b. Find the least common multiple (LCM) of $(x-3)^2$ and x^2-x-6.

$(x-3)^2 = (x-3)^2$

$x^2-x-6 = (x-3) \cdot (x+2)$

$\text{LCM} = (x-3)^2(x+2)$

▶ The LCD of $\dfrac{5}{(x-3)^2}$ and $\dfrac{3x+4}{x^2-x-6}$ is $(x-3)^2(x+2)$.

c. Find the least common multiple of $c-2$ and $2c+7$.

Because $c-2$ and $2c+7$ cannot be factored, they don't have any factors in common. The least common multiple is their product, $(c-2)(2c+7)$.

▶ The LCD of $\dfrac{3}{c-2}$ and $\dfrac{c+8}{2c+7}$ is $(c-2)(2c+7)$.

✓ **GUIDED PRACTICE**   for Example 2

Find the LCD of the rational expressions.

3. $\dfrac{1}{28m}, \dfrac{m+1}{7m^3}$ **4.** $\dfrac{2}{x^2+4x-5}, \dfrac{x^2+2}{x^2+7x+10}$ **5.** $\dfrac{5a}{a+3}, \dfrac{a+6}{a-4}$

DIFFERENT DENOMINATORS To add or subtract rational expressions that have different denominators, use the LCD to write equivalent rational expressions that have the same denominator just as you would for numerical fractions. In the example below, $12x^2$ is the LCD.

WRITE EQUIVALENT EXPRESSIONS
To write an equivalent rational expression, multiply by a fraction that is equal to 1, such as $\dfrac{3x}{3x}$.

$$\dfrac{5}{4x} + \dfrac{11}{6x^2} = \dfrac{5 \cdot 3x}{4x \cdot 3x} + \dfrac{11 \cdot 2}{6x^2 \cdot 2} = \dfrac{15x}{12x^2} + \dfrac{22}{12x^2}$$

Multiply by 3x to get $12x^2$.   **Multiply by 2 to get $12x^2$.**

EXAMPLE 3 Add expressions with different denominators

Find the sum $\dfrac{9}{8x^2} + \dfrac{5}{12x^3}$.

$$\dfrac{9}{8x^2} + \dfrac{5}{12x^3} = \dfrac{9 \cdot 3x}{8x^2 \cdot 3x} + \dfrac{5 \cdot 2}{12x^3 \cdot 2}$$ Rewrite fractions using LCD, $24x^3$.

$$= \dfrac{27x}{24x^3} + \dfrac{10}{24x^3}$$ Simplify numerators and denominators.

$$= \dfrac{27x + 10}{24x^3}$$ Add fractions.

EXAMPLE 4 Subtract expressions with different denominators

Find the difference $\dfrac{10}{3x} - \dfrac{7x}{x + 2}$.

$$\dfrac{10}{3x} - \dfrac{7x}{x + 2} = \dfrac{10(x + 2)}{3x(x + 2)} - \dfrac{7x(3x)}{(x + 2)(3x)}$$ Rewrite fractions using LCD, $3x(x + 2)$.

$$= \dfrac{10(x + 2) - 7x(3x)}{3x(x + 2)}$$ Subtract fractions.

$$= \dfrac{-21x^2 + 10x + 20}{3x(x + 2)}$$ Simplify numerator.

EXAMPLE 5 Subtract expressions with different denominators

Animated Algebra

For an interactive example of adding and subtracting rational expressions, go to **classzone.com**.

Find the difference $\dfrac{x + 4}{x^2 + 3x - 10} - \dfrac{x - 1}{x^2 + 2x - 8}$.

$$\dfrac{x + 4}{x^2 + 3x - 10} - \dfrac{x - 1}{x^2 + 2x - 8}$$

$$= \dfrac{x + 4}{(x - 2)(x + 5)} - \dfrac{x - 1}{(x + 4)(x - 2)}$$ Factor denominators.

$$= \dfrac{(x + 4)(x + 4)}{(x - 2)(x + 5)(x + 4)} - \dfrac{(x - 1)(x + 5)}{(x + 4)(x - 2)(x + 5)}$$ Rewrite fractions using LCD, $(x - 2)(x + 5)(x + 4)$.

$$= \dfrac{(x + 4)(x + 4) - (x - 1)(x + 5)}{(x - 2)(x + 5)(x + 4)}$$ Subtract fractions.

$$= \dfrac{x^2 + 8x + 16 - (x^2 + 4x - 5)}{(x - 2)(x + 5)(x + 4)}$$ Find products in numerator.

$$= \dfrac{4x + 21}{(x - 2)(x + 5)(x + 4)}$$ Simplify.

AVOID ERRORS
Because you are subtracting $x^2 + 4x - 5$ in the numerator, you need to add the opposite of *every* term in $x^2 + 4x - 5$.

✓ **GUIDED PRACTICE** for Examples 3, 4, and 5

Find the sum or difference.

6. $\dfrac{3}{2x} + \dfrac{7}{5x^4}$

7. $\dfrac{y}{y + 1} + \dfrac{3}{y + 2}$

8. $\dfrac{2z - 1}{z^2 + 2z - 8} - \dfrac{z + 1}{z^2 - 4}$

EXAMPLE 6 Solve a rate problem

BOAT TRAVEL A boat travels 24 kilometers upstream (against the current) and 24 kilometers downstream (with the current) as shown in the diagram. Write an equation that gives the total travel time t (in hours) as a function of the boat's average speed r (in kilometers per hour) in still water. Find the total travel time if the boat's average speed in still water is 10 kilometers per hour.

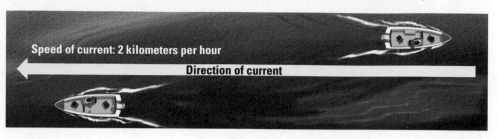

Speed of current: 2 kilometers per hour

Direction of current

Solution

STEP 1 **Write** a verbal model. Then write an equation.

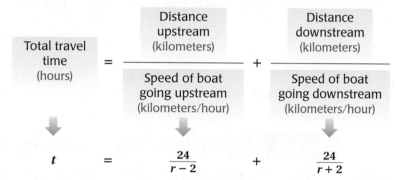

Total travel time (hours)	=	Distance upstream (kilometers)	+	Distance downstream (kilometers)
		Speed of boat going upstream (kilometers/hour)		Speed of boat going downstream (kilometers/hour)

$$t \quad = \quad \frac{24}{r-2} \quad + \quad \frac{24}{r+2}$$

COMBINE SPEEDS

When you go upstream, you subtract the speed of the current from the speed at which you travel in still water. When you go downstream, you add the speeds.

STEP 2 **Combine** the expressions on the right side of the equation.

$t = \dfrac{24}{r-2} + \dfrac{24}{r+2}$ **Write equation.**

$= \dfrac{24(r+2)}{(r-2)(r+2)} + \dfrac{24(r-2)}{(r+2)(r-2)}$ **Rewrite fractions using LCD, $(r-2)(r+2)$.**

$= \dfrac{24(r+2) + 24(r-2)}{(r-2)(r+2)}$ **Add fractions.**

$= \dfrac{48r}{(r-2)(r+2)}$ **Simplify.**

STEP 3 **Find** the value of t when $r = 10$.

$$t = \frac{48(10)}{(10-2)(10+2)} = \frac{480}{(8)(12)} = \frac{480}{96} = 5$$

▶ The total travel time is 5 hours.

✓ **GUIDED PRACTICE** **for Example 6**

9. **WHAT IF?** In Example 6, suppose the speed of the current is 3 kilometers per hour. Find the total travel time.

11.4 EXERCISES

HOMEWORK KEY

◆ = **MULTIPLE CHOICE PRACTICE**
Exs. 12, 22, 37, 52, and 56–58

○ = **HINTS AND HOMEWORK HELP**
for Exs. 7, 29, and 49 at classzone.com

SKILLS · PROBLEM SOLVING · REASONING

1. **VOCABULARY** Copy and complete: The __?__ of two rational expressions is the same as the least common multiple of the denominators of the rational expressions.

2. **WRITING** *Describe* your steps in rewriting the expressions $\dfrac{1}{x+2}$ and $\dfrac{2x}{x^2-4}$ so that they have the same denominator.

EXAMPLE 1
on p. 705
for Exs. 3–12

ADDING AND SUBTRACTING EXPRESSIONS Find the sum or difference.

3. $\dfrac{2}{5x} + \dfrac{3}{5x}$

4. $\dfrac{y+1}{2y} + \dfrac{5}{2y}$

5. $\dfrac{6z}{z^2} - \dfrac{2z}{z^2}$

6. $\dfrac{7}{a+2} - \dfrac{3a}{a+2}$

7. $\dfrac{b}{b-3} + \dfrac{b+1}{b-3}$

8. $\dfrac{c+2}{c-9} + \dfrac{c+5}{c-9}$

9. $\dfrac{7}{m^2+1} - \dfrac{8}{m^2+1}$

10. $\dfrac{2n+1}{n^2-16} - \dfrac{n}{n^2-16}$

11. $\dfrac{3r}{r^2+r-7} + \dfrac{1}{r^2+r-7}$

12. ◆ **MULTIPLE CHOICE** What is the difference of $\dfrac{x+2}{x^2+5}$ and $\dfrac{3x+2}{x^2+5}$?

Ⓐ $\dfrac{2x}{x^2+5}$

Ⓑ $-\dfrac{4x+4}{x^2+5}$

Ⓒ $-\dfrac{2x}{x^2+5}$

Ⓓ $\dfrac{4x-4}{x^2+5}$

EXAMPLE 2
on p. 706
for Exs. 13–22

FINDING THE LCD Find the LCD of the rational expressions.

13. $\dfrac{1}{24x}, \dfrac{x+2}{6x^3}$

14. $\dfrac{3}{15v^2}, \dfrac{v^2-4}{20v^3}$

15. $\dfrac{4w}{w+5}, \dfrac{w+3}{w-2}$

16. $\dfrac{s-1}{s+2}, \dfrac{s+2}{s-1}$

17. $\dfrac{1}{t^2-4t}, \dfrac{6}{t^2-2t-8}$

18. $\dfrac{u+9}{u^2+8u+7}, \dfrac{-3}{u^2-2u-3}$

19. $\dfrac{x-1}{x-2}, \dfrac{x-3}{x-4}$

20. $\dfrac{x+1}{15x}, \dfrac{25}{18x^3}$

21. $\dfrac{3}{12m^3}, \dfrac{m+1}{4m^3}$

22. ◆ **MULTIPLE CHOICE** What is the LCD of $\dfrac{3}{x^2-4x}$ and $\dfrac{4x}{x+2}$?

Ⓐ 1

Ⓑ $3(x+2)$

Ⓒ $4x^2(x-4)$

Ⓓ $x(x+2)(x-4)$

EXAMPLES 3, 4, and 5
on p. 707
for Exs. 23–24

ERROR ANALYSIS *Describe* and correct the error in finding the sum or difference.

23. $\dfrac{8}{2x+3} - \dfrac{4x}{x+2}$

$$\dfrac{8}{2x+3} - \dfrac{4x}{x+2} = \dfrac{8-4x}{2x+3-(x+2)}$$
$$= \dfrac{8-4x}{2x+3-x-2}$$
$$= \dfrac{8-4x}{x+1}$$

24. $\dfrac{5x}{x-4} + \dfrac{2}{x+3}$

$$\dfrac{5x}{x-4} + \dfrac{2}{x+3} = \dfrac{5x(x-4) + 2(x+3)}{(x-4)(x+3)}$$
$$= \dfrac{5x^2 - 20x + 2x + 6}{(x-4)(x+3)}$$
$$= \dfrac{5x^2 - 18x + 6}{(x-4)(x+3)}$$

ADDING AND SUBTRACTING EXPRESSIONS Find the sum or difference.

25. $\dfrac{5x}{4} + \dfrac{2}{5x}$

26. $\dfrac{13}{3y} + \dfrac{2}{11y}$

27. $\dfrac{7}{2z} - \dfrac{2}{3z^2}$

28. $\dfrac{7r}{r-2} - \dfrac{2r}{r-3}$

29. $\dfrac{s}{5s-2} - \dfrac{1}{4s+1}$

30. $\dfrac{c+3}{c-6} + \dfrac{c}{3c+10}$

31. $\dfrac{d-5}{d+7} + \dfrac{d-5}{4d}$

32. $\dfrac{f+3}{7f} - \dfrac{3f}{f+4}$

33. $\dfrac{1}{g^2+5g+6} - \dfrac{1}{g^2-4}$

34. $\dfrac{2j}{j^2-1} + \dfrac{j-1}{j^2-7j+6}$

35. $\dfrac{k+7}{k^2+6k+9} + \dfrac{k-5}{k^2-5k-24}$

36. $\dfrac{v+2}{2v^2-v-15} - \dfrac{v-2}{v^2+2v-15}$

37. ◆ **MULTIPLE CHOICE** What is the sum of $\dfrac{11}{6x}$ and $\dfrac{2}{13x}$?

Ⓐ $\dfrac{9}{7x}$ Ⓑ $\dfrac{13}{19x}$ Ⓒ $\dfrac{155}{78x}$ Ⓓ $\dfrac{13}{26x}$

38. ⊘ **GEOMETRY** The height h of a rectangular prism is given by

$$h = \frac{S}{2(\ell+w)} - \frac{\ell w}{\ell+w}$$

where S is the surface area, ℓ is the length, and w is the width. Find the difference of the expressions on the right side of the equation.

39. **REASONING** One polynomial has degree m and another degree n. What is the maximum degree of the LCM of the two polynomials? What is the minimum degree of the LCM of the two polynomials? *Explain.*

USING ORDER OF OPERATIONS Use the order of operations to write the expression as a single rational expression.

40. $2\left(\dfrac{x}{x+1}\right) - 3\left(\dfrac{x-4}{x+2}\right)$

41. $5\left(\dfrac{3x}{x-2} + \dfrac{4}{x^2+6x-16}\right)$

42. $\dfrac{x-3}{x^2+9x+20} + \dfrac{5x}{x+2} \cdot \dfrac{12}{x+4}$

43. $\dfrac{x+5}{x-9} - \dfrac{3x^2+2x-1}{x+4} \div \dfrac{x^2-3x-4}{x^2-16}$

CONNECT SKILLS TO PROBLEM SOLVING Exercises 44–46 will help you prepare for problem solving.

Use the following information: A smallmouth bass swims 440 centimeters upstream (against the current) and downstream (with the current). Let r equal the swimming rate of the bass in centimeters per second. The rate of the current is 55 centimeters per second.

44. Write an expression for the rate of the bass while swimming upsteam and an expression for the rate of the bass while swimming downstream.

45. Write an expression for the time the bass took to swim upsteam and an expression for the time the bass took to swim downstream.

46. Use the expressions from Exercises 44 and 45 to write an expression for the total time the bass takes to swim upstream and downstream.

47. **DRIVING** Matt drives 200 miles to another city. On the drive back home, his average speed decreases by 5 miles per hour. Write an equation that gives the total driving time t (in hours) as a function of his average speed r (in miles per hour) when driving to the city. Then find the total driving time if he drives to the city at an average speed of 50 miles per hour.

California **@HomeTutor**   for problem solving help at classzone.com

EXAMPLE 6
....
on p. 708
for Exs. 48–51

48. CANOEING A canoeist on Big River near Mendocino, California, travels 16 miles upstream (against the current) and back downstream (with the current). The speed of the current is 1 mile per hour. Write an equation that gives the total travel time t (in hours) as a function of the canoeist's average speed r (in miles per hour) in still water. Then find the total travel time if the canoeist's average speed in still water is 6 miles per hour.

California @HomeTutor for problem solving help at classzone.com

(49.) BIOLOGY A bumblebee flies 500 meters to a flower bed against a wind with a constant speed of 6 meters per second. It then flies back to its hive with the wind. Write an equation that gives the total travel time t (in seconds) as a function of its average speed r (in meters per second). Then find the total flight time if its average speed is 24 meters per second.

50. MULTI-STEP PROBLEM An airplane makes a round trip between two destinations as shown in the diagram. The airplane flies against the wind when traveling west and flies with the wind when traveling east. Assume that the speed of the wind remains constant during each flight.

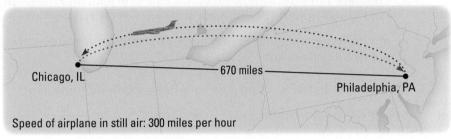

Chicago, IL ———— 670 miles ———— Philadelphia, PA

Speed of airplane in still air: 300 miles per hour

a. Model Write an equation that gives the total flying time t (in hours) as a function of the speed w (in miles per hour) of the wind. Then find the total flying time if the speed of the wind is 15 miles per hour.

b. Decide For what value of w does the flying time one way take half as long as the total flying time? *Explain* your reasoning.

51. ELEVATORS According to California state law, the minimum weight W (in pounds) that a passenger elevator must hold is given by

$$W = \frac{2A^2}{3} + \frac{200A}{3} \text{ if } A \le 50 \qquad \text{and} \qquad W = \frac{7A^2}{150} + (125A - 1367) \text{ if } A > 50$$

where A represents the area (in square feet) of the floor of the elevator.

a. Write the right side of each equation as a single rational expression.

b. What is the minimum weight that an elevator must hold if the area of the floor of the elevator is 30 square feet? 60 square feet?

52. ◆ MULTIPLE CHOICE Radio stations use either amplitude modulation (AM) broadcasting or frequency modulation (FM) broadcasting. The percent a (in decimal form) of commercial AM radio stations during the period 1990–2003 can be modeled by

$$a = \frac{2.8 + 0.085x}{5.3 + 0.30x}$$

where x is the number of years since 1990. Which model gives the percent f (in decimal form) of commercial FM radio stations as a function of x?

(A) $f = \frac{2 + 0.15x}{5.3 + 0.30x}$ **(B)** $f = \frac{2.5 + 0.215x}{5.3 + 0.30x}$ **(C)** $f = \frac{2.9 + 0.025x}{5.3 + 0.30x}$ **(D)** $f = \frac{2.1 + 0.815x}{5.3 + 0.30x}$

53. MULTI-STEP PROBLEM The axle load for a tow vehicle is the weight (in pounds) that an axle on the vehicle supports. The rear axle load R and the front axle load F are given by the formulas

$$R = \frac{t(w + h)}{w} \quad \text{and} \quad F = \frac{th}{w}$$

where t represents the weight (in pounds) that presses down on the hitch by a trailer and w and h represent the distances (in feet) shown.

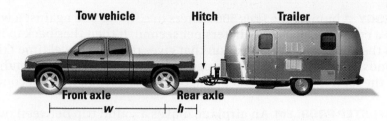

a. Calculate For a certain tow vehicle, $t = 300$, $w = 9$, and $h = 3.5$. Find the rear axle load and the front axle load.

b. Compare Find the difference of the rear axle load and the front axle load found in part (a). *Compare* your answer with the given value of t.

c. Model Write an equation that gives t in terms of R and F. *Justify* your answer algebraically.

54. CHALLENGE Let a, b, c, and d be first-degree polynomials. Find two rational expressions $\frac{a}{b}$ and $\frac{c}{d}$ such that $\frac{a}{b} - \frac{c}{d} = \frac{5x + 7}{(x + 2)(x + 3)}$.

55. CHALLENGE A parallel electric circuit with three resistors and a power source is shown at the right. For a parallel circuit with three resistors, let r_1 represent the resistance (in ohms) of one resistor, let r_2 represent the resistance (in ohms) of a second resistor, and let r_3 represent the resistance (in ohms) of a third resistor. The total resistance r_T is equal to the multiplicative inverse of $\frac{1}{r_1} + \frac{1}{r_2} + \frac{1}{r_3}$. Write $\frac{1}{r_1} + \frac{1}{r_2} + \frac{1}{r_3}$ as a single rational expression. Then write an equation that gives r_T in terms of r_1, r_2, and r_3.

◆ CALIFORNIA STANDARDS SPIRAL REVIEW

Alg. 13.0

56. What is the product of $\frac{5 - 2x}{6}$ and $\frac{24}{10 - 4x}$? *(p. 696)*

  (A) 2 **(B)** $\frac{36x}{60 - x}$ **(C)** $\frac{60 - 12x}{-4x}$ **(D)** $5 - 2x$

Alg. 20.0

57. What are the roots of the polynomial $2x^2 + x - 10$? *(p. 566)*

  (A) $-\frac{5}{2}, 2$ **(B)** $2, 4$ **(C)** $\frac{1}{3}, 3$ **(D)** $3, 7$

Alg. 23.0

58. An athlete kicks a football upward from the ground with an initial vertical velocity of 64 feet per second. After how many seconds does the ball land on the ground? *(p. 549)*

  (A) 2 sec   **(B)** 3 sec   **(C)** 4 sec   **(D)** 5 sec

11.5 Solve Rational Equations

Math and SPORTS
Ex. 31, p. 717

Standards Alg. 13.0 Students add, subtract, multiply, and divide rational expressions and functions. Students solve both computationally and conceptually challenging problems by using these techniques.

Connect *Before* you used rational expressions. *Now* you will solve rational equations.

Key Vocabulary
- rational equation
- extraneous solution
- cross product, *p. 161*
- least common denominator (LCD) of rational expressions, *p. 705*

A **rational equation** is an equation that contains one or more rational expressions. When both sides of the equation are single rational expressions, you can solve the equation by using the cross products property.

EXAMPLE 1 Use the cross products property

Solve $\dfrac{6}{x+4} = \dfrac{x}{2}$. Check your solution.

REVIEW CROSS PRODUCTS
For help with using the cross products property, see p. 161.

$\dfrac{6}{x+4} = \dfrac{x}{2}$	Write original equation.
$12 = x^2 + 4x$	Cross products property
$0 = x^2 + 4x - 12$	Subtract 12 from each side.
$0 = (x+6)(x-2)$	Factor polynomial.
$x + 6 = 0 \quad or \ x - 2 = 0$	Zero-product property
$x = -6 \ or \quad x = 2$	Solve for x.

▸ The solutions are -6 and 2.

CHECK If $x = -6$: If $x = 2$:

$$\dfrac{6}{-6+4} \stackrel{?}{=} \dfrac{-6}{2} \qquad \dfrac{6}{2+4} \stackrel{?}{=} \dfrac{2}{2}$$

$$-3 = -3 \checkmark \qquad\qquad 1 = 1 \checkmark$$

✓ **GUIDED PRACTICE** for Example 1

Solve the equation. Check your solution.

1. $\dfrac{5}{y-2} = \dfrac{y}{3}$

2. $\dfrac{2}{z+5} = \dfrac{z}{7}$

EXTRANEOUS SOLUTIONS Consider the equation $\dfrac{1}{x} = \dfrac{1}{2x}$. Using the cross products property gives $2x = x$, or $x = 0$, but 0 is an excluded value for the expressions in the original equation. In this case, 0 is called an *extraneous solution*. A solution of a transformed equation that is not a solution of the original equation is an **extraneous solution.**

EXAMPLE 2 **Multiply by the LCD**

Solve $\dfrac{x}{x-2} + \dfrac{1}{5} = \dfrac{2}{x-2}$. Check your solution.

Multiply each side of the equation by the LCD to transform the rational equation into a polynomial equation.

$$\dfrac{x}{x-2} + \dfrac{1}{5} = \dfrac{2}{x-2}$$ **Write original equation.**

$$\dfrac{x}{x-2} \cdot 5(x-2) + \dfrac{1}{5} \cdot 5(x-2) = \dfrac{2}{x-2} \cdot 5(x-2)$$ **Multiply by LCD, $5(x-2)$.**

$$\dfrac{x \cdot 5(x-2)}{x-2} + \dfrac{5(x-2)}{5} = \dfrac{2 \cdot 5(x-2)}{x-2}$$ **Multiply, then divide out common factors.**

$$5x + x - 2 = 10$$ **Simplify.**

$$6x - 2 = 10$$ **Combine like terms.**

$$x = 2$$ **Solve for x.**

AVOID ERRORS
Be sure to identify the excluded values for the rational expressions in the original equation.

The solution appears to be 2, but the expressions $\dfrac{x}{x-2}$ and $\dfrac{2}{x-2}$ are undefined when $x = 2$. So, 2 is an extraneous solution.

▶ The rational equation has no solution.

EXAMPLE 3 **Factor to find the LCD**

Solve $\dfrac{3}{x-7} + 1 = \dfrac{8}{x^2 - 9x + 14}$. Check your solution.

Write each denominator in factored form. The LCD is $(x-2)(x-7)$.

$$\dfrac{3}{x-7} + 1 = \dfrac{8}{(x-2)(x-7)}$$

$$\dfrac{3}{x-7} \cdot (x-2)(x-7) + 1 \cdot (x-2)(x-7) = \dfrac{8}{(x-2)(x-7)} \cdot (x-2)(x-7)$$

$$\dfrac{3(x-2)(x-7)}{x-7} + (x-2)(x-7) = \dfrac{8(x-2)(x-7)}{(x-2)(x-7)}$$

$$3(x-2) + (x^2 - 9x + 14) = 8$$

$$x^2 - 6x + 8 = 8$$

$$x^2 - 6x = 0$$

$$x(x-6) = 0$$

$$x = 0 \text{ or } x - 6 = 0$$

$$x = 0 \text{ or } \quad x = 6$$

▶ The solutions are 0 and 6.

CHECK　　If $x = 0$:　　　　　　　　If $x = 6$:

$$\dfrac{3}{0-7} + 1 \overset{?}{=} \dfrac{8}{0^2 - 9 \cdot 0 + 14}$$　　$$\dfrac{3}{6-7} + 1 \overset{?}{=} \dfrac{8}{6^2 - 9 \cdot 6 + 14}$$

$$\dfrac{4}{7} = \dfrac{4}{7} \checkmark$$　　　　　　　　$$-2 = -2 \checkmark$$

EXAMPLE 4 **Solve a multi-step problem**

PAINT MIXING You have an 8 pint mixture of paint that is made up of equal amounts of yellow paint and blue paint. To create a certain shade of green, you need a paint mixture that is 80% yellow. How many pints of yellow paint do you need to add to the mixture?

ANOTHER WAY

For an alternative method for solving the problem in Example 4, turn to page 719 for the **Problem Solving Workshop**.

Solution

Because the amount of yellow paint equals the amount of blue paint in the mixture, the mixture has 4 pints of yellow paint and blue paint. Let p represent the number of pints of yellow paint that you need to add.

STEP 1 **Write** a verbal model. Then write an equation.

$$\frac{\text{Pints of yellow paint in mixture} + \text{Pints of yellow paint needed}}{\text{Pints of paint in mixture} + \text{Pints of yellow paint needed}} = \text{Desired percent yellow in mixture}$$

$$\frac{4 + p}{8 + p} = 0.8$$

STEP 2 **Solve** the equation.

$\dfrac{4 + p}{8 + p} = 0.8$	**Write equation.**
$4 + p = 0.8(8 + p)$	**Cross products property**
$4 + p = 6.4 + 0.8p$	**Distributive property**
$0.2p = 2.4$	**Rewrite equation.**
$p = 12$	**Solve for *p*.**

▶ You need to add 12 pints of yellow paint.

CHECK	$\dfrac{4 + p}{8 + p} = 0.8$	**Write original equation.**
	$\dfrac{4 + 12}{8 + 12} \overset{?}{=} 0.8$	**Substitute 12 for *p*.**
	$\dfrac{16}{20} \overset{?}{=} 0.8$	**Simplify numerator and denominator.**
	$0.8 = 0.8 ✓$	**Write fraction as decimal. Solution checks.**

 GUIDED PRACTICE **for Examples 2, 3, and 4**

3. Solve **(a)** $\dfrac{a}{a + 4} + \dfrac{1}{3} = \dfrac{-12}{a + 4}$ and **(b)** $\dfrac{n}{n - 11} - 1 = \dfrac{22}{n^2 - 5n - 66}$.

4. **WHAT IF?** In Example 4, suppose you need a paint mixture that is 75% yellow. How many pints of yellow paint do you need to add to the mixture?

11.5 EXERCISES

HOMEWORK KEY

◆ = MULTIPLE CHOICE PRACTICE
Exs. 12, 26, 33, and 39–41

◯ = HINTS AND HOMEWORK HELP
for Exs. 7, 17, and 31 at classzone.com

SKILLS · PROBLEM SOLVING · REASONING

1. **VOCABULARY** Copy and complete: The equation $\dfrac{3}{x-1} = \dfrac{7}{x} + 4$ is an example of a(n) ? .

2. **WRITING** *Describe* two methods for solving a rational equation. Which method can you use to solve any kind of rational equation? *Explain.*

EXAMPLE 1
on p. 713
for Exs. 3–14

SOLVING EQUATIONS Solve the equation. Check your solution.

3. $\dfrac{5}{r} = \dfrac{r}{20}$

4. $\dfrac{3}{s-13} = \dfrac{s}{10}$

5. $\dfrac{2}{t} = \dfrac{10}{t-6}$

6. $\dfrac{2}{c+3} = \dfrac{-5}{c-1}$

7. $\dfrac{2m}{m+4} = \dfrac{3}{m-1}$

8. $\dfrac{n-3}{n-6} = \dfrac{n+1}{n+5}$

9. $\dfrac{w}{2} = \dfrac{15}{w+1}$

10. $\dfrac{2x}{4-x} = \dfrac{x}{x-4}$

11. $\dfrac{2y}{y-3} = \dfrac{24}{y}$

12. ◆ **MULTIPLE CHOICE** What are the solutions of the equation $\dfrac{5}{y+2} = \dfrac{y}{3}$?

(A) 0, 3 **(B)** −5, 3 **(C)** 2, 3 **(D)** −5, 5

ERROR ANALYSIS *Describe* and correct the error in solving the equation.

13. $\dfrac{x+1}{2x+2} = \dfrac{3}{2x}$

14. $\dfrac{4x+1}{8x-1} = \dfrac{3}{5}$

$$(x+1)2x = 3(2x+2)$$
$$2x^2 + 2x = 6x + 6$$
$$2x^2 - 4x - 6 = 0$$
$$2(x-3)(x+1) = 0$$
$$x - 3 = 0 \quad \text{or} \quad x + 1 = 0$$
$$x = 3 \quad \text{or} \quad x = -1$$

The solutions are 3 and −1.

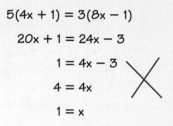

$$5(4x+1) = 3(8x-1)$$
$$20x + 1 = 24x - 3$$
$$1 = 4x - 3$$
$$4 = 4x$$
$$1 = x$$

The solution is 1.

EXAMPLES
2 and 3
on p. 714
for Exs. 15–24

SOLVING EQUATIONS Solve the equation. Check your solution.

15. $\dfrac{6x}{x-11} + 1 = \dfrac{3}{x-11}$

16. $\dfrac{z}{z+7} - 3 = \dfrac{-1}{z+7}$

17. $\dfrac{a+7}{a+4} - 1 = \dfrac{a+10}{2a+8}$

18. $\dfrac{1}{b+3} + 2 = \dfrac{b^2-3}{b^2+12b+27}$

19. $\dfrac{m}{m-2} - \dfrac{3m}{m-4} = \dfrac{-2m+2}{m^2-6m+8}$

20. $\dfrac{3n}{n+1} = \dfrac{12}{n^2-1} + \dfrac{n+4}{n-1}$

21. $\dfrac{3}{p-1} - \dfrac{2}{p-1} = \dfrac{-6}{p^2-3p+2}$

22. $\dfrac{5}{q+4} = \dfrac{q}{q-3} + \dfrac{2q-27}{q^2+q-12}$

23. $\dfrac{r+2}{r^2+6r-7} = \dfrac{8}{r^2+3r-4}$

24. $\dfrac{9}{s^2-4} = \dfrac{4-5s}{s-2}$

25. **REASONING** Consider the equation $\frac{2}{x-a} = \frac{x}{x-a}$ where a is a real number. For what value(s) of a does the equation have exactly one solution? no solution? *Explain* your answers.

26. ◆ **MULTIPLE CHOICE** Let a be a real number. How many solutions does the equation $\frac{2}{x-a} = \frac{1}{x+a} + \frac{2a}{x^2 - a^2}$ have?

   (A) Zero   (B) One   (C) Two   (D) Infinitely many

27. **REASONING** Is the expression $\frac{x+a}{x+1+a}$ ever equivalent to $\frac{x}{x+1}$ for some nonzero value of a? *Justify* your answer algebraically.

CONNECT SKILLS TO PROBLEM SOLVING Exercises 28–30 will help you prepare for problem solving.

Write an equation for the situation.

28. You have made 12 free throws out of the last 20 attempts. Find the number x of consecutive free throws you have to make to raise your free throw percentage to 85%.

29. A fruit punch has 5 cups of fruit juice and 2 cups of sparkling water. Find the number x of cups of sparkling water you need to add so that the fruit punch is 50% sparkling water.

30. A trail mix consists of 3 cups of raisins and 8 cups of assorted nuts. Find the number x of cups of nuts you have to add so that the mixture is 75% nuts.

EXAMPLE 4
on p. 715
for Exs. 31–33

31. **ICE HOCKEY** In ice hockey, a goalie's save percentage (in decimal form) is the number of shots blocked by the goalie divided by the number of shots attempted by an opposing team. Suppose a goalie has blocked 160 out of 200 shots. How many consecutive shots does the goalie need to block in order to raise the save percentage to 0.840?

   California @*HomeTutor* for problem solving help at classzone.com

Goalie saves 160 out of 200 shots.

32. **RUNNING TIMES** You are running a 6000 meter charity race. Your average speed in the first half of the race is 50 meters per minute faster than your average speed in the second half. You finish the race in 27 minutes. What is your average speed in the second half of the race?

   California @*HomeTutor* for problem solving help at classzone.com

33. ◆ **MULTIPLE CHOICE** You have a cleaning solution that consists of 2 cups of vinegar and 7 cups of water. You need a cleaning solution that consists of 5 parts water and 1 part vinegar in order to clean windows. How many cups of water do you need to add to your cleaning solution so that you can use it to clean windows?

   (A) 2 cups   (B) 3 cups   (C) 4 cups   (D) 5 cups

34. TELEVISION The average time t (in minutes) that a person in the United States watched television per day during the period 1950–2000 can be modeled by the function

$$t = \frac{265 + 8.85x}{1 + 0.0114x}$$

where x is the number of years since 1950.

   a. Approximate the year in which a person watched television for an average of 6 hours per day.

   b. About how many years had passed when the average time a person spent watching television per day increased from 5 hours to 7 hours?

35. SCIENCE Atmospheric pressure, measured in pounds per square inch (psi), is the pressure exerted on an object by the weight of the atmosphere above the object. The atmospheric pressure P (in psi) can be modeled by the function

$$P = \frac{14.55(56{,}267 - a)}{55{,}545 + a}$$

where a is the altitude (in feet). Is the change in altitude greater when the atmospheric pressure changes from 10 psi to 9 psi or from 8 psi to 7 psi? *Explain* your answer.

36. WRITING *Explain* how you can solve a rational equation such as

$\frac{x}{x + 1} + \frac{x - 2}{x} = \frac{2x - 1}{4}$ using the cross products property.

37. CHALLENGE Let a and b be real numbers. The solutions of the equation $ax + b = \frac{30}{x + 2} - 1$ are -8 and 8. What are the values of a and b? *Explain* your answer.

38. CHALLENGE Butterfat makes up about 1% of the volume of milk in 1% milk. Butterfat can make up no more than 0.2% of the volume of milk in skim milk. A container holds 15 fluid ounces of 1% milk. How many fluid ounces of butterfat must be removed in order for the milk to be considered skim milk? Round your answer to the nearest hundredth.

◆ CALIFORNIA STANDARDS SPIRAL REVIEW

Alg. 13.0 **39.** What is the difference of $\frac{4}{x + 4}$ and $\frac{7}{5x}$? *(p. 705)*

   (A) $-\frac{3}{5x(x + 4)}$ (B) $\frac{13}{5x(x + 4)}$ (C) $\frac{13x - 28}{5x(x + 4)}$ (D) $\frac{4x - 2}{5x(x + 4)}$

Alg. 11.0 **40.** What is the factored form of $2x^2 + 5x + 3$? *(p. 566)*

   (A) $(2x + 3)(x + 1)$ (B) $(x + 3)(x + 2)$

   (C) $(x + 1)(x + 3)$ (D) $(2x + 1)(x + 3)$

Alg. 5.0 **41.** You are making potato salad for lunch. You can peel 2 potatoes per minute. You need 20 peeled potatoes. How long will you take to finish if you have already peeled 8 potatoes? *(p. 132)*

   (A) 2 min   (B) 4 min   (C) 6 min   (D) 12 min

EXTRA PRACTICE for Lesson 11.5, p. 820   ⟋ **ONLINE QUIZ** at classzone.com

Another Way to Solve Example 4, page 715

In Example 4 on page 715, you saw how to solve a problem about mixing paint by using a rational equation. You can also solve the problem by using a table or by reinterpreting the problem.

PROBLEM

PAINT MIXING You have an 8 pint mixture of paint that is made up of equal amounts of yellow paint and blue paint. To create a certain shade of green, you need a paint mixture that is 80% yellow. How many pints of yellow paint do you need to add to the mixture?

METHOD 1

Use a Table One alternative approach is to use a table.

The mixture has 8 pints of paint. Because the mixture has an equal amount of yellow paint and blue paint, the mixture has $8 \div 2 = 4$ pints of yellow paint.

STEP 1 **Make** a table that shows the percent of the mixture that is yellow paint after you add various amounts of yellow paint.

Yellow paint (pints)	Paint in mixture (pints)	Percent of mixture that is yellow paint
4	8	$\frac{4}{8} = 50\%$
6	10	$\frac{6}{10} = 60\%$
8	12	$\frac{8}{12} \approx 67\%$
10	14	$\frac{10}{14} \approx 71\%$
12	16	$\frac{12}{16} = 75\%$
14	18	$\frac{14}{18} \approx 78\%$
15	19	$\frac{15}{19} \approx 79\%$
16	20	$\frac{16}{20} = 80\%$

A mixture with 6 pints of yellow paint is the result of adding 2 pints of yellow paint to the mixture.

This amount of yellow paint gives you the percent of yellow paint you want.

STEP 2 **Find** the number of pints of yellow paint you need. Subtract the number of pints of yellow paint already in the mixture from the total number of pints of yellow paint you have: $16 - 4 = 12$.

▸ You need to add 12 pints of yellow paint.

METHOD 2

Reinterpret Problem Another alternative approach is to reinterpret the problem.

STEP 1 **Reinterpret** the problem. A mixture with 80% yellow paint means that $\frac{4}{5}$ of the mixture is yellow and $\frac{1}{5}$ of the mixture is blue. So, the ratio of yellow paint to blue paint needs to be 4 : 1. You need 4 times as many pints of yellow paint as pints of blue paint.

STEP 2 **Write** a verbal model. Then write an equation. Let p represent the number of pints of yellow paint that you need to add.

Pints of yellow paint already in mixture	+	Pints of yellow paint you need to add	= 4 ·	Pints of blue paint in mixture
4	+	p	= 4 ·	4

STEP 3 **Solve** the equation.

$4 + p = 4 \cdot 4$ **Write equation.**

$4 + p = 16$ **Multiply.**

$p = 12$ **Subtract 4 from each side.**

▸ You need to add 12 pints of yellow paint to the mixture.

PRACTICE

1. **INVESTING** Jill has $10,000 in various investments, including $1000 in a mutual fund. Jill wants the amount in the mutual fund to make up 20% of the amount in all of her investments. How much money should she add to the mutual fund? Solve this problem using two different methods.

2. **ERROR ANALYSIS** *Describe* and correct the error in solving Exercise 1.

Amount in mutual fund	Amount in all investments	Percent in mutual fund
1000	10,000	10%
1400	10,400	About 13%
1800	10,800	About 17%
2250	11,250	20%

Jill needs to add $2250 to her mutual fund.

3. **BASKETBALL** A basketball player has made 40% of 30 free throw attempts so far. How many consecutive free throws must the player make in order to increase the percent of free throw attempts made to 50%? Solve this problem using two different methods.

4. **WHAT IF?** In Exercise 3, suppose the basketball player instead wants to increase the percent of free throw attempts made to 60%. How many consecutive free throws must the player make?

5. **SNOW SHOVELING** Neil and Alexi are shoveling snow out of a driveway. Neil can shovel the snow alone in 50 minutes. Both Neil and Alexi can shovel the snow in 30 minutes when working together. How many minutes will Alexi take to shovel the snow alone? Solve this problem using two different methods.

11.6 Solve Work Problems

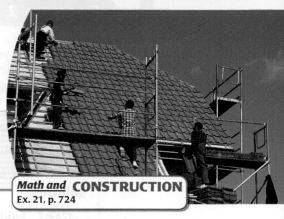

Math and CONSTRUCTION
Ex. 21, p. 724

Standards Alg. 15.0 Students apply algebraic techniques to solve rate problems, **work problems**, and percent mixture problems.

Connect *Before* you solved rational equations. *Now* you will solve work problems.

Key Vocabulary
- least common denominator (LCD) of rational expressions, *p. 705*
- rational equation, *p. 713*

Problems involving work done at a steady pace, such as mowing a lawn, can be solved using this formula:

| Work rate | · | Time | = | Work done |

In the formula, the work rate is the part of a job that is completed in a given amount of time. For example, if you take 2 hours to mow a lawn, then your work rate is $\frac{1}{2}$ job per hour.

EXAMPLE 1 Find the time it takes to complete a job

GROCERY STORE You and a co-worker share responsibilities at a grocery store. You take 40 minutes to place sales tags under each item that is on sale, and your co-worker takes 60 minutes to complete the same job. How long will it take the two of you to place all of the sales tags if you work together?

Solution

STEP 1 **Find** the work rates for you and your co-worker.

Because you can do the entire job in 40 minutes, your work rate is $\frac{1}{40}$ job per minute. Your co-worker's work rate is $\frac{1}{60}$ job per minute.

STEP 2 **Find** the part of the job done by each person.

Let t be the time (in minutes) you take to complete the job together.

Your work done: $\frac{1}{40} \cdot t = \frac{t}{40}$

Co-worker's work done: $\frac{1}{60} \cdot t = \frac{t}{60}$

STEP 3 **Write** an equation for the total work done. Then solve the equation.

The parts of the job found in Step 2 must add up to 1 whole job.

$$\frac{t}{40} + \frac{t}{60} = 1 \qquad \text{Write equation.}$$
$$3t + 2t = 120 \qquad \text{Multiply each side by LCD, 120.}$$
$$t = 24 \qquad \text{Solve for } t.$$

▶ Together, you and your co-worker can place the sales tags in 24 minutes.

Multiple Choice Practice for Lessons 11.4–11.6

In Exercises 1 and 2, use the information below.

The maximum weight W (in pounds) that a truck on a highway can carry on a group of consecutive axles is given by the function

$$W = 500\left(\frac{d}{n-1} + 12n + 36\right)$$

where d is the distance (in feet) between the first axle and the last axle of the group and n is the number of axles in the group.

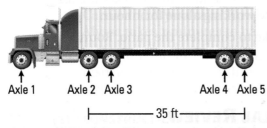

Axle 1   Axle 2   Axle 3   Axle 4   Axle 5

|———— 35 ft ————|

1. What is an equivalent expression for the maximum weight W? **Alg. 13.0**

   Ⓐ $\dfrac{500(12n + d + 36)}{n - 1}$

   Ⓑ $\dfrac{500d + 12n^2 + 24n - 36}{n - 1}$

   Ⓒ $\dfrac{500d + (12n + 36)}{n - 1}$

   Ⓓ $\dfrac{500(12n^2 + 24n + d - 36)}{n - 1}$

2. What is the approximate maximum weight that the truck can carry on the group of axles numbered 2–5? **Alg. 13.0**

   Ⓐ 20,000 lb   Ⓑ 24,000 lb

   Ⓒ 48,000 lb   Ⓓ 52,000 lb

3. What are the solutions of $\dfrac{-3x}{x+1} = \dfrac{-2}{x-1}$?
   Alg. 13.0

   Ⓐ $2, -\dfrac{1}{3}$ Ⓑ $-2, \dfrac{1}{3}$

   Ⓒ $-4, 7$ Ⓓ $2, 3$

4. What is the LCD of $\dfrac{3}{2x^2 + 6x}$ and $\dfrac{x-2}{x^2 - 9}$?
   Alg. 13.0

   Ⓐ $x + 3$ Ⓑ $2x^2 - 18$
   Ⓒ $2x^3 - 18x$ Ⓓ $2x^3 - 12x^2 + 18x$

5. Your sister can prepare a garden salad in 8 minutes. If you work together, you and your sister do the same job in 5 minutes. About how long would you take to prepare a garden salad by yourself? **Alg. 15.0**

   Ⓐ 11.8 min   Ⓑ 12.7 min

   Ⓒ 13.3 min   Ⓓ 13.9 min

6. Debbie cleans her apartment in 2.5 hours. Her roommate cleans the apartment in 3 hours. About how long would Debbie and her roommate take to clean the apartment if they worked together? **Alg. 15.0**

   Ⓐ 1.2 h   Ⓑ 1.4 h

   Ⓒ 1.8 h   Ⓓ 2 h

7. A rower travels 5 miles upstream (against the current) and 5 miles downstream (with the current). The speed of the current is given in the diagram. Which equation gives the total travel time t (in hours) as a function of the rower's average speed r (in miles per hour) in still water? **Alg. 13.0**

Speed of current: 1 mi/h
Direction of current

   Ⓐ $t = \dfrac{10r}{r^2 - 1}$ Ⓑ $t = \dfrac{2r}{5}$

   Ⓒ $t = \dfrac{25}{r^2 - 1}$ Ⓓ $t = \dfrac{10}{r}$

8. What is the simplified form of
   $\dfrac{2}{x+1} + \dfrac{3}{x-2}$? **Alg. 13.0**

   Ⓐ $\dfrac{5}{(x+1)(x-2)}$ Ⓑ $\dfrac{5x - 1}{(x+1)(x-2)}$

   Ⓒ $\dfrac{x+3}{x+2}$ Ⓓ $\dfrac{6}{(x+1)(x-2)}$

BIG IDEAS

For Your Notebook

Big Idea 1

Performing Operations with Rational Expressions

A rational expression is an expression that can be written as a ratio of two polynomials where the denominator is not zero.

Performing operations with rational expressions is similar to performing operations with numerical fractions. Any common factors in the numerator and denominator should be divided out, and the original expression should be used when finding excluded values.

Operation	Rule
Multiplication	$\frac{a}{b} \cdot \frac{c}{d} = \frac{ac}{bd}$ where $b \neq 0$ and $d \neq 0$
Division	$\frac{a}{b} \div \frac{c}{d} = \frac{a}{b} \cdot \frac{d}{c}$ where $b \neq 0$, $c \neq 0$, and $d \neq 0$
Addition	Same denominator: $\frac{a}{c} + \frac{b}{c} = \frac{a+b}{c}$ where $c \neq 0$ Different denominators: Use LCD of rational expressions.
Subtraction	Same denominator: $\frac{a}{c} - \frac{b}{c} = \frac{a-b}{c}$ where $c \neq 0$ Different denominators: Use LCD of rational expressions.

Big Idea 2

Solving Rational Equations

A rational equation is an equation that contains one or more rational expressions. You can use the following steps to solve a rational equation.

STEP 1 **Rewrite** the rational equation by using the cross products property or by multiplying each side by the least common denominator (LCD) of the rational expressions in the equation.

STEP 2 **Solve** the rewritten equation.

STEP 3 **Check** for extraneous solutions.

Big Idea 3

Solving Work Problems

Problems involving work done at a steady pace, such as mowing a lawn, can be solved using this formula:

$$\boxed{\text{Work rate}} \quad \cdot \quad \boxed{\text{Time}} \quad = \quad \boxed{\text{Work done}}$$

You can use the following steps to solve a work problem.

STEP 1 **Find** the work rate for each person.

STEP 2 **Find** the amount of work done by each person.

STEP 3 **Write** an equation for the total work done by adding the work done by each person. Then solve the equation.

11.2 Simplify Rational Expressions

pp. 688–694

Alg. 12.0

EXAMPLE

Simplify $\dfrac{x^2 - 3x - 18}{x^2 + 11x + 24}$. State the excluded values.

$$\frac{x^2 - 3x - 18}{x^2 + 11x + 24} = \frac{(x + 3)(x - 6)}{(x + 3)(x + 8)}$$ Factor numerator and denominator.

$$= \frac{\cancel{(x + 3)}(x - 6)}{\cancel{(x + 3)}(x + 8)}$$ Divide out common factor.

$$= \frac{x - 6}{x + 8}$$ Simplify.

▶ The excluded values are −8 and −3.

EXERCISES

EXAMPLES 1, 2, 3, and 4
on pp. 688–690
for Exs. 8–13

Find the excluded values, if any, of the expression.

8. $\dfrac{x + 3}{2x - 4}$

9. $\dfrac{3}{y^2 - 4y - 12}$

10. $\dfrac{8z}{9z^2 - 1}$

Simplify the expression, if possible. State the excluded values.

11. $\dfrac{5m^3 - 15m^2}{20m^2}$

12. $\dfrac{3n^2 - n - 2}{2n^2 - 3n + 1}$

13. $\dfrac{4 - r^2}{r^2 - r - 2}$

11.3 Multiply and Divide Rational Expressions

pp. 696–703

Alg. 13.0

EXAMPLE

Find the quotient $\dfrac{5x^2 + 3x - 2}{4x} \div (5x - 2)$.

$$\frac{5x^2 + 3x - 2}{4x} \div (5x - 2) = \frac{5x^2 + 3x - 2}{4x} \div \frac{5x - 2}{1}$$ Rewrite polynomial as fraction.

$$= \frac{5x^2 + 3x - 2}{4x} \cdot \frac{1}{5x - 2}$$ Multiply by multiplicative inverse.

$$= \frac{5x^2 + 3x - 2}{4x(5x - 2)}$$ Multiply numerators and denominators.

$$= \frac{(5x - 2)(x + 1)}{4x(5x - 2)}$$ Factor and divide out common factor.

$$= \frac{x + 1}{4x}$$ Simplify.

EXERCISES

EXAMPLES 3 and 4
on pp. 697–698
for Exs. 14–16

Find the product or quotient.

14. $\dfrac{-x^3}{x^2 + 5x - 14} \cdot (2 - x)$

15. $\dfrac{6v^8}{2v^5} \div \dfrac{8v}{14v^5}$

16. $\dfrac{w^2 - 9}{2w + 1} \div \dfrac{w + 3}{4w^2 - 1}$

11.4 Add and Subtract Rational Expressions

pp. 705–712

Alg. 13.0

EXAMPLE

Find the difference $\dfrac{x}{x-4} - \dfrac{5}{x+3}$.

$$\frac{x}{x-4} - \frac{5}{x+3} = \frac{x(x+3)}{(x-4)(x+3)} - \frac{5(x-4)}{(x+3)(x-4)}$$ Rewrite fractions using LCD, $(x-4)(x+3)$.

$$= \frac{x(x+3) - 5(x-4)}{(x-4)(x+3)}$$ Subtract fractions.

$$= \frac{x^2 - 2x + 20}{(x-4)(x+3)}$$ Simplify numerator.

EXERCISES

EXAMPLES
1, 3, 5, and 6
on pp. 705–708
for Exs. 17–20

Find the sum or difference.

17. $\dfrac{x+13}{5x-3} - \dfrac{9x-20}{5x-3}$

18. $\dfrac{5}{6a} + \dfrac{1}{9a^3}$

19. $\dfrac{6}{c+1} - \dfrac{c}{c^2 - 2c - 8}$

20. BICYCLING You ride your bike to a beach that is 15 miles away. Your average speed on the way home is 5 miles per hour less than your average speed on the way to the beach. Write an equation that gives the total travel time t (in hours) as a function of your average speed r (in miles per hour) on the way to the beach. Then find the total travel time if you biked to the beach at an average speed of 15 miles per hour.

11.5 Solve Rational Equations

pp. 713–718

Alg. 13.0

EXAMPLE

Solve $\dfrac{2x}{x-1} + \dfrac{2}{3} = \dfrac{10}{x-1}$.

$$\frac{2x}{x-1} + \frac{2}{3} = \frac{10}{x-1}$$ Write original equation.

$$\frac{2x}{x-1} \cdot 3(x-1) + \frac{2}{3} \cdot 3(x-1) = \frac{10}{x-1} \cdot 3(x-1)$$ Multiply each expression by LCD, $3(x-1)$.

$$\frac{2x \cdot 3(x-1)}{(x-1)} + \frac{2 \cdot 3(x-1)}{3} = \frac{10 \cdot 3(x-1)}{(x-1)}$$ Multiply, then divide out common factors.

$$6x + 2x - 2 = 30$$ Simplify.

$$8x - 2 = 30$$ Combine like terms.

$$x = 4$$ Solve for x.

EXERCISES

EXAMPLES
1, 2, and 3
on pp. 713–714
for Exs. 21–23

Solve the equation. Check your solution.

21. $\dfrac{18}{x-3} = \dfrac{x}{3}$

22. $\dfrac{4}{y+6} - 2 = \dfrac{20}{y^2 + 3y - 18}$

23. $\dfrac{1}{z+3} - \dfrac{5}{6} = \dfrac{2}{z+3}$

Alg. 15.0   **EXAMPLE**

NEWSPAPERS You and a friend share the responsibility of delivering newspapers on a newspaper route. You take 2 hours to deliver the newspapers, and your friend takes 3 hours to complete the same job. How long will the two of you take to deliver the newspapers if you work together?

Solution

STEP 1 **Find** the work rates for you and your friend.

If you deliver the newspapers in 2 hours, your work rate is $\frac{1}{2}$ job per hour. Similarly, your friend's work rate is $\frac{1}{3}$ job per hour.

STEP 2 **Find** the part of the job done by each person.

Let t be the time (in hours) you take to complete the job together.

Your work done: $\frac{1}{2} \cdot t = \frac{t}{2}$

Your friend's work done: $\frac{1}{3} \cdot t = \frac{t}{3}$

STEP 3 **Write** an equation for the total work done. Then solve the equation.

Because the parts of the job completed by you and your friend make up 1 whole job, set the sum of the expressions in Step 2 equal to 1.

$$\frac{t}{2} + \frac{t}{3} = 1 \qquad \text{Write equation.}$$

$$\frac{t}{2} \cdot 6 + \frac{t}{3} \cdot 6 = 1 \cdot 6 \qquad \text{Multiply by LCD, 6.}$$

$$3t + 2t = 6 \qquad \text{Simplify.}$$

$$t = \frac{6}{5} \qquad \text{Solve for } t.$$

▶ Working together, you and your friend can deliver the newspapers in $1\frac{1}{5}$ hours, or 1 hour 12 minutes.

EXERCISES

EXAMPLES 1 and 2
on pp. 721–722
for Exs. 24–25

24. HOUSEKEEPING Jim and Leslie clean rooms for a local hotel. Jim can clean 3 rooms in 20 minutes, and Leslie can clean 3 rooms in 40 minutes. How long will Jim and Leslie take to clean 3 rooms working together?

25. GARDENING You can weed your neighbor's garden in 3 hours. Working with your brother, you can complete the same job in 2 hours. How long would your brother take to complete the gardening job by himself?

1. **VOCABULARY** Copy and complete: The variables x and y show __?__ if $y = \dfrac{k}{x}$ and $k \neq 0$.

2. **VOCABULARY** *Describe* the steps you would take to simplify a rational expression.

Given that y varies inversely with x, use the specified values to write an inverse variation equation that relates x and y. Then find y when $x = 3$.

3. $x = 2, y = 5$

4. $x = 9, y = 9$

5. $x = 4.5, y = 4$

6. Tell whether the table represents inverse variation. If so, write the inverse variation equation.

x	−10	−2	4	5	20
y	0.5	2.5	−1.25	−1	−0.25

Simplify the expression, if possible. State the excluded values.

7. $\dfrac{42x^4}{3x^2}$

8. $\dfrac{2y - 8}{4 - y}$

9. $\dfrac{z^2 - 4z - 77}{z^2 - 13z + 22}$

Find the sum, difference, product, or quotient.

10. $\dfrac{r^2 - 9r + 18}{r^2 + 11r + 30} \cdot \dfrac{r + 5}{r^2 - 36}$

11. $\dfrac{s^2 + 3s - 10}{s^2 - 9} \div \dfrac{s - 2}{s + 3}$

12. $\dfrac{x^2 - 9x}{x + 3} \div (x^2 - 6x - 27)$

13. $\dfrac{a - 4}{-a^3 + 3a^2} \cdot (a^2 - 2a - 3)$

14. $\dfrac{6}{5b^2} + \dfrac{2}{3b}$

15. $\dfrac{2 - 5y}{y - 10} + \dfrac{1}{3y + 2}$

16. $\dfrac{4}{m + 2} - \dfrac{3m}{m - 3}$

17. $\dfrac{2n + 7}{n - 1} - \dfrac{8n}{n + 5}$

18. $\dfrac{p + 1}{p^2 - 49} + \dfrac{p - 1}{p^2 + 10p + 21}$

Solve the equation. Check your solution.

19. $\dfrac{7}{u + 1} = \dfrac{4}{u + 4}$

20. $\dfrac{t + 11}{t - 11} = \dfrac{11t + 121}{t^2 - 6t - 55}$

21. $\dfrac{8}{x + 4} = \dfrac{5x}{x^2 - 2x - 24} - 1$

22. **GOLF** A local golf club offers two payment options to anyone who wants to use its course. The first option is a one-time fee of $750 to join for the season plus $25 for each use of the golf course. The second option is a fee of $45 for each use of the golf course.

   a. Using the first option, write an equation that gives the average cost C (in dollars per use) of the golf course as a function of the number g of times that a golfer uses the golf course.

   b. Using the first option, about how many times will a golfer need to use the golf course before the average cost is less than $45?

23. **CLEANING** You and your brother start a house cleaning business for the summer. Your brother needs twice the time you need to clean a certain room. Working together, the two of you need 60 minutes to clean the room.

   a. Write an equation that you can use to find the time (in minutes) you need to clean the room by yourself. Then solve the equation.

   b. How long will each of you need to clean the room individually?

If you have difficulty solving a multiple choice problem directly, you may be able to use another approach to eliminate incorrect answer choices and obtain the correct answer.

PROBLEM 1

You can fill a swimming pool in 4 hours using hose A. You can fill the same swimming pool in 7 hours using hose B. About how long will you take to fill the swimming pool using hoses A and B together?

A 1.8 h   **B** 2.5 h   **C** 6.9 h   **D** 11.2 h

Strategy 1 SOLVE DIRECTLY

Solve the work problem by writing and solving a rational equation.

STEP 1 **Find** each hose's work rate.

If hose A can fill the pool in 4 hours, it can do $\frac{1}{4}$ job per hour. Similarly, hose B's work rate is $\frac{1}{7}$ job per hour.

STEP 2 **Find** the part of the job done by each hose.

Let t be the time (in minutes) the two hoses take to fill the pool together.

Hose A: $\frac{1}{4} \cdot t = \frac{t}{4}$ **Hose B:** $\frac{1}{7} \cdot t = \frac{t}{7}$

STEP 3 **Write** an equation for the total work done. Then solve the equation.

The parts of the job found in Step 2 must add up to 1 whole job.

$\frac{t}{4} + \frac{t}{7} = 1$ **Write equation.**

$7t + 4t = 28$ **Multiply by LCD, 28.**

$11t = 28$ **Combine like terms.**

$t \approx 2.5$ **Solve for t.**

The correct answer is B. **A** **B** **C** **D**

Strategy 2 ELIMINATE CHOICES

You can eliminate answer choices by using numerical reasoning.

STEP 1 **Consider** how long each hose takes to fill the pool.

Separately, hose A takes 4 hours to fill the pool, and hose B takes 7 hours to fill the pool. The two hoses should take less time to fill the pool together than either hose would take to fill the pool alone. So, the two hoses should take less than 4 hours to fill the pool. You can eliminate choice C and choice D.

STEP 2 **Consider** how long each hose takes to fill half of the pool.

Separately, hose A takes 2 hours to fill half of the pool, and hose B takes 3.5 hours to fill half of the pool. Because neither hose can fill half of the pool in 1.8 hours separately, together the two hoses could not possibly fill the entire pool in 1.8 hours. So, you can eliminate choice A.

The correct answer is B. **A** **B** **C** **D**

PROBLEM 2

Simplify $\dfrac{3x^2 + x - 4}{x^2 + 6x - 7}$ to lowest terms.

(A) $\dfrac{3x + 4}{x + 7}$ (B) $\dfrac{3x - 4}{x - 7}$ (C) $\dfrac{3x + 2}{x + 6}$ (D) $\dfrac{3x + 1}{x + 6}$

Strategy 1 SOLVE DIRECTLY

Factor the numerator and denominator in the rational expression and divide out common factors.

$\dfrac{3x^2 + x - 4}{x^2 + 6x - 7} = \dfrac{(3x + 4)(x - 1)}{(x + 7)(x - 1)}$ **Factor numerator and denominator.**

$= \dfrac{(3x + 4)\cancel{(x - 1)}}{(x + 7)\cancel{(x - 1)}}$ **Divide out common factor.**

$= \dfrac{3x + 4}{x + 7}$ **Simplify.**

The correct answer is A. (A) (B) (C) (D)

Strategy 2 ELIMINATE CHOICES

Evaluate the original expression and the answer choices for various values of x.

STEP 1 Choose $x = 0$.

Original expression: $\dfrac{3(0)^2 + 0 - 4}{(0)^2 + 6(0) - 7} = \dfrac{4}{7}$

A: $\dfrac{3(0) + 4}{0 + 7} = \dfrac{4}{7}$ B: $\dfrac{3(0) - 4}{0 - 7} = \dfrac{4}{7}$

C: $\dfrac{3(0) + 2}{0 + 6} = \dfrac{1}{3}$ D: $\dfrac{3(0) + 1}{0 + 6} = \dfrac{1}{6}$

You can eliminate choices C and D.

STEP 2 Choose $x = 2$.

Original expression: $\dfrac{3(2)^2 + 2 - 4}{(2)^2 + 6(2) - 7} = \dfrac{10}{9}$

A: $\dfrac{3(2) + 4}{2 + 7} = \dfrac{10}{9}$ B: $\dfrac{3(2) - 4}{2 - 7} = -\dfrac{2}{5}$

You can eliminate choice B.

The correct answer is A. (A) (B) (C) (D)

STRATEGY PRACTICE

Explain why you can eliminate the highlighted answer choice.

1. What is the simplified form of $\dfrac{3x^3}{6x^2}$?

(A) $\dfrac{x}{2}$ (B) $2x$ (C) ✗ $\dfrac{3x}{6}$ (D) x

2. What is the least common denominator of $\dfrac{17y^4}{z^2}$ and $\dfrac{8z}{3y}$?

(A) $3yz$ (B) $3yz^2$ (C) ✗ $3y$ (D) yz^2

3. Avi completes a job in 4 hours. Geoff can complete the same job in 2 hours. How long will they take to complete the job working together?

(A) 1.3 h   (B) 2.6 h   (C) 3.4 h   (D) ✗ 4.2 h

11 ◆ MULTIPLE CHOICE PRACTICE

1. What is the solution of the equation

   $\dfrac{2}{x+3} + \dfrac{1}{x} = \dfrac{4}{3x}$? **Alg. 13.0**

   (A) $-\dfrac{1}{3}$

   (B) $\dfrac{3}{5}$

   (C) $\dfrac{5}{7}$

   (D) 2

2. A company forecasts the average price of digital car radios for the period 2004–2007. The average price p (in thousands of dollars) of a digital car radio can be modeled by

   $$p = \dfrac{170x + 60}{190x^2 + 55x + 140}$$

   where x is the number of years since 2004. What is the simplified form of the model? **Alg. 12.0**

   (A) $p = \dfrac{24x + 11}{30x^2 + 7x + 43}$

   (B) $p = \dfrac{17x + 6}{19x^2 + 5x + 14}$

   (C) $p = \dfrac{34x + 12}{38x^2 + 11x + 28}$

   (D) $p = \dfrac{85x + 30}{95x^2 + 27x + 70}$

3. Which equation gives the ratio r of the surface area to the volume of the rectangular prism shown as a function of the height h? **Alg. 13.0**

   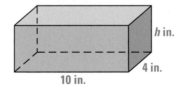

   10 in.

   (A) $r = \dfrac{2}{h} + 0.7$

   (B) $r = \dfrac{1}{20h} + 0.7$

   (C) $r = \dfrac{1}{20h} + 28$

   (D) $r = \dfrac{2}{h} + 0.05$

4. The table shows the amount of time t (in minutes) it takes for p people to complete a job. What inverse variation equation relates t and p? **Alg 15.0**

People, p	Time t (min)
6	200
8	150
10	120
12	100
16	75

   (A) $t = \dfrac{1200}{p}$

   (B) $t = \dfrac{p}{1200}$

   (C) $p = \dfrac{700}{t}$

   (D) $p = \dfrac{t}{700}$

5. It takes 7 minutes to fill a washing machine tub using only the cold water valve. It takes 4 minutes to fill the tub using both the cold water valve and the hot water valve. How many minutes will it take to fill the tub using only the hot water valve? **Alg. 15.0**

   (A) $7\dfrac{1}{2}$ min

   (B) $8\dfrac{2}{3}$ min

   (C) $9\dfrac{1}{3}$ min

   (D) $10\dfrac{4}{5}$ min

6. The variables x and y vary inversely, and $y = 4$ when $x = 2$. What is the constant of variation? **Alg. 15.0**

   (A) 3

   (B) 4

   (C) 8

   (D) 10

7. What is the solution of $\frac{2}{3x+1} + 2 = \frac{2}{3}$?

Alg. 13.0

Ⓐ $-\frac{5}{6}$

Ⓑ $\frac{2}{3}$

Ⓒ 1

Ⓓ 7

8. Marcel runs 12 kilometers against the wind and 12 kilometers with the wind. The speed of the wind is given in the diagram. What equation gives the total travel time t (in hours) as a function of Marcel's average speed r (in kilometers per hour) with no wind? **Alg. 13.0**

Direction of wind
Wind speed: 4 km/h

Ⓐ $t = \frac{24r}{(r-4)(r+4)}$

Ⓑ $t = \frac{2r}{3}$

Ⓒ $t = \frac{144}{(r-4)(r+4)}$

Ⓓ $t = \frac{48}{r}$

9. What is the simplified form of $\frac{t^4}{t^3 + t^2}$?

Alg. 12.0

Ⓐ $\frac{t^4}{t^2(t+1)}$

Ⓑ $\frac{t^2}{t+1}$

Ⓒ $\frac{t^4}{t+1}$

Ⓓ $\frac{t}{t^2 + 1}$

10. The number D (in thousands) of all college degrees earned and the number M (in thousands) of master's degrees earned in the United States during the period 1984–2001 can be modeled by

$$D = \frac{17x^2 + 1800}{1 + 0.0062x^2} \text{ and } M = \frac{2.5x^2 + 280}{1 + 0.0040x^2}$$

where x is the number of years since 1984. What equation gives the percent p of all college degrees that were master's degrees as a function of x? **Alg. 13.0**

Ⓐ $p = \frac{(17x^2 + 1800)(25x^2 + 280)}{(1 + 0.0062x^2)(1 + 0.0040x^2)}$

Ⓑ $p = \frac{17x^2 + 1800}{1 + 0.0062x^2} - \frac{2.5x^2 + 280}{1 + 0.0040x^2}$

Ⓒ $p = \frac{17x^2 + 1800}{1 + 0.0062x^2} + \frac{2.5x^2 + 280}{1 + 0.0040x^2}$

Ⓓ $p = \frac{(2.5x^2 + 280)(1 + 0.0062x^2)}{(1 + 0.0040x^2)(17x^2 + 1800)}$

11. Working together, a painter and an assistant can paint a room in 2 hours. Let t represent the number of hours that the painter needs to paint the room alone.

Person	Work rate	Time worked	Fraction of room painted
Painter	$\frac{1}{t}$	2	$\frac{2}{t}$
Assistant	?	2	$\frac{1}{t}$

What is the missing value in the table?
Alg. 15.0

Ⓐ $\frac{1}{2t}$

Ⓑ $\frac{2}{t}$

Ⓒ $2t$

Ⓓ $\frac{t}{2}$

Evaluate the expression.

1. $2^4 \cdot 3 - 16 \div 4$ *(p. 11)*

2. $|-125| - 34$ *(p. 53)*

3. $\pm\sqrt{2025}$ *(p. 95)*

Solve the equation.

4. $7 - 2x = 13$ *(p. 132)*

5. $-8x + 15 + 5x = 9$ *(p. 139)*

6. $5(2x + 3) = 4x$ *(p. 146)*

Solve the inequality. Graph your solution.

7. $4x - 6 \le 8x - 2$ *(p. 202)*

8. $-2 \le x - 6 < 18$ *(p. 210)*

9. $2x < 6 \text{ or } 4x \ge 8$ *(p. 210)*

Graph the equation.

10. $x = 7$ *(p. 264)*

11. $y = 2x + 3$ *(p. 291)*

12. $4y - 2x = 1$ *(p. 291)*

Write an equation in slope-intercept form of the line with the given characteristics.

13. slope: -3;
    y-intercept: 4 *(p. 322)*

14. passes through $(-2, -8)$
    and $(3, -5.5)$ *(p. 329)*

15. slope: -8; passes
    through $(1, -5)$ *(p. 329)*

Solve the linear system.

16. $x = 4y + 3$ *(p. 383)*
    $2x - 4y = 7$

17. $3x - 7y = 20$ *(p. 398)*
    $-11x + 10y = 5$

18. $-9x + 6y = 0$ *(p. 405)*
    $-12x + 8y = 5$

Simplify the expression. Write your answer using only positive exponents.

19. $(2x^3)^4 \cdot x^9$ *(p. 460)*

20. $(-9x^3)^2\left(-\frac{1}{4}x^6\right)$ *(p. 460)*

21. $\dfrac{(3x)^{-3}y^3}{x^2y^{-1}}$ *(p. 475)*

Tell whether the triangle with the given side lengths is a right triangle.

22. $5, 6, 7$ *(p. 491)*

23. $1.8, 2.4, 3$ *(p. 491)*

24. $9, 40, 41$ *(p. 491)*

Find the sum, difference, product, or quotient.

25. $(6a^2 - 22a) - (a^3 - 7a + 54)$ *(p. 520)*

26. $(-a^4 - 100) + (5a^4 - a^2 + 81)$ *(p. 520)*

27. $(4c + 2)(6c^2 - c + 2)$ *(p. 528)*

28. $(4x^2 + 5) \div (x - 3)$ *(p. 541)*

Factor the polynomial.

29. $a^2 - 15a - 54$ *(p. 556)*

30. $-3b^2 - 22b - 7$ *(p. 566)*

31. $4f^2 + 4fg + g^2$ *(p. 573)*

32. $p^2(p - 5) + 9(5 - p)$ *(p. 579)*

Solve the equation.

33. $(x + 7)(x - 3) = 0$ *(p. 549)*

34. $4x^2 + 9 = 0$ *(p. 633)*

35. $9x^2 - 28x + 3 = 0$ *(p. 643)*

36. $8x^2 + 7 = 36x - 9$ *(p. 649)*

Graph the equation.

37. $y = -2x^2 + 5$ *(p. 605)*

38. $y = -3x^2 + 8x - 5$ *(p. 612)*

39. $y = x^2 - 4x - 5$ *(p. 612)*

40. $y = 0.5(x + 3)(x + 2)$ *(p. 618)*

Find the sum, difference, product, or quotient.

41. $\dfrac{x-2}{x+5} \cdot \dfrac{x+5}{x-8}$ *(p. 696)*   **42.** $\dfrac{x^3-16x}{x^2+3x} \div (x-4)$ *(p. 696)*   **43.** $\dfrac{16}{2x^4} \cdot \dfrac{7x^3}{2x}$ *(p. 696)*

44. $\dfrac{2x}{3-x} + \dfrac{x-9}{3-x}$ *(p. 705)*   **45.** $\dfrac{1}{x+6} + \dfrac{4x}{x+6}$ *(p. 705)*   **46.** $\dfrac{9}{x^2-3x} - \dfrac{3}{x-3}$ *(p. 705)*

47. FERRY TRAVEL Each weekday, two ferries travel from Larkspur, California, to San Francisco. Ferry A can carry 390 passengers per trip, and together the ferries can carry 840 passengers per trip. How many passengers can Ferry B carry per trip? *(p. 26)*

48. VOLLEYBALL The circumference of a volleyball should be 26 inches with an absolute deviation of 0.5 inch. Write and solve an absolute value inequality that describes the acceptable circumferences of a volleyball. *(p. 226)*

49. SAVINGS Two investment accounts are increasing in value at a rate of $200 per year. The two accounts began with $3500 and $4000. Write equations that model the value of each account as a function of the number of years since the account was opened. How are the graphs of the equations related? *Justify* your answer. *(p. 291)*

50. MARATHON Two runners are training for the California International Marathon in Sacramento, California. One runner begins running 6 minutes after the other. The speed of the first runner is 11.4 miles per hour. The speed of the second runner is 12 miles per hour. After how many minutes does the second runner pass the first runner? *(p. 413)*

51. COMPUTER MEMORY You check the amount of free space available on the hard drive of your computer. There are 512 megabytes (MB) of free space. You know that $1 \text{ MB} = 2^{20}$ bytes and that $512 = 2^9$. How many bytes of free space are available? Express your answer as a power of 2. *(p. 460)*

52. CONSTRUCTION A construction worker is cutting the square piece of sheet metal shown into two pieces along one of the diagonals. How long a cut does the worker have to make? Round your answer to the nearest tenth of an inch. *(p. 491)*

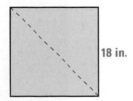
18 in.

53. STONE ARCH The shape of a stone arch can be modeled by the graph of the equation $y = -0.5x^2 + 4x + 4$ where x is the horizontal distance (in feet) from one end of the arch and y is the vertical distance (in feet) above the ground. What is the maximum height of the arch? *Explain* how you found your answer. *(p. 605)*

54. HEATING RATES An electric heater takes 8 minutes to heat an entire apartment to the desired temperature. A wood stove and an electric heater together take 6 minutes to heat the apartment. How many minutes does it take the wood stove alone to heat the apartment to the desired temperature? *(p. 721)*

12 Probability: Review and Preview

Before

In previous courses, you learned the following skills, which you'll use in Chapter 12:

- Performing operations with fractions, decimals, and percents
- Using counting methods

Now

In Chapter 12 you'll study these **Big Ideas:**

1 Finding theoretical and experimental probabilities

2 Finding the number of permutations and combinations

3 Finding probabilities of compound events

Why?

So you can solve real-world problems about . . .

- Field goals, p. 749
- Movies, p. 754
- Band competitions, p. 754
- Photography, p. 759
- Walruses, p. 767
- Chess, p. 766

 **Algebra**

at *classzone.com*

Get-Ready Games

SUNNY DAYS

California Standards

Review comparing fractions. **Gr. 6 NS 1.1**
Prepare for probabilities as ratios. **Gr. 6 SDAP 3.3**

Upland: There are 5 sunny days for every 2 cloudy days.

Zellwood: There are 6 sunny days per week.

Ashton: There are 11 sunny days every 2 weeks.

Arlington: 17 out of 21 days are sunny.

Yellowfield: For every 3 days, 2 are sunny.

Milltown: 5 out of 21 days are cloudy.

How to Play

Find the name and state of the sunniest city in the United States.

- For each sentence given above, write a ratio, in fraction form, of sunny days to cloudy days.
- Order the fractions from least to greatest. Write the first letters of the towns in the same order as the corresponding fractions.

CALIFORNIA STANDARDS

- **Alg. 2 18.0** Students use fundamental counting principles to compute combinations and permutations. *(Lessons 12.2, 12.3)*

- **Alg. 2 19.0** Students use combinations and permutations to compute probabilities. *(Lessons 12.2, 12.3)*

- **Gr. 6 SDAP 3.0** Students determine theoretical and experimental probabilities and use these to make predictions about events. *(Lesson 12.1)*

LIGHTNING MATH

California Standards

Review using ratios. **Gr. 6 NS 1.2**
Prepare for finding probabilities. **Gr. 6 SDAP 3.0**

How to Play

Use the numbers on the clouds above to form ratios that are equivalent to the ratios on the lightning bolts. Find all such ratios.

Games Wrap-Up

Draw Conclusions

Complete these exercises after playing the games.

1. **WRITING** *Describe* the steps you used to order the fractions in *Sunny Days*.

2. **REASONING** Use the cloud numbers in *Lightning Math* to write four ratios that are different from the ratios shown on the lightning bolts in *Lightning Math*.

Prerequisite Skills

California @HomeTutor

Prerequisite skills practice
at classzone.com

REVIEW VOCABULARY

- common factor, *p. 785*
- percent, *p. 791*
- simplest form of a fraction, *p. 792*
- Venn diagram, *p. 809*

VOCABULARY CHECK

Copy and complete the statement.

1. A(n) __?__ is a fraction whose denominator is 100.

2. A(n) __?__ uses shapes to show how sets are related.

SKILLS CHECK

Write the fraction in simplest form. *(Review p. 786 for 12.1–12.4.)*

3. $\frac{5}{80}$ 4. $\frac{16}{56}$ 5. $\frac{88}{100}$ 6. $\frac{63}{96}$

Write the percent as a decimal and as a fraction.
(Review pp. 791–792 for 12.1–12.4.)

7. 14%   8. 78%   9. 2.55%   10. 0.6%

Perform the indicated operation. *(Review p. 788 for 12.4.)*

11. $\frac{1}{6} + \frac{5}{8}$ 12. $\frac{2}{5} - \frac{1}{3}$ 13. $\frac{1}{8} \times \frac{3}{4}$ 14. $\frac{7}{8} - \frac{1}{5}$

Notetaking Skills

NOW YOU TRY

Make a *summary triangle* for multiplying fractions.

Focus on Graphic Organizers

You can use a *summary triangle* to summarize details about a mathematical concept, such as writing a fraction as a percent.

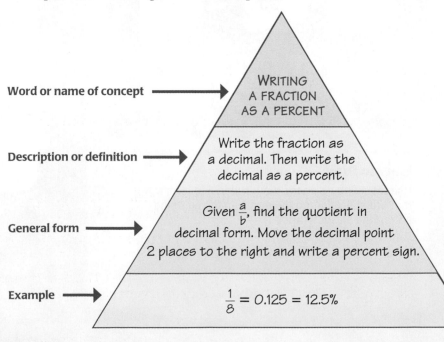

Word or name of concept → WRITING A FRACTION AS A PERCENT

Description or definition → Write the fraction as a decimal. Then write the decimal as a percent.

General form → Given $\frac{a}{b}$, find the quotient in decimal form. Move the decimal point 2 places to the right and write a percent sign.

Example → $\frac{1}{8} = 0.125 = 12.5\%$

12.1 Find a Probability

MATERIALS • paper bag • pieces of paper

Standards Review

Gr. 6 SDAP 3.2 Use data to estimate the probability of future events (e.g., batting averages or number of accidents per mile driven).

> **QUESTION** **What is the chance that you select the initials of a student in your class from a bag of letters?**

You can perform an experiment and record the results to approximate the likelihood of selecting the initials of a student in your class.

> **EXPLORE** **Perform an experiment**

STEP 1 *Select letters*

Write each of the 26 letters of the alphabet on separate pieces of paper. Put all of the letters into a bag. Select a letter at random (without looking into the bag). Replace the letter and select a second letter at random.

STEP 2 *Record the results*

Record the results of the selections in a table like the one shown below.

- If the first letter is the first initial (but the second letter is not the last initial) of any student in your class, put a tally mark in the "first initial" column.
- If the second letter is the last initial (but the first letter is not the first initial) of any student in your class, put a tally mark in the "last initial" column.
- If the two letters are the first and last initials of any student in your class, put a tally mark in the "both initials" column.

Perform the experiment 30 times.

	First initial	Last initial	Both initials
Tally	IIII	IIIIII	I
Frequency	?	?	?

STEP 3 *Record the frequencies*

Record the *frequency*, the total number of tally marks, of each possible result.

> **DRAW CONCLUSIONS** **Use your observations to complete these exercises**

1. For what fraction of the times that you performed the experiment did you select the first initial of a student in your class? the last initial? both?

2. Which result do you think is least likely to happen if you repeat the experiment 30 more times? *Explain* your choice.

3. **REASONING** You perform the experiment 90 times. How many times do you expect to select both initials of a student in your class? *Explain*.

12.1 Find Theoretical and Experimental Probabilities

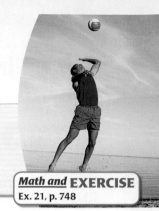

Standards Review Gr. 6 SDAP 3.0 Students determine theoretical and experimental probabilities and use these to make predictions about events.

Connect *Before* you wrote and simplified rational numbers. *Now* you will use rational numbers to review Grade 6 SDAP Standard 3.0.

Math and **EXERCISE**
Ex. 21, p. 748

Key Vocabulary
• outcome
• sample space
• event
• probability
• theoretical probability
• experimental probability

REVIEW TREE DIAGRAMS
For help with tree diagrams, see p. 805.

A possible result of an experiment is an **outcome**. For instance, when you roll a number cube there are 6 possible outcomes: 1, 2, 3, 4, 5, or 6. The set of all possible outcomes is called a **sample space**. An **event** is an outcome or a collection of outcomes, such as rolling an odd number.

EXAMPLE 1 Find a sample space

You flip a coin and roll a number cube. How many possible outcomes are in the sample space? List the possible outcomes.

Solution

Use a tree diagram to find the outcomes in the sample space.

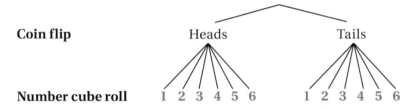

Coin flip   Heads   Tails

Number cube roll   1 2 3 4 5 6   1 2 3 4 5 6

The sample space has 12 possible outcomes. They are listed below.

Heads, 1   Heads, 2   Heads, 3   Heads, 4   Heads, 5   Heads, 6
Tails, 1   Tails, 2   Tails, 3   Tails, 4   Tails, 5   Tails, 6

✓ **GUIDED PRACTICE** for Example 1

1. You flip 2 coins and roll a number cube. How many possible outcomes are in the sample space? List the possible outcomes.

PROBABILITY The **probability of an event** is a measure of the likelihood, or chance, that the event will occur. Probability is a number from 0 to 1 and can be expressed as a decimal, fraction, or percent.

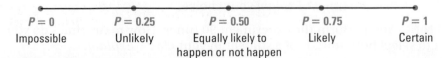

$P = 0$	$P = 0.25$	$P = 0.50$	$P = 0.75$	$P = 1$
Impossible	Unlikely	Equally likely to happen or not happen	Likely	Certain

THEORETICAL PROBABILITY The outcomes for a specified event are called *favorable outcomes*. When all outcomes are equally likely, the **theoretical probability** of the event is defined as follows:

$$\text{Theoretical probability} = \frac{\text{Number of favorable outcomes}}{\text{Total number of outcomes}}$$

The probability of event A is written as $P(A)$.

EXAMPLE 2 **Find a theoretical probability**

T-SHIRTS You and your friends designed T-shirts with silk-screened emblems, and you are selling the T-shirts to raise money. The table below shows the number of T-shirts that you have in each design. A student chooses a T-shirt at random. What is the probability that the student chooses a red T-shirt?

	Gold emblem	Silver emblem
Green T-shirt	10	8
Red T-shirt	6	6

Solution

You and your friends have a total of $10 + 6 + 8 + 6 = 30$ T-shirts. So, there are 30 possible outcomes. Of all the T-shirts, 12 T-shirts are red. There are 12 favorable outcomes.

$$P(\text{red T-shirt}) = \frac{\text{Number of favorable outcomes}}{\text{Total number of outcomes}}$$

$$= \frac{\text{Number of red T-shirts}}{\text{Total number of T-shirts}}$$

$$= \frac{12}{30}$$

$$= \frac{2}{5}$$

WRITE PROBABILITIES
In Example 2, the probability can be expressed as $\frac{2}{5}$, 0.4, or 40%.

✓ **GUIDED PRACTICE** for Example 2

2. **T-SHIRTS** In Example 2, what is the probability that the student chooses a T-shirt with a gold emblem?

3. You toss a coin and roll a number cube. What is the probability that the coin shows tails and the number cube shows 4?

EXPERIMENTAL PROBABILITY An **experimental probability** is based on repeated *trials* of an experiment. The number of trials is the number of times the experiment is performed. Each trial in which a favorable outcome occurs is called a *success*.

$$\text{Experimental probability} = \frac{\text{Number of successes}}{\text{Number of trials}}$$

EXAMPLE 3 **Find theoretical and experimental probabilities**

Each section of the spinner shown has the same area. The spinner was spun 20 times. The table shows the results. For which color is the experimental probability of stopping on the color the same as the theoretical probability?

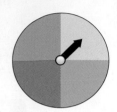

Spinner Results			
Red	Green	Blue	Yellow
5	9	3	3

Animated Algebra

For an interactive example of finding probabilities, go to **classzone.com**.

Solution

The theoretical probability of stopping on each of the four colors is $\frac{1}{4}$.

Use the outcomes in the table to find the experimental probabilities.

$P(\text{red}) = \frac{5}{20} = \frac{1}{4}$ $P(\text{green}) = \frac{9}{20}$ $P(\text{blue}) = \frac{3}{20}$ $P(\text{yellow}) = \frac{3}{20}$

▶ The experimental probability of stopping on red is the same as the theoretical probability of stopping on red.

EXAMPLE 4   **◆ Multiple Choice Practice**

Wendy has 8 black pens, 13 blue pens, and 4 red pens in a desk drawer. What is the probability that, without looking, Wendy will pick a red pen from the drawer?

Ⓐ 4%   Ⓑ 16%   Ⓒ 19%   Ⓓ 25%

Solution

$P(\text{red pen}) = \dfrac{\text{Number of favorable outcomes}}{\text{Total number of outcomes}}$

$= \dfrac{\text{Number of red pens}}{\text{Total number of pens}}$

$= \dfrac{4}{25}$

$= 16\%$

▶ The correct answer is B. Ⓐ Ⓑ Ⓒ Ⓓ

 GUIDED PRACTICE   for Examples 3 and 4

4. In Example 3, for which color is the experimental probability of stopping on the color greater than the theoretical probability?

5. David has 16 red marbles, 14 blue marbles, and 10 yellow marbles. He randomly chooses one marble. What is the probability that David chooses a blue marble?

12.1 EXERCISES

SKILLS · PROBLEM SOLVING · REASONING

1. **VOCABULARY** Copy and complete: A number that describes the likelihood of an event is the __?__ of the event.

2. **WRITING** *Explain* the difference between theoretical probability and experimental probability.

EXAMPLE 1
on p. 744
for Exs. 3–6

SAMPLE SPACE **In Exercises 3–6, find the number of possible outcomes in the sample space. Then list the possible outcomes.**

3. A bag contains 4 red cards numbered 1–4, 4 white cards numbered 1–4, and 4 black cards numbered 1–4. You choose a card at random.

4. You toss two coins.

5. You roll a number cube and toss three coins.

6. You roll two number cubes.

EXAMPLES
3 and 4
on p. 746
for Exs. 7–13

THEORETICAL AND EXPERIMENTAL PROBABILITIES **In Exercises 7–13, refer to the spinner shown. The spinner is divided into sections with the same area.**

7. What is the probability that the spinner stops on a multiple of 3?

8. What is the probability that the spinner stops on a multiple of 4?

9. What is the probability that the spinner does *not* stop on a number less than 12?

10. **ERROR ANALYSIS** *Describe* and correct the error in finding the theoretical probability that the spinner stops on a multiple of 9.

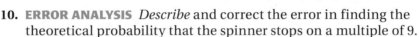

$$\frac{\text{Number of favorable outcomes}}{\text{Total number of outcomes}} = \frac{2}{10} = \frac{1}{5} \quad \times$$

11. You spin the spinner 30 times. It stops on 12 three times. What is the experimental probability of stopping on 12?

12. You spin the spinner 10 times. It stops on an even number 6 times. What is the experimental probability of stopping on an even number?

13. **ERROR ANALYSIS** You spin the spinner 20 times. It stops on a multiple of 4 five times. *Describe* and correct the error in finding the experimental probability that the spinner stops on a multiple of 4.

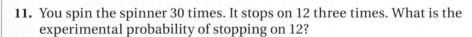

$$\frac{\text{Number of successes}}{\text{Total number of trials}} = \frac{4}{20} = \frac{1}{5} \quad \times$$

14. ◆ **MULTIPLE CHOICE** The probability that an event occurs is $\frac{5}{13}$. What is the probability that the event does *not* occur?

    A $\frac{5}{18}$ **B** $\frac{8}{13}$ **C** $\frac{18}{13}$ **D** $\frac{13}{5}$

15. ◆ **MULTIPLE CHOICE** A bag contains 9 red marbles, 5 yellow marbles, and 6 green marbles. You randomly choose one marble from the bag. What is the probability that you choose a yellow marble?

    A 5%   **B** 20%   **C** 25%   **D** 30%

16. **NUMBER CUBES** Make a table showing all of the possible sums that result from rolling two number cubes. (Columns represent the possible outcomes of the first number cube. Rows represent the possible outcomes of the second number cube. The cells of the table represent the sums of the two outcomes.) Then find the probability of rolling each sum.

CONNECT SKILLS TO PROBLEM SOLVING Exercises 17–19 will help you prepare for problem solving.

Use the following information: A car is randomly chosen from the cars at a dealership. The table shows the number of new and used cars and the number of cars at the dealership with two-wheel and four-wheel drive.

17. What is the total number of outcomes?

18. What is the number of favorable outcomes for choosing a new car with four-wheel drive?

19. What is the number of favorable outcomes for choosing a used car with two-wheel drive?

	Two-wheel drive	Four-wheel drive
New	40	27
Used	19	4

EXAMPLE 2
on p. 745
for Exs. 20–21

20. ◆ **MULTIPLE CHOICE** You have created a playlist of 7 songs on your MP3 player. You play these songs in a random shuffle, where each song has an equally likely chance of being played. What is the probability that the second song on the list will be played first?

    A $\frac{1}{7}$ **B** $\frac{2}{7}$ **C** $\frac{3}{7}$ **D** $\frac{6}{7}$

California @HomeTutor for problem solving help at classzone.com

21. **SURVEY** A survey asked a total of 600 students (100 male students and 100 female students who were 11, 13, and 15 years old) about their exercise habits. The table shows the numbers of students who said they exercise 2 hours or more each week.

	11-years-olds	13-years-olds	15-years-olds
Female	53	57	51
Male	65	68	67

a. What is the probability that a randomly selected female student who participated in this survey exercises 2 hours or more each week?

b. What is the probability that a randomly selected 15-year-old student who participated in this survey exercises 2 hours or more each week?

c. What is the probability that a randomly selected student who participated in this survey exercises 2 hours or more each week?

California @HomeTutor for problem solving help at classzone.com

22. FOOTBALL The table shows the 2003 National Football League regular season field goal statistics for kicker Adam Vinatieri.

	Point difference at end of game		
	0–7 points	8–14 points	≥ 15 points
Field goals attempted	20	11	3
Field goals made	16	7	2

   a. During the 2003 regular season, what was the probability that Adam Vinatieri would make an attempted field goal, regardless of the point difference?

   b. Find the probabilities that Vinatieri made an attempted field goal when the point difference at the end of the game was 0–7 points, 8–14 points, and at least 15 points.

   c. During what kinds of games was Adam Vinatieri most likely to make attempted field goals? *Justify* your answer.

 at classzone.com

Adam Vinatieri

23. CHALLENGE The table shows the results of Congressional elections that involved incumbent candidates (representatives or senators who ran for re-election) during the period 1980–2000.

	Incumbent representatives		Incumbent senators	
	Ran	Re-elected	Ran	Re-elected
Presidential election year	2373	2235	163	130
Midterm election year	1984	1873	145	130

   a. Did a *representative* or a *senator* have a better chance of being re-elected? *Justify* your answer using the data in the table.

   b. During what type of election year did a member of Congress have a better chance of being re-elected? *Justify* your answer.

◆ CALIFORNIA STANDARDS SPIRAL REVIEW

Alg. 20.0

24. Which of the following is a solution of $x^2 - 4x + 1 = 0$? *(p. 649)*

   Ⓐ $-2 + \sqrt{2}$ Ⓑ $2 + \sqrt{3}$ Ⓒ $3 + \sqrt{2}$ Ⓓ $3 + \sqrt{3}$

Alg. 12.0

25. Which expression is equivalent to $\dfrac{x^2 - 4x + 4}{x^2 - 4}$? *(p. 688)*

   Ⓐ $\dfrac{x - 2}{x + 2}$ Ⓑ $\dfrac{x + 2}{x - 2}$ Ⓒ $4x$ Ⓓ -1

Alg. 23.0

26. The height h (in feet) of a coin dropped from a bridge can be modeled by $h = -16t^2 + 100$ where t is the time (in seconds) since the coin was dropped. How long will it take the coin to reach the water below? *(p. 633)*

   Ⓐ 1 sec   Ⓑ 1.5 sec   Ⓒ 2 sec   Ⓓ 2.5 sec

12.2 Find Probabilities Using Permutations

Standards Preview

Alg. 2 18.0 Students use fundamental counting principles to compute combinations and **permutations.**

Alg. 2 19.0 Students use combinations and **permutations** to compute probabilities.

Connect *Before* you used counting methods to count possibilities. *Now* you will find permutations to prepare for Algebra 2 Standards 18.0 and 19.0.

Math and **BANDS**
Ex. 45, p. 754

Key Vocabulary
• **permutation**
• *n* **factorial**

A **permutation** is an arrangement of objects in which order is important. For instance, the 6 possible permutations of the letters A, B, and C are shown.

ABC   ACB   BAC   BCA   CAB   CBA

EXAMPLE 1   Count permutations

Consider the number of permutations of the letters in the word JULY.

  a. In how many ways can you arrange all of the letters?

  b. In how many ways can you arrange 2 of the letters?

Solution

REVIEW COUNTING PRINCIPLE

For help with using the counting principle, see p. 805.

  a. Use the counting principle to find the number of permutations of the letters in the word JULY.

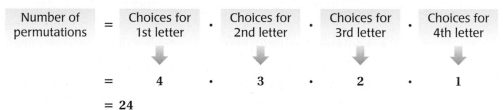

$$= 4 \cdot 3 \cdot 2 \cdot 1$$

$$= 24$$

  ▶ There are 24 ways you can arrange all of the letters in the word JULY.

  b. When arranging 2 letters of the word JULY, you have 4 choices for the first letter and 3 choices for the second letter.

$$\begin{array}{c} \text{Number of} \\ \text{permutations} \end{array} = \begin{array}{c} \text{Choices for} \\ \text{1st letter} \end{array} \cdot \begin{array}{c} \text{Choices for} \\ \text{2nd letter} \end{array}$$

$$= 4 \cdot 3$$

$$= 12$$

  ▶ There are 12 ways you can arrange 2 of the letters in the word JULY.

✓ **GUIDED PRACTICE**   for Example 1

  1. In how many ways can you arrange all the letters in the word MOUSE? just 3 letters in the word MOUSE?

FACTORIAL In Example 1, you evaluated the expression $4 \cdot 3 \cdot 2 \cdot 1$. This expression can be written as 4! and is read "4 *factorial*." For any positive integer n, the product of the integers from 1 to n is called ***n* factorial** and is written as $n!$. The value of 0! is defined to be 1.

$$n! = n \cdot (n-1) \cdot (n-2) \cdot \ldots \cdot 3 \cdot 2 \cdot 1 \text{ and } 0! = 1$$

In Example 1, you also found the number of permutations of 4 objects taken 2 at a time. You can use the formulas below to find the number of permutations.

KEY CONCEPT   *For Your Notebook*

Permutations

Formulas	**Examples**
The number of permutations of n objects is given by: $$_nP_n = n!$$	The number of permutations of 4 objects is: $$_4P_4 = 4! = 4 \cdot 3 \cdot 2 \cdot 1 = 24$$
The number of permutations of n objects taken r at a time, where $r \leq n$, is given by: $$_nP_r = \frac{n!}{(n-r)!}$$	The number of permutations of 4 objects taken 2 at a time is: $$_4P_2 = \frac{4!}{(4-2)!} = \frac{4 \cdot 3 \cdot \cancel{2!}}{\cancel{2!}} = 12$$

EXAMPLE 2 **Use a permutations formula**

CD RECORDING Your band has written 12 songs and plans to record 9 of them for a CD. In how many ways can you arrange the songs on the CD?

You record 9 songs.

Solution

To find the number of permutations of 9 songs chosen from 12, find $_{12}P_9$.

$_{12}P_9 = \dfrac{12!}{(12-9)!}$ **Permutations formula**

$= \dfrac{12!}{3!}$ **Subtract.**

$= \dfrac{12 \cdot 11 \cdot 10 \cdot 9 \cdot 8 \cdot 7 \cdot 6 \cdot 5 \cdot 4 \cdot \cancel{3!}}{\cancel{3!}}$ **Expand factorials.**
   Divide out common factor, 3!.

$= 79,833,600$ **Multiply.**

▶ There are 79,833,600 ways to arrange 9 songs out of 12.

> **DIVIDE COMMON FACTORS**
> When you divide out common factors, remember that 3! is a factor of 12!.

✓ **GUIDED PRACTICE** **for Example 2**

2. **WHAT IF?** In Example 2, suppose your band has written 15 songs. You will record 9 of them for a CD. In how many ways can you arrange the songs on the CD?

EXAMPLE 3 ◆ **Multiple Choice Practice**

A trailer license plate once issued by California had 2 letters followed by 4 digits. The letters I, O, and Q were not used. Each letter and digit was used only once. How many different trailer license plates were possible?

(A) 506

(B) 5040

(C) 2,550,240

(D) 18,144,000

ELIMINATE CHOICES
If all the characters on the plate were (different) digits there would be $_{10}P_6 = 151{,}200$ possibilities. Because two characters are letters, there are even more possibilities. So, eliminate choices A and B.

Solution

STEP 1 **Find** the number of permutations of 2 letters chosen from 23.

$$_{23}P_2 = \frac{23!}{(23-2)!} = \frac{23!}{21!} = \frac{23 \cdot 22 \cdot \cancel{21!}}{\cancel{21!}} = 506$$

STEP 2 **Find** the number of permutations of 4 digits chosen from 10.

$$_{10}P_4 = \frac{10!}{(10-4)!} = \frac{10!}{6!} = \frac{10 \cdot 9 \cdot 8 \cdot 7 \cdot \cancel{6!}}{\cancel{6!}} = 5040$$

STEP 3 **Calculate** the number of possible trailer license plates.

Find the product of the number of permutations of letters and the number of permutations of digits.

$$_{23}P_2 \cdot {_{10}P_4} = 506 \cdot 5040 = 2{,}550{,}240$$

There were 2,550,240 possible trailer license plates.

▶ The correct answer is C. (A) (B) (C) (D)

EXAMPLE 4 **Find a probability using permutations**

PARADE For a town parade, you will ride on a float with your soccer team. There are 12 floats in the parade, and their order is chosen at random. Find the probability that your float is first and the float with the school chorus is second.

Solution

STEP 1 **Write** the number of possible outcomes as the number of permutations of the 12 floats in the parade. This is $_{12}P_{12} = 12!$.

STEP 2 **Write** the number of favorable outcomes as the number of permutations of the other floats, given that the soccer team is first and the chorus is second. This is $_{10}P_{10} = 10!$.

STEP 3 **Calculate** the probability.

$$P\binom{\text{soccer team is first and}}{\text{chorus is second}} = \frac{10!}{12!}$$

Form a ratio of favorable to possible outcomes.

$$= \frac{\cancel{10!}}{12 \cdot 11 \cdot \cancel{10!}}$$

Expand factorials. Divide out common factor, 10!.

$$= \frac{1}{132}$$

Simplify.

3. **WHAT IF?** In Example 3, suppose the letters I, O, and Q, and the digits 0 and 1 are *not* used. How many different trailer license plates are possible?

4. **WHAT IF?** In Example 4, suppose there are 14 floats in the parade. Find the probability that the float with the soccer team is first and the float with the chorus is second.

12.2 **EXERCISES**

HOMEWORK KEY

◆ = **MULTIPLE CHOICE PRACTICE**
Exs. 16, 35, 40, 42, and 48–50

○ = **HINTS AND HOMEWORK HELP**
for Exs. 9, 27, and 41 at classzone.com

SKILLS · PROBLEM SOLVING · REASONING

1. **VOCABULARY** Copy and complete: An arrangement of objects in which order is important is called a(n) __?__ .

2. **NOTETAKING SKILLS** Make a summary triangle like the one on page 742 for permutations.

EXAMPLE 1
on p. 750
for Exs. 3–14

COUNTING PERMUTATIONS Find the number of ways you can arrange (a) all of the letters in the given California city name and (b) just 2 of the letters in the city name. Ignore the space between parts of a city's name.

3. BREA
4. ACTON
5. ORANGE
6. SAN JOSE

7. FRESNO
8. NORWALK
9. SAN PEDRO
10. MOUNT BALDY

11. PLYMOUTH
12. HEALDSBURG
13. MONTCLAIR
14. MUIR BEACH

EXAMPLE 2
on p. 751
for Exs. 15–35

15. **OPEN-ENDED** *Describe* a real-world situation where the number of possibilities is given by $_5P_2$.

16. ◆ **MULTIPLE CHOICE** What is the value of $_8P_3$?

    (A) 6
    (B) 336
    (C) 6720
    (D) 40,320

FACTORIALS AND PERMUTATIONS Evaluate the expression.

17. $1!$
18. $3!$
19. $5!$
20. $7!$

21. $8!$
22. $10!$
23. $12!$
24. $13!$

25. $_5P_2$
26. $_9P_1$
27. $_7P_3$
28. $_6P_5$

29. $_8P_8$
30. $_{12}P_0$
31. $_{30}P_2$
32. $_{25}P_5$

ERROR ANALYSIS *Describe* and correct the error in evaluating the expression.

33.
$$_{11}P_7 = \frac{11!}{11-7} = \frac{11!}{4} = 9{,}979{,}200 \quad ✗$$

34.
$$_5P_3 = \frac{5!}{3!} = \frac{5 \cdot 4 \cdot \cancel{3!}}{\cancel{3!}} = 20 \quad ✗$$

35. ◆ **MULTIPLE CHOICE** What is the value of $_{10}P_3 \cdot {}_4P_2$?

    (A) 1440
    (B) 8640
    (C) 10,080
    (D) 7,257,600

CONNECT SKILLS TO PROBLEM SOLVING Exercises 36–38 will help you prepare for problem solving.

Use the following information: You have 10 beads, each a different color. You place the beads, in random order, on a string.

36. How many different ways can you arrange the beads on the string?

37. How many different ways can you arrange the remaining beads if a green bead is first and a yellow bead is second?

38. What is the probability that you randomly place a green bead first and a yellow bead second?

EXAMPLE 3
on p. 752
for Exs. 39–42

39. **MOVIES** Six friends go to a movie theater. In how many different ways can they sit together in a row of 6 empty seats?

California **@HomeTutor** for problem solving help at classzone.com

40. ◆ **MULTIPLE CHOICE** You plan to visit 4 stores during a shopping trip. In how many orders can you visit these stores?

(A) 4   (B) 16   (C) 24   (D) 256

California **@HomeTutor** for problem solving help at classzone.com

41. **PASSWORDS** You are creating a password for your new e-mail account. You decide to use 3 letters followed by 5 digits for your password. You will not repeat any letter or digit. How many different passwords are possible?

42. ◆ **MULTIPLE CHOICE** The judges in an art contest award prizes for first, second, and third place out of 11 entries. Which expression gives the number of ways the judges can award first, second, and third place?

(A) $\dfrac{3!}{11!}$ (B) $\dfrac{8!}{11!}$ (C) $\dfrac{11!}{8!}$ (D) $\dfrac{11!}{3!}$

EXAMPLE 4
on p. 752
for Exs. 43–45

43. **HISTORY EXAM** On an exam, you are asked to list 5 historical events in the order in which they occurred. You guess the order of the events at random. What is the probability that you choose the correct order?

44. **SPIRIT** You make 6 posters to hold up at a basketball game. Each poster has a letter of the word TIGERS. You and 5 friends sit next to each other in a row. The posters are distributed at random. What is the probability that TIGERS is spelled correctly when you hold up the posters?

45. **BAND COMPETITION** Seven marching bands will perform at a competition. The order of the performances is determined at random. What is the probability that your school band will perform first, followed by the band from the one other high school in your town?

46. CHALLENGE Consider a set of 4 objects and a set of n objects.

  a. Are there more permutations of all 4 of the objects or of 3 of the 4 objects? *Justify* your answer using an organized list.

  b. In general, are there more permutations of n objects taken n at a time or of n objects taken $n - 1$ at a time? *Justify* your answer using the formula for the number of permutations.

47. CHALLENGE You and a friend are 2 of the 10 performers in a school talent show. The order of the performances is determined at random. The first five performers go on stage before the intermission, while the remaining five performers go on stage after the intermission.

  a. What is the probability that you are the last performer before the intermission and your friend performs immediately before you?

  b. What is the probability that you are *not* the first performer?

◆ CALIFORNIA STANDARDS SPIRAL REVIEW

Alg. 14.0
48. What number must you add to each side of the quadratic equation $x^2 + 12x = -8$ to complete the square? *(p. 643)*

Ⓐ -8 Ⓑ -6 Ⓒ 6 Ⓓ 36

Alg. 16.0
49. Which relation is a function? *(p. 249)*

Ⓐ $\{(5, 1), (4, 2), (3, 3), (2, 4)\}$ Ⓑ $\{(0, 0), (1, 1), (2, 2), (2, 3)\}$

Ⓒ $\{(1, 1), (1, 4), (4, 4), (4, 1)\}$ Ⓓ $\{(0, 0), (0, -4), (-4, 0), (-4, -4)\}$

Alg. 2.0
50. A fence is built around a square garden. The area of the garden is 256 square yards. What is the length of the fence? *(p. 95)*

Ⓐ 40 yd   Ⓑ 48 yd   Ⓒ 56 yd   Ⓓ 64 yd

QUIZ *for Lessons 12.1–12.2*

Evaluate the expression. *(p. 750)*

1. $2!$ **2.** $4!$ **3.** $0!$ **4.** $6!$

5. $_5P_4$ **6.** $_3P_1$ **7.** $_9P_9$ **8.** $_7P_6$

9. MARBLES A bag contains 16 red marbles, 8 white marbles, and 12 blue marbles. You randomly select one marble from the bag. *(p. 744)*

  a. What is the probability that you select a red marble?

  b. What is the probability that you do *not* select a blue marble?

10. CD SHUFFLE You are playing a CD with 14 songs on random shuffle. Your CD player selects a song at random, plays it, then selects another song at random and plays it. No song is repeated until every song is played. What is the probability that song 3 is played first and song 1 is played second? *(p. 750)*

12.3 Find Probabilities Using Combinations

Standards Preview

Alg. 2 18.0 Students use fundamental counting principles to compute **combinations** and permutations.

Alg. 2 19.0 Students use **combinations** and permutations **to** compute **probabilities**.

Connect *Before* you used permutations to count possibilities. *Now* you will use combinations to prepare for Algebra 2 Standards 18.0 and 19.0.

Math and **PHOTOGRAPHY**
Ex. 31, p. 759

Key Vocabulary
• combination

A **combination** is a selection of objects in which order is *not* important. For instance, in a drawing for 3 identical prizes, you would use combinations, because the order of the winners would not matter. If the prizes were different, you would use permutations, because the order would matter.

EXAMPLE 1   Count combinations

Count the combinations of 2 letters from the list A, B, C, D.

Solution

List all of the permutations of 2 letters in the list A, B, C, D. Because order is not important in a combination, cross out any duplicate pairs.

AB	AC	AD	~~BA~~	BC	BD ←
~~CA~~	~~CB~~	CD	~~DA~~	~~DB~~	~~DC~~

→ BD and DB are the same pair.

▶ There are 6 possible combinations of 2 letters from the list A, B, C, D.

Animated Algebra

For an interactive example of counting combinations, go to **classzone.com**.

✓ **GUIDED PRACTICE**   for Example 1

1. Count the combinations of 3 letters from the list A, B, C, D.

COMBINATIONS Instead of making an organized list, you can find the number of combinations using the formula below (see Exercise 24).

KEY CONCEPT   *For Your Notebook*

Combinations

Formula

The number of combinations of *n* objects taken *r* at a time, where $r \leq n$, is given by:

$$_nC_r = \frac{n!}{(n-r)! \cdot r!}$$

Example

The number of combinations of 4 objects taken 2 at a time is:

$$_4C_2 = \frac{4!}{(4-2)! \cdot 2!} = \frac{4 \cdot 3 \cdot 2!}{2! \cdot (2 \cdot 1)} = 6$$

EXAMPLE 2 Use the combinations formula

LUNCH MENU You order a sandwich at a restaurant. You can choose 2 side dishes from a list of 8. How many combinations of side dishes are possible?

Solution

The order in which you choose the side dishes is not important. So, to find the number of combinations of 8 side dishes taken 2 at a time, find $_8C_2$.

$$_8C_2 = \frac{8!}{(8-2)! \cdot 2!} \quad \text{Combinations formula}$$

$$= \frac{8!}{6! \cdot 2!} \quad \text{Subtract.}$$

$$= \frac{8 \cdot 7 \cdot \cancel{6!}}{\cancel{6!} \cdot (2 \cdot 1)} \quad \begin{array}{l}\text{Expand factorials.} \\ \text{Divide out common factor, 6!.}\end{array}$$

$$= 28 \quad \text{Simplify.}$$

▶ There are 28 different combinations of side dishes you can order.

EXAMPLE 3 ◆ **Multiple Choice Practice**

Julie and Nathan are among 12 student members of the school board. Two student board members will be selected at random to serve as spokespersons. What is the probability that Julie and Nathan will be the 2 student board members selected?

(A) $\frac{1}{66}$ **(B)** $\frac{1}{33}$ **(C)** $\frac{1}{12}$ **(D)** $\frac{1}{6}$

STEP 1 **Write** the number of possible outcomes as the number of combinations of 12 people chosen 2 at a time, or $_{12}C_2$, because the order in which the members are chosen is not important.

$$_{12}C_2 = \frac{12!}{(12-2)! \, 2!} = \frac{12!}{10! \, 2!} = \frac{12 \cdot 11 \cdot \cancel{10!}}{\cancel{10!} \cdot 2!} = 66$$

STEP 2 **Find** the number of favorable outcomes. Only one of the possible combinations includes both Julie and Nathan.

STEP 3 **Calculate** the probability.

$$P(\text{Julie and Nathan}) = \frac{1}{66}$$

▶ The correct answer is A. (A) (B) (C) (D)

 GUIDED PRACTICE   for Examples 2 and 3

2. **WHAT IF?** In Example 2, suppose you can choose 3 side dishes out of the list of 8 side dishes. How many combinations are possible?

3. **WHAT IF?** In Example 3, suppose there are 20 student members on the school board. Find the probability that Julie and Nathan will be the 2 students selected at random to serve as spokespersons.

12.3 EXERCISES

HOMEWORK KEY

◆ = **MULTIPLE CHOICE PRACTICE**
Exs. 17, 18, 32, and 38–40

○ = **HINTS AND HOMEWORK HELP**
for Exs. 13, 21, and 31 at classzone.com

SKILLS · PROBLEM SOLVING · REASONING

1. **VOCABULARY** Copy and complete: A(n) __?__ is a selection of objects in which order is not important.

2. **WRITING** *Explain* how a combination differs from a permutation.

EXAMPLE 1
on p. 756
for Exs. 3–6

COMBINATIONS Count the combinations of 2 letters from the following lists.

3. A, B, C

4. A, B, C, D, E

5. A, B, C, D, E, F

6. **ERROR ANALYSIS** *Describe* and correct the error in listing all of the possible combinations of 2 letters from the list X, Y, Z.

XY	YX	ZX
XZ	YZ	ZY

✗

EXAMPLE 2
on p. 757
for Exs. 7–18

7. **ERROR ANALYSIS** *Describe* and correct the error in evaluating $_9C_4$.

$$_9C_4 = \frac{9!}{(9-4)!} = \frac{9!}{5!} = 3024 \quad ✗$$

8. **COMBINATIONS** Consider the digits 0–9. How many combinations of 4 digits are possible?

COMBINATIONS Evaluate the expression.

9. $_5C_1$

10. $_9C_5$

11. $_9C_9$

12. $_8C_6$

13. $_{12}C_3$

14. $_{11}C_4$

15. $_{15}C_8$

16. $_{20}C_5$

17. ◆ **MULTIPLE CHOICE** What is the value of $_{10}C_6$?

(A) 7

(B) 60

(C) 210

(D) 151,200

18. ◆ **MULTIPLE CHOICE** You have the first season of your favorite television show on a set of DVDs. The set contains 13 episodes. You have time to watch 3 episodes. How many combinations of 3 episodes can you watch?

(A) 286

(B) 572

(C) 1716

(D) 589,680

REASONING In Exercises 19–22, tell whether the question can be answered using *combinations* or *permutations*. *Explain* your choice, then answer the question.

19. Four students from your class of 120 students will be selected to organize a fundraiser. How many groups of 4 students are possible?

20. Ten students are auditioning for 3 different roles in a play. In how many ways can the 3 roles be filled?

21. To complete an exam, you must answer 8 questions from a list of 10 questions. In how many ways can you complete the exam?

22. In how many ways can 5 people sit in a car that holds 5 passengers?

23. **WRITING** Which is greater, $_6P_r$ or $_6C_r$? *Justify* your answer.

24. REASONING Complete the following and explain your reasoning: $_nP_r = \underline{\ ?\ } \cdot {_nC_r}$. Then use this equation to obtain the formula for $_nC_r$.

CONNECT SKILLS TO PROBLEM SOLVING Exercises 25–28 will help you prepare for problem solving.

Use the following information: You and your friend are 2 of the 9 students entered in a raffle. A teacher will randomly choose 2 of the students to win prizes. What is the probability that you and your friend are chosen as the winners?

25. Should you answer this question using combinations or permutations? *Explain*.

26. What is the number of possible outcomes?

27. What is the number of favorable outcomes?

28. Calculate the probability.

EXAMPLE 2
on p. 757
for Ex. 29

29. RESTAURANT You are ordering a burrito with 2 main ingredients and 3 toppings. The menu below shows the possible choices. How many different burritos are possible?

MAIN INGREDIENTS
chicken   black beans
steak   red beans
pork   rice

TOPPINGS
peppers   salsa
onions   pico de gallo
guacamole   extra cheese
jalapeños   black olives

California @HomeTutor for problem solving help at classzone.com

EXAMPLE 3
on p. 757
for Exs. 30–34

30. WORK SCHEDULE You work 3 evenings each week at a bookstore. Your supervisor assigns you 3 evenings at random from the 7 possibilities. What is the probability that your schedule this week includes working on Friday?

California @HomeTutor for problem solving help at classzone.com

31. PHOTOGRAPHY A yearbook editor has selected 14 photos, including one of you and one of your friend, to use in a collage for the yearbook. The photos are placed at random. There is room for 2 photos at the top of the page. What is the probability that your photo and your friend's photo are the 2 photos placed at the top of the page?

32. ◆ MULTIPLE CHOICE You and your friend are 2 of the 10 eighth graders on your school's soccer team. Your coach randomly chooses 2 eighth graders to be team captains. What is the probability that your coach chooses you and your friend?

   A $\frac{1}{5}$
   B $\frac{2}{45}$
   C $\frac{1}{45}$
   D $\frac{1}{90}$

33. ◆ **GEOMETRY** Use the figure at the right.

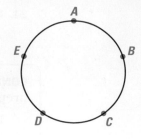

a. *Explain* how you can use combinations to determine how many different line segments you can draw using the labeled points as endpoints. Then find the number of segments.

b. How many different triangles can you draw using the labeled points as vertices?

c. How many different quadrilaterals can you draw using the labeled points as vertices?

34. **SHORT RESPONSE** On a television game show, 9 members of the studio audience are randomly selected to be eligible contestants.

a. Six of 9 eligible contestants are randomly chosen to play a game on the stage. How many combinations of 6 players from the group of eligible contestants are possible?

b. You and your 2 friends are part of the group of 9 eligible contestants. What is the probability that all 3 of you are chosen to play the game on stage? *Explain* how you found your answer.

35. **FRUIT DRINKS** The ad at the right is for a restaurant. You can choose from 1 to 4 juices to make a fruit drink.

a. Is the claim about the possible number of fruit drinks reasonable? *Explain* your reasoning.

b. Suppose you have 10 fruit juices from which to choose 1 to 4 juices. How many drinks are possible? *Explain*.

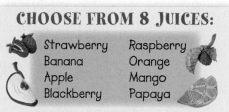

CHOOSE FROM 8 JUICES:

Strawberry	Raspberry
Banana	Orange
Apple	Mango
Blackberry	Papaya

Over 200 fruit drinks possible!
(Each fruit drink can contain up to four juices.)

36. **CHALLENGE** Prove that $_nC_r = {_n}C_{n-r}$. *Explain* why this makes sense.

37. **CHALLENGE** There are 30 students in your class. Your science teacher will choose 5 students at random to complete a group project. Find the probability that you and your 2 friends in the science class are chosen to work in the group. *Explain* how you found your answer.

◆ **CALIFORNIA STANDARDS SPIRAL REVIEW**

Alg. 21.0

38. The graph of $y = \frac{1}{2}x^2 + bx - 6$ passes through $(-2, 0)$. What is the value of b? *(p. 612)*

(A) −4 **(B)** −2 **(C)** 1 **(D)** 2

Alg. 17.0

39. The domain of the function $y = 8 - 3x$ is $\{-1, 0, 2, 5\}$. What is the range of the function? *(p. 257)*

(A) $\{-7, 2, 5, 8\}$ **(B)** $\{0, 2, 5, 8\}$ **(C)** $\{-7, 2, 8, 11\}$ **(D)** $\{1, 2, 2\frac{2}{3}, 3\}$

Alg. 13.0

40. Subtract: $\frac{4}{3x^2} - \frac{5}{4x}$. *(p. 705)*

(A) $\frac{16 - 5x}{12x^2}$ **(B)** $\frac{16 - 15x}{12x^2}$ **(C)** $\frac{-1}{3x^2 - 4x}$ **(D)** $\frac{16 - 15x}{12x}$

EXTRA PRACTICE for Lesson 12.3, p. 821 ✍ **ONLINE QUIZ** at classzone.com

12.3 Find Permutations and Combinations

Standards Preview

Alg. 2 19.0 Students use combinations and permutations to compute probabilities.

QUESTION How can you find permutations and combinations using a graphing calculator?

EXAMPLE 1 Find permutations and combinations

Evaluate (a) $_{16}P_5$ and (b) $_{12}C_7$.

Solution

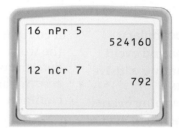

a. Find $_nP_r$ with $n = 16$ and $r = 5$. Enter 16 for n. Press MATH and go to the PRB menu. Select $_nP_r$. Then enter 5 for r. $_{16}P_5 = 524{,}160$.

b. Find $_nC_r$ with $n = 12$ and $r = 7$. Enter 12 for n. Press MATH and go to the PRB menu. Select $_nC_r$. Then enter 7 for r. $_{12}C_7 = 792$.

EXAMPLE 2 Find a probability

SOFTBALL There are 15 players on your softball team. Only 9 of the players can start a game. Your coach randomly chooses 9 starting players. What is the probability that your coach chooses you?

Solution

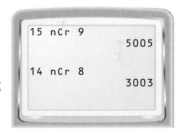

Step 1 **Find** the total number of outcomes. The number of ways to choose 9 starting players from 15 players is $_{15}C_9$. Use your calculator to find that $_{15}C_9 = 5005$.

Step 2 **Find** the number of favorable outcomes. If you are one of the starting players, the coach must choose 8 players from the remaining 14 players. Use your calculator to find that $_{14}C_8 = 3003$.

Step 3 **Calculate** the probability.

$$\frac{\text{Number of favorable outcomes}}{\text{Total number of outcomes}} = \frac{3003}{5005} = \frac{3}{5}$$

PRACTICE

Evaluate the expression.

1. $_7C_4$ **2.** $_{10}C_3$ **3.** $_9P_5$ **4.** $_{11}P_8$

5. GROUP PROJECT Your teacher randomly selects 3 students from a class of 28 students to work on a group project. What is the probability that your teacher selects you for the project?

12.4 Find Probabilities of Compound Events

Math and **NATURE**
Ex. 22, p. 767

> **Standards Review**
>
> **Gr. 6 SDAP 3.4** Understand that the probability of either of two disjoint events occurring is the sum of the two individual probabilities and that the probability of one event following another, in independent trials, is the product of the two probabilities.
>
> **Gr. 6 SDAP 3.5** Understand the difference between independent and dependent events.

> **Connect**
>
> *Before* you found the probability of a simple event. *Now* you will find the probability of a compound event to review Grade 6 SDAP Standards 3.4 and 3.5.

Key Vocabulary
• compound event
• mutually exclusive events
• overlapping events
• independent events
• dependent events

A **compound event** combines two or more events, using the word *and* or the word *or*. To find the probability that either event *A* or event *B* occurs, determine how the events are related. **Mutually exclusive events**, or *disjoint events*, have no common outcomes. **Overlapping events** have at least one common outcome.

For instance, suppose you roll a number cube.

REVIEW VENN DIAGRAMS
For help with using Venn diagrams, see p. 809.

Mutually Exclusive Events	**Overlapping Events**
Event *A*: Roll a 3.	**Event *A*:** Roll an odd number.
Event *B*: Roll an even number.	**Event *B*:** Roll a prime number.

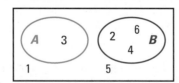

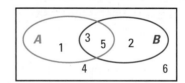

Set *A* has **1** number, and set *B* has **3** numbers. There are no numbers in both sets.

$P(3 \text{ or even}) = \frac{1}{6} + \frac{3}{6}$

$P(A \text{ or } B) = P(A) + P(B)$

Set *A* has **3** numbers, and set *B* has **3** numbers. There are **2** numbers in both sets.

$P(\text{odd or prime}) = \frac{3}{6} + \frac{3}{6} - \frac{2}{6}$

$P(A \text{ or } B) = P(A) + P(B) - P(A \text{ and } B)$

EXAMPLE 1 **Find the probability of *A* or *B***

You roll a number cube. Find the probability that you roll a 2 or an odd number.

Solution

Because 2 is an even number, rolling a 2 and rolling an odd number are mutually exclusive events.

$P(2 \text{ or odd}) = P(2) + P(\text{odd}) = \frac{1}{6} + \frac{3}{6} = \frac{4}{6} = \frac{2}{3}$

EXAMPLE 2 **Find the probability of *A* or *B***

You roll a number cube. Find the probability that you roll an even number or a prime number.

Solution

Because 2 is both an even number and a prime number, rolling an even number and rolling a prime number are overlapping events. There are 3 even numbers (2, 4, 6), 3 prime numbers (2, 3, 5), and 1 number that is both (2).

$$P(\text{even or prime}) = P(\text{even}) + P(\text{prime}) - P(\text{even and prime})$$

$$= \frac{3}{6} + \frac{3}{6} - \frac{1}{6}$$

$$= \frac{5}{6}$$

 GUIDED PRACTICE for Examples 1 and 2

1. You roll a number cube. Find the probability that you roll a 2 or a 5.

2. You roll a number cube. Find the probability that you roll a number less than 4 or an odd number.

INDEPENDENT AND DEPENDENT EVENTS To find the probability that event *A* and event *B* both occur, determine how the events are related. Two events are **independent events** if the occurrence of one event has no effect on the occurrence of the other. Two events are **dependent events** if the occurrence of one event affects the occurrence of the other.

For instance, consider the probability of choosing a green marble and then a blue marble from the bag shown. If you choose one marble and replace it before choosing the second, then the events are independent. If you do not replace the first marble, then the sample space has changed, and the events are dependent.

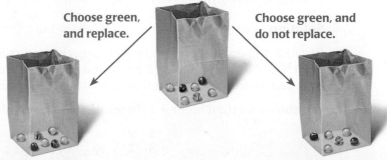

Choose green, and replace.

Choose green, and do not replace.

READING
The expression *P*(*B* given *A*) represents the probability that event *B* occurs given that event *A* has occurred. If *A* and *B* are independent events, *P*(*B* given *A*) = *P*(*B*).

Independent Events

With replacement:

$$P(\text{green and blue}) = \frac{4}{7} \cdot \frac{1}{7} = \frac{4}{49}$$

$$\boldsymbol{P(A \text{ and } B) = P(A) \cdot P(B)}$$

Dependent Events

Without replacement:

$$P(\text{green and blue}) = \frac{4}{7} \cdot \frac{1}{6} = \frac{2}{21}$$

$$\boldsymbol{P(A \text{ and } B) = P(A) \cdot P(B \text{ given } A)}$$

EXAMPLE 3 Find the probability of *A* and *B*

BUS SCHEDULE John takes a city bus from his neighborhood to a location within walking distance of a park. The express bus arrives at his neighborhood between 7:30 and 7:36. The local bus arrives at his neighborhood between 7:30 and 7:40. John arrives at the bus stop at 7:33. Find the probability that he misses both the express bus and the local bus.

Local bus arrives between 7:3 and 7:40.

ANOTHER WAY
For alternative methods for solving the problem in Example 3, turn to page 769 for the **Problem Solving Workshop**.

Solution

The events are independent. The arrival of one bus does not affect the arrival of the other bus.

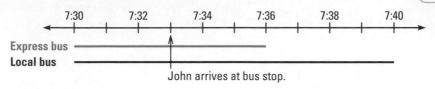

John arrives at bus stop.

There are 6 minutes when the express bus can arrive. John is not at the bus stop for 3 of those minutes.	There are 10 minutes when the local bus can arrive. John is not at the bus stop for 3 of those minutes.
P(**John misses express bus**) $= \dfrac{3}{6} = \dfrac{1}{2}$	P(**John misses local bus**) $= \dfrac{3}{10}$

Multiply the probabilities of the two events:

$$P(\text{John misses both buses}) = \frac{1}{2} \cdot \frac{3}{10} = \frac{3}{20}$$

▸ The probability that John misses both buses is $\dfrac{3}{20}$.

EXAMPLE 4 Find the probability of *A* and *B*

PEN COLORS A box contains 3 blue pens and 5 black pens. You choose one pen at random, do not replace it, then choose a second pen at random. What is the probability that both pens are blue?

Solution

Because you do not replace the first pen, the events are dependent. Before you choose a pen, there are 8 pens, and 3 of them are blue. After you choose a blue pen, there are 7 pens left and 2 of them are blue.

$$P(\text{blue and then blue}) = P(\text{blue}) \cdot P(\text{blue given blue})$$

$$= \frac{3}{8} \cdot \frac{2}{7} = \frac{6}{56} = \frac{3}{28}$$

✔ **GUIDED PRACTICE** for Examples 3 and 4

3. MARBLES A bag contains 4 red, 5 green, and 2 blue marbles. You randomly draw 2 marbles, one at a time. Find the probabililty that both are red if:

a. you replace the first marble.   **b.** you do not replace the first marble.

12.4 EXERCISES

HOMEWORK KEY

◆ = **MULTIPLE CHOICE PRACTICE**
Exs. 8, 13, 24, and 28–30

○ = **HINTS** and **HOMEWORK HELP**
for Exs. 5, 15, and 23 at classzone.com

SKILLS · PROBLEM SOLVING · REASONING

1. **VOCABULARY** Copy and complete: The probability of __?__ events is found using the formula $P(A \text{ and } B) = P(A) \cdot P(B \text{ given } A)$.

2. **WRITING** *Explain* how overlapping events differ from mutually exclusive events.

EXAMPLES
1 and 2
on pp. 762–763
for Exs. 3–8

PROBABILITY OF A OR B In Exercises 3–6, you roll a number cube. Tell whether the events *A* and *B* are *mutually exclusive* or *overlapping*. Then find $P(A \text{ or } B)$.

3. **Event A:** Roll a 6.
   Event B: Roll a prime number.

4. **Event A:** Roll an even number.
   Event B: Roll a 5.

5. **Event A:** Roll an odd number.
   Event B: Roll a number less than 5.

6. **Event A:** Roll a multiple of 3.
   Event B: Roll an even number.

7. **ERROR ANALYSIS** A bag contains 7 yellow marbles, 4 red marbles, and 5 blue marbles. *Describe* and correct the error in finding the probability that you randomly draw a yellow or blue marble.

$$P(\text{yellow or blue}) = P(\text{yellow}) \cdot P(\text{blue}) = \frac{7}{16} \cdot \frac{5}{16} = \frac{35}{256}$$ ✗

8. ◆ **MULTIPLE CHOICE** A bag contains 10 tiles with the numbers 1–10 on them. You randomly choose a tile from the bag. What is the probability that you choose an even number or a number less than 5?

   A 0.7   **B** 0.8   **C** 0.9   **D** 1

EXAMPLES
3 and 4
on p. 764
for Exs. 9–12

PROBABILITY OF A AND B In Exercises 9–12, tell whether the events *A* and *B* are *dependent* or *independent*. Then find $P(A \text{ and } B)$.

9. You roll two number cubes.
   Event A: You roll a 2 first.
   Event B: You roll a 5 next.

10. You flip a coin and roll a number cube.
    Event A: The coin shows heads.
    Event B: The number cube shows 2.

11. You write each of the letters of the word BIOLOGY on pieces of paper and place them in a bag. You randomly draw one letter, do not replace it, then randomly draw a second letter.
    Event A: The first letter is O.
    Event B: The second letter is B.

12. A bowl contains 3 apples, 3 oranges, and 4 pears. You choose a piece of fruit at random, eat it, then choose a second piece of fruit at random.
    Event A: You choose a pear first.
    Event B: You choose a pear next.

13. ◆ **MULTIPLE CHOICE** A vase holds 7 red roses and 5 pink roses. You randomly choose a rose, place it in a different vase, then randomly choose another rose. What is the approximate probability that both roses are red?

(**A**) 0.29   (**B**) 0.32   (**C**) 0.34   (**D**) 0.37

CHESS PIECES In Exercises 14–17, consider a bag that contains all of the pieces in a chess set, as shown in the diagram.

	King	Queen	Bishop	Rook	Knight	Pawn
Black	1	1	2	2	2	8
White	1	1	2	2	2	8

14. You choose one piece at random. Find the probability that you choose a black piece or a queen.

15. You choose one piece at random, replace it, then choose a second piece at random. Find the probability that you choose a rook, then a bishop.

16. You choose one piece at random, do not replace it, then choose a second piece at random. Find the probability that you choose a king, then a pawn.

17. **ERROR ANALYSIS** *Describe* and correct the error in finding the probability that you randomly choose a pawn and then a second pawn, without replacement.

$$P(\text{pawn and pawn}) = P(\text{pawn}) \cdot P(\text{pawn})$$
$$= \frac{16}{32} \cdot \frac{16}{32} = \frac{1}{4}$$

CONNECT SKILLS TO PROBLEM SOLVING Exercises 18–20 will help you prepare for problem solving.

Given events *A* and *B*, determine which path along the decision tree you should use to find the probability. *Explain* your reasoning.

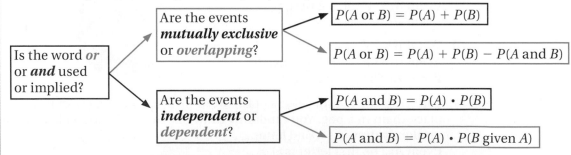

18. You roll a number cube. Find the probability of rolling a 3 or a 4.

19. A bag contains 5 red marbles and 6 black marbles. Find the probability of choosing a black marble, not replacing it, then choosing a red marble.

20. You flip a coin and roll a number cube. Find the probability of getting tails and rolling a 5.

EXAMPLES
3 and 4
·········
on p. 764
for Exs. 21–22

21. CONTEST You can win concert tickets from a radio station if you are the first person to call when the song of the day is played, or if you are the first person to answer the trivia question correctly. The song of the day is played between 5:00 and 5:30 P.M. The trivia question is asked between 5:15 and 5:45 P.M. You begin listening to the radio station at 5:20 P.M. Find the probability that you miss the song of the day and the trivia question.

California @*HomeTutor* for problem solving help at classzone.com

22. WALRUS When a walrus looks for food, it waves its flipper to move sediment 70% of the time. When using the flipper wave technique, a walrus uses its right flipper 89% of the time. Find the probability that a walrus looking for food uses a flipper and it is the right flipper.

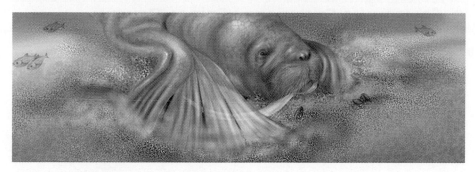

California @*HomeTutor* for problem solving help at classzone.com

EXAMPLES
1, 2, 3, and 4
·············
on pp. 762–764
for Ex. 23

(23.) SHORT RESPONSE A survey of 887,403 households found that 270,658 households have a dog, 326,591 have a cat, and 81,641 have both.

a. What is the probability that one of the households surveyed, chosen at random, has a dog and a cat?

b. What is the probability that one of the households surveyed, chosen at random, has a dog or a cat?

c. *Explain* how your answers to parts (a) and (b) are related.

24. ◆ MULTIPLE CHOICE The table shows the ranges of annual mean temperature and precipitation for 57 cities in the United States. Find the probability that a city in this study has an annual mean temperature in the range 39°F–52°F or an annual precipitation in the range 0–24 inches.

Precipitation (inches)	Temperature (degrees Fahrenheit)	
	39–52	53–66
0–24	7	7
25–49	21	22

(A) $\dfrac{28}{57}$ (B) $\dfrac{35}{57}$ (C) $\dfrac{42}{57}$ (D) $\dfrac{50}{57}$

25. REASONING *Explain* why $P(not\ A) = 1 - P(A)$ for an event A.

26. CHALLENGE The sections of the spinner shown all have the same area. You spin the spinner.

a. Find the probability that the spinner stops on red *or* a prime number *or* a multiple of 3. You may want to draw a Venn diagram to find the answer.

b. Write a general formula for $P(A\ or\ B\ or\ C)$ where A, B, and C are overlapping events. *Explain* your reasoning.

27. **CHALLENGE** You have 5 tickets to a play. You invite 4 friends to see the play. You hand out the tickets at random. One ticket is for an aisle seat, and the other tickets are for the next 4 seats in the row.

Number of tickets: 5

a. What is the probability that you will get the aisle seat?

b. What is the probability that you will get the aisle seat and your best friend will get the ticket for the seat next to you?

c. *Explain* how you could solve the problem in part (b) using permutations.

◆ CALIFORNIA STANDARDS SPIRAL REVIEW

Alg. 6.0

28. Which of the following is the graph of $x - 2y > -6$? *(p. 425)*

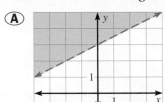
Ⓐ

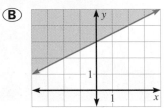
Ⓑ

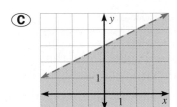
Ⓒ

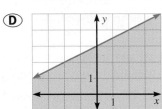
Ⓓ

Alg. 8.0

29. Which line is perpendicular to $3x + 4y = 4$? *(p. 354)*

Ⓐ $-3x + 4y = 4$ Ⓑ $-4x + 3y = 3$ Ⓒ $4x + 3y = 3$ Ⓓ $3x + 4y = -4$

Alg. 25.3

30. Which statement is true for any real number x? *(p. 102)*

Ⓐ $-|x|$ is always positive.   Ⓑ $-|-x|$ is always positive.

Ⓒ $|-x|$ is never negative.   Ⓓ $|-x|$ is sometimes negative.

QUIZ *for Lessons 12.3–12.4*

Evaluate the expression. *(p. 756)*

1. $_6C_3$ 2. $_7C_2$ 3. $_{12}C_8$ 4. $_{15}C_5$

5. **ELECTIVES** Your school offers 10 elective courses each semester. You have time in your schedule for 2 of these courses. How many combinations of 2 elective courses can you choose? *(p. 756)*

6. **NUMBER TILES** A bag contains 30 number tiles labeled 1–30. *(p. 762)*

a. You select one tile at random. What is the probability that you select an odd number or a prime number?

b. You replace the tile in part (a), then randomly choose a second tile. What is the probability that both tiles are odd numbers?

Using ALTERNATIVE METHODS

Another Way to Solve Example 3, page 764

In Example 3 on page 764, you saw how to solve the problem about a bus schedule by using a number line and a formula. You can also solve the problem by performing a simulation or using geometry.

PROBLEM

BUS SCHEDULE John takes a city bus from his neighborhood to a location within walking distance of a park. The express bus arrives at his neighborhood between 7:30 and 7:36. The local bus arrives at his neighborhood between 7:30 and 7:40. John arrives at the bus stop at 7:33. Find the probability that John misses both the express bus and the local bus.

METHOD 1

Performing a Simulation One alternative approach is to perform a simulation.

STEP 1 **Read** the problem. Notice that there is a 6 minute interval when the express bus could arrive and a 10 minute interval when the local bus could arrive. Let 1 represent the first minute, from 7:30 to 7:31, that a bus could arrive. Let 2 represent the second minute, from 7:31 to 7:32, that a bus could arrive. Continue to number the minutes when a bus could arrive.

STEP 2 **Generate** random integers. Use a graphing calculator to generate a random integer from 1 to 6. This number represents the minute that the express bus arrives. Then generate a random integer from 1 to 10. This number represents the minute that the local bus arrives. Perform this simulation 10 times.

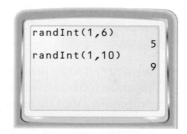

```
randInt(1,6)
                    5
randInt(1,10)
                    9
```

John is not at the bus stop until the fourth minute, so if both numbers that you generate are less than 4, then John misses both buses.

First number	5	4	2	5	2	1	2	3	3	1
Second number	9	1	1	8	4	7	9	10	6	2
Miss both buses?	No	No	Yes	No	No	No	No	No	No	Yes

STEP 3 **Find** the experimental probability that John misses both buses.

$$P(\text{John misses both buses}) = \frac{2}{10} = \frac{1}{5}$$

METHOD 2 **Using Geometry** Another approach is to use geometry. Use the formula for the area of a rectangle to find the number of possible outcomes and the number of favorable outcomes.

STEP 1 **Draw** a rectangle whose side lengths represent the number of minutes that each bus could arrive.

STEP 2 **Draw** a square within the rectangle to represent the number of minutes that John is *not* at the bus stop.

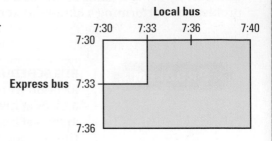

STEP 3 **Calculate** the area of the rectangle that represents the time a bus could arrive. Also calculate the area of the square that represents the time that John is *not* at the bus stop.

Time a bus could arrive: Time John is *not* at the bus stop:
$A = 6 \cdot 10 = 60$ $A = 3 \cdot 3 = 9$

STEP 4 **Find** the probability that John misses both buses by forming the ratio of the areas from Step 2.

$$P(\text{John misses both buses}) = \frac{9}{60} = \frac{3}{20}$$

PRACTICE

1. **WHAT IF?** In the problem on page 769, suppose John arrives at 7:34. What is the probability that he misses both buses?

2. **VISITING FRIENDS** Two friends are planning to visit you this evening. You expect one friend to arrive at your house between 7:00 and 7:30 P.M. You expect the other friend to arrive between 7:10 and 7:20 P.M. You have to run an errand from 7:00 until 7:15 P.M. What is the probability that you are home when both friends arrive? Solve this problem using two different methods.

3. **WHAT IF?** In Exercise 2, suppose a third friend plans to visit you this evening. This friend plans to arrive at your house between 7:00 and 7:20 P.M. What is the probability that you are home when all three of your friends arrive? *Explain* how you found your answer.

4. **RAFFLE** You enter two different raffles during your neighborhood's street fair. The winner of the first raffle will be announced between 6:00 and 6:30 P.M. The winner of the second raffle will be announced between 6:15 and 6:45 P.M. You leave the fair at 5:00 P.M. and return at 6:20 P.M. What is the probability that you hear the winner of each raffle announced? Solve this problem using two different methods.

5. **ERROR ANALYSIS** A student solved the problem in Exercise 4 as shown. *Describe* and correct the error.

$$P(\text{hear both winners}) = \frac{\text{Favorable time}}{\text{Total time}}$$

$$= \frac{10 \text{ minutes}}{30 \text{ minutes}} = \frac{1}{3}$$

MIXED REVIEW of Skills and Problem Solving

Multiple Choice Practice for Lessons 12.1–12.4

1. A study surveyed 100 male and 100 female 13-year-olds as well as 100 male and 100 female 15-year-olds. The table shows the numbers of those surveyed who eat fruit every day. For which of the following groups is a randomly selected person most likely to eat fruit every day? **Gr. 6 SDAP 3.3**

	13-year-olds	15-year-olds
Male	60	53
Female	61	58

   (A) 15-year-old females

   (B) 13-year-old males

   (C) 13-year-olds

   (D) 15-year-old males

2. In NCAA women's basketball tournaments from 1982 to 2003, the teams seeded, or ranked, number one have won 283 games and lost 71 games in the tournament. What is the probability that a team, chosen at random from all those that have been seeded number one, lost a game in the tournament? **Gr. 6 SDAP 3.3**

   (A) $\frac{71}{354}$ (B) $\frac{71}{283}$ (C) $\frac{212}{283}$ (D) $\frac{283}{354}$

3. In how many ways can you arrange 3 letters from the word EQUATION? **Alg. 2 18.0**

   (A) 56   (B) 336

   (C) 6270   (D) 40,320

4. Each section of the spinner shown has the same area. You spin the spinner. What is the probability that the spinner lands on blue or an even number? **Gr. 6 SDAP 3.4**

   (A) $\frac{1}{8}$

   (B) $\frac{1}{2}$

   (C) $\frac{3}{4}$

   (D) $\frac{7}{8}$

5. You arrange the letters shown below at random. What is the probability that you arrange the letters so that the word ANGLE is spelled? **Alg. 2 19.0**

   A L G E N

   (A) $\frac{1}{5}$ (B) $\frac{1}{10}$ (C) $\frac{1}{60}$ (D) $\frac{1}{120}$

6. What is $_6C_2$? **Alg. 2 18.0**

   (A) 6   (B) 15   (C) 24   (D) 30

7. You are ordering an omelet with two toppings. You can choose your toppings from the list shown below. How many possible omelets can you choose? **Alg. 2 18.0**

   OMELET TOPPINGS
   CHEESE, MUSHROOMS, SPINACH, TOMATOES, PEPPERS, BROCCOLI, ONIONS, CHICKEN

   (A) 15   (B) 28   (C) 56   (D) 64

8. Your friend is competing in a talent show. There are 5 contestants in the show, and the order of the contestants is determined randomly. You are running late and will miss the first 2 contestants. What is the probability that you will *not* miss your friend's performance? **Alg. 2 19.0**

   (A) 30%   (B) 36%

   (C) 60%   (D) 80%

9. A jar contains 7 pennies, 9 nickels, 6 dimes, and 14 quarters. You randomly choose one coin from the jar, do not replace it, then randomly choose a second coin. What is the probability that you choose a dime and then a quarter? **Gr. 6 SDAP 3.5**

   (A) $\frac{1}{15}$ (B) $\frac{1}{6}$ (C) $\frac{5}{9}$ (D) $\frac{17}{30}$

BIG IDEAS
For Your Notebook

Big Idea 1

Finding Theoretical and Experimental Probabilities

Theoretical probability	All outcomes are equally likely.	$P(A) = \dfrac{\text{Number of favorable outcomes}}{\text{Total number of outcomes}}$
Experimental probability	Based on repeated trials of an experiment	$P(A) = \dfrac{\text{Number of successes}}{\text{Number of trials}}$

Big Idea 2

Finding the Number of Permutations and Combinations

A *permutation* is an arrangement of objects in which order is important.

Formula	Example
Number of permutations of n objects is: $$_nP_n = n! = n \cdot (n - 1) \cdot \ldots \cdot 2 \cdot 1$$	Number of permutations of 5 objects is: $$_5P_5 = 5! = 5 \cdot 4 \cdot 3 \cdot 2 \cdot 1 = 120$$
Number of permutations of n objects taken r at a time, where $r \leq n$, is: $$_nP_r = \dfrac{n!}{(n - r)!}$$	Number of permutations of 5 objects taken 2 at a time is: $$_5P_2 = \dfrac{5!}{(5 - 2)!} = \dfrac{5 \cdot 4 \cdot \cancel{3!}}{\cancel{3!}} = 20$$

A *combination* is a selection of objects in which order is *not* important.

Formula	Example
Number of permutations of n objects taken r at a time, where $r \leq n$, is: $$_nC_r = \dfrac{n!}{(n - r)! \cdot r!}$$	Number of combinations of 5 objects taken 2 at a time is: $$_5C_2 = \dfrac{5!}{(5 - 2)! \cdot 2!} = \dfrac{5 \cdot 4 \cdot \cancel{3!}}{\cancel{3!} \cdot 2!} = \dfrac{20}{2!} = 10$$

Combinations and permutations can be used to find probabilities.

Big Idea 3

Finding Probabilities of Compound Events

Two events can be *mutually exclusive* or *overlapping*.

Mutually exclusive	Events A and B have no common outcomes.	$P(A \text{ or } B) = P(A) + P(B)$
Overlapping	Events A and B have at least one common outcome.	$P(A \text{ or } B) = P(A) + P(B) - P(A \text{ and } B)$

Two events can be *independent* or *dependent*.

Independent	Occurrence of event A has no effect on occurrence of event B.	$P(A \text{ and } B) = P(A) \cdot P(B)$
Dependent	Occurrence of event A affects occurrence of event B.	$P(A \text{ and } B) = P(A) \cdot P(B \text{ given } A)$

APPLYING THE BIG IDEAS

Big Idea 1
You find theoretical and experimental probabilities in **Step 1**, **Step 3**, and **Ex. 2**.

Big Idea 2
You find the number of combinations in **Ex. 1**.

Big Idea 3
You find probabilities of compound events in **Step 3**.

PROBLEM How can you calculate the probability of winning a best of five series?

STEP 1 Find an experimental probability.

With a partner, play the game "rock, paper, scissors." Recall that paper beats rock, scissors beats paper, and rock beats scissors. Play the game 10 times with your partner. Keep track of how many games each player wins. Any time you and your partner have a tie, that game must be played over until there is a winner.

Use your results to calculate the experimental probability of winning 1 game. What is the experimental probability of losing 1 game?

STEP 2 Find the possible outcomes of winning a best of five series.

In a best of five series, the first person to win 3 games wins the series. Let W represent a win, and let L represent a loss. Three possible outcomes of winning a best of five series are:

WWW   Win the series in 3 games.

WWLW   Win the series in 4 games, losing the third game.

LWLWW   Win the series in 5 games, losing the first and third games.

List all the remaining possible outcomes of winning a best of five series.

STEP 3 Find the probability of winning the series.

Use your results from Step 1 and the fact that each game is an independent event to calculate the probability of each outcome found in Step 2. Add the probabilities together to find the probability of winning a best of five series.

Extending the Problem

1. Look at the list of possible outcomes from Step 2. Notice that when a series is won in four games, a loss occurs in 1 of 3 places. So, the number of possible outcomes when a series is won in four games is $_3C_1 = 3$. Use the same reasoning to write and evaluate a combinations expression for the number of possible outcomes when a series is won in five games. Then verify that the total number of possible outcomes found in Step 2 is correct.

2. Copy and complete the table below. What observations can you make?

Probability of winning 1 game	Probability of winning a best of five series	Probability of winning a best of seven series
0.38	?	?
0.74	?	?

REVIEW KEY VOCABULARY

- outcome, event, *p. 744*
- sample space, *p. 744*
- event, *p. 744*
- probability of an event, *p. 744*
- theoretical probability, *p. 745*

- experimental probability, *p. 745*
- permutation, *p. 750*
- *n* factorial, *p. 751*
- combination, *p. 756*
- compound event, *p. 762*

- mutually exclusive events, *p. 762*
- overlapping events, *p. 762*
- independent events, *p. 763*
- dependent events, *p. 763*

VOCABULARY EXERCISES

1. Copy and complete: An event that combines two or more events is a(n) __?__.

2. Copy and complete: A possible result of an experiment is a(n) __?__.

3. **NOTETAKING SKILLS** Make a summary triangle like the one on page 742 for independent events.

4. **WRITING** *Explain* what the notation $_9P_2$ represents. What is the value of this expression?

REVIEW EXAMPLES AND EXERCISES

Use the review examples and exercises below to check your understanding of the concepts you have learned in each lesson of Chapter 12.

12.1 Find Theoretical and Experimental Probabilities
pp. 744–749

Gr.6 SDAP 3.0

EXAMPLE

A bag contains 15 red checkers and 15 black checkers. You choose a checker at random. Find the probability that you choose a black checker.

$$P(\text{black checker}) = \frac{\text{Number of black checkers}}{\text{Total number of checkers}}$$

$$= \frac{15}{30}$$

$$= \frac{1}{2}$$

EXERCISES

EXAMPLE 2
on p. 745
for Exs. 5, 6

5. **CHECKERS** In the example above, suppose an extra red checker is added to the bag. Find the probability of randomly choosing a black checker.

6. **BAG OF LETTERS** A bag contains tiles. Each tile has one letter from the word HAPPINESS on it. You choose a tile at random. What is the probability that you choose a tile with the letter S?

12.2 Find Probabilities Using Permutations

Alg. 2 19.0

EXAMPLE

Mary has to enter a 4 digit code in order to enter the building where she works. The digits are 4 different numbers from 1 to 5. She forgot the code and tries to guess it. Find the probability that Mary guesses correctly.

STEP 1 **Write** the number of possible outcomes as the number of permutations of 4 out of the 5 possible digits. This is $_5P_4$.

$$_5P_4 = \frac{5!}{(5-4)!} = \frac{5!}{1!} = 5! = 5 \cdot 4 \cdot 3 \cdot 2 \cdot 1 = 120$$

STEP 2 **Find** the probability. Because only one of the permutations is the correct code, the probability that she guesses the correct code is $\frac{1}{120}$.

EXERCISES

EXAMPLE 2
on p. 751
for Exs. 7–11

Evaluate the expression.

7. $_7P_6$ **8.** $_6P_2$ **9.** $_8P_5$ **10.** $_{13}P_{10}$

11. MUSIC You downloaded 6 songs. You randomly choose 4 of these songs to play. Find the probability that you play the first 4 songs that you downloaded in the order in which you downloaded them.

12.3 Find Probabilities Using Combinations

Alg. 2 18.0

EXAMPLE

For a government class, Sara must choose 3 states in the United States to research. Sara decides to choose from the 6 New England states. How many combinations of states are possible?

The order in which Sara chooses the states is not important. So, to find the number of combinations of 6 states taken 3 at a time, find $_6C_3$.

$$_6C_3 = \frac{6!}{(6-3)! \cdot 3!}$$ **Combinations formula**

$$= \frac{6 \cdot 5 \cdot 4 \cdot \cancel{3!}}{\cancel{3!} \cdot (3 \cdot 2 \cdot 1)}$$ **Expand factorials.** **Divide out common factor, 3!.**

$$= 20$$ **Simplify.**

EXERCISES

EXAMPLE 2
on p. 757
for Exs. 12–16

Evaluate the expression.

12. $_7C_6$ **13.** $_6C_2$ **14.** $_8C_5$ **15.** $_{13}C_{10}$

16. TICKETS You win 5 tickets to a concert. In how many ways can you choose 4 friends out of a group of 9 to take with you to the concert?

Chapter Review   775

12.4 Find Probabilities of Compound Events

pp. 762–768

Gr. 6 SDAP 3.4 **EXAMPLE**

The sections of the spinner shown all have the same area. You spin the spinner. Find the probability that the spinner stops on red or on an even number.

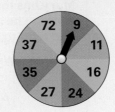

Because 24 is an even number on a red section, stopping on red and stopping on an even number are overlapping events.

$$P(\text{red or even}) = \mathbf{P(red)} + \mathbf{P(even)} - \mathbf{P(red\ and\ even)}$$

$$= \frac{3}{8} + \frac{3}{8} - \frac{1}{8}$$

$$= \frac{5}{8}$$

EXERCISES

EXAMPLES
1 and 2
·················
on pp. 762–763
for Exs. 17–20

You spin the spinner shown above. Find the specified probability.

17. $P(\text{green or odd})$

18. $P(\text{blue or prime number})$

19. $P(\text{blue or even})$

20. $P(\text{red or multiple of 3})$

Gr. 6 SDAP 3.4 **EXAMPLE**

A bag contains 5 red marbles, 3 blue marbles, 6 white marbles, and 2 green marbles. You choose one marble at random, put the marble aside, then choose a second marble at random. What is the probability that both marbles are blue?

Because you do not replace the first marble, the events are dependent. Before you choose a marble, there are 16 marbles, and 3 of them are blue. After you choose a blue marble, there are 2 blue marbles among the 15 marbles left.

$$P(\text{blue and then blue}) = \mathbf{P(blue)} \cdot \mathbf{P(blue\ given\ blue)}$$

$$= \frac{3}{16} \cdot \frac{2}{15}$$

$$= \frac{6}{240}$$

$$= \frac{1}{40}$$

EXERCISES

EXAMPLES
3 and 4
·················
on p. 764
for Exs. 21, 22

You randomly choose 2 marbles from the bag described in the example above.

21. Find the probability that both are green if you replace the first marble.

22. Find the probability that both are green if you do not replace the first marble.

1. **VOCABULARY** The set of all possible outcomes of an experiment is called a(n) __?__ .

2. **VOCABULARY** For any positive integer n, the product of the integers from 1 to n is called __?__ .

You roll a number cube. Find the probability of the event.

3. You roll a 4.

4. You roll an even number.

5. You roll a number less than 3.

6. You roll a multiple of 3.

Evaluate the expression.

7. $_8P_3$

8. $_6C_3$

9. $_{12}C_7$

In Exercises 10 and 11, tell whether the question can be answered using *combinations* **or** *permutations*. ***Explain* your choice, then answer the question.**

10. Eight swimmers participate in a race. In how many ways can the swimmers finish in first, second, and third place?

11. A restaurant offers 7 different side dishes. In how many different ways can you choose 2 side dishes?

In Exercises 12 and 13, you spin the spinner shown. The sections of the spinner have the same area. Tell whether the events A and B are *mutually exclusive* or *overlapping*. Then find $P(A \text{ or } B)$.

12. **Event A:** The spinner stops on a multiple of 3.
Event B: The spinner stops on yellow.

13. **Event A:** The spinner stops on 5.
Event B: The spinner stops on blue.

Exercises 14 and 15 refer to a bag containing 12 tiles numbered 1–12.

14. You choose a tile at random. What is the probability that you choose a number less than 10 or an odd number?

15. You choose a tile at random, replace it, and choose a second tile at random. What is the probability that you choose a number greater than 3, then an odd number?

16. **GO KARTS** You and your friend enter a go kart race. There are 8 other entries in the race. The starting order is selected at random. What is the probability that you start first and your friend starts second?

17. **MARBLES** A bag contains 5 red marbles, 3 blue marbles, and 2 green marbles. You randomly choose one marble from the bag, then you choose a second marble without replacing the first. Are events A and B, described below, *dependent* or *independent*? Find $P(A \text{ and } B)$.

Event A: The first marble is green.
Event B: The second marble is blue.

12 ◆ MULTIPLE CHOICE STRATEGIES

STRATEGIES YOU'LL USE:
• SOLVE DIRECTLY
• ELIMINATE CHOICES

Standards Review/Preview

Gr. 6 SDAP 3.4, 3.5;
Alg. 2 18.0

If you have difficulty solving a multiple choice problem directly, you may be able to use another approach to eliminate incorrect answer choices and obtain the correct answer.

PROBLEM 1

During track practice, you and 7 team members compete against each other in a 400 meter race. The running order on the track is chosen at random. What is the probability that you are in lane 1 and your friend is in lane 2?

Ⓐ 0　　　**Ⓑ** $\frac{1}{56}$　　　**Ⓒ** $\frac{1}{4}$　　　**Ⓓ** $\frac{15}{56}$

Strategy 1　SOLVE DIRECTLY

Let A represent the event that you are in lane 1, and let B represent the event that your friend is in lane 2. Because your being placed in lane 1 affects which runner can be placed in lane 2, the events A and B are dependent.

STEP 1 **Determine** the probability that you are in lane 1.

$$P(A) = \frac{1}{8}$$

STEP 2 **Determine** the probability that your friend is in lane 2, given that you are in lane 1.

$$P(B \text{ given } A) = \frac{1}{7}$$

STEP 3 **Calculate** the probability that you are in lane 1 and your friend is in lane 2.

$$P(A \text{ and } B) = P(A) \cdot P(B \text{ given } A)$$
$$= \frac{1}{8} \cdot \frac{1}{7}$$
$$= \frac{1}{56}$$

The correct answer is B. Ⓐ **Ⓑ** Ⓒ Ⓓ

Strategy 2　ELIMINATE CHOICES

Because it is possible for you to be placed in lane 1 and your friend in lane 2, the probability cannot be 0. You can eliminate choice A.

Now consider a race with 2 people. Let A represent you and B represent your friend.

Lane 1:　**A**　B　　Possible outcomes are arranged
Lane 2:　B　　A　　vertically, favorable in red.

So, the probability that you are in lane 1 and your friend is in lane 2 is $\frac{1}{2}$.

Now consider a race with 3 people. Let A represent you, B represent your friend, and C represent a third person.

Lane 1:　**A**　A　B　B　C　C
Lane 2:　**B**　C　A　C　A　B
Lane 3:　**C**　B　C　A　B　A

So, the probability that you are in lane 1 and your friend is in lane 2 is $\frac{1}{6}$.

As more people run, the probability decreases. Because $\frac{1}{4}$ and $\frac{15}{56}$ are each greater than $\frac{1}{6}$, you can eliminate choices C and D.

The correct answer is B. Ⓐ **Ⓑ** Ⓒ Ⓓ

PROBLEM 2

How many combinations of 2 letters from the 26 letters of the alphabet are possible?

(A) 13   (B) 325   (C) 650   (D) 26!

Strategy 1 | SOLVE DIRECTLY

To find the number of combinations of 26 letters taken 2 at a time, find $_{26}C_2$.

$$_{26}C_2 = \frac{26!}{(26-2)! \cdot 2!} \quad \textbf{Combinations formula}$$

$$= \frac{26!}{24! \cdot 2!} \quad \textbf{Subtract.}$$

$$= \frac{26 \cdot 25 \cdot 24!}{24! \cdot (2 \cdot 1)} \quad \begin{array}{l}\textbf{Expand factorials. Divide}\\ \textbf{out common factor, 24!.}\end{array}$$

$$= 325 \quad \textbf{Simplify.}$$

There are 325 possible combinations of 2 letters from the 26 letters of the alphabet.

The correct answer is B. (A) **(B)** (C) (D)

Strategy 2 | ELIMINATE CHOICES

Pairing the letter A with each of the remaining 25 letters will form 25 pairings. So, eliminate choice A.

Pairing the letter B with each of the remaining 24 letters will form 24 pairings. If you continue down to the last pairing, Y with Z, the total number of pairings is $25 + 24 + \ldots + 2 + 1$. This sum is less than $25 \cdot 24 \cdots \cdot 2 \cdot 1$, which is less than 26!. So, eliminate choice D.

Consider partial sums (5 numbers at a time):

$$25 + 24 + 23 + 22 + 21 < 25 \cdot 5 = 125$$
$$20 + 19 + 18 + 17 + 16 < 20 \cdot 5 = 100$$
$$15 + 14 + 13 + 12 + 11 < 15 \cdot 5 = 75$$
$$10 + 9 + 8 + 7 + 6 < 10 \cdot 5 = 50$$
$$\underline{5 + 4 + 3 + 2 + 1 < 5 \cdot 5 = 25}$$
$$25 + 24 + \ldots + 2 + 1 < 375$$

So, eliminate choice C.

The correct answer is B. (A) **(B)** (C) (D)

STRATEGY PRACTICE

Explain why you can eliminate the highlighted answer choice.

1. You roll a number cube. What is the probability that you roll a prime number or an odd number?

   (A) $\frac{1}{3}$ (B) $\frac{1}{2}$ (C) $\frac{2}{3}$ (D)✗ 1

2. In how many ways can you arrange all of the letters of the word SIX?

   (A)✗ 1   (B) 3   (C) 6   (D) 720

3. You have 4 quarters from the years 1974, 1980, 1991, and 2006. You randomly choose 3 of the quarters. What is the probability that the remaining quarter is the oldest?

   (A) $\frac{1}{6}$ (B) $\frac{1}{4}$ (C) $\frac{1}{2}$ (D)✗ $\frac{3}{4}$

Standards Review Handbook

pages 783–809

Number Sense

Quotients and Remainders	783
Factors and Multiples	784
Finding Equivalent Fractions and Simplifying Fractions	786
Mixed Numbers and Improper Fractions	787
Adding and Subtracting Fractions	788
Multiplying and Dividing Fractions	789
Comparing and Ordering Decimals	790
Fractions, Decimals, and Percents	791
Finding Percents of Numbers	793

Algebra and Functions

The Coordinate Plane	794
Converting Units of Measurement	795

Measurement and Geometry

Perimeter and Area	796
Circumference and Area of a Circle	798
Surface Area and Volume	799
Translations and Reflections	801

Statistics, Data Analysis, and Probability

Mean, Median, and Mode	803
Line Graphs	804
Counting Methods	805

Mathematical Reasoning

Problem Solving Strategies	807
Venn Diagrams and Logical Reasoning	809

Extra Practice for Chapters 1–12

pages 810–821

Tables

pages 822–829

Symbols	822
Formulas	823
Properties	825
Measures	828
Squares and Square Roots	829

English-Spanish Glossary

pages 830–858

Index

pages 859–872

Credits

pages 873–874

Selected Answers

page SA1

Quotients and Remainders 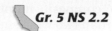 *Gr. 5 NS 2.2*

When dividing a whole number a, called the **dividend**, by a nonzero whole number b, called the **divisor**, you must find the following:

1. the greatest whole number q, called the **quotient**, such that $bq \leq a$

2. the difference r, called the **remainder**, of a and bq

You can check the results of a division using multiplication and addition:

$$a = bq + r, \text{ or } dividend = (divisor)(quotient) + remainder$$

EXAMPLE   **Divide 321 by 7. Check your answer.**

```
                    45  ←——— quotient
    divisor ——→  7)321  ←——— dividend
                    28
                    41
                    35
                     6  ←——— remainder
```

▶ $321 \div 7 = 45 \text{ R}6$

CHECK $7(45) + 6 \overset{?}{=} 321$

$315 + 6 \overset{?}{=} 321$

$321 = 321 \checkmark$

A whole number that has a remainder of 0 when divided by 2 is called **even** and can be written in the form $2q$ where q is the quotient. A whole number that has a remainder of 1 when divided by 2 is called **odd** and can be written as $2q + 1$.

EXAMPLE   **Tell whether (a) 587 and (b) 1624 are even or odd. Then write each number in the form $2q$ or $2q + 1$.**

a. $587 \div 2 = 293 \text{ R}1$. Therefore, 587 is odd and can be written as $2(293) + 1$.

b. $1624 \div 2 = 812 \text{ R}0$. Therefore, 1624 is even and can be written as $2(812)$.

PRACTICE

Find the quotient and remainder. Check your answer.

1. $98 \div 6$ **2.** $483 \div 5$ **3.** $3926 \div 8$ **4.** $1828 \div 4$

5. $917 \div 13$ **6.** $4826 \div 17$ **7.** $836 \div 51$ **8.** $9620 \div 22$

Tell whether the number is even or odd. Then write it in the form $2q$ or $2q + 1$.

9. 94   **10.** 293   **11.** 966   **12.** 551

13. 1834   **14.** 3561   **15.** 1   **16.** 12,367

Factors and Multiples 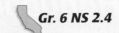 *Gr. 6 NS 2.4*

A **prime number** is a whole number that is greater than 1 and has exactly two whole number factors, 1 and itself. A **composite number** is a whole number that is greater than 1 and has more than two whole number factors. The table below shows that the first five prime numbers are 2, 3, 5, 7, and 11.

Number	Product(s)	Factor(s)	Prime or composite?
1	1 · 1	1	Neither
2	1 · 2	1, 2	Prime
3	1 · 3	1, 3	Prime
4	1 · 4, 2 · 2	1, 2, 4	Composite
5	1 · 5	1, 5	Prime
6	1 · 6, 2 · 3	1, 2, 3, 6	Composite
7	1 · 7	1, 7	Prime
8	1 · 8, 2 · 4	1, 2, 4, 8	Composite
9	1 · 9, 3 · 3	1, 3, 9	Composite
10	1 · 10, 2 · 5	1, 2, 5, 10	Composite
11	1 · 11	1, 11	Prime
12	1 · 12, 2 · 6, 3 · 4	1, 2, 3, 4, 6, 12	Composite

When you write a composite number as a product of prime numbers, you are writing its **prime factorization**. You can use a **factor tree** to write the prime factorization of a number.

EXAMPLE **Write the prime factorization of 120.**

Write 120 at the top of your factor tree. Draw two branches and write 120 as the product of two factors. Continue to draw branches until all the factors are prime numbers (shown in red). Here are two possible factor trees for 120.

Start with 120 = 2 · 60.   Start with 120 = 10 · 12.

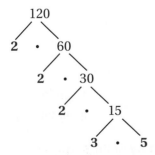
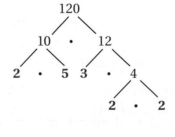

Both factor trees show that $120 = 2 \cdot 2 \cdot 2 \cdot 3 \cdot 5$, or $120 = 2^3 \cdot 3 \cdot 5$.

▶ The prime factorization of 120 is $2^3 \cdot 3 \cdot 5$.

For two or more nonzero whole numbers, a **common factor** is a whole number that is a factor of each number. The **greatest common factor (GCF)**, or *greatest common divisor*, of two or more nonzero whole numbers is the greatest of their common factors.

EXAMPLE   **Find the greatest common factor of 30 and 84.**

Write the prime factorization of each number. The GCF is the product of the common prime factors.

$30 = \textbf{2} \cdot \textbf{3} \cdot 5$ and $84 = \textbf{2} \cdot 2 \cdot \textbf{3} \cdot 7$

The common prime factors are **2** and **3**. The GCF is the product $2 \cdot 3 = 6$.

▶ The greatest common factor of 30 and 84 is 6.

A **multiple** of a nonzero whole number is the product of the number and any nonzero whole number. A **common multiple** of two or more nonzero whole numbers is a multiple of each number. The **least common multiple (LCM)** of two or more nonzero whole numbers is the least of their common multiples.

EXAMPLE   **Find the least common multiple of 12 and 30.**

Write the prime factorization of each number using exponents. Circle the greatest power of each prime factor. The LCM is the product of these powers.

$12 = \boxed{2^2} \cdot \boxed{3}$ and $30 = 2 \cdot 3 \cdot \boxed{5}$

The LCM is the product $2^2 \cdot 3 \cdot 5 = 60$.

▶ The least common multiple of 12 and 30 is 60.

PRACTICE

Write the prime factorization of the number if it is not a prime number. If the number is prime, write *prime*.

1. 28	**2.** 16	**3.** 11	**4.** 100
5. 81	**6.** 49	**7.** 60	**8.** 53
9. 180	**10.** 19	**11.** 51	**12.** 72

Find the greatest common factor of the pair of numbers.

13. 4, 8	**14.** 5, 6	**15.** 60, 18	**16.** 2, 10
17. 36, 27	**18.** 15, 21	**19.** 12, 16	**20.** 24, 108
21. 48, 88	**22.** 8, 12	**23.** 20, 28	**24.** 3, 5

Find the least common multiple of the pair of numbers.

25. 6, 9	**26.** 3, 8	**27.** 5, 45	**28.** 16, 20
29. 10, 65	**30.** 12, 15	**31.** 9, 30	**32.** 8, 9
33. 2, 14	**34.** 28, 32	**35.** 7, 49	**36.** 4, 6

Finding Equivalent Fractions and Simplifying Fractions

Gr. 4 NS 1.5, Gr. 6 NS 2.4

A **fraction** is a number of the form $\frac{a}{b}$ where a is the **numerator** and b is the

denominator. The value of b cannot be 0.

The number lines show the graphs of two fractions, $\frac{1}{2}$ and $\frac{2}{4}$.

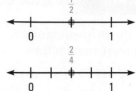

These fractions represent the same number. Two fractions that represent the same number are called **equivalent fractions**.

To write equivalent fractions, you can multiply or divide the numerator and the denominator of the original fraction by the same nonzero number.

EXAMPLE Write two fractions that are equivalent to $\frac{6}{8}$.

Multiply the numerator and denominator by 3.

$$\frac{6}{8} = \frac{6 \times 3}{8 \times 3} = \frac{18}{24} \quad \text{Equivalent fraction}$$

Divide the numerator and denominator by 2.

$$\frac{6}{8} = \frac{6 \div 2}{8 \div 2} = \frac{3}{4} \quad \text{Equivalent fraction}$$

A fraction is in **simplest form** when its numerator and its denominator have no common factors besides 1.

EXAMPLE Write the fraction $\frac{10}{15}$ in simplest form.

Divide the numerator and denominator by 5, the greatest common factor of 10 and 15.

$$\frac{10}{15} = \frac{10 \div 5}{15 \div 5} = \frac{2}{3} \quad \text{Simplest form}$$

PRACTICE

Write two fractions that are equivalent to the given fraction.

1. $\frac{9}{12}$ **2.** $\frac{4}{6}$ **3.** $\frac{1}{2}$ **4.** $\frac{2}{5}$ **5.** $\frac{10}{14}$

Write the fraction in simplest form.

6. $\frac{16}{24}$ **7.** $\frac{3}{12}$ **8.** $\frac{30}{48}$ **9.** $\frac{5}{40}$ **10.** $\frac{8}{20}$

11. $\frac{4}{16}$ **12.** $\frac{64}{72}$ **13.** $\frac{35}{100}$ **14.** $\frac{21}{81}$ **15.** $\frac{44}{55}$

16. $\frac{15}{20}$ **17.** $\frac{12}{28}$ **18.** $\frac{15}{39}$ **19.** $\frac{24}{78}$ **20.** $\frac{60}{96}$

Mixed Numbers and Improper Fractions

A **mixed number** is the sum of a whole number and a fraction. An **improper fraction** is a fraction with a numerator that is greater than or equal to the denominator.

The number line at the right shows the graph of the mixed number $1\frac{3}{4}$ and the improper fraction $\frac{7}{4}$.

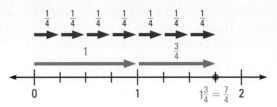

EXAMPLE Write $2\frac{7}{8}$ as an improper fraction and graph it on a number line.

$$2\frac{7}{8} = 2 + \frac{7}{8}$$ Definition of mixed number

$$= \frac{16}{8} + \frac{7}{8}$$ 1 whole $= \frac{8}{8}$, so 2 wholes $= \frac{16}{8}$.

$$= \frac{23}{8}$$ Add.

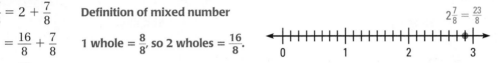

$2\frac{7}{8} = \frac{23}{8}$

EXAMPLE Write $\frac{17}{5}$ as a mixed number and graph it on a number line.

$$\begin{array}{r} 3 \\ 5\overline{)17} \\ \underline{15} \\ 2 \end{array}$$

Divide the numerator by the denominator: $17 \div 5$.
The quotient is 3 and the remainder is 2.

▶ $\frac{17}{5} = 3\frac{2}{5}$ Write the remainder as a fraction, $\frac{\text{remainder}}{\text{divisor}}$.

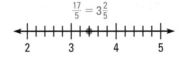

$\frac{17}{5} = 3\frac{2}{5}$

PRACTICE

Write the mixed number as an improper fraction and graph it on a number line.

1. $1\frac{2}{3}$ 2. $3\frac{1}{4}$ 3. $10\frac{3}{10}$ 4. $2\frac{3}{5}$ 5. $4\frac{1}{2}$

6. $9\frac{1}{3}$ 7. $1\frac{1}{6}$ 8. $2\frac{3}{4}$ 9. $6\frac{5}{8}$ 10. $5\frac{9}{10}$

11. $8\frac{1}{8}$ 12. $6\frac{3}{5}$ 13. $7\frac{2}{9}$ 14. $2\frac{3}{7}$ 15. $12\frac{2}{3}$

Write the improper fraction as a mixed number and graph it on a number line.

16. $\frac{5}{2}$ 17. $\frac{12}{5}$ 18. $\frac{15}{8}$ 19. $\frac{25}{4}$ 20. $\frac{37}{3}$

21. $\frac{7}{4}$ 22. $\frac{27}{8}$ 23. $\frac{29}{10}$ 24. $\frac{68}{9}$ 25. $\frac{54}{5}$

26. $\frac{31}{4}$ 27. $\frac{22}{5}$ 28. $\frac{13}{3}$ 29. $\frac{43}{9}$ 30. $\frac{35}{6}$

Adding and Subtracting Fractions  *Gr. 6 NS 2.1*

To add or subtract two fractions with the same denominator, write the sum or difference of the numerators over the denominator.

Sum and Difference Rules ($c \neq 0$)
$\dfrac{a}{c} + \dfrac{b}{c} = \dfrac{a+b}{c}$ $\qquad$ $\dfrac{a}{c} - \dfrac{b}{c} = \dfrac{a-b}{c}$

EXAMPLE Add or subtract: **a.** $\dfrac{1}{10} + \dfrac{3}{10}$ **b.** $\dfrac{7}{8} - \dfrac{3}{8}$

a. $\dfrac{1}{10} + \dfrac{3}{10} = \dfrac{4}{10}$ **Add numerators.**

$\quad = \dfrac{2}{5}$ **Simplify.**

b. $\dfrac{7}{8} - \dfrac{3}{8} = \dfrac{4}{8}$ **Subtract numerators.**

$\quad = \dfrac{1}{2}$ **Simplify.**

The **least common denominator (LCD)** of two fractions is the least common multiple of the denominators. To add or subtract two fractions with different denominators, use the LCD of the fractions to write equivalent fractions that have the same denominator.

EXAMPLE Add: $\dfrac{1}{4} + \dfrac{5}{6}$

The LCD of the fractions is 12, so write $\dfrac{1}{4}$ as $\dfrac{1 \times 3}{4 \times 3} = \dfrac{3}{12}$ and $\dfrac{5}{6}$ as $\dfrac{5 \times 2}{6 \times 2} = \dfrac{10}{12}$.

$\dfrac{1}{4} + \dfrac{5}{6} = \dfrac{3}{12} + \dfrac{10}{12}$ **Write equivalent fractions.**

$\quad = \dfrac{13}{12}$ **Add.**

$\quad = 1\dfrac{1}{12}$ **Write as a mixed number.**

PRACTICE

Add or subtract.

1. $\dfrac{1}{16} + \dfrac{3}{16}$
2. $\dfrac{1}{5} + \dfrac{2}{5}$
3. $\dfrac{7}{12} - \dfrac{5}{12}$
4. $\dfrac{2}{3} - \dfrac{1}{3}$
5. $\dfrac{5}{8} + \dfrac{3}{8}$

6. $\dfrac{3}{4} + \dfrac{3}{4}$
7. $\dfrac{7}{8} - \dfrac{3}{8}$
8. $\dfrac{17}{20} + \dfrac{9}{20}$
9. $\dfrac{7}{10} + \dfrac{1}{2}$
10. $\dfrac{3}{10} + \dfrac{3}{5}$

11. $\dfrac{3}{8} - \dfrac{3}{16}$
12. $\dfrac{1}{3} + \dfrac{1}{10}$
13. $\dfrac{7}{12} - \dfrac{1}{16}$
14. $\dfrac{2}{3} - \dfrac{1}{4}$
15. $\dfrac{5}{6} + \dfrac{7}{8}$

16. $\dfrac{3}{4} - \dfrac{5}{8}$
17. $\dfrac{3}{4} - \dfrac{1}{5}$
18. $\dfrac{5}{12} + \dfrac{2}{3}$
19. $1 - \dfrac{1}{5}$
20. $4 - \dfrac{3}{16}$

21. $2\dfrac{5}{8} + 4\dfrac{1}{8}$
22. $2\dfrac{9}{10} - 1\dfrac{7}{10}$
23. $1\dfrac{5}{6} + 3\dfrac{1}{6}$
24. $2\dfrac{1}{2} + 2\dfrac{3}{8}$
25. $1\dfrac{3}{4} - \dfrac{11}{16}$

Multiplying and Dividing Fractions

Gr. 6 NS 2.1

To multiply two fractions, write the product of the numerators over the product of the denominators.

Product Rule (*b*, *d* ≠ 0)

$$\frac{a}{b} \times \frac{c}{d} = \frac{ac}{bd}$$

EXAMPLE Multiply: $\frac{3}{5} \times \frac{7}{8}$

$\frac{3}{5} \times \frac{7}{8} = \frac{3 \times 7}{5 \times 8}$ **Use product rule.**

$= \frac{21}{40}$ **Simplify.**

Two nonzero numbers whose product is 1 are **reciprocals**.

For example, 6 and $\frac{1}{6}$ are reciprocals because $6 \times \frac{1}{6} = 1$.

Every number except 0 has a reciprocal. To divide by a fraction, multiply by its reciprocal.

Quotient Rule (*b*, *c*, *d* ≠ 0)

$$\frac{a}{b} \div \frac{c}{d} = \frac{a}{b} \times \frac{d}{c}$$

EXAMPLE Divide: $\frac{5}{7} \div \frac{3}{4}$

The reciprocal of $\frac{3}{4}$ is $\frac{4}{3}$ because $\frac{3}{4} \times \frac{4}{3} = 1$, so multiply $\frac{5}{7}$ by $\frac{4}{3}$.

$\frac{5}{7} \div \frac{3}{4} = \frac{5}{7} \times \frac{4}{3}$ **Use quotient rule.**

$= \frac{20}{21}$ **Use product rule.**

PRACTICE

Multiply or divide.

1. $\frac{3}{4} \times \frac{2}{3}$ 2. $\frac{1}{5} \times \frac{5}{8}$ 3. $\frac{1}{6} \div \frac{1}{3}$ 4. $\frac{2}{3} \div \frac{2}{3}$ 5. $\frac{9}{10} \div \frac{4}{5}$

6. $\frac{1}{12} \times \frac{3}{4}$ 7. $\frac{3}{8} \times \frac{1}{8}$ 8. $\frac{5}{6} \div \frac{1}{4}$ 9. $\frac{1}{2} \times \frac{1}{4}$ 10. $\frac{7}{10} \div \frac{5}{8}$

11. $\frac{3}{4} \div \frac{1}{2}$ 12. $\frac{5}{6} \times \frac{3}{10}$ 13. $\frac{2}{5} \div \frac{4}{5}$ 14. $\frac{9}{10} \times \frac{1}{3}$ 15. $\frac{1}{4} \div \frac{7}{8}$

16. $\frac{3}{16} \times \frac{2}{5}$ 17. $\frac{2}{5} \div 20$ 18. $18 \times \frac{1}{3}$ 19. $\frac{1}{10} \times 6$ 20. $24 \div \frac{3}{8}$

21. $5\frac{1}{2} \times \frac{9}{16}$ 22. $8\frac{1}{4} \div \frac{3}{10}$ 23. $1\frac{7}{8} \times 2\frac{1}{3}$ 24. $3\frac{3}{4} \div 6\frac{1}{2}$ 25. $2\frac{1}{2} \div 1\frac{7}{8}$

Comparing and Ordering Decimals  *Gr. 6 NS 1.1*

You can use a number line to compare and order decimals. From left to right, the numbers on a number line appear in order from least to greatest.

EXAMPLE Copy and complete the statement using <, >, or =.

a. 9.67 __?__ 9.59

9.67 is to the right of 9.59, so 9.67 is greater than 9.59.

▶ 9.67 > 9.59

b. 0.08 __?__ 0.12

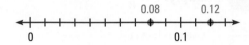

0.08 is to the left of 0.12, so 0.08 is less than 0.12.

▶ 0.08 < 0.12

EXAMPLE Order the numbers 0.4, 0.56, 0.48, and 0.515 from least to greatest.

Graph all the numbers on a number line.

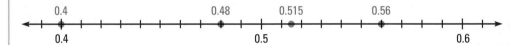

Write the numbers as they appear on the number line from left to right.

▶ The numbers in order from least to greatest are 0.4, 0.48, 0.515, and 0.56.

PRACTICE

Copy and complete the statement using <, >, or =.

1. 1.48 __?__ 1.413
2. 0.809 __?__ 0.81
3. 5.47 __?__ 5.43

4. 0.01 __?__ 0.005
5. 35.2 __?__ 35
6. 6.24 __?__ 6.2

7. 1.674 __?__ 1.678
8. 20.05 __?__ 20.3
9. 9.018 __?__ 9.017

10. 2.71 __?__ 2.711
11. 0.683 __?__ 0.683
12. 148.7 __?__ 14.87

Order the numbers from least to greatest.

13. 2.5, 2.3, 2.45, 2.38
14. 7.01, 7.13, 7.3, 7.03
15. 10.19, 10.2, 10, 10.4

16. 0.3, 0.47, 0.9, 0.15
17. 1.3, 1.05, 1.11, 1.0
18. 12.6, 10.9, 11, 11.9

19. 6.1, 6.89, 7.25, 7
20. 3.1, 3.3, 0.3, 1.33
21. 5.46, 5.4, 5.64, 5.6

22. 4.66, 4.6, 5, 4.666
23. 0.75, 0.6, 0.81, 0.58
24. 61, 60.01, 60, 60.1

Fractions, Decimals, and Percents

A **percent** is a fraction whose denominator is 100. The symbol for percent is %. In the model at the right, there are 100 squares in all, and 49 of the 100 squares are shaded. You can write the shaded part of the model as a fraction, a decimal, or a percent.

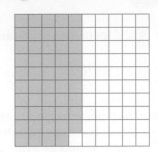

Fraction: forty-nine out of one hundred, or $\frac{49}{100}$

Decimal: forty-nine hundredths, or 0.49

Percent: forty-nine percent, or 49%

EXAMPLE Write the fraction as a decimal: **a.** $\frac{1}{8}$ **b.** $\frac{5}{12}$

a.
$$8\overline{)1.000} \quad \text{0.125}$$
Divide.

▶ $\frac{1}{8} = 0.125$

b.
$$12\overline{)5.00000\ldots} \quad \text{0.41666}\ldots$$
Divide.

▶ $\frac{5}{12} = 0.41666\ldots = 0.41\overline{6}$

EXAMPLE Write the decimal as a fraction: **a.** 0.7 **b.** 0.32

a. 0.7 = seven tenths

$$= \frac{7}{10}$$

b. 0.32 = thirty-two hundredths

$$= \frac{32}{100}$$

$$= \frac{8}{25}$$

To write a percent as a decimal, move the decimal point two places to the left and remove the percent sign.

EXAMPLE Write the percent as a decimal: **a.** 16% **b.** 5%

a. 16% = 16%

= 0.16

b. 5% = 05%

= 0.05

To write a decimal as a percent, move the decimal point two places to the right and write a percent sign.

EXAMPLE Write the decimal as a percent: **a.** 0.83 **b.** 0.195

a. 0.83 = 0.83

= 83%

b. 0.195 = 0.195

= 19.5%

EXAMPLE Write the percent as a fraction: **a. 98%** **b. 5%**

a. $98\% = \dfrac{98}{100}$ **Definition of percent**

$= \dfrac{49}{50}$ **Simplify.**

b. $5\% = \dfrac{5}{100}$ **Definition of percent**

$= \dfrac{1}{20}$ **Simplify.**

To write a fraction as a percent, you may be able to rewrite the fraction using a denominator of 100. If the denominator of the fraction is not a factor of 100, you can first write the fraction as a decimal and then as a percent.

EXAMPLE Write the fraction as a percent: **a.** $\dfrac{2}{5}$ **b.** $\dfrac{5}{8}$

a. $\dfrac{2}{5} = \dfrac{2(20)}{5(20)}$ **Write as a fraction with denominator 100.**

$= \dfrac{40}{100} = 40\%$ **Write as a percent.**

b. $\dfrac{5}{8} = 0.625$ **Write as a decimal.**

$= 62.5\%$ **Write as a percent.**

The table below gives commonly used fractions, decimals, and percents written in increasing order.

$\dfrac{1}{100} = 0.01 = 1\%$	$\dfrac{1}{16} = 0.0625 = 6.25\%$	$\dfrac{1}{10} = 0.1 = 10\%$	$\dfrac{1}{8} = 0.125 = 12.5\%$
$\dfrac{1}{5} = 0.2 = 20\%$	$\dfrac{1}{4} = 0.25 = 25\%$	$\dfrac{1}{3} = 0.\overline{3} = 33\tfrac{1}{3}\%$	$\dfrac{3}{8} = 0.375 = 37.5\%$
$\dfrac{2}{5} = 0.4 = 40\%$	$\dfrac{1}{2} = 0.5 = 50\%$	$\dfrac{3}{5} = 0.6 = 60\%$	$\dfrac{5}{8} = 0.625 = 62.5\%$
$\dfrac{2}{3} = 0.\overline{6} = 66\tfrac{2}{3}\%$	$\dfrac{3}{4} = 0.75 = 75\%$	$\dfrac{4}{5} = 0.8 = 80\%$	$\dfrac{7}{8} = 0.875 = 87.5\%$

PRACTICE

Write the percent as a decimal and as a fraction.

1. 70% **2.** 12% **3.** 3% **4.** 55% **5.** 35%

6. 9% **7.** 110% **8.** 225% **9.** 0.3% **10.** 0.5%

Write the decimal as a fraction and as a percent.

11. 0.28 **12.** 0.13 **13.** 0.05 **14.** 0.36 **15.** 0.52

16. 0.004 **17.** 0.025 **18.** 4 **19.** 1.5 **20.** 2.3

Write the fraction as a decimal and as a percent. Round decimals to the nearest thousandth. Round percents to the nearest tenth of a percent.

21. $\dfrac{3}{16}$ **22.** $\dfrac{1}{9}$ **23.** $\dfrac{61}{100}$ **24.** $\dfrac{3}{20}$ **25.** $\dfrac{19}{100}$

26. $\dfrac{17}{25}$ **27.** $\dfrac{9}{25}$ **28.** $\dfrac{5}{6}$ **29.** $\dfrac{4}{7}$ **30.** $\dfrac{5}{12}$

Finding Percents of Numbers

 *Gr. 5 NS 1.2*

Just as "half of 8" means to multiply $\frac{1}{2}$ and 8, "50% of 8" means to multiply 50% and 8. To find a percent of a number, multiply the percent by the number. One method is to write the percent as a fraction before multiplying.

EXAMPLE Find the percent of the number: **a. 25% of 36**   **b. 80% of 13**

a. $25\% \text{ of } 36 = 25\% \times 36$

$= \frac{1}{4} \times 36$

$= \frac{36}{4}$

$= 9$

b. $80\% \text{ of } 43 = 80\% \times 13$

$= \frac{4}{5} \times 13$

$= \frac{52}{5}$

$= 10\frac{2}{5}$

Another method of finding the percent of a number is to write the percent as a decimal and then multiply.

EXAMPLE Find the percent of the number: **a. 5% of 94**   **b. 110% of 7**

a. $5\% \text{ of } 94 = 5\% \times 94$

$= 0.05 \times 94$

$= 4.7$

b. $110\% \text{ of } 7 = 110\% \times 7$

$= 1.1 \times 7$

$= 7.7$

PRACTICE

Find the percent of the number by rewriting the percent as a fraction.

1. 50% of 40
2. 25% of 80
3. $33\frac{1}{3}\%$ of 66
4. $66\frac{2}{3}\%$ of 39

5. 20% of 185
6. 75% of 8
7. 60% of 54
8. 40% of 33

9. 37.5% of 120
10. 6.25% of 96
11. 87.5% of 56
12. 1% of 294

13. 6% of 500
14. 150% of 1000
15. $133\frac{1}{3}\%$ of 300
16. $233\frac{1}{3}\%$ of 48

Find the percent of the number by rewriting the percent as a decimal.

17. 20% of 90
18. 35% of 160
19. 95% of 240
20. 80% of 65

21. 17% of 29
22. 63% of 18
23. 38% of 152
24. 44% of 11

25. 9% of 85
26. 4% of 419
27. 32.9% of 382
28. 72.5% of 565

29. 183% of 15
30. 1010% of 22
31. 0.57% of 392
32. 8.17% of 5

The Coordinate Plane  *Gr. 5 AF 1.4*

A **coordinate plane** has a horizontal **x-axis** and a vertical **y-axis** that intersect at a point called the **origin** and divide the plane into four **quadrants**. The origin is labeled *O*.

In an **ordered pair**, the order of the numbers is important. When an ordered pair is graphed, the first number is the **x-coordinate** and the second number is the **y-coordinate**. The coordinates of the origin are (0, 0). The point $P(-2, 1)$ is graphed at the right.

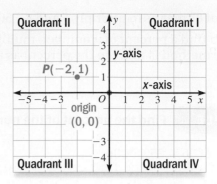

EXAMPLE Give the coordinates of points A and B.

Point *A* is 3 units to the right of the origin and 2 units up, so the x-coordinate is 3 and the y-coordinate is 2.

▸ The coordinates of point *A* are (3, 2).

Point *B* is 0 units to the right of the origin and 4 units down, so the x-coordinate is 0 and the y-coordinate is −4.

▸ The coordinates of point *B* are (0, −4).

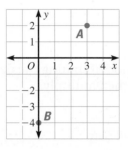

EXAMPLE Plot C(5, 0) and D(−1, −3) in a coordinate plane.

To plot the point $C(5, 0)$, begin at the origin and move 5 units right, then 0 units up.

To plot the point $D(-1, -3)$, begin at the origin and move 1 unit left, then 3 units down.

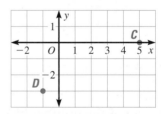

PRACTICE

Give the coordinates of the point.

1. *A*	**2.** *B*	**3.** *C*
4. *D*	**5.** *E*	**6.** *F*
7. *G*	**8.** *H*	**9.** *J*
10. *K*	**11.** *L*	**12.** *M*

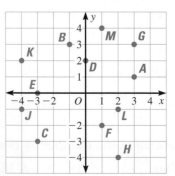

Plot the point in a coordinate plane.

13. $N(-4, 2)$	**14.** $P(0, -4)$	**15.** $Q(-1, -1)$
16. $R(-5, -2)$	**17.** $S(-1, -5)$	**18.** $T(1, 3)$
19. $U(2, -1)$	**20.** $V(3, -1)$	**21.** $W(2, -5)$
22. $X(-5, 3)$	**23.** $Y(-2, 0)$	**24.** $Z(0, 1)$

Converting Units of Measurement  *Gr. 6 AF 2.1*

The Table of Measures on page 828 gives many statements of equivalent measures. You can write two different conversion factors for each statement, as shown below. Each conversion factor is equal to 1.

Statement of Equivalent Measures	Conversion Factors	
100 cm = 1 m	$\dfrac{100 \text{ cm}}{1 \text{ m}} = 1$	$\dfrac{1 \text{ m}}{100 \text{ cm}} = 1$

To convert from one unit of measurement to another, multiply by a conversion factor that will eliminate the starting unit and result in the desired unit.

Convert meters to centimeters:

Use $\dfrac{100 \text{ cm}}{1 \text{ m}}$.

$3 \text{ m} \times \dfrac{100 \text{ cm}}{1 \text{ m}} = 300 \text{ cm}$

Convert centimeters to meters:

Use $\dfrac{1 \text{ m}}{100 \text{ cm}}$.

$400 \text{ cm} \times \dfrac{1 \text{ m}}{100 \text{ cm}} = 4 \text{ m}$

Sometimes you need to use more than one conversion factor.

EXAMPLE Copy and complete: 2 d = _?_ sec

STEP 1 **Find** the appropriate statements of equivalent measures.

24 h = 1 d, 60 min = 1 h, and 60 sec = 1 min

STEP 2 **Write** conversion factors.

$\dfrac{24 \text{ h}}{1 \text{ d}}, \dfrac{60 \text{ min}}{1 \text{ h}},$ and $\dfrac{60 \text{ sec}}{1 \text{ min}}$

STEP 3 **Multiply** by conversion factors to convert days to seconds.

$2 \text{ d} \times \dfrac{24 \text{ h}}{1 \text{ d}} \times \dfrac{60 \text{ min}}{1 \text{ h}} \times \dfrac{60 \text{ sec}}{1 \text{ min}} = 172{,}800 \text{ sec}$

▸ 2 d = 172,800 sec

PRACTICE

Copy and complete.

1. 300 sec = _?_ min
2. 2.6 g = _?_ kg
3. 64 oz = _?_ lb
4. 4 gal = _?_ qt
5. 72 in. = _?_ ft
6. 94 mm = _?_ cm
7. 42 ft = _?_ yd
8. 5 d = _?_ h
9. 3 m = _?_ cm
10. 2 yd = _?_ in.
11. 70 L = _?_ mL
12. 10 mi = _?_ ft
13. 1.5 ton = _?_ lb
14. 4500 mL = _?_ L
15. 15,000 mg = _?_ g
16. 1 mi = _?_ in.
17. 80 fl oz = _?_ qt
18. 5 gal = _?_ c
19. 1 km = _?_ mm
20. 20 c = _?_ qt
21. 8 h = _?_ sec

Perimeter and Area  *Gr. 7 MG 2.1*

The **perimeter** *P* of a figure is the distance around it.

Perimeter of a Square	Perimeter of a Rectangle	Perimeter of a Triangle
	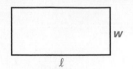	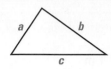
$P = s + s + s + s$ $= 4s$	$P = \ell + w + \ell + w$ $= 2\ell + 2w$	$P = a + b + c$

EXAMPLE   Find the perimeter of the figure.

a. Square

9 cm

$P = 4s$

$= 4(9)$

$= 36$ cm

b. Rectangle

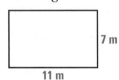

7 m

11 m

$P = 2\ell + 2w$

$= 2(11) + 2(7)$

$= 22 + 14 = 36$ m

c. Triangle

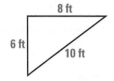

8 ft

6 ft   10 ft

$P = a + b + c$

$= 6 + 8 + 10$

$= 24$ ft

The **area** *A* of a figure is the number of square units enclosed by the figure.

Area of a Square	Area of a Rectangle	Area of a Parallelogram
	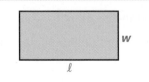	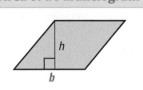
$A = s^2$	$A = \ell w$	$A = bh$

Area of a Triangle	Area of a Trapezoid
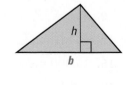	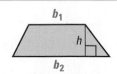
$A = \frac{1}{2}bh$	$A = \frac{1}{2}(b_1 + b_2)h$

EXAMPLE Find the area of the figure.

a. Rectangle

15 cm

9 cm

$A = \ell w$

$= 9(15)$

$= 135 \text{ cm}^2$

b. Triangle

6 in.

12 in.

$A = \frac{1}{2}bh$

$= \frac{1}{2}(12)(6)$

$= 36 \text{ in.}^2$

c. Parallelogram

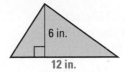

32 yd

25 yd

$A = bh$

$= 25(32)$

$= 800 \text{ yd}^2$

PRACTICE

Find the perimeter of the figure.

1. Square

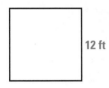

12 ft

2. Rectangle

8 mm

6 mm

3. Triangle

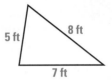

5 ft   8 ft

7 ft

Find the area of the figure.

4. Square

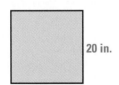

20 in.

5. Rectangle

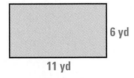

6 yd

11 yd

6. Triangle

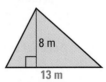

8 m

13 m

7. Parallelogram

11 in.

10 in.

8. Trapezoid

17 m

10 m

9 m

9. Parallelogram

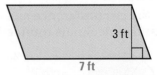

3 ft

7 ft

10. Trapezoid

13 m

24 m   12 m

11. Triangle

14 yd

10 yd

12. Rectangle

8 in.

18 in.

Circumference and Area of a Circle

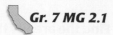 *Gr. 7 MG 2.1*

A circle consists of all points in a plane that are the same distance from a fixed point called the **center**.

The distance between the center and any point on the circle is the **radius**. The distance across the circle through the center is the **diameter**. The diameter of a circle is twice its radius.

The **circumference** of a circle is the distance around the circle. For any circle, the ratio of its circumference to its diameter is

π (pi), a number that is approximately equal to 3.14 or $\frac{22}{7}$.

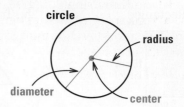

Circumference and Area of a Circle
To find the circumference C of a circle with radius r or diameter d, use the formula $C = 2\pi r$ or $C = \pi d$.   To find the area A of a circle with radius r, use the formula $A = \pi r^2$.

EXAMPLE Find the circumference and area of the circle. Give your answers in terms of π and as decimals rounded to the nearest tenth.

5 cm

Circumference

$C = 2\pi r$

$\quad = 2\pi(5)$

$\quad = 10\pi$ cm   **Exact answer**

$\quad \approx 10(3.14)$

$\quad = 31.4$ cm   **Decimal approximation**

Area

$A = \pi r^2$

$\quad = \pi(5^2)$

$\quad = 25\pi$ cm^2 **Exact answer**

$\quad \approx 25(3.14)$

$\quad = 78.5$ cm^2 **Decimal approximation**

PRACTICE

Find the circumference and area of the circle. Give your answers in terms of π and as decimals rounded to the nearest tenth.

1.
6 in.

2.
3 cm

3.
8 in.

4.
4 m

5.
4 ft

6.
14 cm

7.
18 m

8.
2 ft

Surface Area and Volume 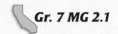 *Gr. 7 MG 2.1*

A **solid** is a three-dimensional figure that encloses part of space. The
surface area S of a solid is the sum of the areas of all of its surfaces.
The **volume** V of a solid is the amount of space that the solid occupies.
In the formulas for surface area and volume, the number π (pi) is
approximately equal to 3.14 or $\frac{22}{7}$.

Right Rectangular Prism	Right Circular Cylinder

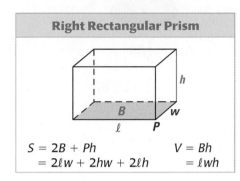

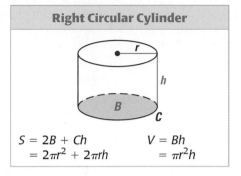

$S = 2B + Ph$ $\quad$ $V = Bh$	$S = 2B + Ch$ $\quad$ $V = Bh$
$= 2\ell w + 2hw + 2\ell h$ $\quad$ $= \ell wh$	$= 2\pi r^2 + 2\pi rh$ $\quad$ $= \pi r^2 h$

Regular Pyramid	Right Circular Cone	Sphere

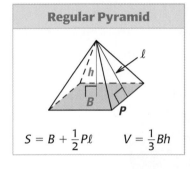

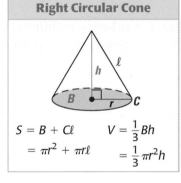

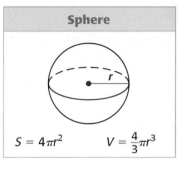

$S = B + \frac{1}{2}P\ell$ $\quad$ $V = \frac{1}{3}Bh$	$S = B + C\ell$ $\quad$ $V = \frac{1}{3}Bh$	$S = 4\pi r^2$ $\quad$ $V = \frac{4}{3}\pi r^3$
	$= \pi r^2 + \pi r\ell$ $\quad$ $= \frac{1}{3}\pi r^2 h$	

In this book, the adjectives *right* and *circular* will be assumed and therefore
will not be used in naming solids.

EXAMPLE **Find the surface area of the solid.**

a. Sphere

$S = 4\pi r^2$

$\quad = 4\pi(6^2)$

$\quad = 144\pi$ in.^{2}

$\quad \approx 144(3.14)$

$\quad \approx 452.2$ in.^{2}

b. Cylinder

1 m

5 m

$S = 2\pi r^2 + 2\pi rh$

$\quad = 2\pi(1^2) + 2\pi(1)(5)$

$\quad = 2\pi + 10\pi$

$\quad = 12\pi$ m^2

$\quad \approx 12(3.14) \approx 37.7$ m^2

c. Cone

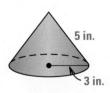

5 in.

3 in.

$S = \pi r^2 + \pi r\ell$

$\quad = \pi(3^2) + \pi(3)(5)$

$\quad = 9\pi + 15\pi$

$\quad = 24\pi$ in.^{2}

$\quad \approx 24(3.14) \approx 75.4$ in.^{2}

EXAMPLE Find the volume of the solid.

a. Rectangular prism

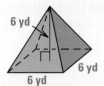

8 ft

5 ft

5 ft

$V = Bh$

$= 25(8)$

$= 200 \text{ ft}^3$

b. Regular pyramid

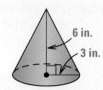

6 yd

6 yd

6 yd

$V = \frac{1}{3}Bh$

$= \frac{1}{3}(36)6$

$= 72 \text{ yd}^3$

c. Cone

6 in.

3 in.

$V = \frac{1}{3}Bh$

$= \frac{1}{3}\pi(3^2)(6)$

$= 18\pi \text{ in.}^3$

$\approx 18(3.14) \approx 56.5 \text{ in.}^3$

PRACTICE

Find the surface area and volume of the solid. For spheres, cylinders, and cones, give your answers in terms of π and as decimals rounded to the nearest tenth.

1. Rectangular prism

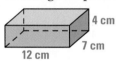

4 cm

7 cm

12 cm

2. Cylinder

4 in.

5 in.

3. Sphere

15 m

4. Cylinder

8 ft

13 ft

5. Cone

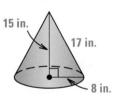

15 in.

17 in.

8 in.

6. Rectangular prism

3 mm

4 mm

5 mm

7. Regular pyramid

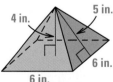

5 in.

4 in.

6 in.

6 in.

8. Sphere

10 in.

9. Cylinder

16 in.

43 in.

10. Rectangular prism

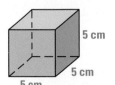

5 cm

5 cm

5 cm

11. Cone

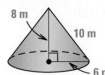

8 m

10 m

6 m

12. Regular pyramid

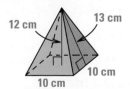

12 cm

13 cm

10 cm

10 cm

Translations and Reflections 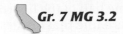 *Gr. 7 MG 3.2*

A **transformation** is a change made to the location or to the size of a figure. The new figure formed by a transformation is called an **image**. In this book, original figures are shown in blue and images in red.

A **translation** is a transformation in which each point of a figure moves the same distance in the same direction. A figure and its translated image are identical in size and shape.

To translate a figure in the coordinate plane, you change the coordinates of its points by using the rules below, where a and b are positive.

Translation	Rule
Slide to the right a units	$x \rightarrow x + a$
Slide to the left a units	$x \rightarrow x - a$
Slide up b units	$y \rightarrow y + b$
Slide down b units	$y \rightarrow y - b$

EXAMPLE **Translate figure *ABCD* 4 units to the right and 5 units down.**

To find the coordinates of the images of points A, B, C, and D, add 4 to the x-coordinates and subtract 5 from the y-coordinates.

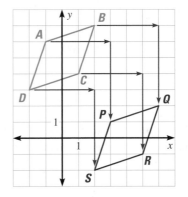

Original				Image
$A(-1, 6)$	$\rightarrow$	$P(-1 + 4, 6 - 5)$	$=$	$P(3, 1)$
$B(2, 7)$	$\rightarrow$	$Q(2 + 4, 7 - 5)$	$=$	$Q(6, 2)$
$C(1, 4)$	$\rightarrow$	$R(1 + 4, 4 - 5)$	$=$	$R(5, -1)$
$D(-2, 3)$	$\rightarrow$	$S(-2 + 4, 3 - 5)$	$=$	$S(2, -2)$

A **reflection** is a transformation in which a figure is reflected, or flipped, in a line, called the *line of reflection*. A figure and its reflected image are identical in size and shape.

EXAMPLE **Reflect the line segment in the given line.**

For each endpoint, find the distance from the endpoint to the line of reflection. Move the same distance on the opposite side of the line of reflection and plot the image point. Draw a segment connecting the two points.

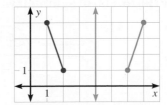

A figure has **line symmetry** if one half of the figure is a mirror image of the other half. A **line of symmetry** is a line that divides the figure such that each half is a reflection in the line of the other half.

EXAMPLE Find the number of lines of symmetry for each figure.

 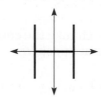

a. One line of symmetry   b. Two lines of symmetry   c. No lines of symmetry

PRACTICE

The coordinates of the vertices of a polygon are given. Draw the polygon. Then find the coordinates of the vertices of the image after the specified translation and draw the image.

1. (2, 7), (6, 7), (6, 5), (2, 5); translate 1 unit to the right and 4 units down

2. (4, 4), (6, 4), (6, 7); translate 3 units to the left and 3 units up

3. (−4, 1), (−1, −1), (2, 1); translate 3 units to the right and 3 units up

4. (3, 0), (5, −3), (1, −4); translate 4 units to the left

5. (1, 3), (5, 2), (2, 1), (0, −2); translate 2 units down

6. (0, 0), (−1, 5), (3, 2), (3, −3); translate 1 unit to the left and 6 units down

For the figure shown, find the coordinates of the vertices of the image after a reflection in the given line. Then draw the image.

7. 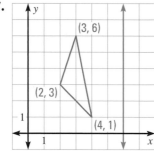   8. 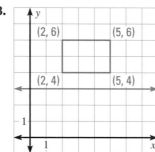   9.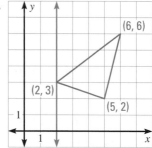

For the figure shown, tell whether the figure has line symmetry. If so, copy the figure and draw the line(s) of symmetry.

10.   11.    12.   13.

Mean, Median, and Mode 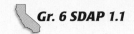 *Gr. 6 SDAP 1.1*

Three measures of central tendency are mean, median, and mode.

The **mean** of a data set is the sum of the values divided by the number of values.	The **median** of a data set is the middle value when the values are written in numerical order. If a data set has an even number of values, the median is the mean of the two middle values.	The **mode** of a data set is the value that occurs most often. A data set can have no mode, one mode, or more than one mode.

EXAMPLE **Find the mean, median, and mode(s) of the data in the table.**

Mean

Add the values. Then divide by 8, the number of values.

Sum = 251 + 222 + 222 + 220 + 215 + 207 + 188 + 178
   = 1703

▶ Mean = $\frac{1703}{8}$ = 212.875

Median

Write the values in order from least to greatest. Then find the middle value(s).

   178, 188, 207, **215**, **220**, 222, 222, 251

Find the mean of the two middle values.

▶ Median = $\frac{215 + 220}{2} = \frac{435}{2}$ = 217.5

Mode

Find the value that occurs most often.

▶ Mode = 222

Lengths of School Years	
Country	**School year (days)**
China	251
Korea	222
Taiwan	222
Japan	220
Israel	215
Switzerland	207
Canada	188
United States	178

PRACTICE

Find the mean, median, and mode(s) of the data.

1. Test scores: 90, 88, 95, 94, 87, 85, 92, 99, 100, 94

2. Daily high temperatures (°F) for a week: 68, 70, 67, 68, 75, 75, 74

3. Ages of employees: 24, 52, 21, 55, 39, 49, 28, 33, 52, 41, 30, 64, 45

4. Numbers of students in classes: 21, 24, 27, 28, 25, 18, 22, 25, 26, 22, 27, 20

5. Movie ticket prices: $6.75, $7.50, $7.25, $6.75, $6.25, $7.50, $7.25, $6.75, $7

6. Hourly rates of pay: $14.50, $8.75, $7, $11, $16.50, $18, $12, $10.25

7. Numbers of children in families: 0, 0, 1, 1, 1, 2, 2, 2, 2, 2, 3, 3, 4, 4, 4, 5

8. Ages of students in a high school class: 3 sixteen-year-olds, 10 seventeen-year-olds, and 7 eighteen-year-olds

Line Graphs 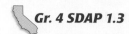 *Gr. 4 SDAP 1.3*

You can use a **line graph** to show how numerical data change over time.

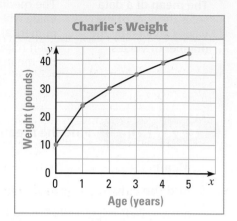

Charlie's Weight

> **EXAMPLE** **Use the line graph, which shows Charlie's weight from birth to 5 years old. (a) How much weight did Charlie gain in 5 years? (b) At what age did Charlie weigh 30 pounds? (c) In which year did Charlie gain the most weight?**
>
> **a.** The lowest point on the graph shows that Charlie weighed 10 pounds at birth. The highest point on the graph shows he weighed 42.5 pounds at age 5.
>
> $42.5 - 10 = 32.5$
>
> ▸ Charlie gained 32.5 pounds in 5 years.
>
> **b.** The point on the graph to the right of 30 on the weight axis corresponds to an age of 2.
>
> ▸ Charlie weighed 30 pounds at age 2.
>
> **c.** The graph is steepest from birth to age 1.
>
> ▸ Charlie gained the most weight in his first year.

> **PRACTICE**

In Exercises 1–5, use the line graph above.

1. How much did Charlie weigh on his first birthday?

2. How old was Charlie when he weighed 40 pounds?

3. In which year did Charlie gain the least weight?

4. How much weight did Charlie gain his first year?

5. How much weight did Charlie gain from age 1 to age 4?

In Exercises 6–14, use the line graph, which shows Abby's height from birth to 4 years old.

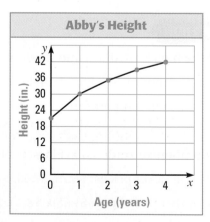

Abby's Height

6. How tall was Abby when she was born?

7. How old was Abby when she was 35 inches tall?

8. In which year did Abby grow the most?

9. In which year did Abby grow the least?

10. How many inches did Abby grow from age 3 to age 4?

11. In which year did Abby grow 5 inches?

12. How many inches did Abby grow in 4 years?

13. At what age was Abby's height double her height at birth?

14. If Abby maintains the same growth rate from age 4 to age 5 that she had from age 3 to age 4, how tall will she be when she is 5?

Counting Methods  *Gr. 4 SDAP 2.1*

There are several methods for counting the number of possibilities in a situation.

EXAMPLE **Make a list to find the number of possible lunch specials.**

Pair each soup with each sandwich.

    Chicken soup with turkey sandwich

    Chicken soup with tuna sandwich

    Chicken soup with cheese sandwich

    Tomato soup with turkey sandwich

    Tomato soup with tuna sandwich

    Tomato soup with cheese sandwich

Count the number of lunch specials in the list.

▸ There are 6 possible lunch specials.

Lunch Special $6.95	
Choose 1 soup and 1 sandwich.	
Soups	**Sandwiches**
Chicken	Turkey
Tomato	Tuna
	Cheese

EXAMPLE **Draw a tree diagram to find the number of possible lunch specials given the choices in the example above.**

Arrange the soups and sandwiches in a tree diagram.

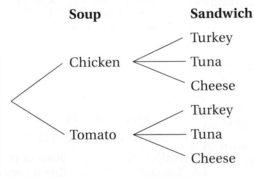

Soup	Sandwich	Lunch
	Turkey	Chicken soup, turkey sandwich
Chicken	Tuna	Chicken soup, tuna sandwich
	Cheese	Chicken soup, cheese sandwich
	Turkey	Tomato soup, turkey sandwich
Tomato	Tuna	Tomato soup, tuna sandwich
	Cheese	Tomato soup, cheese sandwich

▸ There are 6 possible lunch specials.

Another way to count the number of possible lunch specials described in the examples above is to multiply. Since there are 2 choices of soup and 3 choices of sandwich, there are $2 \times 3 = 6$ possible lunch specials. This method uses the counting principle.

The Counting Principle
If one event can occur in *m* ways, and for each of these ways a second event can occur in *n* ways, then the number of ways that the two events can occur together is *m* · *n*.

The counting principle can be extended to three or more events.

EXAMPLE Greta must choose a 4-digit password for her cell phone mailbox. Use the counting principle to find the number of possible 4-digit passwords.

For each of the 4 digits in the password, there are 10 choices: 0, 1, 2, 3, 4, 5, 6, 7, 8, and 9.

10 choices for first digit	×	10 choices for second digit	×	10 choices for third digit	×	10 choices for fourth digit

$10 \times 10 \times 10 \times 10 = 10{,}000$

▶ There are 10,000 possible 4-digit passwords.

PRACTICE

In Exercises 1–3, use the indicated counting method to answer the question.

1. Andrew, Bettina, and Carl are triplets. In how many different ways can the triplets stand in a row for a photo? (Make a list.)

2. The sign at the right shows the color and size choices for school T-shirts. How many different types of school T-shirts are available? (Draw a tree diagram.)

3. A 3-letter monogram consists of the first letter of a person's first name, middle name, and last name. For example, Matthew David Weaver's monogram is MDW. How many different 3-letter monograms are possible? (Use the counting principle.)

School T-Shirts $9.99	
Choose 1 color and 1 size.	
Colors:	**Sizes:**
Black, Gold, or White	S, M, L, or XL

In Exercises 4–8, answer the question using any counting method you choose.

4. How many different pizzas with 2 different toppings are available for the large pizza special advertised at the right?

5. Lance must choose 4 characters for his computer password. Each character can be any letter A–Z or any digit 0–9. How many different computer passwords are possible?

6. Mia must choose 3 whole numbers less than 50 for her locker combination. The numbers may be repeated. How many different locker combinations are possible?

7. A restaurant offers a dinner special. You can choose a main course, a vegetable, and a salad from a choice of 6 main courses, 4 vegetables, and 3 salads. How many different dinners are available?

8. Each day Scott walks, rides the bus, or gets a ride to school. He has each of the same possibilities for getting home each day. How many combinations of travel to and from school does Scott have?

Large Pizza Special	
Any 2 toppings for $12.49	
Pepperoni	Black olive
Sausage	Green pepper
Ground beef	Red onion
Extra cheese	Mushroom

Problem Solving Strategies  *Gr. 7 MR 1.0, Gr. 7 MR 2.0*

The following are strategies that you can use to solve problems.

Strategy	When to use	How to use
Draw a diagram	Draw a diagram when a problem involves any relationships that you can represent visually.	Draw a diagram that shows the given information. Label any unknowns in your diagram and look for relationships between givens and unknowns.
Look for a pattern	Look for a pattern when a problem includes a series of numbers or diagrams that you need to analyze.	Look for a pattern in any given information. Apply, extend, or generalize the pattern to help you solve the problem.
Guess, check, and revise	Guess, check, and revise when you need a place to start or you want to see what happens for a particular number.	Make a reasonable guess. Check to see if your guess solves the problem. If it does not, revise your guess and check again.
Act it out	Act out a problem that involves any relationships that you can represent with physical objects and movement.	Act out the problem, using objects described in the problem or other items that represent those objects.
Make a list or table	Make a list or table when you need to record, generate, or organize information.	Generate a list systematically, accounting for all possibilities. Look for relationships across rows or down columns within a table.
Solve a simpler or related problem	Solve a simpler or related problem when a problem seems difficult and can be made easier by using simpler numbers or conditions.	Think of a way to make the problem easier. Solve the simpler or related problem. Use what you learned to help you solve the original problem.
Work backward	Work backward when a problem gives you an end result and you need to find beginning conditions.	Work backward from the given information until you solve the problem. Work forward through the problem to check your answer.
Break into parts	Break into parts when a problem cannot be solved all at once, but can be solved in parts or stages.	Break the problem into parts and solve each part. Put the answers together to help you solve the original problem.

EXAMPLE **Fletcher baked brownies in a rectangular pan that measures 9 inches by 13 inches. He wants to cut rectangular brownies that are at least 2 inches on each side, with all brownies the same size. What is the greatest number of brownies Fletcher can cut?**

Draw a diagram of the rectangular pan. Label the sides with their lengths. Think about each side of the rectangle.

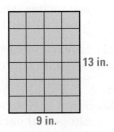

$9 \div 2 = 4.5$, so cut 4 brownies along the 9 inch side.
Check: $9 \div 4 = 2.25$, and $2.25 > 2$.

$13 \div 2 = 6.5$, so cut 6 brownies along the 13 inch side.
Check: $13 \div 6 \approx 2.17$, and $2.17 > 2$.

Use your diagram to count the brownies: $4 \times 6 = 24$.

▶ The greatest number of brownies Fletcher can cut is 24.

STANDARDS REVIEW HANDBOOK

1. Four friends hosted a party. The table shows the amount of money each friend spent. The friends want to share the party expenses equally, and Pam will pay the entire amount she owes to one person. Who owes money to whom?

Person	Party expenses
Barb	$11 for drinks
Bonnie	$15 for food
Pam	$6 for invitations
Holly	$8 for decorations

2. Six people can be seated at a rectangular table, with one person at each end. How many people can be seated at five of these tables if they are placed end to end?

3. Bob is 55 years old. In 5 years, Bob will be twice as old as his son. How old is Bob's son?

4. Maddie and Rob are sharing a pack of 25 pens. Maddie offers to let Rob have 3 pens for every 2 pens she gets. If they use the entire package of pens, how many pens will each person get?

5. In how many different ways can you make $.50 in change using quarters, dimes, and nickels?

6. The diagram shows two cuts through the center of a pizza. How many cuts through the center are needed to divide a pizza into 12 equal pieces?

7. Deb is flying to Seattle. Her flight leaves at 4:15 P.M. She wants to arrive at the airport 2 hours early to check in and get through security. The taxi ride from her office to the airport takes about 30 minutes. What time should Deb ask the taxi driver to pick her up at the office?

8. Dan wants to enclose a rectangular area with a fence. He has 12 fence posts to use, and the fence posts will be placed 10 feet apart. The diagram shows a possible shape for the area. Find another shape that would use all the fence posts, placed 10 feet apart, and would increase the area by 100 square feet.

9. A soccer league has a 7 week season, and there are 7 teams in the league. Each team plays a game with every other team once during the season. How many soccer games must be played each week of the season?

10. Julia is setting up a display of cracker boxes at a grocery store. She wants one box in the top row, two boxes in the second row down, three boxes in the third row down, and so on, as shown. Each box is 8 inches tall, and her display will be 6 feet tall. How many cracker boxes will be in the display?

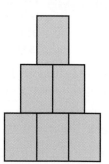

11. Five friends line up for tetherball. William is first in line, Mac is between Quinn and Benjamin, and Nate is next to William and Benjamin. Which friend is last in line?

12. The 4 members of the Buckner family usually drink 3 gallons of milk altogether each week. For 12 weeks in the summer, they will have a fifth family member staying with them. How many gallons of milk would you expect the 5 family members to drink over the 12 weeks?

Venn Diagrams and Logical Reasoning

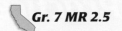 *Gr. 7 MR 2.5*

A **Venn diagram** uses shapes to show how sets are related.

EXAMPLE **Draw a Venn diagram of the whole numbers less than 10 where set *A* consists of prime numbers and set *B* consists of even numbers.**

Whole numbers less than 10:
0, 1, 2, 3, 4, 5, 6, 7, 8, 9

Set *A*: 2, 3, 5, 7

Set *B*: 0, 2, 4, 6, 8

Both set *A* and set *B*: 2

Neither set *A* nor set *B*: 1, 9

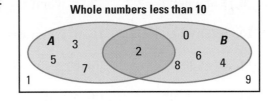

You can use a Venn diagram to answer questions about sets.

EXAMPLE **Use the Venn diagram above to answer the question.**

a. Is the statement below *true* or *false*? Explain.

No whole number less than 10 is prime.

▸ False. The whole number 2 is less than 10 and is prime.

b. Is the statement below *always*, *sometimes*, or *never* true? Explain.

A whole number less than 10 is either even or prime.

▸ Sometimes. Each of the numbers 0, 2, 3, 4, 5, 6, 7, and 8 are either even or prime, but the numbers 1 and 9 are not even and not prime.

PRACTICE

Draw a Venn diagram of the sets described.

1. Of the whole numbers less than 10, set *A* consists of factors of 10 and set *B* consists of odd numbers.

2. Of the whole numbers less than 10, set *A* consists of factors of 6 and set *B* consists of even numbers.

Use the Venn diagrams you drew in Exercises 1 and 2 to answer the question.

3. Are the following statements *true* or *false*? Explain.

   a. *If a whole number less than 10 is odd, then it must be a factor of 10.*

   b. *A whole number less than 10 that is a factor of 10 must be odd.*

4. Are the following statements *always*, *sometimes*, or *never* true? Explain.

   a. *A whole number that is even and less than 10 is a factor of 6.*

   b. *A factor of 6 that is less than 10 is even.*

Extra Practice

Chapter 1

Evaluate the expression.

1.1
1. $k + 9$ when $k = 7$
2. $21 - x$ when $x = 3$
3. $3.5 + t$ when $t = 0.9$
4. $y - \frac{3}{8}$ when $y = \frac{7}{12}$
5. $\frac{m}{4}$ when $m = 9.6$
6. $1.5t$ when $t = 2.3$
7. z^3 when $z = \frac{2}{3}$
8. p^4 when $p = 0.2$
9. $\frac{12}{n}$ when $n = 3$
10. $0.75r$ when $r = 3.5$
11. x^2 when $x = \frac{6}{5}$
12. $\frac{2}{3}v^2$ when $v = \frac{3}{4}$

1.2
13. $25 - 7 + 8$
14. $67 - 3 \cdot 4$
15. $8^2 \div 4 + 12$
16. $9 + 6 \div 3$
17. $\frac{3^3 - 7}{2}$
18. $\frac{1}{3}(7 - 5.5)^2$
19. $3 + 4(3 + 24)$
20. $\frac{3}{5}[27 - (2 + 5)]^2$
21. $\frac{2^3 + 6}{7}$
22. $\frac{2}{9}(5 - 2)^3$
23. $12 - \frac{1}{2}(8 + 7)$
24. $2[20 - \frac{3}{4}(30 - 14)]$

1.3 Translate the verbal phrase into an expression.

25. $\frac{3}{4}$ of a number m
26. the quotient of a number x and 7
27. the difference of a number y and 3
28. 6 more than 3 times a number n
29. 5 less than $\frac{1}{2}$ of a number t
30. 3 more than the quotient of a number y and 4

1.3 Write an expression for the situation.

31. Number of minutes left in a 45 minute class after m minutes have gone by
32. Number of students in a class if 19 students are present and b are not
33. Number of meters in c centimeters

1.4 Write an equation or an inequality.

34. The quotient of a number n and 8 is at least 24.
35. The product of 12 and the difference of a number r and 4 is 72.
36. The difference of a number q and 18 is greater than 10 and less than 15.

1.4 Solve the equation using mental math.

37. $d - 13 = 25$
38. $12z = 96$
39. $23 - m = 7$
40. $\frac{k}{6} = 12$

1.5 Identify what you know and what you need to find out. You do *not* need to solve the problem.

41. One day the temperature in Quito, Ecuador, was 18°C. The temperature in Monterey, California, was 63°F. Which temperature was higher?
42. What is the interest on $100 invested for 3 years in an account that earns simple interest at a rate of 2% per year?
43. On Monday, Katherine walked at a rate of 0.08 mile per minute for 40 minutes. On Tuesday, she walked at a rate of 0.07 mile per minute for 50 minutes. How far did Katherine walk altogether?

Chapter 2

2.1 Tell whether each number belongs to each of the following sets: whole numbers, integers, and rational numbers. Then order the numbers from least to greatest.

1. $0.25, -\dfrac{1}{8}, -\dfrac{1}{10}, -\dfrac{1}{5}$

2. $-2.5, -3, \dfrac{5}{2}, -\dfrac{9}{4}$

3. $-4, 3, -5, 0$

2.2 Find the sum.

4. $-6 + 10$

5. $-25 + (-36)$

6. $-75 + 58$

7. $8 + (-15) + 7$

8. $-2.8 + 4.3$

9. $-8.2 + (-11.5)$

10. $3\dfrac{2}{3} + \left(-5\dfrac{3}{8}\right)$

11. $-12\dfrac{3}{5} + 8\dfrac{1}{6}$

2.3 Find the difference.

12. $-17 - 20$

13. $16 - (-50)$

14. $-9 - (-12)$

15. $\dfrac{4}{5} - \dfrac{1}{2}$

16. $-\dfrac{1}{2} - \dfrac{2}{3}$

17. $-\dfrac{1}{3} - \left(-\dfrac{3}{4}\right)$

18. $-6.4 - 15$

19. $-12.8 - (-5.6)$

2.3 Evaluate the expression when $x = 1.5$ and $y = -4$.

20. $y - x$

21. $-y - (-x)$

22. $x - (10 - y)$

23. $-7 - (x - y)$

2.4 Find the product.

24. $-\dfrac{2}{3}(-36)$

25. $64\left(-\dfrac{5}{8}\right)$

26. $-4.1(-3.5)$

27. $(1.1)(-0.5)(-4)$

2.4 Identify the property illustrated.

28. $(-5)(8)(2) = (-5)(2)(8)$

29. $6 \cdot (7 \cdot 2) = (6 \cdot 7) \cdot 2$

30. $1(mn) = mn$

31. $0 \cdot (134) = 0$

32. $y \cdot (-1) = (-1) \cdot y$

33. $(-1)(-9) = 9$

2.5 Use the distributive property to write an equivalent expression.

34. $8(x + 4)$

35. $5(6 - y)$

36. $(m + 7)(-8)$

37. $-3(k - 14)$

38. $\dfrac{3}{5}(-15r - 5)$

39. $\dfrac{7}{12}(24s + 12)$

40. $(9v - 18)\dfrac{1}{3}$

41. $-\dfrac{5}{6}(-6w - 30)$

2.6 Find the quotient.

42. $-35 \div 7$

43. $-92 \div (-4)$

44. $36 \div -\dfrac{3}{4}$

45. $-56 \div -\dfrac{7}{8}$

46. $\dfrac{5}{9} \div (-5)$

47. $-\dfrac{5}{12} \div \dfrac{1}{2}$

48. $-\dfrac{4}{3} \div \dfrac{4}{3}$

49. $-\dfrac{5}{6} \div -\dfrac{6}{5}$

2.7 Approximate the square root to the nearest integer.

50. $\sqrt{135}$

51. $-\sqrt{75}$

52. $-\sqrt{160}$

53. $\sqrt{250}$

2.8 Determine whether the statement is *sometimes*, *always*, or *never* true.

54. If a number is irrational, then it is not an integer.

55. $|x + 3| - 3 > 0$ for a real number x.

56. If a number is a perfect square, then it is also a prime number.

Chapter 3

Solve the equation. Check your solution.

3.1
1. $x + 4 = 20$
2. $8 = m - 13$
3. $t + 2 = -10$
4. $z - 8 = -7$
5. $7h = 63$
6. $-4t = -44$
7. $\frac{b}{4} = 13$
8. $\frac{y}{-3} = 8$

3.2
9. $4x + 3 = 27$
10. $6m - 4 = 14$
11. $50 = 7y - 6$
12. $\frac{t}{4} - 3 = 9$
13. $\frac{x}{7} + 3 = -2$
14. $6p - 2p = 28$

3.3
15. $6x + 3x + 8 = 35$
16. $12w - 5 - 3w = 40$
17. $4d - 3 - 2d = -15$
18. $7m + 3(m + 2) = -24$
19. $5x - 3(x - 5) = 13$
20. $\frac{3}{4}(2y - 8) = 6$

3.4
21. $8x - 4 = 3x + 6$
22. $10 - 2x = 3x - 20$
23. $5 - 5x = 14 - 8x$
24. $3(2y - 5) = 4y - 7$
25. $9 + 4y = 2(3 - y)$
26. $3x - 3 = \frac{3}{4}(2x + 12)$
27. $12a + 5 = 6(2a + 5)$
28. $2(8m - 7) = 16m - 14$
29. $\frac{4}{5}(15c - 35) = 9c - 7$

3.5 Solve the proportion. Check your solution.

30. $\frac{7}{2} = \frac{x}{16}$
31. $\frac{m}{9} = \frac{6}{27}$
32. $\frac{z}{4} = \frac{48}{12}$
33. $\frac{30}{50} = \frac{t}{10}$
34. $\frac{2a}{5} = \frac{18}{15}$
35. $\frac{10}{4} = \frac{5w}{14}$
36. $\frac{3 + c}{7} = \frac{27}{21}$
37. $\frac{12}{8} = \frac{k - 1}{20}$

3.5 Write the sentence as a proportion. Then solve the proportion.

38. 5 is to 7 as 15 is to x.
39. 9 is to 3 as x is to 12.
40. g is to 9 as 16 is to 12.
41. 6 is to 18 as y is to 3.

3.6 Solve the proportion. Check your solution.

42. $\frac{12}{x} = \frac{6}{7}$
43. $\frac{6x}{4} = \frac{18}{12}$
44. $\frac{9}{2x} = \frac{21}{28}$
45. $\frac{7y}{8} = \frac{35}{20}$
46. $\frac{7}{x + 13} = \frac{4}{12}$
47. $\frac{y + 5}{y} = \frac{10}{8}$
48. $\frac{a - 3}{a} = \frac{6}{24}$
49. $\frac{4d}{5 + 3d} = \frac{9}{8}$
50. $\frac{2x + 6}{x} = \frac{7}{2}$
51. $\frac{3b}{5b - 7} = \frac{8}{11}$
52. $\frac{8}{2x + 12} = \frac{6}{x + 8}$
53. $\frac{4.8 - 2x}{8} = \frac{0.4 + x}{10}$

3.7 Solve the literal equation for x. Then use the solution to solve the specific equation.

54. $ax - b = c$; $6x - 5 = 25$
55. $a(b - x) = c$; $2(8 - x) = -6$
56. $\frac{a}{x} + b = c$; $\frac{42}{x} + 4 = 11$
57. $\frac{x}{a} + b = cx - d$; $\frac{x}{2} + 8 = 3x - 2$

3.7 Solve the equation for y.

58. $5x + y = 10$
59. $8x - 2y = 16$
60. $7x + 3y = 6 - 5x$
61. $21 = 6x + 7y$
62. $1 - 9x = 7 + 3y$
63. $4x + 5y = 19x - 20$
64. $6x - 11 = 8y - 7$
65. $4 - 18x = 6y + 12$

Chapter 4

Solve the inequality. Graph your solution.

4.1
1. $y - 2 > 3$
2. $5 + x \le 2$
3. $4 \ge x - 3$
4. $m + 3 < 2$

5. $2 + n \le 4\frac{1}{2}$
6. $2\frac{3}{4} + n < -3\frac{5}{8}$
7. $1\frac{7}{8} > 6\frac{3}{4} + z$
8. $3\frac{2}{5} \ge 1\frac{1}{3} + k$

9. $-8.5 \le t - 10$
10. $r + 4 < -0.7$
11. $-6.9 > -1.4 + y$
12. $1.48 - m \ge -3.13$

13. $\frac{2}{3} + p \ge \frac{3}{4}$
14. $7 < 12 - n$
15. $5\frac{1}{6} - x > 3$
16. $y - 3.2 \le -2.4$

4.2
17. $3p \le 27$
18. $-13t > 26$
19. $\frac{x}{3} \ge 2$
20. $\frac{y}{-2} < 5$

21. $-6m \ge -9$
22. $-3 \ge \frac{n}{2}$
23. $0.3z \le 2.4$
24. $25 > -2.5s$

25. $4.8z \le 3.2$
26. $0.09d < -1.8$
27. $\frac{y}{0.3} > -15$
28. $-1.8t < 9$

29. $-\frac{n}{3} < \frac{3}{4}$
30. $3.6 > -0.3r$
31. $-2.4x \ge -7.2$
32. $\frac{3}{4}y \le -\frac{3}{8}$

4.3
33. $3x + 5 \ge 20$
34. $6z - 5 < 13$
35. $8(t + 4) > -8$

36. $7 - 8n \le 4n - 17$
37. $6d - 4 \ge 14 + 3d$
38. $\frac{2}{3}y + 28 > 20 + 2y$

4.3 **Solve the inequality, if possible.**

39. $5 + 7x \le 2x - 9x + 2$
40. $d - 5d - 1 < 4d + 2$
41. $4(3y + 4) \le 3(7 + 4y)$

42. $6 + 12m < \frac{1}{2}(24m - 10)$
43. $6(-5 + 3p) \ge 3(6p - 10)$
44. $\frac{5}{6}(12z - 24) > \frac{2}{5}(25z - 25)$

4.4 **Solve the inequality. Graph your solution.**

45. $2 \le y - 4 < 7$
46. $-27 < 9x < 27$
47. $2 < 6z - 10 < 20$

48. $15 < \frac{5}{9}(18a - 9) \le 30$
49. $2v > 12 \ or \ v + 2 < 6$
50. $3r + 7 < -5 \ or \ 32 \le 7r + 46$

51. $-4m < 8 \ or \ 2m - 2 < -12$
52. $9t - 20 \ge 4t \ or \ 4 < \frac{1}{-2}t$
53. $-n - 1 > 1 \ or \ 2n + 8 > n + 8$

4.5 **Solve the equation, if possible.**

54. $|x| = 8$
55. $|y| = -10$
56. $|m + 6| = 5$
57. $|4z - 2| = 14$

58. $|t - 7| = 21$
59. $6|z - 4| = 36$
60. $4|6s + 11| = -52$
61. $|r + 3| - 16 = -4$

62. $|5r| + 10 = 15$
63. $2|3s + 4| = 14$
64. $-4|7v + 2| = 32$
65. $12\left|\frac{5}{6}w - 4\right| - 4 = 8$

4.6 **Solve the inequality. Graph your solution.**

66. $|x| \le 3$
67. $|y| \ge 5$
68. $|s| > 1.2$
69. $|q| < \frac{2}{5}$

70. $|x + 2| > 6$
71. $|y + 3| \le 5$
72. $|8 - m| < 3$
73. $|4n - 1| \ge 7$

74. $3|p - 3| \le 12$
75. $|3q + 2| - 3 \ge 8$
76. $2|5a - 1| + 3 \le 11$
77. $4\left|\frac{2}{3}c + 2\right| < 64$

EXTRA PRACTICE

Extra Practice **813**

Chapter 5

5.1 Identify the domain and range of the relation.

1. $\{(4, 1), (6, 2), (10, 3), (16, 4)\}$

2. $\{(-15, 4), (-11, 1), (7, 5), (9, 8)\}$

3.

x	3	4	5	6	7
y	9	11	13	15	17

4.

x	-3	-1	0	1	3
y	3	1	0	-1	-3

5. The domain of the function $y = 1.25x + 5$ is $-2, 0, 2, 4, 6$. Identify the range of the function.

5.2 Graph the equation.

6. $y = x + 2$; domain 0, 1, 2, 3

7. $y = 3x - 3$; domain $-2, -1, 0, 2, 3$

8. $y = 1.5x$; domain 0, 20, 40, 60

9. $y = \frac{1}{4}x + 4$; domain $-12, -4, 4, 8$

5.3 Graph the equation.

10. $y - x = 3$

11. $y + 3x = 5$

12. $y - 4x = 10$

13. $y = 4$

14. $2x - y = 0$

15. $3x + y = 0$

16. $3x + 2y = -6$

17. $x = 0.5$

5.4 Find the x-intercept and the y-intercept of the graph of the equation.

18. $2x - y = 12$

19. $-5x - 2y = 20$

20. $-4x + 1.5y = 4$

21. $y = \frac{3}{4}x - 15$

5.4 Graph the equation. Label the points where the line crosses the axes.

22. $y = 3x - 6$

23. $4x + 5y = -20$

24. $\frac{2}{3}x + \frac{1}{2}y = 10$

25. $0.3x - y = 6$

5.5 Find the slope of the line that passes through the points.

26. $(4, 2)$ and $(6, 8)$

27. $(-3, 0)$ and $(2, -5)$

28. $(-5, 3)$ and $(-8, 10)$

29. $(9, 4)$ and $(0, 1)$

30. $(-2, 5)$ and $(-2, 10)$

31. $(6, -4)$ and $(4, -4)$

32. $(6, 1)$ and $(4, 3)$

33. $(5, -7)$ and $(0, -7)$

34. $(4, 1)$ and $(12, 8)$

5.6 Identify the slope and y-intercept of the line with the given equation.

35. $y = 7x + 8$

36. $y = 10x - 6$

37. $y = 3 - 4x$

38. $y = x$

5.6 Rewrite the equation in slope-intercept form. Then identify the slope and the y-intercept of the line.

39. $2x + y = 8$

40. $10x - y = 20$

41. $5x + 2y = 10$

42. $-2x - y = 3$

5.6 Graph the equation.

43. $y = 2x - 4$

44. $y = -\frac{3}{4}x + 1$

45. $2x + y = 1$

46. $-2x + 3y = -9$

5.7 Graph the direct variation equation.

47. $y = 2x$

48. $y = -x$

49. $y = 4x$

50. $5x + y = 0$

51. $x - 2y = 0$

52. $3x + y = 0$

53. $2y = 9x$

54. $y - \frac{5}{4}x = 0$

Chapter 6

6.1 Write an equation of the line with the given slope and *y*-intercept.

1. slope: 3
y-intercept: 6

2. slope: −2
y-intercept: 4

3. slope: 5
y-intercept: −1

4. slope: −1
y-intercept: −3

5. slope: $\frac{1}{2}$
y-intercept: −5

6. slope: $-\frac{7}{10}$
y-intercept: 8

6.1 Write an equation of the line that passes through the given points.

7. $(-2, 3), (0, 5)$

8. $(4, -8), (0, -2)$

9. $(3, 0), (0, -4)$

6.2 Write an equation of the line that passes through the given point and has the given slope *m*.

10. $(3, 8); m = 2$

11. $(-1, 5); m = -4$

12. $(-6, 3); m = \frac{2}{3}$

6.2 Write an equation of the line that passes through the given points.

13. $(2, 4), (5, 13)$

14. $(1, -2), (-2, 13)$

15. $\left(2, \frac{1}{3}\right), (6, 3)$

16. $(3, -10), (-5, 6)$

17. $(5, 7), (-4, 2)$

18. $\left(\frac{1}{4}, \frac{1}{4}\right), \left(\frac{3}{4}, \frac{1}{2}\right)$

6.3 Graph the equation.

19. $y - 3 = -3(x + 4)$

20. $y + 5 = -2(x - 1)$

21. $y - 6 = \frac{2}{3}(x - 3)$

6.3 Write an equation in point-slope form of the line that passes through the given point and has the given slope *m* or that passes through the two given points.

22. $(-3, 5), m = -2$

23. $(2, 4), m = \frac{1}{2}$

24. $(-1, -6), m = -\frac{3}{2}$

25. $(-4, 2), (-2, 16)$

26. $(3, 9), (-7, 4)$

27. $(10, -2), (12, -6)$

6.4 Write two equations in standard form that are equivalent to the given equation.

28. $-2x + y = 6$

29. $3x - 4y = 5$

30. $x - 3y = -2$

6.4 Write an equation in standard form of the line that passes through the given point and has the given slope *m* or that passes through the two given points.

31. $(2, 7), m = -4$

32. $(5, 11), m = 3$

33. $(-3, 0) m = 2$

34. $(1, -2), (-2, 4)$

35. $(-1, -1), (0, 4)$

36. $(4, -6), (11, -13)$

6.5 Write an equation of the line that passes through the given point and is parallel to the given line.

37. $(5, 4), y = 3x + 5$

38. $(-3, -7), y = -5x - 2$

39. $(8, -3), y = \frac{3}{4}x + 5$

6.5 Write an equation of the line that passes through the given point and is perpendicular to the given line.

40. $(-12, -2), y = 3x + 2$

41. $(15, -11), y = \frac{3}{5}x - 8$

42. $(7, -6), 4x + 6y = 7$

Chapter 7

7.1 Solve the linear system by graphing. Check your solution.

1. $y = x - 1$
$y = -x + 5$

2. $y = 3x + 12$
$y = -4x - 2$

3. $3x - 2y = -5$
$4x + 3y = -18$

4. $\frac{2}{3}x + \frac{1}{3}y = \frac{16}{3}$
$-\frac{2}{5}x + y = \frac{8}{5}$

7.2 Solve the linear system using substitution.

5. $y = 2x + 6$
$x = y - 3$

6. $y = 3x + 5$
$x + y = -1$

7. $x = 2y - 5$
$2x - y = 11$

8. $\frac{1}{2}x + \frac{3}{4}y = 5$
$x - \frac{1}{2}y = 6$

Solve the linear system using elimination.

7.3 **9.** $x + 2y = 2$
$-x + 3y = 13$

10. $3x - 4y = -16$
$x - 4y = -40$

11. $5x + 4y = 6$
$7x + 4y = 14$

12. $4x - 3y = 39$
$7y = 4x - 79$

7.4 **13.** $x + y = -3$
$5x + 7y = -9$

14. $8x - 3y = 61$
$2x - 5y = -23$

15. $4x - 3y = -2$
$6x + 4y = 31$

16. $15x - 8y = 6$
$25x - 12y = 16$

7.5 Graph the linear system. Then use the graph to tell whether the linear system has *one solution*, *no solution*, or *infinitely many solutions*.

17. $2x + y = -3$
$y = -2x + 5$

18. $2y - 4x = 10$
$-2y - 2x = 8$

19. $5x + 2y = -19$
$10x - 7y = -16$

20. $10x + 5y = -15$
$y = -2x - 3$

7.6 **21.** During a canoe ride, a canoe travels upstream at a speed of 4 miles per hour and then travels the same distance downstream at a speed of 8 miles per hour. The speed of the current remains constant. What is the average speed of the canoe in still water?

22. During the last kilometer of a race, John has a 40 second lead over Mary. John runs at a speed of 1.5 meters per second, and Mary runs at a speed of 2 meters per second. How long will it take Mary to overtake John?

7.7 **23.** A food store sells a mixture of dried fruit and nuts. The dried fruit sells for $.60 per ounce, and the nuts sell for $.50 per ounce. The store wants to make a 20 ounce mixture that sells for $.54 per ounce. How many ounces of dried fruit and nuts should the store owner mix?

7.7 **24.** Becky is mixing a 10% saline solution with an 18% saline solution. She would like to obtain a 20 gram mixture that is 13% saline. How many grams of each solution should she use to obtain the desired mixture?

7.8 Graph the inequality.

25. $y \geq x + 5$

26. $y < x - 1$

27. $4x + y > 3$

28. $x \leq -5$

29. $3(x - 8) \leq 6y$

30. $2(x - 1) \geq 1 - y$

31. $x - 8 < y + 2$

32. $3(y - 8) > x - 9$

7.9 Graph the system of inequalities.

33. $y \geq -5$
$y \leq -2$

34. $x \geq -3$
$y < 1$

35. $y < -2x - 3$
$x - y > -4$

36. $x + 4y \geq -8$
$y - 4x < 8$
$x > -1$

Chapter 8

Simplify the expression. In exercises involving numerical bases only, write your answer using exponents.

8.1 **1.** $5^3 \cdot 5^4$ **2.** $6 \cdot 6$ **3.** $[(-4)^3]^2$ **4.** $(8 \cdot 4)^5$

   5. $n^2 \cdot n^4 \cdot n^5$ **6.** $(y^3)^5$ **7.** $(-2x)^3$ **8.** $(3d^2)^3 \cdot 2d^2$

8.2 **9.** $\dfrac{8^7}{8^2}$ **10.** $\left(-\dfrac{2}{3}\right)^5$ **11.** $7^9 \cdot \left(\dfrac{1}{7}\right)^4$ **12.** $\dfrac{1}{t^9} \cdot t^{13}$

   13. $\left(\dfrac{p}{q}\right)^7$ **14.** $\left(\dfrac{6x^9}{3y^4}\right)^2$ **15.** $\left(\dfrac{4y^5}{3}\right)^3 \cdot \dfrac{1}{y^6}$ **16.** $\left(\dfrac{2}{u^2}\right)^3 \cdot \left(\dfrac{3u^4}{z^2}\right)^4$

8.3 Evaluate the expression.

   17. 3^{-4} **18.** $(-5)^{-3}$ **19.** 7^0 **20.** $4^{-5} \cdot 4^3$

   21. $\left(\dfrac{1}{2}\right)^{-3}$ **22.** $(3^{-2})^3$ **23.** $\dfrac{1}{2^{-5}}$ **24.** $\dfrac{8^{-4}}{8^{-6}}$

8.3 Simplify the expression. Write your answer using only positive exponents.

   25. y^{-10} **26.** $(3c)^{-4}$ **27.** $10b^{-3}c^5$ **28.** $(2d^5e^{-2})^{-3}$

   29. $\dfrac{x^{-4}}{y^{-5}}$ **30.** $\dfrac{1}{6t^{-5}u^3}$ **31.** $\dfrac{3}{(-2z)^{-5}}$ **32.** $\dfrac{(2e)^{-4}g^5}{e^5g^{-3}}$

8.4 Simplify the expression.

   33. $\sqrt{98}$ **34.** $\sqrt{300}$ **35.** $\sqrt{128x^3}$ **36.** $\sqrt{112} \cdot \sqrt{63}$

   37. $\sqrt{27x^5} \cdot \sqrt{48x}$ **38.** $\sqrt{\dfrac{19}{49}}$ **39.** $\sqrt{\dfrac{1}{6x^2}}$ **40.** $\dfrac{3}{\sqrt{5}}$

   41. $\dfrac{\sqrt{7}}{\sqrt{8k}}$ **42.** $\sqrt{\dfrac{5}{27}}$ **43.** $2\sqrt{3} + \sqrt{7} + \sqrt{3}$ **44.** $2\sqrt{11} + \sqrt{99}$

   45. $\sqrt{45} + 3\sqrt{20}$ **46.** $\sqrt{3}(12 - \sqrt{15})$ **47.** $3\sqrt{6}(4\sqrt{6} - \sqrt{600})$ **48.** $(6 - \sqrt{7})(6 - \sqrt{7})$

8.5 Let a and b represent the lengths of the legs of a right triangle, and let c represent the length of the hypotenuse. Find the unknown length.

   49. $a = 6, b = 8$ **50.** $a = 10, c = 26$ **51.** $b = 40, c = 41$ **52.** $a = 2, c = 5$

8.5 Tell whether the triangle with the given side lengths is a right triangle.

   53. 10, 24, 26 **54.** 12, 14, 16 **55.** 14, 15, 21 **56.** 1.4, 4.8, 5

8.6 Evaluate the expression.

   57. $\sqrt[3]{125}$ **58.** $-\sqrt[3]{64}$ **59.** $\sqrt[3]{8} + \sqrt{16}$ **60.** $\sqrt{4} - \sqrt[3]{27}$

   61. $81^{1/2}$ **62.** $9^{-3/2}$ **63.** $8^{4/3}$ **64.** $1^{-1/3}$

8.6 Simplify the expression. Write your answer using only positive exponents.

   65. $11^{9/2} \cdot 11^{-5/2}$ **66.** $\left(\dfrac{1}{8}\right)^{1/3}\left(\dfrac{1}{4}\right)^{1/2}$ **67.** $x^{-7/3}(x^{1/3})^2$ **68.** $\dfrac{\sqrt{n} \cdot m^{-3/2}}{(n^6)^{-1/3}}$

Chapter 9

9.1 **Find the sum or difference.**

1. $(6x^2 + 7) + (x^2 - 9)$

2. $(8y^2 - 3y - 10) + (-11y^2 + 2y - 7)$

3. $(10m^2 - 7m + 2) - (3m^2 - 2m + 5)$

4. $(2t^3 - 3t^2 + 5t) - (6t^3 + 3t^2 - 5t)$

5. $(6b^3 + 12b^2 - b) - (15b^2 + 7b - 8)$

6. $(r^2 - 8 + 4r^3 + 5r) - (7r^3 - 3r^2 + 5)$

Find the product.

9.2 7. $5x^4(2x^3 - 3x^2 + 5x - 1)$

8. $(x^2 + 4x + 2)(x + 7)$

9. $(2x + 3)(4x + 2)$

10. $(2x^2 - 5x + 6)(3x - 2)$

11. $(3x - 7)(x + 5)$

12. $(9t - 2)(2t - 3)$

9.3 13. $(x + 10)^2$

14. $(m + 8)(m - 8)$

15. $(4x - 2)(4x + 2)$

16. $(3x - 4y)(3x + 4y)$

17. $(6 - 3t)(6 + 3t)$

18. $(-11x - 4y)^2$

9.4 **Divide.**

19. $-12x^6 \div 3x^3$

20. $9x^2 \div (-27x^8)$

21. $(30x^4 - 12x^3 + 6x^2) \div (-6x)$

22. $(9y^2 + 3y - 6) \div (3y - 2)$

23. $(3v^2 + 2v + 12) \div (v + 2)$

24. $(9m^2 - 6) \div (3m - 4)$

9.5 **Solve the equation.**

25. $(m + 8)(m - 2) = 0$

26. $(2y - 6)(y + 3) = 0$

27. $(5y - 3)(2y - 4) = 0$

28. $3b^2 + 9b = 0$

29. $-12m^2 - 3m = 0$

30. $14k^2 = 28k$

9.6 **Factor the trinomial.**

31. $y^2 + 7y + 12$

32. $x^2 - 12x + 35$

33. $q^2 + 3q - 40$

9.6 **Solve the equation.**

34. $m^2 - 7m + 10 = 0$

35. $n^2 + 8 = 6n$

36. $r^2 - 15r = -8r - 10$

9.7 **Factor the trinomial.**

37. $-x^2 + 5x - 6$

38. $3k^2 - 10k + 8$

39. $4k^2 - 12k + 5$

40. $6t^2 - 5t - 6$

41. $-3s^2 - 7s - 2$

42. $2v^2 - 5v + 3$

9.7 **Solve the equation.**

43. $-3x^2 + 14x - 8 = 0$

44. $3p^2 - 28 = 17p$

45. $t(6t - 7) = 3$

9.8 **Factor the polynomial.**

46. $y^2 - 36$

47. $9y^2 - 49$

48. $12y^2 - 27$

49. $x^2 - 8x + 16$

50. $4x^2 - 12x + 9$

51. $27x^2 - 36x + 12$

52. $g^2 + 10g + 25$

53. $9b^2 + 24b + 16$

54. $4w^2 + 28w + 49$

9.9 **Factor the polynomial completely.**

55. $2x^2 + 8x + 6$

56. $3z^2 - 16z + 5$

57. $3y^3 + 15y^2 + 2y + 10$

58. $30z^3 - 14z^2 - 8z$

59. $98m^3 - 18m$

60. $2h^3 - 3h^2 - 18h + 27$

EXTRA PRACTICE

Chapter 10

10.1 **Graph the function. Compare the graph with the graph of $y = x^2$.**

1. $y = 4x^2$

2. $y = -5x^2$

3. $y = \frac{1}{2}x^2$

4. $y = -\frac{2}{5}x^2$

5. $y = x^2 + 3$

6. $y = x^2 - 2$

7. $y = 3x^2 + 4$

8. $y = -4x^2 - 3$

10.2 **Graph the function. Label the vertex and axis of symmetry.**

9. $y = x^2 + 4x + 4$

10. $y = -x^2 - 2x + 3$

11. $y = 2x^2 - 6x + 5$

12. $y = 3x^2 + 12x + 8$

13. $y = -2x^2 + 6$

14. $y = \frac{3}{4}x^2 - 3x$

10.3 **Graph the quadratic function. Label the vertex, axis of symmetry, and x-intercept(s).**

15. $y = (x - 2)(x - 3)$

16. $y = -2(x - 1)(x - 6)$

17. $y = -\frac{3}{2}(x + 5)(x + 4)$

18. $y = (x - 5)^2$

19. $y = \frac{1}{4}(x + 6)^2$

20. $y = -(x + 2)^2$

21. $y = -3x^2 + 27$

22. $y = -x^2 + 8x - 7$

23. $y = 6x^2 + 5x - 4$

10.4 **Solve the equation by graphing.**

24. $x^2 + 3x - 10 = 0$

25. $x^2 + 14 = 9x$

26. $-x^2 + 3x = -18$

27. $2x^2 + 3x - 20 = 0$

28. $2x^2 + x = 6$

29. $\frac{1}{2}x^2 - x = 12$

10.5 **Solve the equation.**

30. $2x^2 - 20 = 78$

31. $3y^2 + 16 = 4$

32. $16y^2 - 6 = 3$

33. $48 - x^2 = -52$

34. $5m^2 - 5 = 10$

35. $2 - 5t^2 = 4$

10.6 **Solve the equation by completing the square.**

36. $x^2 + 4x - 21 = 0$

37. $g^2 - 10g = 24$

38. $w^2 - 7w + 6 = 0$

39. $y^2 - \frac{3}{4}y = \frac{1}{4}$

40. $x^2 - 6x + 3 = 0$

41. $4m^2 + 8m - 7 = 0$

42. $\frac{1}{3}t^2 - 4t + 5 = 3$

43. $\frac{1}{2}b^2 - 8b + 8 = -15$

44. $3x^2 - 6x + 2 = 27$

10.7 **Use the quadratic formula to solve the equation.**

45. $h^2 + 6h - 72 = 0$

46. $3x^2 - 7x + 2 = 0$

47. $2k^2 - 5k + 2 = 0$

48. $n^2 + 1 = 5n$

49. $2z + 4 = 3z^2$

50. $5x^2 - 4x = 2$

51. $7r^2 - 2r = 6$

52. $3n^2 - 4n + 3 = 5$

53. $4x^2 + 6x = 3x^2 - 4x + 1$

10.8 **Tell whether the equation has *two solutions*, *one solution*, or *no solution*.**

54. $m^2 - 2m + 1 = 0$

55. $3x^2 + 6x + 2 = 0$

56. $2q^2 + 3q + 5 = 0$

57. $\frac{3}{4}x^2 - x + 2 = 0$

58. $2w^2 - 5w + 6 = 8$

59. $2y^2 + 10y - 5 = 3y^2 - 30$

60. $-\frac{1}{2}r^2 - 3r = 2r - 6$

61. $5p^2 + p - 4 = 3$

62. $-3x^2 - 1 = 2x^2 + 5x - 3$

Chapter 11

11.1 Graph the inverse variation equation.

1. $y = \dfrac{-1}{x}$ **2.** $y = \dfrac{8}{x}$ **3.** $y = \dfrac{12}{x}$ **4.** $y = \dfrac{-14}{x}$

11.1 Given that y varies inversely with x, use the specified values to write an inverse variation equation that relates x and y. Then find the value of y when $x = 2$.

5. $x = 3, y = 4$ **6.** $x = -2, y = 5$ **7.** $x = 8, y = -6$ **8.** $x = -7, y = -7$

11.2 Simplify the rational expression, if possible. State the excluded values.

9. $\dfrac{44x^3}{24x}$ **10.** $\dfrac{3y + 6}{y + 2}$ **11.** $\dfrac{3a - 15}{4a - 20}$ **12.** $\dfrac{2b - 8}{4 - b}$

13. $\dfrac{r^2 - 2r - 15}{r^2 + r - 6}$ **14.** $\dfrac{s + 3}{2s^2 + 3s - 9}$ **15.** $\dfrac{2m^2 + 8m - 24}{3m^3 + 24m^2 + 36m}$ **16.** $\dfrac{6n^3 - 18n^2}{3n^3 - 27n}$

Find the sum, difference, product, or quotient.

11.3 **17.** $\dfrac{x^2 + 3x - 10}{2x - 4} \cdot \dfrac{5x}{x^2 + 2x - 15}$ **18.** $\dfrac{2y^6}{6y^3 + 8y^2} \cdot (3y + 4)$

19. $\dfrac{3z^2 + 2z - 1}{z + 3} \cdot \dfrac{z^2 - 9}{z + 1}$ **20.** $\dfrac{4a^2}{6a - 1} \div \dfrac{2a^3 - 6a^2}{-18a + 3}$

21. $\dfrac{3r^2 - 12}{r - 2} \div \dfrac{2r^2 + 7r + 6}{2r^2 - r - 6}$ **22.** $\dfrac{3s^2 + 11s + 10}{s + 2} \div (-3s^2 + s + 10)$

11.4 **23.** $\dfrac{8}{5t} + \dfrac{3}{2t^2}$ **24.** $\dfrac{3}{u + 2} + \dfrac{4}{2u + 1}$

25. $\dfrac{5}{2b - 3} + \dfrac{1}{b - 6}$ **26.** $\dfrac{4}{5t^2} - \dfrac{10}{3t}$

27. $\dfrac{3}{c^2 - 9} - \dfrac{2}{2c^2 - 3c - 9}$ **28.** $\dfrac{k + 4}{k^2 + 4k + 4} - \dfrac{k - 4}{k^2 - k - 6}$

11.5 Solve the equation. Check your solution.

29. $\dfrac{2}{x + 2} = \dfrac{x - 5}{9}$ **30.** $\dfrac{y}{y - 1} + \dfrac{1}{4} = \dfrac{6}{y - 1}$

31. $\dfrac{z}{z + 3} + 2 = \dfrac{5}{z - 1}$ **32.** $\dfrac{1}{w + 5} - \dfrac{2}{w + 3} = \dfrac{6}{w^2 + 5w + 6}$

33. $\dfrac{3}{h + 4} - 4 = \dfrac{6}{h^2 + h - 12}$ **34.** $\dfrac{2}{a + 2} - \dfrac{5}{a + 2} = \dfrac{4}{a^2 + 4a + 4}$

11.6 **35.** Jin and Suzie are building a model. Jin can build a model in 4 hours working by herself, and Suzie can build a model in 2 hours and 30 minutes working by herself. How long will Jin and Suzie take to build a model working together?

36. Working together, computer A and computer B process 10 images that are transmitted from a satellite in 100 seconds. Working by itself, computer A could complete the same job in 180 seconds. How long would it take computer B to process 10 images working by itself?

Chapter 12

12.1 In Exercises 1 and 2, use the following information. A bag contains 4 pens, 3 pencils, and 8 markers. You choose one item from the bag at random.

1. What is the probability that you choose a marker?

2. What is the probability that you do *not* choose a pen?

12.1 In Exercises 3–5, use the following information. A bag contains 3 red, 3 blue, and 3 yellow marbles. You toss a coin and then draw a marble out of the bag at random.

3. Find the number of possible outcomes in the sample space. Then list the possible outcomes.

4. What is the probability that the coin shows tails and the marble is blue?

5. What is the probability that the coin shows heads and the marble is *not* red?

12.2 6. In how many ways can you arrange the letters in the word SPRING?

7. In how many ways can you arrange 3 of the letters in the word TULIP?

12.2 In Exercises 8–15, evaluate the expression.

8. $7!$

9. $11!$

10. $\dfrac{5!}{3!}$

11. $\dfrac{10!}{8!}$

12. $_6P_6$

13. $_7P_4$

14. $_8P_2$

15. $_{12}P_5$

12.3 16. You can choose 3 books from a list of 5 books to read for English class. How many combinations of 3 books are possible?

17. An amusement park has 15 rides. You want to go on 10 of them. How many different combinations of rides can you go on?

12.3 Evaluate the expression.

18. $_5C_0$

19. $_7C_4$

20. $_{10}C_7$

21. $_{11}C_1$

22. $_4C_2$

23. $_7C_6$

24. $_{14}C_7$

25. $_{21}C_{19}$

12.4 In Exercises 26–29, you roll a number cube. Tell whether the events A and B are *mutually exclusive* or *overlapping*. Then find $P(A \text{ or } B)$.

26. **Event A:** Roll a 5.
    Event B: Roll a prime number.

27. **Event A:** Roll a 4.
    Event B: Roll a multiple of 3.

28. **Event A:** Roll a 6.
    Event B:: Roll a number less than 3.

29. **Event A:** Roll a multiple of 2.
    Event B: Roll a number greater than 3.

12.4 30. A bag contains 3 red, 4 blue, and 5 yellow marbles. You randomly draw two marbles, one at a time. Find the probability that both are blue if **(a)** you replace the first marble and **(b)** you do *not* replace the first marble.

31. There are 5743 known amphibian species in the world. Of these, 1856 species are judged to be at risk of extinction, and another 113 species may already be extinct. Find the probability that two different amphibian species, each chosen at random, are at risk of extinction.

Tables

Symbols

Symbol	Meaning	Page
$3 \cdot x$ $3x$ $3(x)$	3 times x	5
$\dfrac{a}{b}$	a divided by b, $b \neq 0$	5
a^4	the fourth power of a, or $a \cdot a \cdot a \cdot a$	6
( )	parentheses—a grouping symbol	12
[ ]	brackets—a grouping symbol	12
$=$	is equal to	26
$<$	is less than	26
$>$	is greater than	26
$\leq$	is less than or equal to	26
$\geq$	is greater than or equal to	26
$\stackrel{?}{=}$	is equal to?	27
$\ldots$	continues on	53
$\{1, 2, 3\}$	a set with elements 1, 2, and 3	53
$-a$	the opposite of a	55
$|a|$	the absolute value of a	55
$\dfrac{1}{a}$	the reciprocal of a, $a \neq 0$	88
$\sqrt{a}$	the nonnegative square root of a, $a \geq 0$	95
$\pm$	plus or minus	95

Symbol	Meaning	Page
$\approx$	is approximately equal to	96
$\{\}$ or $\emptyset$	empty set	148
$a : b$	the ratio of a to b	155
$\{x : x \geq 0\}$	the set of all x such that x is greater than or equal to 0	266
$f(x)$	the value of the function f at x	269
m	slope	282
b	y-intercept	291
k	constant of variation	297
a^{-n}	$\dfrac{1}{a^n}$, $a \neq 0$	475
$\sqrt[3]{a}$	the cube root of a	498
$a^{1/2}$	the nonnegative square root of a, $\sqrt{a}$, where $a \geq 0$	499
$a^{1/3}$	the cube root of a, $\sqrt[3]{a}$	499
$P(A)$	the probability of an event A	745
$n!$	n factorial, or $n \cdot (n-1) \cdot \ldots \cdot 2 \cdot 1$, n is a nonnegative integer	751
${}_nP_r$	the number of permutations of n objects taken r at a time, $r \leq n$	751
${}_nC_r$	the number of combinations of n objects taken r at a time, $r \leq n$	756

Geometric Formulas

Pythagorean Theorem (p. 491)

In a right triangle, $a^2 + b^2 = c^2$ where a and b are the lengths of the legs and c is the length of the hypotenuse.

Square (p. 796)

Area
$A = s^2$

Perimeter
$P = 4s$

Rectangle (p. 796)

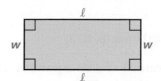

Area
$A = \ell w$

Perimeter
$P = 2\ell + 2w$

Parallelogram (p. 796)

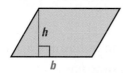

Area
$A = bh$

Triangle (p. 796)

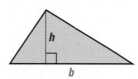

Area
$A = \frac{1}{2}bh$

Trapezoid (p. 796)

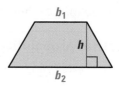

Area
$A = \frac{1}{2}(b_1 + b_2)h$

Circle (p. 798)

Circumference
$C = \pi d$ or
$C = 2\pi r$

Area
$A = \pi r^2$

Prism (p. 799)

Surface Area
$S = 2B + Ph$

Volume
$V = Bh$

Cylinder (p. 799)

Surface Area
$S = 2B + Ch$
$\quad = 2\pi r^2 + 2\pi rh$

Volume
$V = Bh$
$\quad = \pi r^2 h$

Pyramid (p. 799)

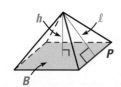

Surface Area
$S = B + \frac{1}{2}P\ell$

Volume
$V = \frac{1}{3}Bh$

Cone (p. 799)

Surface Area
$S = B + \pi r\ell$
$\quad = \pi r^2 + \pi r\ell$

Volume
$V = \frac{1}{3}Bh$
$\quad = \frac{1}{3}\pi r^2 h$

Sphere (p. 799)

Surface Area
$S = 4\pi r^2$

Volume
$V = \frac{4}{3}\pi r^3$

Other Formulas

Slope (p. 282)	The slope m of a nonvertical line passing through the two points (x_1, y_1) and (x_2, y_2) is $m = \dfrac{y_2 - y_1}{x_2 - x_1}$.
Total cost (p. 418)	$\boxed{\text{Unit cost}} \cdot \boxed{\text{Amount}} = \boxed{\text{Total cost}}$
Amount of a component in a solution (p. 419)	$\boxed{\begin{array}{c}\text{Amount of}\\\text{solution}\end{array}} \cdot \boxed{\begin{array}{c}\text{Percent of}\\\text{component}\\\text{in solution}\end{array}} = \boxed{\begin{array}{c}\text{Amount of}\\\text{component}\end{array}}$
Quadratic formula (p. 649)	The real-number solutions of the quadratic equation $ax^2 + bx + c = 0$ are $x = \dfrac{-b \pm \sqrt{b^2 - 4ac}}{2a}$ where $a \neq 0$ and $b^2 - 4ac \geq 0$.
Work done (p. 721)	$\boxed{\text{Work rate}} \cdot \boxed{\text{Time}} = \boxed{\text{Work done}}$
Theoretical probability (p. 745)	The probability of an event when all the outcomes are equally likely is $P(\text{event}) = \dfrac{\text{Number of favorable outcomes}}{\text{Total number of outcomes}}$.
Experimental probability (p. 745)	For repeated trials of an experiment, the probability of an event is $P(\text{event}) = \dfrac{\text{Number of successes}}{\text{Number of trials}}$.
Permutations (p. 751)	The number of permutations of n objects taken r at a time, where $r \leq n$, is given by ${}_nP_r = \dfrac{n!}{(n-r)!}$.
Combinations (p. 756)	The number of combinations of n objects taken r at a time, where $r \leq n$, is given by ${}_nC_r = \dfrac{n!}{(n-r)! \cdot r!}$.
Probability of mutually exclusive or overlapping events (p. 762)	If A and B are mutually exclusive events, then $P(A \text{ or } B) = P(A) + P(B)$. If A and B are overlapping events, then $P(A \text{ or } B) = P(A) + P(B) - P(A \text{ and } B)$.
Probability of independent or dependent events (p. 763)	If A and B are independent events, then $P(A \text{ and } B) = P(A) \cdot P(B)$. If A and B are dependent events, then $P(A \text{ and } B) = P(A) \cdot P(B \text{ given } A)$.

Properties

Properties of Addition and Multiplication

Commutative Properties (pp. 62, 75) The order in which you add two numbers does not change the sum.	$a + b = b + a$
The order in which you multiply two numbers does not change the product.	$a \cdot b = b \cdot a$
Associative Properties (pp. 62, 75) The way you group three numbers in a sum does not change the sum.	$(a + b) + c = a + (b + c)$
The way you group three numbers in a product does not change the product.	$(a \cdot b) \cdot c = a \cdot (b \cdot c)$
Identity Properties (pp. 62, 75) The sum of a number and the additive identity, 0, is the number.	$a + 0 = 0 + a = a$
The product of a number and the multiplicative identity, 1, is the number.	$a \cdot 1 = 1 \cdot a = a$
Inverse Properties (pp. 62, 88) The sum of a number and its additive inverse, or opposite, is 0.	$a + (-a) = -a + a = 0$
The product of a nonzero number and its multiplicative inverse, or reciprocal, is 1.	$a \cdot \frac{1}{a} = \frac{1}{a} \cdot a = 1 \ (a \neq 0)$
Closure Properties (pp. 62, 75) A set of numbers is closed under addition if the sum of any two numbers in the set is also a number in the set.	Example: The set of whole numbers is closed under addition.
A set of numbers is closed under multiplication if the product of any two numbers in the set is also a number in the set.	Example: The set of integers is closed under multiplication.
Distributive Property (p. 81) You can multiply a number and a sum by multiplying each term of the sum by the number and then adding these products. The same property applies to the product of a number and a difference.	$a(b + c) = ab + ac$ $(b + c)a = ba + ca$ $a(b - c) = ab - ac$ $(b - c)a = ba - ca$

Properties of Equality

Reflexive Property of Equality (p. 104) A quantity is equal to itself.	$a = a$
Symmetric Property of Equality (p. 104) If one quantity equals a second, then the second quantity equals the first.	If $a = b$, then $b = a$.
Transitive Property of Equality (p. 104) If one quantity equals a second and the second quantity equals a third, then the first quantity equals the third.	If $a = b$ and $b = c$, then $a = c$.

Properties of Equality

Addition Property of Equality (p. 125) Adding the same number to each side of an equation produces an equivalent equation.	If $x - a = b$, then $x - a + a = b + a$, or $x = b + a$.
Subtraction Property of Equality (p. 125) Subtracting the same number from each side of an equation produces an equivalent equation.	If $x + a = b$, then $x + a - a = b - a$, or $x = b - a$.
Multiplication Property of Equality (p. 126) Multiplying each side of an equation by the same nonzero number produces an equivalent equation.	If $\frac{x}{a} = b$ and $a \neq 0$, then $a \cdot \frac{x}{a} = a \cdot b$, or $x = ab$.
Division Property of Equality (p. 126) Dividing each side of an equation by the same nonzero number produces an equivalent equation.	If $ax = b$ and $a \neq 0$, then $\frac{ax}{a} = \frac{b}{a}$, or $x = \frac{b}{a}$.

Properties of Inequality

Addition Property of Inequality (p. 190) Adding the same number to each side of an inequality produces an equivalent inequality.	If $a < b$, then $a + c < b + c$. If $a > b$, then $a + c > b + c$.
Subtraction Property of Inequality (p. 191) Subtracting the same number from each side of an inequality produces an equivalent inequality.	If $a < b$, then $a - c < b - c$. If $a > b$, then $a - c > b - c$.
Multiplication Property of Inequality (p. 196) Multiplying each side of an inequality by a *positive* number produces an equivalent inequality. Multiplying each side of an inequality by a *negative* number and *reversing the direction of the inequality symbol* produces an equivalent inequality.	If $a < b$ and $c > 0$, then $ac < bc$. If $a < b$ and $c < 0$, then $ac > bc$.
Division Property of Inequality (p. 197) Dividing each side of an inequality by a *positive* number produces an equivalent inequality. Dividing each side of an inequality by a *negative* number and *reversing the direction of the inequality symbol* produces an equivalent inequality.	If $a < b$ and $c > 0$, then $\frac{a}{c} < \frac{b}{c}$. If $a > b$ and $c < 0$, then $\frac{a}{c} > \frac{b}{c}$.

Properties of Exponents

Product of Powers Property (p. 460) To multiply powers having the same base, add the exponents.	$a^m \cdot a^n = a^{m+n}$
Power of a Power Property (p. 461) To find a power of a power, multiply exponents.	$(a^m)^n = a^{mn}$
Power of a Product Property (p. 462) To find a power of a product, find the power of each factor and multiply.	$(ab)^m = a^m b^m$
Quotient of Powers Property (p. 467) To divide powers having the same nonzero base, subtract exponents.	$\dfrac{a^m}{a^n} = a^{m-n}, a \neq 0$
Power of a Quotient Property (p. 468) To find a power of a quotient, find the power of the numerator and the power of the denominator and divide.	$\left(\dfrac{a}{b}\right)^m = \dfrac{a^m}{b^m}, b \neq 0$

Other Properties

Cross Products Property (p. 161) The cross products of a proportion are equal.	If $\dfrac{a}{b} = \dfrac{c}{d}$ $(b, d \neq 0)$, then $ad = bc$.
Product Property of Radicals (pp. 483, 503) The square root of a product equals the product of the square roots of the factors. The cube root of a product equals the product of the cube roots of the factors.	$\sqrt{ab} = \sqrt{a} \cdot \sqrt{b}, a \geq 0$ and $b \geq 0$ $\sqrt[3]{ab} = \sqrt[3]{a} \cdot \sqrt[3]{b}$
Quotient Property of Radicals (pp. 484, 503) The square root of a quotient equals the quotient of the square roots of the numerator and denominator. The cube root of a quotient equals the quotient of the cube roots of the numerator and denominator.	$\sqrt{\dfrac{a}{b}} = \dfrac{\sqrt{a}}{\sqrt{b}}, a \geq 0$ and $b > 0$ $\sqrt[3]{\dfrac{a}{b}} = \dfrac{\sqrt[3]{a}}{\sqrt[3]{b}}, b \neq 0$

Measures

Time

60 seconds (sec) = 1 minute (min)	365 days ⎤
60 min = 1 hour (h)	52 weeks (approx.) ⎬ = 1 year
24 h = 1 day	12 months ⎦
7 days = 1 week	10 years = 1 decade
4 weeks (approx.) = 1 month	100 years = 1 century

Metric	**United States Customary**
Length	**Length**
10 millimeters (mm) = 1 centimeter (cm) $\left.\begin{array}{l}100 \text{ cm} \\ 1000 \text{ mm}\end{array}\right]$ = 1 meter (m) 1000 m = 1 kilometer (km)	12 inches (in.) = 1 foot (ft) $\left.\begin{array}{r}36 \text{ in.} \\ 3 \text{ ft}\end{array}\right]$ = 1 yard (yd) $\left.\begin{array}{l}5280 \text{ ft} \\ 1760 \text{ yd}\end{array}\right]$ = 1 mile (mi)
Area	**Area**
100 square millimeters = 1 square centimeter (mm^2) (cm^2) 10,000 cm^2 = 1 square meter (m^2) 10,000 m^2 = 1 hectare (ha)	144 square inches (in.^{2}) = 1 square foot (ft^2) 9 ft^2 = 1 square yard (yd^2) $\left.\begin{array}{l}43{,}560 \text{ ft}^2 \\ 4840 \text{ yd}^2\end{array}\right]$ = 1 acre (A)
Volume	**Volume**
1000 cubic millimeters = 1 cubic centimeter (mm^3) (cm^3) 1,000,000 cm^3 = 1 cubic meter (m^3)	1728 cubic inches (in.^{3}) = 1 cubic foot (ft^3) 27 ft^3 = 1 cubic yard (yd^3)
Liquid Capacity	**Liquid Capacity**
$\left.\begin{array}{r}1000 \text{ milliliters (mL)} \\ 1000 \text{ cubic centimeters (cm}^3)\end{array}\right]$ = 1 liter (L) 1000 L = 1 kiloliter (kL)	8 fluid ounces (fl oz) = 1 cup (c) 2 c = 1 pint (pt) 2 pt = 1 quart (qt) 4 qt = 1 gallon (gal)
Mass	**Weight**
1000 milligrams (mg) = 1 gram (g) 1000 g = 1 kilogram (kg) 1000 kg = 1 metric ton (t)	16 ounces (oz) = 1 pound (lb) 2000 lb = 1 ton
Temperature Degrees Celsius (°C)	**Temperature Degrees Fahrenheit (°F)**
0°C = freezing point of water 37°C = normal body temperature 100°C = boiling point of water	32°F = freezing point of water 98.6°F = normal body temperature 212°F = boiling point of water

TABLES

Squares and Square Roots

No.	Square	Sq. Root	No.	Square	Sq. Root	No.	Square	Sq. Root
1	1	1.000	51	2601	7.141	101	10,201	10.050
2	4	1.414	52	2704	7.211	102	10,404	10.100
3	9	1.732	53	2809	7.280	103	10,609	10.149
4	16	2.000	54	2916	7.348	104	10,816	10.198
5	25	2.236	55	3025	7.416	105	11,025	10.247
6	36	2.449	56	3136	7.483	106	11,236	10.296
7	49	2.646	57	3249	7.550	107	11,449	10.344
8	64	2.828	58	3364	7.616	108	11,664	10.392
9	81	3.000	59	3481	7.681	109	11,881	10.440
10	100	3.162	60	3600	7.746	110	12,100	10.488
11	121	3.317	61	3721	7.810	111	12,321	10.536
12	144	3.464	62	3844	7.874	112	12,544	10.583
13	169	3.606	63	3969	7.937	113	12,769	10.630
14	196	3.742	64	4096	8.000	114	12,996	10.677
15	225	3.873	65	4225	8.062	115	13,225	10.724
16	256	4.000	66	4356	8.124	116	13,456	10.770
17	289	4.123	67	4489	8.185	117	13,689	10.817
18	324	4.243	68	4624	8.246	118	13,924	10.863
19	361	4.359	69	4761	8.307	119	14,161	10.909
20	400	4.472	70	4900	8.367	120	14,400	10.954
21	441	4.583	71	5041	8.426	121	14,641	11.000
22	484	4.690	72	5184	8.485	122	14,884	11.045
23	529	4.796	73	5329	8.544	123	15,129	11.091
24	576	4.899	74	5476	8.602	124	15,376	11.136
25	625	5.000	75	5625	8.660	125	15,625	11.180
26	676	5.099	76	5776	8.718	126	15,876	11.225
27	729	5.196	77	5929	8.775	127	16,129	11.269
28	784	5.292	78	6084	8.832	128	16,384	11.314
29	841	5.385	79	6241	8.888	129	16,641	11.358
30	900	5.477	80	6400	8.944	130	16,900	11.402
31	961	5.568	81	6561	9.000	131	17,161	11.446
32	1024	5.657	82	6724	9.055	132	17,424	11.489
33	1089	5.745	83	6889	9.110	133	17,689	11.533
34	1156	5.831	84	7056	9.165	134	17,956	11.576
35	1225	5.916	85	7225	9.220	135	18,225	11.619
36	1296	6.000	86	7396	9.274	136	18,496	11.662
37	1369	6.083	87	7569	9.327	137	18,769	11.705
38	1444	6.164	88	7744	9.381	138	19,044	11.747
39	1521	6.245	89	7921	9.434	139	19,321	11.790
40	1600	6.325	90	8100	9.487	140	19,600	11.832
41	1681	6.403	91	8281	9.539	141	19,881	11.874
42	1764	6.481	92	8464	9.592	142	20,164	11.916
43	1849	6.557	93	8649	9.644	143	20,449	11.958
44	1936	6.633	94	8836	9.695	144	20,736	12.000
45	2025	6.708	95	9025	9.747	145	21,025	12.042
46	2116	6.782	96	9216	9.798	146	21,316	12.083
47	2209	6.856	97	9409	9.849	147	21,609	12.124
48	2304	6.928	98	9604	9.899	148	21,904	12.166
49	2401	7.000	99	9801	9.950	149	22,201	12.207
50	2500	7.071	100	10,000	10.000	150	22,500	12.247

TABLES

A

absolute deviation (p. 222) The absolute deviation of a number x from a given value is the absolute value of the difference of x and the given value:

$$\text{absolute deviation} = |x - \text{given value}|$$

desviación absoluta (pág. 222) La desviación absoluta de un número x con respecto a un valor dado es el valor absoluto de la diferencia entre x y el valor dado:

$$\text{desviación absoluta} = |x - \text{valor dado}|$$

If the absolute deviation of x from 2 is 3, then $|x - 2| = 3$.

Si la desviación absoluta de x con respecto a 2 es 3, entonces $|x - 2| = 3$.

---

absolute value (p. 55) The absolute value of a number a is the distance between a and 0 on a number line. The symbol $|a|$ represents the absolute value of a.

valor absoluto (pág. 55) El valor absoluto de un número a es la distancia entre a y 0 en una recta numérica. El símbolo $|a|$ representa el valor absoluto de a.

$|2| = 2$, $|-5| = 5$, and $|0| = 0$

$|2| = 2$, $|-5| = 5$ y $|0| = 0$

---

absolute value equation (p. 220) An equation that contains an absolute value expression.

ecuación de valor absoluto (pág. 220) Ecuación que contiene una expresión de valor absoluto.

$|x + 2| = 3$ is an absolute value equation.

$|x + 2| = 3$ es una ecuación de valor absoluto.

---

additive identity (p. 62) The number 0 is the additive identity, because the sum of any number and 0 is the number: $a + 0 = 0 + a = a$.

identidad de la suma (pág. 62) El número 0 es la identidad de la suma ya que la suma de cualquier número y 0 es ese número: $a + 0 = 0 + a = a$.

$$-2 + 0 = -2, 0 + \tfrac{3}{4} = \tfrac{3}{4}$$

---

additive inverse (p. 62) The additive inverse of a number a is its opposite, $-a$. The sum of a number and its additive inverse is 0: $a + (-a) = -a + a = 0$.

inverso aditivo (pág. 62) El inverso aditivo de un número a es su opuesto, $-a$. La suma de un número y su inverso aditivo es 0: $a + (-a) = -a + a = 0$.

The additive inverse of -5 is 5, and $-5 + 5 = 0$.

El inverso aditivo de -5 es 5, y $-5 + 5 = 0$.

---

algebraic expression (p. 5) An expression that includes at least one variable. Also called *variable expression*.

expresión algebraica (pág. 5) Expresión que incluye por lo menos una variable. También llamada *expresión variable*.

$5n$, $\frac{14}{y}$, $6 + c$, and $8 - x$ are algebraic expressions.

$5n$, $\frac{14}{y}$, $6 + c$ y $8 - x$ son expresiones algebraicas.

asymptotes of a hyperbola (p. 682) Lines that a hyperbola approaches but does not intersect.

asíntotas de una hipérbola (pág. 682) Rectas a las que la hipérbola se acerca pero sin intersecarlas.

See hyperbola.

Ver hipérbola.

---

axis of symmetry (p. 605) The line that passes through the vertex and divides the parabola into two symmetric parts.

eje de simetría (pág. 605) La recta que pasa por el vértice y divide a la parábola en dos partes simétricas.

The axis of symmetry of the graph of $y = -x^2 + 2x + 1$ **is the line** $x = 1$.

El eje de simetría de la gráfica de $y = -x^2 + 2x + 1$ **es la recta** $x = 1$.

B

base of a power (p. 6) The number or expression that is used as a factor in a repeated multiplication.

base de una potencia (pág. 6) El número o la expresión que se usa como factor en una multiplicación repetida.

In the power 3^4, **the base is 3.**

En la potencia 3^4, **la base es 3.**

---

binomial (p. 521) A polynomial with two terms.

binomio (pág. 521) Polinomio con dos términos.

$t^3 - 4t$ **and** $2x + 5$ **are binomials.**

$t^3 - 4t$ **y** $2x + 5$ **son binomios.**

---

branches of a hyperbola (p. 682) The two symmetrical parts of a hyperbola.

ramas de una hipérbola (pág. 682) Las dos partes simétricas de la hipérbola.

See hyperbola.

Ver hipérbola.

C

coefficient (p. 82) The number part of a term with a variable part.

coeficiente (pág. 82) La parte numérica de un término que tiene una variable.

The coefficient of $-6x$ **is** -6.

El coeficiente de $-6x$ **es** -6.

combination (p. 756) A selection of objects in which order is *not* important.	There are 6 combinations of two of the letters from the list A, B, C, D: AB, AC, AD, BC, BD, and CD.
combinación (pág. 756) Selección de objetos en la que el orden *no* es importante.	Hay 6 combinaciones de dos de las letras de la lista A, B, C, D: AB, AC, AD, BC, BD y CD.
completing the square (p. 643) The process of rewriting a quadratic expression so that it is a perfect square trinomial.	To write $x^2 - 16x$ as a perfect square trinomial, add $\left(\frac{-16}{2}\right)^2$, or $(-8)^2$. This gives $x^2 - 16x + (-8)^2 = (x - 8)^2$.
completar el cuadrado (pág. 643) El proceso de escribir una expresión cuadrática de manera que sea un trinomio cuadrado perfecto.	Para escribir $x^2 - 16x$ como trinomio cuadrado perfecto, suma $\left(\frac{-16}{2}\right)^2$, o $(-8)^2$. Así resulta $x^2 - 16x + (-8)^2 = (x - 8)^2$.
compound event (p. 762) An event that combines two or more events, using the word *and* or the word *or*.	When you roll a number cube, the event "roll a 2 or an odd number" is a compound event.
evento compuesto (pág. 762) Evento que combina dos o más eventos usando la palabra *y* o la palabra *o*.	Cuando lanzas un cubo numerado, el evento "salir el 2 ó número impar" es un evento compuesto.
compound inequality (p. 210) Two inequalities joined by *and* or *or*.	$-2 < x$ *and* $x < 1$, which can be written as $-2 < x < 1$, is a compound inequality, as is $x < -1$ *or* $x > 0$.
desigualdad compuesta (pág. 210) Dos desigualdades unidas por *y* u *o*.	$-2 < x$ *y* $x < 1$, que puede escribirse $-2 < x < 1$, es una desigualdad compuesta, al igual que $x < -1$ *ó* $x > 0$.
conditional statement (p. 55) A statement with a hypothesis and a conclusion. **enunciado condicional** (pág. 55) Enunciado que tiene una hipótesis y una conclusión.	**conditional statement** **enunciado condicional** If $a > 0$, then $\lvert a \rvert = a$. hypothesis conclusion hipótesis conclusión
conjecture (p. 102) A statement that is believed to be true but not yet shown to be true.	A conclusion reached using inductive reasoning is a conjecture.
conjetura (pág. 102) Enunciado que se considera verdadero sin que haya sido demostrado todavía.	Una conclusión que se saca mediante el razonamiento inductivo es una conjetura.

consistent dependent system (p. 405) A linear system with infinitely many solutions. The graphs of the equations of a consistent dependent system coincide.

sistema dependiente compatible (pág. 405) Sistema lineal con infinitas soluciones. Las gráficas de las ecuaciones de un sistema dependiente compatible coinciden.

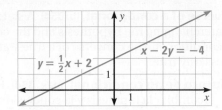

The linear system $x - 2y = -4$ and $y = \frac{1}{2}x + 2$ is a consistent dependent system because the graphs of the equations coincide.

El sistema lineal $x - 2y = -4$ e $y = \frac{1}{2}x + 2$ es un sistema dependiente compatible ya que las gráficas de las ecuaciones coinciden.

---

consistent independent system (p. 376) A linear system with exactly one solution. The graphs of the equations of a consistent independent system intersect.

sistema independiente compatible (pág. 376) Sistema lineal con una sola solución. Las gráficas de las ecuaciones de un sistema independiente compatible se intersecan.

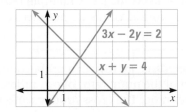

The linear system $3x - 2y = 2$ and $x + y = 4$ is a consistent independent system because the graphs of the equations intersect.

El sistema lineal $3x - 2y = 2$ y $x + y = 4$ es un sistema independiente compatible ya que las gráficas de las ecuaciones se intersecan.

---

constant of variation (pp. 297, 680) The nonzero constant k in a direct variation equation $y = kx$ or in an inverse variation equation $y = \frac{k}{x}$.

constante de variación (págs. 297, 680) La constante k distinta de cero de una ecuación de variación directa $y = kx$ o de una ecuación de variación inversa $y = \frac{k}{x}$.

The constant of variation in the direct variation equation $y = \frac{2}{3}x$ is $\frac{2}{3}$, and the constant of variation in the inverse variation equation $y = \frac{-1}{x}$ is -1.

La constante de variación de la ecuación de variación directa $y = \frac{2}{3}x$ es $\frac{2}{3}$, y la constante de variación de la ecuación de variación inversa $y = \frac{-1}{x}$ es -1.

---

constant term (p. 82) A term that has no variable part.

término constante (pág. 82) Término que no tiene una parte variable.

In the expression $3x + (-4) + (-6x) + 2$, the constant terms are -4 and 2.

En la expresión $3x + (-4) + (-6x) + 2$, los términos constantes son -4 y 2.

converse of a conditional (p. 354) A statement formed by interchanging the hypothesis and the conclusion of the conditional. The converse of a true statement is not necessarily true.

The converse of the statement "If $x = 5$, then $|x| = 5$" is "If $|x| = 5$, then $x = 5$." The original statement is true, but the converse is false.

recíproco de un condicional (pág. 354) Enunciado formado al intercambiar la hipótesis y la conclusión del condicional. El recíproco de un enunciado verdadero no es necesariamente verdadero.

El recíproco del enunciado "Si $x = 5$, entonces $|x| = 5$" es "Si $|x| = 5$, entonces $x = 5$". El enunciado original es verdadero, pero el recíproco es falso.

---

counterexample (p. 55) An example used to show that an if-then statement is false.

The statement "If a number is a whole number, then the number is positive" is false because 0 is a whole number that is not a positive number.

contraejemplo (pág. 55) Ejemplo utilizado para demostrar que un enunciado de "si…, entonces…" es falso.

El enunciado "Si un número es un número natural, entonces es positivo" es falso ya que 0 es un número natural que no es positivo.

---

cross product (p. 161) In a proportion, a cross product is the product of the numerator of one ratio and the denominator of the other ratio. The cross products of a proportion are equal.

The cross products of the proportion $\frac{3}{4} = \frac{6}{8}$ are $3 \cdot 8 = 24$ and $4 \cdot 6 = 24$.

producto cruzado (pág. 161) En una proporción, un producto cruzado es el producto del numerador de una de las razones y el denominador de la otra razón. Los productos cruzados de una proporción son iguales.

Los productos cruzados de la proporción $\frac{3}{4} = \frac{6}{8}$ son $3 \cdot 8 = 24$ y $4 \cdot 6 = 24$.

---

cube root (p. 498) The cube root of a real number a is a real number b such that $b^3 = a$.

2 is the cube root of 8 because $2^3 = 8$.

raíz cúbica (pág. 498) La raíz cúbica de un número real a es un número real b tal que $b^3 = a$.

2 es la raíz cúbica de 8 ya que $2^3 = 8$.

D

deductive reasoning (p. 102) A form of reasoning in which a conclusion is based on statements that are assumed or shown to be true.

$(x + 2) + (-2)$
$= x + [2 + (-2)]$ Associative property of addition
$= x + 0$ Inverse property of addition
$= x$ Identity property of addition

razonamiento deductivo (pág. 102) Tipo de razonamiento en el que una conclusión se basa en enunciados que se suponen o se demuestran verdaderos.

$(x + 2) + (-2)$
$= x + [2 + (-2)]$ Propiedad asociativa de la suma
$= x + 0$ Propiedad del elemento inverso de la suma
$= x$ Propiedad de identidad de la suma

degree of a monomial (p. 520) The sum of the exponents of the variables in the monomial. The degree of a nonzero constant term is 0.	The degree of $4ab^2$ is $1 + 2$, or 3.
grado de un monomio (pág. 520) La suma de los exponentes de las variables del monomio. El grado de un término constante distinto de cero es 0.	El grado de $4ab^2$ es $1 + 2$, ó 3.
degree of a polynomial (p. 520) The greatest degree of the terms of the polynomial.	The polynomial $2x^2 + x - 5$ has a degree of 2.
grado de un polinomio (pág. 520) El mayor grado de los términos del polinomio.	El polinomio $2x^2 + x - 5$ tiene un grado de 2.
dependent events (p. 763) Two events such that the occurrence of one event affects the occurrence of the other event.	A bag contains 3 red marbles and 5 white marbles. You randomly draw one marble, do not replace it, then randomly draw another marble. The events "draw a red marble first" and "draw a white marble second" are dependent events because the first marble was not replaced.
eventos dependientes (pág. 763) Dos eventos tales que la ocurrencia de uno de ellos afecta a la ocurrencia del otro.	Una bolsa contiene 3 canicas rojas y 5 blancas. Sacas al azar una canica sin reemplazarla y luego sacas al azar otra canica. Los eventos "sacar primero una canica roja" y "sacar después una canica blanca" son eventos dependientes, ya que la primera canica no fue reemplazada.
dependent variable (p. 250) The output variable of a function.	In the function equation $y = x + 3$, y is the dependent variable.
variable dependiente (pág. 250) La variable de salida de una función.	En la ecuación de función $y = x + 3$, y es la variable dependiente.
direct variation (p. 297) The relationship of two variables x and y if there is a nonzero number k such that $y = kx$. If $y = kx$, then y is said to vary directly with x.	The equation $2x - 3y = 0$ represents direct variation because it is equivalent to the equation $y = \frac{2}{3}x$. The equation $y = x + 5$ does *no*t represent direct variation.
variación directa (pág. 297) La relación entre dos variables x e y si hay un número k distinto de cero tal que $y = kx$. Si $y = kx$, entonces se dice que y varía directamente con x.	La ecuación $2x - 3y = 0$ representa una variación directa ya que es equivalente a la ecuación $y = \frac{2}{3}x$. La ecuación $y = x + 5$ *no* representa una variación directa.

discriminant (p. 657) The expression $b^2 - 4ac$ of the associated equation $ax^2 + bx + c = 0$; also the expression under the radical sign in the quadratic formula.

The value of the discriminant of the equation $3x^2 - 2x - 7 = 0$ is:
$$b^2 - 4ac = (-2)^2 - 4(3)(-7) = 88$$

discriminante (pág. 657) La expresión $b^2 - 4ac$ de la ecuación asociada $ax^2 + bx + c = 0$; también es la expresión colocada bajo el signo radical de la fórmula cuadrática.

El valor del discriminante de la ecuación $3x^2 - 2x - 7 = 0$ es:
$$b^2 - 4ac = (-2)^2 - 4(3)(-7) = 88$$

---

distributive property (p. 81) A property that can be used to find the product of a number and a sum or difference:
$$a(b + c) = ab + ac$$
$$(b + c)a = ba + ca$$
$$a(b - c) = ab - ac$$
$$(b - c)a = ba - ca$$

propiedad distributiva (pág. 81) Propiedad que sirve para hallar el producto de un número y una suma o una diferencia:
$$a(b + c) = ab + ac$$
$$(b + c)a = ba + ca$$
$$a(b - c) = ab - ac$$
$$(b - c)a = ba - ca$$

$$3(4 + 2) = 3(4) + 3(2),$$
$$(8 - 6)4 = (8)4 - (6)4$$

---

domain of a relation (p. 249) The domain of a relation represented by a set of ordered pairs (x, y) is the set of all x values.

See relation.

dominio de una relación (pág. 249) El dominio de una relación representado por un conjunto de pares ordenados (x, y) es el conjunto de todos los valores x.

Ver relación.

---

equation (p. 26) A mathematical sentence formed by placing the symbol $=$ between two expressions.

$2k - 8 = 12$ is an equation.

ecuación (pág. 26) Enunciado matemático formado al colocar el símbolo $=$ entre dos expresiones.

$2k - 8 = 12$ es una ecuación.

---

equivalent equations (p. 125) Equations that have the same solution(s).

$x + 7 = 4$ and $x = -3$ are equivalent equations.

ecuaciones equivalentes (pág. 125) Ecuaciones que tienen la misma solución o soluciones.

$x + 7 = 4$ y $x = -3$ son ecuaciones equivalentes.

equivalent expressions (p. 81) Two expressions that have the same value for all values of the variable. **expresiones equivalentes** (pág. 81) Dos expresiones que tienen el mismo valor para todos los valores de la variable.	$3(x + 2) + x$ and $4x + 6$ are equivalent expressions. $3(x + 2) + x$ y $4x + 6$ son expresiones equivalentes.
equivalent inequalities (p. 190) Inequalities that have the same solutions. **desigualdades equivalentes** (pág. 190) Desigualdades con las mismas soluciones.	$2t < 4$ and $t < 2$ are equivalent inequalities, because the solutions of both inequalities are all real numbers less than 2. $2t < 4$ y $t < 2$ son desigualdades equivalentes ya que las soluciones de ambas son todos los números reales menores que 2.
evaluate an algebraic expression (p. 5) To find the value of an algebraic expression by substituting a number for each variable and performing the operation(s). **evaluar una expresión algebraica** (pág. 5) Hallar el valor de una expresión algebraica sustituyendo cada variable por un número y realizando la operación u operaciones.	The value of $n - 1$ when $n = 3$ is $3 - 1 = 2$. El valor de $n - 1$ cuando $n = 3$ es $3 - 1 = 2$.
event (p. 744) An outcome or a collection of outcomes. **evento** (pág. 744) Resultado o colección de resultados.	When you roll a number cube, "roll an odd number" is an event. Cuando lanzas un cubo numerado, "salir número impar" es un evento.
excluded value (p. 688) A number that makes a rational expression undefined. **valor excluido** (pág. 688) Número que hace que una expresión racional sea indefinida.	3 is an excluded value of the expression $\frac{2}{x - 3}$ because 3 makes the value of the denominator 0. 3 es un valor excluido de la expresión $\frac{2}{x - 3}$ ya que 3 hace que el valor del denominador sea 0.
experimental probability (p. 745) A probability based on repeated trials of an experiment. The experimental probability of an event is the ratio of the number of successes (trials in which a favorable outcome occurs) to the number of trials. **probabilidad experimental** (pág. 745) Probabilidad basada en la realización repetida de los ensayos de un experimento. La probabilidad experimental de un evento es la razón entre el número de resultados deseados (ensayos en las que se produce un resultado favorable) y el número de ensayos.	You spin a spinner 20 times and it stops on yellow 3 times. The experimental probability that the spinner stops on yellow is $\frac{3}{20}$, 15%, or 0.15. Giras una ruleta 20 veces y ésta se detiene en el amarillo 3 veces. La probabilidad experimental de que la ruleta se detenga en el amarillo es $\frac{3}{20}$, 15% o 0.15.

exponent (p. 6) The number or variable that represents the number of times the base of a power is used as a factor.	In the power 3^4, the exponent is 4.
exponente (pág. 6) El número o la variable que representa la cantidad de veces que se usa la base de una potencia como factor.	En la potencia 3^4, el exponente es 4.
extraneous solution (p. 713) A solution of a transformed equation that is not a solution of the original equation.	The rational equation $\frac{1}{x} = \frac{1}{2x}$ can be transformed using the cross products property. The resulting equation $2x = x$ has one solution, 0, but 0 is an extraneous solution because it does not satisfy the original equation $\frac{1}{x} = \frac{1}{2x}$.
solución extraña (pág. 713) Solución de una ecuación transformada que no es solución de la ecuación original.	La ecuación racional $\frac{1}{x} = \frac{1}{2x}$ puede ser transformada usando la propiedad de los productos cruzados. La ecuación resultante $2x = x$ tiene una solución, 0, pero 0 es una solución extraña, porque no resuelve la ecuación original $\frac{1}{x} = \frac{1}{2x}$.

F

factor by grouping (p. 579) To factor a polynomial with four terms by grouping, factor a common monomial from pairs of terms, and then look for a common binomial factor.	$$\begin{aligned} x^3 + 3x^2 + 5x + 15 &= (x^3 + 3x^2) + (5x + 15) \\ &= x^2(x + 3) + 5(x + 3) \\ &= (x + 3)(x^2 + 5) \end{aligned}$$
factorizar por grupos (pág. 579) Para factorizar por grupos un polinomio con cuatro términos, factoriza un monomio común a partir de los pares de términos y luego busca un factor binómico común.	
factor completely (p. 580) A factorable polynomial with integer coefficients is factored completely if it is written as a product of unfactorable polynomials with integer coefficients.	The polynomial $x^3 - x$ is *not* factored completely when written as $x(x^2 - 1)$ but is factored completely when written as $x(x + 1)(x - 1)$.
factorizar completamente (pág. 580) Un polinomio que puede descomponerse en factores y que tiene coeficientes enteros está completamente factorizado si está escrito como producto de polinomios que no pueden descomponerse en factores y que tienen coeficientes enteros.	El polinomio $x^3 - x$ *no* está completamente factorizado cuando se escribe $x(x^2 - 1)$, pero sí está completamente factorizado cuando se escribe $x(x + 1)(x - 1)$.
formula (p. 34) An equation that relates two or more quantities.	The formula $d = rt$ relates the distance traveled to the rate of speed and travel time.
fórmula (pág. 34) Ecuación que relaciona dos o más cantidades.	La fórmula $d = rt$ relaciona la distancia recorrida con la velocidad y el tiempo transcurrido.

function (p. 249) A relation in which there is exactly one range element for each domain element.

función (pág. 249) Relación en que hay exactamente un elemento del rango por cada elemento del dominio.

The relation represented by the table below is a function, because each element of the domain is paired with exactly one element of the range.

La relación representada en la tabla es una función, porque cada elemento del dominio está asociado con exactamente un elemento del rango.

Domain, x Dominio, x	0	1	2	3	4
Range, y Rango, y	3	4	5	6	7

---

function notation (p. 269) A way to name a function using the symbol $f(x)$ instead of y. The symbol $f(x)$ is read as "the value of f at x" or as "f of x."

notación de función (pág. 269) Forma de nombrar una función usando el símbolo $f(x)$ en lugar de y. El símbolo $f(x)$ se lee "el valor de f en x" o "f de x".

The function $y = 2x - 9$ can be written in function notation as $f(x) = 2x - 9$.

La función $y = 2x - 9$ escrita en notación de función es $f(x) = 2x - 9$.

---

graph of an equation in two variables (p. 264) The set of points in a coordinate plane that represent all solutions of the equation.

gráfica de una ecuación con dos variables (pág. 264) El conjunto de puntos de un plano de coordenadas que representan todas las soluciones de la ecuación.

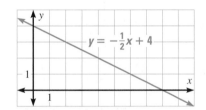

The line is the graph of the equation $y = -\frac{1}{2}x + 4$.

La recta es la gráfica de la ecuación $y = -\frac{1}{2}x + 4$.

---

graph of an inequality in one variable (p. 189) On a number line, the set of points that represent all solutions of the inequality.

gráfica de una desigualdad con una variable (pág. 189) En una recta numérica, el conjunto de puntos que representan todas las soluciones de la desigualdad.

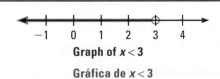

Graph of $x < 3$

Gráfica de $x < 3$

graph of an inequality in two variables (p. 425) In a coordinate plane, the set of points that represent all solutions of the inequality.

gráfica de una desigualdad con dos variables (pág. 425) En un plano de coordenadas, el conjunto de puntos que representa todas las soluciones de la desigualdad.

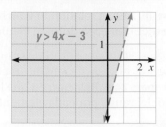

The graph of $y > 4x - 3$ is the shaded half-plane.

La gráfica de $y > 4x - 3$ es el semiplano sombreado.

---

graph of a system of linear inequalities (p. 433) The graph of all solutions of the system.

gráfica de un sistema de desigualdades lineales (pág. 433) La gráfica de todas las soluciones del sistema.

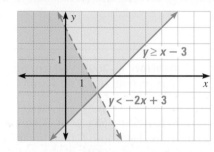

The graph of the system $y < -2x + 3$ and $y \geq x - 3$ is the intersection of the half-planes.

La gráfica del sistema $y < -2x + 3$ e $y \geq x - 3$ es la intersección de los semiplanos.

H

half-plane (p. 425) In a coordinate plane, the region on either side of a boundary line.

semiplano (pág. 425) En un plano de coordenadas, la región situada a cada lado de una recta límite.

See graph of an inequality in two variables.

Ver gráfica de una desigualdad con dos variables.

---

hyperbola (p. 682) The graph of the inverse variation equation $y = \frac{a}{x}$ $(a \neq 0)$. A hyperbola has two symmetrical parts called branches. A hyperbola approaches but doesn't intersect lines called asymptotes.

hipérbola (pág. 682) La gráfica de la ecuación de variación inversa $y = \frac{a}{x}$ $(a \neq 0)$. La hipérbola tiene dos partes simétricas llamadas ramas. La hipérbola se acerca a las rectas llamadas asíntotas pero sin intersecarlas.

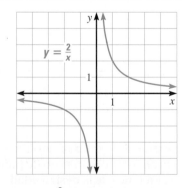

The graph of $y = \frac{2}{x}$ is a hyperbola. The asymptotes of the hyperbola are the lines $x = 0$ and $y = 0$.

La gráfica de $y = \frac{2}{x}$ es una hipérbola. Las asíntotas de la hipérbola son las rectas $x = 0$ e $y = 0$.

hypotenuse (p. 491) The hypotenuse of a right triangle is the side opposite the right angle.

hipotenusa (pág. 491) La hipotenusa de un triángulo rectángulo es el lado opuesto al ángulo recto.

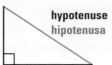
hypotenuse
hipotenusa

identity (p. 148) An equation that is true for all values of the variable.

identidad (pág. 148) Ecuación que es verdadera para todos los valores de la variable.

The equation $2x + 10 = 2(x + 5)$ is an identity.

La ecuación $2x + 10 = 2(x + 5)$ es una identidad.

---

if-then statement (p. 55) A conditional statement with an *if* part and a *then* part. The *if* part contains the hypothesis, and the *then* part contains the conclusion.

enunciado de "si…, entonces…" (pág. 55) Enunciado condicional con una parte de *si* y otra de *entonces*. La parte de *si* contiene la hipótesis, y la parte de *entonces* contiene la conclusión.

If $a = -1$, then $|a| = 1$.
The hypothesis is $a = -1$.
The conclusion is $|a| = 1$.

Si $a = -1$, entonces $|a| = 1$.
La hipótesis es $a = -1$.
La conclusión es $|a| = 1$.

---

inconsistent system (p. 405) A linear system with no solution. The graphs of the equations of an inconsistent system are parallel lines.

sistema incompatible (pág. 405) Sistema lineal sin solución. Las gráficas de las ecuaciones de un sistema incompatible son rectas paralelas.

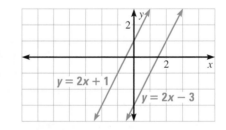

The linear system $y = 2x + 1$ and $y = 2x - 3$ is inconsistent because the graphs of the equations are parallel lines.

El sistema lineal $y = 2x + 1$ e $y = 2x - 3$ es incompatible ya que las gráficas de las ecuaciones son rectas paralelas.

---

independent events (p. 763) Two events such that the occurrence of one event has no effect on the occurrence of the other event.

eventos independientes (pág. 763) Dos eventos tales que la ocurrencia de uno de ellos no afecta a la ocurrencia del otro.

You roll a number cube twice. The events "roll a 3 first" and "roll a 6 second" are independent events.

Lanzas un cubo numerado dos veces. Los eventos "salir primero el 3" y "salir después el 6" son eventos independientes.

independent variable (p. 250) The input variable of a function. **variable independiente** (pág. 250) La variable de entrada de una función.	In the function equation $y = x + 3$, x is the **independent variable**. En la ecuación de función $y = x + 3$, x es la variable independiente.
inductive reasoning (p. 102) A form of reasoning in which a conclusion is based on several examples. **razonamiento inductivo** (pág. 102) Tipo de razonamiento en el que la conclusión se basa en varios ejemplos.	You add several pairs of odd numbers and notice that the sum is even. You conclude that the sum of any two odd numbers is even. Sumas varias parejas de números impares y observas que la suma es par. Sacas la conclusión de que la suma de dos números impares cualesquiera es par.
inequality (p. 26) A mathematical sentence formed by placing one of the symbols $<$, $\leq$, $>$, or $\geq$ between two expressions. **desigualdad** (pág. 26) Enunciado matemático formado al colocar uno de los siguientes símbolos entre dos expresiones: $<$, $\leq$, $>$ o $\geq$.	$6n \geq 24$ and $x - 2 < 7$ are inequalities. $6n \geq 24$ y $x - 2 < 7$ son desigualdades.
integers (p. 53) Elements of $\{\ldots, -3, -2, -1, 0, 1, 2, 3, \ldots\}$, a set consisting of the negative integers, zero, and the positive integers. **números enteros** (pág. 53) Elementos de $\{\ldots, -3, -2, -1, 0, 1, 2, 3, \ldots\}$, un conjunto formado por los números enteros negativos, el cero y los números enteros positivos.	-8 and 46 are integers. $-8\frac{1}{2}$ and 46.2 are *not* integers. -8 y 46 son números enteros. $-8\frac{1}{2}$ y 46.2 *no* son números enteros.
intercept form of a quadratic function (p. 618) A quadratic function in the form $y = a(x - p)(x - q)$ where $a \neq 0$. The x-intercepts of the graph of the function are p and q. **forma de intersección de una función cuadrática** (pág. 618) Función cuadrática de la forma $y = a(x - p)(x - q)$, donde $a \neq 0$. Las intersecciones en x de la gráfica de la función son p y q.	The quadratic function $y = -(x + 1)(x - 5)$ is in intercept form. The intercepts of the graph of the function are -1 and 5. La función cuadrática $y = -(x + 1)(x - 5)$ está en la forma de intersección. Las intersecciones de la gráfica de la función son -1 y 5.
inverse operations (p. 125) Two operations that undo each other. **operaciones inversas** (pág. 125) Dos operaciones que se anulan entre sí.	Addition and subtraction are inverse operations. Multiplication and division are also inverse operations. La suma y la resta son operaciones inversas. La multiplicación y la división también son operaciones inversas.

ENGLISH-SPANISH GLOSSARY

inverse variation (p. 680) The relationship of two variables x and y if there is a nonzero number k such that $y = \frac{k}{x}$. If $y = \frac{k}{x}$, then y is said to vary inversely with x.

variación inversa (pág. 680) La relación entre dos variables x e y si hay un número k distinto de cero tal que $y = \frac{k}{x}$. Si $y = \frac{k}{x}$, entonces se dice que y varía inversamente con x.

The equations $xy = 4$ and $y = \frac{-1}{x}$ represent inverse variation.

Las ecuaciones $xy = 4$ e $y = \frac{-1}{x}$ representan una variación inversa.

---

irrational number (p. 96) A number that cannot be written as the quotient of two integers. The decimal form of an irrational number neither terminates nor repeats.

número irracional (pág. 96) Número que no puede escribirse como cociente de dos números enteros. La forma decimal de un número irracional no termina ni se repite.

$\sqrt{945} = 30.74085\ldots$ is an irrational number. $1.666\ldots$ is *not* an irrational number.

$\sqrt{945} = 30.74085\ldots$ es un número irracional. $1.666\ldots$ *no* es un número irracional.

 L

---

leading coefficient (p. 520) When a polynomial is written so that the exponents of a variable decrease from left to right, the coefficient of the first term is the leading coefficient.

coeficiente inicial (pág. 520) Cuando un polinomio se escribe de tal manera que los exponentes de una variable disminuyen de izquierda a derecha, el coeficiente del primer término es el coeficiente inicial.

The leading coefficient of the polynomial $2x^3 + x^2 - 5x + 12$ is 2.

El coeficiente inicial del polinomio $2x^3 + x^2 - 5x + 12$ es 2.

---

least common denominator (LCD) of rational expressions (p. 706) The least common multiple of the denominators of the rational expressions.

mínimo común denominador (m.c.d.) de las expresiones racionales (pág. 706) El mínimo común múltiplo de los denominadores de expresiones racionales.

The LCD of $\frac{5}{(x-3)^2}$ and $\frac{3x+4}{(x-3)(x+2)}$ is $(x-3)^2(x+2)$.

El m.c.d. de $\frac{5}{(x-3)^2}$ y $\frac{3x+4}{(x-3)(x+2)}$ es $(x-3)^2(x+2)$.

---

legs of a right triangle (p. 491) The two sides that form the right angle.

catetos de un triángulo rectángulo (pág. 491) Los dos lados que forman el ángulo recto.

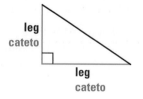

---

like terms (p. 82) Terms that have identical variable parts with corresponding variables raised to the same power. Constant terms are also like terms.

términos semejantes (pág. 82) Términos que tienen partes variables idénticas con variables correspondientes elevadas a la misma potencia. Los términos constantes también son términos semejantes.

In the expression $3x + (-4) + (-6x) + 2$, $3x$ and $-6x$ are like terms, and -4 and 2 are like terms.

En la expresión $3x + (-4) + (-6x) + 2$, $3x$ y $-6x$ son términos semejantes, y -4 y 2 también son términos semejantes.

| **linear equation** (p. 265) An equation whose graph is a line or part of a line. | *See* **standard form of a linear equation.** |
| **ecuación lineal** (pág. 265) Una ecuación cuya gráfica es una recta o parte de una recta. | *Ver* **forma general de una ecuación lineal.** |

| **linear function** (p. 266) The equation $Ax + By = C$ represents a linear function provided $B \neq 0$. | The equation $2x - y = 3$ represents a linear function. The equation $x = 3$ does *not* represent a linear function. |
| **función lineal** (pág. 266) La ecuación $Ax + By = C$ representa una función lineal siempre que $B \neq 0$. | La ecuación $2x - y = 3$ representa una función lineal. La ecuación $x = 3$ *no* representa una función lineal. |

| **linear inequality in two variables** (p. 425) An inequality that is the result of replacing the $=$ sign in a linear equation with $<$, $\leq$, $>$, or $\geq$. | $x - 3y < 6$ is a linear inequality in two variables, x and y. |
| **desigualdad lineal con dos variables** (pág. 425) Desigualdad que se obtiene al reemplazar el símbolo $=$ de la ecuación lineal por $<$, $\leq$, $>$ o $\geq$. | $x - 3y < 6$ es una desigualdad lineal con dos variables, x e y. |

| **literal equation** (p. 167) An equation in which letters are used to replace the coefficients and constants of another equation. | The equation $5(x + 3) = 20$ can be written as the literal equation $a(x + b) = c$. |
| **ecuación literal** (pág. 167) Ecuación en la que se usan letras para reemplazar los coeficientes y las constantes de otra ecuación. | La ecuación $5(x + 3) = 20$ puede escribirse como la ecuación literal $a(x + b) = c$. |

M

maximum value (p. 613) For $y = ax^2 + bx + c$ where $a < 0$, the y-coordinate of the vertex is the maximum value of the function.

valor máximo (pág. 613) Para $y = ax^2 + bx + c$ donde $a < 0$, la coordenada y del vértice es el valor máximo de la función.

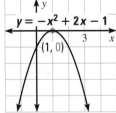

$$y = -x^2 + 2x - 1$$

$(1, 0)$

The maximum value of the function
$y = -x^2 + 2x - 1$ **is 0.**

El valor máximo de la función
$y = -x^2 + 2x - 1$ **es 0.**

minimum value (p. 613) For $y = ax^2 + bx + c$ where $a > 0$, the y-coordinate of the vertex is the minimum value of the function.

valor mínimo (pág. 613) Para $y = ax^2 + bx + c$ donde $a > 0$, la coordenada y del vértice es el valor mínimo de la función.

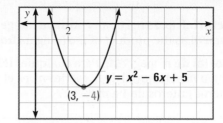

The minimum value of the function $y = x^2 - 6x + 5$ is -4.

El valor mínimo de la función $y = x^2 - 6x + 5$ es -4.

---

monomial (p. 520) A number, a variable with a positive integer exponent, or the product of a number and one or more variables with positive integer exponents.

$10, 3x, \frac{1}{2}ab^2$, and $-1.8m^5$ are monomials.

monomio (pág. 520) Un número, una variable cuyo exponente es un número entero positivo, o el producto de un número y una o más variables cuyos exponentes son números enteros positivos.

$10, 3x, \frac{1}{2}ab^2$ y $-1.8m^5$ son monomios.

---

multiplicative identity (p. 75) The number 1 is the multiplicative identity, because the product of any number and 1 is the number: $a \cdot 1 = 1 \cdot a = a$.

identidad de la multiplicación (pág. 75) El número 1 es la identidad de la multiplicación ya que el producto de cualquier número y 1 es ese número: $a \cdot 1 = 1 \cdot a = a$.

$$3.6(1) = 3.6, \, 1(-7) = -7$$

---

multiplicative inverse (p. 88) The multiplicative inverse of a nonzero number a is its reciprocal, $\frac{1}{a}$. The product of a nonzero number and its multiplicative inverse is 1: $a \cdot \frac{1}{a} = \frac{1}{a} \cdot a = 1, a \neq 0$.

The multiplicative inverse of $-\frac{1}{5}$ is -5 because $-\frac{1}{5} \cdot (-5) = 1$.

inverso multiplicativo (pág. 88) El inverso multiplicativo de un número a distinto de cero es su recíproco, $\frac{1}{a}$. El producto de un número distinto de cero y su inverso multiplicativo es 1: $a \cdot \frac{1}{a} = \frac{1}{a} \cdot a = 1, a \neq 0$.

El inverso multiplicativo de $-\frac{1}{5}$ es -5 ya que $-\frac{1}{5} \cdot (-5) = 1$.

---

mutually exclusive events (p. 762) Events that have no common outcome. Also called *disjoint events*.

When you roll a number cube, "roll a 3" and "roll an even number" are mutually exclusive events.

eventos mutuamente excluyentes (pág. 762) Eventos que no tienen ningún caso en común. También son llamados *eventos disjuntos*.

Cuando lanzas un cubo numerado, "salir el 3" y "salir número par" son eventos mutuamente excluyentes.

n factorial (p. 751) For any positive integer n, n factorial, written $n!$, is the product of the integers from 1 to n; $0! = 1$.

factorial de n (pág. 751) Para cualquier número entero positivo n, el factorial de n, escrito $n!$, es el producto de los números enteros de 1 a n; $0! = 1$.

$$5! = 5 \cdot 4 \cdot 3 \cdot 2 \cdot 1 = 120$$

---

negative exponent (p. 475) If $a \neq 0$, then a^{-n} is the reciprocal of a^n; $a^{-n} = \dfrac{1}{a^n}$.

exponente negativo (pág. 475) Si $a \neq 0$, entonces a^{-n} es el recíproco de a^n; $a^{-n} = \dfrac{1}{a^n}$.

$$3^{-2} = \frac{1}{3^2} = \frac{1}{9}$$

---

negative integers (p. 53) The integers that are less than 0.

números enteros negativos (pág. 53) Los números enteros menores que 0.

$$-1, -2, -3, -4, \ldots$$

---

open sentence (p. 26) An equation or an inequality that contains an algebraic expression.

enunciado con variables (pág. 26) Ecuación o desigualdad que contiene una expresión algebraica.

$2k - 8 = 12$ and $6n \geq 24$ are open sentences, but $20 - 8 = 12$ and $30 \geq 24$ are not.

$2k - 8 = 12$ y $6n \geq 24$ son enunciados con variables pero $20 - 8 = 12$ y $30 \geq 24$ no lo son.

---

opposites (p. 55) Two numbers that are the same distance from 0 on a number line but are on opposite sides of 0.

opuestos (pág. 55) En una recta numérica, dos números que están a la misma distancia de 0 pero en lados opuestos de 0.

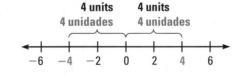

4 and −4 are opposites.

4 y −4 son opuestos.

---

order of magnitude of a quantity (p. 462) The power of 10 nearest the quantity.

orden de magnitud de una cantidad (pág. 462) La potencia de 10 más próxima a la cantidad.

The order of magnitude of 91,000 is 10^5, or 100,000.

El orden de magnitud de 91,000 es 10^5, o 100,000.

---

order of operations (p. 11) Rules for evaluating an expression involving more than one operation.

To evaluate $24 - (3^2 + 1)$, evaluate the power, then add within the parentheses, and then subtract:
$$24 - (3^2 + 1) = 24 - (9 + 1) = 24 - 10 = 14$$

orden de operaciones (pág. 11) Reglas para evaluar una expresión relacionada con más de una operación.

Para evaluar $24 - (3^2 + 1)$, evalúa la potencia, suma las cantidades entre paréntesis y después resta:
$$24 - (3^2 + 1) = 24 - (9 + 1) = 24 - 10 = 14$$

outcome (p. 744) A possible result of an experiment.

resultado (pág. 744) Solución posible de un experimento.

When you roll a number cube, there are 6 possible outcomes: 1, 2, 3, 4, 5, or 6.

Cuando lanzas un cubo numerado, hay 6 resultados posibles: 1, 2, 3, 4, 5 ó 6.

overlapping events (p. 762) Events that have at least one common outcome.

eventos de intersección (pág. 762) Eventos que tienen al menos un resultado en común.

When you roll a number cube, "roll a 3" and "roll an odd number" are overlapping events.

Cuando lanzas un cubo numerado, "salir el 3" y "salir número impar" son eventos de intersección.

P

parabola (p. 605) The U-shaped graph of a quadratic function.

parábola (pág. 605) La gráfica en forma de U de una función cuadrática.

The graph of $y = x^2 - 6x + 5$ is a parabola.

La gráfica de $y = x^2 - 6x + 5$ es una parábola.

parallel lines (p. 293) Two lines in the same plane that do not intersect.

rectas paralelas (pág. 293) Dos rectas del mismo plano que no se intersecan.

perfect square (p. 96) A number that is the square of an integer.

cuadrado perfecto (pág. 96) Número que es el cuadrado de un número entero.

49 is a perfect square, because $49 = 7^2$.

49 es un cuadrado perfecto ya que $49 = 7^2$.

perfect square trinomials (p. 574) Trinomials of the form $a^2 + 2ab + b^2$ and $a^2 - 2ab + b^2$.

trinomios cuadrados perfectos (pág. 574) Trinomios de la forma $a^2 + 2ab + b^2$ y $a^2 - 2ab + b^2$.

$x^2 + 6x + 9$ and $x^2 - 10x + 25$ are perfect square trinomials.

$x^2 + 6x + 9$ y $x^2 - 10x + 25$ son trinomios cuadrados perfectos.

permutation (p. 750) An arrangement of objects in which order is important.	There are 6 permutations of the numbers 1, 2, and 3: 123, 132, 213, 231, 312, and 321.
permutación (pág. 750) Disposición de objetos en la que el orden es importante.	Existen 6 permutaciones de los números 1, 2 y 3: 123, 132, 213, 231, 312 y 321.
perpendicular lines (p. 355) Two lines in the same plane that intersect to form a right angle.	Horizontal and vertical lines are perpendicular to each other.
rectas perpendiculares (pág. 355) Dos rectas del mismo plano que al intersecarse forman un ángulo recto.	Las rectas horizontales y verticales son perpendiculares entre sí.
point-slope form (p. 340) An equation of a nonvertical line written in the form $y - y_1 = m(x - x_1)$ where the line passes through a given point (x_1, y_1) and has a slope of m.	The equation $y + 3 = 2(x - 4)$ is in point-slope form. The graph of the equation is a line that passes through the point $(4, -3)$ and has a slope of 2.
forma de punto y pendiente (pág. 340) Ecuación de una recta no vertical escrita en la forma $y - y_1 = m(x - x_1)$, donde la recta pasa por un punto dado (x_1, y_1) y tiene pendiente m.	La ecuación $y + 3 = 2(x - 4)$ está en la forma de punto y pendiente. La gráfica de la ecuación es una recta que pasa por el punto $(4, -3)$ y tiene pendiente 2.
polynomial (p. 520) A monomial or a sum of monomials, each called a term of the polynomial.	$9, 2x^2 + x - 5$, and $7bc^3 + 4b^4c$ are polynomials.
polinomio (pág. 520) Monomio o suma de monomios en donde cada uno se llama término del polinomio.	$9, 2x^2 + x - 5$ y $7bc^3 + 4b^4c$ son polinomios.
positive integers (p. 53) The integers that are greater than 0.	$1, 2, 3, 4, \ldots$
números enteros positivos (pág. 53) Los números enteros mayores que 0.	
power (p. 6) An expression that represents repeated multiplication of the same factor.	81 is a power of 3, because $81 = 3 \cdot 3 \cdot 3 \cdot 3 = 3^4$.
potencia (pág. 6) Expresión que representa la multiplicación repetida del mismo factor.	81 es una potencia de 3 ya que $81 = 3 \cdot 3 \cdot 3 \cdot 3 = 3^4$.
probability of an event (p. 744) A number from 0 to 1 that measures the likelihood, or chance, that the event will occur.	*See* experimental probability *and* theoretical probability.
probabilidad de un evento (pág. 744) Número de 0 a 1 que mide la posibilidad de que ocurra un evento.	*Ver* probabilidad experimental *y* probabilidad teórica.
proportion (p. 156) An equation that states that two ratios are equivalent: $\frac{a}{b} = \frac{c}{d}$ where $b \neq 0$ and $d \neq 0$.	$\frac{3}{4} = \frac{6}{8}$ and $\frac{11}{6} = \frac{x}{30}$ are proportions.
proporción (pág. 156) Ecuación que establece que dos razones son equivalentes: $\frac{a}{b} = \frac{c}{d}$ donde $b \neq 0$ y $d \neq 0$.	$\frac{3}{4} = \frac{6}{8}$ y $\frac{11}{6} = \frac{x}{30}$ son proporciones.

Pythagorean theorem (p. 491) If a triangle is a right triangle, then the sum of the squares of the lengths a and b of the legs equals the square of the length c of the hypotenuse: $a^2 + b^2 = c^2$.

teorema de Pitágoras (pág. 491) Si un triángulo es rectángulo, entonces la suma de los cuadrados de las longitudes a y b de los catetos es igual al cuadrado de la longitud c de la hipotenusa: $a^2 + b^2 = c^2$.

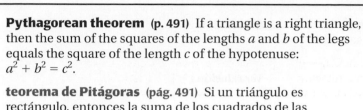

$$5^2 + 12^2 = 13^2$$

Q

quadratic equation (p. 624) An equation that can be written in the standard form $ax^2 + bx + c = 0$ where $a \neq 0$.

ecuación cuadrática (pág. 624) Ecuación que puede escribirse en la forma general $ax^2 + bx + c = 0$, donde $a \neq 0$.

The equations $x^2 - 2x = 3$ and $0.1x^2 = 40$ are quadratic equations.

$x^2 - 2x = 3$ y $0.1x^2 = 40$ son ecuaciones cuadráticas.

quadratic formula (p. 649) The formula below that can be used to find the solutions of the quadratic equation $ax^2 + bx + c = 0$ where $a \neq 0$ and $b^2 - 4ac \geq 0$:
$$x = \frac{-b \pm \sqrt{b^2 - 4ac}}{2a}$$

fórmula cuadrática (pág. 649) La fórmula de abajo puede utilizarse para hallar las soluciones de la ecuación cuadrática $ax^2 + bx + c = 0$ donde $a \neq 0$ y $b^2 - 4ac \geq 0$:
$$x = \frac{-b \pm \sqrt{b^2 - 4ac}}{2a}$$

To solve $3x^2 + 5x - 8 = 0$, substitute 3 for a, 5 for b, and -8 for c in the quadratic formula:
$$x = \frac{-5 \pm \sqrt{5^2 - 4(3)(-8)}}{2(3)}$$
$$x = 1 \text{ or } x = -\frac{8}{3}$$

Para resolver $3x^2 + 5x - 8 = 0$, sustituye a por 3, b por 5 y c por -8 en la fórmula cuadrática:
$$x = \frac{-5 \pm \sqrt{5^2 - 4(3)(-8)}}{2(3)}$$
$$x = 1 \text{ ó } x = -\frac{8}{3}$$

quadratic function (p. 605) A nonlinear function that can be written in the standard form $y = ax^2 + bx + c$ where $a \neq 0$.

función cuadrática (pág. 605) Función no lineal que puede escribirse en la forma general $y = ax^2 + bx + c$, donde $a \neq 0$.

$y = 2x^2 + 5x - 3$ is a quadratic function.

$y = 2x^2 + 5x - 3$ es una función cuadrática.

R

radical expression (p. 483) An expression that contains a radical, such as a square root, cube root, or other root.

expresión radical (pág. 483) Expresión que contiene un radical, como una raíz cuadrada, una raíz cúbica u otra raíz.

$3\sqrt{2x}$ and $\sqrt[3]{x - 1}$ are radical expressions.

$3\sqrt{2x}$ y $\sqrt[3]{x - 1}$ son expresiones radicales.

radicand (p. 95) The number or expression inside a radical symbol.

radicando (pág. 95) El número o la expresión que aparece bajo el signo radical.

The radicand of $\sqrt{9}$ and $-\sqrt{9}$ is 9.

El radicando de $\sqrt{9}$ y $-\sqrt{9}$ es 9.

range of a relation (p. 249) The range of a relation represented by a set of ordered pairs (x, y) is the set of all y values.	*See* relation.
rango de una relación (pág. 249) El rango de una relación representado por un conjunto de pares ordenados (x, y) es el conjunto de todos los valores y.	*Ver* relación.
rate (p. 21) A fraction that compares two quantities measured in different units.	$\frac{110 \text{ miles}}{2 \text{ hours}}$ and $\frac{55 \text{ miles}}{1 \text{ hour}}$ are rates.
tasa (pág. 21) Fracción que compara dos cantidades medidas en unidades diferentes.	$\frac{110 \text{ millas}}{2 \text{ horas}}$ y $\frac{55 \text{ millas}}{1 \text{ hora}}$ son tasas.
rate of change (p. 284) A comparison of a change in one quantity to a change in another quantity. In real-world situations, you can interpret the slope of a line as a rate of change.	You pay \$7 for 2 hours of computer use and \$14 for 4 hours of computer use. The rate of change is $\frac{\text{change in cost}}{\text{change in time}} = \frac{14 - 7}{4 - 2} = 3.5$, or \$3.50 per hour.
tasa de cambio (pág. 284) Comparación entre el cambio producido en una cantidad y el cambio producido en otra cantidad. En situaciones de la vida real, se puede interpretar la pendiente de una recta como una tasa de cambio.	Pagas \$7 por usar la computadora 2 horas y \$14 por usarla 4 horas. La tasa de cambio es $\frac{\text{cambio en el costo}}{\text{cambio en el tiempo}} = \frac{14 - 7}{4 - 2} = 3.5$, o \$3.50 por hora.
ratio (p. 155) A comparison of two numbers using division. The ratio of a and b, where $b \neq 0$, can be written as a to b, as $a : b$, or as $\frac{a}{b}$.	The ratio of 5 wins to 2 losses can be written as 5 to 2, as $5 : 2$, or as $\frac{5}{2}$.
razón (pág. 155) Comparación de dos números mediante la división. La razón entre a y b, donde $b \neq 0$, puede escribirse a a b, $a : b$ o $\frac{a}{b}$.	La razón de 5 victorias a 2 derrotas puede escribirse 5 a 2, $5 : 2$ ó $\frac{5}{2}$.
rational equation (p. 713) An equation that contains one or more rational expressions.	The equations $\frac{6}{x + 4} = \frac{x}{2}$ and $\frac{x}{x - 2} + \frac{1}{5} = \frac{2}{x - 2}$ are rational equations.
ecuación racional (pág. 713) Ecuación que contiene una o más expresiones racionales.	$\frac{6}{x + 4} = \frac{x}{2}$ y $\frac{x}{x - 2} + \frac{1}{5} = \frac{2}{x - 2}$ son ecuaciones racionales.
rational expression (p. 688) An expression that can be written as a ratio of two polynomials where the denominator is not 0.	$\frac{x + 8}{10x}$ and $\frac{5}{x^2 - 1}$ are rational expressions.
expresión racional (pág. 688) Expresión que puede escribirse como razón de dos polinomios, donde el denominador no es 0.	$\frac{x + 8}{10x}$ y $\frac{5}{x^2 - 1}$ son expresiones racionales.

rational function (p. 690) A function whose rule is given by a fraction whose numerator and denominator are polynomials and whose denominator is not 0.	The equations $y = \frac{-1}{x}$ and $y = \frac{2x-1}{x-2}$ are rational functions.
función racional (pág. 690) Función cuya regla viene dada por una fracción cuyo numerador y denominador son polinomios y cuyo denominador no es 0.	Las ecuaciones $y = \frac{-1}{x}$ e $y = \frac{2x-1}{x-2}$ son funciones racionales.
rational number (p. 53) A number that can be written as $\frac{a}{b}$ where a and b are integers and $b \neq 0$.	$4 = \frac{4}{1}, 0 = \frac{0}{1}, 2\frac{1}{3} = \frac{7}{3}, -\frac{3}{4} = \frac{-3}{4}$, and $0.6 = \frac{3}{5}$ are all rational numbers.
número racional (pág. 53) Número que puede escribirse $\frac{a}{b}$, donde a y b son números enteros y $b \neq 0$.	$4 = \frac{4}{1}, 0 = \frac{0}{1}, 2\frac{1}{3} = \frac{7}{3}, -\frac{3}{4} = \frac{-3}{4}$ y $0.6 = \frac{3}{5}$ son todos números racionales.
rationalizing the denominator (p. 485) The process of eliminating a radical from an expression's denominator by multiplying the expression by an appropriate form of 1.	To rationalize the denominator of $\frac{5}{\sqrt{7}}$, multiply the expression by $\frac{\sqrt{7}}{\sqrt{7}}$: $$\frac{5}{\sqrt{7}} = \frac{5}{\sqrt{7}} \cdot \frac{\sqrt{7}}{\sqrt{7}} = \frac{5\sqrt{7}}{\sqrt{49}} = \frac{5\sqrt{7}}{7}$$
racionalizar el denominador (pág. 485) El proceso de eliminar el radical del denominador de una expresión multiplicando la expresión por la forma apropiada de 1.	Para racionalizar el denominador de $\frac{5}{\sqrt{7}}$, multiplica la expresión por $\frac{\sqrt{7}}{\sqrt{7}}$: $$\frac{5}{\sqrt{7}} = \frac{5}{\sqrt{7}} \cdot \frac{\sqrt{7}}{\sqrt{7}} = \frac{5\sqrt{7}}{\sqrt{49}} = \frac{5\sqrt{7}}{7}$$
real numbers (p. 97) The set of all rational and irrational numbers.	$8, -6.2, \frac{6}{7}, \pi$, and $\sqrt{2}$ are real numbers.
números reales (pág. 97) El conjunto de todos los números racionales e irracionales.	$8, -6.2, \frac{6}{7}, \pi$ y $\sqrt{2}$ son números reales.
relation (p. 249) A pairing of the elements of one set, called the domain, with the elements of another set, called the range.	The pairing in the table below is a relation.
relación (pág. 249) La asociación en pares de los elementos de un conjunto, llamado dominio, y de los elementos de otro conjunto, llamado rango.	La correspondencia en la tabla de abajo es una relación.

Domain / Dominio	4	4	5	6	7
Range / Rango	0	1	2	3	4

root (p. 550) A root of a polynomial involving x is a value of x for which the corresponding value of the polynomial is 0.	The roots of the polynomial $x^2 - 2x - 8 = (x-4)(x+2)$ are 4 and -2.
raíz (pág. 550) La raíz de un polinomio con x es un valor de x para el cual el valor correspondiente del polinomio es 0.	Las raíces del polinomio $x^2 - 2x - 8 = (x-4)(x+2)$ son 4 y -2.

sample space (p. 744) The set of all possible outcomes.

When you roll a number cube there are 6 possible outcomes, so the sample space is 1, 2, 3, 4, 5, and 6.

espacio muestral (pág. 744) El conjunto de todos los resultados posibles.

Si lanzas un cubo numerado, hay 6 resultados posibles, de forma que el espacio muestral es 1, 2, 3, 4, 5 y 6.

---

scale (p. 163) A ratio that relates the dimensions of a scale drawing or scale model and the actual dimensions.

The scale 1 in. : 12 ft on a floor plan means that 1 inch in the floor plan represents an actual distance of 12 feet.

escala (pág. 163) Razón que relaciona las dimensiones de un dibujo a escala o un modelo a escala con las dimensiones reales.

La escala 1 pulg. : 12 pies en un diagrama de planta significa que 1 pulgada en el diagrama de planta representa una distancia real de 12 pies.

---

scale drawing (p. 163) A two-dimensional drawing of an object in which the dimensions of the drawing are in proportion to the dimensions of the object.

A floor plan of a house is a scale drawing.

dibujo a escala (pág. 163) Dibujo bidimensional de un objeto en el que las dimensiones del dibujo guardan proporción con las dimensiones del objeto.

El diagrama de planta de una casa es un dibujo a escala.

---

scale model (p. 163) A three-dimensional model of an object in which the dimensions of the model are in proportion to the dimensions of the object.

A globe is a scale model of Earth.

modelo a escala (pág. 163) Modelo tridimensional de un objeto en el que las dimensiones del modelo guardan proporción con las dimensiones del objeto.

El globo terráqueo es un modelo a escala de la Tierra.

---

simplest form of a radical expression (p. 483) A radical expression containing a square root that has no perfect square factors other than 1 in the radicand, no fractions in the radicand, and no radicals appearing in the denominator of a fraction.

In simplest form, $\sqrt{32}$ is written as $4\sqrt{2}$, and $\frac{5}{\sqrt{7}}$ is written as $\frac{5\sqrt{7}}{7}$.

forma más simple de una expresión radical (pág. 483) Expresión radical que contiene una raíz cuadrada que no tiene en el radicando fracciones ni factores cuadrados perfectos distintos de 1 y que no tiene radicales en el denominador de la fracción.

En la forma más simple, $\sqrt{32}$ se escribe $4\sqrt{2}$, y $\frac{5}{\sqrt{7}}$ se escribe $\frac{5\sqrt{7}}{7}$.

---

simplest form of a rational expression (p. 689) A rational expression whose numerator and denominator have no factors in common other than 1.

The simplest form of $\frac{2x}{x(x-3)}$ is $\frac{2}{x-3}$.

forma más simple de una expresión racional (pág. 689) Expresión racional cuyo numerador y denominador no tienen más factores en común que el 1.

La forma más simple de $\frac{2x}{x(x-3)}$ es $\frac{2}{x-3}$.

slope (p. 282) The slope m of a nonvertical line is the ratio of the vertical change (the *rise*) to the horizontal change (the *run*) between any two points (x_1, y_1) and (x_2, y_2) on the line: $m = \dfrac{y_2 - y_1}{x_2 - x_1}$.

pendiente (pág. 282) La pendiente m de una recta no vertical es la razón del cambio vertical (*distancia vertical*) al cambio horizontal (*distancia horizontal*) entre dos puntos cualesquiera (x_1, y_1) y (x_2, y_2) de la recta: $m = \dfrac{y_2 - y_1}{x_2 - x_1}$.

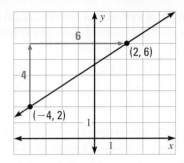

The slope of the line shown is $\dfrac{4}{6}$, or $\dfrac{2}{3}$.

La pendiente de la recta indicada es $\dfrac{4}{6}$, ó $\dfrac{2}{3}$.

---

slope-intercept form (p. 291) A linear equation written in the form $y = mx + b$ where m is the slope and b is the y-intercept of the equation's graph.

forma de pendiente e intersección (pág. 291) Ecuación lineal escrita en la forma $y = mx + b$, donde m es la pendiente y b es la intersección en y de la gráfica de la ecuación.

$y = 3x + 4$ is in slope-intercept form. The slope of the line is 3, and the y-intercept is 4.

$y = 3x + 4$ está en la forma de pendiente e intersección. La pendiente de la recta es 3, y la intersección en y es 4.

---

solution of an equation in one variable (p. 27) A number that produces a true statement when substituted for the variable in an equation.

solución de una ecuación con una variable (pág. 27) Número que, al sustituirse por la variable de la ecuación, produce un enunciado verdadero.

The number 3 is a solution of the equation $8 - 2x = 2$, because $8 - 2(3) = 2$.

El número 3 es una solución de la ecuación $8 - 2x = 2$ ya que $8 - 2(3) = 2$.

---

solution of an equation in two variables (p. 264) An ordered pair that produces a true statement when the coordinates of the ordered pair are substituted for the variables in the equation.

solución de una ecuación con dos variables (pág. 264) Par ordenado que, al ser sustituidas sus coordenadas por las variables de la ecuación, produce un enunciado verdadero.

$(1, -4)$ is a solution of $3x - y = 7$, because $3(1) - (-4) = 7$.

$(1, -4)$ es una solución de $3x - y = 7$ ya que $3(1) - (-4) = 7$.

---

solution of an inequality in one variable (p. 27) A number that produces a true statement when substituted for the variable in an inequality.

solución de una desigualdad con una variable (pág. 27) Número que, al sustituirse por la variable de la desigualdad, produce un enunciado verdadero.

The number 3 is a solution of the inequality $5 + 3n \leq 20$, because $5 + 3(3) = 14$ and $14 \leq 20$.

El número 3 es una solución de la desigualdad $5 + 3n \leq 20$ ya que $5 + 3(3) = 14$ y $14 \leq 20$.

---

solution of an inequality in two variables x and y (p. 425) An ordered pair (x, y) that produces a true statement when the values of x and y are substituted into the inequality.

solución de una desigualdad con las dos variables x e y (pág. 425) Par ordenado (x, y) que, al sustituirse los valores de x e y en la desigualdad, produce un enunciado verdadero.

$(-1, 2)$ is a solution of the inequality $x - 3y < 6$ because $-1 - 3(2) = -7$ and $-7 < 6$.

$(-1, 2)$ es una solución de la desigualdad $x - 3y < 6$ ya que $-1 - 3(2) = -7$ y $-7 < 6$.

solution of a system of linear equations (p. 376) An ordered pair that is a solution of each equation in the system.	**(3, 2) is a solution of the system of linear equations** $$x + 2y = 7$$ $$3x - 2y = 5$$ because each equation is a true statement when 3 is substituted for x and 2 is substituted for y.
solución de un sistema de ecuaciones lineales (pág. 376) Par ordenado que es una solución de cada ecuación del sistema.	**(3, 2) es una solución del sistema de ecuaciones lineales** $$x + 2y = 7$$ $$3x - 2y = 5$$ ya que cada ecuación es un enunciado verdadero cuando x se sustituye por 3 e y se sustituye por 2.
solution of a system of linear inequalities (p. 433) An ordered pair that is a solution of each inequality in the system.	**(6, −5) is a solution of the system of inequalities** $$x - y > 7$$ $$2x + y < 8$$ because each inequality is a true statement when 6 is substituted for x and −5 is substituted for y.
solución de un sistema de desigualdades lineales (pág. 433) Par ordenado que es una solución de cada desigualdad del sistema.	**(6, −5) es una solución del sistema de desigualdades** $$x - y > 7$$ $$2x + y < 8$$ ya que cada desigualdad es un enunciado verdadero cuando x se sustituye por 6 e y se sustituye por −5.
square root (p. 95) A square root of a real number a is a real number b such that $b^2 = a$.	The square roots of 9 are 3 and −3, because $3^2 = 9$ and $(-3)^2 = 9$. So, $\sqrt{9} = 3$ and $-\sqrt{9} = -3$.
raíz cuadrada (pág. 95) La raíz cuadrada de un número real a es un número real b, tal que $b^2 = a$.	Las raíces cuadradas de 9 son 3 y −3 ya que $3^2 = 9$ y $(-3)^2 = 9$. Así pues, $\sqrt{9} = 3$ y $-\sqrt{9} = -3$.
standard form of a linear equation (p. 265) $Ax + By = C$ where A, B, and C are real numbers and A and B are not both zero.	The linear equation $y = 2x - 3$ can be written in standard form as $2x - y = 3$.
forma general de una ecuación lineal (pág. 265) $Ax + By = C$ donde A, B y C son números reales, y donde A y B no son ambos cero.	La ecuación lineal $y = 2x - 3$ puede escribirse en la forma general como $2x - y = 3$.
standard form of a quadratic equation (p. 624) A quadratic equation in the form $ax^2 + bx + c = 0$ where $a \neq 0$.	The quadratic equation $x^2 - 2x - 3 = 0$ is in standard form.
forma general de una ecuación cuadrática (pág. 624) Ecuación cuadrática de la forma $ax^2 + bx + c = 0$, donde $a \neq 0$.	La ecuación cuadrática $x^2 - 2x - 3 = 0$ está en la forma general.

standard form of a quadratic function (p. 605) A quadratic function in the form $y = ax^2 + bx + c$ where $a \neq 0$.

forma general de una función cuadrática (pág. 605) Función cuadrática de la forma $y = ax^2 + bx + c$, donde $a \neq 0$.

The quadratic function $y = 2x^2 + 5x - 3$ is in standard form.

La función cuadrática $y = 2x^2 + 5x - 3$ está en la forma general.

---

system of linear equations (p. 376) Two or more linear equations in the same variables; also called a *linear system*.

sistema de ecuaciones lineales (pág. 376) Dos o más ecuaciones lineales con las mismas variables; llamado también *sistema lineal*.

The equations below form a system of linear equations:
$$x + 2y = 7$$
$$3x - 2y = 5$$

Las siguientes ecuaciones forman un sistema de ecuaciones lineales:
$$x + 2y = 7$$
$$3x - 2y = 5$$

---

system of linear inequalities in two variables (p. 433) Two or more linear inequalities in the same variables; also called a *system of inequalities*.

sistema de desigualdades lineales con dos variables (pág. 433) Dos o más desigualdades lineales con las mismas variables; llamado también *sistema de desigualdades*.

The inequalities below form a system of linear inequalities in two variables:
$$x - y > 7$$
$$2x + y < 8$$

Las siguientes desigualdades forman un sistema de desigualdades lineales con dos variables:
$$x - y > 7$$
$$2x + y < 8$$

T

terms of an expression (p. 82) The parts of an expression that are added together.

términos de una expresión (pág. 82) Las partes de una expresión que se suman.

The terms of the expression $3x + (-4) + (-6x) + 2$ are $3x$, -4, $-6x$, and 2.

Los términos de la expresión $3x + (-4) + (-6x) + 2$ son $3x$, -4, $-6x$ y 2.

---

theoretical probability (p. 745) When all outcomes are equally likely, the theoretical probability of an event is the ratio of the number of favorable outcomes to the total number of possible outcomes. The probability of event A is written as $P(A)$.

probabilidad teórica (pág. 745) Cuando todos los resultados son igualmente posibles, la probabilidad teórica de un evento es la razón entre el número de resultados favorables y el número total de resultados posibles. La probabilidad del evento A se escribe $P(A)$.

A bag of 20 marbles contains 8 red marbles. The theoretical probability of randomly choosing a red marble from the bag is $\frac{8}{20} = \frac{2}{5}$, 40%, or 0.4.

Una bolsa de 20 canicas contiene 8 canicas rojas. La probabilidad teórica de sacar al azar una canica roja de la bolsa es $\frac{8}{20} = \frac{2}{5}$, 40% o 0.4.

---

trinomial (p. 521) A polynomial with three terms.

trinomio (pág. 521) Polinomio con tres términos.

$2x^2 + x - 5$ is a trinomial.

$2x^2 + x - 5$ es un trinomio.

uniform motion (p. 413) An object moving at a constant rate is said to be in uniform motion.

movimiento uniforme (pág. 413) Se dice que un objeto está en movimiento uniforme cuando se mueve a una tasa constante.

A car traveling at a constant speed of 50 miles per hour is in uniform motion.

Un carro que viaja a una velocidad constante de 50 millas por hora está en movimiento uniforme.

---

unit rate (p. 21) A rate in which the denominator of the fraction is 1 unit.

relación unitaria (pág. 21) Relación en la que el denominador de la fracción es 1 unidad.

$\dfrac{55 \text{ miles}}{1 \text{ hour}}$, or 55 mi/h, is a unit rate.

$\dfrac{55 \text{ millas}}{1 \text{ hora}}$, ó 55 mi/h, es una relación unitaria.

---

variable (p. 5) A letter that is used to represent one or more numbers.

variable (pág. 5) Letra que sirve para representar uno o más números.

In the expressions $5n$, $n + 1$, and $8 - n$, the letter n is the variable.

En las expresiones $5n$, $n + 1$ y $8 - n$, la letra n es la variable.

---

verbal model (p. 20) A verbal model describes a real-world situation using words as labels and using math symbols to relate the words.

modelo verbal (pág. 20) Un modelo verbal describe una situación de la vida real mediante palabras que la exponen y símbolos matemáticos que relacionan esas palabras.

A verbal model and algebraic expression for dividing a dollars in a tip jar among 6 people:

Un modelo verbal y una expresión algebraica utilizados para dividir entre 6 personas a dólares del recipiente de las propinas:

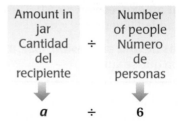

---

vertex of a parabola (p. 605) The lowest or highest point on a parabola.

vértice de una parábola (pág. 605) El punto más bajo o más alto de la parábola.

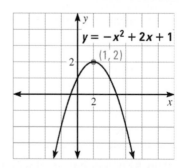

The vertex of the graph of $y = -x^2 + 2x + 1$ is the point $(1, 2)$.

El vértice de la gráfica de $y = -x^2 + 2x + 1$ es el punto $(1, 2)$.

vertical motion model (p. 551) A model for the height of an object that is propelled into the air but has no power to keep itself in the air.

modelo de movimiento vertical (pág. 551) Modelo para representar la altura de un objeto que es lanzado hacia arriba pero que no tiene potencia para mantenerse en el aire.

The vertical motion model for an object thrown upward with an initial vertical velocity of 20 feet per second from an initial height of 8 feet is $h = -16t^2 + 20t + 8$ where h is the height (in feet) of the object t seconds after it is thrown.

El modelo de movimiento vertical de un objeto lanzado hacia arriba con una velocidad vertical inicial de 20 pies por segundo desde una altura inicial de 8 pies es $h = -16t^2 + 20t + 8$, donde h es la altura (en pies) del objeto t segundos después del lanzamiento.

whole numbers (p. 53) Elements of {0, 1, 2, 3, . . . }.

números naturales (pág. 53) Elementos de {0, 1, 2, 3, . . . }.

0, 8, and **106 are whole numbers.**
−1 and 0.6 are *not* whole numbers.

0, 8 y 106 son números naturales.
−1 y 0.6 *no* son números naturales.

x-intercept (p. 273) The x-coordinate of a point where a graph crosses the x-axis.

intersección en x (pág. 273) La coordenada x de un punto donde la gráfica interseca con el eje x.

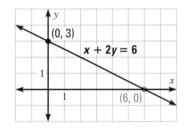

The x-intercept is 6.

La intersección en x es 6.

y-intercept (p. 273) The y-coordinate of a point where a graph crosses the y-axis.

intersección en y (pág. 273) La coordenada y de un punto donde la gráfica interseca con el eje y.

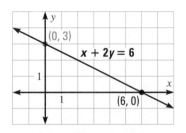

The y-intercept is 3.

La intersección en y es 3.

zero exponent (p. 626) If $a \neq 0$, then $a^0 = 1$. **exponente cero** (pág. 626) Si $a \neq 0$, entonces $a^0 = 1$.	$(-7)^0 = 1$
zero of a function (p. 626) Given y as a function of x, a zero of the function is an x-value for which $y = 0$. **cero de una función** (pág. 626) Si se da y como una función de x, un cero de la función es un valor de x para el cual $y = 0$.	The zero of $y = 2x - 4$ is 2 because $y = 0$ when $x = 2$. El cero de $y = 2x - 4$ es 2 porque $y = 0$ cuando $x = 2$.

Index

A

About the Standards, 27, 55, 62, 81, 139, 147, 202, 203, 293, 323, 347, 384, 435, 483, 550, 551, 649, 683, 708

Absolute deviation, 222, 224–225
  relative, 231

Absolute error, 222

Absolute value, 55–59, 110, 112, 113, 220
  equations, 220–225, 237
  inequalities, 226–231, 233, 238

ACT, *See* Multiple choice questions

Act it out, problem solving strategy, 807–808

Activities, *See also* Graphing calculator; Spreadsheet
  completing the square, 642
  the discriminant, 656
  dividing polynomials, 540
  factoring trinomials, 555, 565
  finding probability, 743
  if-then statements and their converses, 353
  inequalities with negative coefficients, 195
  linear inequalities in two variables, 424
  linear systems and elimination, 390
  modeling addition of polynomials, 519
  modeling equations with variables on both sides, 145
  modeling linear relationships, 321
  multiplication by –1, 73
  multiplying binomials, 527
  patterns and expressions, 18
  products and powers, 459
  properties of radicals, 482
  relationships between dimensions of a rectangle, 679
  scatter plots and functions, 256
  slope, 281
  slope and *y*-intercept, 290
  solving linear systems, 375
  statements with *and* and *or*, 209
  writing statements in if-then form, 94
  zero and negative exponents, 474

Addition
  of fractions, 2, 50–51, 52, 123, 788
  of inequalities, 190–194, 235

integer, 60–66, 123
  as inverse of subtraction, 125
  of monomials, 521, 523
  order of operations and, 11
  of polynomials, 519–525, 588, 590
  modeling, 519
  properties, 62, 110, 125, 175, 190, 233, 825
  of radicals, 485–490
  of rational expressions, 705–712, 727, 731
  real number, 60–66, 110, 113
  repeated, 73
  for solving linear systems, 391–397, 442, 445
  verbal phrases for, 19
  whole number, 50–51

Addition property of equality, 104, 125, 175

Addition property of inequality, 190, 233

Additive identity, 62

Additive inverse, 62

Algebraic expression, *See* Expression(s)

Algebra tiles
  for factoring trinomials, 555, 565
  for modeling addition of polynomials, 519
  for modeling completing the square, 642
  for modeling division of polynomials, 540
  for modeling linear equations, 145
  for modeling multiplication of binomials, 527
  for solving linear systems, 390

Alternative methods, *See* Another Way; Problem Solving Workshop

***And* statements,** 209
  for compound inequalities, 210–218, 233, 237
  for compound probabilities, 762–767, 769–770, 772, 776

Animated Algebra, *Throughout. See for example* 10, 12, 18, 33, 67, 76, 79, 131, 146, 168, 170, 191

Another Way, 32, 63, 83, 90, 141, 157, 162, 204, 213, 249, 330, 348, 398, 420, 522, 633, *See also* Problem Solving Workshop

Applications
  advertising, 136, 262, 305, 654, 702

agriculture, 473
amusement parks, 239, 287, 306, 396, 638
apparel, 225, 302, 366, 397, 403, 411, 745
architecture, 495, 616, 622
art, 10, 100, 407
astronomy, 54, 157, 160, 213, 306, 465, 469, 472, 486, 506, 514, 639
aviation, 198, 288, 413, 414, 416, 417, 449, 452, 525, 617, 687, 703, 711
baseball/softball, 39, 207, 230, 328, 432, 436, 496, 522, 525, 572, 598, 630, 637, 663, 699, 725, 761
basketball, 28, 105, 138, 222, 278, 317, 396, 417, 536, 717, 720, 754, 771
biking, 28, 37, 130, 230, 239, 302, 303, 332, 337, 601, 685, 731
biology, 23, 24, 31, 131, 334, 359, 502, 661, 694, 711
botany, 24, 303, 479
bowling, 172, 237
business, 58, 63, 65, 86, 113, 120, 204, 206, 239, 313, 338, 345, 370, 378, 385, 389, 504, 599, 662, 675, 686, 693, 694, 728, 733, 736
camping, 24, 151, 204, 239, 432
cheerleading, 224
chemistry, 80, 299, 304–305, 419, 422, 423, 441, 447, 449, 452, 465, 479, 503, 554, 578, 717
computer/internet, 151, 152, 193, 228, 300, 327, 335, 345, 385, 389, 403, 472, 481, 739
construction, 100, 172, 179, 317, 361, 493, 504, 532, 561, 585, 587, 629, 647, 663, 715, 724, 725
consumer economics, 10, 15, 16, 23, 25, 29, 36, 37, 43, 45, 48, 115, 136, 137, 143, 150, 159, 185, 194, 201, 206, 207, 208, 217, 219, 240, 242, 243, 245, 249, 253, 267, 284, 293, 296, 315, 317, 327, 331, 334, 338, 339, 342, 343, 351, 361, 364, 370, 410, 412, 544, 546, 702
containers, 7, 42, 339, 582, 585, 589, 595, 597, 599, 611, 728, 736

contests, 59, 86, 159, 225, 230, 242, 279, 439, 617, 662, 754, 767, 771, 777, 781

crafts, 34, 35, 36, 44, 130, 245, 288, 311, 380, 387, 400, 440, 452, 455, 533, 561, 572, 645, 648

dance, 39, 136

design, 176, 493, 533, 561, 564, 571, 599, 601, 728

diving, 37, 86, 92, 134, 138, 571, 780

domestic animals, 151, 351, 553

earth science, 70, 76, 78, 79, 109, 121, 130, 154, 172, 235, 262, 270, 327, 465, 466, 472, 507

education, 151, 397, 737, 768, 775

employment, 20, 30, 31, 87, 134, 144, 150, 159, 200, 240, 242, 277, 296, 301, 302, 428, 431, 655, 686, 721–725, 732, 737

energy, 610, 611

entertainment, 9, 215, 369, 389, 403, 411, 617, 683, 768

exercise, 83, 87, 254, 381, 438, 443, 748

finance, 35, 39, 48, 58, 65, 78, 92, 119, 121, 143, 154, 200, 208, 211, 245, 254, 269, 279, 359, 360, 380, 381, 489, 693, 720, 739

food preparation, 30, 36, 58, 156, 165, 201, 208, 230, 232, 269, 270, 314, 317, 403, 422, 447, 452, 717, 718, 726, 807

football, 16, 166, 178, 193, 222, 387, 396, 403, 497, 504, 538, 622, 654, 702, 712, 749

fundraising, 25, 30, 39, 45, 194, 388, 592, 686

games, 71, 100, 208, 225, 538, 548, 585, 665, 766, 773, 808

gardening, 34, 116, 172, 174, 245, 278, 295, 351, 421, 422, 423, 530, 548, 732

geography, 58, 622

golf, 58, 66, 70, 629, 733

government, 159, 259, 749, 757

gymnastics, 224, 236, 238

hiking, 36, 288, 339, 504

history, 44, 216, 232, 504, 533, 651, 654, 655, 661

hockey, 295, 359, 393, 553, 635, 640, 717

home decor, 96, 109, 138, 334, 338, 547, 578, 585, 599, 675

manufacturing, 72, 200, 245, 301

maps, 163, 165, 359, 363, 370, 473, 514, 515, 711

measurement, 25, 44, 47, 48, 49, 58, 71, 93, 193, 412, 464, 479, 481, 489, 509, 515, 704, 718

movies, 6, 85, 160, 181, 201, 287, 381, 448, 651, 754

music, 15, 30, 43, 48, 58, 66, 86, 117, 137, 155, 206, 217, 234, 240, 241, 242, 243, 251, 262, 280, 324, 396, 402, 431, 439, 455, 694, 748, 751, 755, 781

nutrition, 41, 305, 351, 431

oceanography, 288, 502, 638

Olympics, 128

performing arts, 285, 562

photography, 23, 165, 169, 327, 363, 410, 439, 596, 686, 759

physics, 65, 80, 107, 160, 219, 230, 272, 477, 480, 585, 674, 687, 711, 712, 718

physiology, 15, 17, 83, 231, 305, 313, 439, 539, 804

population, 80, 508, 524

recreation, 31, 130, 151, 387, 410, 439, 441, 524, 546, 577, 601

recycling, 278, 346

running, 30, 32, 35, 38, 49, 137, 200, 263, 267, 312, 346

skateboarding, 137, 287, 496, 530, 675

skating, 279, 280, 315, 378, 410

soccer, 9, 100, 159, 224, 400, 492, 497, 553, 629, 752, 759, 808

speed, 36, 404, 413, 414, 415–417, 490, 708, 710, 711

structures, 65, 78, 101, 157, 173, 224, 243, 292, 371, 431, 496, 502, 510, 511, 546, 554, 572, 577, 601, 610, 614, 659, 711, 739

surveys, 174, 466, 748, 771, 780

swimming, 38, 114, 143, 184, 416, 492

telephone, 21, 31, 232, 270, 327, 367, 396, 547, 654, 691, 806

television, 105, 245, 345, 368, 380, 693, 718, 758, 760

temperature, 35, 39, 58, 65, 68, 70, 80, 89, 92, 101, 117, 121, 152, 172, 189, 190, 213, 215, 216, 224, 262, 270, 767

tennis, 193, 403, 671

track and field, 70, 230, 502, 568, 627, 686, 717, 737, 778

transportation, 130, 345, 352

travel, 35, 37, 46, 47, 49, 150, 173, 191, 200, 269, 270, 288, 302, 316, 349, 365, 367, 453

vehicles, 68, 118, 136, 144, 147, 182, 194, 275, 295, 396, 413, 414, 415, 416, 417, 447, 455, 503, 524, 674, 701, 711, 712, 726, 739, 764, 769

volleyball, 93, 155, 587, 665, 673, 739

volunteering, 13, 449

walking, 173, 284

water sports, 200, 367, 610

weather, 59, 65, 92, 105, 113, 230, 271, 335, 538

wildlife, 9, 23, 115, 141, 162, 201, 206, 215, 216, 231, 388, 462, 463, 477, 551, 553, 571, 572, 577, 595, 617, 620, 767

winter sports, 71, 154, 160, 181, 194, 216, 411, 431, 447, 548, 648, 686

Approximation, *See* Estimation

Area, 796
    of a circle, 798
    of a parallelogram, 796–797
    of a rectangle, 34, 796–797
    of a rhombus, 174
    of a square, 7, 796–797
    of a trapezoid, 796–797
    of a triangle, 168, 796–797

Area model
    for completing the square, 642
    for the distributive property, 81
    for dividing polynomials, 540
    for factoring trinomials, 555, 565
    for possible outcomes, 536, 538, 770
    to show percent, 791
    to show the Pythagorean theorem, 495
    to solve problems, 770
    for the square of a binomial, 534

Argument (direct and indirect), *See* Proof

Arrangements
    combinations, 349, 351–352, 756–761, 772, 773, 775
    permutations, 750–755, 761, 772, 775

Assertion, *See* Conditional statement; Conjecture

Assessment, *See also* Multiple choice questions
    Chapter Test, 45, 117, 181, 239, 313, 367, 449, 511, 595, 671, 733, 777
    Pre-Course Test, SG17–SG18
    Prerequisite Skills quiz, 4, 52, 124, 188, 248, 320, 374, 458, 518, 604, 678, 742

Quiz, *Throughout. See for example* 24, 37, 71, 86, 108, 152, 173, 201, 217, 231, 263, 279, 303

Standards Practice, SG2–SG16

Associative property
of addition, 62, 110
of multiplication, 75, 110

Asymptote(s), 682

Average, 803, *See also* Mean; Median; Mode

Avoid Errors, *See* Error analysis

Axis of symmetry, 605, 612–613

Base, of a power, 6

Big ideas
applying, 41, 111, 176, 234, 308, 363, 443, 506, 589, 665, 728, 773
summarizing, 40, 110, 175, 233, 307, 362, 442, 505, 588, 664, 727, 772

Binomials, 521, *See also* Polynomial(s)
dividing by, 542–545
multiplying, 527, 529–538, 676–677
square of a binomial pattern, 534–539
sum and difference pattern, 535–539

Boundary line, of a linear inequality, 425

Breaking a problem into parts, problem solving strategy, 87, 807–808

Calculator, *See also* Graphing calculator
for approximating square root, 96
for evaluating fractional exponents, 500
for exploring radical properties, 482
for subtracting real numbers, 68

California @Home Tutor, *Throughout. See for example* 9, 15, 23, 30, 36, 42, 58, 78, 92, 100, 112

California Standards Spiral Review, *Throughout. See for example* 10, 16, 24, 31, 37, 59, 66, 71, 79, 86, 93, 101

Case diagram, graphic organizer, 374, 408, 444

Center, of a circle, 798

Central tendency, measures of, 89, 91, 92–93, 111, 803

Challenge, exercises, *Throughout. See for example* 10, 16, 24, 31, 37, 59, 66, 71, 79, 86, 93, 101, 108

Change
evaluating, 68, 69
line graphs and, 804
negative, 68
positive, 68
rate of, 284–289, 299, 324, 362

Chapter Problem, 41, 111, 176, 234, 308, 363, 443, 506, 589, 665, 728, 773

Chapter Review, 42–44, 112–116, 177–180, 235–238, 309–312, 364–366, 444–448, 507–510, 590–594, 666–670, 729–732, 774–776

Chapter Summary, 40, 110, 175, 233, 307, 362, 442, 505, 588, 664, 727, 772

Checking solutions
using a calculator, 68, 526, 530, 567, 580, 658, 696
using a graph, 355, 384, 433, 434, 435, 437, 526, 530, 567, 580, 644, 658, 696
using inverse operations, 519, 542, 543, 579, 783
using substitution, 27–31, 33, 44, 47, 132, 133, 134, 140, 162, 186, 190, 196, 274, 376–379, 383, 384, 391, 398, 399, 549, 581, 624, 713, 715, 807
using a table, 147, 157, 204
using unit analysis, 324

Circle
area of, 798
circumference of, 798

Circumference, of a circle, 798

Claimed assertion, *See* Conjecture

Classifying
functions, 249–250, 252
lines by slope, 284
numbers, 53, 54, 57, 97, 99, 110
polynomials, 521, 523

Closure property
of addition, 62–66, 110
of multiplication, 75–79, 110

Coefficient
negative, 195
of a term, 82

Combinations, 349, 351–352, 756–761, 772, 773, 775
formula, 756

on a graphing calculator, 761
probability and, 756–761, 773

Common factor, 785, *See also* Greatest common monomial factor
permutations and, 751
of polynomial terms, 550, 568

Common misconceptions, *See* Error analysis

Common monomial factor, 550, 568

Common multiple, 785

Communication
describing in words, *Throughout. See for example* 8, 9, 14, 18, 22, 23, 29, 31, 35, 56, 57, 59, 64
Reading in Math, 16, 79, 144, 201, 270, 335, 431, 465, 539, 655, 686
reading math, *Throughout. See for example* 6, 21, 27, 53, 55, 76, 82, 96, 133, 156
writing in math, *Throughout. See for example* 6, 8, 14, 18, 22, 29, 35, 56, 64, 69, 77, 84

Commutative property
of addition, 62–66, 110
of multiplication, 75–79, 110

Compare, exercises, 10, 59, 66, 207, 256, 569, 685, 712

Comparing
decimals, 790
graphs of inequalities, 218
graphs of quadratic functions, 605–611
inductive and deductive reasoning, 102
integers, 53, 56
rates of change, 285
slopes of lines, 290
y-intercepts of lines, 290

Completing the square, 643–648, 664, 669
for the quadratic formula, 649

Composite number, 784–785

Compound event, 762
probability of, 762–770, 772, 773, 776

Compound inequalities, 210–218, 234, 237, 374
absolute value and, 226–231, 238

Concept circle, graphic organizer, 52, 63, 112

Concepts, *See* Big ideas; Chapter Summary; Key Concepts

Concept Summary, 90, 148, 228, 260, 284, 331, 401, 408, 580, 627, 651, 682

Conclusion, 55–56, 57, 94, 353
conjecture and, 102
Conditional statement, 55–56, 57, 94,
98, 99, 353, 354
Cone, surface area and volume of,
799–800
Conjecture, 102, *See also* Conditional
statement
proving, 103–108, 482, 584
Connections, *See* Applications
Connect Skills to Problem Solving,
exercises, *Throughout. See for
example* 9, 15, 23, 30, 36, 58,
65, 70, 78, 85, 92, 100
Consistent dependent system, 405,
406
Consistent independent system, 376
Constant term, 82
Constant of variation, 297, 298, 680
Converse
of an if-then statement, 353, 354
of the Pythagorean theorem,
493–496, 510
Conversion factor, 795
Coordinate plane, 794
graphing linear functions in,
266–271, 282–289, 307, 308,
310, 318
graphing quadratic functions in,
605–631
half-plane, 425
plotting points in, 246–247, 794
transformations in, 801–802
Coordinates
of ordered pairs, 249, 257, 794
of transformations, 801–802
Counterexample, 55–56, 57, 353
exercises, 94, 99
Counting methods, 805–806
Counting principle, 750, 805–806
Critical thinking, *See* Reasoning
Cross multiplication, *See* Cross
products property
Cross products property, 161
to solve proportions, 161–166, 175,
180
to solve rational equations,
713–718
Cube root, 498
fractional exponents and, 499–503
Cumulative Review, 244–245,
454–455, 600–601, 738–739
Cylinder
surface area of, 183, 728, 799–800
volume of, 173, 466, 728, 799–800

Data, *See also* Graphs; Statistics
analyzing
using deviation from the mean,
111
using measures of central
tendency, 89, 91, 93, 111, 803
collecting, 111, 256, 308
experimental, 424, 743, 773
using random numbers, 769–770
using simulation, 769–770
organizing
counting methods, 805–806
in a line graph, 804
in a scatter plot, 256
in a table, 73, 138, 157, 208, 234,
290, 338, 387, 389, 424, 472,
479, 563, 564, 638, 719, 748,
807–808
in a tree diagram, 744, 766, 784,
805
Decimal(s)
comparing, 790
fractions and, 791–792
ordering, 790
percent and, 791–792
repeating, 54
terminating, 54
Decision tree, graphic organizer, 604,
621, 666, 766
Deductive reasoning, 102–108, 482,
See also Proof; Reasoning
Degree
of a monomial, 520
of a polynomial, 520
Denominator, 786
Dependent events, 763
probability of, 763–767, 772, 776
Dependent variable, 250
Deviation, from the mean, 111
Diagnosing readiness, *See* Readiness
Diagrams
drawing to solve problems, 38, 589,
807–808
tree, 744, 766, 784, 805
Venn, 53, 97, 209, 762, 809
Diameter, of a circle, 798
Difference of two squares pattern,
573
Dimensional analysis, 21, 679, *See
also* Unit analysis
Direct variation, 297–305, 312, 680,
682, 684
Discrete mathematics
counting methods, 805–806
counting principle, 750, 805–806

inductive reasoning, 102–108
scatter plot, 256
sets, 53, 62, 97, 809
tree diagram, 744, 766, 784, 805
Discriminant, 656, 657
Disjoint events, 762
probability of, 762–769
Distributive property, 81, 110
applying to real numbers, 81–87
for factoring polynomials, 579–580,
582–586
FOIL pattern and, 529–533
modeling, 81
for simplifying radical expressions,
485–490, 509
for solving equations, 139–144
Dividend, 783
Division
exponents and, 467–473
for finding equivalent fractions,
786
of fractions, 789
as inverse of multiplication, 126
of monomials, 541, 545
order of operations and, 11
of polynomials, 540–547, 588, 592
modeling, 540
properties, 126, 175, 197, 233
of radicals, 484–490
of rational expressions, 696,
698–703, 727, 730
ratios and, 155
real number, 88–93, 115
for solving an inequality, 197–201,
236
verbal phrases for, 19
whole number, 783
Division property of equality, 126,
175
Division property of inequality, 197,
233
Divisor, 783
Domain
of a linear function, 266–271
restricted, 267
of a quadratic function, 608
of a relation, 249–250, 252
Draw conclusions, *Throughout. See
for example* 18, 72, 73, 94, 106,
145, 153, 195, 209, 218, 256,
281, 290
Draw a diagram, problem solving
strategy, 38, 589, 807–808
Draw a graph, problem solving
strategy, 304

Eliminate choices, *See also* Multiple choice questions
  examples, *Throughout. See for example* 13, 46, 47, 118, 119, 182, 183, 240, 241, 273, 314, 315
Elimination method, for solving linear systems, 391–404
Equality, properties of, 104, 125, 126, 175, 825, 826
Equation(s) in one variable, 26, 125–131, 135–137, 139–144, 178, 187, 248
  absolute value, 220–225, 237
  checking solutions of, 27–31, 44
  equivalent, 125
  mental math and, 27–31, 122
  multi-step, 139–144, 178, 248
  one-step, 125–131, 177
  polynomial, 549–586
  quadratic, 624–655, 664, 665, 668–670
    factoring, 556–562, 566–572
  rational, 713–725
  solution of, 27
  solving on a spreadsheet, 153
  two-step, 132–138, 178
  with variables on both sides, 145–152, 179
    modeling, 145
  verbal sentences for, 26–31, 229
  writing, 26–31, 40, 41, 44
Equations in two or more variables, 108–173, 175, 176, 349, 351–352, *See also* Linear equation(s); Linear functions
  direct variation, 297–305, 312
  of horizontal lines, 265–266, 348
  inverse variation, 679–687
  literal, 167–173
  of parallel lines, 354–360, 362, 366
  of perpendicular lines, 355–360, 362, 366
  radical, 486, 489, 490
  rewriting, 167–173, 175, 180
  systems of, 375–388, 390–411
  of vertical lines, 265–266, 348
Equivalent equations, 125
Equivalent expressions, 81
Equivalent fractions, 786
Equivalent inequalities, 190
Error analysis
  Avoid Errors, *Throughout. See for example* 5, 12, 19, 20, 55, 68, 89, 156, 197, 221, 282

  exercises, *Throughout. See for example* 8, 9, 14, 22, 23, 29, 35, 38, 57, 64, 69, 78, 84
Estimation
  exercises, 225, 346, 506, 691, 699, 718
  overestimate, 424
  of points of intersection, 377–382
  of square roots, 96–100, 116
    using a calculator, 96
  underestimate, 424
  of zeros of a quadratic function, 626–631
Even number, 783
Events, 744
  compound, 762–770, 772, 773, 776
  dependent, 763–767, 772, 776
  disjoint, 762–769
  independent, 763–767, 772, 773, 776
  mutually exclusive, 762–770
  overlapping, 762–767, 772
Excluded value, 688, 691
Experiment(s)
  performing, 424, 743, 773
  trials of, 745
Experimental probability, 743, 745–749, 772, 773, 774
Exponent(s)
  expressions using, 6–10, 460–465, 467–473
  fractional, 498–503, 505, 510
  negative, 475–480, 505, 508–509
  order of magnitude and, 462–466
  properties of, 459–480, 505, 506, 507–509, 827
  zero as, 474, 475, 505, 508–509
Expression(s)
  equivalent, 81
  evaluating, 5–10, 40, 41, 42, 43
    using the distributive property, 81–87
    using exponential properties, 460–465, 467–473, 475–480, 499–503, 507–509
    using a graphing calculator, 17
    using order of operations, 11–16, 43
  for even numbers, 783
  exponential, 6–10
  for odd numbers, 783
  order of operations and, 11–16, 43
  parts of, 82
  for patterns, 18
  radical, 483–490, 509
  rational, 688–694, 696–703, 705–712

  square root, 95–101
  terms of, 82
  variables and, 5–10
  verbal phrases for, 19–24
  writing, 19–24, 40, 43
Extraneous solution, 713
Extra Practice, 810–821

Factor(s), 784–785
  common, 785
  conversion, 795
  greatest common, 785
  prime, 784–785
Factoring
  polynomials, 550–562, 565–586, 588, 589, 592–594, 604
  $ax^2 + bx + c$, 565–572, 593
  completely, 579–586
  using difference of two squares pattern, 573–578
  by grouping, 579–580, 582–586
  using perfect square trinomial pattern, 574–578
  second-degree, 556–562, 565–586
  special products, 573–578, 591, 594
  third-degree, 579–586
  quadratic equations, 556–562, 633, 640
  trinomials, 555–562, 565–572, 593
    using models, 555, 565
  whole numbers, 784–785
Factor tree, 784
Favorable outcome, 745
Find the error, *See* Error analysis
FOIL pattern, 529–533
Formula(s)
  area
    of a circle, 798
    of a parallelogram, 796
    of a rectangle, 34, 796
    of a rhombus, 174
    of a square, 7, 796
    of a trapezoid, 796
    of a triangle, 168, 796
  circumference of a circle, 34, 798
  combination, 756
  distance traveled, 34, 413
  Doyle log rule, 639
  n factorial, 751
  perimeter
    of a rectangle, 168, 321, 796
    of a square, 171, 796
    of a triangle, 796

permutation, 751
profit, 34
quadratic, 649
rewriting, 167–173, 180
simple interest, 34
slope, 282, 340
using to solve problems, 34–37
surface area
    of a cylinder, 183, 728, 799
    of a regular pyramid, 799
    of a right circular cone, 799
    of a right rectangular prism, 589, 799
    of a sphere, 799
table of, 823, 824
temperature
    Celsius/Kelvin conversion, 101
    Fahrenheit/Celsius conversion, 34, 172, 213, 255
velocity, 490
volume
    of a cube, 7
    of a regular pyramid, 799
    of a right circular cone, 799
    of a right circular cylinder, 173, 466, 728, 799
    of a right rectangular prism, 180, 589, 799
    of a sphere, 465, 799
work, 721
Formula triangle, graphic organizer, 4, 35, 42
Four square diagram, graphic organizer, 320, 343, 364
Fraction(s), 786
    adding, 52, 788
    decimals and, 791–792
    dividing, 789
    equivalent, 786
    as exponents, 498–503, 505, 510
    improper, 787
    mixed numbers and, 787
    multiplying, 789
    percents and, 742, 791–792
    product rule, 789
    quotient rule, 789
    simplest form of, 786
    simplifying, 786
    square root of, 634
    subtracting, 788
    sum and difference rules, 788
Fractional powers, 498–503, 505, 510, *See also* Exponent(s)
Fraction bar, as a grouping symbol, 12
Frequency, of an experimental result, 743

Function(s), 249, *See also* Linear functions; Quadratic function(s)
    classifying, 249–250, 252
    equations of, 250–251, 253–254
    graphing, 256–271, 282–284, 526, 605–631, 664–668
    input, 249
    linear, 266–271
        graphing, 266–271, 282–284
    output, 249
    polynomial, 526
    quadratic, 605–631, 664–668
    rational, 681–682, 695, 696, 699, 701–703, 708, 710–712
    relations and, 249–250, 252
    as tables, 249–255, 307, 308, 309
    scatter plots and, 256
    sets of ordered pairs for, 258–263
    zero of, 626–631, 664
Function notation, 269
Function rule(s), 250–254
    for a graph, 258–263
    writing, 251, 253, 254, 258, 261, 308

G

Geometric formulas, table of, 823
Geometry, *See also* Geometric formulas; Measurement
    Pythagorean theorem, 491–496, 510
        converse, 493–496, 510
    transformations, 801–802
Get-Ready Games, 2–3, 50–51, 122–123, 186–187, 246–247, 318–319, 372–373, 456–457, 516–517, 602–603, 676–677, 740–741
Graph-and-check method, to solve linear systems, 377–382
Graphic organizers
    case diagram, 374, 408, 444
    concept circle, 52, 63, 112
    decision tree, 604, 621, 666
    formula triangle, 4, 35, 42
    four square diagram, 320, 343, 364
    information frame, 124, 128, 177
    information wheel, 518, 531, 590
    notetaking organizer, 188, 205, 235
    parallel processes diagram, 678, 700, 729
    property and examples chart, 458, 463, 507
    sequence diagram, 248, 276, 309
    summary triangle, 742, 753, 774

Graphing calculator, *See also* Calculator
    activities
        find permutations and combinations, 761
        find zeros of a function, 631
        graph linear equations, 272
        graph polynomial functions, 526
        graph rational functions, 695
        make a table, 255
        use order of operations, 17
        solve compound inequalities, 218
        solve linear systems by graphing, 382
    checking solutions, 526, 530, 567, 580, 644, 658
    entering equations, 255, 272, 526, 627, 631, 695
    entering inequalities, 218
    exercises, 610, 616, 629, 665
    generating random numbers, 769
    graph feature, 218, 382, 526, 695
    intersect feature, 382
    setting the window, 272, 382, 631
    to solve quadratic equations, 627, 631
    table setup, 255, 695
    trace feature, 272, 627
    zero feature, 631
Graphs
    of compound inequalities, 210–218, 233
    of direct variation, 298–305
    of functions, 256–271, 307, 309
        linear, 266–271, 282–284, 307, 308, 309, 310
        polynomial, 526
        quadratic, 605–631, 664–668
        rational, 681–682, 695, 696
    of horizontal lines, 265–266, 348
    of inequalities, 189–194, 196, 197, 202, 203, 226–227, 233, 235, 236, 237, 238
        in two variables, 424–432
    of integers, 53–55, 56
    interpreting, 285, 288–289
    inverse variation, 679, 681–682, 684
    line, 804
    of linear equations, 264–279, 291–296, 307, 310, 311, 312, 322–338, 340–341, 344, 347–349, 364, 365, 366, 518
    of linear systems, 376–382, 405–406, 408, 409, 442, 444
    making to solve problems, 564
    of ordered pairs, 256–271, 310, 794

INDEX

of real numbers, 97
of relations, 258, 261, 263
scatter plot, 256
of systems of linear inequalities, 433–440
of transformations, 801–802
of vertical lines, 265–266, 348
Greatest common factor (GCF), 785
of polynomial terms, 550, 568
Greatest common monomial factor, 550, 568
Grouping, to factor polynomials, 579–580, 582–586
Grouping symbols, order of operations and, 11–16
Guess, check, and revise, problem solving strategy, 33, 807–808

Half-plane(s), 425
intersection of, 433–434
Horizontal line
equation of, 265–266, 348
graph of, 265–266, 348
slope of, 283, 284, 286
Hyperbola, 682
asymptotes of, 682
branches of, 682
Hypotenuse, 491
Hypothesis, 55–56, 57, 94, 353

Identity, 148
Identity property
for addition, 62, 110
for multiplication, 75, 110
If-then statement, 55–56, 57, 94, 98, 99, 493
converse of, 353, 493
Image, 801
Improper fraction(s), 787
mixed numbers and, 787
Inconsistent system, 405
Independent events, 763
probability of, 763–767, 772, 773, 776
Independent variable, 250
Indirect measurement, Pythagorean theorem and, 492, 495, 496
Indirect proof, 488
Inductive reasoning, 102–108, 482, *See also* Reasoning
Inequality (Inequalities) in one variable, 26, 189–194, 196–207, 374
absolute value, 226–231, 238
addition and subtraction, 189–194, 235
checking solutions of, 27–31, 44, 195
combining, 26
compound, 210–218, 226–231, 234, 237, 374
equivalent, 190
graphs of, 189–194, 196, 197, 202, 203, 233, 235, 236, 237, 238
multiplication and division, 196–201, 236
multi-step, 202–208, 228, 236
with negative coefficients, 195
properties of, 190, 191, 233
solution of, 27
solution set for, 202, 203
symbols for, 26, 189
writing, 26–31, 40, 44
Inequality (Inequalities) in two variables
boundary line of, 425
solution of, 425
systems of, 433–440, 442, 443, 448
writing, 428, 430, 431, 432
Information frame, graphic organizer, 124, 128, 177
Information wheel, graphic organizer, 518, 531, 590
Input, of a function, 249
Integers, 53, 97, 110
adding, 60–66
properties of, 62
rule for, 61
graphing, 53–55, 56
multiplying, 73–79
properties of, 75
rule for, 74
negative, 53
operations with, 123
positive, 53
as roots of a perfect square, 96
subtracting, 67–72
Intercept form, of a quadratic function, 618
Intercepts, 273–279, 311
Intersection, of graphs of inequalities, 210
Inverse operations
addition and subtraction, 125
multiplication and division, 126
Inverse property
of addition, 62, 110
of multiplication, 88, 110
Inverse variation, 679–687, 729
equations, 679–687, 729
graphing, 679, 681–682, 684
modeling, 679
Investigating algebra, *See* Activities
Irrational number, 96, 97, 110

Judge the validity, *See* Error analysis
Justify, *See also* Proof; Reasoning
an answer, 10, 31, 194, 328, 334, 336, 353, 358, 359, 554, 571, 749, 755, 758
steps, 76, 77, 86, 103–108, 114, 146–148, 202–204, 212–213, 616

Key Concept, *Throughout. See for example* 11, 19, 26, 32, 55, 61, 67, 74, 75, 81, 88, 89, 95

L

Leading coefficient, 520
Least common denominator (LCD), 788
of rational expressions, 706–712, 714–718
Least common multiple (LCM), 785
Legs, of a right triangle, 491
Likelihood, 744, *See also* Probability
of an event, 744
of an experimental result, 743
Like terms, 82
combining, 82–86
to solve equations, 133, 135, 139
to solve linear systems, 390–397, 398–404
Linear equation(s), 265, *See also* Linear system(s)
direct variation, 297–305, 312, 320
given slope and a point, 322, 324–328
given two points, 323–328, 330, 331, 333–338
graphs of, 264–279, 307, 310, 311, 312, 518
horizontal lines and, 265–266, 348
intercepts and, 273–279, 311
modeling, 275, 321, 324, 363
parallel lines and, 354–360, 362, 363, 366
perpendicular lines and, 354–360, 362, 363, 366
point-slope form, 323, 340–346, 362, 365

INDEX

slope-intercept form, 290–296, 322–338, 362, 364–365

standard form, 265, 347–352, 362, 366

vertical lines and, 265–266, 348

Linear functions, 266–271

graphs of, 266–271, 282–289, 307, 309, 310

scatter plots and, 256

Linear inequalities, *See* Inequality (Inequalities) in two variables

Linear model, 275, 362, 363

Linear system(s), 375

consistent dependent, 405, 406

consistent independent, 376

graphing, 376–382, 405–406, 408, 409, 442, 443, 444

on a graphing calculator, 382

identifying the number of solutions, 406, 408, 442, 446

inconsistent, 405

with infinitely many solutions, 406–411

mixture problems and, 418–423, 447

with no solution, 405–411

rate and, 413–417, 447

solution of, 375, 376

solving

by adding or subtracting, 390–397, 442, 445

using algebra tiles, 390

using the elimination method, 391–404

using graph-and-check method, 377–382

by graphing, 376–382, 443

by multiplying first, 398–404, 442, 446

by substitution, 383–388, 442, 445

summary of methods for, 401

using tables, 375, 389

types of, 376

writing, 378, 380–381, 385, 387–388, 393, 395–397, 400, 402–403, 407, 410–411, 413–417, 418–423, 443

Line graph, 804

Line of reflection, 801

Line of symmetry, 802

List, making to solve problems, 756, 807–808

Literal equation, 167–173

Logical argument, *See* Justify; Proof; Reasoning

Logical deduction, *See* Conditional statement; Deductive reasoning; If-then statement

Lowest terms, *See* Simplest form

Make a list, problem solving strategy, 756, 807–808

Manipulatives

algebra tiles, 145, 390, 519, 527, 540, 555, 565, 642

index cards, 195

measuring tools, 256, 281, 321

square tiles, 679

stop watch, 424

tangram pieces, 424

Mathematical model, 20

Maximum value, of a quadratic function, 613–614, 616

Mean, 89, 91–93, 111, 803

deviation from, 111

Mean absolute deviation, 222, 224–225

Measurement

area, 7, 34, 168, 174, 796–797

converting units, 795

distance, 34, 413

indirect, using the Pythagorean theorem, 492, 495, 496

perimeter, 168, 171, 173, 321, 796

surface area, 183, 589, 728, 799

temperature, 34, 101, 172, 213, 255

volume, 7, 173, 180, 465, 466, 589, 728, 799

Measures, table of, 826

Measures of central tendency, 89, 91–93, 111, 803

Median, 803

Mental math

for finding products, 535

for solving equations, 27–31, 47, 122

Minimum value, of a quadratic function, 613–614, 616

Mixed numbers, 787

Mixed Review of Skills and Problem Solving, 25, 39, 80, 109, 154, 174, 219, 232, 280, 306, 339, 361, 412, 441, 481, 504, 548, 587, 632, 663, 704, 726, 771

Mixture problems, 418–423, 447

percent, 419–423

Mode, 803

Modeling

absolute value, 220

absolute value inequalities, 226

addition of polynomials, 519

completing the square, 642

direct variation, 300, 301–303

the distributive property, 81

division of polynomials, 540

equivalent expressions, 81

equivalent fractions, 786

factorization of trinomials, 555, 565

fractions, decimals, and percents, 791

integer addition, 60, 61

inverse variation, 679

likelihood, 744

linear equations, 145

using linear equations, 292, 293, 295–296, 321, 324, 327–328, 331, 332, 335–336

using linear models, 275, 277–279, 342–343, 345–346, 362

linear relationships, 275, 277–279, 321

mixed numbers, 787

multiplication of polynomials, 527, 534

mutually exclusive events, 762

opposites, 55

overlapping events, 762

parabolic path, 620, 622–623

possible outcomes, 536, 538, 744

Pythagorean theorem, 495

quadratic functions, 620, 622–623, 665

using rational expressions, 683, 685–687, 693–694, 699, 701–703

real number addition, 60, 61

using simulation, 769–770

slope, 281

solutions to linear systems, 390

time, 764

using unit analysis, 21, 28, 168, 284, 324, 328, 336

using a Venn diagram, 53, 97, 209, 762, 809

using a verbal model, *Throughout.* *See for example* 20, 28, 33, 40, 43, 46, 76, 83, 118, 128, 134

vertical motion, 551, 553–554, 568, 571, 572, 575, 577, 588

Monomial(s), 519, 520, *See also* Polynomial(s)

adding, 521, 523

degree of, 520

dividing by, 541, 545

dividing out, 689–694

INDEX

multiplying, 528
subtracting, 521, 523
Motion of an object under the force of gravity, *See* Vertical motion model
Multiples, 784–785
Multiple Choice Practice, 48–49, 120–121, 184–185, 242–243, 316–317, 370–371, 452–453, 514–515, 598–599, 674–675, 736–737, 780–781
Multiple choice questions, *See also* California Standards Spiral Review; Mixed Review of Skills and Problem Solving; Multiple Choice Practice; Multiple Choice Strategies
examples, *Throughout. See for example* 34, 54, 62, 75, 127, 132, 140, 146, 202, 221, 227
exercises, *Throughout. See for example* 8, 9, 10, 14, 16, 22, 23, 29, 30, 35, 36, 39
Multiple Choice Strategies, 46–47, 118–119, 182–183, 240–241, 314–315, 368–369, 450–451, 512–513, 596–597, 672–673, 734–735, 778–779
Multiple representations, *Throughout. See for example* 62, 67, 74, 75, 81, 88, 95, 125, 126, 161, 190, 191, 196
Multiplication
of binomials, 527, 528–538
by −1, 73–77
to check division, 783
cross products and, 161–166
division of real numbers and, 88–93
exponents and, 459–466, 505, 507
to find equivalent fractions, 786
of fractions, 789
as inverse of division, 126
using mental math, 535
order of operations and, 11
of polynomials, 527–539, 588, 591, 697, 699–703
properties, 74, 75, 110, 126, 175, 196, 233, 549, 825
of radicals, 483–490
of rational expressions, 696–703, 727, 730
real number, 73–79, 110
as repeated addition, 73
to solve inequalities, 196–201, 236
to solve linear systems, 398–404, 442, 446

verbal phrases for, 19
whole number, 50–51
Multiplication property of equality, 126, 175
Multiplication property of inequality, 196, 233
Multiplicative identity, 75
Multiplicative inverse, 88
Multi-step equations, 139–144, 178
Multi-step inequalities, 202–208, 228, 236
Multi-step problems
examples, *Throughout. See for example* 20, 21, 28, 32–33, 46, 76, 83, 134, 145, 157, 167
exercises, *Throughout. See for example* 9, 15, 36, 59, 65, 79, 93, 101, 131, 137, 151, 160
Mutually exclusive events, 762
probability of, 762–767, 772

N

n **factorial,** 751
Negative change, 68
Negative coefficient, 195
Negative exponent, 474–480, 505, 508–509
Negative slope, 283–289
Negative square root, 95
Notetaking, *See* Chapter Summary; Concept Summary; Graphic organizers; Key Concept
Notetaking organizer, graphic organizer, 188, 205, 235
Number line
for comparing and order decimals, 790
for graphing inequalities, 189–194, 196, 197, 202, 203
for modeling absolute value, 220
for modeling absolute value inequalities, 226–227
for modeling integer addition, 60, 61
for modeling integers, 53
for modeling likelihood, 744
for modeling opposites, 55
for modeling time, 764
for ordering rational numbers, 54, 112
for ordering real numbers, 97, 116
for showing equivalent fractions, 786
for showing improper fractions and mixed numbers, 787

Numbers
absolute value of, 55–57, 112, 113, 220
classifying, 53, 54, 57, 97, 99, 110
comparing, 53, 56
composite, 784–785
even, 783
decimal, 54, 790
integer, 53, 97, 110
irrational, 96, 97, 110
odd, 783
opposite, 55, 57
ordering, 54, 57, 97, 99, 112–113, 116, 790
perfect square, 96
prime, 784–785
real, 53, 110
whole, 53, 97, 110
Numerator, 786

O

Odd number, 783
Online Quiz, *Throughout. See for example* 10, 16, 24, 31, 37, 59, 66, 71, 79, 86, 93, 101
Open-ended problems, *Throughout. See for example* 31, 130, 150, 209, 277, 358, 379, 403, 464, 471, 692, 753
Open sentence, 26, 30
Opposites, 55, 57
additive inverse and, 62
inverse property of addition and, 62
rational expressions and, 690
Ordered pair, 249, 257, 794
graphing, 256–271, 310, 794
as solution to a linear equation, 264
as solution to a linear inequality, 425
as solution to a linear system, 375, 376
Ordering
decimals, 790
rational numbers, 54, 57, 112–113
ratios, 740
real numbers, 97, 99, 116
Order of magnitude, 462–466, 508, 512
Order of operations, 11–16, 43
on a graphing calculator, 17
Origin, 794
Or **statements,** 209
compound inequalities and, 210–218, 233, 237

in compound probability, 762–770, 772, 776
Outcome(s)
of an experiment, 744
favorable, 745
modeling possible, 536, 538, 744
Output, of a function, 249
Overestimate, 424
Overlapping events, 762
probability of, 762–767, 772

Parabola, 605
Parallel lines
equations for, 354–360, 362, 363, 366
linear systems and, 405–411
slope and, 293, 294–295
Parallel processes diagram, graphic organizer, 678, 700, 729
Pattern(s)
difference of two squares, 573
exercises, 472, 479
exponential, 474
expressions and, 18
extending, 73
finding to solve problems, 807–808
FOIL, 529–533
perfect square trinomial, 574
products and powers, 459
square of a binomial, 534–539
sum and difference, 535–539
Percent(s), 791
decimals and, 791–792
fractions and, 742, 791–792
mixture problems and, 419–423, 447
of numbers, 793
Percent mixture problems, *See* Mixture problems
Perfect square, 96
Perfect square of a binomial, 574, *See also* Perfect square trinomial pattern
Perfect square trinomial, 574
Perfect square trinomial pattern, 574
Perimeter, 168, 171, 321, 796–797
Permutations, 750–755, 772, 775
formula, 751
on a graphing calculator, 761
probability and, 752–755, 761, 775
Perpendicular lines
equations for, 354–360, 362, 363, 366
slope and, 355–360

Pi, 798
Points
in the coordinate plane, 794
on a line, 265, 268
Point-slope form, 323, 340–346, 362, 365
Polynomial(s), 519, 520
adding, 519–525, 588, 590
classifying, 521, 523
degree of, 520
dividing, 540–547, 588, 592
dividing rational expressions by, 698–703
factoring, 549–562, 565–586, 588, 589, 592–594, 604
$ax^2 + bx + c$, 565–572, 593
completely, 579–586
using difference of two squares pattern, 573–578
by grouping, 579–580, 582–586
using a model, 555, 565
using perfect square trinomials pattern, 574–578
second-degree, 556–562, 565–586
special products, 573–578, 591, 594
third-degree, 579–586
FOIL pattern and, 529–533
multiplying, 527–539, 588, 591, 678
multiplying a rational expression by, 698, 699–703
prime, 580
roots of, 550, 552, 559, 627, 650, 652
square of a binomial pattern, 534–539
subtracting, 521–525, 588, 590
sum and difference pattern, 535–539
terms of, 520
in two variables, 560
Polynomial equations, 549–586, 588, 592–594, *See also* Polynomial(s)
writing, 568–569, 571–572, 589
Positive integer, 53
Power of a power property, 461, 505
Power of a product property, 462, 505
Power of a quotient property, 468, 505
Powers, 6–10, 459–466, *See also* Exponent(s)
Pre-Course Test, SG17–SG18
Prediction, *See also* Probability
exercises, 225, 290, 308, 328, 336, 424

simulation and, 769–770
Prerequisite Skills, 4, 52, 124, 188, 248, 320, 374, 458, 518, 604, 678, 742, 783–809
Prime factorization, 784–785
Prime factors, 784–785
of polynomials, 579–586
Prime number, 784–785
Prime polynomial, 580
Principle square root, 95
Prism
surface area of, 589, 799–800
volume of, 180, 589, 799–800
Probability
combinations and, 756–761, 773
compound events, 762–770, 772, 773, 776
counting methods, 805–806
dependent events, 763–767, 772, 776
disjoint events, 762–769
event, 744
experimental, 743, 745–749, 772, 773, 774
independent events, 763–767, 772, 773, 776
likelihood and, 743, 744
mutually exclusive events, 762–770
notation, 745
outcome, 744
overlapping events, 762–770
permutation and, 752–755, 761, 775
possible outcomes, 536, 538
sample space, 744
simulation and, 769–770
theoretical, 744–749, 772, 773, 774
trials, 745
Problem solving plan, 32–38, 40, 44
Problem solving strategies, 807–808, *See also* Eliminate choices; Problem Solving Workshop
act it out, 807–808
use an area model, 770
break a problem into parts, 87, 807–808
draw a diagram, 38, 589, 807–808
draw a graph, 304, 564
guess, check, and revise, 33, 807–808
look for a pattern, 807–808
make a list, 756, 807–808
make a table, 338, 389, 719, 807–808
perform a simulation, 769–770
reinterpret the problem, 720

INDEX

solve a simpler problem, 807–808
work backward, 208, 807–808
write a proportion, 305
Problem Solving Workshop, 38, 87,
138, 208, 304–305, 337–338,
389, 497, 563–564, 640–641,
719–720, 769–770
Product of powers property, 460, 505
Product property of radicals, 483,
505
Product rule, 789
Profit formula, 34
Projectile, 551
vertical motion and, 551, 553–554
Proof, *See also* Justify; Reasoning
of a conjecture, 103–108, 482, 584
indirect, 488
of the quadratic formula, 649
solution as a, 147
of a statement, 203
two-column, 104
Property (Properties)
of addition, 62, 104, 110, 125, 175
closure, 62, 75, 110
distributive, 81–86
of division, 126, 175
of equality, 104, 125, 126
of exponents
division, 467–473, 505, 508
multiplication, 459–466, 505, 507
negative, 475–480, 505, 508–509
zero, 474–480, 505, 508–509
of inequality, 190, 191, 196, 197,
233
of multiplication, 74, 75, 110, 126,
175, 549
of –1, 73–75
of a quadratic function, 613
of radicals, 482–490
of subtraction, 125, 175, 458
table of, 825–827
zero product, 549
Property and examples chart,
graphic organizer, 458, 463,
507
Property of zero
converse of, 549
for multiplication, 75
Proportion(s), 156
ratio and, 156–160, 179
reading, 156
scale and, 163, 165–166, 176
setting up, 156
solving, 156–160
using cross products, 161–166,
175, 180

Prove or disprove, *See* Proof
Pyramid
surface area of, 799–800
volume of, 799–800
Pythagorean theorem, 491–496, 510
converse of, 493–496, 510

Q

Quadrants, 794
Quadratic equation(s), *See also*
Polynomial(s)
the discriminant and, 656–662,
664, 670
number of solutions of, 624–625,
664
solving, 624–655, 664, 665, 668–670
by completing the square,
642–648, 664, 669
by factoring, 556–562, 633, 640
by graphing, 624–631, 664, 668
methods, 651
using the quadratic formula,
649–655, 664, 670
using a table, 641
using square roots, 633–639, 664,
669
standard form, 624
Quadratic formula, 649
deriving, 649
discriminant and, 656–662, 664,
670
to solve quadratic equations,
649–655, 664, 670
Quadratic function(s), 605–631
domain of, 608
graphing, 605–631, 664, 665,
666–668
axis of symmetry, 605, 612–613
in intercept form, 618–623
in standard form, 605–617
vertex, 605, 612
x-intercepts, 618–623
maximum value of, 613–614, 616
minimum value of, 613–614, 616
modeling a parabolic path with,
620, 622–623, 665
properties of, 612
range of, 608
standard form, 605
writing, 620–623
zeros of, 626
estimating, 626–631
Quotient, 783
Quotient of powers property, 467,
505

Quotient property of radicals, 484,
505
Quotient rule, 789

R

Radical equations, 486, 489, 490
Radical expressions, 483
rationalizing the denominator,
485–490
simplest form of, 483
simplifying, 483–490, 509
Radicals
fractional exponents and, 499–504
operations with, 483–490, 505, 509
properties of, 482–490, 505, 506,
509
Pythagorean theorem and,
491–496, 510
in solutions of quadratic
equations, 634, 636
Radical symbol, 95
Radicand, 95
Radius, of a circle, 798
Random integers, generate using a
graphing calculator, 769
Range
of a linear function, 266–271, 443
of a quadratic function, 608
of a relation, 249–250, 252
Rate(s), 21, 155
of change, 284–289, 299, 311, 324,
331–332, 334–336, 342, 362
linear systems and, 413–417, 447
rational functions and, 708,
710–712, 731
relationship to time and distance,
413–417, 447
of speed, 413–417
uniform motion and, 413
unit, 21, 22
work and, 721–725
Rate problems, 413–417, 447
Ratio(s), 155
direct variation, 300
equivalent, 741
ordering, 740
proportion and, 155–160, 179
slope, 281, 282
Rational equations, 699, 701–703,
708, 710–712, 713
cross products property and,
713–718
solving, 713–725, 727, 731, 732
work problems and, 721–725, 727,
732

Rational expression(s), 688, 727
  adding, 705–712, 727, 731
  dividing, 696, 698–703, 727, 730
  excluded values and, 688, 691
  least common denominator of,
    706–712, 714–718
  multiplying, 696–703, 727, 730
  opposite factors and, 690
  simplest form, 689
  simplifying, 688–694, 727, 730
  subtracting, 705–712, 727, 731
  in two variables, 693
  undefined, 688
Rational functions, 690
  adding, 708
  dividing, 699, 701, 702–703
  graphing, 681–682, 696
    on a graphing calculator, 695
  multiplying, 701, 702–703
Rationalizing the denominator,
    485–490
Rational numbers, 53–57, 110
  classifying, 97
  ordering, 54, 57, 112
Readiness
  Prerequisite Skills, 4, 52, 124, 188,
    248, 320, 374, 458, 518, 604,
    678, 742
  Standards Review Handbook,
    783–809
Reading in Math, 16, 79, 144, 201,
    270, 335, 431, 465, 539, 655,
    686
Reading math, *Throughout. See for
    example* 6, 21, 27, 53, 55, 76,
    82, 95, 96, 133, 144, 156
Real number(s), 53, 110
  adding, 60–66, 113
  applying the distributive property
    to, 81–86
  comparing, 97, 116
  dividing, 88–93, 115
  as domain of a linear function, 266
  integers, 53, 97, 110
  irrational numbers, 96, 97, 110
  multiplying, 73–79, 114
  opposites, 55, 57
  ordering, 97, 99, 116
  repeating decimals, 54
  as solutions of inequalities, 203
  square root of, 95–101
  subtracting, 67–72, 114
  terminating decimals, 54
Reasoning
  all or *none* statements, 94
  and statements, 209, 233
  conclusion, 55–57, 353

  conditional statements, 55–57, 353
  conjecture, 102
    proving, 103–108, 482, 584
  converse of a statement, 353, 354
  counterexample, 55–56, 57, 353
  counting methods, 805–806
  deductive, 102–108, 116, 482
  dimensional analysis, 21, 679
  draw conclusions, *Throughout. See
    for example* 18, 72, 73, 94, 145,
    153, 195, 209, 218, 256, 290
  exercises, *Throughout. See for
    example* 15, 65, 70, 77, 92, 99,
    106, 107, 108, 129, 136, 144
  hypothesis, 55–57, 353
  if-then statements, 55–57, 94, 98
  indirect proof, 488
  inductive, 102–108, 116, 482
  or statements, 209, 233
  sometimes, always, never
    questions, 106–107, 117
  true or *false* statements, 56, 57, 65,
    70, 78, 85, 92, 94, 98, 99, 108,
    116, 117, 209, 215, 230
  Venn diagrams and, 53, 97, 209,
    762, 809
Reciprocals, 88, 789
  to divide real numbers, 88–93
  negative exponents and, 475–480
  slopes of perpendicular lines and,
    355–360
  solving equations with, 127–131,
    140–144
Reflections, 801–802
  quadratic functions and, 606
Relations, 249
  functions and, 249–250, 252
  graphs of, 258, 261, 263
  sets of ordered pairs for, 258, 261,
    263
Remainder, 783
Repeating decimal, 54
Reviews, *See* Chapter Review;
    Chapter Summary;
    Cumulative Review; Mixed
    Review of Skills and Problem
    Solving; Standards Review
    Handbook
Right triangle
  hypotenuse of, 491
  legs of, 491
  Pythagorean theorem and, 491–496
Roots
  of a polynomial, 550, 552, 559, 627,
    650, 652
  relationship to zeros, 626, 627
  x-intercepts as, 618, 627

Sample space, 744
SAT, *See* Multiple choice questions
Scale, 163, 165–166, 176
Scale drawing, 163, 165–166, 176, 497
Scale model, 163, 165–166
Scatter plot, 256
Second-degree polynomial, *See*
    Polynomial(s)
Sequence diagram, graphic
    organizer, 248, 276, 309
Set(s)
  closure and, 62, 75
  for domain and range, 249
  notation, 190, 266
  of numbers, 53, 97, 809
  of ordered pairs, 258, 261, 263
  solution for an inequality, 202
  Venn diagrams and, 53, 97, 209,
    809
Set notation, 190
  for domain and range, 266
Short response questions,
    Throughout. See for example
    36, 100, 107, 131, 137, 143,
    166, 334, 344, 358, 387, 395
Simplest form
  fraction, 786
  ratio, 155
  rational expression, 689
Simulation, 769–770
Slope, 281, 282
  classifying lines by, 284, 286
  formula, 282
  of a horizontal line, 283, 284, 286
  line, 282–296, 311
  linear systems and, 405–411
  modeling, 281
  parallel lines and, 354–360
  perpendicular lines and, 355–360
  rate of change and, 282–289, 311
  undefined, 284, 286
  of a vertical line, 283, 284, 286, 348
  y-intercept and, 290–296
  zero, 284, 286
Slope-intercept form
  for graphing linear equations,
    290–296, 312
  for writing linear equations,
    322–338, 362, 364–365
Solid, 799
Solution(s), 624, 633, 657
  of an equation, 27
    absolute value, 222
    quadratic, 624–625, 627, 656,
      657, 664, 670

in two variables, 264
extraneous, 713
of an inequality, 27, 190, 203
    in two variables, 425
of a linear system, 375, 376
    of inequalities, 433
number of, 148, 664, 670

Solution set
for an inequality, 202
for a system of linear inequalities,
    435

Spreadsheet
for solving equations, 153
for subtracting real numbers, 72

Square of a binomial pattern, 534

Square root(s), 95–101, 116, *See also*
        Radicals
on a calculator, 96
of a fraction, 634
fractional exponents and, 499–503
perfect square, 96
principal, 95
simplifying, 634
to solve quadratic equations,
    633–639, 664, 669
table of, 829

Squares, table of, 829

Standard form
of a linear equation, 265, 347–352,
    362, 366
    special cases, 265–266
of a quadratic equation, 624
of a quadratic function, 605

Standards Practice, SG2–SG16

Standards Review Handbook,
        783–809
the coordinate plane, 794
    transformations in, 801–802
counting methods, 805–806
decimals
    comparing, 790
    fractions and, 791–792
    ordering, 790
    percent and, 791–792
fractions
    decimals and, 791–792
    equivalent, 786
    improper, 787
    mixed numbers and, 787
    operations with, 788–789
    percent and, 791–792
    simplifying, 786
mean, median, and mode, 803
measurement
    circumference and area of a
        circle, 798
    converting units of, 795

perimeter and area, 796–797
    surface area and volume,
        799–800
number sense
    even and odd numbers, 783
    factors and multiples, 784–785
    prime and composite numbers,
        784–785
    quotients and remainders, 783
percent
    decimals and, 791–792
    fractions and, 791–792
    of a number, 793
problem solving strategies,
    807–808
transformations, 801–802
Venn diagrams and logical
    reasoning, 809

Statistics, *See also* Data; Graphs;
        Probability
mean absolute deviation, 222,
    224–225
measures of central tendency, 89,
    91, 92–93, 111, 803

Subset, 75

Substitution
for checking solutions,
    Throughout. See for example
    27–31, 33, 40, 43, 47, 132, 133
for solving linear systems, 383–388,
    442, 445

Subtraction
of fractions, 788
of inequalities, 191–194, 235
as inverse of addition, 125
of monomials, 521, 523
order of operations and, 11
of polynomials, 521–525, 588, 590
properties, 125, 175, 191, 233, 458
of radicals, 485–490
of rational expressions, 705–712,
    727, 731
real number, 67–72, 114
for solving linear systems, 392–397,
    442, 445
verbal phrases for, 19
whole number, 50–51

Subtraction property of equality,
    125, 175

Subtraction property of inequality,
    191, 233

Subtraction rule, 67, 458

Sum and difference pattern, 535

Sum and difference rules, for
        fractions, 788

Summary triangle, graphic
        organizer, 742, 753, 774

Surface area
of a regular pyramid, 799–800
of a right circular cone, 799–800
of a right circular cylinder, 183,
    728, 799–800
of a right rectangular prism, 589,
    799–800
of a sphere, 799–800

Symbol(s)
absolute value, 55, 220
break in axis, 256
function notation, 269
grouping, 11
inequality, 26, 189
plus or minus, 95
radical, 95
table of, 822

**System of two linear equations in
    two variables,** *See* Linear
        system(s)

**System of two linear inequalities in
    two variables,** 433–440, 442,
    446

T

Table
for finding a pattern, 474, 482
for graphing a function, 257–271
    quadratic, 605–611
for graphing an inverse variation
    equation, 681
of ordered pairs, 249–255
    on a graphing calculator, 255
to represent a function, 334, 338
for solving an equation, 153
for solving a linear system, 389
for solving a quadratic equation,
    641
for solving problems, 73, 138, 157,
    208, 234, 290, 338, 387, 389,
    424, 472, 479, 563, 564, 638,
    719, 748, 807–808

**Table of equivalent fractions,
    decimals, and percents,** 792

Table of Formulas, 823–824

Table of Measures, 828

Table of Properties, 825–827

Table of Squares and Square Roots,
    829

Table of Symbols, 822

Technology, *See* Graphing calculator;
        Spreadsheet

Technology support, *See* Animated
        Algebra; California @Home
        Tutor; Online Quiz

INDEX

Temperature
  Celsius/Kelvin conversion, 101
  Fahrenheit/Celsius conversion, 34, 172, 213, 255
Term(s)
  constant, 82
  of an expression, 82
  like, 82
    combining, 82–86
  of a polynomial, 520
Terminating decimal, 54
Theorem, 491
Theoretical probability, 744–749, 772, 773, 774
Third-degree polynomial, *See* Polynomial(s)
Transformations, 801–802
  of quadratic functions, 606, 607, 609
Translating verbal statements, 19–24, 26–31, 210–211, 214–217, 227, 229
Translations, 801–802
  of quadratic functions, 606, 607, 609
Tree diagram
  for counting possibilities, 805
  for possible outcomes, 744
  for prime factorization, 784
Trial, of a probability experiment, 745
Trinomial(s), 521, *See also* Polynomial(s)
  factoring, 555–562, 593
    using models, 555, 565
  perfect square, 574
  in two variables, 560
***True* or *false* statements,** 56, 57, 65, 70, 78, 85, 92, 94, 98, 99, 108, 116, 117, 209, 215, 230
Two-column proof, 104

Undefined rational expression, 688
Undefined slope, 284, 286
Underestimate, 424
Uniform motion, 413
Union, of graphs of inequalities, 210
Unit analysis, 21, 28, 168, 284, 324, 328, 336
Unit rate, 21, 23

Variable(s), 5
  choosing, 20, 251

dependent, 250
eliminating to solve linear systems, 391–397
in a fraction, 167
independent, 250
literal equations and, 167–173
Variation
  constant of, 297, 298, 680
  direct, 297–305, 312, 680, 682, 684
  inverse, 679–687, 729
Venn diagrams, 809
  for *and* and *or* statements, 209
  showing mutually exclusive events, 762
  showing overlapping events, 762
  showing sets of numbers, 53, 97, 809
Verbal model, 20
  examples, *Throughout. See for example* 28, 33, 40, 43, 46, 76, 83, 87, 118, 128, 134
Verbal phrases, translating, 19–24
Verbal sentences, translating, 26–31, 229
Vertex, of a parabola, 605, 612
Vertical line
  equation for, 265–266, 348
  graph of, 265–266, 348
  slope of, 283, 284, 286
Vertical line test, 258, 261, 262, 263
Vertical motion model, 551, 553, 568, 571, 572, 575, 577
Visual thinking, *See* Graphs; Manipulatives; Modeling; Multiple representations; Transformations
Vocabulary
  prerequisite, 4, 52, 124, 188, 248, 320, 374, 458, 518, 604, 678, 742
  review, 42, 112, 177, 235, 309, 364, 444, 507, 590, 666, 729, 774
Volume
  of a cube, 7
  of a prism, 180, 589, 799–800
  of a regular pyramid, 799–800
  of a right circular cone, 799–800
  of a right circular cylinder, 173, 466, 728, 799–800
  of a sphere, 799–800

What If? questions, *Throughout. See for example* 6, 7, 13, 20, 21, 28, 33, 63, 83, 87, 128, 134
Whole numbers, 53, 97, 110

Work backward, problem solving strategy, 208, 807–808
Work problems, 721–725, 727, 732
Writing
  and and *or* statements, 209
  function rules, 251, 253, 254
    for a graph, 258, 261
  if-then statements, 94
  probabilities, 745
  proofs, 104–108
    indirect, 488
  proportions, 156–160, 162–166
  radicals, 484
  ratios, 155, 158

x-axis, 794
x-coordinate, 794
x-intercept(s), 273, 274
  discriminant and, 656–662, 664
  graphs of quadratic functions and, 618–623, 627, 664
  graphs of linear equations and, 273–279

y-axis, 794
y-coordinate, 794
y-intercept(s), 273, 274
  graphs of linear equations and, 273–279, 290–296, 322–338
  graphs of linear systems and, 405–411

Zero
  as additive identity, 62
  as a constant, 520
  division by, 89
  as an exponent, 474, 475, 505, 508–509
  of a function, 626–631, 664
  multiplication by, 88
  of a quadratic function, 626–631
  square root of, 95
Zero-product property, 549–554, 618–623
Zero slope, 284, 286

INDEX

Credits

Photography

Cover
Ty Allison/Getty Images

Authors, Teacher Advisors, and Reviewers
Aguilar Maritza Chang/ Fantastic Shots; *Austin* Jostens Photography/Lifetouch; *Birbeck* Courtesy of Edie Birbeck; *Boswell* Robert C. Jenks, Jenks Studio; *Bryson* Margaret L. Kidd; *Carter* Lifetouch; *Chavez* Courtesy of Mark Chavez; *Cliffe* Courtesy of Karen Cliffe; *Davis* Shawn Davis; *Duffy* Courtesy of Ellen Duffy; *Fox* Courtesy of Barry Fox ; *Kanold* McDougal Littell/ Houghton Mifflin Co.; *Kohn* Sharon Kohn; *Kuykendall* Courtesy of Brent Kuykendall; *Larson* Meridian Creative Group; *Martinez* Courtesy of Chris Martinez; *Miyata* Courtesy of Greg Miyata; *Okamoto* Akiko Okamoto; *Pacheco* Nila Pacheco; *Phair* James F. Phair; *Sass* Courtesy of Rudy Sass; *Smith* Jessica Smith; *Stiff* Jerry Head Jr.; *Walker-Jennels* Courtesy of Gwendolyn Walker-Jennels.

TOC1 Royalty-Free/Corbis; **TOC2** Tim Tadder/Corbis; **TOC3** David Zaninger/Alamy; **TOC4** Vision of America, LLC/Alamy; **TOC5** Thomas & Pat Leeson/Photo Researchers, Inc.; **TOC6** Paul Mounce/Corbis; **TOC7** John Elk III/Lonely Planet Images; **TOC8** Anup Shah/Getty Images; **TOC9** Thomas Winz/Lonely Planet Images; **TOC10** Jeff Flindt/NewSport/Corbis; **TOC11** David Trood/Getty Images; **TOC12** Brown W. Cannon III/Getty Images; **TOC13** John Post/Panoramic Images; **SG1** Royalty-Free/Corbis; **SG18** School Division/Houghton Mifflin Company; **SG19** PhotoSpin; **2** Royalty-Free/Corbis; **3** Joseph Sohm-Visions of America/PhotoDisc Red/Getty Images; **5** *top right* Randy Faris/ Corbis; **9** *center right* James Balog/Getty Images; **10** Scott S. Warren/Aurora Photos; **11** Royalty-Free/Comstock Images; **13** David Young-Wolff/PhotoEdit; **16** Donald Miralle/Staff/Getty Images; **19** *printer* Ryan McVay/PhotoDisc/Getty Images; *photo* Royalty-Free/Stockbyte; **21** Steve Dunwell/Index Stock Imagery; **23** Patrick Ward/Corbis; **26** Robert F. Bukaty, Staff/AP Images; **28** Seb Rogers/Alamy; **29** *center left* Chris Collins/Corbis; *center right* PhotoDisc; **30** Elaine Thompson, Staff/AP Images; **31** Najlah Feanny/Corbis; **32** Michael Stevens/Fog Stock; **36** Scott Warren/Aurora Photos; **41** Spencer Grant/PhotoEdit; **53** Jonathan Nourok/PhotoEdit; **54** John Chumack/Photo Researchers, Inc.; **60** Patrik Glardino/Corbis; **63** Bob Krist/ Corbis; **65** LLC, FogStock/Index Stock Imagery; **67** Stephen Alvarez/Aurora Photos; **70** Myrleen Ferguson Cate/PhotoEdit; **72** Ron Chapple/Getty Images; **74** Natphoto/Getty Images; **76** Peter Essick/Aurora Photos; **78** Philip Coblentz/Getty Images; **80** Charles D. Winters/Photo Researchers, Inc.; **81** Patrik Glardino/ Corbis; **83** Bob Daemmrich/The Image Works, Inc.; **88** Jonathan Ferrey/Getty Images; **89** Duncan Adams/AP Images; **92** Photo courtesy of Mehgan Heaney-Grier, Freedive Champion & Jim Edds, photographer; **93** *both* USGS; **95** Sylvain Grandadam/ Getty Images; **100** Photo from the New York Hall of Science/www. minotaurmazes.com; **102** Richard Hutchings/PhotoEdit; **111** Roy Morsch/age fotostock; **122** NASA; **123** *planet* NASA; *astronuat* NASA/Corbis; **125** Barros & Barros/Getty Images; **128** Anja Niedringhaus/AP Images; **131** Gary Bell/Oceanwide Images; **132** Stephen Frink/Corbis; **134** Royalty-Free/Corbis; **136** M. Spencer Green/AP Images; **139** Michael Newman/PhotoEdit; **141** Steve Kaufman/Corbis; **146** Mark Lennihan/AP Images; **155** Reuters/Corbis; **157** Lowell Georgia/Corbis; **159** Marc Muench/ Getty Images; **161** Marcus Bradbury; **167** Nancy Ney/Getty Images; **172** Royalty-Free/Corbis; **176** David Young-Wolff/ PhotoEdit; **185** Gary Cralle/Getty Images; **189** Royalty-Free/ Corbis; **191** Sergio Piumatti; **193** Rob Tringali/SportsChrome; **196** Jonathan Nourok/PhotoEdit; **198** John Powell Photographer/ Alamy; **201** William Albert Allard/National Geographic Image Collection; **202** Roy Toft/National Geographic/Getty Images; **204** Eric Risberg/AP Images; **206** Melanie Acevedo/Botanica/ Jupiterimages; **208** Eric Risberg/AP Images; **210** Courtesy of www.apcamcar.com; **213** DLR/NASA; **215** Garold W. Sneegas; **216** Courtesy of and Copyright, Peabody Essex Museum, Salem, Massachusetts; **220** AP Images; **222** Darren Sweet/ PictureChasers.com; **224** Neal Preston/Corbis; **226** Tony Avelar/ Animals Animals; **230** David Barber/PhotoEdit; **231** D. Robert & Lorri Franz/Corbis; **234** David Young-Wolff/PhotoEdit; **246** *clipboard & pencils* PhotoDisc; **249** Michael Newman/ PhotoEdit; **251** Aneal Vohra/Index Stock Imagery; **257** Mitchell Funk/Getty Images; **259** David J. & Janice L. Frent Collection/ Corbis; **262** PhotoDisc; **264** U.S. Navy photo by Photographer's Mate 3rd Class Ramon Preciado; **267** David Madison/Getty Images; **273** Alexis Rosenfeld/Photo Researchers, Inc.; **275** Alexis Rosenfeld/Photo Researchers, Inc.; **277** Michael S. Yamashita/ Corbis; **280** Jim Cooper/AP Images; **281** *all* McDougal Littell/ Houghton Mifflin Co.; **282** Scott Markewitz/Getty Images; **284** *café* Paul Edmondson/Getty Images; *soup* Judd Pilossof/Jupiter Images; **288** Kevin Fleming/Corbis; **291** Peter Williams/AP Images; **292** Kevin P. Casey/Corbis; **295** Robert Laberge/Getty Images; **297** Lionel Cironneau/AP Images; **299** The North Platte Telegraph, Kristina Jergensen/AP Images; **300** *top right* Hugh Threlfall/Alamy; **302** Rodolfo Arpia/Alamy; **308** Visions of America, LLC/Alamy; **322** Jim Cummins/Getty Images; **324** Comstock Images/Alamy; **327** Yann Arthus-Bertrand/Corbis; **329** Tony Ashby/AFP/Getty Images; **331** Masterfile; **332** Lester Lefkowitz/Corbis; **340** Bongarts/Sportschrome; **342** R. Ian Lloyd/ Masterfile; **345** Robert W. Ginn/PhotoEdit; **347** The Photo Library Wales/Alamy; **349** Richard Cummins/Corbis; **354** Phillip Colla/ www.OceanLight.com; **373** Christie's Images/Corbis; **376** Liu Liqun/Corbis; **381** *top left* Royalty-Free/Corbis; *top center* Elliptical Trainer photo courtesy of NordicTrack.com; *top right* Royalty-Free/Corbis; **383** Gary Pearl/StockShot/Alamy; **387** David Young-Wolff/PhotoEdit; **388** Jeremy Woodhouse/ PhotoDisc Blue/Getty Images; **391** Purestock/Alamy; **393** Niklas Larsson/AP Images; **396** Janet Bailey/Masterfile; **397** Spencer Grant/PhotoEdit; **398** José Antonio Jiménez/age fotostock; **400** Royalty-Free/Corbis; **403** Jose Carillo/PhotoEdit; **405** Bobby Model/Getty Images; **410** Thomas Shjarback/Alamy; **413** Dennis MacDonald/PhotoEdit; **416** Paul McMahon/Heartland Images; **417** Nick Rowe/PhotoDisc/Getty Images; **418** OnRequest Images, Inc./Alamy; **422** Joel Wolfson Photographer, LLC; **425** Greig Cranna/Index Stock Imagery; **428** Keith Woods/Getty Images; **431** Paul J. Sutton/Duomo/Corbis; **433** Pierre Ducharme/Reuters/Corbis; **436** Jeff Lewis/AP Images; **439** Jonathan Nourok/PhotoEdit; **443** Ryan McVay/PhotoDisc Green/ Getty Images; **460** Scott Camazine/Photo Researchers, Inc.; **463** Michael Busselle/Corbis; **465** Royalty-Free/Getty Images; **467** Roger Ressmeyer/Corbis; **469** Paul J. Mayo - Australia; **472** Akira Fujii/ESA; **475** Juan Silva/Getty Images; **477** *both* Ted Kinsman/ Photo Researchers, Inc.; **479** *left* Carlyn Iverson/Photo Researchers, Inc.; *right* mediacolor's/Alamy; **483** John Elk/Elk Photography; **490** Tony Freeman/PhotoEdit; **491** Joseph Pobereskin/Getty Images; **498** Michael Newman/PhotoEdit; **502** Vince Streano/Corbis; **506** Andrea Dupree (Harvard-Smithsonia CfA), Ronald Gilliland (STScI), NASA and ESA; **514** *center left* JPL/NASA; **520** Tom Bean/Corbis; **522** Bill Aron/PhotoEdit; **524** Digtial Vision/Corbis; **525** Robert Galbraith/Reuters/Corbis; **528** Neale Haynes/ImageState/Alamy; **533** *photo* Will Hart/ PhotoEdit; *frame* PhotoSpin; **534** David Young-Wolff/PhotoEdit; **536** PhotoSpin; **538** *football* Royalty-Free/Corbis; *grass* PhotoSpin; **539** Royalty-Free/Corbis; **541** Ace Stock Limited/

Selected Answers

Chapter 1

1.1 Exercises (pp. 8–10) **1.** exponent: 12, base: 6 **3.** 60
5. 12 **7.** 7 **9.** 0.4 **11.** 4.5 **13.** 0.9 **15.** $\frac{1}{3}$ **17.** $1\frac{2}{3}$
19. twelve to the fifth power, $12 \cdot 12 \cdot 12 \cdot 12 \cdot 12$
21. three tenths to the fourth power, $0.3 \cdot 0.3 \cdot 0.3 \cdot 0.3$
23. one half to the eighth power, $\frac{1}{2} \cdot \frac{1}{2} \cdot \frac{1}{2} \cdot \frac{1}{2} \cdot \frac{1}{2} \cdot \frac{1}{2} \cdot \frac{1}{2} \cdot \frac{1}{2}$
25. y to the sixth power, $y \cdot y \cdot y \cdot y \cdot y \cdot y$ **27.** 0.4 was
multiplied by 2 instead of squared; $(0.4)^2 = (0.4)(0.4) =$
0.16. **29.** 9 **31.** 1 **33.** 125 **35.** 64 **37.** $\frac{1}{16}$ **39.** $\frac{27}{125}$
41. $\frac{9}{16}$ **43.** 64 **45.** 17.4 **47.** 6.7 **49.** 55 **51.** The value
of a was substituted for b and the value of b was
substituted for a; $\frac{a}{b} = \frac{48}{12} = 4$. **55.** 50 cents **57.** 30 m

1.2 Exercises (pp. 14–16) **1.** Square 4. **3.** 8 **5.** 14
7. $3\frac{3}{5}$ **9.** $63\frac{3}{4}$ **11.** 21 **13.** $73\frac{1}{2}$ **15.** $12\frac{1}{2}$ **17.** 48
19. 7 + 7 was added before dividing 14 by 7; $14 \div 7 + 7 =$
$2 + 7 = 9$. **23.** 16 **25.** 126 **27.** 0.75 **29.** 3 **33.** 52
35. 2 **37.** 115 cents **39.** 132 oz
45. 933 points

1.2 Graphing Calculator Activity (p. 17) **1.** 5 **3.** 0.429
5. 0.188 **7.** 40.9 BMI units

1.3 Exercises (pp. 22–24) **1.** rate **3.** $x + 8$ **5.** $\frac{1}{2}m$
7. $7 - n$ **9.** $\frac{2t}{12}$ **11.** $2k - 7$ **15.** $4v$ **17.** $\frac{2.97}{p}$ **19.** $7 - d$
21. $12y$ **23.** 1.5 pints per serving **25.** $6.80 per share
27. Feet should cancel out, not be squared; $48.
29. Total cost (dollars) = Cost for bus (dollars) + Cost per
ticket (dollars/ticket) • Number of tickets **31.** Amount
paid (dollars) = Amount of bill (dollars) ÷ Number of
friends + Amount of tip (dollars) **33.** $98g$; 1960 tons
35. $500

1.4 Exercises (pp. 29–31) **1.** *Sample answer:* $3x + 5 =$
30 **3.** $42 + n = 51$ **5.** $9 - \frac{t}{6} = 5$ **7.** $9(t + 5) < 6$
9. $8 < b + 3 < 12$ **11.** $10 < t - 7 < 20$ **13.** $p \geq 12.99$
15. The algebraic expression is reversed; $t - 4.2 = 15$.
17. solution **19.** not a solution **21.** not a solution
23. solution **25.** solution **27.** not a solution
29. 5 **31.** 12 **33.** 9 **35.** $3x - 2 = x + 5$; solution
39. $60 - a < 45$ **41.** 7.5 mi **43.** 46 participants

1.5 Exercises (pp. 35–37) **1.** *Sample answer:*
$P = 2\ell + 2w$ **3.** You know how many collars you have
made, how much you have spent to make them, and how
much money you want to make. You need to find out
what to charge for each collar so you make $90.

5. You know the temperature in Rome and the
temperature in Dallas. You know the formula to
convert Fahrenheit temperatures to Celsius
temperatures. You need to find the higher temperature.
7. The formula for perimeter should be used, not area;
$P = 2(200) + 2(150) = 700$; $10(700) = 7000.
9. $P = I - E$ **11.** $d = rt$ **15.** You know the horse's
speed, the distance traveled, and the number of feet
in a yard. You need to find out how many minutes the
horse ran. **17.** 2.8 min **19.** $126 **23.** 10.35 oz

Chapter Review (pp. 42–44) **1.** 7, 12 **3.** algebraic
expression **5.** 16 **7.** 10 **9.** 400 **11.** 25 in.^{2} **13.** 9
15. 8 **17.** $\frac{1}{3}$ **19.** 52 **21.** 18 **23.** $z - 5$ **25.** $3x^2$
27. $2.95n + 2.19$ **29.** $13 + t \geq 24$ **31.** solution
33. 240 ft^2

Chapter 2

2.1 Exercises (pp. 56–59) **1.** rational number **5.** 7
7. -5 **9.** 5 **11.** -1 **13.** -2 **15.** 1.6: rational number,
1: whole number, integer, rational number, -4: integer,
rational number, 0: whole number, integer, rational
number; $-4, 0, 1, 1.6$ **17.** $-\frac{2}{3}$; rational number, -0.6:
rational number, -1: integer, rational number, $\frac{1}{3}$: rational
number; $-1, -\frac{2}{3}, -0.6, \frac{1}{3}$ **19.** 16: whole number, integer,
rational number, -1.66: rational number, $\frac{5}{3}$: rational
number, -1.6: rational number; $-1.66, -1.6, \frac{5}{3}, 16$
21. -4.99: rational number, 5: whole number, integer,
rational number, $\frac{16}{3}$: rational number, -5.1: rational
number; $-5.1, -4.99, 5, \frac{16}{3}$ **25.** The number $-\lvert -0.2 \rvert$
is a negative number. *Sample answer:* For the number
$-\lvert -0.2 \rvert$, remove the negative sign outside the absolute
value bars. **27.** 3, 3 **29.** 0, 0 **31.** $-2.7, 2.7$
33. 7.9, 7.9 **35.** $\frac{5}{6}, \frac{5}{6}$ **37.** $-1\frac{1}{3}, 1\frac{1}{3}$ **39.** Hypothesis:
a number is negative, conclusion: its absolute value is
negative; false. *Sample answer:* $\lvert -3 \rvert$ is 3, a positive
number. **41.** Hypothesis: a number is an integer,
conclusion: the number is a rational number; true.
43. Hypothesis: a number is an integer, conclusion: its
absolute value is a whole number; true. **47.** 1
49. 1.75 **51.** 2.25 **53.** 1.5 **55.** $-2.4°F$ **57.** 3.941 oz
59. May **61.** -12 **65. a.** $-10°F$ with a wind speed
of 10 mi/h **b.** decreases

2.2 Exercises (pp. 63–66) **1.** 0 **3.** -8 **5.** 6 **7.** -13 **9.** -6 **11.** 1.5 **13.** -5.9 **15.** -13.6 **17.** $-5\frac{3}{10}$ **19.** $-5\frac{17}{20}$ **21.** $-18\frac{5}{28}$ **23.** The answer should be negative; $-13 + (-15) = -(13 + 15) = -28$. **25.** Inverse property of addition **27.** Commutative property of addition **29.** Associative property of addition **31.** The identity property states that the sum of a number and zero is the number; the property that states that the sum of a number and its opposite is zero is the inverse property. **33.** -15 **35.** -5.13 **37.** $-20\frac{1}{5}$ **41.** -3 **43.** -9.5 **45.** $7\frac{23}{60}$ **47.** 0 **49.** 7.4 **51. a.** 4, 4; true **b.** Commutative property; $-3 + (2 + 5)$; Associative property **53.** $-5 + 75$ **55.** $550 + (-350)$ **57.** 55 ft **61. a.** your friend **b.** No; you and your friend will have the same total score, -7.

2.3 Exercises (pp. 69–71) **1.** $-3 + (-6)$ **3.** 18 **5.** -8 **7.** 14.1 **9.** -25.8 **11.** $-\frac{1}{3}$ **13.** $\frac{3}{4}$ **15.** 8 was substituted for y instead of -8; $3 - (-8) + 2 = 3 + 8 + 2 = 13$. **17.** 4.6 **19.** 10.6 **21.** 7.7 **23.** 7.6 **25.** 1.8 **27.** 107°F **29.** -1280 m **31.** 127.1 ft **33.** 158°C **35.** -14 **37.** -14 **39.** 34.1 **45.** $-3 - 12$ **47.** $14 - (-3)$ **49.** 14.6°C **51.** -0.3 sec; yes; Sue's time of 341.7 seconds is 0.3 second under the qualifying time of 342 seconds, so she qualifies for the race.

2.3 Spreadsheet Activity (p. 72) **1.** 6 hand grips **3.** The 4.902 in. handgrip; the difference with the smallest absolute value is the difference for the 4.902 in. hand grip.

2.4 Exercises (pp. 77–79) **1.** 1 **3.** -28 **5.** 90 **7.** -36 **9.** 7 **11.** -43.89 **13.** -40 **15.** -80 **17.** $2\frac{2}{5}$ **19.** multiplicative property of zero **21.** identity property of multiplication **23.** associative property of multiplication **25.** identity property of multiplication **27.** multiplicative property of -1 **29.** $16y$. Sample answer: $y(-2)(-8) = y[(-2)(-8)] = y(16) = 16y$; Justifications: Associative property of multiplication, Product of -2 and -8 is 16, Commutative property of multiplication. **31.** $-3q$. Sample answer: $\frac{3}{5}(-5q = \left[\frac{3}{5}(-5)\right]q = -3q$; Justifications: Associative property of multiplication, Product of $\frac{3}{5}$ and -5 is -3. **33.** $42z$. Sample answer: $-5(-4)(-2.1)(-z) = 20(-2.1)(-z) = -42(-z) = -42[(-1 \cdot z)] = [(-42)(-1)]z = 42z$; Justifications: Product of -5 and -4 is 20, Product of 20 and -2.1 is -42, Multiplicative property of -1, Associative property of multiplication, Product of -42 and -1 is 42. **35.** $5t^2$. Sample answer: $-5t(-t) = -5t[(-1 \cdot t)] = -5[t \cdot (-1)]t = -5(-1 \cdot t)t = [(-5)(-1)](t)(t) = 5(t)(t) = 5[(t)(t)] = 5t^2$; Justifications: Multiplicative property of -1, Associative property of multiplication, Commutative property of multiplication, Associative property of multiplication, Product of -5 and -1 is 5, Associative property of multiplication,

Product of t and t is t^2. **37.** $-\frac{3}{10}m^2$. Sample answer:
$$\frac{1}{3}\left(-\frac{9}{10}\right)(-m)(-m) = -\frac{3}{10}(-m)(-m) =$$
$$-\frac{3}{10}(-1 \cdot m)(-1 \cdot m) = -\frac{3}{10}(-1)(m \cdot -1)m =$$
$$-\frac{3}{10}(-1)(-1 \cdot m)m = -\frac{3}{10}[(-1)(-1)](m)(m) =$$
$$-\frac{3}{10}(1)(m)(m) = -\frac{3}{10}(m)(m) = -\frac{3}{10}[(m)(m)] = -\frac{3}{10}m^2;$$
Justifications: Product of $\frac{1}{3}$ and $-\frac{9}{10}$ is $-\frac{3}{10}$, Multiplicative property of -1, Associative property of multiplication, Commutative property of multiplication, Associative property of multiplication, Product of -1 and -1 is 1, Identity property of multiplication, Associative property of multiplication, Product of m and m is m^2. **39.** -0.4 **41.** -12.6 **43.** -6.6 **45.** 9 **47.** 0.9 **49.** In the third step, the product $(-8)(-5)$ should be 40, not -40; $40(z \cdot z) = 40z^2$. **51. a.** -108, -108; true **b.** $-9 \cdot (3 \cdot 4)$; Commutative property **53.** $-1200(3.5)$ **55.** about 632.3 km^2 **59.** 4.19027 km^3

2.5 Exercises (pp. 84–86) **1.** 4, -9 **3.** In the first step the last minus sign should be a plus sign, because when you use the distributive property to remove the parentheses you must multiply each term inside the parentheses by -1; $5y - (2y - 8) = 5y + (-1)(2y) + (-1)(-8) = 5y - 2y + 8 = 3y + 8$. **5.** $4x + 12$ **7.** $5m + 25$ **9.** $-8p + 24$ **11.** $4r - 6$ **13.** $6v^2 + 6v$ **15.** $-6x + 2x^2$ **17.** $\frac{1}{4}m - 2$ **19.** $4n - 6$ **23.** terms: 9, $7y$, -2, $-5y$; like terms: 9 and -2, $7y$ and $-5y$; coefficients: 7, -5; constant terms: 9, -2 **25.** terms: $-3y^2$, $3y^2$, -7, 9; like terms: $-3y^2$ and $3y^2$, -7 and 9; coefficients: -3, 3; constant terms: -7, 9 **27.** terms: $6xy$, $-11xy$, $2xy$, $-4xy$; like terms: $6xy$, $-11xy$, $2xy$, $-4xy$, coefficients: 6, -11, 2, -4; constant terms: none **29.** $-4x$ **31.** $2n + 7$ **33.** $6 - 4c$ **35.** $14t + 4$ **37.** $-5v - 6$ **39.** $30 - 4z$ **41.** $2v + 16$, $5v + 15$ **43.** $2x + 5.4$, $2.1x + 1.26$ **45.** yes; no; yes **47.** no; no; yes **49.** $2x + 2(x + 11)$ **51.** $\frac{1}{2}x(x + 1)$ **53.** $C = 3r - 6$; $\$5.97$ **55. a.** $y = -15x + 700$ **b.** $\$475$

2.6 Exercises (pp. 90–93) **1.** The multiplicative inverse of a number a is the number $\frac{1}{a}$ provided $a \neq 0$. **3.** $-\frac{1}{18}$ **5.** -1 **7.** $-1\frac{1}{3}$ **9.** $\frac{3}{13}$ **13.** 3 **15.** -20 **17.** $-\frac{1}{3}$ **19.** $\frac{1}{30}$ **21.** $\frac{5}{6}$ **23.** $-\frac{1}{5}$ **25.** $-1\frac{2}{3}$ **27.** $2\frac{1}{4}$ **29.** -2 **31.** 0.1 **33.** $3x - 7$ **35.** $-3z + 2$ **37.** $\frac{1}{2} - 2\frac{1}{2}q$ **39.** $3a + 1\frac{1}{4}$ **41.** $4 - 3c$ **43.** $10\left(-\frac{1}{5}\right) = -2$, not 2; $\frac{-15x - 10}{-5} =$ $(-15x - 10) \cdot \left(-\frac{1}{5}\right) = -15x\left(-\frac{1}{5}\right) - 10\left(-\frac{1}{5}\right) = 3x - (-2) =$ $3x + 2$. **45.** -9 **47.** 9 **53.** $\frac{-54}{4.5}$ **55.** $\frac{-120 + 125 + (-150)}{3}$ **57.** -14.75°C **61. a.** -0.034 **b.** Yes; the player's ace efficiency will increase by 0.022 to -0.012.

2.7 Exercises (pp. 98–101) **1.** irrational number
5. -7 **7.** ± 1 **9.** ± 11 **11.** -16 **13.** 19 **15.** -40
17. The radical symbol with a $\pm$ sign in front of it represents both the positive and negative square roots of the radicand; $\pm\sqrt{400} = \pm 20$. **19.** -4 **21.** 12 **23.** 6
25. -8 **27.** $\sqrt{49}$: real number, rational number, integer, whole number, 8: real number, rational number, integer, whole number, $-\sqrt{4}$: real number, rational number, integer, -3: real number, rational number, integer; -3, $-\sqrt{4}, \sqrt{49}, 8$ **29.** -11.5: real number, rational number, $-\sqrt{121}$: real number, rational number, integer, -10: real number, rational number, integer, $\frac{25}{2}$: real number, rational number, $\sqrt{144}$: real number, rational number, integer, whole number; $-11.5, -\sqrt{121}, -10, \sqrt{144}, \frac{25}{2}$

31. $-\frac{8}{3}$: real number, rational number, $-\sqrt{5}$: real number, irrational number, 2.6: real number, rational number, -1.5: real number, rational number, $\sqrt{5}$: real number, irrational number; $-\frac{8}{3}, -\sqrt{5}, -1.5, \sqrt{5}, 2.6$ **33.** If a number is a whole number, then it is a real number; true.
35. If a number is a perfect square, then it is not a whole number; false. *Sample answer:* 9 is a perfect square that is also a whole number. **43.** 51 in. **45.** 60 in. **47.** 35 ft, 24 ft, 48 ft, 30 ft; they are all rational numbers.

51. a.

Quotient of pyramids	Quotient of areas of bases	Quotient of side lengths of bases
$\frac{\text{Khafre}}{\text{Menafaure}}$	3.94	1.99
$\frac{\text{Khufu}}{\text{Menafaure}}$	4.59	2.14
$\frac{\text{Khufu}}{\text{Khafre}}$	1.16	1.08

b. The quotient of the side lengths is the square root of the quotient of the areas.

2.8 Exercises (pp. 105–108) **1.** A conjecture is a statement that is believed to be true but not yet shown to be true. **3.** inductive **5.** deductive **7.** *Sample answer:* The number of inches of rain in June will be 1.2 inches.
9. Your school will score at least fifty points in the next game. **11.** The perimeter of the room is 80 feet and the area of the room is 375 square feet.
13. transitive property **15.** symmetric property
17. The associative properties of addition and multiplication cannot be used together. *Sample answer:* The equation $(2y + 8) \cdot 4y = (2y \cdot 4y) + (8 \cdot 4y)$ is always true because of the distributive property.
19–29. Sample explanations are given.
19. Sometimes; it is true for all values of n except $n = 0$.
21. Sometimes; this is only true when $x = 0$.

23. Always; two times any number is always greater than the number. **25.** Never; the square of any number is always greater than or equal to zero. **27.** Always; two times any integer is even and one less than any even integer is an odd integer. **29.** Sometimes; this is true for $x > 0$ and false for $x < 0$, when it will equal -1.
39. Multiplicative property of -1; $[a \cdot (-1)]b$; Commutative property of multiplication; Associative property of multiplication; $-(ab)$

Chapter Review (pp. 112–116) **1.** terms: $-3x$, -5, $-7x$, -9; coefficients: -3, -7; constant terms: -5, -9; like terms: $-3x$ and $-7x$, -5 and -9 **3.** real number, rational number **5.** real number, rational
number, integer **7.** $-6, -5.2, -\frac{3}{8}, -\frac{1}{4}, 0.3$ **9.** $-\frac{2}{3}$,
$-0.666, -0.6, 0.66, \frac{2}{3}$ **11.** 0.2, 0.2 **13.** $-\frac{7}{8}, \frac{7}{8}$
15. Wednesday **17.** -10 **19.** -5.4 **21.** $\frac{7}{60}$

23. -11 **25.** -8.6 **27.** $-1\frac{1}{3}$ **29.** -8 **31.** -3.4
33. 60 **35.** $-28y$. *Sample answer:* $-4(-y)(-7) = -4[(-y)(-7)] = -4[(-7)(-y)] = [(-4)(-7)](-y) = 28(-y) = 28(-1 \cdot y) = [28(-1)]y = -28y$; Justifications: Associative property of multiplication, Commutative property of multiplication, Associative property of multiplication, Product of -4 and -7 is 28, Multiplicative property of -1, Associative property of multiplication, Product of 28 and -1 is -28. **37.** $20z$. *Sample answer:* $2.5(-4z)(-2) = [2.5(-4)](z)(-2) = -10(z)(-2) = -10[(z)(-2)] = -10[(-2) \cdot z] = [(-10)(-2)]z = 20z$; Justifications: Associative property of multiplication, Product of 2.5 and -4 is -10, Associative property of multiplication, Commutative property of multiplication, Associative property of multiplication, Product of -10 and -2 is 20. **39.** $40 - 8x$ **41.** $-z^2 + 4z$
43. $-3.7 - 4m$ **45.** $C = -2p + 130$; $122 **47.** -26
49. -347 m **51.** $-6m + 3$ **53.** 11 **55.** ± 9
57. 10 **59.** -12 **61.** $-\sqrt{49}, -6.8, 1.58, \sqrt{3}, 2$ **63.** If a number is a real number, then it is an irrational number; false. *Sample answer:* 5 is a real number that is not irrational. **65.** deductive

Chapter 3

3.1 Exercises (pp. 128–131) **1.** inverse operations
3. 3 **5.** 5 **7.** -3 **9.** -20 **11.** 7 **13.** 11 **15.** 13
17. -2 **21.** 4 **23.** 6 **25.** -13 **27.** -15 **29.** -11
31. 28 **33.** 91 **35.** -486 **37.** 22 **39.** 3.8 should have been subtracted from both sides; $x + 3.8 - 3.8 = 2.3 - 3.8$, $x = -1.5$. **41.** 3.5 **43.** -1.1 **45.** -2.05
47. $\frac{5}{8}$ **49.** 0.06 **51.** 96 **53.** 12 **55.** -49 **57.** -65
59. $\frac{1}{6}$ **61.** -2 **63.** Add -9 to each side of the equation.
65. 9 **67.** $6 = \frac{5}{C}$ **69.** 1046.6 ft **77.** 47.5 ft^2

3.2 Exercises (pp. 135–137) **1.** like terms **3.** 4 **5.** 2 **7.** -3 **9.** 6 **11.** 40 **13.** 18 **15.** 4 **17.** 9 **19.** -4
23. Unlike terms were combined; $-3x = 5$, $x = -\frac{5}{3}$.
25. $y = 3x + 7$; -5 **27.** $y = 10x - 9$; 2 **29.** 4 **31.** 5
33. 0.5 **35.** 15.9 **37.** 6.9 **39.** A **41.** B **43.** 1.5 h

3.3 Exercises (pp. 141–144) **1.** $\frac{5}{3}$ **3.** 3 **5.** 6 **7.** -2
9. -8 **11.** -8 **13.** -2 **15.** 2 **17.** 3 **19.** 5 **21.** 5
23. 3 **27.** 12 **29.** -2 **31.** -50 **33.** 5 **35.** 22
37. Multiply each side by 2, not $\frac{1}{2}$; $2x - 10 = 8$, $2x = 18$, $x = 9$. **39.** 0.5 **41.** 0.1 **43.** 1.2 **45.** 21 **47.** $5\frac{1}{3}$
51. $8x + 2x + 5 = 55$ **53.** $2x + 2(x - 5) = 102$ **55.** 0.75 ft
57. 33 mo **59.** After the work crews merged; before the work crews merged they were working at a rate of $115 + 137 = 252$ feet per month, and after merging, at a rate of 307 feet per month.

3.4 Exercises (pp. 149–152) **1.** identity **3.** -2 **5.** -4
7. -7 **9.** 8 **11.** -4 **13.** -3 **19.** 2 **21.** -7
23. no solution **25.** no solution **29.** Because the original equation is equivalent to the equation $0 = 0$, the equation is true for all values of y, not just for $y = 0$. The equation is an identity and all real numbers are solutions.
31. $-\frac{1}{2}$ **33.** no solution **35.** -4 **37.** 10 **39.** 6
41. 3 **43.** -24 **45.** -4 **47.** 120 ft **49.** 136 ft
51. $60(x - 3) = 40x$ **53.** $3x = 4(x - 2)$ **55.** 4 mo
57. 30 visits

3.4 Spreadsheet Activity (p. 153) **1.** 7 is the value of x that makes the left side and right side values equal.
3. 29

3.5 Exercises (pp. 158–160) **1.** ratios **3.** no; 7 to 9
5. yes **7.** $\frac{6}{5}$ **9.** 22 **11.** 48 **13.** 15 **15.** 40 **17.** 12
19. 9 **21.** 57 **25.** Each side should be multiplied by 6, not $\frac{1}{6}$; $6 \cdot \frac{3}{4} = 6 \cdot \frac{x}{6}$, $\frac{9}{2} = x$. **27.** $\frac{3}{8} = \frac{x}{32}$ **29.** $\frac{x}{4} = \frac{8}{16}$
31. $\frac{b}{10} = \frac{7}{2}$ **33.** $\frac{12}{18} = \frac{d}{27}$ **35.** 1.8 **37.** 2.4 **39.** 4 **41.** 4
43. 2 **45.** 3.5 **47.** Sample answer: $\frac{2}{3} = \frac{4}{6}$; 7 ways
49. Sample answer: $\frac{3}{30} = \frac{x}{480}$ **51.** $\frac{2}{145}$ **53.** $\frac{2}{5}$ **55.** $\frac{1}{2}$
57. 45 goals

3.6 Exercises (pp. 164–166) **1.** cross product **3.** 6
5. 24 **7.** 1 **9.** -49 **11.** 2 **13.** -4 **15.** 27 **17.** -7
21. The cross products property should be used to multiply the numerator of each ratio by the denominator of the other ratio, not to multiply the numerator of one ratio by the numerator of the other ratio; $4 \cdot x = 3 \cdot 16$, $4x = 48$, $x = 12$. **23.** 15 **25.** 10 **27.** 5.5 **29.** -3.4
31. 4.2 **33.** 3 **35.** -2.3 **37.** 0.25 **41.** Sample answer: $\frac{1}{50} = \frac{x}{550}$ **43.** 5 c **45.** about 171 km **47.** about 171 km
49. about 211.5 cm

3.7 Exercises (pp. 170–173) **1.** literal equation
3. $x = \frac{c}{b - a}$; -2 **5.** $x = \frac{c}{a} + b$; 15 **7.** $x = \frac{ab}{c}$; 3
9. $x = a(c - b)$; 28 **11.** b should have been subtracted from both sides, not added to the right side; $ax = -b$, $x = -\frac{b}{a}$. **13.** $y = -2x + 7$ **15.** $y = -3x + 4$
17. $y = \frac{6}{7}x + 2$ **19.** $y = \frac{2}{5}x - \frac{62}{5}$ **21.** $y = \frac{9}{5}x - 6$
23. $y = 7x + 1$ **27.** $h = \frac{S - 2B}{P}$ **31.** $y = 2.1x - 8.4$
33. $y = 5x - 20$ **35.** $y = -2x + 1.5$ **37.** $\ell = \frac{S - \pi r^2}{\pi r}$; 13.03 cm **41.** 1 cm, 2 cm, 4 cm, 8 cm **43. a.** $\ell = \frac{s + 2}{4}$
b. 1.75 in., 3.5 in., 4.5 in., 5.5 in. **47.** $F = \frac{9}{5}C + 32$
a. 37°F **b.** 45°F

Chapter Review (pp. 177–180) **1.** scale drawing
3. Combining like terms on each side, the equation becomes $10x = 10x$, which is true for all values of x.
7. 13 **9.** -15 **11.** -36 **13.** 2 **15.** 18 **17.** 5 **19.** 2
21. -6 **23.** 14 **25.** 1 **27.** -4 **29.** no solution
31. 7 **33.** all real numbers **35.** 3 **37.** 7 **39.** 26
41. 15 **43.** 2.5 gal **45.** 2.5 **47.** -4 **49.** -13
51. $y = \frac{-x}{7}$ **53.** $y = \frac{1}{5}x + 4$

Chapter 4

4.1 Exercises (pp. 192–194) **1.** open; left
3. $s \le 60$;
5. $h > 48$;
7. $x < 10$ **9.** $x \ge -2$
15. $w > -17.6$;
21. $c \le 8.8$;
25. The number line should be shaded to the right of -3, not the left.
27. $n - 15 \le 37$; $n \le 52$;
29. $x + 29.7 < 51.3$, $x < 21.6$ **31.** You can add -3 to both sides of the inequality to get $x > -8$. **33.** $4 + r > 12$
35. $b + 75 \le 100$ **37.** at least 25 additional touchdowns

4.2 Exercises (pp. 198–201)
1. division property of inequality
7. $y > 6$;
11. $g > -120$;

31. You can use the division property of inequality to divide each side of the inequality by a (and reverse the inequality symbol if $a < 0$), or you can use the multiplication property of inequality to multiply each side of the inequality by $\frac{1}{a}$ (and reverse the inequality symbol if $a < 0$).   **33.** Both sides of the inequality were multiplied by a positive number, so the inequality symbol should not have been reversed; $x \le -63$.

35. $-15y \le 90$; $y \ge -6$;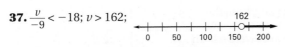

37. $\frac{v}{-9} < -18$; $v > 162$;

39. always   **41.** sometimes   **43.** $6.5t \ge 10$
45. $7.5h \ge 100$ **47.** at least 200 words   **49.** at least 3.2 in.
51. $400h \le 6400$, $h \le 16$ horses   **53.** A corral that is 100 feet by 100 feet can accommodate 9 additional horses, but a corral that is 120 feet by 80 feet can accommodate just 8 additional horses. Increasing both dimensions adds more area to the corral.

4.3 Exercises (pp. 205–207)   **1.** equivalent inequalities
5. $v \ge -1$;

11. $p < \frac{1}{2}$;

17. The distributive property was not used correctly; $-8x + 12 < 28$; $-8x < 16$; $x > -2$.   **19.** $s \ge 0$ **21.** all real numbers   **23.** all real numbers   **25.** all real numbers
27. all real numbers   **29.** no solution
31. $2(x + 8) > 32 - 6x$; $x > 2$;

35. $\frac{1}{2}(8)(x + 1) \ge 44$; $x \ge 10$ **37.** $60 - 5t \le 15$

39. at most 11 songs   **43.** $53 + 3p \le 105$, $p \le 17\frac{1}{3}$, at most 17 pitches   **45.** $a = 3$ and $b \ge 2$; $a = 3$ and $b < 2$

4.4 Exercises (pp. 214–217)   **1.** compound inequality
5. $-1.5 \le x < 9.2$;

9. $-4 \le m \le \frac{1}{4}$;

15. $s < -22$ or $s \ge 3$;

23. no solution   **25.** 3 was subtracted from only 2 of the 3 expressions of the inequality; $1 < -2x < 6$; $-\frac{1}{2} > x > -3$.

27. $x + 5 < 8$ or $x - 3 > 5$; $x < 3$ or $x > 8$;

33. true   **35.** False. *Sample answer:* $a = -7$
37. $68 < T < 80$ **39.** $a < 6$ or $a > 65$
41. $-4 \le t \le 5$;

43. $3.2 \le f \le 6.4$ **45.** less than 129.31 cm or greater than 189.66 cm   **47. a.** $8 \le \frac{w}{300} \le 10$, $2400 \le w \le 3000$; 2400 watts to 3000 watts   **b.** Yes; no; the amplification per person for 350 people is $\frac{2900}{350} \approx 8.3$ watts, which is between 8 watts and 10 watts; the amplification per person for 400 people is $\frac{2900}{400} = 7.25$ watts, which is not between 8 watts and 10 watts.

4.4 Graphing Calculator Activity (p. 218)   **1.** $4 < x < 7$; the graphs are the same.   **3.** $3 \le x \le 7$ **5.** $8 \le x \le 48$
7. $x \le 4\frac{1}{2}$ or $x \ge 5$

4.5 Exercises (pp. 223–225)   **1.** absolute value equation
3. $5, -5$ **5.** $0.7, -0.7$ **7.** $\frac{1}{2}, -\frac{1}{2}$ **9.** $4, -10$ **11.** $-1, -3\frac{2}{3}$
13. $2, -9$ **15.** $4, 9$ **17.** $8\frac{1}{2}, -3\frac{1}{2}$ **19.** $-\frac{1}{2}, -2\frac{1}{2}$
23. The absolute value of a number is never negative, so it is incorrect to rewrite this absolute value equation as two equations; there are no solutions.   **25.** no solution
27. no solution   **29.** $0, 16$ **31.** $6, -3$ **33.** $13.5, 14.5$
35. $0.25, -1.25$ **37.** $13, -3$ **39.** $-7.5, -10.7$
41. $|x - 3| + 4 = 8$; $7, -1$ **45.** $|t - 52| = 21$
47. 39 in., 45 in.   **49. a.** 6.628 points, 8.654 points
b. 0.231 point   **51.** 11.4 carats, 12.6 carats

4.6 Exercises (pp. 229–231)   **1.** equivalent inequalities
9. $d \le -7$ or $d \ge -1$;

15. $r < -8$ or $r > -4$;

21. The compound inequality should use *or*; $x + 4 < -13$ or $x + 4 > 13$; $x < -17$ or $x > 9$.
25. $|2x + 7| \ge 15$; $x \le -11$ or $x \ge 4$;

27. $4|x - 9| < 8$; $7 < x < 11$;
29. true   **31.** False. *Sample answer:* $a = 20$
33. $|r - 3| \le 0.5$ **35.** $|d - 5| \ge 0.25$ **37.** greater than 7.6 or less than 7.2   **39.** $|p - 350| \le 50$; at least 300 lb and at most 400 lb

Chapter Review (pp. 235–238) **1.** $|x - 19| = 8$
3. graph of an inequality
9. $s < -2.7$;
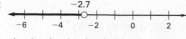
13. $y \geq 9$;
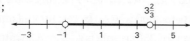
19. no solution; ←————————————→
21. at most 5 tickets
23. $-1 < x < 3\frac{2}{3}$;

$3\frac{2}{3}$

27. $-4, -8$ **29.** $5, 1$ **31.** $1\frac{1}{6}; \frac{1}{6}$
33. $-8 \leq m \leq 8$;

37. $x \leq -2\frac{1}{3}$ or $x \geq -1$;

$-2\frac{1}{3}$

39. at least 78.35 in. and at most 79.15 in.

Chapter 5

5.1 Exercises (pp. 252–254) **1.** domain; range
3. domain: $-2, 0, 2$; range: $3, 5$ **5.** domain: $8, 18, 28$;
range: $-1, 9, 20$ **7.** domain: $3, 5, 7, 8$; range: $-3, -2, 5, 7$
11. function **13.** function **15.** function
17. The numbers listed are the domain elements. The range is 6, 7, 8, and 9.

21.

x	−5	−2	7	8	12
y = x + 3.5	−1.5	1.5	10.5	11.5	15.5

range: $-1.5, 1.5, 10.5, 11.5, 15.5$

23.

x	4	6	9	11
$y = \frac{1}{2}x + 3$	5	6	$7\frac{1}{2}$	$8\frac{1}{2}$

range: $5, 6, 7\frac{1}{2}, 8\frac{1}{2}$

25.

x	−4	0	2	4	6
$y = \frac{0.5x + 1}{2}$	$-\frac{1}{2}$	$\frac{1}{2}$	1	$1\frac{1}{2}$	2

range: $-\frac{1}{2}, \frac{1}{2}, 1, 1\frac{1}{2}, 2$ **27.** $y = x - 8$ **29.** $y = 2x$
35. $a \neq c; a = c$

5.1 Graphing Calculator Activity (p. 255) **1.** 50°F; scroll down until you see the output 10, and look across the row to see that the input value is 50.

3.

x	0	1	2	3	4
y	5	5.75	6.5	7.25	8

5.

x	1	2	3	4	5
y	7	14.5	22	29.5	37

5.2 Exercises (pp. 260–263) **1.** domain; range

3.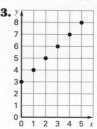

11. When graphing the points, the positive and negative axes were used backwards.

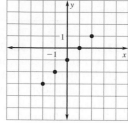

13. function **15.** not a function **17.** $y = 2x - 2$;
domain: 0, 1, 2, 3; range: $-2, 0, 2, 4$ **21.** The input values are the number of years since 2004; the output values are the heights in inches of a plant. *Sample answer:* Let $t = $ years since 2004 and let $h = $ height in inches.
23. The input values are the number of school play tickets purchased; the output values are the cost in dollars for the tickets. *Sample answer:* Let $n = $ number of tickets purchased and let $c = $ cost in dollars for the tickets.

25.

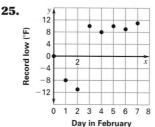

No vertical line can be drawn through more than one point.

27. a.

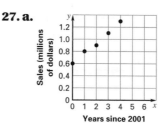

b. No vertical line can be drawn through more than one point.
c. The sales are increasing each year by about $200,000.

5.3 Exercises (pp. 268–271) **1.** linear function
3. solution **5.** not a solution **7.** not a solution
9. solution **11.** not a solution

17.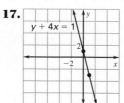

25.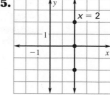

27. does not lie on the line   **29.** does not lie on the line
31. does not lie on the line   **33.** lies on the line

37. 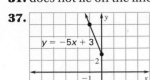 $y \geq 3$

45. 35; 8; −10   **47.** −8; −11; −13   **49.** $-2\frac{2}{3}; -\frac{1}{6}; 1\frac{1}{2}$

51. domain   **53. a.** 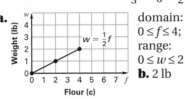 domain: $0 \leq f \leq 4$; range: $0 \leq w \leq 2$ **b.** 2 lb

57. 20°C   **59.** The temperature increases by 25°C.

5.3 Graphing Calculator Activity (p. 272)   **1.** 5.6   **3.** −5.3

5.4 Exercises (pp. 276–279)   **1.** x-intercept
3. The intercepts are switched; the x-intercept is −2, and the y-intercept is 1.   **5.** 3; −3   **7.** 1; 4   **9.** 12; −3
11. 64; 4   **13.** −12; 24   **15.** 0.25; 1.2   **17.** 20; −12

21. 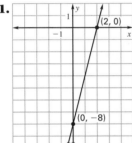   **25.**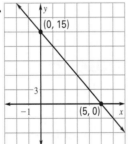

35. 3; −2   **37.**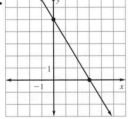

47. The d-intercept represents the number of dimes you have if you have no nickels, and the n-intercept represents the number of nickels you have if you have no dimes.   **49.** The b-intercept represents the number of hours you spent babysitting if you do not spend any time walking dogs, and the d-intercept represents the number of hours you spent walking dogs if you do not spend any time babysitting.

51. a. x-intercept, 14; y-intercept, 7
b. *Sample answer:*
2 small and 6 large,
4 small and 5 large,
6 small and 4 large

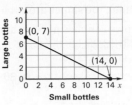

5.5 Exercises (pp. 286–289)   **1.** slope
3. The denominator should be 2 − 5, not 5 − 2;
$m = \dfrac{6-3}{2-5} = \dfrac{3}{-3} = -1$.   **5.** undefined   **7.** The slope was calculated using $\dfrac{\text{run}}{\text{rise}}$, not $\dfrac{\text{rise}}{\text{run}}$; $m = \dfrac{0-3}{12-6} = \dfrac{-3}{6} = -\dfrac{1}{2}$.
9. undefined   **11.** $-\dfrac{5}{2}$ **13.** 1   **15.** 0   **19.** $2.25 per day; it costs $2.25 per day to rent a movie.   **21.** 0.3   **23.** 0.1
25. −2   **27.** −3   **29.** −15   **31.** 60 mi/h   **33.** The first hour; the line segment for the first hour is steeper than the line segment for the second hour.   **35. a.** 0 h to 1.5 h
b. 4.65 h to 8.95 h   **37.** *Sample answer:* The hiker begins climbing up the hill because the elevation is increasing. The hiker then rests because the elevation remains the same. Finally, the hiker descends the hill since the elevation is decreasing.

5.6 Exercises (pp. 294–296)   **1.** parallel   **3.** 2; 1
5. −3; 6   **7.** −4; 1   **9.** 2; 3

11. $-\dfrac{1}{10}; -2$ **15.**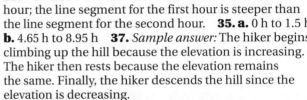

17.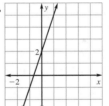

23. The y-intercept is −1, not 1.

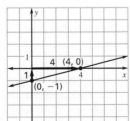

25. red, blue, and green   **27.** Parallel; both slopes are 3.

29. Not parallel; the slopes are -4 and $-\frac{1}{4}$.   **31.** 2; 8; the plant grows 2 inches per day and is 8 inches high when planted.   **33.** 12.95; 35; the jeans cost $35 and each T-shirt costs $12.95.

35. a. 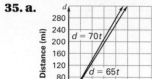   **b.** 20 mi

37. a. 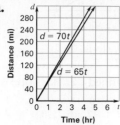   **b.** $80

5.7 Exercises (pp. 300–303)   **1.** direct variation
3. direct variation; 1   **5.** not direct variation
7. direct variation; -4

13. 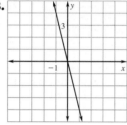   **15.**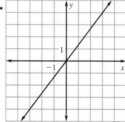

23. $y = -x$; -8 **25.** $y = -\frac{3}{4}x$; -6 **27.** direct variation;
$y = 5x$ **29.** $y = 3x$ **31.** $y = \frac{2}{9}x$ **33.** $y = 12x$
35. a. $d = 2r$ **b.** 3000 m

Chapter Review (pp. 309–312)   **1.** slope
3. a. not slope-intercept form; $y = -3x + 6$
b. slope-intercept form
c. not slope-intercept form; $y = \frac{1}{4}x + \frac{1}{4}$
d. slope-intercept form

5.

x	−2	2	3	5	9
y = 3x + 1	−5	7	10	16	28

range: $-5, 7, 10, 16, 28$

7. $y = \frac{1}{2}x - 1$; domain: $-2, 0, 2, 4$; range: $-2, -1, 0, 1$

9. 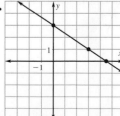   **11.**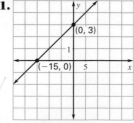

13.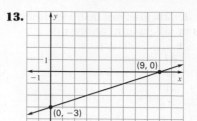

15. $-\frac{1}{3}$ **17.** -2 **19.** 0

21. 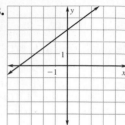   **23.**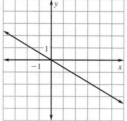

25. not direct variation   **27.** direct variation; 4

29.

Chapter 6

6.1 Exercises (pp. 325–328)   **1.** slope   **3.** $y = 2x + 9$
5. $y = -3x$ **7.** $y = \frac{2}{3}x - 9$ **11.** $y = -\frac{3}{2}x + 4$
13. $y = -\frac{1}{2}x$ **15.** $y = -x - 3$ **17.** The slope was not calculated using corresponding values from the points; $\frac{1-4}{5-0} = -\frac{3}{5}$, $y = -\frac{3}{5}x + 4$.   **19.** $y = 4x + 4$ **21.** $y = -\frac{4}{3}x$
23. $y = 2x - 2$ **25.** $y = -x - 5$ **27.** $y = -\frac{1}{16}x + 4$
29. $y = -4x - 24$ **31.** -3 **33.** $-\frac{3}{2}$ **35.** $-\frac{1}{3}$
37. The values for x and y were reversed; $2 = m(-8) - 2$; $4 = -8m$; $m = -\frac{1}{2}$.   **39.** $y = \frac{1}{2}x$ **43.** starting value: $25, rate of change: $37.80 per month   **47. a.** $C = 44m + 48$ **b.** $312   **49. a.** $t = 0.7d + 2$ **b.** 16 min

6.2 Exercises (pp. 333–336)   **1.** y-intercept
3. $y = 3x - 2$ **5.** $y = -5x - 13$ **7.** $y = -\frac{3}{4}x + 2$
11. $y = 4x - 15$ **13.** $y = -\frac{1}{2}x + \frac{1}{2}$ **15.** $y = \frac{1}{3}x - \frac{4}{3}$
17. $y = 3x + 1$ **19.** $y = -\frac{2}{5}x - 1$ **21.** $y = -\frac{1}{2}x - \frac{7}{4}$
25. $y = \frac{1}{4}x - 2$ **27.** $y = -\frac{1}{2}x + 3$

29. Yes; you can find the slope and then substitute the value of m and the coordinates of one of the points in $y = mx + b$ to find the value of b. Then you can write the slope-intercept equation. **31.** No; many lines have the same slope but different y-intercepts. **33.** 18 should have been substituted for m, not b; $81 = 18(2) + b$, $81 = 36 + b$, $b = \$45$. **35.** (5, 276.50) and (3, 177.30) **37.** $\frac{3}{4}$ ft per yr; 6 ft **41.** $y = 11.8x + 584$ **43.** No; the model predicts about 985 Sunday newspapers but the domain of the function is $0 \le x \le 30$, so the model is not expected to be accurate when $x > 30$. **45.** The 3 points lie on the same line. If you use 2 points to find an equation of the line and check to see that the third point is a solution, you find that all 3 points lie on the line $y = \frac{3}{4}x + 1$. **47.** The 3 points do not lie on the same line. If you use 2 points to find an equation of the line and check to see whether the third point is a solution, you find that the 3 points do not lie on the same line.

6.3 Exercises (pp. 343–346)
1. -2; $(-5, 5)$
3. $y - 1 = 2(x - 2)$ **5.** $y + 1 = -6(x - 7)$
7. $y - 2 = 5(x + 8)$ **9.** $y + 3 = -9(x + 11)$
11. $y + 12 = -\frac{2}{5}\left(x - \frac{1}{2}\right)$ **13.** The form is $y - y_1$, so the left side should be $y - (-5)$, or $y + 5$; $y + 5 = -2(x - 1)$.

15. 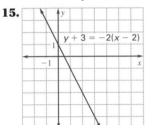 **21.**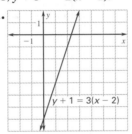

23. $y - 1 = 2(x - 3)$ or $y + 3 = 2(x - 1)$
25. $y - 4 = -\frac{1}{2}(x + 5)$ or $y - 2 = -\frac{1}{2}(x + 1)$
27. $y + 2 = \frac{1}{2}(x - 6)$ or $y - 1 = \frac{1}{2}(x - 12)$
29. $y - 5 = \frac{5}{4}(x - 4)$ or $y + 5 = \frac{5}{4}(x + 4)$
31. $y + 19 = \frac{16}{5}(x + 5)$ or $y - 13 = \frac{16}{5}(x - 5)$
33. $y - 9 = -\frac{1}{4}x$ or $y - 7 = -\frac{1}{4}(x - 8)$
35. $y - 18 = -\frac{5}{3}(x + 5)$ or $y - 13 = -\frac{5}{3}(x + 2)$
37. $y + 8 = -3(x + 7)$ or $y - 4 = -3(x + 11)$
41. Yes; the increase is at a constant rate; $y - 1.2 = 0.2(x - 1)$. **43.** Yes; the increase is at a constant rate of \$8.75 per hour; $C = 8.75t$.
45. a. $y = 130x + 530$ **b.** \$1570 **49.** *Sample answer:* $y - 17.6 = -0.06(x - 60)$; 16.4 ft/sec

6.4 Exercises (pp. 350–352)
1. standard form **3.** point-slope form **5–9.** Sample answers are given.
5. $2x + 2y = -20$, $3x + 3y = -30$ **7.** $x - 2y = -9$, $-2x + 4y = 18$ **9.** $3x - y = -4$, $6x - 2y = -8$
11. $-x + y = 5$ **13.** $2x + y = 5$ **15.** $\frac{3}{2}x + y = -10$

17. $\frac{2}{3}x + y = -\frac{4}{3}$ **19.** $-\frac{4}{3}x + y = -1$ **21.** $-\frac{1}{2}x + y = 1$
23. $y = 2$, $x = 3$ **25.** $y = 3$, $x = -1$ **27.** $y = 4$, $x = -1$
33. $\frac{1}{2}$; $x - 8y = -2$ **35.** 11; $8x + 11y = 4$
37. $\frac{2}{7}$; $14x + 2y = -28$ **39.** $7p + 14h = 56$
41. a. 15 oz **b.** $12c + 15w = 120$ **c.** 10 corn, 0 wheat; 5 corn, 4 wheat; 0 corn, 8 wheat **45. a.** $0.75b + s = 63$
b. 18 times; if you ride the bus 60 times, it costs $60(\$.75) = \$45$ without the pass. The pass costs \$63, so you need to spend \$18 on subway rides; $\frac{\$18}{\$1/\text{ride}} = 18$ rides.

6.5 Exercises (pp. 357–360)
1. perpendicular
3. $y = 2x + 5$ **5.** $y = -\frac{3}{5}x + 2$ **7.** $y = 6x + 1$
9. $y = 2x + 9$ **11.** $y = 3x + 30$ **13.** neither
15. perpendicular **17.** parallel: none; perpendicular: none **21.** $y = -\frac{1}{3}x - 1$ **23.** $y = -\frac{1}{5}x + 2$
25. $y = \frac{7}{2}x + 3$ **27.** $y = -\frac{2}{3}x + 5$ **29.** $y = 2x - 17$
35. Lines a and c since each has a slope of 1, and lines b and d since each has a slope of -1. **37. a.** $y = 2x + 8$
b. $y = -2x + 8$ **c.** No; the slopes 2 and -2 are not negative reciprocals.

Chapter Review (pp. 364–366)
1. converse
3. perpendicular **5.** $y = 3x - 10$ **7.** $y = -\frac{2}{11}x + 7$
9. $y = x + 6$ **11.** $y = -1.25x + 25$; \$22.50 **13.** $y = x + 3$
15. $y - 7 = -6(x - 4)$ or $y - 1 = -6(x - 5)$
17. $y + 2 = -\frac{6}{11}(x + 3)$ or $y + 8 = -\frac{6}{11}(x - 8)$
19. $4x + y = -1$ **21.** $0.07r + 0.04s = 5$. *Sample answer:* 4 yd organza, 118 yd satin; 20 yd organza, 90 yd satin; 60 yd organza, 20 yd satin **23. a.** $y = -2x + 1$
b. $y = \frac{1}{2}x - 4$

Chapter 7

7.1 Exercises (pp. 378–381)
1. solution **3.** solution
5. not a solution **9.** (4, 2) **11.** The solution $(3, -1)$ is not a solution of Equation 2. The graph of Equation 2 is incorrect; if properly graphed, the lines would intersect at $(-3, -3)$.

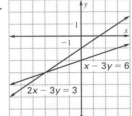

13. (4, 0) **15.** $(-3, -5)$ **17.** $(10, -15)$ **19.** $(7, -5)$
21. $(-5, 2)$ **23.** (3, 6) **25.** (8, 2) **31.** $x + y = 10$, $y = 2x + 1$ **33.** 2040 **35.** 15 small cards and 10 large cards

7.1 Graphing Calculator Activity (p. 382)
1. $(-1.5, 2.5)$
3. $(0.2, -1.44)$

7.2 Exercises (pp. 386–388) **1.** system of linear equations **3.** (5, 3) **5.** (2, −1) **7.** (−4, 5) **9.** (2, 1) **11.** (−3, −4) **13.** (8, −7) **15.** (5, −8) **17.** (4, 3) **19.** (−1, 1) **25.** $x + y = 35, x = 4y$ **27.** $2x + 2y = 32$, $x = 3y$ **31.** 4 in. *Sample answer:* (4, 5) is the solution of the linear system $1.5x = 1.2y$ and $x + y = 9$, so $x = 4$.

7.3 Exercises (pp. 394–397) **1.** *Sample answer:* $x + y = 10, x − y = 5$ **3.** (1, 6) **5.** (−1, −5) **7.** (5, 7) **9.** (3, 5) **11.** (7, −11) **13.** (−2, 2) **15.** (0, −10) **17.** (−3, 1) **19.** (2, 13) **23.** (2, −3) **25.** (−18, 4) **27.** (4, −3) **29.** (−1, −4) **33.** *Sample answer:* When you add $3x$ to each side of Equation 2, you get $3x + 5y = 60$, not $−3x + 5y = 60$; you then subtract the equations; $3x − 2y = −3$ and $3x + 5y = 60, −7y = −63, y = 9$. **35.** $2\ell + 2w = 14, 2\ell = 4w − 1; \ell = 4.5$ ft, $w = 2.5$ ft **39.** $x + y = 14, x − y = 10$ **41.** $x + y = 28, y = x + 2$ **43.** twice **47.** monophonic ring tone, $1.95; polyphonic ring tone, $3.50 **49.** 18 field goals

7.4 Exercises (pp. 401–404) **1.** 36 **3.** (1, 1) **5.** (5, −4) **7.** (−2, −3) **9.** (8, 1) **11.** (3, 3) **13.** (2, 1) **17.** (−7, −12) **19.** (5, 6) **21.** (−1, 7) **23.** (−6, 10) **25.** (1, 2) **27.** (7, 6) **29.** *Sample answer:* The equations should be subtracted, not added; $−x = −9, x = 9$. **33.** $x + y = 17, 1.5x + y = 22$ **35.** $x + y = 12, 18x + 10y = 208$ **37.** $.99; $1.99 **39. a.** Let x represent the number of student tickets and y represent the number of adult tickets; $3x + 5y = 3000$, $x + y = 720$, 300 student tickets and 420 adult tickets were sold. **b.**

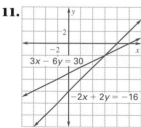

yes

7.5 Exercises (pp. 408–411) **1.** inconsistent system **5.** B; one solution **7.** A; infinitely many solutions

9.

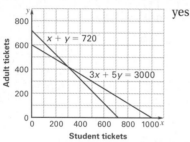

infinitely many solutions

11.

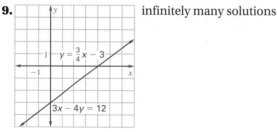

one solution

15. (−3, 4) **17.** (3, 7) **19.** (2, 2) **21.** no solution **23.** (0, 3) **27.** infinitely many solutions **29.** infinitely many solutions **31.** infinitely many solutions **35.** $6a + 8p = 6.4, 4a + 5p = 4.1$ **37.** $0.05x + 0.10y = 1.50$, $0.05(2x) + 0.10(8y) = 3.00$ **39.** Yes. *Sample answer:* There is one solution to the resulting linear system.

7.6 Exercises (pp. 415–417) **1.** An object moving at a constant rate is in uniform motion. **3.** 220 mi **5.** 1.6 km **7.** 15 cm per h **9.** 4.5 m per sec **11.** 4 sec **13.** 2.6 sec **17. a.** $r + c = 30$ **b.** $r − c = 25$ **19.** $x = y + 1.2$; $1.8x = 1.9y$ **21.** $x − y = 4.3, x + y = 4.9$; speed in still water: 4.6 m per sec, speed of current: 0.3 m per sec

7.7 Exercises (pp. 421–423) **3.** $5 per lb **5.** $.45 per oz **7.** $.60 per oz **9.** $13.45 per lb **11.** $1.22 per lb **13.** 5% **15.** 25% **17.** 4% **19.** 2.4% **21.** 0.5 g **23.** 3.85 mg **25.** $x + y = 25, 0.28x + 0.34y = 7.5$ **27.** $x + y = 8, 2.6x + 2y = 19$; 5 oz of daisy seeds and 3 oz of cosmos seeds **31.** 0.5 gal

7.8 Exercises (pp. 429–432) **1.** solution **3.** not a solution **5.** not a solution **7.** not a solution **9.** solution **11.** solution **13.** not a solution **15.** solution **17.** solution

21.

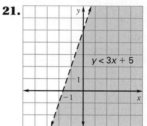

29.

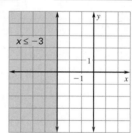

41. The boundary line should be solid.

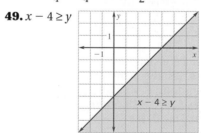

43. $y > −\frac{5}{4}x + \frac{7}{4}$ **45.** $y > \frac{1}{2}x + 2$ **47.** $y \ge 2$

49. $x − 4 \ge y$

53. $y > 0$ **55.** $y < 0$ **59.** $d \le 7t$

61. $x + y \le 860$

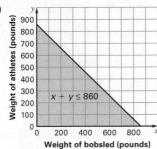

Sample answer: The solution (450, 400) means that the bobsled can weigh 450 pounds when the combined weight of the athletes is 400 pounds.

65. $y \le 0.3x$

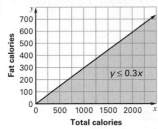

67. About 31.3%; you have consumed 400 calories out of 2000 calories so far, and 100 fat calories out of a maximum of 600 calories. So, you can consume up to 500 more fat calories out of 1600 total calories, or about 31.3% of the remaining calories.

7.9 Exercises (pp. 437–440) **1.** solutions
3. not a solution **5.** not a solution **7.** C **9.** B

11.

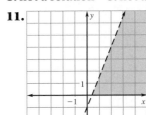

17.

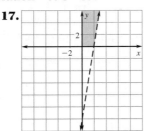

21. The graph is shaded to include $x + y > 3$, instead of $x + y < 3$.

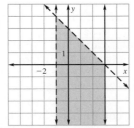

23. $y > -1, y < 2$ **25.** $y \ge x + 2, y \le x + 4, x \le 0, y \ge 0$
27. $y > -\dfrac{2}{3}x - 3, y \le x - 3, y > -5, y \le 0$
29. $x \ge 20, y \ge 10, x + y \le 40$

31. $x \le 60, y \le 40,$
$x > 0, y > 0$

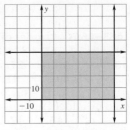

33. a. $s \le 15, r \le 10,$
$s + r \le 15, s \ge 0, r \ge 0$

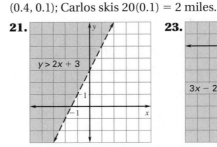

b. no

Chapter Review (pp. 444–448) **1.** system of linear inequalities **3.** *Sample answer:* $y = 2x + 3, 2y = 4x + 6$; the lines intersect (are consistent) and the equations are equivalent (are dependent). **5.** $(-1, 1)$ **7.** $(3, -1)$
9. $(-3, -9)$ **11.** $(-2, 2)$ **13.** $(-2, 5)$ **15.** $(2, 4)$
17. Infinitely many solutions. *Sample answer:* The two equations have the same slope and the same y-intercept. Therefore, they both result in the same line and have an infinite number of solutions. **19.** $5x = 20y, x + y = \dfrac{1}{2}$;
$(0.4, 0.1)$; Carlos skis $20(0.1) = 2$ miles.

21.

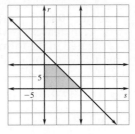

23.

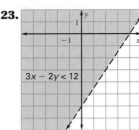

25.

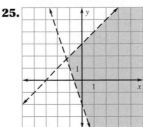

27.

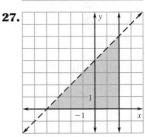

Chapter 8

8.1 Exercises (pp. 463–466) **1.** order of magnitude
3. 4^8 **5.** 3^4 **7.** $(-7)^9$ **9.** 2^{14} **11.** 3^{10} **13.** $(-5)^{12}$
15. $15^3 \cdot 29^3$ **17.** $132^6 \cdot 9^6$ **19.** x^6 **21.** z^6 **23.** x^{16}
25. $(b-2)^{12}$ **27.** $25x^2$ **29.** $49x^2y^2$ **31.** $100x^{14}$
33. $96d^{22}$ **35.** $12p^{19}$ **37.** $108x^{29}$ **39.** *Sample answer:*
The exponents should be added, not multiplied;
$c^1 \cdot c^4 \cdot c^5 = c^{1+4+5} = c^{10}$. **45.** 2 **47.** 2 **49.** $x^{13}y^{12}z^{17}$
55. 10^7 **57.** 10^8 **61. a.** $10^{24}, 10^{25}, 10^{26}, 10^{27}, 10^{28}$
b. $10^5 \cdot 10^{23}$; 10^{28} atoms **63.** 10^6 nanometers
65. a. 10^4 **b.** 10^{10} **c.** Increases the volume by 10^8;
since the radius is squared in the formula for volume,
multiplying the radius by 10 would raise the volume by a
factor of $10 \cdot 10$, or 10^2. **67. a.** 2^{13}

8.2 Exercises (pp. 470–473) **1.** base, exponent

3. 5^4 **5.** 3^4 **7.** $(-4)^3$ **9.** $\dfrac{1}{3^5}$ **11.** $\dfrac{(-5)^4}{4^4}$ **13.** 7^7

15. $9 \cdot 6^3$ **17.** 3^8 **21.** z **23.** $\dfrac{j^{11}}{k^{11}}$ **25.** $-\dfrac{1}{x^5}$

27. $\dfrac{a^4}{b^4}$ **29.** $\dfrac{a^{35}}{32b^5}$ **31.** $\dfrac{27x^{15}}{343y^6}$ **33.** $\dfrac{9x^4}{4y^2}$ **35.** $\dfrac{100x^6}{y^6}$

37. The denominator was not squared; $\dfrac{4^2 \cdot x^2}{5^2} = \dfrac{16x^2}{25}$.

39. 4 **41.** 14 **43.** $\dfrac{16f^4g^8}{81}$ **45.** $\dfrac{m^8n^8}{100}$ **49.** 10^2 **51.** 10^2

55. a. Polaris; 10^3 times greater **b.** 10^{11} hr
57. a. 2^{10} kilobytes; 2^{20} kilobytes

8.3 Exercises (pp. 478–480) **1.** Product of powers
property and definition of zero exponent; the expression
simplifies using the product of powers property to 30,
which by definition equals 1. **3.** $\dfrac{1}{64}$ **5.** $-\dfrac{1}{3}$ **7.** 1 **9.** $\dfrac{49}{4}$

11. $\dfrac{1}{32}$ **13.** $\dfrac{1}{32}$ **15.** 27 **17.** $\dfrac{1}{243}$ **19.** $\dfrac{8}{3}$ **21.** 16

25. $\dfrac{2}{y^3}$ **27.** $\dfrac{1}{121h^2}$ **29.** $\dfrac{5}{m^3n^4}$ **31.** 1 **33.** $\dfrac{1}{x^5y^2}$ **35.** $\dfrac{y^8}{15x^{10}}$

37. $243d^3$ **39.** $\dfrac{3x^{12}y^5}{4}$ **43.** In the denominator, the

exponent -3 does not apply to the factor 5;
$\dfrac{2x}{5x^{-3}} = \dfrac{2x}{5} \cdot \dfrac{x^3}{1} = \dfrac{2x^4}{5}$. **45.** $\dfrac{10^{-5}}{10^{-7}}$ **47.** about 10^6 grains

of salt **49.** about 10^{11} red blood cells **51. a.** $\dfrac{1}{2}, \dfrac{1}{4}, \dfrac{1}{8}$

b. $\left(\dfrac{1}{2}\right)^x$ **53.** *Sample answer:* It approaches 0.

8.4 Exercises (pp. 487–490) **1.** rationalizing the
denominator **3.** $2\sqrt{5}$ **5.** $4\sqrt{6}$ **7.** $5\sqrt{5b}$ **9.** $9m\sqrt{m}$

11. $5\sqrt{6}$ **13.** $2x\sqrt{7}$ **15.** $2a^2b^2\sqrt{b}$ **17.** mn **19.** $\dfrac{2}{7}$

21. $\dfrac{a\sqrt{a}}{11}$ **25.** The square root must also be applied

to the denominator; $\sqrt{\dfrac{4}{9}} = \dfrac{\sqrt{4}}{\sqrt{9}} = \dfrac{2}{3}$. **27.** $\sqrt{2}$

29. $\dfrac{\sqrt{15}}{12}$ **31.** $\dfrac{3\sqrt{a}}{a}$ **33.** $\dfrac{x\sqrt{10}}{5}$ **35.** $8\sqrt{2}$ **37.** $37\sqrt{2}$

39. $8\sqrt{3} + 2\sqrt{6}$ **41.** $5\sqrt{5} - 5$ **43.** $6\sqrt{6} - 12$

45. $69 + 28\sqrt{5}$ **49.** $16s^3t\sqrt{2rt}$ **51.** $\dfrac{h\sqrt{10gf}}{5f^2}$ **53.** $\dfrac{\sqrt{5}}{10}$

55. $\dfrac{3\sqrt{x} + 4x\sqrt{x}}{x^2}$ **57.** $(a\sqrt{b} + c\sqrt{d})(a\sqrt{b} - c\sqrt{d}) =$
$a^2b - ac\sqrt{bd} + ac\sqrt{bd} - c^2d = a^2b - c^2d$

61. $x\sqrt{2}$ ft **63.** $\dfrac{4x\sqrt{7}}{7}$ cm **67.** $v = 8\sqrt{d}$; $16\sqrt{5}$ ft

8.5 Exercises (pp. 494–496) **1.** hypotenuse
3. $b = 4$ **5.** $c = \sqrt{61}$ **7.** $c = 8\sqrt{2}$ **9.** $c = 4\sqrt{13}$
11. $a = 8$ **13.** $a = 1.6$ **17.** 12 **19.** 7.5
21. not a right triangle **23.** not a right triangle
25. right triangle **29.** leg **31.** hypotenuse **33.** 16 ft
35. No; the sum of the squares of the two shorter sides is
not equal to the square of the longest side.

8.6 Exercises (pp. 501–503) **1.** cube root **3.** 10
5. -3 **7.** 11 **9.** -8 **11.** 12 **13.** 5 **17.** 2

19. $\dfrac{1}{125}$ **21.** 32 **23.** $\dfrac{1}{25}$ **25.** 144 **27.** $\dfrac{1}{64}$ **29.** $\dfrac{1}{16}$

31. $x^{9/2}$ **33.** To find the product of powers, add
the exponents rather than subtract them;

$27^{-2/3} \cdot 27^{1/3} = 27^{-2/3 + 1/3} = 27^{-1/3} = \dfrac{1}{27^{1/3}} = \dfrac{1}{3}$

35. $4x^{13}$ **37.** $\dfrac{x^2}{2y^4}$ **39.** 24 in.^{2} **41.** 216 in.^{2}

45. about 11.9 m per sec

Chapter Review (pp. 507–510) **1.** *Sample answer:*
Use the product of powers property to write $2^{-4} \cdot 2^4 =$
$2^{-4+4} = 2^0 = 1$, or use the definition of negative
exponent and the quotient of powers property to write
$2^{-4} \cdot 2^4 = \dfrac{1}{2^4} \cdot 2^4 = \dfrac{2^4}{2^4} = 1$ **5.** $(-3)^8$ **7.** y^{20} **9.** $(b+2)^{24}$

11. $-64x^2y^2$ **13.** 10^{21} **15.** 5^3 **17.** 17^4 **19.** $\dfrac{49x^{10}}{y^4}$

21. $\dfrac{6r^{15}}{7s^5}$ **23.** 1 **25.** $\dfrac{27}{8}$ **27.** $\dfrac{25d^2}{c^6}$ **29.** $\dfrac{9}{m^2}$ **31.** 10^6

33. $7\sqrt{2}$ **35.** $\sqrt{42}$ **37.** $14x^2$ **39.** $\dfrac{\sqrt{5}}{x}$ **41.** $\dfrac{2\sqrt{5}}{5}$ **43.** $\dfrac{x\sqrt{3}}{3}$

47. $19\sqrt{3}$ **47.** $5 + 5\sqrt{2}$ **49.** $b = \sqrt{341}$ **51.** $c = \sqrt{370}$
53. $a = 2.5$ **55.** 12 **57.** 1 **59.** 8.25 lb

Chapter 9

9.1 Exercises (pp. 523–525) **1.** monomial **3.** $9m^5$; 5, 9
5. $2x^2y^2 - 8xy$; 4, 2 **7.** $3z^4 + 2z^3 - z^2 + 5z$; 4, 3
11. not a polynomial; variable exponent **13.** polynomial;
1, binomial **15.** polynomial; 3, trinomial **17.** $3b$
19. $13z^5$ **21.** $13a^2 - 4$ **23.** $m^2 + 9m + 9$
25. $6c^2 + 14$ **27.** $-2n^3 + n - 12$
29. $-15d^3 + 3d^2 - 3d + 2$ **31.** Two unlike terms,
$-4x^2$ and $8x$, were combined; $-2x^3 - 4x^2 + 8x + 1$.
33. No. *Sample answer:* $4x^2 - 2$ and $-4x^2 + 1$ are both of
degree 2, but their sum, $(4x^2 - 2) + (-4x^2 + 1)$, is -1,
a monomial of degree 0. **35.** $12x - 3$
37. $-x^2 + 10xy + y^2$ **39.** $6a^2b - 6a + 4b - 19$
41. $30,000 + 800t$ **43.** $20,000 + 400t$

9.1 Graphing Calculator Activity (p. 526)
1. $7x^2 + 2x + 1$ **3.** correct

9.2 Exercises (pp. 531–533) **1.** binomials **3.** $9x^6$
5. $20m^4$ **7.** $-4y^4 - 8y^2 - 4y$ **9.** $24c^7 - 3c^5 - 9c^4 + 15c^3$
11. $-20b^8 + 10b^6 - 5b^4 + 55b^3$ **13.** $2y^2 - 7y - 15$
15. $5s^2 + 42s + 16$ **17.** $24n^2 - 63n + 30$ **19.** When
combining like terms, the exponents on the variables
should stay the same, rather than being added together;
$2x^3 + 11x^2 - 25x - 28$. **21.** $10x^2 - 41x + 40$
23. $b^3 - 3b^2 + 3b - 2$ **25.** $-2r^3 + 15r^2 + 2r - 63$
27. $4y^3 + 29y^2 - 48y + 18$ **31.** $21a^2 - 34a + 8$
33. $48t^2 + 58t - 11$ **35.** $40z^2 + 47z + 12$
37. $7x^3 + 3x^2 - 4x + 6$ **39.** $4w^6 - 14w^4 + 3w^3 + 2w^2$
41. $2x^2 + x - 45$ **43.** $80 - 6x^2$ **45.** B **47.** C
49. a. $4x^2 + 84x + 440$ **b.** 840 in.^{2}

9.3 Exercises (pp. 537–539) **1.** *Sample answer:* $x - 5$,
$x + 5$ **3.** $x^2 + 16x + 64$ **5.** $4y^2 + 20y + 25$
7. $t^2 - 14t + 49$ **9.** $36b^2 - 12b + 1$ **11.** $100k^2 - 60k + 9$
13. The middle term of the product should be twice the
product of the terms of the binomial; $4d^2 - 40d + 100$.
15. $m^2 - 36$ **17.** $9x^2 - 1$ **19.** $9s^2 - 64$ **21.** $4s^2 - 1.21$
23. $\frac{1}{16} - 25a^2$ **25.** $144 - \frac{1}{9}b^2$ **29.** Use the sum and
difference pattern to find the product $(30 - 2)(30 + 2)$.
31. Use the sum and difference pattern to find the
product $(90 + 1)(90 - 1)$. **33.** Use the square of a
binomial pattern to find the product $(40 + 4)^2$.
35. Use the square of a binomial pattern to find the
product $(60 + 3)^2$. **37.** $36x^2 + 60x + 25$
39. $49a^2 - 64b^2$ **41.** $169 - 52x + 4x^2$ **43.** $81 - 16t^2$
45. $16a^2 - 100b^2$ **47.** $64m^2 - n^2$ **49.** $4a^2 - 25b^2$
51. a. $c^2 - d^2$ **b.** length: $c + d$, width: $c - d$ **c.** the sum
and difference pattern, $(c + d)(c - d) = c^2 - d^2$
53. B and C

55.

	First Game	
	Don't reach last level: 55%	Reach last level: 45%
Don't reach last level: 55%	Not reach twice	1 reach 1 not reach
Reach last level: 45%	1 not reach 1 reach	Reach twice

(Second Game — left label)   49.5%

57. a. About 88.1%; find the sum of the three areas that
represent completing either one or two passes:
$(0.655)^2 + (0.345 \cdot 0.655) + (0.345 \cdot 0.655) \approx 0.881$.
b. The outcome of each attempted pass is modeled
by $0.655C + 0.345I$, so the possible outcomes of two
attempted passes are modeled by $(0.655C + 0.345I)^2 = 0.429C^2 + 0.452CI + 0.119I^2$. The coefficient of the
C^2 term, 0.429, is interpreted to mean that 42.9% of the
time Drew Brees will complete both of two attempted
passes. The coefficient of the CI term, 0.452, is interpreted
to mean that 45.2% of the time Drew Brees will complete
exactly one of two attempted passes. The coefficient
of the I^2 term, 0.119, is interpreted to mean that 11.9%
of the time Drew Brees will complete neither of two
attempted passes. **59.** $36\pi - 12\pi w + \pi w^2$

9.4 Exercises (pp. 545–547) **1.** binomial **3.** $-\dfrac{c^4}{9}$
5. $-\dfrac{4}{x^2}$ **7.** $7y^5$ **9.** $-\dfrac{p^3}{4}$ **11.** $2x^2 - 3x + 4$
13. $-2r^3 + 5r + 12$ **15.** $3v + 5$ **17.** $m - 4$
19. $3p - 13 + \dfrac{18}{p + 3}$ **21.** $x + 3 + \dfrac{-12}{x + 6}$ **23.** $-t - 3 + \dfrac{-4}{t - 3}$
27. The remainder, -4, should be placed over
the divisor, $x + 2$, not over the dividend, $5x + 6$;
$(5x + 6) \div (x + 2) = 5 + \dfrac{-4}{x + 2}$. **29.** 10 **31.** $\dfrac{7}{6} + \dfrac{2}{\ell}$
33. $20 + 0.5x$ **35.** $\dfrac{20 + 0.5x}{x + 2}$ **37.** $C = \dfrac{80}{d} + 3$

9.5 Exercises (p. 552–554) **1.** The vertical motion
model is the equation $h = -16t^2 + vt + s$, where h is
the height (in feet) of a projectile after t seconds in
the air, given an initial velocity of v feet per second
nd an initial height of s feet. **3.** 5, -3 **5.** 13, 14
7. 7, $-\dfrac{4}{3}$ **9.** $-\dfrac{1}{3}$, -6 **11.** $\dfrac{3}{4}$, $-\dfrac{7}{6}$ **13.** Each factor must
be set equal to zero; $z - 15 = 0$ or $z + 21 = 0$, $z = 15$ or
$z = -21$. **15.** $3(2x^2 - 5y)$ **17.** $d^5(5d + 2)$
19. $3m^2(3m^5 - 1)$ **21.** $4a(3a^4 + 2)$ **23.** A common
monomial factor, $3x$, was factored out, but not the
greatest common factor, which is $3x^3$; $3x^3(3x - 2)$.
25. 0, 1 **27.** 0, $-\dfrac{15}{2}$ **29.** 0, $-\dfrac{3}{4}$ **31.** 0, $-\dfrac{2}{7}$
33. 0, 2 **35.** 0, $\dfrac{5}{2}$ **37.** 0, -4 **41.** $2ab(4a - 3b)$
43. $v(v^2 - 5v + 9)$ **45.** $3q^2(2q^3 - 7q^2 - 5)$
47. $h = -16t^2 + 3t$ **49.** $h = -16t^2 + 5t + 2$
51. a. $h = -16t^2 + 2.4t$ **b.** 0.09 ft **53.** about 0.73 sec

57. a.

x (feet)	y (feet)
0	0
1	6
2	8
3	6
4	0

b.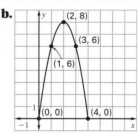

c. 4 ft

9.6 Exercises (pp. 559–562) **1.** factors
3. $(x + 3)(x + 1)$ **5.** $(b - 9)(b - 8)$ **7.** $(z + 12)(z - 4)$
9. $(y - 9)(y + 2)$ **11.** $(x + 10)(x - 7)$
13. $(m - 15)(m + 8)$ **15.** $(p + 16)(p + 4)$
17. $(c + 11)(c + 4)$ **19.** In order to have a product of
-60, p and q cannot both be negative; $(s - 20)(s + 3)$.
23. 10, -3 **25.** -10, 5 **27.** -5, -4 **29.** -22, -1
31. -9, -2 **33.** 16, 2 **35.** 8, -3 **37.** -9, 8
39. -17, -2 **41.** -5, 11 **43.** -3, 17 **45.** -6, 30
49. 17 m, 2 m **51.** 17 ft, 14 ft **53.** $(y - 5z)(y - z)$
55. $(r + 10s)(r + 5s)$ **57.** $(x + 13y)(x - 5y)$
59. $(u - 12v)(u + 9v)$ **61.** $(s + 7t)(s - 5t)$
63. $(w + 13x)(w - 7x)$ **65.** top rectangle: $x(50 - x)$,
bottom rectangle: $30x$ **67.** top rectangle: 600 ft^2, bottom
rectangle: 600 ft^2 **69. a.** $x^2 + 82x + 1600$ **b.** 8 ft

9.7 Exercises (pp. 569–572) **1.** trinomial
3. $-(y-4)(y+2)$ **5.** $-(a-3)(a-9)$
7. $-(3p+1)(p+3)$ **9.** $(2t-9)(t+7)$
11. $(3n-2)(n-5)$ **13.** $-(2k+3)(3k+2)$
15. $(4m+5)(m+1)$ **17.** $(4a-3)(a+3)$
19. $-(5b-2)(b-1)$ **21.** Using 3 and -5 as the factors of -15 gives a middle term of $-10x+3x=-7x$ instead of $7x$; $2x^2+7x-15=(2x-3)(x+5)$.   **25.** $-\frac{1}{3},-7$

27. $-\frac{1}{4},\frac{2}{5}$ **29.** $\frac{1}{3},-5$ **31.** $\frac{1}{7},\frac{1}{4}$ **33.** $\frac{5}{7},-1$ **35.** $-\frac{7}{6},2$

37. $\frac{2}{5},1$ **39.** $-\frac{4}{5},2$ **41.** $\frac{7}{2},6$ **43.** The factorization of the polynomial should be $(3x+2)(4x-1)$ instead of $(3x-1)(4x+2)$; $12x^2+5x-2=0$, $(3x+2)(4x-1)=0$, $3x+2=0$ or $4x-1=0$, $x=-\frac{2}{3}$ or $x=\frac{1}{4}$.   **47.** $-\frac{1}{4},\frac{5}{2}$

51. $2x^2-9x-5=0$. *Sample answer:* Any root $x=\frac{r}{s}$ of $ax^2+bx+c=0$ comes from setting the factor $sx-r$ equal to zero after ax^2+bx+c is written in factored form; so, the roots $-\frac{1}{2}$ and 5 come from the factors $2x-(-1)$, or $2x+1$, and $x-5$. The product of these factors is $(2x+1)(x-5)=2x^2-10x+x-5=2x^2-9x-5$.   **59.** 70 m, 31 m

9.8 Exercises (pp. 576–578) **1.** perfect square
3. $(x+5)(x-5)$ **5.** $(9c+2)(9c-2)$
7. $-3(m+4n)(m-4n)$ **9.** $(x-2)^2$ **11.** $(7a+1)^2$

13. $\left(m+\frac{1}{2}\right)^2$ **15.** $4(c+10)(c-10)$ **17.** $(2s+3r)(2s-3r)$

19. $8(3+2y)(3-2y)$ **21.** $(2x)^2-3^2$ is in the form a^2-b^2, so it must be factored using the difference of two squares pattern; $9(2x+3)(2x-3)$.   **25.** -4

27. ±3 **29.** $\frac{5}{6}$ **31.** $\pm\frac{4}{3}$ **33.** $0,1$ **35.** -2 **37.** $\pm\frac{4}{3}$

39. ±6 **41.** A   **43.** 1.25 sec   **45. a.** $h=-16t^2+8t$
b. 0.25 sec   **47. a.** $4d^2-9$ **b.** 10 in.

9.9 Exercises (pp. 583–586) **1.** The polynomial is written as a product of unfactorable polynomials with integer coefficients.   **3.** $(x-8)(x+1)$
5. $(z-4)(6z-7)$ **7.** $(b^2-3)(b+5)$ **9.** $(x+13)(x-1)$
11. $(5z^2+12)(z-1)$ **13.** $(x^2+2)(x+1)$
15. $(z^2+3)(z-4)$ **17.** $(a^2-5)(a+13)$
19. $(n^2+5)(5n-4)$ **21.** $(y+1)(y+5x)$
23. $x^2(x+1)(x-1)$ **25.** $3n^2(n+4)(n-4)$
27. $3c^7(5c+1)(5c-1)$ **29.** $8s^2(2s+1)(2s-1)$
31. not factorable   **33.** $3w^2(w+4)^2$
35. $(b-5)(b+2)(b-2)$ **37.** $(t^2+2)(9t-1)$

39. $7ab^3(a+3)(a-3)$ **43.** $-1,\pm2$ **45.** $\frac{7}{4},\pm2$

47. $0,-5,-3$ **49.** $0,\pm9$ **51.** $0,\pm2$ **53.** $-\frac{1}{3},\pm1$

55. ±2 **57.** $0,\pm6$ **59.** $\frac{1}{5},\pm3$ **63.** 12 ft, 4 ft, 2 ft

67. 8 ft long by 3 ft wide   **69.** 12 ft long by 2 ft wide
71. a. $4w^2+16w$ **b.** 4 in. long by 4 in. wide by 8 in. high
73. a. 1, about -0.2 **b.** The t-value -0.2 has no meaning because time cannot be negative in this situation. The t-value 1 means that the ball hits the ground 1 second after you throw it.

Chapter Review (pp. 590–594) **1.** degree of the polynomial   **5.** A   **7.** x^3-8x^2+15x
9. $11y^5+4y^2-y-3$ **11.** $5s^3-7s+13$
13. x^3-5x^2+7x-3 **15.** x^2-2x-8 **17.** $z^2-3z-88$
19. $18n^2+27n+7$ **21.** $3x^2+10x-8$
23. $36y^2+12y+1$ **25.** $16a^2-24a+9$ **27.** $9s^2-25$
29. $y-2+\frac{-14}{y-3}$ **31.** $a-1+\frac{1}{3a+3}$ **33.** $0,-13$

35. $0,\frac{1}{2}$ **37.** $0,-10$ **39.** $(n+13)(n+2)$
41. $(b-7)(b+2)$ **43.** $(t-9)(t-15)$ **45.** $(p+7)(p+2)$
47. $(y-7)(y-3)$ **49.** $(2r+3)(r+3)$
51. $(4n-3)(n-1)$ **53.** $(3a+4)(a-2)$
55. $(a+4y)(a-4y)$ **57.** $(x+10)^2$ **59.** $-2(y-8)^2$
61. $(a^2+6)(a-5)$ **63.** $(x-11)(x+1)(x-1)$
65. $3n^3(7n+1)(7n-1)$ **67.** $(x+1)(x-1)(x+5)$
69. $(x^2-6)(x+1)$

Chapter 10

10.1 Exercises (pp. 608–611) **1.** parabola
7. 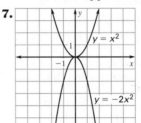 The graph is a reflection in the x-axis of the graph of $y=2x^2$ and is narrower than the graph of $y=x^2$.

19. 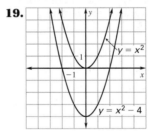 The graph is a vertical translation (of 4 units down) of the graph of $y=x^2$.

29. 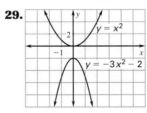 The graph is a vertical translation (of 2 units down) of a reflection in the x-axis of the graph of $y=3x^2$ and is narrower than the graph of $y=x^2$.

31. 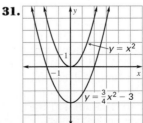 The graph is a vertical translation (of 3 units down) of the graph of $y=\frac{3}{4}x^2$ and is wider than the graph of $y=x^2$.

39. The graph of $y = 3x^2 - 11$ is a vertical translation (of 5 units up) of the graph of $y = 3x^2 - 16$.   **43.** 3 ft; 2 ft

45. a.

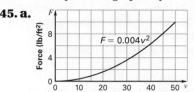

b. about 16 knots
c. about 35 knots

47. $h = -16t^2 + 45$, $h = -16t^2 + 32$. *Sample answer:* The graph of $h = -16t^2 + 45$ is a vertical translation (of 13 units up) of the graph of $h = -16t^2 + 32$.

10.2 Exercises (pp. 615–617)   1. When the function is in standard form, $y = ax^2 + bx + c$, it will have a minimum value if $a > 0$ and a maximum value if $a < 0$.

3. $x = 2$, $(2, -2)$ **5.** $x = 4$, $(4, 26)$ **7.** $x = -\frac{1}{2}$, $\left(-\frac{1}{2}, -\frac{3}{2}\right)$

9. $x = 0$, $(0, -1)$ **11.** $x = 6$, $(6, 7)$ **13.** The equation of the axis of symmetry is $x = -\frac{b}{2a}$, not $x = \frac{b}{2a}$; $x = -\frac{b}{2a} = -\frac{16}{2(2)} = -4$, so the axis of symmetry is $x = -4$.

17.

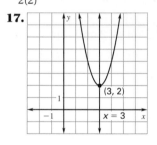

21.

29. maximum value; 7   **31.** maximum value; -8
33. maximum value; $\frac{81}{8}$ **35.** maximum value; 54
39. half the width (in feet) of the arch at its base
41. The x-coordinate of the vertex is half the width (in feet) of the arch at its base, and the y-coordinate of the vertex is the height (in feet) of the arch.
43. about 0.091 sec; about 80 mm

10.3 Exercises (pp. 621–623)   1. x-intercepts
3. $-5, -2$ **5.** $-7, -2$ **7.** $-4, 2$

11.

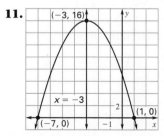

15.

25. The intercept form is $y = a(x - p)(x - q)$, not $y = a(x + p)(x + q)$; $y = (x + 2)(x - 6)$, $y = (x - (-2))(x - 6)$, the intercepts are -2 and 6.   **27.** $y = (x + 3)(x - 3)$

29. $y = -2(x - 3)(x - 5)$ **31.** $y = (x + 7)(x + 7)$ **35.** No. *Sample answer:* A polynomial with three roots p, q, and r will have the form $a(x - p)(x - q)(x - r)$, which is the factored form of a third-degree polynomial, not a second-degree polynomial.   **37. a.** $(0, 2)$ **b.** 2 ft

39. $y = -\frac{27}{5780}x(x - 340)$

10.4 Exercises (pp. 628–630)   1. $2x^2 - 9x + 11 = 0$
3. 4, 1   **5.** $-4, -2$ **7.** 8, -2 **9.** 3   **11.** -5 **13.** -7
15. no solution   **17.** no solution   **19.** $-6, 2$ **23.** $-1, 2$
25. $-1, 4$ **27.** $-3, 4$ **29.** $-5, 2$ **31.** $-5, 4$ **33.** 1, 11
35. $-\frac{3}{2}, 1$ **37.** $\frac{1}{2}$ **39.** no solution   **41.** $-3.4, -0.6$
43. $-1.4, 3.4$ **45.** 0.8, 6.2   **47.** $-1.3, 0.8$ **49.** $-4.7, -1.3$
53. The difference between the x-intercepts is the width (in feet) of the arch at its base.   **55.** about 24.1 ft

10.4 Graphing Calculator Activity (p. 631)   1. -1.11, 3.61   **3.** -1.61, 5.61   **5.** -3.90, 0.90

10.5 Exercises (pp. 636–639)   1. square root   **3.** ± 1
5. ± 10 **7.** 0   **9.** $\pm\frac{1}{2}$ **11.** $\pm\frac{7}{3}$ **13.** 0   **17.** $\pm\sqrt{7}$

19. no solution   **21.** 0   **23.** $\pm\sqrt{5}$ **25.** $\pm\frac{10\sqrt{7}}{7}$ **27.** $\pm\frac{\sqrt{7}}{2}$
31. Negative numbers do not have real-number square roots, so $\pm\sqrt{-2}$ are not real numbers; $d^2 = -2$, there is no solution.   **33.** $3 + \sqrt{5}, 3 - \sqrt{5}$ **35.** $-5 + \sqrt{10}, -5 - \sqrt{10}$
37. $-14 + \sqrt{7}, -14 - \sqrt{7}$ **39.** $-1 + \sqrt{22}, -1 - \sqrt{22}$

41. 12 in.   **43.** 11.66 ft   **45.** ± 3 **47.** $-16, 26$ **49.** $\pm\frac{\sqrt{15}}{2}$
53. Substitute 20 for h in the given equation and solve for t.   **55.** 1.54 sec

10.6 Exercises (pp. 646–648)   1. completing the square
3. 9; $(x + 3)^2$ **5.** 4; $(x - 2)^2$ **7.** $\frac{9}{4}$; $\left(x - \frac{3}{2}\right)^2$

9. 1.44; $(x + 1.2)^2$ **11.** $\frac{4}{9}$; $\left(x - \frac{2}{3}\right)^2$ **13.** $\frac{9}{64}$; $\left(x - \frac{3}{8}\right)^2$

17. $-12, 2$ **19.** $-6, 12$ **21.** $-7, 3$ **23.** $-\frac{21}{2}, -\frac{1}{2}$

25. $4 + \sqrt{23}, 4 - \sqrt{23}$ **27.** $-\frac{5}{2}, -\frac{1}{2}$
29. When completing the square, you must add the same number to each side of the equation, not just to the side of the equation for which you complete the square; $x^2 - 14x + 49 = 11 + 49$; $(x - 7)^2 = 60$; $x - 7 = \pm\sqrt{60}$; $x = 7 \pm \sqrt{60}$; $x = 7 \pm 2\sqrt{15}$.   **31.** $2 + \sqrt{11}, 2 - \sqrt{11}$
33. $8 + \sqrt{51}, 8 - \sqrt{51}$ **35.** $-\frac{11}{3}, -\frac{1}{3}$
37. $6 + \frac{\sqrt{357}}{3}, 6 - \frac{\sqrt{357}}{3}$ **39.** $2 + \sqrt{7}, 2 - \sqrt{7}$
41. $-5 + \sqrt{21}, -5 - \sqrt{21}$ **43.** 12   **45. a.** $(2 + \sqrt{11})^2 - 4(2 + \sqrt{11}) = 4 + 4\sqrt{11} + 11 - 8 - 4\sqrt{11} = 15 - 8 = 7$
b. *Sample answer:* The other solution is $2 - \sqrt{11}$; to test this conjecture, substitute $(2 - \sqrt{11})$ for x in the expression $x^2 - 4x$ and show that it simplifies to 7; the conjecture is correct.   **47.** $x(x - 4) = 45$ **49.** 3 ft

10.7 Exercises (pp. 652–655) **1.** quadratic formula

3. $\dfrac{3+\sqrt{5}}{2}, \dfrac{3-\sqrt{5}}{2}$ **5.** $-1, \dfrac{5}{2}$ **7.** $\dfrac{1+\sqrt{37}}{6}, \dfrac{1-\sqrt{37}}{6}$

9. $-13, 8$ **11.** $-2, \dfrac{7}{3}$ **13.** $\dfrac{1+\sqrt{57}}{2}, \dfrac{1-\sqrt{57}}{2}$

15. $-\dfrac{5}{2}$ **17.** $\dfrac{9+\sqrt{273}}{12}, \dfrac{9-\sqrt{273}}{12}$ **19.** $-2, 7$ **21.** $-1, \dfrac{9}{7}$

23. $5 + \sqrt{3}, 5 - \sqrt{3}$ **25.** $\dfrac{7+\sqrt{129}}{8}, \dfrac{7-\sqrt{129}}{8}$

27. $\dfrac{3+\sqrt{149}}{14}, \dfrac{3-\sqrt{149}}{14}$ **29.** $\dfrac{-7+\sqrt{13}}{6}, \dfrac{-7-\sqrt{13}}{6}$

33. Before identifying the values of a, b, and c, the equation must be written in standard form $ax^2 + bx + c = 0$: $-2x^2 + 3x - 1 = 0$, so $c = -1$, not 1; $x = \dfrac{-3 \pm \sqrt{3^2 - 4(-2)(-1)}}{2(-2)}$, $x = \dfrac{-3 \pm \sqrt{1}}{-4}$, $x = \dfrac{1}{2}$ and $x = 1$. **35–41.** Sample answers are given. **35.** Using square roots, the equation can be written in the form $x^2 = d$. **37.** Factoring, the expression $m^2 + 5m + 6$ factors easily. **39.** Factoring, you can rewrite the equation as $10g^2 - 13g + 4 = 0$ and then factor the left-hand side as $(5g - 4)(2g - 1)$. **41.** Quadratic formula, the equation does not factor easily. **43.** ± 4

45. $-1 + \sqrt{7}, -1 - \sqrt{7}$ **47.** $-2 + \sqrt{13}, -2 - \sqrt{13}$

49. $-5 + \sqrt{29}, -5 - \sqrt{29}$ **51.** no solution

53. $1 + \sqrt{2}, 1 - \sqrt{2}$ **57.** No. *Sample answer:* If $b^2 - 4ac < 0$, then the number under the radical symbol in the quadratic formula is negative, and the equation $ax^2 + bx + c = 0$ has no real-number solutions and the graph of the related function has no x-intercepts.

59. $0 = -0.336x^2 + 1.73x - 1.4$ **61.** 1993

63. a. $h = -16t^2 + 45t + 2.5$ **b.** about 2.7 sec

65. about 22 sec

10.8 Exercises (pp. 660–662) **1.** $x = \dfrac{-b \pm \sqrt{(b^2 - 4ac)}}{2a}$

3. no solution **5.** two solutions **7.** two solutions

9. no solution **11.** one solution

15. When substituting into the quadratic formula, the value of c should have been -4, not 4; $y = 0$ when $x = \dfrac{-3 \pm \sqrt{3^2 - 4(2)(-4)}}{2(2)} = \dfrac{-3 \pm \sqrt{41}}{4}$, the graph has two x-intercepts because the discriminant is positive.

17. 2 **19.** 2 **21.** 2 **23.** 1 **25.** 1 **27.** 2 **29.** 0

31–33. Sample answers are given. **31. a.** 0 **b.** 1

c. 2 **33. a.** 8 **b.** 9 **c.** 10 **35.** One; the value of the discriminant is $(-6)^2 - 4(3)(3) = 0$, so the graph has exactly one x-intercept. A parabola that has exactly one x-intercept must have its vertex on the x-axis.

37. *Sample answer:* $x^2 + x - 1$ cannot be factored, but the graph of $y = x^2 + x - 1$ has two x-intercepts, $\dfrac{-1+\sqrt{5}}{2}$ and $\dfrac{-1-\sqrt{5}}{2}$. **39.** Yes. *Sample answer:* Substitute 27 for h in the equation $h = -16t^2 + 40t + 2$ and write the equation in standard form: $16t^2 - 40t + 25 = 0$. The discriminant is $b^2 - 4ac = (-40)^2 - 4(16)(25) = 0$, so the equation has one solution and the object reaches a height of 27 feet. **41. a.** Substitute 25 for y in the equation and then write the resulting quadratic equation in standard form: $25 = 0.06x^2 - 4x + 87$, or $0 = 0.06x^2 - 4x + 62$. Evaluate the discriminant: $b^2 - 4ac = (-4)^2 - 4(0.06)(62) = 1.12 > 0$. Because the discriminant is positive, the equation $25 = 0.06x^2 - 4x + 87$ does have

solutions, so it is possible for a parakeet to consume 25 milliliters of oxygen per gram of body mass per hour. **b.** 24.5 km/h, 42.2 km/h **43.** No. *Sample answer:* To determine if there is any point of the arch at a height of 4 feet, substitute 4 for y in the equation and then determine if the equation has any positive solutions. The equation is $4 = -0.18x^2 + 1.6x$, or $0 = -0.18x^2 + 1.6x - 4$. Evaluate the discriminant: $b^2 - 4ac = (1.6)^2 - 4(-0.18)(-4) = -0.32 < 0$. Because the discriminant is negative, the equation has no solution; thus, a child who is 4 feet tall cannot walk under one of the arches without having to bend over.

Chapter Review (pp. 666–670) **1.** axis of symmetry

5. 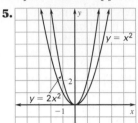 The graph is narrower than the graph of $y = x^2$.

7. 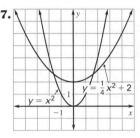 The graph is a vertical translation (of 2 units up) of the graph of $y = \dfrac{1}{4}x^2$ and is wider than the graph of $y = x^2$.

9. $x = \dfrac{7}{3}, \left(\dfrac{7}{3}, \dfrac{25}{3}\right)$

11. 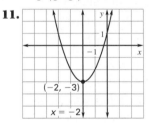 **13.**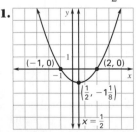

15. minimum value; -3 **17.** maximum value; $-\dfrac{17}{2}$

19. minimum value; $-\dfrac{49}{5}$ **21.**

23. no solution **25.** $-8, 1$ **27.** $\pm\dfrac{4}{5}$ **29.** about 1.9 sec

31. $-3 \pm \sqrt{11}$ **33.** $\dfrac{1 \pm \sqrt{5}}{2}$ **35.** $\dfrac{-7+\sqrt{73}}{4}, \dfrac{-7-\sqrt{73}}{4}$

37. $\dfrac{7+\sqrt{29}}{10}, \dfrac{7-\sqrt{29}}{10}$ **39.** $-\dfrac{11}{9}, 1$ **41.** $\dfrac{3+\sqrt{149}}{14}, \dfrac{3-\sqrt{149}}{14}$

43. no solution **45.** two solutions **47.** two solutions

Chapter 11

11.1 Exercises (pp. 684–687) **1.** -3 **3.** direct variation
5. neither **7.** inverse variation **9.** direct variation
11. inverse variation **13.** direct variation

17. 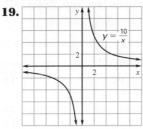 **19.**

29. $y = \dfrac{10}{x}$; 5 **31.** $y = \dfrac{-20}{x}$; -10 **33.** $y = \dfrac{225}{x}$; 112.5

35. $y = \dfrac{24}{x}$; 12 **37.** $y = \dfrac{9}{x}$; 4.5 **39.** $y = \dfrac{-120}{x}$; -60

41. $y = \dfrac{-136}{x}$; -68 **43.** $y = \dfrac{156}{x}$; 78 **45.** not inverse

variation **47.** inverse variation; $y = \dfrac{300}{x}$ **51.** $2\pi r = C$;

direct variation **53.** $Bh = 400$; inverse variation

55. $t = \dfrac{k}{v}$ **57.** $p = \dfrac{k}{t}$ **59.** $d = \dfrac{175{,}000}{p}$; 350 units

61. 3.6 min or 3 min 36 sec **63.** 8.75 mm

65. $t = \dfrac{200}{r}$; yes, the
equation is in the
form $y = \dfrac{a}{x}$.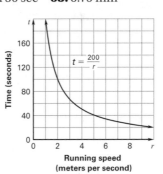

11.2 Exercises (pp. 691–694) **1.** excluded value

3. none **5.** -1 **7.** none **9.** $0, \dfrac{1}{2}$ **11.** When finding the
excluded values you must find the values for which the
denominator of the original expression, $2x^2 - 11x + 12$,
is 0; the excluded values are $\dfrac{3}{2}$ and 4. **13.** $\dfrac{2x}{5}$; none

15. $-3a$; 0 **17.** 3; -11 **19.** -2; 3 **21.** $\dfrac{2}{f^2 - 9}$; ± 3

23. $\dfrac{1}{h - 4}$; $-3, 4$ **25.** $\dfrac{-6}{2w - 5}$; $0, \dfrac{5}{2}$ **27.** 3; 0, 4

29. $\dfrac{s + 8}{s - 1}$; 1, -8 **31.** $\dfrac{1}{m^2 + 5m}$; 0, -5 **35.** $\dfrac{4}{5x}$ **37.** $\dfrac{3}{x}$

39. $\dfrac{x - 2}{2y}$; $x \neq 7$ and $y \neq 0$ **41.** $\dfrac{5x + y}{4x + y}$; $x \neq \dfrac{2}{5}y$ and $x \neq -\dfrac{1}{4}y$

43. $p = \dfrac{7500}{7500 + 31c}$ **45.** $p = \dfrac{3x^2 - 12}{22x^2 + 2500}$; about 11%

47. a. $y = \dfrac{2r + 2\ell}{r\ell}$ **b.** $y = \dfrac{50 + \ell}{25\,\ell}$ **c.** *Sample answer:*
As the length increases, the ratio decreases.

11.2 Graphing Calculator Activity (p. 695)
1. *Sample answer:* The value $x = -2$ does not result
in a denominator of 0 for y_2, but it does make the
denominator 0 for y_1.

11.3 Exercises (pp. 700–703) **1.** multiplicative inverse

3. $\dfrac{15}{14p^2}$ **5.** $\dfrac{-(v - 3)}{5(v + 1)}$ **7.** $\dfrac{x + 4}{2x + 1}$ **9.** $\dfrac{-3m}{m - 2}$ **13.** Before

dividing out the common factor $(x - 2)$, you must
first rewrite the factor $(2 - x)$ in the denominator as
$-1(x - 2)$, leaving a factor of -1 in the denominator:

$\dfrac{(x - 2)x}{-1(x + 5)(x - 2)} = \dfrac{-x}{x + 5}$. **15.** $\dfrac{5s^6}{9}$ **17.** $\dfrac{c(c + 1)}{c + 6}$

19. $\dfrac{3 - 2x}{7}$ **21.** $\dfrac{t - 11}{(5t - 1)^2}$ **25.** *Sample answer:*

$\dfrac{x^2 - 4x - 12}{x^2 - 2x - 24}$; $\dfrac{x^2 - x - 6}{x^2 - 9x + 18}$ **27.** $(x - 1)(x + 4)$.

Sample answer: 4 **29.** $C = \dfrac{49 + 14x}{(1 - 0.05x)(630 + 7x)}$

31. $p = \dfrac{100 + 2.2x}{(1 - 0.014x)(1500 + 63x)}$; about 7%

35. $p = \dfrac{(90 + 43x)(1 - 0.015x)}{(1 - 0.016x)(650 + 185x)}$; about 24%

11.4 Exercises (pp. 709–712) **1.** least common

denominator **3.** $\dfrac{1}{x}$ **5.** $\dfrac{4}{z}$ **7.** $\dfrac{2b + 1}{b - 3}$ **9.** $-\dfrac{1}{m^2 + 1}$

11. $\dfrac{3r + 1}{r^2 + r - 7}$ **13.** $24x^3$ **15.** $(w + 5)(w - 2)$

17. $t(t + 2)(t - 4)$ **19.** $(x - 2)(x - 4)$ **21.** $12m^3$
23. Rational expressions are not subtracted by
subtracting their numerators and subtracting their
denominators. Instead, you must write the expressions
with a common denominator and then subtract the
numerators over the common denominator;

$\dfrac{8}{2x + 3} - \dfrac{4x}{x + 2} = \dfrac{8(x + 2)}{(2x + 3)(x + 2)} - \dfrac{4x(2x + 3)}{(2x + 3)(x + 2)} =$

$\dfrac{8x + 16 - 8x^2 - 12x}{(2x + 3)(x + 2)} = \dfrac{-8x^2 - 4x + 16}{(2x + 3)(x + 2)}$.

25. $\dfrac{25x^2 + 8}{20x}$ **27.** $\dfrac{21z - 4}{6z^2}$ **29.** $\dfrac{4s^2 - 4s + 2}{(5s - 2)(4s + 1)}$

31. $\dfrac{5d^2 - 18d - 35}{4d(d + 7)}$ **33.** $\dfrac{-5}{(g + 2)(g + 3)(g - 2)}$

35. $\dfrac{2k^2 - 3k - 71}{(k - 8)(k + 3)^2}$ **41.** $\dfrac{15x^2 + 120x + 20}{(x - 2)(x + 8)}$ **43.** $\dfrac{-3x^2 + 29x - 4}{x - 9}$

45. $\dfrac{440}{r - 55}$; $\dfrac{440}{r + 55}$ **47.** $t = \dfrac{440r - 1000}{r(r - 5)}$; about 8.4 h

49. $t = \dfrac{1000r}{(r - 6)(r + 6)}$; about 44 sec

51. a. $\dfrac{2A^2 + 200A}{3}$; $\dfrac{7A^2 + 18{,}750A - 205{,}050}{150}$

b. 2600 lb; 6301 lb

11.5 Exercises (pp. 716–718) **1.** rational equation

3. ± 10 **5.** $-1\dfrac{1}{2}$ **7.** $-1\dfrac{1}{2}$, 4 **9.** $-6, 5$ **11.** 6

13. The solutions must be checked in the original
equation. The solution $x = -1$ is extraneous because it is
an excluded value for the original equation. The correct
solution is 3. **15.** 2 **17.** no solution **19.** 1 **21.** -4

23. $-6, 8$ **25.** All real numbers except 2; 2; two fractions with equal denominators must also have equal numerators, so $x = 2$, and the denominator of both fractions is $2 - a$. The equation has this one solution as long as the denominator $2 - a$ is not 0; so, the equation has no solution when $a = 2$.   **29.** $\frac{2 + x}{7 + x} = 0.5$

31. 50 consecutive shots   **35.** From 8 psi to 7 psi; substitute the given psi values for p in the given equation and then solve for a: for $P = 10$, $a \approx 10{,}722$; for $P = 9$, $a \approx 13{,}536$; for $P = 8$, $a \approx 16{,}600$; for $P = 7$, $a \approx 19{,}948$. The change in altitude when the atmospheric pressure changes from 9 psi to 10 psi is about $13{,}536 - 10{,}722 = 2814$, and the change in altitude when the atmospheric pressure changes from 7 psi to 8 psi is about $19{,}948 - 16{,}600 = 3348$.

11.6 Exercises (pp. 723–725)   1. rational equation
3. $\frac{1}{4}$ **5.** $\frac{12}{17}$ **7.** $\frac{1}{3}$ job per h   **9.** 2 h   **11.** $\frac{t}{180}$ **13.** $\frac{15}{4t}$
15. $\frac{15t + 175}{7t}$ **17.** *Sample answer:* The amount of work done is rate $\times$ time, not rate $\times \frac{1}{\text{time}}$; work done is $\frac{1}{5} \cdot t = \frac{t}{5}$ **19.** C   **21.** $5\frac{5}{11}$ h   **25.** If each person's rate is $\frac{1}{m}$ job per hour, then the combined rate for all n persons is $\frac{n}{m}$ job(s) per hour; as n increases, the time needed for 1 job decreases.

Chapter Review (pp. 729–732)   1. asymptote
5. $y = \frac{63}{x}$; 12.6   **7.** 15 min   **9.** $-2, 6$ **11.** $\frac{m-3}{4}$; 0
13. $-\frac{r+2}{r+1}$; $-1, 2$ **15.** $\frac{21v^7}{4}$ **17.** $\frac{-8x + 33}{5x - 3}$
19. $\frac{5c^2 - 13c - 48}{(c+1)(c-4)(c+2)}$ **21.** $-6, 9$ **23.** $-4\frac{1}{5}$ **25.** 6 h

Chapter 12

12.1 Exercises (pp. 747–749)   1. probability
3. 12 outcomes; R1, R2, R3, R4, W1, W2, W3, W4, B1, B2, B3, B4   **5.** 48 outcomes; 1HHH, 1HHT, 1HTH, 1HTT, 1THH, 1THT, 1TTH, 1TTT, 2HHH, 2HHT, 2HTH, 2HTT, 2THH, 2THT, 2TTH, 2TTT, 3HHH, 3HHT, 3HTH, 3HTT, 3THH, 3THT, 3TTH, 3TTT, 4HHH, 4HHT, 4HTH, 4HTT, 4THH, 4THT, 4TTH, 4TTT, 5HHH, 5HHT, 5HTH, 5HTT, 5THH, 5THT, 5TTH, 5TTT, 6HHH, 6HHT, 6HTH, 6HTT, 6THH, 6THT, 6TTH, 6TTT   **7.** $\frac{9}{10}$ **9.** $\frac{7}{10}$ **11.** $\frac{1}{10}$
13. The number of successes was five, so the numerator should be 5, not 4; $\frac{5}{20} = \frac{1}{4}$.   **17.** 90 outcomes
19. 19 outcomes   **21. a.** $\frac{161}{300}$ **b.** $\frac{59}{100}$ **c.** $\frac{361}{600}$

12.2 Exercises (pp. 753–755)   1. permutation
3. a. 24 ways   **b.** 12 ways   **5. a.** 720 ways   **b.** 30 ways
7. a. 720 ways   **b.** 30 ways   **9. a.** 40,320 ways
b. 56 ways   **11. a.** 40,320 ways   **b.** 56 ways
13. a. 362,880 ways   **b.** 72 ways   **17.** 1   **19.** 120
21. 40,320   **23.** 479,001,600   **25.** 20   **27.** 210
29. 40,320   **31.** 870   **33.** The denominator of the

fraction should be $(11 - 7)!$, not $(11 - 7)$; $\frac{11!}{(11 - 7)!} = \frac{11!}{4!} = 1{,}663{,}200$.   **37.** 40,320 ways   **39.** 720 ways
41. 471,744,000 passwords   **43.** $\frac{1}{120}$ **45.** $\frac{1}{42}$

12.3 Exercises (pp. 758–760)   1. combination
3. 3 combinations   **5.** 15 combinations   **7.** $\frac{9!}{(9 - 4)!}$ is $_9P_4$ not $_9C_4$, which must also have a factor of 4! in its denominator; $_9C_4 = \frac{9!}{(9-4)! \cdot 4!} = \frac{9!}{5! \cdot 4!} = 126$.   **9.** 5
11. 1   **13.** 220   **15.** 6435   **19.** Combinations; the order in which the students are picked for the group does not matter; 8,214,570 groups.   **21.** Combinations; the order in which you answer the questions does not matter; 45 ways.   **25.** Combinations; the order in which the winners are chosen does not matter.   **27.** 1

29. 840 burritos   **31.** $\frac{1}{91}$ **33. a.** Each line segment that can be drawn is determined by its two endpoints, so the number of different line segments that can be drawn is the number of combinations of 2 endpoints chosen from 5 possible endpoints; 10 segments.   **b.** 10 triangles
c. 5 quadrilaterals   **35. a.** No. *Sample answer:* The total number of possible drinks is the sum of the number of 1-juice drinks, the number of 2-juice drinks, the number of 3-juice drinks, and the number of 4-juice drinks: $_8C_1 + {}_8C_2 + {}_8C_3 + {}_8C_4 = 8 + 28 + 56 + 70 = 162 < 200$ drinks.
b. 385 drinks. *Sample answer:* The total number of possible drinks is the sum of the number of 1-juice drinks, the number of 2-juice drinks, the number of 3-juice drinks, and the number of 4-juice drinks: $_{10}C_1 + {}_{10}C_2 + {}_{10}C_3 + {}_{10}C_4 = 10 + 45 + 120 + 210 = 385$ drinks.

12.3 Graphing Calculator Activity (p. 761)   1. 35
3. 15,120   **5.** $\frac{3}{28}$, or about 10.7%

12.4 Exercises (pp. 765–768)   1. dependent
3. mutually exclusive; $\frac{2}{3}$ **5.** overlapping; $\frac{5}{6}$ **7.** To find the probability that you draw a yellow or a blue marble, the probabilities of the individual events should be added, not multiplied; $\frac{7}{16} + \frac{5}{16} = \frac{12}{16} = \frac{3}{4}$.
9. independent; $\frac{1}{36}$ **11.** dependent; $\frac{1}{21}$ **15.** $\frac{1}{64}$
17. If you first draw a pawn and do not replace it, then the probability of drawing a second pawn is $\frac{15}{31}$, not $\frac{16}{32}$; $\frac{16}{32} \cdot \frac{15}{31} = \frac{15}{62}$.   **19.** And, dependent, $P(A \text{ and } B) = P(A) \cdot P(B \text{ given } A)$. *Sample answer:* Because the black marble is not replaced, the first outcome of the choice affects the outcome of the second choice, so the events are dependent.   **21.** $\frac{1}{9}$ **25.** *Sample answer:* Since event A must either occur or not occur, $P(A) + P(\text{not } A) = 1$. Subtracting $P(A)$ from each side of this equation gives the result $P(\text{not } A) = 1 - P(A)$.

Chapter Review (pp. 774–776)   1. compound event
5. $\frac{15}{31}$ **7.** 5040   **9.** 6720   **11.** $\frac{1}{360}$ **13.** 15   **15.** 286
17. $\frac{7}{8}$ **19.** $\frac{3}{4}$ **21.** $\frac{1}{64}$

Standards Review Handbook

Quotients and Remainders (p. 783)   **1.** 16 R2   **3.** 490 R6
5. 70 R7   **7.** 16 R20   **9.** even; 2(47)   **11.** even; 2(483)
13. even; 2(917)   **15.** odd; 2(0) + 1

Factors and Multiples (p. 785)   **1.** $2^2 \cdot 7$ **3.** prime
5. 3^4 **7.** $2^2 \cdot 3 \cdot 5$ **9.** $2^2 \cdot 3^2 \cdot 5$ **11.** $3 \cdot 17$ **13.** 4
15. 6   **17.** 9   **19.** 4   **21.** 8   **23.** 4   **25.** 18   **27.** 45
29. 130   **31.** 90   **33.** 14   **35.** 49

Finding Equivalent Fractions and Simplifying Fractions
(p. 786)   1–5. Sample answers are given.   **1.** $\frac{3}{4}$ and $\frac{18}{24}$
3. $\frac{2}{4}$ and $\frac{3}{6}$ **5.** $\frac{5}{7}$ and $\frac{20}{28}$ **7.** $\frac{1}{4}$ **9.** $\frac{1}{8}$ **11.** $\frac{1}{4}$ **13.** $\frac{7}{20}$
15. $\frac{4}{5}$ **17.** $\frac{3}{7}$ **19.** $\frac{4}{13}$

Mixed Numbers and Improper Fractions (p. 787)
1. $\frac{5}{3}$

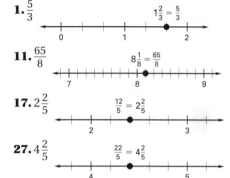

11. $\frac{65}{8}$

17. $2\frac{2}{5}$

27. $4\frac{2}{5}$

Adding and Subtracting Fractions (p. 788)   **1.** $\frac{1}{4}$ **3.** $\frac{1}{6}$
5. 1   **7.** $\frac{1}{2}$ **9.** $1\frac{1}{5}$ **11.** $\frac{3}{16}$ **13.** $\frac{25}{48}$ **15.** $1\frac{17}{24}$ **17.** $\frac{11}{20}$
19. $\frac{4}{5}$ **21.** $6\frac{3}{4}$ **23.** 5   **25.** $1\frac{1}{16}$

Multiplying and Dividing Fractions (p. 789)   **1.** $\frac{1}{2}$ **3.** $\frac{1}{2}$
5. $1\frac{1}{8}$ **7.** $\frac{3}{64}$ **9.** $\frac{1}{8}$ **11.** $1\frac{1}{2}$ **13.** $\frac{1}{2}$ **15.** $\frac{2}{7}$ **17.** $\frac{1}{50}$ **19.** $\frac{3}{5}$
21. $3\frac{3}{32}$ **23.** $4\frac{3}{8}$ **25.** $1\frac{1}{3}$

Comparing and Ordering Decimals (p. 790)   **1.** >
3. >   **5.** >   **7.** <   **9.** >   **11.** =   **13.** 2.3, 2.38, 2.45, 2.5
15. 10, 10.19, 10.2, 10.4   **17.** 1.0, 1.05, 1.11, 1.3
19. 6.1, 6.89, 7, 7.25   **21.** 5.4, 5.46, 5.6, 5.64
23. 0.58, 0.6, 0.75, 0.81

Fractions, Decimals, and Percents (p. 792)   **1.** 0.7, $\frac{7}{10}$
3. 0.03, $\frac{3}{100}$ **5.** 0.35, $\frac{7}{20}$ **7.** 1.1, $1\frac{1}{10}$ **9.** 0.003, $\frac{3}{1000}$
11. $\frac{7}{25}$, 28%   **13.** $\frac{1}{20}$, 5%   **15.** $\frac{13}{25}$, 52%   **17.** $\frac{1}{40}$, 2.5%
19. $1\frac{1}{2}$, 150%   **21.** 0.188, 18.8%   **23.** 0.61, 61%
25. 0.19, 19%   **27.** 0.36, 36%   **29.** 0.571, 57.1%

Finding Percents of Numbers (p. 793)   **1.** 20   **3.** 22
5. 37   **7.** $32\frac{2}{5}$ **9.** 45   **11.** 49   **13.** 30   **15.** 400   **17.** 18
19. 228   **21.** 4.93   **23.** 57.76   **25.** 7.65   **27.** 125.678
29. 27.45   **31.** 2.2344

The Coordinate Plane (p. 794)   **1.** (3, 1)   **3.** (−3, −3)
5. (−3, 0)   **7.** (3, 3)   **9.** (−4, −1)   **11.** (2, −1)

Converting Units of Measurement (p. 795)   **1.** 5   **3.** 4
5. 6   **7.** 14   **9.** 300   **11.** 70,000   **13.** 3000   **15.** 15
17. 2.5   **19.** 1,000,000   **21.** 28,800

Perimeter and Area (p. 797)   **1.** 48 ft   **3.** 20 ft
5. 66 yd^2 **7.** 110 in.^{2} **9.** 21 ft^2 **11.** 70 yd^2

Circumference and Area of a Circle (p. 798)   **1.** 12π in.
or 37.7 in., 36π in.^{2} or 113.0 in.^{2} **3.** 16π in. or 50.2 in.,
64π in.^{2} or 201.0 in.^{2} **5.** 4π ft or 12.6 ft, 4π ft^2 or 12.6 ft^2
7. 18π m or 56.5 m, 81π m^2 or 254.3 m^2

Surface Area and Volume (p. 800)   **1.** 320 cm^2, 336 cm^3
3. 900π m^2 or 2826 m^2, 4500π m^3 or 14,130 m^3
5. 200π in.^{2} or 628 in.^{2}, 320π in.^{3} or 1004.8 in.^{3} **7.** 96 in.^{2},
48 in.^{3} **9.** 1888π in.^{2} or 5928.3 in.^{2}, 11,008π in.^{3} or
34,565.1 in.^{3} **11.** 96π m^2 or 301.4 m^2, 96π m^3 or 301.4 m^3

Translations and Reflections (p. 801–802)

1. (3, 3), (7, 3), (7, 1), (3, 1)

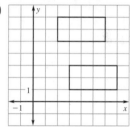

5. (1, 1), (5, 0), (2, −1), (0, −4)

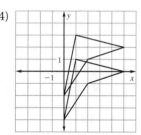

7. (9, 6), (8, 1), (10, 3)

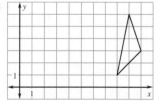

9. (−2, 6), (−1, 2), (2, 3)

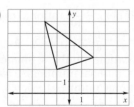

11. no **13.** yes

Mean, Median, and Mode (p. 803)
1. 92.4; 93; 94
3. 41; 41; 52 **5.** $7; $7; $6.75 **7.** 2.25; 2; 2

Line Graphs (p. 804)
1. about 24 lb **3.** his fifth yr
5. about 15 lb **7.** about 2 yr old **9.** her fourth yr
11. her second yr **13.** about 4 yr

Counting Methods (p. 805)
1. 6 ways
3. 17,576 3-letter monograms **5.** 1,679,616 computer
passwords **7.** 72 dinners

Problem Solving Strategies (p. 808)
1. Pam owes
$4 that she can pay to Bonnie who is owed a total of
$5. Holly should pay both Barb and Bonnie $1.
3. 25 years old **5.** 10 ways **7.** 1:45 P.M.
9. 3 soccer games per week **11.** Quinn

Venn Diagrams and Logical Reasoning (p. 809)
1.

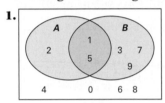

3. a. False; 3, 7, and 9 are whole numbers less than 10 that
are odd but are not factors of 10. **b.** False; 2 is a whole
number less than 10 that is a factor of 10 but is not odd.

Extra Practice

Chapter 1 (p. 810)
1. 16 **3.** 4.4 **5.** 2.4 **7.** $\frac{8}{27}$
9. 4 **11.** $\frac{36}{25}$ **13.** 26 **15.** 28 **17.** 10 **19.** 111
21. 2 **23.** 4.5 **25.** $\frac{3}{4}m$ **27.** $y - 3$ **29.** $\frac{1}{2}t - 5$
31. $45 - m$ **33.** $\frac{c}{100}$ **35.** $12(r - 4) = 72$ **37.** 38
39. 16 **41.** *Sample answer:* You know the temperature
in Quito in degrees Celsius and the temperature in
Monterey in degrees Fahrenheit. You need to find out
which one is greater. **43.** *Sample answer:* You know the
rate and time Katherine walked each day. You need to
find out the distance she walked during the 2 days.

Chapter 2 (p. 811)
1. 0.25: rational numbers; $-\frac{1}{8}$:
rational numbers; $-\frac{1}{10}$: rational numbers; $-\frac{1}{5}$: rational
numbers; $-\frac{1}{5}, -\frac{1}{8}, -\frac{1}{10}, 0.25$ **3.** -4: integers, rational
numbers; 3: whole numbers, integers, rational numbers;
-5: integers, rational numbers; 0: whole numbers,
integers, rational numbers; $-5, -4, 0, 3$ **5.** -61
7. 0 **9.** -19.7 **11.** $-4\frac{13}{30}$ **13.** 66 **15.** $\frac{3}{10}$ **17.** $\frac{5}{12}$
19. -7.2 **21.** 5.5 **23.** -12.5 **25.** -40 **27.** 2.2

29. associative property of multiplication **31.** property
of zero **33.** property of -1 **35.** $30 - 5y$ **37.** $-3k + 42$
39. $14s + 7$ **41.** $5w + 25$ **43.** 23 **45.** 64 **47.** $-\frac{5}{6}$
49. $\frac{25}{36}$ **51.** -9 **53.** 16 **55.** sometimes

Chapter 3 (p. 812)
1. 16 **3.** -12 **5.** 9 **7.** 52 **9.** 6
11. 8 **13.** -35 **15.** 3 **17.** -6 **19.** -1 **21.** 2 **23.** 3
25. $-\frac{1}{2}$ **27.** no solution **29.** 7 **31.** 2 **33.** 6 **35.** 7
37. 31 **39.** $\frac{9}{3} = \frac{x}{12}$; 36 **41.** $\frac{6}{18} = \frac{y}{3}$; 1 **43.** 1 **45.** 2
47. 20 **49.** 9 **51.** 8 **53.** 1.6 **55.** $x = b - \frac{c}{a}$; 11
57. $x = \frac{a(-b - d)}{1 - ac}$; 4 **59.** $y = 4x - 8$ **61.** $y = -\frac{6}{7}x + 3$
63. $y = 3x - 4$ **65.** $y = -3x - \frac{4}{3}$

Chapter 4 (p. 813)
3. $x \le 7$
27. $y > -4.5$
39. $x \le -\frac{3}{14}$ **41.** all real numbers **43.** all real numbers
45. $6 \le y < 11$
51. $m < -5$ or $m > -2$
55. no solution **57.** $-3, 4$ **59.** $-2, 10$ **61.** $-15, 9$
63. $-3\frac{2}{3}, 1$ **65.** $3\frac{3}{5}, 6$
67. $y \le -5$ or $y \ge 5$
69. $-\frac{2}{5} < q < \frac{2}{5}$

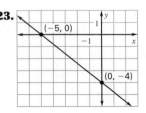

Chapter 5 (p. 814)
1. domain: 4, 6, 10, 16; range: 1, 2,
3, 4 **3.** domain: 3, 4, 5, 6, 7; range: 9, 11, 13, 15, 17
5. 2.5, 5, 7.5, 10, 12.5

7.
11.

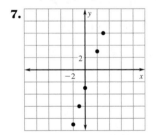
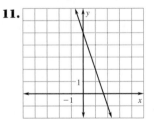

19. $-4; -10$ **21.** 20; -15 **23.**

27. -1 **29.** $\frac{1}{3}$ **31.** 0 **33.** 0 **35.** $7; 8$ **37.** $-4; 3$

39. $y = -2x + 8; -2; 8$ **41.** $y = -\frac{5}{2}x + 5; -\frac{5}{2}; 5$

45.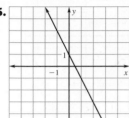

49.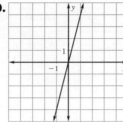

51.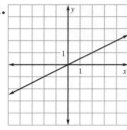

Chapter 6 (p. 815) **1.** $y = 3x + 6$ **3.** $y = 5x - 1$

5. $y = \frac{1}{2}x - 5$ **7.** $y = x + 5$ **9.** $y = \frac{4}{3}x - 4$

11. $y = -4x + 1$ **13.** $y = 3x - 2$ **15.** $y = \frac{2}{3}x - 1$

17. $y = \frac{5}{9}x + \frac{38}{9}$

19.

21.

23. $y - 4 = \frac{1}{2}(x - 2)$ **25.** $y - 2 = 7(x + 4)$ or $y - 16 = 7(x + 2)$ **27.** $y + 2 = -2(x - 10)$ or $y + 6 = -2(x - 12)$
29. *Sample answer:* $-3x + 4y = -5, 6x - 8y = 10$
31. $4x + y = 15$ **33.** $2x - y = -6$ **35.** $5x - y = -4$
37. $y = 3x - 11$ **39.** $y = \frac{3}{4}x - 9$ **41.** $y = -\frac{5}{3}x + 14$

Chapter 7 (p. 816) **1.** $(3, 2)$ **3.** $(-3, -2)$ **5.** $(-3, 0)$

7. $(9, 7)$ **9.** $(-4, 3)$ **11.** $\left(4, -\frac{7}{2}\right)$ **13.** $(-6, 3)$ **15.** $\left(\frac{5}{2}, 4\right)$

17. no solution

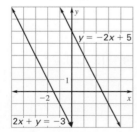

19. one solution

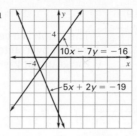

21. 6 mi/h **23.** 8 oz dried fruit, 12 oz nuts

25.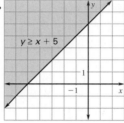

31.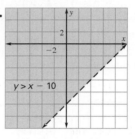

33.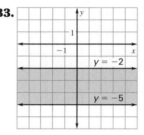

35.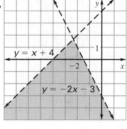

Chapter 8 (p. 817) **1.** 5^7 **3.** $(-4)^6$ **5.** n^{11} **7.** $-8x^3$
9. 8^5 **11.** 7^5 **13.** $\frac{p^7}{q^7}$ **15.** $\frac{64y^9}{27}$ **17.** $\frac{1}{81}$ **19.** 1 **21.** 8
23. 32 **25.** $\frac{1}{y^{10}}$ **27.** $\frac{10c^5}{b^3}$ **29.** $\frac{y^5}{x^4}$ **31.** $-96z^5$ **33.** $7\sqrt{2}$
35. $8x\sqrt{2x}$ **37.** $36x^3$ **39.** $\frac{\sqrt{6}}{6x}$ **41.** $\frac{\sqrt{14k}}{4k}$ **43.** $3\sqrt{3} + \sqrt{7}$
45. $9\sqrt{5}$ **47.** -108 **49.** $c = 10$ **51.** $a = 9$
53. right triangle **55.** not a right triangle **57.** 5
59. 6 **61.** 9 **63.** 16 **65.** 11^2 **67.** $\frac{1}{x^{5/3}}$

Chapter 9 (p. 818) **1.** $7x^2 - 2$ **3.** $7m^2 - 5m - 3$
5. $6b^3 - 3b^2 - 8b + 8$ **7.** $10x^7 - 15x^6 + 25x^5 - 5x^4$
9. $8x^2 + 16x + 6$ **11.** $3x^2 + 8x - 35$ **13.** $x^2 + 20x + 100$
15. $16x^2 - 4$ **17.** $36 - 9t^2$ **19.** $-4x^3$
21. $-5x^3 + 2x^2 - x$ **23.** $3v - 4 + \frac{20}{v + 2}$ **25.** $-8, 2$
27. $\frac{3}{5}, 2$ **29.** $-\frac{1}{4}, 0$ **31.** $(y + 4)(y + 3)$ **33.** $(q + 8)(q - 5)$
35. $2, 4$ **37.** $-(x - 3)(x - 2)$ **39.** $(2k - 1)(2k - 5)$
41. $-(3s + 1)(s + 2)$ **43.** $\frac{2}{3}, 4$ **45.** $-\frac{1}{3}, \frac{3}{2}$
47. $(3y + 7)(3y - 7)$ **49.** $(x - 4)^2$ **51.** $3(3x - 2)^2$
53. $(3b + 4)^2$ **55.** $2(x + 1)(x + 3)$ **57.** $(3y^2 + 2)(y + 5)$
59. $2m(7m + 3)(7m - 3)$

Chapter 10 (p. 819)

1. 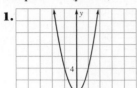 The graph is a vertical stretch by a factor of 4 of the graph of $y = x^2$.

5. 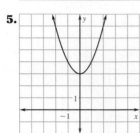 The graph is a vertical translation 3 units up of the graph of $y = x^2$.

9. 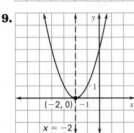 **13.**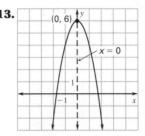

15. 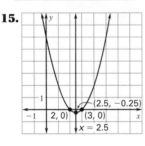 **21.**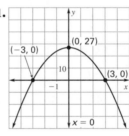

25. $2, 7$ **27.** $-4, \dfrac{5}{2}$ **29.** $-4, 6$ **31.** no solution

33. ± 10 **35.** no solution **37.** $-2, 12$ **39.** $-\dfrac{1}{4}, 1$

41. $-1 \pm \dfrac{\sqrt{11}}{2}$ **43.** $8 \pm 3\sqrt{2}$ **45.** $-12, 6$ **47.** $\dfrac{1}{2}, 2$

49. $\dfrac{1 \pm \sqrt{13}}{3}$ **51.** $\dfrac{1 \pm \sqrt{43}}{7}$ **53.** $-5 \pm \sqrt{26}$

55. two solutions **57.** no solution **59.** two solutions
61. two solutions

Chapter 11 (p. 820)

1. 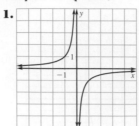 **3.**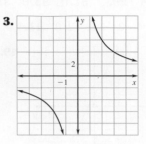

5. $y = \dfrac{12}{x}$; 6 **7.** $y = \dfrac{-48}{x}$; -24 **9.** $\dfrac{11x^2}{6}$; 0 **11.** $\dfrac{3}{4}$; 5

13. $\dfrac{r-5}{r-2}$; $2, -3$ **15.** $\dfrac{2m-4}{3m^2+6m}$; $-6, -2, 0$ **17.** $\dfrac{5x}{2x-6}$

19. $3z^2 - 10z + 3$ **21.** $3r - 6$ **23.** $\dfrac{16t + 15}{10t^2}$

25. $\dfrac{7b - 33}{(2b-3)(b-6)}$ **27.** $\dfrac{4c+3}{(c+3)(c-3)(2c+3)}$ **29.** $-4, 7$

31. $-\dfrac{7}{3}, 3$ **33.** $-3, \dfrac{11}{4}$ **35.** $1\dfrac{7}{13}$ h or about 1 h 32 min

Chapter 12 (p. 821) **1.** $\dfrac{8}{15}$ **3.** 6 possible outcomes: heads, yellow; heads, red; heads, blue; tails, yellow; tails, red; tails, blue **5.** $\dfrac{1}{3}$ **7.** 60 ways **9.** 39,916,800

11. 90 **13.** 840 **15.** 95,040 **17.** 3003 combinations

19. 35 **21.** 11 **23.** 7 **25.** 210 **27.** mutually exclusive; $\dfrac{1}{2}$

29. overlapping; $\dfrac{2}{3}$ **31.** about 10.4%